BIG IDEAS MATH®
Modeling Real Life

Grade 8
Common Core Edition

TEACHING EDITION

Ron Larson
Laurie Boswell

Big Ideas Learning™

Erie, Pennsylvania
BigIdeasLearning.com

Big Ideas Learning, LLC
1762 Norcross Road
Erie, PA 16510-3838
USA

For product information and customer support, contact Big Ideas Learning
at **1-877-552-7766** or visit us at ***BigIdeasLearning.com***.

Cover Image:
Valdis Torms, cobalt88/Shutterstock.com

Front Matter:
xxxvii Heyourelax/iStock/Getty Images Plus; **xxxviii** Valengilda/iStock/Getty Images Plus; **xxxix** Juanmonino/E+/
Getty Images; **xl** stockcam/iStock/Getty Images Plus; **xli** supergenijalac/iStock/Getty Images Plus; **xliii** tawan/
Shutterstock.com; **xliv** uatp2/iStock/Getty Images Plus; **xlv** carlosgaw/E+/Getty Images

Printed in the U.S.A.

IBSN 13: 978-1-63708-869-2

5 6 7 8 9 10 11 26 25 24 23 22

One Voice from Kindergarten Through Algebra 2

Written by renowned authors, Dr. Ron Larson and Dr. Laurie Boswell, *Big Ideas Math* offers a seamless math pedagogy from elementary through high school. Together, Ron and Laurie provide a consistent voice that encourages students to make connections through cohesive progressions and clear instruction. Since 1992, Ron and Laurie have authored over 50 mathematics programs.

> *Each time Laurie and I start working on a new program, we spend time putting ourselves in the position of the reader. How old is the reader? What is the reader's experience with mathematics? The answers to these questions become our writing guides. Our goal is to make the learning targets understandable and to develop these targets in a clear path that leads to student success.*

Ron Larson

Ron Larson, Ph.D., is well known as lead author of a comprehensive and widely used mathematics program that ranges from elementary school through college. He holds the distinction of Professor Emeritus from Penn State Erie, The Behrend College, where he taught for nearly 40 years. He received his Ph.D. in mathematics from the University of Colorado. Dr. Larson engages in the latest research and advancements in mathematics education and consistently incorporates key pedagogical elements to ensure focus, coherence, rigor, and student self-reflection.

> *My passion and goal in writing is to provide an essential resource for exploring and making sense of mathematics. Our program is guided by research around the learning and teaching of mathematics in the hopes of improving the achievement of all students. May this be a successful year for you!*

Laurie Boswell

Laurie Boswell, Ed.D., is the former Head of School at Riverside School in Lyndonville, Vermont. In addition to authoring textbooks, she provides mathematics consulting and embedded coaching sessions. Dr. Boswell received her Ed.D. from the University of Vermont in 2010. She is a recipient of the Presidential Award for Excellence in Mathematics Teaching and later served as president of CPAM. Laurie has taught math to students at all levels, elementary through college. In addition, Laurie has served on the NCTM Board of Directors and as a Regional Director for NCSM. Along with Ron, Laurie has co-authored numerous math programs and has become a popular national speaker.

Big Ideas Learning would like to express our gratitude to the mathematics education and instruction experts who served as our advisory panel, contributing specialists, and reviewers during the writing of *Big Ideas Math: Modeling Real Life*. Their input was an invaluable asset during the development of this program.

Contributing Specialists and Reviewers

- **Sophie Murphy**, Ph.D. Candidate, Melbourne School of Education, Melbourne, Australia
  Learning Targets and Success Criteria Specialist and Visible Learning Reviewer

- **Linda Hall**, Mathematics Educational Consultant, Edmond, OK
  Advisory Panel and Teaching Edition Contributor

- **Michael McDowell**, Ed.D., Superintendent, Ross, CA
  Project-Based Learning Specialist

- **Kelly Byrne**, Math Supervisor and Coordinator of Data Analysis, Downingtown, PA
  Advisory Panel and Content Reviewer

- **Jean Carwin**, Math Specialist/TOSA, Snohomish, WA
  Advisory Panel and Content Reviewer

- **Nancy Siddens**, Independent Language Teaching Consultant, Las Cruces, NM
  English Language Learner Specialist

- **Nancy Thiele**, Mathematics Consultant, Mesa, AZ
  Teaching Edition Contributor

- **Kristen Karbon**, Curriculum and Assessment Coordinator, Troy, MI
  Advisory Panel and Content Reviewer

- **Kery Obradovich**, K–8 Math/Science Coordinator, Northbrook, IL
  Advisory Panel and Content Reviewer

- **Jennifer Rollins**, Math Curriculum Content Specialist, Golden, CO
  Advisory Panel

- **Becky Walker**, Ph.D., School Improvement Services Director, Green Bay, WI
  Advisory Panel

- **Anthony Smith**, Ph.D., Associate Professor, Associate Dean, University of Washington Bothell, Seattle, WA
  Reading/Writing Reviewer

- **Nicole Dimich Vagle**, Educator, Author, and Consultant, Hopkins, MN
  Assessment Reviewer

- **Jill Kalb**, Secondary Math Content Specialist, Arvada, CO
  Content Reviewer

- **Janet Graham**, District Math Specialist, Manassas, VA
  Response to Intervention and Differentiated Instruction Reviewer

- **Sharon Huber**, Director of Elementary Mathematics, Chesapeake, VA
  Universal Design for Learning Reviewer

Student Reviewers

- Jackson Currier
- Mason Currier
- Taylor DeLuca
- Ajalae Evans
- Malik Goodwine
- Majesty Hamilton
- Reilly Koch

- Kyla Kramer
- Matthew Lindemuth
- Greer Lippert
- Zane Lippert
- Jeffrey Lobaugh
- Riley Moran
- Zoe Morin

- Deke Patton
- Brooke Smith
- Dylan Throop
- Jenna Urso
- Madison Whitford
- Jenna Wigham

Research

Ron Larson and Laurie Boswell used the latest in educational research, along with the body of knowledge collected from expert mathematics instructors, to develop the *Modeling Real Life* series. By implementing the work of renowned researchers from across the world, *Big Ideas Math* offers at least a full year's growth within a full year's learning while also encouraging a growth mindset in students and teachers. Students take their learning from surface-level to deep-level, then transfer that learning by modeling real-life situations. For more information on how this program uses learning targets and success criteria to enhance teacher clarity, see pages xiv–xv.

The pedagogical approach used in this program follows the best practices outlined in the most prominent and widely accepted educational research, including:

- *Visible Learning*
  John Hattie © 2009

- *Visible Learning for Teachers*
  John Hattie © 2012

- *Visible Learning for Mathematics*
  John Hattie © 2017

- *Principles to Actions: Ensuring Mathematical Success for All*
  NCTM © 2014

- *Adding It Up: Helping Children Learn Mathematics*
  National Research Council © 2001

- *Mathematical Mindsets: Unleashing Students' Potential through Creative Math, Inspiring Messages and Innovative Teaching*
  Jo Boaler © 2015

- *What Works in Schools: Translating Research into Action*
  Robert Marzano © 2003

- *Classroom Instruction That Works: Research-Based Strategies for Increasing Student Achievement*
  Marzano, Pickering, and Pollock © 2001

- *Principles and Standards for School Mathematics*
  NCTM © 2000

- *Rigorous PBL by Design: Three Shifts for Developing Confident and Competent Learners*
  Michael McDowell © 2017

- Common Core State Standards for Mathematics National Governors Association Center for Best Practices and Council of Chief State School Officers © 2010

- *Universal Design for Learning Guidelines*
  CAST © 2011

- Rigor/Relevance Framework®
  International Center for Leadership in Education

- *Understanding by Design*
  Grant Wiggins and Jay McTighe © 2005

- Achieve, ACT, and The College Board

- *Elementary and Middle School Mathematics: Teaching Developmentally*
  John A. Van de Walle and Karen S. Karp © 2015

- *Evaluating the Quality of Learning: The SOLO Taxonomy*
  John B. Biggs & Kevin F. Collis © 1982

- *Unlocking Formative Assessment: Practical Strategies for Enhancing Students' Learning in the Primary and Intermediate Classroom*
  Shirley Clarke, Helen Timperley, and John Hattie © 2004

- *Formative Assessment in the Secondary Classroom*
  Shirley Clarke © 2005

- *Improving Student Achievement: A Practical Guide to Assessment for Learning*
  Toni Glasson © 2009

Instructional Design

A single authorship team from Kindergarten through Algebra 2 results in a logical progression of focused topics with meaningful coherence from course to course.

FOCUS

A focused program reflects the balance in grade-level standards while simultaneously supporting and engaging students to develop conceptual understanding of the major work of the grade.

The Learning Target and Success Criteria for each section focus the learning into manageable chunks, using clear teaching text and Key Ideas within the Student Edition.

2.1 Multiplying Integers

Learning Target: Find products of integers.

Success Criteria:
- I can explain the rules for multiplying integers.
- I can find products of integers with the same sign.
- I can find products of integers with different signs.

Key Idea

Ratios

Words A **ratio** is a comparison of two quantities. The **value of the ratio** a to b is the number $\frac{a}{b}$, which describes the multiplicative relationship between the quantities in the ratio.

Examples 2 snails *to* 6 fish

$\frac{1}{2}$ cup of milk *for every* $\frac{1}{4}$ cup of cream

Algebra The ratio of a to b can be written as $a : b$.

Laurie's Notes prepare you for the math concepts in each chapter and section and make connections to the threads of major topics for the course.

Laurie's Notes

Chapter 5 Overview

The study of ratios and proportions in this chapter builds upon and connects to prior work with rates and ratios in the previous course. Students should have an understanding of how ratios are represented and how ratio tables are used to find equivalent ratios. Tape diagrams and double number lines were also used to represent and solve problems involving equivalent ratios.

a Single Authorship Team

COHERENCE

A single authorship team built a coherent program that has intentional progression of content within each grade and between grade levels. Your students will build new understanding on foundations from prior grades and connect concepts throughout the course.

The authors developed content that progresses from prior chapters and grades to future ones. In addition to charts like this one, Laurie's Notes provide point of use insights about where your students have come from and where they are going in their learning progression.

Through the Grades		
Grade 7	**Grade 8**	**High School**
• Use samples to draw inferences about populations. • Compare two populations from random samples using measures of center and variability. • Approximate the probability of a chance event and predict the approximate relative frequency given the probability.	• Construct and interpret scatter plots. • Find and assess lines of fit for scatter plots. • Use equations of lines to solve problems and interpret the slope and the y-intercept. • Construct and interpret a two-way table summarizing data. Use relative frequencies to describe possible association between the two variables.	• Classify data as quantitative or qualitative, choose and create appropriate data displays, and analyze misleading graphs. • Make and use two-way tables to recognize associations in data by finding marginal, relative, and conditional relative frequencies. • Interpret scatter plots, determine how well lines of fit model data, and distinguish between correlation and causation.

One author team thoughtfully wrote each course, creating a seamless progression of content from Kindergarten to Algebra 2.

See pages xxviii and xxix for the K–8 Progressions chart.

Gra			Grade 4	Grade 5	Grade 6	Grade 7	Grade 8
			Operations and Algebraic Thinking		**Expressions and Equations**		
oblems involving h and subtraction 0. roperties of ons. ith addition and ion equations. s 1–5, 10, 11	Solve problems involving addition and subtraction within 20. Work with equal groups of objects. *Chapters 1–6, 15*	Solve problems involving multiplication and division within 100. Apply properties of multiplication. Solve problems involving the four operations, and identify and explain patterns in arithmetic. *Chapters 1–5, 8, 9, and 14*	Use the four operations with whole numbers to solve problems. Understand factors and multiples. Generate and analyze patterns. *Chapters 2–6, 12*	Write and interpret numerical expressions. Analyze patterns and relationships. *Chapters 2, 12*	Perform arithmetic with algebraic expressions. *Chapter 3* Solve one-variable equations and inequalities. *Chapters 6, 8* Analyze relationships between dependent and independent variables. *Chapter 6*	Write equivalent expressions. *Chapter 3* Use numerical and algebraic expressions, equations, and inequalities to solve problems. *Chapters 3, 4, 6*	Understand the connections between proportional relationships, lines, and linear equations. *Chapter 4* Solve linear equations and systems of linear equations. *Chapters 1, 5* Work with radicals and integer exponents. *Chapters 8, 9*
							Functions
							Define, evaluate, and compare functions, and use functions to model relationships between quantities.

You have used number lines to find sums of positive numbers, which involve movement to the right. Now you will find sums with negative numbers, which involve movement to the left.

Throughout each course, lessons build on prior learning as new concepts are introduced. Here the students are reminded of the use of number lines with positive numbers.

Using Number Lines to Find Sums

a. Find $4 + (-4)$.

Draw an arrow from 0 to 4 to represent 4. Then draw an arrow 4 units to the left to represent adding -4.

Rigor in Math: A Balanced Approach

Instructional Design

The authors wrote every chapter and every section to give you a meaningful balance of rigorous instruction.

RIGOR

A rigorous program provides a balance of three important building blocks.

- **Conceptual Understanding**
  Discovering why
- **Procedural Fluency**
  Learning how
- **Application**
  Knowing when to apply

Conceptual Understanding

Students have the opportunity to develop foundational concepts central to the *Learning Target* in each *Exploration* by experimenting with new concepts, talking with peers, and asking questions.

EXPLORATION 1 **Understanding Quotients Involving N**

Work with a partner.

a. Discuss the relationship between multiplication your partner.

b. **INDUCTIVE REASONING** Complete the table. The for dividing (i) two integers with the same sign ar different signs.

Expression	Type of Quotient	Quoti
$-15 \div 3$	Integers	
$12 \div (-6)$		
$10 \div (-2)$		

Conceptual Thinking

Ask students to think deeply with conceptual questions.

29. **MP** **NUMBER SENSE** Without solving, determine whether $\dfrac{x}{4} = \dfrac{15}{3}$ and $\dfrac{x}{15} = \dfrac{4}{3}$ have the same solution. Explain your reasoning.

EXAMPLE 1 **Graphing a Linear Equation in Standard Form**

Graph $-2x + 3y = -6$.

Step 1: Write the equation in slope-intercept form.

$$-2x + 3y = -6 \qquad \text{Write the equation.}$$
$$3y = 2x - 6 \qquad \text{Add } 2x \text{ to each side.}$$
$$y = \frac{2}{3}x - 2 \qquad \text{Divide each side by 3.}$$

Step 2: Use the slope and the y-intercept to graph the equation.

$$y = \frac{2}{3}x + (-2)$$

slope y-intercept

Procedural Fluency

Solidify learning with clear, stepped-out teaching and examples.

Then shift conceptual understanding into procedural fluency with *Try Its, Self-Assessments, Practice,* and *Review & Refresh.*

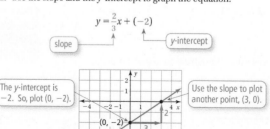

The y-intercept is -2. So, plot $(0, -2)$.

Use the slope to plot another point, $(3, 0)$.

$(0, -2)$

STEAM Video: "Trophic Status"

Name_____ Date_____

Chapter 3 Performance Task

Chlorophyll in Plants

What is needed for photosynthesis? How can you use the amount of chlorophyll in a lake to determine the level of biological productivity?

Photosynthesis is the process by which plants acquire energy from the sun. Sunlight, carbon dioxide, and water are used by a plant to produce glucose and dioxygen.

Before: After:
6 Carbon Dioxide + 6 Water ——→ Glucose + 6 Dioxygen

1. You want to make models of the molecules involved in photosynthesis for a science fair project. The table shows the number of each element used for each molecule. Let x, y, and z represent the costs of a model carbon atom, model hydrogen atom, and

	Number of Atoms		
Molecule	Carbon	Hydrogen	Oxygen
Carbon Dioxide	1	0	2
Water	0	2	1

36. **DIG DEEPER!** The *girth* of a package is the distance around the perimeter of a face that does not include the length as a side. A postal service says that a rectangular package can have a maximum combined length and girth of 108 inches.

   a. Write an inequality that represents the allowable dimensions for the package.

   b. Find three different sets of allowable dimensions that are reasonable for the package. Find the volume of each package.

THE PROBLEM-SOLVING PLAN

1. **Understand the Problem**
   Think about what the problem is asking, what information you know, and how you might begin to solve.

2. **Make a Plan**
   Plan your solution pathway before jumping in to solve. Identify any relationships and decide on a problem-solving strategy.

3. **Solve and Check**
   As you solve the problem, be sure to evaluate your progress and check your answers. Throughout the problem-solving process, you must continually ask, "Does this make sense?" and be willing to change course if necessary.

Embedded Mathematical Practices

Encouraging Mathematical Mindsets

Developing proficiency in the **Mathematical Practices** is about becoming a mathematical thinker. Students learn to ask why, and to reason and communicate with others as they learn. Use this guide to communicate opportunities in your classroom for students to develop proficiency with the mathematical practices.

1

One way to **Make Sense of Problems and Persevere in Solving Them** is to use the Problem-Solving Plan. Students should take time to analyze the given information and what the problem is asking to help them plan a solution pathway.

Look for labels such as:
- Explain the Meaning
- Find Entry Points
- Analyze Givens
- Make a Plan
- Interpret a Solution
- Consider Similar Problems
- Consider Simpler Forms
- Check Progress
- Problem Solving

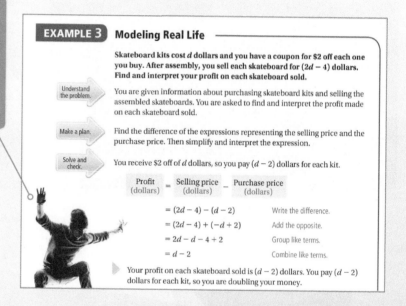

EXAMPLE 3 **Modeling Real Life**

Skateboard kits cost d dollars and you have a coupon for \$2 off each one you buy. After assembly, you sell each skateboard for $(2d - 4)$ dollars. Find and interpret your profit on each skateboard sold.

Understand the problem. You are given information about purchasing skateboard kits and selling the assembled skateboards. You are asked to find and interpret the profit made on each skateboard sold.

Make a plan. Find the difference of the expressions representing the selling price and the purchase price. Then simplify and interpret the expression.

Solve and check. You receive \$2 off of d dollars, so you pay $(d - 2)$ dollars for each kit.

$$\underset{\text{(dollars)}}{\text{Profit}} = \underset{\text{(dollars)}}{\text{Selling price}} - \underset{\text{(dollars)}}{\text{Purchase price}}$$

$= (2d - 4) - (d - 2)$ Write the difference.

$= (2d - 4) + (-d + 2)$ Add the opposite.

$= 2d - d - 4 + 2$ Group like terms.

$= d - 2$ Combine like terms.

Your profit on each skateboard sold is $(d - 2)$ dollars. You pay $(d - 2)$ dollars for each kit, so you are doubling your money.

2

Students **Reason Abstractly** when they explore a concrete example and represent it symbolically. Other times, students **Reason Quantitatively** when they see relationships in numbers or symbols and draw conclusions about a concrete example.

a. Represent each table in the same coordinate plane. Which graph represents a proportional relationship? How do you know?

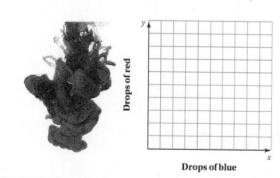

Drops of blue

Look for labels such as:
- Make Sense of Quantities
- Use Equations
- Use Expressions
- Understand Quantities
- Use Operations
- Number Sense
- Reasoning

Math Practice

Reasoning

How is the graph of the proportional relationship different from the other graph?

b. Which property can you use to solve each of the equations modeled by the algebra tiles? Solve each equation and explain your method.

46. **MP** **LOGIC** When you multiply or divide each side of an inequality by the same negative number, you must reverse the direction of the inequality symbol. Explain why.

Math Practice

Make Conjectures
Can you use algebra tiles to solve any equation? Explain your reasoning.

3

When students **Construct Viable Arguments and Critique the Reasoning of Others**, they make and justify conclusions and decide whether others' arguments are correct or flawed.

Look for labels such as:

- Use Assumptions
- Use Definitions
- Use Prior Results
- Make Conjectures
- Build Arguments
- Analyze Conjectures
- Use Counterexamples

- Justify Conclusions
- Compare Arguments
- Construct Arguments
- Listen and Ask Questions
- You Be the Teacher
- Logic

36. **MP** **APPLY MATHEMATICS** You decide to make and sell bracelets. The cost of your materials is $84.00. You charge $3.50 for each bracelet.

a. Write a function that represents the profit P for selling b bracelets.

b. Which variable is independent? dependent? Explain.

c. You will *break even* when the cost of your materials equals your income. How many bracelets must you sell to break even?

Look for labels such as:

- Apply Mathematics
- Simplify a Solution
- Use a Diagram
- Use a Table
- Use a Graph

- Use a Formula
- Analyze Relationships
- Interpret Results
- Modeling Real Life

4

To Model with Mathematics, students apply the math they have learned to a real-life problem, and they interpret mathematical results in the context of the situation.

BUILDING TO FULL UNDERSTANDING

Throughout each course, students have opportunities to demonstrate specific aspects of the mathematical practices. Labels throughout the book indicate gateways to those aspects. Collectively, these opportunities will lead students to a full understanding of each mathematical practice. Developing these mindsets and habits will give meaning to the mathematics they learn.

Embedded Mathematical Practices (continued)

5 To **Use Appropriate Tools Strategically**, students need to know what tools are available and think about how each tool might help them solve a mathematical problem. When students choose a tool to use, remind them that it may have limitations.

Look for labels such as:
- Choose Tools
- Recognize Usefulness of Tools
- Use Other Resources
- Use Technology to Explore
- Using Tools

d. Enter the function $y = \left(\dfrac{1}{10}\right)^x$ into your graphing calculator. Use the *table* feature to evaluate the function for positive integer values of x until the calculator displays a y-value that is not in standard form. Do the results support your answer in part (c)? Explain.

Math Practice

Use Technology to Explore

How can writing $\dfrac{1}{10}$ as a power of 10 help you understand the calculator display?

6 When students **Attend to Precision**, they are developing a habit of being careful in how they talk about concepts, label their work, and write their answers.

Look for labels such as:
- Communicate Precisely
- Use Clear Definitions
- State the Meaning of Symbols
- Specify Units
- Label Axes
- Calculate Accurately
- Precision

Add $1.459 + 23.7$.

$$
\begin{array}{r}
\overset{1}{} \\
1.459 \\
+\ 23.700 \\
\hline
25.159
\end{array}
$$

Insert zeros so that both numbers have the same number of decimal places.

Math Practice

Calculate Accurately

Why is it important to line up the decimal points when adding or subtracting decimals?

49. **MP** **PRECISION** Consider the equation $c = ax - bx$, where a, b, and c are whole numbers. Which of the following result in values of a, b, and c so that the original equation has exactly one solution? Justify your answer.

| $a - b = 1, c = 0$ | $a = b, c \neq 0$ | $a = b, c = 0$ | $a \neq b, c = 0$ |

MP STRUCTURE Tell whether the triangles are similar. Explain.

14.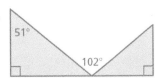

15.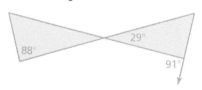

Find the sum of the areas of the faces.

Surface Area	=	Area of bottom	+	Area of a side	+	Area of a side	+	Area of a side	+	Area of a side	
S	=	49	+	35	+	35	+	35	+	35	= 189

Students **Look For and Make Use of Structure** by looking closely to see structure within a mathematical statement, or stepping back for an overview to see how individual parts make one single object.

Look for labels such as:
- Look for Structure
- Look for Patterns
- View as Components
- Structure
- Patterns

Math Practice

Look for Patterns

How can you find the surface area of a square pyramid by calculating the area of only two of the faces?

35. **MP REPEATED REASONING** You have been assigned a nine-digit identification number.

  a. Should you use the Fundamental Counting Principle or a tree diagram to find the total number of possible identification numbers? Explain.

  b. How many identification numbers are possible?

When students **Look For and Express Regularity in Repeated Reasoning**, they can notice patterns and make generalizations. Remind students to keep in mind the goal of a problem, which will help them evaluate reasonableness of answers along the way.

Look for labels such as:
- Repeat Calculations
- Find General Methods
- Maintain Oversight
- Evaluate Results
- Repeated Reasoning

Making Learning Visible

Knowing the learning intention of a chapter or section helps learners focus on the purpose of an activity, rather than simply completing it in isolation. This program supports visible learning through the consistent use of Learning Targets and Success Criteria to ensure positive outcomes for all students.

> Every chapter and section shows a Learning Target and related Success Criteria. These are purposefully integrated into each carefully written lesson.

4.4 Writing and Graphing Inequalities

Learning Target: Write inequalities and represent solutions of inequalities on number lines.

Success Criteria:
- I can write word sentences as inequalities.
- I can determine whether a value is a solution of an inequality.
- I can graph the solutions of inequalities.

Chapter Learning Target:
Understand equations and inequalities.

Chapter Success Criteria:
- ☐ I can identify key words and phrases to write equations and inequalities.
- ☐ I can write word sentences as equations and inequalities.
- ☐ I can solve equations and inequalities using properties.
- ☐ I can use equations and inequalities to model and solve real-life problems.

> The Chapter Review reminds students to rate their understanding of the learning targets.

Chapter Self-Assessment

As you complete the exercises, use the scale below to rate your understanding of the success criteria in your journal.

1	2	3	4
I do not understand.	I can do it with help.	I can do it on my own.	I can teach someone else.

6.1 Writing Equations in One Variable (pp. 245–250)

Learning Target: Write equations in one variable and write equations that represent real-life problems.

Write the word sentence as an equation.

. The product of a number m and 2 is 8.

> Students review each section with a reminder of that section's learning target.

> ◉ Icons throughout Laurie's Notes suggest ways to target where students are in their learning.

> ◉ **Fist of Five:** Ask students to indicate their understanding of the first and second success criterion. Then select students to explain each one.

QUESTIONS FOR LEARNERS

As students progress through a section, they should be able to answer the following questions.

- What are you learning?
- Why are you learning this?
- Where are you in your learning?
- How will you know when you have learned it?
- Where are you going next?

Success Criteria, and Self-Assessment

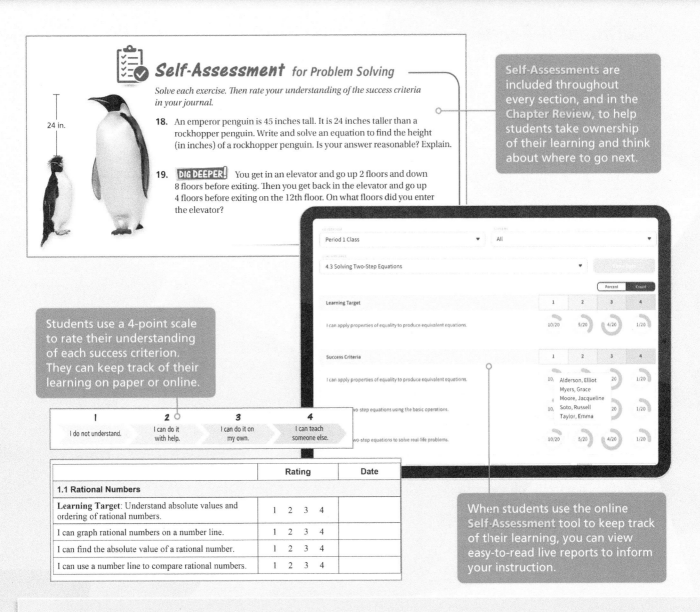

Self-Assessment for Problem Solving

Solve each exercise. Then rate your understanding of the success criteria in your journal.

24 in.

18. An emperor penguin is 45 inches tall. It is 24 inches taller than a rockhopper penguin. Write and solve an equation to find the height (in inches) of a rockhopper penguin. Is your answer reasonable? Explain.

19. **DIG DEEPER!** You get in an elevator and go up 2 floors and down 8 floors before exiting. Then you get back in the elevator and go up 4 floors before exiting on the 12th floor. On what floors did you enter the elevator?

Self-Assessments are included throughout every section, and in the Chapter Review, to help students take ownership of their learning and think about where to go next.

Students use a 4-point scale to rate their understanding of each success criterion. They can keep track of their learning on paper or online.

1	2	3	4
I do not understand.	I can do it with help.	I can do it on my own.	I can teach someone else.

	Rating	Date
1.1 Rational Numbers		
Learning Target: Understand absolute values and ordering of rational numbers.	1 2 3 4	
I can graph rational numbers on a number line.	1 2 3 4	
I can find the absolute value of a rational number.	1 2 3 4	
I can use a number line to compare rational numbers.	1 2 3 4	

When students use the online Self-Assessment tool to keep track of their learning, you can view easy-to-read live reports to inform your instruction.

Ensuring Positive Outcomes

John Hattie's *Visible Learning* research consistently shows that using Learning Targets and Success Criteria can result in two years' growth in one year, ensuring positive outcomes for student learning and achievement.

Sophie Murphy, M.Ed., wrote the chapter-level learning targets and success criteria for this program. Sophie is currently completing her Ph.D. at the University of Melbourne in Australia with Professor John Hattie as her leading supervisor. Sophie completed her Master's thesis with Professor John Hattie in 2015. Sophie has over 20 years of experience as a teacher and school leader in private and public school settings in Australia.

Purposeful Focus

Many of the things we do as educators have a positive effect on student learning, but which ones have the greatest impact? This program purposefully integrates **five key strategies** proven to have some of the highest impact on student achievement.

TEACHER CLARITY

Before starting a new topic, make clear the learning target. As students explore and learn, continue to connect their experiences back to the success criteria so they know where they are in their learning.

✓ *Self-Assessment* for Concepts & Skills

- Identify the reasons for incorrect answers for Exercises 9–14. Are the errors computational? Do students complete Exercises 9–12 with ease but struggle with Exercises 13 and 14? Are the negative numbers the issue? Make sure students are aware of the reasons for their mistakes.

- Exercise 15 asks students to explain the relationship between using the Distributive Property to simplify an expression and to factor an expression. Students' responses will provide information about their level of understanding.

Try It

- These exercises provide a review of three additional data displays.
- **Turn and Talk:** Have students discuss their answers. Remind them of *Talk Moves* that they can use in their discussions. Then review the answers as a class.

FEEDBACK

Actively listen as you probe for student understanding, being mindful of the feedback that you provide. When students provide you with feedback, you see where your students are in their learning and make instructional decisions for where to go next.

CLASSROOM DISCUSSION

Encourage your students to talk together! This solidifies understanding while honing their ability to reason and construct arguments. Students benefit from hearing the reasoning of classmates and hearing peers critique their own reasoning.

Daily Support from a Master Educator

In Laurie's Notes, master educator Laurie Boswell uses her professional training and years of experience to help you guide your students to better understanding.

Laurie studied Professor John Hattie's research on *Visible Learning* and met with Hattie on multiple occasions to ensure she was interpreting his research accurately and embedding it effectively. Laurie's expertise continues with an ongoing collaboration with Sophie Murphy, who is pursuing her Ph.D. under Professor Hattie.

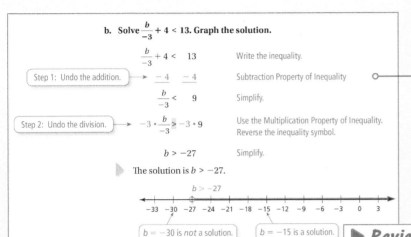

b. Solve $\dfrac{b}{-3} + 4 < 13$. Graph the solution.

$\dfrac{b}{-3} + 4 < 13$		Write the inequality.
Step 1: Undo the addition. → $-4 \quad -4$		Subtraction Property of Inequality
$\dfrac{b}{-3} < 9$		Simplify.
Step 2: Undo the division. → $-3 \cdot \dfrac{b}{-3} > -3 \cdot 9$		Use the Multiplication Property of Inequality. Reverse the inequality symbol.
$b > -27$		Simplify.

▶ The solution is $b > -27$.

$b > -27$

$-33 \quad -30 \quad -27 \quad -24 \quad -21 \quad -18 \quad -15 \quad -12 \quad -9 \quad -6 \quad -3 \quad 0 \quad 3$

$b = -30$ is *not* a solution. $b = -15$ is a solution.

DIRECT INSTRUCTION
Follow exploration and discovery with explicit instruction to build procedural skill and fluency. Teach with clear Key Ideas and powerful stepped-out examples that have been carefully designed to meet the success criteria.

▶ Review & Refresh

Solve the inequality. Graph the solution.

1. $-3x \geq 18$
2. $\dfrac{2}{3}d > 8$
3. $2 \geq \dfrac{g}{-4}$

Find the missing values in the ratio table. Then write the equivalent ratios.

4.
Flutes	7		28
Clarinets	4	12	

5.
Boys	6	3	
Girls	10		50

6. What is the volume of the cube?

   A. $8\,\text{ft}^3$
   B. $16\,\text{ft}^3$
   C. $24\,\text{ft}^3$
   D. $32\,\text{ft}^3$

   2 ft

SPACED PRACTICE
Effective practice does not just focus on a single topic of new learning; students must revisit concepts over time so deeper learning occurs. This program cohesively offers multiple opportunities for students to build their conceptual understanding by intentionally revisiting and applying concepts throughout subsequent lessons and chapters. *Review & Refresh* exercises in every section also provide continual practice on the major topics.

We focus on **STRATEGIES** with some of the **HIGHEST IMPACT** on student achievement—up to 2 years of learning for a year of input.

Five Strategies for Purposeful Focus

Professor John Hattie, in his *Visible Learning* network, identified more than 250 influences on student learning, and developed a way of ranking them. He conducted meta-analyses and compared the influences by their **effect size**—the impact the factor had on student learning.

Average effect size 0.4: 1 year of growth for a year of input

DIRECT INSTRUCTION (0.59)
FEEDBACK (0.64)
SPACED PRACTICE (0.65)
TEACHER CLARITY (0.76)
CLASSROOM DISCUSSION (0.82)

Effect size 0.8: 2 years' growth for a year of input

Effect size

0.1 0.2 0.3 0.4 0.5 0.6 0.7 0.8 0.9 1.0 0 −0.1 −0.2

Negative Low Medium High

Developmental effects

Typical effects of one year of teaching on students

Decreased achievement

Zone of desired effects

Barometer of Influences

How to Use This Program: Plan

Taking Advantage of Your Resources

You play an indispensable role in your students' learning. This program provides rich resources for learners of all levels to help you **Plan**, **Teach**, and **Assess**.

> Plan every chapter and section with tools in the Teaching Edition such as Suggested Pacing, Progression Tables, and chapter and section Overviews written by Laurie Boswell.

Suggested Pacing

Chapter Opener	1 Day
Section 1	2 Days
Section 2	2 Days
Section 3	2 Days
Section 4	2 Days
Section 5	

Preparing to Teach

- Students should be familiar with organizing the results of an experiment in a table.
- **Model with Mathematics:** In this exploration, students will gain a conceptual sense of probability by performing activities to determine the likelihood of an event. They will pursue the concept of possible outcomes, which leads to describing the likelihood of an event.

Through the Chapter

Standard	7.1	7.2	7.3	7.4	
8.F.A.1 Understand that a function is a rule that assigns to each input exactly one output. The graph of a function is the set of ordered pairs consisting of an input and the corresponding output.	●	★			
8.F.A.2 Compare properties of two functions each represented in a different way (algebraically, graphically, numerically in tables, or by verbal descriptions).			★		
8.F.A.3 Interpret the equation $y = mx + b$ as defining a linear function, whose graph is a straight line; give examples of functions that are not			●	★	

Find Your Resources Digitally

Use the resources page that is available on your *BigIdeasMath.com* dashboard. Here, you can download, customize, and print these planning resources and many more. Use the filters to view resources specific to a chapter or section.

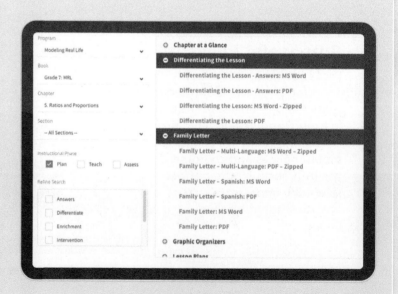

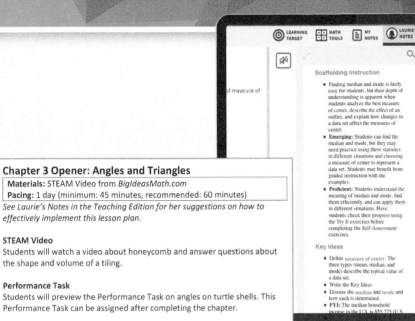

Chapter 3 Opener: Angles and Triangles

Materials: STEAM Video from *BigIdeasMath.com*
Pacing: 1 day (minimum: 45 minutes, recommended: 60 minutes)

See Laurie's Notes in the Teaching Edition for her suggestions on how to effectively implement this lesson plan.

STEAM Video
Students will watch a video about honeycomb and answer questions about the shape and volume of a tiling.

Performance Task
Students will preview the Performance Task on angles on turtle shells. This Performance Task can be assigned after completing the chapter.

Chapter Exploration
Students will preview skills taught in the chapter.
- properties of angles formed by a transversal

Access all planning resources of the Teaching Edition in the *Dynamic Classroom*. Use the customizable Lesson Plans to help teach each lesson to meet your specific classroom needs.

Review topics using the Skills Review Handbook to support students. Each topic includes a key concept and vocabulary and contains examples and exercises.

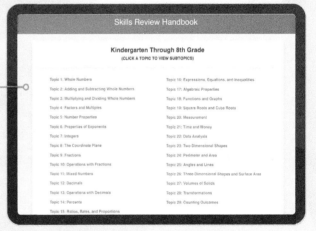

Plan Online

Remember as you are planning, that the *Dynamic Classroom* has the same interactive tools, such as the digital *Sketchpad*, that students will use to model concepts. Plan ahead by practicing these tools to guide students as they use these manipulatives and models.

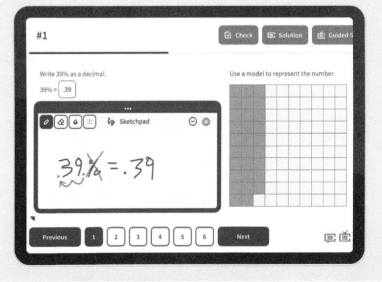

How to Use This Program: Teach

Multiple Pathways for Instruction

Big Ideas Learning provides everything at your fingertips to help you make the best instructional choices for your students.

Present all content digitally using the **Dynamic Classroom.** Send students a page link on-the-fly with **Flip-To** to direct where you want your students to go.

Have students think ahead about chapter concepts in the world around them with a **STEAM video.** Then, students transfer their learning in the **Connecting Concepts** and **Performance Task** at the end of the chapter.

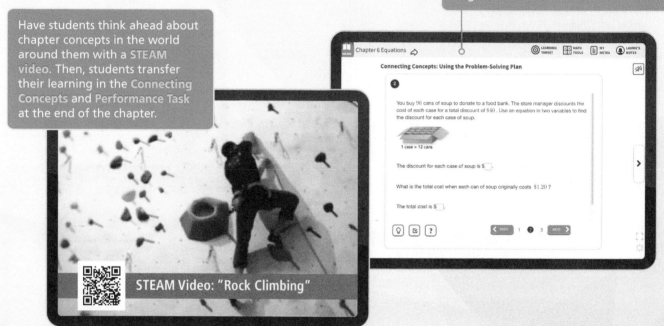

STEAM Video: "Rock Climbing"

Chapter 6 Equations

Connecting Concepts: Using the Problem-Solving Plan

You buy 96 cans of soup to donate to a food bank. The store manager discounts the cost of each case for a total discount of $40 . Use an equation in two variables to find the discount for each case of soup.

1 case = 12 cans

The discount for each case of soup is $☐ .

What is the total cost when each can of soup originally costs $1.20 ?

The total cost is $☐ .

Engage students with a creative hook at the beginning of each section with **Motivate.** This activity, written by master educator Laurie Boswell, provides a conceptual introduction for the section. Then, encourage mathematical discovery with **Exploration.**

4.1 Solving Equations Using Addition or Subtraction

Learning Target: Write and solve equations using addition or subtraction.

Success Criteria:
- I can apply the Addition and Subtraction Properties of Equality to produce equivalent equations.
- I can solve equations using addition or subtraction.
- I can apply equations involving addition or subtraction to solve real-life problems.

Motivate

? Show students a collection of algebra tiles and ask, "Can the collection be simplified? Can you remove zero pairs? What is the expression represented by the collection?"
- **Model:** As a class, model the equations $x + 3 = 7$ and $x + 2 = 5$ using algebra tiles. These do not require a zero pair to solve and will help remind students how to solve equations using algebra tiles.
- Remind students that they need to think of subtracting as *adding the opposite* when using algebra tiles (i.e., $x - 3$ as $x + (-3)$).

? "What does it mean to solve an equation?" To find the value of the variable that makes the equation true.

EXPLORATION 1 **Using Algebra Tiles to Solve Equations**

Work with a partner.

a. Use the examples to explain the meaning of each property.

Addition Property of Equality: $x + 2 = 1$
$x + 2 + 5 = 1 + 5$

Subtraction Property of Equality: $x + 2 = 1$
$x + 2 - 1 = 1 - 1$

Are these properties true for equations involving negative numbers? Explain your reasoning.

b. Write the four equations modeled by the algebra tiles. Explain how you can use algebra tiles to solve each equation. Then find the solutions.

EXAMPLE 1 Determining Whether Two Quantities are Proportional

Tell whether x and y are proportional. Explain your reasoning.

a.

x	1	2	3	4
y	−2	0	2	4

Plot the points. Draw a line through the points.

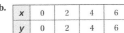

b.

x	0	2	4	6
y	0	2	4	6

Plot the points. Draw a line through the points.

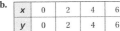

The line does *not* pass through the origin. So, x and y are not proportional.

The line passes through the origin. So, x and y are proportional.

EXAMPLE 3 Modeling Real Life

The graph shows the area y (in square feet) that a robotic vacuum cleans in x minutes. Find the area cleaned in 10 minutes.

The graph is a line through the origin, so x and y are proportional. You can write an equation to represent the relationship between area and time.

Because the graph passes through the point (1, 16), the unit rate is 16 square feet per minute and the constant of proportionality is $k = 16$. So, an equation of the line is $y = 16x$. Substitute to find the area cleaned in 10 minutes.

Robotic Vacuum

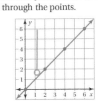

$$y = 16x \qquad \text{Write the equation.}$$
$$= 16(10) \qquad \text{Substitute 10 for } x.$$
$$= 160 \qquad \text{Multiply.}$$

So, the vacuum cleans 160 square feet in 10 minutes.

Scaffolding Instruction

- In the exploration, students discussed various methods of solving proportions. They will continue this work in the lesson.
- **Emerging:** Students may be able to create a ratio table but may struggle to write and/or solve the proportion. Students will benefit from close examination of the examples.
- **Proficient:** Students can write and solve proportions using a variety of methods (including tables). Students should review Examples 4 and 5 before proceeding to the Self-Assessment exercises.

Name _____ Date _____

Lesson 7.1 Extra Practice

You randomly choose one of the tiles shown.

1 2 3 4 5 6 7 8 9

1. How many possible outcomes are there?

2. What are the favorable outcomes of choosing a number greater than 6?

3. In how many ways can choosing a number divisible by 2 occur?

How to Use This Program: Assess

Powerful Assessment Tools

Gain insight into your students' learning with these powerful formative and summative assessment tools tailored to every learning target and standard.

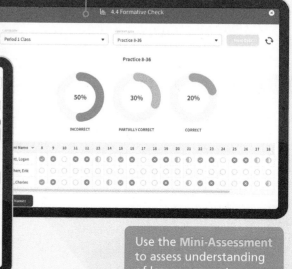

Access real-time data and navigate easily through student responses with **Formative Check**.

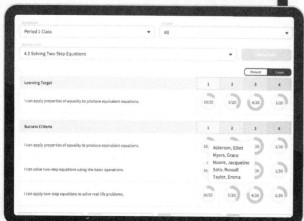

Use the **Mini-Assessment** to assess understanding of lesson concepts.

Scaffold **Practice** from the **Assignment Guide and Concept Check**. Assign print or digital versions, and project answers and solutions in class using the **Answer Presentation Tool**.

Mini-Assessment

Write the word sentence as an inequality.

1. A number a is at least 5. $a \geq 5$

2. Four times a number b is no more than -4.73. $4b \leq -4.73$

3. Tell whether -2 is a solution of $6g - 14 > -21$. not a solution

4. A rollercoaster is at most 45 meters high. Write and graph an inequality that represents the height of the rollercoaster.

   $h \leq 45;$ 40 41 42 43 44

Scaffold assignments to support all students in their learning progression. The suggested assignments are a starting point. Continue to assign additional exercises and revisit with spaced practice to move every student toward proficiency.

6.1 Practice

▶ Review & Refresh

Find the missing dimension. Use the scale 1 : 15.

	Item	Model	Actual
1.	Figure skater	Height: in.	Height: 67.5 in.
2.	Pipe	Length: 5 ft	Length: ft

Simplify the expression.

3. $2(3p - 6) + 4p$

4. $5n - 3(4n + 1)$

Assignment Guide and Concept Check

Level	Assignment 1	Assignment 2
Emerging	4, 8, 9, 10, 11, 14, 16, 17, 26, 27, 31	18, 19, 32, 33, 35, 36, 39, 40, 41, 42
Proficient	4, 8, 9, 10, 11, 17, 18, 19, 26, 28, 30, 32, 48	25, 33, 35, 37, 39, 40, 42, 43, 47
Advanced	4, 8, 9, 12, 13, 14, 23, 25, 26, 30, 32, 33, 48	38, 40, 45, 46, 47, 49, 50, 51

- Assignment 1 is for use after students complete the Self-Assessment for Concepts & Skills.
- Assignment 2 is for use after students complete the Self-Assessment for Problem Solving.
- The red exercises can be used as a concept check.

Assign Quizzes or Chapter Tests to assess understanding of section or chapter content or use Alternative Assessments and Performance Tasks, which include scoring rubrics.

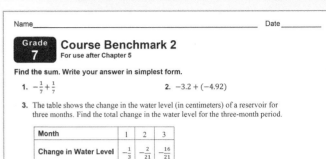

Name_____ Date_____

Grade 7 **Course Benchmark 2**
For use after Chapter 5

Find the sum. Write your answer in simplest form.

1. $-\frac{1}{7} + \frac{1}{7}$

2. $-3.2 + (-4.92)$

3. The table shows the change in the water level (in centimeters) of a reservoir for three months. Find the total change in the water level for the three-month period.

Month	1	2	3
Change in Water Level	$-\frac{1}{3}$	$-\frac{2}{21}$	$-\frac{16}{21}$

Find the difference. Write your answer in simplest form.

4. $-\frac{2}{5} - \left(-\frac{9}{5}\right)$

5. $-8.3 - 6.8$

6. At 4 P.M., the total snowfall is 3 centimeters. At 8 P.M., the total snowfall is 14 centimeters. What is the mean hourly snowfall?

Assess student learning of standards throughout the year with cumulative Course Benchmark Tests to measure progress. Use the results to help plan instruction and intervention.

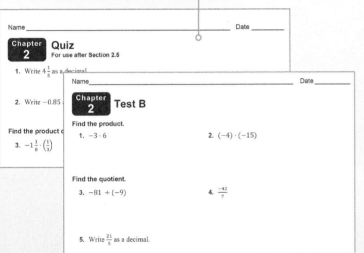

Name_____ Date_____

Chapter 2 **Quiz**
For use after Section 2.5

1. Write $4\frac{1}{5}$ as a decimal.

2. Write -0.85

Find the product

3. $-1\frac{1}{8} \cdot \left(\frac{1}{3}\right)$

Name_____ Date_____

Chapter 2 **Test B**

Find the product.

1. $-3 \cdot 6$

2. $(-4) \cdot (-15)$

Find the quotient.

3. $-81 \div (-9)$

4. $\frac{-42}{7}$

5. Write $\frac{21}{5}$ as a decimal.

Measure learning across grades with adaptive Progression Benchmark Tests.

Use the Assignment Builder to assign digital versions of the print Quizzes, Chapter Tests, and Course Benchmark Tests. Receive immediate feedback through robust reporting.

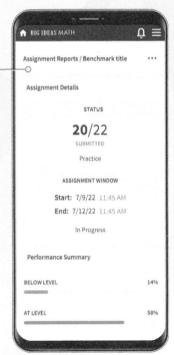

Assessment item point values are weighted. You can customize an item's total point value to fit your needs.

Strategic Support for All Learners

Support for English Language Learners

Big Ideas Learning supports English Language Learners (ELLs) with a blend of print and digital resources available in Spanish. Look to your Teaching Edition for opportunities to support all students with the language development needed for mathematical understanding.

Students' WIDA scores are a starting point. As the year progresses, students may move in and out of language levels with varying language demands of the content and as students change and grow.

Clarify, Connect, and Scaffold

- Clarify language that may be difficult or confusing for ELLs
- Connect new learning to something students already know
- Differentiate student comprehension while completing practice exercises
- Target Beginner, Intermediate, and Advanced ELLs, which correspond to **WIDA** reading, writing, speaking, and listening language mastery levels

Practice Language and Content

- Practice math while improving language skills
- Use language as a resource to develop procedural fluency

Assess Understanding

- Check for development of mathematical reasoning
- Informally assess student comprehension of concepts

WIDA 1: Entering
WIDA 2: Emerging

WIDA 3: Developing
WIDA 4: Expanding

WIDA 5: Bridging
WIDA 6: Reaching

ELL Support

After demonstrating Example 1, have students practice language by working in pairs to complete Try It Exercises 1–3. Have one student ask another, "What is the first step? Do you add or subtract? What is the solution?" Have students alternate roles.

- **Beginner:** Write the steps and provide one-word answers.
- **Intermediate:** Answer with phrases or simple sentences such as, "First, I add five."
- **Advanced:** Answer with detailed sentences such as, "First, I add five to each side of the equation."

Family Letters in multiple languages

Nome_____

Capítulo 2 **Multiplicando e dividindo números racionais**

Prezada Família,

Toda família t...
ingredientes s...
molhos, crosta...
possibilidades...

Você e seu(ua)...
que decidir qu...
houver apenas...
Mas para um g...

Você pode est...
grande. Multip...

Nom_____

Chapitre 2 **Multiplier et diviser les nombres rationnels**

Chère famille,

Chaque famille a une pizza préférée. Les pizzas sont inhabituelles dans le sens où les ingrédients sont généralement personnalisés. La variété des viandes, des légumes, des sauces, des croûtes, des herbes et des épices produit un grand éventail de possibilités.

Vous pourriez vous amusez avec votre élève à faire une pizza maison. Tout d'abord, vous devez décider du nombre de pizzas dont vous avez besoin et de la taille de chacune. Si deux personnes vont manger seulement, une petite pizza pourrait faire le truc. Mais pour un grand groupe, vous aurez peut-être besoin de plusieurs pizzas.

Perímetro y área/Geometría

Big Ideas Math® Game Closet

Elige Su Polígono

Materiales:
- Tablero de juego
- Lápiz
- Papel

Instrucciones:
Juega en pares. Alumnos se turnan para elegir un polígono y hallar su área. El juego continúa como alumnos añaden cada nueva área a sus áreas anteriores, hasta que todos los polígonos sean usados. Polígonos pueden ser usados solamente una vez. Todas las medidas son pulgadas.

Games available in Spanish

Multi-Language Glossary

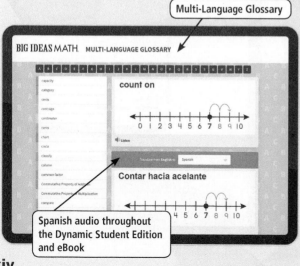

BIG IDEAS MATH. MULTI-LANGUAGE GLOSSARY

capacity
category
cents
cent sign
centimeter
cents
chart
circle
classify
column
common factor
Commutative Property of Addition
Commutative Property of Multiplication
compare

count on

0 1 2 3 4 5 6 7 8 9 10

Translate from English to Spanish

Contar hacia acelante

4 5 6 7 8 9 10

Spanish audio throughout the Dynamic Student Edition and eBook

Nombre _____ Fecha_____

Capítulo 1 **Examen A**

Encuentra el valor absoluto.

1. $|-4|$

2. $\left|-\frac{5}{8}\right|$

Encuentra la suma o la resta. Escribe fracciones en su mínima expresión.

3. $-7 + (-3)$

4. $8 - (-5)$

Assess students with Spanish quizzes and chapter tests

Students Get the Support They Need, When They Need It

There will be times throughout this course when students may need help. Whether students missed a section, did not understand the content, or just want to review, take advantage of the resources provided in the *Dynamic Student Edition*.

Students use the **Self-Assessment** tool to keep track of their understanding of the section's Learning Target and Success Criteria.

Students can take notes throughout the lesson using the **My Notes** function. These notes will be organized for them by chapter and section.

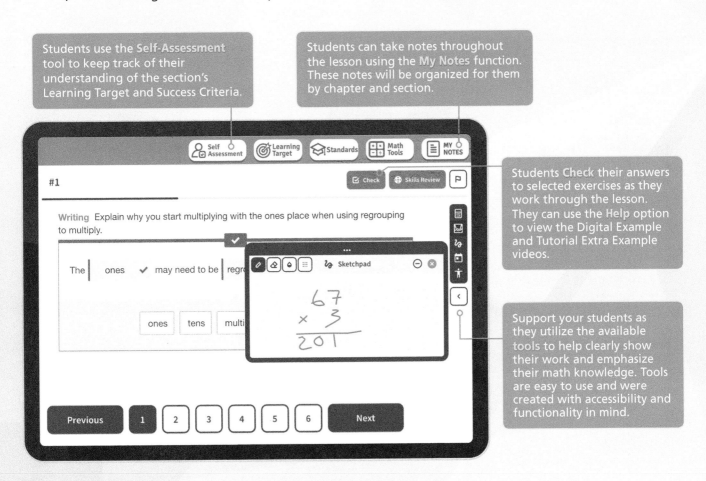

Students **Check** their answers to selected exercises as they work through the lesson. They can use the **Help** option to view the Digital Example and Tutorial Extra Example videos.

Support your students as they utilize the available tools to help clearly show their work and emphasize their math knowledge. Tools are easy to use and were created with accessibility and functionality in mind.

USE THESE QR CODES TO EXPLORE ADDITIONAL RESOURCES

Multi-Language Glossary

View definitions and examples of vocabulary words

Skills Trainer

Practice previously learned skills

Interactive Tools

Visualize mathematical concepts

Skills Review Handbook

A collection of review topics

Meeting the Needs of All Learners

Resources at Your Fingertips

This robust, innovative program utilizes a mixture of print and digital resources that allow for a variety of instructional approaches. The program encompasses hands-on activities, interactive explorations, videos, scaffolded instruction, learning support, and many more resources that appeal to students and teachers alike.

PRINT RESOURCES

Student Edition

Teaching Edition

Student Journal

Resources by Chapter
- Family Letter
- Warm-Ups
- Extra Practice
- Reteach
- Enrichment and Extension
- Chapter Self-Assessment
- Puzzle Time

Assessment Book
- Prerequisite Skills Practice
- Pre- and Post-Course Tests
- Course Benchmark Tests
- Quizzes
- Chapter Tests
- Alternative Assessments
- STEAM Performance Tasks

Rich Math Tasks
Skills Review Handbook

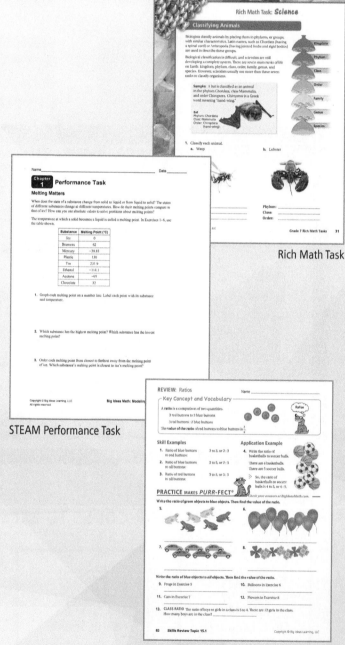

Rich Math Task

STEAM Performance Task

Skills Review Handbook

Through Program Resources

TECHNOLOGY RESOURCES

Dynamic Student Edition
- Interactive Tools
- Interactive Explorations
- Digital Examples
- Tutorial Extra Example Videos
- Self-Assessments

Dynamic Classroom
- Laurie's Notes
- Interactive Tools
- Interactive Explorations
- Digital Examples with PowerPoints
- Formative Check
- Flip-To
- Digital Warm-Ups and Closures
- Mini-Assessments

Resources
- Answer Presentation Tool
- Chapter at a Glance
- Complete Materials List
- Cross-Curricular Projects
- Skills Trainer
- Vocabulary Flash Cards
- STEAM Videos
- Game Library
- Multi-Language Glossary
- Lesson Plans
- Differentiating the Lesson
- Graphic Organizers
- Pacing Guides
- Worked-Out Solutions Key
- Math Tool Paper
- Family Letters
- Homework App
- Skills Review Handbook

Dynamic Assessment System
- Practice
- Assessments
- Progression Benchmark Tests
- Detailed Reports

Video Support for Teachers
- Life on Earth Videos
- Professional Development Videos
- Concepts and Tools Videos

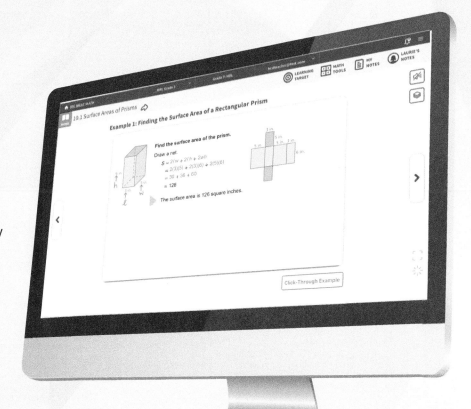

Cohesive Progressions

		Grade K	Grade 1	Grade 2	Grade 3
Number and Quantity		**Counting and Cardinality**			
		Know number names and the count sequence. Count to tell the number of objects. Compare numbers. *Chapters 1–4, 6, 8–10*			
		Number and Operations – Base Ten			
		Work with numbers 11–19 to gain foundations for place value. *Chapter 8*	Extend the counting sequence. Use place value and properties of operations to add and subtract. *Chapters 6–9*	Use place value and properties of operations to add and subtract. *Chapters 2–10, 14*	Use place value and properties of operations to perform multi-digit arithmetic. *Chapters 7–9, 12*
					Num. and Oper. – Fractions
					Understand fractions as numbers. *Chapters 10, 11, 14*
Algebra and Functions		**Operations and Algebraic Thinking**			
		Understand addition as putting together and adding to, and understand subtraction as taking apart and taking from. *Chapters 5–7*	Solve problems involving addition and subtraction within 20. Apply properties of operations. Work with addition and subtraction equations. *Chapters 1–5, 10, 11*	Solve problems involving addition and subtraction within 20. Work with equal groups of objects. *Chapters 1–6, 15*	Solve problems involving multiplication and division within 100. Apply properties of multiplication. Solve problems involving the four operations, and identify and explain patterns in arithmetic. *Chapters 1–5, 8, 9, and 14*
Geometry		**Geometry**			
		Identify and describe shapes. Analyze, compare, create, and compose shapes. *Chapters 11, 12*	Reason with shapes and their attributes. *Chapters 12, 14*	Reason with shapes and their attributes. *Chapter 15*	Reason with shapes and their attributes. *Chapters 10, 13*
Measurement, Data, and Probability		**Measurement and Data**			
		Describe and compare measurable attributes. Classify objects and count the number of objects in each category. *Chapters 4, 11, 13*	Measure lengths indirectly and by iterating length units. Tell and write time. Represent and interpret data. *Chapters 10–12*	Measure and estimate lengths in standard units. Relate addition and subtraction to length. Work with time and money. Represent and interpret data. *Chapters 11–14*	Solve problems involving measurement and estimation of intervals of time, liquid volumes, and masses of objects. Represent and interpret data. Understand the concepts of area and perimeter. *Chapters 6, 12, 14, 15*

Through the Grades

Grade 4	Grade 5	Grade 6	Grade 7	Grade 8
Number and Operations – Base Ten		**The Number System**		
Generalize place value understanding for multi-digit whole numbers. Use place value and properties of operations to perform multi-digit arithmetic. *Chapters 1–5*	Understand the place value system. Perform operations with multi-digit whole numbers and with decimals to hundredths. *Chapters 1, 3–7*	Perform operations with multi-digit numbers and find common factors and multiples. *Chapter 1* Divide fractions by fractions. *Chapter 2* Extend understanding of numbers to the rational number system. *Chapter 8*	Perform operations with rational numbers. *Chapters 1, 2*	Extend understanding of numbers to the real number system. *Chapter 9*
Number and Operations – Fractions		**Ratios and Proportional Relationships**		
Extend understanding of fraction equivalence and ordering. Build fractions from unit fractions. Understand decimal notation for fractions, and compare decimal fractions. *Chapters 7–11*	Add, subtract, multiply, and divide fractions. *Chapters 6, 8–11*	Use ratios to solve problems. *Chapters 3, 4*	Use proportional relationships to solve problems. *Chapters 5, 6*	
Operations and Algebraic Thinking		**Expressions and Equations**		
Use the four operations with whole numbers to solve problems. Understand factors and multiples. Generate and analyze patterns. *Chapters 2–6, 12*	Write and interpret numerical expressions. Analyze patterns and relationships. *Chapters 2, 12*	Perform arithmetic with algebraic expressions. *Chapter 5* Solve one-variable equations and inequalities. *Chapters 6, 8* Analyze relationships between dependent and independent variables. *Chapter 6*	Write equivalent expressions. *Chapter 3* Use numerical and algebraic expressions, equations, and inequalities to solve problems. *Chapters 3, 4, 6*	Understand the connections between proportional relationships, lines, and linear equations. *Chapter 4* Solve linear equations and systems of linear equations. *Chapters 1, 5* Work with radicals and integer exponents. *Chapters 8, 9*
				Functions
				Define, evaluate, and compare functions, and use functions to model relationships between quantities. *Chapter 7*
Geometry				
Draw and identify lines and angles, and classify shapes by properties of their lines and angles. *Chapters 13, 14*	Graph points on the coordinate plane. Classify two-dimensional figures into categories based on their properties. *Chapters 12, 14*	Solve real-world and mathematical problems involving area, surface area, and volume. *Chapter 7*	Draw, construct, and describe geometrical figures and describe the relationships between them. *Chapters 5, 9, 10* Solve problems involving angle measure, area, surface area, and volume. *Chapters 9, 10*	Understand congruence and similarity. *Chapters 2, 3* Use the Pythagorean Theorem. *Chapter 9* Solve problems involving volumes of cylinders, cones, and spheres. *Chapter 10*
Measurement and Data		**Statistics and Probability**		
Solve problems involving measurement and conversion of measurements from a larger unit to a smaller unit. Represent and interpret data. Understand angles and measure angles. *Chapters 10–13*	Convert measurement units within a given measurement system. Represent and interpret data. Understand volume. *Chapters 11, 13*	Develop understanding of statistical variability and summarize and describe distributions. *Chapters 9, 10*	Make inferences about a population, compare two populations, and use probability models. *Chapters 7, 8*	Investigate patterns of association in bivariate data. *Chapter 6*

Standard Code	Standard	Grade 8
The Number System		
8.NS.A.1	Know that numbers that are not rational are called irrational. Understand informally that every number has a decimal expansion; for rational numbers show that the decimal expansion repeats eventually, and convert a decimal expansion which repeats eventually into a rational number.	**9.4, 9.5**
8.NS.A.2	Use rational approximations of irrational numbers to compare the size of irrational numbers, locate them approximately on a number line diagram, and estimate the value of expressions (e.g., π^2).	**9.5**
Expressions and Equations		
8.EE.A.1	Know and apply the properties of integer exponents to generate equivalent numerical expressions.	**8.2, 8.3, 8.4, 8.5, 8.6, 8.7**
8.EE.A.2	Use square root and cube root symbols to represent solutions to equations of the form $x^2 = p$ and $x^3 = p$, where p is a positive rational number. Evaluate square roots of small perfect squares and cube roots of small perfect cubes. Know that $\sqrt{2}$ is irrational.	**9.1, 9.2, 9.3,** 9.5, 9.6, 10.1, 10.2, 10.3
8.EE.A.3	Use numbers expressed in the form of a single digit times an integer power of 10 to estimate very large or very small quantities, and to express how many times as much one is than the other.	**8.5, 8.6, 8.7**
8.EE.A.4	Perform operations with numbers expressed in scientific notation, including problems where both decimal and scientific notation are used. Use scientific notation and choose units of appropriate size for measurements of very large or very small quantities (e.g., use millimeters per year for seafloor spreading). Interpret scientific notation that has been generated by technology.	8.5, **8.6, 8.7**
8.EE.B.5	Graph proportional relationships, interpreting the unit rate as the slope of the graph. Compare two different proportional relationships represented in different ways.	**4.3, 7.2, 7.3**
8.EE.B.6	Use similar triangles to explain why the slope m is the same between any two distinct points on a non-vertical line in the coordinate plane; derive the equation $y = mx$ for a line through the origin and the equation $y = mx + b$ for a line intercepting the vertical axis at b.	**4.2, 4.3, 4.4**

Boldface indicates a lesson in which the standard is a primary focus.

Mathematical Content Correlated to Grade 8

Standard Code	Standard	Grade 8
8.EE.C.7	Solve linear equations in one variable.	
	a. Give examples of linear equations in one variable with one solution, infinitely many solutions, or no solutions. Show which of these possibilities is the case by successively transforming the given equation into simpler forms, until an equivalent equation of the form $x = a$, $a = a$, or $a = b$ results (where a and b are different numbers).	**1.1, 1.2, 1.3,** 5.4
	b. Solve linear equations with rational number coefficients, including equations whose solutions require expanding expressions using the distributive property and collecting like terms.	**1.1, 1.2, 1.3,** 2.6, 2.7, 3.1, 3.2, 3.3, 3.4, 4.1, 4.3, 4.5, 4.6, 5.2, 5.3, 5.4, 6.2, 7.2, 10.1, 10.2, 10.4
8.EE.C.8	Analyze and solve pairs of simultaneous linear equations.	
	a. Understand that solutions to a system of two linear equations in two variables correspond to points of intersection of their graphs, because points of intersection satisfy both equations simultaneously.	**5.1,** 5.2, 5.3, **5.4**
	b. Solve systems of two linear equations in two variables algebraically, and estimate solutions by graphing the equations. Solve simple cases by inspection.	**5.1, 5.2, 5.3, 5.4**
	c. Solve real-world and mathematical problems leading to two linear equations in two variables.	**5.1, 5.2, 5.3, 5.4**
Functions		
8.F.A.1	Understand that a function is a rule that assigns to each input exactly one output. The graph of a function is the set of ordered pairs consisting of an input and the corresponding output.	**7.1, 7.2,** 7.3, 7.4
8.F.A.2	Compare properties of two functions each represented in a different way (algebraically, graphically, numerically in tables, or by verbal descriptions).	**7.3,** 7.4
8.F.A.3	Interpret the equation $y = mx + b$ as defining a linear function, whose graph is a straight line; give examples of functions that are not linear.	**7.3,** 7.4

Boldface indicates a lesson in which the standard is a primary focus.

Common Core State Standards for

Standard Code	Standard	Grade 8
8.F.B.4	Construct a function to model a linear relationship between two quantities. Determine the rate of change and initial value of the function from a description of a relationship or from two (x, y) values, including reading these from a table or from a graph. Interpret the rate of change and initial value of a linear function in terms of the situation it models, and in terms of its graph or a table of values.	**4.6, 4.7**, 5.1, 5.2, 5.3, 5.4, 6.2, **7.2**, **7.3**, 7.4
8.F.B.5	Describe qualitatively the functional relationship between two quantities by analyzing a graph (e.g., where the function is increasing or decreasing, linear or nonlinear). Sketch a graph that exhibits the qualitative features of a function that has been described verbally.	**7.5**
Geometry		
8.G.A.1	Verify experimentally the properties of rotations, reflections, and translations:	
	a. Lines are taken to lines, and line segments to line segments of the same length.	**2.1, 2.2, 2.3**, 2.4, **3.1**
	b. Angles are taken to angles of the same measure.	**2.1, 2.2, 2.3**, 2.4, **3.1**
	c. Parallel lines are taken to parallel lines.	**2.1, 2.2, 2.3**, 2.4, **3.1**
8.G.A.2	Understand that a two-dimensional figure is congruent to another if the second can be obtained from the first by a sequence of rotations, reflections, and translations; given two congruent figures, describe a sequence that exhibits the congruence between them.	**2.4**, 2.6
8.G.A.3	Describe the effect of dilations, translations, rotations, and reflections on two-dimensional figures using coordinates	**2.1, 2.2, 2.3, 2.4, 2.5**, 2.6
8.G.A.4	Understand that a two-dimensional figure is similar to another if the second can be obtained from the first by a sequence of rotations, reflections, translations, and dilations; given two similar two-dimensional figures, describe a sequence that exhibits the similarity between them.	**2.6**, 3.4, 4.2

Boldface indicates a lesson in which the standard is a primary focus.

Mathematical Content Correlated to Grade 8

Standard Code	Standard	Grade 8
8.G.A.5	Use informal arguments to establish facts about the angle sum and exterior angle of triangles, about the angles created when parallel lines are cut by a transversal, and the angle-angle criterion for similarity of triangles.	**3.1, 3.2, 3.4**
8.G.B.6	Explain a proof of the Pythagorean Theorem and its converse.	**9.2, 9.6**
8.G.B.7	Apply the Pythagorean Theorem to determine unknown side lengths in right triangles in real-world and mathematical problems in two and three dimensions.	**9.2**, 9.5, 9.6
8.G.B.8	Apply the Pythagorean Theorem to find the distance between two points in a coordinate system.	**9.2**, 9.5, 9.6
8.G.C.9	Know the formulas for the volumes of cones, cylinders, and spheres and use them to solve real-world and mathematical problems.	**10.1, 10.2, 10.3**
Statistics and Probability		
8.SP.A.1	Construct and interpret scatter plots for bivariate measurement data to investigate patterns of association between two quantities. Describe patterns such as clustering, outliers, positive or negative association, linear association, and nonlinear association.	**6.1, 6.2**
8.SP.A.2	Know that straight lines are widely used to model relationships between two quantitative variables. For scatter plots that suggest a linear association, informally fit a straight line, and informally assess the model fit by judging the closeness of the data points to the line.	**6.2**
8.SP.A.3	Use the equation of a linear model to solve problems in the context of bivariate measurement data, interpreting the slope and intercept.	**6.2**
8.SP.A.4	Understand that patterns of association can also be seen in bivariate categorical data by displaying frequencies and relative frequencies in a two-way table. Construct and interpret a two-way table summarizing data on two categorical variables collected from the same subjects. Use relative frequencies calculated for rows or columns to describe possible association between the two variables.	**6.3**

Boldface indicates a lesson in which the standard is a primary focus.

Suggested Pacing

Chapters 1–10   146 Days

Chapter 1   (13 Days)

Chapter Opener	1 Day
Section 1.1	2 Days
Section 1.2	2 Days
Section 1.3	3 Days
Section 1.4	2 Days
Connecting Concepts	1 Day
Chapter Review	1 Day
Chapter Test	1 Day
Year-To-Date	**13 Days**

Chapter 2   (18 Days)

Chapter Opener	1 Day
Section 2.1	2 Days
Section 2.2	2 Days
Section 2.3	2 Days
Section 2.4	2 Days
Section 2.5	2 Days
Section 2.6	2 Days
Section 2.7	2 Days
Connecting Concepts	1 Day
Chapter Review	1 Day
Chapter Test	1 Day
Year-To-Date	**31 Days**

Chapter 3   (12 Days)

Chapter Opener	1 Day
Section 3.1	2 Days
Section 3.2	2 Days
Section 3.3	2 Days
Section 3.4	2 Days
Connecting Concepts	1 Day
Chapter Review	1 Day
Chapter Test	1 Day
Year-To-Date	**43 Days**

Chapter 4   (18 Days)

Chapter Opener	1 Day
Section 4.1	2 Days
Section 4.2	2 Days
Section 4.3	2 Days
Section 4.4	2 Days
Section 4.5	2 Days
Section 4.6	2 Days
Section 4.7	2 Days
Connecting Concepts	1 Day
Chapter Review	1 Day
Chapter Test	1 Day
Year-To-Date	**61 Days**

Chapter 5   (12 Days)

Chapter Opener	1 Day
Section 5.1	2 Days
Section 5.2	2 Days
Section 5.3	2 Days
Section 5.4	2 Days
Connecting Concepts	1 Day
Chapter Review	1 Day
Chapter Test	1 Day
Year-To-Date	**73 Days**

Chapter 6   (13 Days)

Chapter Opener	1 Day
Section 6.1	2 Days
Section 6.2	3 Days
Section 6.3	2 Days
Section 6.4	2 Days
Connecting Concepts	1 Day
Chapter Review	1 Day
Chapter Test	1 Day
Year-To-Date	**86 Days**

Chapter 7 (14 Days)

Chapter Opener	1 Day
Section 7.1	2 Days
Section 7.2	2 Days
Section 7.3	2 Days
Section 7.4	2 Days
Section 7.5	2 Days
Connecting Concepts	1 Day
Chapter Review	1 Day
Chapter Test	1 Day
Year-To-Date	**100 Days**

Chapter 8 (18 Days)

Chapter Opener	1 Day
Section 8.1	2 Days
Section 8.2	2 Days
Section 8.3	2 Days
Section 8.4	2 Days
Section 8.5	2 Days
Section 8.6	2 Days
Section 8.7	2 Days
Connecting Concepts	1 Day
Chapter Review	1 Day
Chapter Test	1 Day
Year-To-Date	**118 Days**

Chapter 9 (16 Days)

Chapter Opener	1 Day
Section 9.1	2 Days
Section 9.2	2 Days
Section 9.3	2 Days
Section 9.4	2 Days
Section 9.5	2 Days
Section 9.6	2 Days
Connecting Concepts	1 Day
Chapter Review	1 Day
Chapter Test	1 Day
Year-To-Date	**134 Days**

Chapter 10 (12 Days)

Chapter Opener	1 Day
Section 10.1	2 Days
Section 10.2	2 Days
Section 10.3	2 Days
Section 10.4	2 Days
Connecting Concepts	1 Day
Chapter Review	1 Day
Chapter Test	1 Day
Year-To-Date	**146 Days**

An editable version of the Pacing Guide is available in two forms (regular and block scheduling) at *BigIdeasMath.com*.

Equations

■ Major Topic
■ Supporting Topic
■ Additional Topic

Transformations

Angles and Triangles

■ Major Topic
■ Supporting Topic
■ Additional Topic

Graphing and Writing Linear Equations

4

5 Systems of Linear Equations

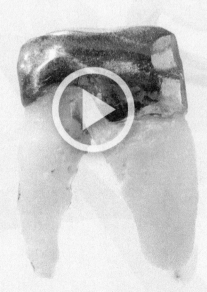

■ Major Topic
■ Supporting Topic
■ Additional Topic

Data Analysis and Displays

xli

7 Functions

■ Major Topic
■ Supporting Topic
■ Additional Topic

Exponents and Scientific Notation

8

Real Numbers and the Pythagorean Theorem

■ Major Topic
■ Supporting Topic
■ Additional Topic

Volume and Similar Solids

1 Equations

Chapter Learning Target:
Understand equations.

Chapter Success Criteria:
- I can identify key words and phrases to solve equations.
- I can write word sentences as equations.
- I can explain how to solve equations.
- I can model different types of equations to solve real-life problems.

STEAM Video: "Training for a Half Marathon"

Laurie's Notes

Chapter 1 Overview

Welcome to a new school year and a class of young teenagers with high energy, varied interests, and great excitement about the year to come. Sharing what the classroom climate and culture will be, along with an overview of the first chapter, will help students form a positive mindset as they begin the year.

From the first day, you want to establish a norm in your classroom that each student will discuss mathematical problems with a partner or group. Explorations at the beginning of each lesson, and Formative Assessment Tips such as *Turn and Talk*, are explicit opportunities for student engagement. I hope you find the suggestions in Laurie's Notes to be helpful in promoting student dialogue and engagement.

A major strand in this course is expressions and equations, content that naturally connects to later work with functions. In this chapter, students will build upon prior skills with equation solving while integrating a review of operations with rational numbers. You will learn a great deal about the strengths and misconceptions your students have. Be alert to two common areas of difficulty, computational errors and representation.

Students who are not proficient in rational-number operations will be challenged to solve equations without making errors. Trust that there will be opportunities throughout the year to practice and reinforce these skills. Integrate a review by writing equations in different forms as shown below.

$$-0.8x = -9.6 \qquad -\frac{4}{5}x = -9\frac{3}{5}$$

Representation is another area of difficulty. All of the equations shown are equivalent.

$$-\frac{x}{5} + 3 = -11 \qquad 3 - \frac{1}{5}x = -11 \qquad -11 = -\frac{1}{5}x + 3$$

The underlying mathematics of why they are equivalent must be shared with students, so they become more confident in understanding which operations are being represented.

Chapter 1 assumes that students have prior knowledge of solving one- and two-step equations. Algebra tiles can be used in the first three lessons to support learners. The visual models help students make sense of the problem-solving process.

$$4x \quad - \quad 7 \quad = \quad 3x \quad - \quad 1$$

The chapter concludes with a lesson on literal equations, where students will rewrite equations and formulas.

Suggested Pacing

Chapter Opener	1 Day
Section 1	2 Days
Section 2	2 Days
Section 3	3 Days
Section 4	2 Days
Connecting Concepts	1 Day
Chapter Review	1 Day
Chapter Test	1 Day
Total Chapter 1	13 Days
Year-to-Date	13 Days

Chapter Learning Target
Understand equations.

Chapter Success Criteria
- Identify key words and phrases to solve equations.
- Write word sentences as equations.
- Explain how to solve equations.
- Model different types of equations to solve real-life problems.

Chapter 1 Learning Targets and Success Criteria

Section	Learning Target	Success Criteria
1.1 Solving Simple Equations	Write and solve one-step equations.	• Apply properties of equality to produce equivalent equations. • Solve equations using addition, subtraction, multiplication, or division. • Use equations to model and solve real-life problems.
1.2 Solving Multi-Step Equations	Write and solve multi-step equations.	• Apply properties to produce equivalent equations. • Solve multi-step equations. • Use multi-step equations to model and solve real-life problems.
1.3 Solving Equations with Variables on Both Sides	Write and solve equations with variables on both sides.	• Explain how to solve an equation with variables on both sides. • Determine whether an equation has one solution, no solution, or infinitely many solutions. • Use equations with variables on both sides to model and solve real-life problems.
1.4 Rewriting Equations and Formulas	Solve literal equations for given variables and convert temperatures.	• Use properties of equality to rewrite literal equations. • Use a formula to convert temperatures.

Progressions

Grade 7	Grade 8	High School
• Add, subtract, factor, and expand linear expressions with rational coefficients. • Solve multi-step problems posed with positive and negative rational numbers. • Solve two-step equations. Compare algebraic solutions to arithmetic solutions.	• Show that a linear equation in one variable has one solution, infinitely many solutions, or no solution by transforming the equation into simpler forms. • Solve linear equations with rational number coefficients, including equations whose solutions require expanding expressions using the distributive property and collecting like terms.	• Solve multi-step linear equations and use them to solve real-life problems. • Rewrite and use literal equations and common formulas. • Solve systems of linear equations by graphing, by substitution, and by elimination.

Through the Chapter

Standard	1.1	1.2	1.3	1.4
8.EE.C.7 Solve linear equations in one variable.	●	●		■
8.EE.C.7a Give examples of linear equations in one variable with one solution, infinitely many solutions, or no solutions. Show which of these possibilities is the case by successively transforming the given equation into simpler forms, until an equivalent equation of the form $x = a$, $a = a$, or $a = b$ results (where a and b are different numbers).	●	●	★	
8.EE.C.7b Solve linear equations with rational number coefficients, including equations whose solutions require expanding expressions using the distributive property and collecting like terms.	●	●	★	

Key

▲ = preparing   ★ = complete
● = learning   ■ = extending

STEAM Video

1. 8.2 mi

2. 4.1875 mi

Performance Task

Sample answer: age, activity level

Mathematical Practices

Students have opportunities to develop aspects of the mathematical practices throughout the chapter. Here are some examples.

1. **Make Sense of Problems and Persevere in Solving Them**
   1.2 Math Practice note, *p. 11*
2. **Reason Abstractly and Quantitatively**
   1.1 Exercise 51, *p. 10*
3. **Construct Viable Arguments and Critique the Reasoning of Others**
   1.4 Exercise 19, *p. 29*
4. **Model with Mathematics**
   1.2 Exercise 28, *p. 16*
5. **Use Appropriate Tools Strategically**
   1.1 Math Practice note, *p. 3*
6. **Attend to Precision**
   1.3 Exercise 49, *p. 24*
7. **Look for and Make Use of Structure**
   1.3 Math Practice note, *p. 19*
8. **Look for and Express Regularity in Repeated Reasoning**
   1.4 Math Practice note, *p. 25*

STEAM Video

Before the Video

- To introduce the STEAM Video, read aloud the first paragraph of Training for a Half Marathon and discuss the question with your students.
- ❓ "How can a runner develop a routine to help train for a half marathon?"

During the Video

- The video shows Alex and Enid training for a half marathon.
- ❓ Pause the video at **0:59** and ask, "How many miles do Alex and Enid want to average per day?" 4.37 miles
- ❓ "How can they find the average number of miles they run per day?" Find the total number of miles and divide by the number of days.
- ❓ "Do Alex and Enid need to run 4.37 miles each day? Explain." No, they can run more miles on some days and less on others.
- Watch the remainder of the video.

After the Video

- ❓ "How did Alex and Enid calculate how many miles they must run on Friday?" They subtracted the total number of miles without Friday from the total number of miles they want to run for the whole week.
- Have students work with a partner to answer Questions 1 and 2.
- As students discuss and answer the questions, listen for understanding of writing and solving simple equations.

Performance Task

- Use this information to spark students' interest and promote thinking about real-life problems.
- ❓ Ask, "What factors might affect the range of a person's target heart rate?"
- After completing the chapter, students will have gained the knowledge needed to complete "Target Heart Rates."

Training for a Half Marathon

A half marathon is a race that is 13.1 miles long. How can a runner develop a routine to help train for a half marathon?

Watch the STEAM Video "Training for a Half Marathon." Then answer the following questions.

1. Alex and Enid are training for a half marathon. They run four days each week, as shown in the table. How far do they have to run on Saturday to average 4.75 miles per running day in Week Nine?

	Distance Ran (miles)			
	Monday	**Wednesday**	**Friday**	**Saturday**
Week Six	2.5	2.6	2.4	7.0
Week Seven	3.3	2.8	2.9	7.0
Week Eight	3.3	3.1	2.6	8.5
Week Nine	3.7	3.0	4.1	x

2. Assuming they meet their goal on Saturday in Week Nine, what is the average number of miles per running day over the 4 weeks in the table?

Target Heart Rates

After completing this chapter, you will be able to use the concepts you learned to answer the questions in the *STEAM Video Performance Task*. You will be given information about a person's heart rate.

Resting heart rate

$$\text{Day } 1 = x$$
$$\text{Day } 2 = x$$
$$\text{Day } 3 = x \quad \Big\} \quad \text{5-day average} = 62$$
$$\text{Day } 4 = x$$
$$\text{Day } 5 = 58$$

You will be asked to find the range of a person's target heart rate. What factors might affect the range of a person's target heart rate?

Getting Ready for Chapter

Chapter Exploration

1. **Work with a partner. Use algebra tiles to model and solve each equation.**

   a. $x + 3 = -3$

   $\boxed{+} = +1$ $\boxed{-} = -1$ $\boxed{+} = x$

   $\boxed{+}\ \boxed{+}\ \boxed{+}\ \boxed{+} = \boxed{-}\ \boxed{-}\ \boxed{-}$ Model the equation $x + 3 = -3$.

   Add three -1 tiles to each side.

   Remove the zero pairs from the left side.

   Write the solution of the equation.

   b. $-3 = x - 2$

   $\boxed{-}\ \boxed{-}\ \boxed{-} = \boxed{+}\ \boxed{-}\ \boxed{-}$ Model the equation $-3 = x - 2$.

   Add two $+1$ tiles to each side.

   Remove the zero pairs from the each side.

   Write the solution of the equation.

   c. $x - 4 = 1$ **d.** $x + 5 = -2$ **e.** $-7 = x + 4$

   f. $x + 6 = 7$ **g.** $-5 + x = -3$ **h.** $-4 = x - 4$

2. **WRITE GUIDELINES** Work with a partner. Use your models in Exercise 1 to summarize the *algebraic steps* that you can use to solve an equation.

Vocabulary

The following vocabulary term is defined in this chapter. Think about what the term might mean and record your thoughts.

literal equation

Laurie's Notes

Chapter Exploration

- **MP2 Reason Abstractly and Quantitatively:** Students should be familiar with algebra tiles from previous courses. Algebra tiles can help students make sense of equations. Algebra tiles are concrete representation, deepening students' understanding of what it means to solve an equation.

- **?** "What does it mean to solve an equation using algebra tiles?" To get one variable tile by itself. Remind students that this is called "isolating the variable."

- For Exercise 1, work through parts (a) and (b) as a class. Then have students solve the remaining equations with a partner. Have each pair compare their answers with another pair. Discuss any discrepancies as a class.

- Allow time for pairs to complete Exercise 2 before discussing their guidelines as a class.

Vocabulary

- These terms represent some of the vocabulary that students will encounter in Chapter 1. Discuss the terms as a class.

- Where have students heard the term *literal equation* outside of a math classroom? In what contexts? Students may not be able to write the actual definition, but they may write phrases associated with a *literal equation*.

- Allowing students to discuss these terms now will prepare them for understanding the terms as they are presented in the chapter.

- When students encounter a new definition, encourage them to write in their *Student Journals.* They will revisit these definitions during the Chapter Review.

ELL Support

Write the phrases *is greater than, is less than,* and *is equal to* in one column. Write the symbols >, <, and = in a second column, randomly ordered. Have students match the symbols to their meanings. Then write the word *equation.* Ask how it is similar to any of the phrases they reviewed. Underline *equa.* Explain that the root word *equa* means "similar" or "the same." Review that an equation is a mathematical sentence that uses an equal sign to show that two expressions are equal. Tell students that a strategy for guessing the meaning of a word is to look for a root word they already know within the unknown word.

Topics for Review

- Checking a Solution
- Equations
- Equivalent Equations
- Formulas
- Inverse Operations
- Operations with Rational Numbers
- Order of Operations
- Reciprocals
- Simplifying Algebraic Expressions
- Solutions
- Two-Step Equations

Chapter Exploration

1. **a.** $x = -6$
    b. $x = -1$
    c. $x = 5$
    d. $x = -7$
    e. $x = -11$
    f. $x = 1$
    g. $x = 2$
    h. $x = 0$

2. *Sample answer:* Apply properties of equality to isolate the variable.

STATE STANDARDS
8.EE.C.7a, 8.EE.C.7b

Learning Target

Write and solve one-step equations.

Success Criteria

- Apply properties of equality to produce equivalent equations.
- Solve equations using addition, subtraction, multiplication, or division.
- Use equations to model and solve real-life problems.

Warm Up

Cumulative, vocabulary, and prerequisite skills practice opportunities are available in the *Resources by Chapter* or at *BigIdeasMath.com*.

ELL Support

Students may be familiar with the word *property* from everyday life as it refers to real estate (a home) or possessions that someone owns. Remind them that in math the word *property* refers to a rule. Ask students to give examples of properties they may remember from previous courses. Explain that in this lesson students will use the Addition, Subtraction, Multiplication, and Division Properties of Equality.

Exploration 1

a. See Additional Answers.

b. Subtraction Property of Equality; $x = -10$; Subtract 8 from each side of the equation $x + 8 = -2$.

   Addition Property of Equality; $x = 5$; Add 11 to each side of the equation $x - 11 = -6$.

   Division Property of Equality; $x = -8$; Divide each side of the equation $-2x = 16$ by -2.

c. Check students' work.

Laurie's Notes

Preparing to Teach

- In the previous course, students solved one- and two-step equations. In this chapter, they will build upon their understanding to solve linear equations with rational number coefficients, which may include collecting like terms.
- **MP5 Use Appropriate Tools Strategically:** Algebra tiles can help students make sense of equations. Algebra tiles are a concrete representation, deepening students' understanding of what it means to solve an equation. Students should be familiar with algebra tiles from previous courses.

Motivate

- Tell students that you are going to play a quick game of *REVERSO*. The directions are simple: give a command to a student and the student must give the reverse (inverse) command to undo the original command. For example, say, "Take 3 steps forward," and the student would say, "Take 3 steps backward."
- Sample commands: turn lights on, step up on a chair, turn to your right, fold 2 sheets of paper, draw a square, open the door
- After you play a few rounds with students, have students play with partners.
- The goal is for students to think about inverse operations.

Exploration 1

- Have students work with a partner to explain the meaning of each property.
- Ask volunteers to explain each property before students move on to part (b).
- Students should have access to algebra tiles throughout the entire chapter. There are templates for algebra tiles available at *BigIdeasMath.com*. Print them on card stock and cut them out. Prepare bags of algebra tiles before class. It might be helpful for each student to have his or her own set of algebra tiles to use whenever needed.
- Discuss the results of parts (b) and (c) as a class.

1.1 Solving Simple Equations

Learning Target: Write and solve one-step equations.

Success Criteria:
- I can apply properties of equality to produce equivalent equations.
- I can solve equations using addition, subtraction, multiplication, or division.
- I can use equations to model and solve real-life problems.

EXPLORATION 1

Using Properties of Equality

Work with a partner.

a. You have used the following properties in a previous course. Explain the meaning of each property.

- Addition Property of Equality

- Subtraction Property of Equality

- Multiplication Property of Equality

- Division Property of Equality

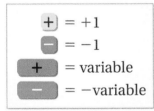

b. Which property can you use to solve each of the equations modeled by the algebra tiles? Solve each equation and explain your method.

Math Practice

Recognize Usefulness of Tools

Can you use algebra tiles to solve any equation? Explain your reasoning.

c. Write an equation that can be solved using one property of equality. Exchange equations with another pair and find the solution.

1.1 Lesson

 Key Ideas

Remember

Addition and subtraction are inverse operations.

Addition Property of Equality

Words Adding the same number to each side of an equation produces an equivalent equation.

Algebra If $a = b$, then $a + c = b + c$.

Subtraction Property of Equality

Words Subtracting the same number from each side of an equation produces an equivalent equation.

Algebra If $a = b$, then $a - c = b - c$.

EXAMPLE 1 **Solving Equations Using Addition or Subtraction**

a. **Solve $x - 7 = -6$.**

$$x - 7 = -6 \quad \text{Write the equation.}$$

Undo the subtraction. $\longrightarrow$ $\underline{+ 7 \quad\quad + 7}$ Addition Property of Equality

$$x = \quad 1 \quad \text{Simplify.}$$

▷ The solution is $x = 1$.

Check

$$x - 7 = -6$$
$$1 - 7 \overset{?}{=} -6$$
$$-6 = -6 \checkmark$$

b. **Solve $1 = w + 6$.**

$$1 = w + 6 \quad \text{Write the equation.}$$

Undo the addition. $\longrightarrow$ $\underline{- 6 \quad\quad - 6}$ Subtraction Property of Equality

$$-5 = w \quad \text{Simplify.}$$

▷ The solution is $w = -5$.

Check

$$1 = w + 6$$
$$1 \overset{?}{=} -5 + 6$$
$$1 = 1 \checkmark$$

c. **Solve $y + 3.4 = 0.5$.**

$$y + 3.4 = \quad 0.5 \quad \text{Write the equation.}$$

Undo the addition. $\longrightarrow$ $\underline{- 3.4 \quad - 3.4}$ Subtraction Property of Equality

$$y = \quad -2.9 \quad \text{Simplify.}$$

▷ The solution is $y = -2.9$.

Try It **Solve the equation. Check your solution.**

1. $b + 2 = -5$

2. $-3 = k + 3$

3. $t - \dfrac{1}{4} = -\dfrac{3}{4}$

Laurie's Notes

Scaffolding Instruction

- Students used algebra tiles to illustrate the properties of equality and to solve simple equations. Students will continue to use the properties of equality to solve one-step equations.
- **Emerging:** Students may struggle with the properties of equality, forgetting to apply the operations to both sides of the equation. They will benefit from guided instruction for the examples.
- **Proficient:** Students can solve one-step equations involving whole numbers, fractions, and decimals with ease. They should work on Try It Exercises 1–7 before checking their understanding with the Self-Assessment exercises.

Key Ideas

- Write the Key Ideas.
- Remind students that two equations that have the same solution are *equivalent equations.*
- **Teaching Tip:** Use an alternate color to show adding (subtracting) c to (from) each side of the equation.
- Remind students of the big idea. Whatever you do to one side of the equation, you must do to the other side of the equation.

EXAMPLE 1

- Work through each part. Note that the vertical format of equation solving is used. The number being added to or subtracted from each side of the equation is written vertically below the number with which it will be combined.
- Remind students to always show their work, as the process is as important as the solution. They should get in the habit of always checking their solutions.
- Students may need to be reminded about operations with positive and negative numbers.
- In part (b), some students may be confused with the variable on the right side of the equation.
- **?** "Can you rewrite the equation with the variable on the left side? Explain."
  Yes, because equality goes both ways, you can switch the sides of the equation, $w + 6 = 1$.
- It might be helpful for struggling students to use algebra tiles for parts (a) and (b).

Try It

- Have students solve the equations and check their solutions independently. Then have students compare their work with their neighbors and resolve any discrepancies.
- Circulate as students work on these exercises. Remind them that it is the practice of *representing* their work that is important in these exercises.

Scaffold instruction to support all students in their learning. Learning is individualized and you may want to group students differently as they move in and out of these levels with each skill and concept. Student self-assessment and feedback help guide your instructional decisions about how and when to layer support for all students to become proficient learners.

Extra Example 1

a. Solve $d - \dfrac{1}{4} = -\dfrac{1}{2}$. $d = -\dfrac{1}{4}$

b. Solve $m + 4.8 = 9.2$. $m = 4.4$

c. Solve $2 = r - 6$. $r = 8$

Try It

1. $b = -7$
2. $k = -6$
3. $t = -\dfrac{1}{2}$

Key Ideas

- Write the Key Ideas.
- **Representation:** Review different ways in which multiplication is represented.

  $$a\,(c) = b\,(c) \qquad ac = bc \qquad a \times c = b \times c \qquad a \cdot c = b \cdot c$$

- Generally, when there are variables in equations, you do not want to use $\times$ to represent multiplication because it can be mistaken for a variable.
- **Representation:** Review different ways in which division is represented.

  $$a \div c = b \div c \qquad \frac{a}{c} = \frac{b}{c} \qquad a/c = b/c$$

EXAMPLE 2

- Remind students that the goal is to solve for the variable so that it has a coefficient of 1.
- ? "What is the inverse operation of multiplying by $-\frac{3}{4}$?" dividing by $-\frac{3}{4}$
- ? "What operation is equivalent to dividing by $-\frac{3}{4}$? Explain." multiplying by $-\frac{4}{3}$; When dividing by a fraction, multiply by the reciprocal of the fraction.
- Remind students that the Multiplicative Inverse Property states that the product of a number and its reciprocal is 1. In this case, $-\frac{4}{3} \cdot \left(-\frac{3}{4}\right) = 1$.
- The purpose of part (b) is to practice working with π in an algebraic expression.
- Have students check their solutions.

Extra Example 2

a. Solve $\frac{2}{5}m = -4$. $m = -10$

b. Solve $3\pi p = -\frac{2}{3}\pi$. $p = -\frac{2}{9}$

Try It

4. $y = -28$

5. $z = -9$

6. $w = 20$

7. $x = 6$

Try It

- Circulate as students work on these exercises independently. Stress representation with students. Do not let them short-cut the process and simply record the answer. They should show what operation is being performed on each side of the equation.
- **Common Error:** In Exercise 7, students may try to subtract 6π from πx or subtract πx from 6π. Remind them that the variable they are solving for is x.
- ⊙ **Thumbs Up:** Have students indicate their understanding of the first two success criteria.

ELL Support

After demonstrating Example 2, have students work in groups to discuss and solve Try It Exercises 4–7. Provide guiding questions: What property is most useful? How do you apply it? What is the solution? Expect students to perform according to their language levels.

Beginner: Write out each step of the process.

Intermediate: Discuss the problem using phrases or simple sentences.

Advanced: Use detailed sentences and help guide discussion.

 **Key Ideas**

Multiplication Property of Equality

Words Multiplying each side of an equation by the same number produces an equivalent equation.

Algebra If $a = b$, then $a \cdot c = b \cdot c$.

Division Property of Equality

Words Dividing each side of an equation by the same number produces an equivalent equation.

Algebra If $a = b$, then $a \div c = b \div c$, $c \neq 0$.

Remember

Multiplication and division are inverse operations.

EXAMPLE 2 **Solving Equations Using Multiplication or Division**

a. Solve $-\dfrac{3}{4}n = -2$.

$$-\frac{3}{4}n = -2 \qquad \text{Write the equation.}$$

$$-\frac{4}{3} \cdot \left(-\frac{3}{4}n\right) = -\frac{4}{3} \cdot (-2) \qquad \text{Multiplication Property of Equality}$$

$$n = \frac{8}{3} \qquad \text{Simplify.}$$

▶ The solution is $n = \dfrac{8}{3}$.

Math Practice

Maintain Oversight

Describe the relationship between $-\dfrac{4}{3}$ and $-\dfrac{3}{4}$. Then explain why it makes sense to multiply each side of the equation by $-\dfrac{4}{3}$.

b. Solve $\pi x = 3\pi$.

$$\pi x = 3\pi \qquad \text{Write the equation.}$$

Undo the multiplication. → $$\frac{\pi x}{\pi} = \frac{3\pi}{\pi} \qquad \text{Division Property of Equality}$$

$$x = 3 \qquad \text{Simplify.}$$

▶ The solution is $x = 3$.

Check
$$\pi x = 3\pi$$
$$\pi(3) \stackrel{?}{=} 3\pi$$
$$3\pi = 3\pi \ \checkmark$$

Try It **Solve the equation. Check your solution.**

4. $\dfrac{y}{4} = -7$

5. $-\dfrac{2z}{3} = 6$

6. $0.09w = 1.8$

7. $6\pi = \pi x$

EXAMPLE 3 **Identifying the Solution of an Equation**

What value of k makes the equation $k + 4 \div 0.2 = 5$ true?

A. -15 **B.** -5 **C.** -3 **D.** 1.5

$k + 4 \div 0.2 = 5$	Write the equation.
$k + 20 = 5$	Divide 4 by 0.2.
$\underline{-20 \quad -20}$	Subtraction Property of Equality
$k = -15$	Simplify.

▶ The correct answer is **A.**

Check

$$k + 4 \div 0.2 = 5$$
$$-15 + 4 \div 0.2 \stackrel{?}{=} 5$$
$$-15 + 20 \stackrel{?}{=} 5$$
$$5 = 5 \checkmark$$

Try It **Solve the equation. Check your solution.**

8. $p - 8 \div \dfrac{1}{2} = -3$ **9.** $q + \left| -10 \right| = 2$

Self-Assessment *for Concepts & Skills*

Solve each exercise. Then rate your understanding of the success criteria in your journal.

WRITING Are the equations equivalent? Explain.

10. $x + 3 = 4$ and $x = 1$ **11.** $-\dfrac{y}{5} = 2$ and $y = 10$

12. OPEN-ENDED Write an equation that you can use the Division Property of Equality to solve.

SOLVING EQUATIONS Solve the equation. Check your solution.

13. $-5 = w - 3$ **14.** $-\dfrac{2}{3}n = 8$

15. $p - 9 \div \dfrac{1}{3} = 6$ **16.** $q + \left| 3 \right| = -5$

17. WHICH ONE DOESN'T BELONG? Which equation does *not* belong with the other three? Explain your reasoning.

$x - 2 = 4$	$x - 3 = 9$	$x - 5 = 1$	$x - 6 = 0$

Laurie's Notes

EXAMPLE 3

- "What is $10 + 4 \div 2$?" 12 Listen for students using the order of operations.
- Students could use *Guess, Check, and Revise*; however, it is more efficient to use the order of operations and then solve the equation.
- Students may think they should first multiply both sides of the equation by 0.2, but this would make the variable term $0.2k$. It is more efficient to use the order of operations to simplify the expression on the left side of the equal sign before using properties of equality.

Try It

- Remind students to follow the order of operations.
- **Common Error:** Students may think $8 \div \frac{1}{2} = 4$ instead of 16.
- "In Exercise 9, what does $|-10|$ mean?" absolute value of -10, which equals 10

✔ Self-Assessment for Concepts & Skills

- Students should work independently on these exercises and then compare with their neighbors to discuss any discrepancies. Go over the exercises with the class, especially Exercise 17. Listen carefully to students' reasoning.
- ⊙ Remind students to rate their understanding of the success criteria in their journals.

ELL Support

Proceed as described in Laurie's Notes, but allow students to work in pairs for extra support. Then have two pairs form a group to discuss their answers. Check answers for Exercises 10 and 11 by asking students to use a thumbs up to answer *yes* and a thumbs down to answer *no*. Have pairs display their answers for Exercises 13–16 on whiteboards for your review.

The Success Criteria Self-Assessment chart can be found in the *Student Journal* or online at *BigIdeasMath.com*.

Extra Example 3

What value of w makes the equation $w - 4 \div \frac{1}{2} = 5$ true?

A. 6 **B.** 7
C. 13 **D.** 14

C

Try It

8. $p = 13$
9. $q = -8$

Self-Assessment
for Concepts & Skills

10. yes; *Sample answer:* The solution of $x + 3 = 4$ is $x = 1$.
11. no; *Sample answer:* The solution of $-\frac{y}{5} = 2$ is $y = -10$, not $y = 10$.
12. *Sample answer:* $3x = 6$
13. $w = -2$
14. $n = -12$
15. $p = 33$
16. $q = -8$
17. $x - 3 = 9$; The solution of $x - 3 = 9$ is $x = 12$. The solution of the other equations is $x = 6$.

Extra Example 4
The melting point of ice is $\frac{2}{9}$ of the melting point of candle wax. The melting point of ice is 32°F. What is the melting point of candle wax? $\frac{2}{9}x = 32$; 144°F

EXAMPLE 4

- **Teaching Tip:** The problems on the last page of each lesson can involve much of a class period. Having students work on the problems in class, where you and other students can support their learning, is more productive than solving application problems for homework and having little support.
- It is important to practice using problem-solving techniques with your students. Ask a student to read the problem and another to explain the problem. Explanations may sound something like, "The temperature starts at 0°C and drops a certain amount every hour. You want to know when the temperature will reach −50°C."
- Go over the verbal model, asking students to explain each part.
- Work through the remainder of the solution.
- Remind students that the numerical solution does not always answer the question. Tell students to always refer back to the question when they write their solutions.

✓ Self-Assessment for Problem Solving

Self-Assessment
for Problem Solving

18. 100

19. 2 boxes; $8x = 40$, $x = 5$. So, you have 5 boxes in stock and need to order 2 more.

20. $1.05x = 7350$; 7000 steps

- The goal for all students is to feel comfortable with the problem-solving plan. It is important for students to problem-solve in class, where they may receive support from you and their peers. Keep in mind that some students may only be ready for the first step.
- Students should read each problem and write a verbal model independently. Then have students check their verbal models with their neighbors. Circulate and check for understanding. If necessary, have a class discussion about the verbal models. Students should solve and check the problems independently.
- ⊙ **Thumbs Up:** Have students indicate their understanding of the third success criterion.

The Success Criteria Self-Assessment chart can be found in the *Student Journal* or online at *BigIdeasMath.com.*

Closure

- Describe in words how to solve a one-step equation.
- Write and solve a one-step equation.

Learning Target
Write and solve one-step equations.

Success Criteria
- Apply properties of equality to produce equivalent equations.
- Solve equations using addition, subtraction, multiplication, or division.
- Use equations to model and solve real-life problems.

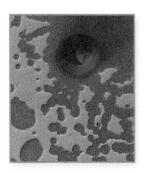

EXAMPLE 4 **Modeling Real Life**

The temperature in a crater on Mars is 0°C at 1 P.M. The temperature decreases 8°C every hour. When will the temperature be −50°C?

To determine when the temperature will be −50°C, find how long it will take the temperature to decrease by 50°C. Write and solve an equation to find the time.

Verbal Model	Change in temperature (°C)	=	Hourly change in temperature (°C per hour)	•	Time (hours)

Variable Let t be the time for the temperature to decrease 50°C.

Equation $-50 \qquad = \qquad -8 \qquad • \qquad t$

> The changes in temperature are negative because the temperatures are decreasing.

$-50 = -8t$ Write the equation.

$\dfrac{-50}{-8} = \dfrac{-8t}{-8}$ Division Property of Equality

$6.25 = t$ Simplify.

The temperature will be −50°C at 6.25 hours after 1 P.M., or 6 hours and 15 minutes after 1 P.M.

▷ So, the temperature will be −50°C at 7:15 P.M.

Self-Assessment for Problem Solving

Solve each exercise. Then rate your understanding of the success criteria in your journal.

18. A shipwreck is 300 meters away from a diving station. An undersea explorer travels away from the station at a speed of 2 meters per second. The explorer is x meters away from the station and will reach the shipwreck in 100 seconds. What is the value of x?

19. You conduct an inventory for a hardware store and count 40 rolls of duct tape. Your manager wants to keep 7 boxes of duct tape in stock. If each box holds 8 rolls of duct tape, how many boxes should you order? Justify your answer.

20. **DIG DEEPER!** Your fitness tracker overestimates the number of steps you take by 5%. The tracker indicates that you took 7350 steps today. Write and solve an equation to find the actual number of steps you took today.

1.1 Practice

Go to *BigIdeasMath.com* to get HELP with solving the exercises.

▶ Review & Refresh

Evaluate the expression.

1. $(3^2 - 8) + 4$

2. $1 + 5 \times 3^2$

3. $4 \times 3 + 10^2$

Identify the terms, coefficients, and constants in the expression.

4. $11q + 2$

5. $h + 9 + g$

6. $6m^2 + 7n$

Write the phrase as an expression.

7. the quotient of 22 and a number a

8. the difference of a number t and 9

▶▶ Concepts, Skills, & Problem Solving

USING PROPERTIES OF EQUALITY Which property of equality can you use to solve the equation modeled by the algebra tiles? Solve the equation and explain your method. (See Exploration 1, p. 3.)

9.
```
 ┌───┐ ┌─┐┌─┐
 │ + │ │─││─│    ┌─┐
 └───┘ │─││─│  = │─│
       │─││─│    └─┘
       └─┘│─│
          └─┘
```

10.
```
 ┌───┐   ┌─┐┌─┐┌─┐
 │ + │   │+││+││+│
 └───┘   └─┘└─┘└─┘
 ┌───┐   ┌─┐┌─┐┌─┐
 │ + │ = │+││+││+│
 └───┘   └─┘└─┘└─┘
 ┌───┐   ┌─┐┌─┐┌─┐
 │ + │   │+││+││+│
 └───┘   └─┘└─┘└─┘
```

SOLVING EQUATIONS USING ADDITION OR SUBTRACTION Solve the equation. Check your solution.

11. $x + 12 = 7$

12. $g - 16 = 8$

13. $-9 + p = 12$

14. $2.5 + y = -3.5$

15. $x - 8\pi = \pi$

16. $4\pi = w - 6\pi$

17. $\dfrac{5}{6} = \dfrac{1}{6} + d$

18. $\dfrac{3}{8} = r + \dfrac{2}{3}$

19. $n - 1.4 = -6.3$

20. **MP MODELING REAL LIFE** A discounted concert ticket costs $14.50 less than the original price p. You pay $53 for a discounted ticket. Write and solve an equation to find the original price.

21. **MP PROBLEM SOLVING** A game of bowling has ten frames. After five frames, your friend's bowling score is 65 and your bowling score is 8 less than your friend's score.

   a. Write and solve an equation to find your score.

   b. By the end of the game, your friend's score doubles and your score increases by 80. Who wins the game? Explain.

Assignment Guide and Concept Check

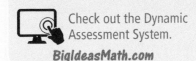
Scaffold assignments to support all students in their learning progression. The suggested assignments are a starting point. Continue to assign additional exercises and revisit with spaced practice to move every student toward proficiency.

Level	Assignment 1	Assignment 2
Emerging	1, 3, 5, 7, 9, 11, 13, 15, 22, 23, 26, 31, 39, 41	17, 18, 20, 21, 27, 28, 32, 33, 42, 45, 46, 49
Proficient	1, 3, 5, 7, 10, 12, 14, 16, 24, 26, 28, 31, 38, 40	18, 30, 34, 35, 36, 37, 41, 42, 45, 46, 47, 49
Advanced	1, 3, 5, 7, 10, 16, 18, 25, 28, 29, 31, 41, 43, 47	34, 36, 37, 44, 45, 46, 48, 49, 50, 51, 52, 53

- Assignment 1 is for use after students complete the Self-Assessment for Concepts & Skills.
- Assignment 2 is for use after students complete the Self-Assessment for Problem Solving.
- The red exercises can be used as a concept check.

Review & Refresh Prior Skills

Exercises 1–3   Using Order of Operations
Exercises 4–6   Identifying Parts of Algebraic Expressions
Exercises 7 and 8   Writing Expressions

For Your Information

- **Exercise 21** Students may not be familiar with the bowling term *frame*. Each set of ten pins is called a frame. An entire game has ten frames.

Common Errors

- **Exercises 11–19** Students may perform the same operation that they are trying to undo instead of the inverse operation. Remind students that to solve for the variable, they must use the inverse operation on both sides of the equation. Demonstrate that using the same operation will not work. For example:

Incorrect	Correct
$x + 12 = \quad 7$	$x + 12 = \quad 7$
$\underline{+\ 12\quad +\ 12}$	$\underline{-\ 12\quad -\ 12}$
$x + 24 = \quad 19$	$x = \quad -5$

Review & Refresh

1. 5
2. 46
3. 112
4. terms: $11q$, 2
   coefficient: 11
   constant: 2
5. terms: h, 9, g
   coefficients: 1, 1
   constant: 9
6. terms: $6m^2$, $7n$
   coefficients: 6, 7
   constant: none
7. $\dfrac{22}{a}$
8. $t - 9$

Concepts, Skills, & Problem Solving

9. Addition Property of Equality; $x = 4$; Add 5 to each side of the equation $x - 5 = -1$.
10. Division Property of Equality; $x = 3$; Divide each side of the equation $3x = 9$ by 3.
11. $x = -5$
12. $g = 24$
13. $p = 21$
14. $y = -6$
15. $x = 9\pi$
16. $w = 10\pi$
17. $d = \dfrac{2}{3}$
18. $r = -\dfrac{7}{24}$
19. $n = -4.9$
20. $p - 14.50 = 53$; \$67.50
21. **a.** $x + 8 = 65$; 57

    b. you;
    your friend's score:
    $2(65) = 130$
    your score: $57 + 80 = 137$

Concepts, Skills, & Problem Solving

22. $x = 5$

23. $n = -5$

24. $w = -48$

25. $m = 7.3\pi$

26. $g = -6$

27. $k = 1\frac{2}{3}$

28. $x = 0.2$

29. $p = -2\frac{1}{3}$

30. $d = 4$

31. no; Your friend should have added 1.5 to each side.

32. $3x = 42$

33. $6.50 per hour

34. 7:35 A.M.

35. $60

36. 6 mi

37. 145 ft

Common Errors

- **Exercises 22–30** Students may perform the same operation that they are trying to undo instead of the inverse operation. Remind students that to solve for the variable, they must use the inverse operation on both sides of the equation. Demonstrate that using the same operation will not work. For example:

Incorrect	Correct
$7x = 35$	$7x = 35$
$7 \cdot 7x = 35 \cdot 7$	$\dfrac{7x}{7} = \dfrac{35}{7}$
$49x = 245$	$x = 5$

- **Exercise 37** Students may skip the step of writing the equation and just subtract the difference in height from the height of the Millennium Force. Encourage students to develop the problem-solving technique of writing the equation before solving. This skill will be useful when solving more difficult problems.

SOLVING EQUATIONS USING MULTIPLICATION OR DIVISION Solve the equation. Check your solution.

22. $7x = 35$

23. $4 = -0.8n$

24. $6 = -\dfrac{w}{8}$

25. $\dfrac{m}{\pi} = 7.3$

26. $-4.3g = 25.8$

27. $\dfrac{3}{2} = \dfrac{9}{10}k$

28. $-7.8x = -1.56$

29. $-2 = \dfrac{6}{7}p$

30. $3\pi d = 12\pi$

31. **MP YOU BE THE TEACHER** Your friend solves the equation. Is your friend correct? Explain your reasoning.

$$-1.5 + k = 8.2$$
$$k = 8.2 + (-1.5)$$
$$k = 6.7$$

32. **MP STRUCTURE** A gym teacher orders 42 tennis balls. The tennis balls come in packs of 3. Which of the following equations represents the number x of packs?

$$x + 3 = 42 \qquad 3x = 42 \qquad \dfrac{x}{3} = 42 \qquad x = \dfrac{3}{42}$$

33. **MP MODELING REAL LIFE** You clean a community park for 6.5 hours. You earn $42.25. How much do you earn per hour?

34. **MP MODELING REAL LIFE** A rocket is scheduled to launch from a command center in 3.75 hours. What time is it now?

35. **MP MODELING REAL LIFE** After earning interest, the balance of an account is $420. The new balance is $\dfrac{7}{6}$ of the original balance. How much interest did it earn?

36. **MP MODELING REAL LIFE** After a cleanup, algae covers 2 miles of a coastline. The length of the coastline covered after the cleanup is $\dfrac{1}{3}$ of the previous length. How many miles of the coast did the algae previously cover?

Launch Time 11:20 A.M.

Roller Coasters at Cedar Point	
Coaster	Height (feet)
Top Thrill Dragster	420
Millennium Force	310
Valravn	225
Rougarou	?

37. **MP PROBLEM SOLVING** Cedar Point, an amusement park in Ohio, has some of the tallest roller coasters in the United States. The Rougarou is 165 feet shorter than the Millennium Force. What is the height of the Rougarou?

SOLVING AN EQUATION **Solve the equation. Check your solution.**

38. $-3 = h + 8 \div 2$

39. $12 = w - |-7|$

40. $q + |6.4| = 9.6$

41. $d - 2.8 \div 0.2 = -14$

42. $\dfrac{8}{9} = x + \dfrac{1}{3}(7)$

43. $p - \dfrac{1}{4} \cdot 3 = -\dfrac{5}{6}$

44. **GEOMETRY** The volume V of the prism is 1122 cubic inches. Use the formula $V = Bh$ to find the height h of the prism.

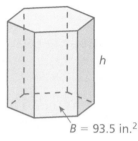

$B = 93.5 \text{ in.}^2$

SOLVING AN EQUATION **Write and solve an equation to find the value of x.**

45. The angles are complementary.

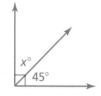

$x°$
$45°$

46. The angles are supplementary.

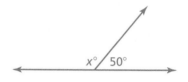

$x°$ $50°$

47. **CRITICAL THINKING** Which of the operations $+$, $-$, $\times$, and $\div$ are inverses of each other? Explain.

48. **MP** **LOGIC** Without solving, determine whether the solution of $-2x = -15$ is *greater than* or *less than* -15. Explain.

49. **OPEN-ENDED** Write a subtraction equation and a division equation so that each has a solution of -2. Justify your answer.

50. **MP** **MODELING REAL LIFE** Ants of a particular species can carry 50 times their body weight. It takes 32 ants of that species to carry the cherry shown. About how much does each ant weigh?

4800 mg

51. **MP** **REASONING** One-fourth of the girls and one-eighth of the boys in a grade retake their school pictures. The photographer retakes pictures for 16 girls and 7 boys. How many students are in the grade?

52. **DIG DEEPER!** You use a crowdfunding website to raise money. The website keeps 5% of each donation. Five of your friends each donate the same amount. The total funding you receive is $47.50. How much does each friend donate?

53. **CRITICAL THINKING** A neighbor pays you and two friends $90 to paint her garage. You divide the money three ways in the ratio $2 : 3 : 5$.

    a. How much does each person receive?

    b. What is one possible reason the money is not divided evenly?

Common Errors

- **Exercises 38–43** Students may forget to use the order of operations when solving for the variable. Remind them to use the order of operations before solving.

Mini-Assessment

Solve the equation. Check your solution.

1. $t + 17 = 3$ $t = -14$
2. $-2\pi + d = -3\pi$ $d = -\pi$
3. $-13.5 = 2.7s$ $s = -5$
4. $\frac{2}{3}j = 8$ $j = 12$
5. You earn \$9.65 per hour. This week, you earned \$308.80 before taxes. Write and solve an equation to find the number of hours you worked this week.
   $9.65x = 308.8$; You worked 32 hours this week.

Section Resources

Surface Level	Deep Level
Resources by Chapter • Extra Practice • Reteach • Puzzle Time Student Journal • Self-Assessment • Practice Differentiating the Lesson Tutorial Videos Skills Review Handbook Skills Trainer	Resources by Chapter • Enrichment and Extension Graphic Organizers Dynamic Assessment System • Section Practice

Concepts, Skills, & Problem Solving

38. $h = -7$
39. $w = 19$
40. $q = 3.2$
41. $d = 0$
42. $x = -1\frac{4}{9}$
43. $p = -\frac{1}{12}$
44. 12 in.
45. $x + 45 = 90$; $x = 45$
46. $x + 50 = 180$; $x = 130$
47. $+$ and $-$ are inverses; Adding a number and subtracting that same number cancel each other out.

    $\times$ and $\div$ are inverses; Multiplying by a number and dividing by that same number cancel each other out.
48. greater than; A negative number divided by a negative number is a positive number.
49. *Sample answer:*

    $x - 2 = -4, \dfrac{x}{2} = -1$;

    $(-2) - 2 \stackrel{?}{=} -4 \qquad \dfrac{-2}{2} \stackrel{?}{=} -1$

    $-4 = -4 \qquad \phantom{\dfrac{-2}{2}}-1 = -1$
50. 3 mg
51. 120 students
52. \$10
53. **a.** \$18, \$27, \$45

    b. *Sample answer:* Everyone did not do an equal amount of painting.

Learning Target

Write and solve multi-step equations.

Success Criteria

- Apply properties to produce equivalent equations.
- Solve multi-step equations.
- Use multi-step equations to model and solve real-life problems.

Warm Up

Cumulative, vocabulary, and prerequisite skills practice opportunities are available in the *Resources by Chapter* or at *BigIdeasMath.com.*

ELL Support

Explain that the word *multi-step* is a compound hyphenated word and you can guess its meaning by looking at its parts. Students may be familiar with the word *step* as one level of a staircase or a movement you make when walking. Explain that it also refers to one action taken in a process. Point out that the prefix *multi-* means "many." A multi-step equation is an equation that requires more than one action (or operation) to solve it.

Exploration 1

a. $36°, 36°, 108°; q + q + 3q = 180,$
$q = 36$

b. $42.5°, 85°, 52.5°;$
$m + 2m + (m + 10) = 180,$
$m = 42.5$

c. $55°, 65°, 60°;$
$x + (x + 10) + (x + 5) = 180,$
$x = 55$

d. $60°, 30°, 90°;$
$y + (y - 30) + 90 = 180, y = 60$

e. See Additional Answers.

Laurie's Notes

Preparing to Teach

- In the previous course, students gained familiarity with the sum of the angle measures of a triangle when they constructed triangles with given side lengths and/or angles. This rule will be formally discussed in Chapter 3.
- **MP1 Make Sense of Problems and Persevere in Solving Them:** Mathematically proficient students look for entry points in a problem. In solving a multi-step equation, they analyze the given information and determine how they can begin the solution.

Motivate

- Make a card for each student in your class. Write a variable term on each card. Students will walk around to find others with a card containing a *like term* to the one they are holding. Samples: $5x, -13x, 5y, 6xy, x, 3.8x, \frac{1}{2}y, -3.8y$
- Ask students to explain what it means for terms to be *like* terms.

Exploration 1

❓ Ask a few questions to prepare students for the exploration.
- "What is the sum of the angle measures of a triangle?" 180°
- "If two angles measure 65° and 75°, what does the third angle measure? Explain." 40°; 180 − (65 + 75) = 40
- "If the angles of a triangle measure $x°$, $2x°$, and $3x°$, can you determine the measure of each angle?" yes
- Model how to write and solve the equation $x + 2x + 3x = 180$. Be sure to mention like terms when solving. Ask about the coefficient of x.
- **Common Error:** After solving the equation, students sometimes forget to substitute the value into each angle expression to find each angle measure.
- **FYI:** The triangles are drawn to scale, so the angle measures can be checked using a protractor.
- Ask volunteers to show a few of the solutions at the board.
❓ "Why are there only two angles with variable expressions written in part (d)?" The third angle is a right angle.
- I like to work through part (e) with students. Display the diagram on the board using an interactive whiteboard or document camera. Make a list of all the unknown measures. Ask several students to write the measure next to a letter in the list and on the diagram. The student should explain his or her reasoning.
❓ If students cannot find an entry point, ask, "What do you know?" Answers may vary, but students often say that $n = 60$ because of the equiangular triangle.
- Discuss results and strategies for finding the angle measures. Listen for right angles at the vertices of the rectangle, the sum of angle measures forming a straight angle equals 180°, the sum of angle measures about a point equals 360°, and the sum of the angle measures of a triangle equals 180°.
- Most students will not write formal equations, but the thinking models equations. For example, $k + m + s = 180$. If you know k and m, you can use mental math to solve for s.
- **Extension:** Ask students to classify each triangle by its angles and by its sides.

1.2 Solving Multi-Step Equations

Learning Target: Write and solve multi-step equations.

Success Criteria:
- I can apply properties to produce equivalent equations.
- I can solve multi-step equations.
- I can use multi-step equations to model and solve real-life problems.

EXPLORATION 1

Finding Angle Measures

Work with a partner. Find each angle measure in each figure. Use equations to justify your answers.

a.
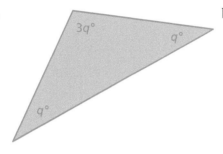

b.
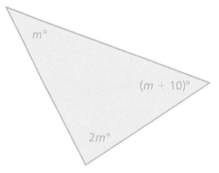

c.
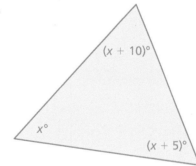

d.
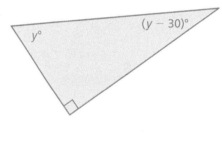

e.
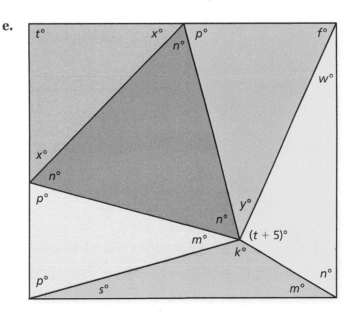

Math Practice

Find Entry Points

How do you decide which triangle to solve first? Explain.

1.2 Lesson

 **Key Idea**

Solving Multi-Step Equations

To solve multi-step equations, use inverse operations to isolate the variable.

EXAMPLE 1 **Solving a Two-Step Equation**

Solve $3x + 15 = 24$.

	$3x + 15 =$	24	Write the equation.
Undo the addition. →	-15	-15	Subtraction Property of Equality
	$3x =$	9	Simplify.
Undo the multiplication. →	$\dfrac{3x}{3} =$	$\dfrac{9}{3}$	Division Property of Equality
	$x =$	3	Simplify.

Check

$3x + 15 = 24$

$3(3) + 15 \stackrel{?}{=} 24$

$24 = 24$ ✓

▶ The solution is $x = 3$.

Try It Solve the equation. Check your solution.

1. $2z - 1 = -5$ **2.** $-3z + 1 = 7$ **3.** $\dfrac{1}{2}x - 9 = -25$

EXAMPLE 2 **Solving a Multi-Step Equation**

Solve $8x - 6x - 25 = -35$.

	$8x - 6x - 25 =$	-35	Write the equation.
	$2x - 25 =$	-35	Combine like terms.
Undo the subtraction. →	$+25$	$+25$	Addition Property of Equality
	$2x =$	-10	Simplify.
Undo the multiplication. →	$\dfrac{2x}{2} =$	$\dfrac{-10}{2}$	Division Property of Equality
	$x =$	-5	Simplify.

▶ The solution is $x = -5$.

Try It Solve the equation. Check your solution.

4. $-4n - 8n + 17 = 23$ **5.** $10 = 3n + 20 - n$

Laurie's Notes

Scaffolding Instruction

- In the exploration, students developed an intuitive understanding about solving multi-step equations. Now they will solve multi-step equations by using inverse operations to isolate the variable.
- **Emerging:** Students may struggle with identifying the signs of the terms in an equation, as well as solving multi-step equations. Make sure students show their steps as you provide guided instruction for the examples.
- **Proficient:** Students can solve multi-step equations. They should complete Try It Exercises 6 and 7 before working on the Self-Assessment exercises.

Key Idea

- **Connection:** When you evaluate an expression, you follow the order of operations. Solving an equation undoes the evaluating, in reverse order. The goal is to isolate the variable term and then solve for the variable.

EXAMPLE 1

- Work through the problem as shown.
- Remind students to show all of their steps and check their solutions.

Try It

- **Think-Pair-Share:** Students should work on the problems independently, showing all of their steps. Have each student check with a neighbor. Then have each pair share with another pair and resolve any discrepancies.
- In Exercise 3, students may divide both sides by $\frac{1}{2}$ incorrectly and get $x = -8$. Remind students that dividing by $\frac{1}{2}$ is the same as multiplying by 2.

EXAMPLE 2

- Work through the problem as shown.
- **?** "Why is $8x - 6x = 2x$?" The Distributive Property can be used to subtract the terms: $8x - 6x = (8 - 6)x = 2x$.

Try It

- **Think-Pair-Share:** Students should read each exercise independently and then work in pairs to solve the equations. Have each pair compare their solutions with another pair and discuss any discrepancies.

ELL Support

After demonstrating Example 2, have students work in groups to discuss and complete Try It Exercises 4 and 5. Provide guiding questions: What like terms can be combined? What properties are useful? How are they applied? What is the solution? Expect students to perform according to their language levels.

Beginner: Write out each step of the process.

Intermediate: Discuss the problem using simple sentences.

Advanced: Use detailed sentences and help guide discussion.

Scaffold instruction to support all students in their learning. Learning is individualized and you may want to group students differently as they move in and out of these levels with each skill and concept. Student self-assessment and feedback help guide your instructional decisions about how and when to layer support for all students to become proficient learners.

Formative Assessment Tip

Think-Pair-Share
This technique allows students to share their thinking about a problem with their partners after they have had time to consider the problem alone. Once partners have discussed the problem, small groups or the whole class should discuss the problem.

The initial time working alone is important for students to develop their own understanding of the mathematics. "Private think time" is what I call it. Once students have engaged in the problem, sharing with partners helps confirm their understanding or perhaps the need to modify their thinking. Sharing their thinking with the whole class is more comfortable for students when they have had the chance to discuss their thinking with partners.

Extra Example 1
Solve $4t - 5 = 19$. $t = 6$

Try It

1. $z = -2$
2. $z = -2$
3. $x = -32$
4. $n = -0.5$
5. $n = -5$

Extra Example 2
Solve $-2m + 4m + 5 = -3$. $m = -4$

Extra Example 3

Solve $-4(3g - 5) + 10g = 19$. $g = 0.5$

Try It

6. $x = -1.5$
7. $d = -1$

Self-Assessment
for Concepts & Skills

8. $x = -6$
9. $x = -9$
10. $n = -7$
11. $n = 2$
12. $x = 4$
13. $d = 2$
14. $2 + 3x = 17; x = 5$
15. *Sample answer:* Subtract 9 from each side. Divide each side by 2. Add 11 to each side. Divide each side by 4.
16. Divide each side by 3, then subtract 2 from each side.

Laurie's Notes

EXAMPLE 3

💡 "What operations are involved in this equation?" multiplication (by 2), subtraction, multiplication (by 5), and addition

- **Note:** Combining like terms in the third step is not obvious to students. When the like terms are not adjacent, students are unsure of how to combine them. Rewrite the left side of the equation as $2 + (-10)x + 4$.
- **Another Method:** Take time to work through the Another Method note and discuss the steps. Instead of using the Distributive Property, both sides of the equation are divided by 2 in the third step. This will not be obvious to students, nor will they know why it is okay to do this.
  - Explain that the left side of the equation is 2 times an expression. When the expression $2(1 - 5x)$ is divided by 2, it leaves the expression $1 - 5x$. In the next step, students want to add 1 to each side because of the subtraction operation shown. Again, it is helpful to write $1 - 5x$ as $1 + (-5)x$ so that it makes sense to students why 1 is subtracted from each side.

Try It

- Encourage students to work in pairs. Students need to be careful with multi-step equations and it is helpful to have a partner check each step.

✓ Self-Assessment for Concepts & Skills

- **Neighbor Check:** Have students work independently and then have their neighbors check their work. Have students discuss any discrepancies.
- ◉ Divide students into six groups. Assign each group one of Exercises 8–13. Ask each group to identify the operations involved and explain them to the class.

ELL Support

Allow students to work in pairs for extra support. Have pairs display their answers for Exercises 8–14 on whiteboards for your review. Have two pairs form a group to discuss and answer Exercises 15 and 16. After groups have finalized their answers, have each group present their answers to another group. The two groups must reach an agreement if their ideas differ. Monitor discussions and provide support.

The Success Criteria Self-Assessment chart can be found in the *Student Journal* or online at *BigIdeasMath.com*.

EXAMPLE 3 **Using the Distributive Property to Solve an Equation**

Solve $2(1 - 5x) + 4 = -8$.

$2(1 - 5x) + 4 = -8$	Write the equation.
$2(1) - 2(5x) + 4 = -8$	Distributive Property
$2 - 10x + 4 = -8$	Multiply.
$-10x + 6 = -8$	Combine like terms.
$\underline{\; -6 \quad -6}$	Subtraction Property of Equality
$-10x = -14$	Simplify.
$\dfrac{-10x}{-10} = \dfrac{-14}{-10}$	Division Property of Equality
$x = 1.4$	Simplify.

▶ The solution is $x = 1.4$.

Math Practice

Look for Structure
Show how to solve the equation without using the Distributive Property.

Try It **Solve the equation. Check your solution.**

6. $-3(x + 2) + 5x = -9$

7. $5 + 1.5(2d - 1) = 0.5$

Self-Assessment *for Concepts & Skills*

Solve each exercise. Then rate your understanding of the success criteria in your journal.

SOLVING AN EQUATION **Solve the equation. Check your solution.**

8. $-5x + 1 = 31$

9. $\dfrac{1}{3}x - 9 = -12$

10. $-n - 6n + 4 = 53$

11. $14 = 6n + 6 - 2n$

12. $-8(x + 1) + 2x = -32$

13. $3 + 4.5(2d - 3) = 7.5$

14. **WRITING** Write the sentence as an equation, then solve.

2 more than 3 times a number x is 17.

15. **OPEN-ENDED** Explain how to solve the equation $2(4x - 11) + 9 = 19$.

16. **CRITICAL THINKING** How can you solve $3(x + 2) = 9$ without distributing the 3?

EXAMPLE 4 **Modeling Real Life**

Find the number x of miles you need to run on Friday so that the mean number of miles run per day is 1.5.

Day	Miles
Monday	2
Tuesday	0
Wednesday	1.5
Thursday	0
Friday	x

Understand the problem.

You are given the number of miles you run each day from Monday through Thursday. You are asked how many miles you need to run on Friday so that your daily average for the five days is 1.5 miles.

Make a plan.

Write and solve an equation using the definition of *mean*.

Solve and check.

$$\frac{2 + 0 + 1.5 + 0 + x}{5} = 1.5 \qquad \frac{\text{sum of the data}}{\text{number of values}} = \text{mean}$$

$$\frac{3.5 + x}{5} = 1.5 \qquad \text{Combine like terms.}$$

$$5 \cdot \frac{3.5 + x}{5} = 5 \cdot 1.5 \qquad \begin{array}{l}\text{Multiplication Property} \\ \text{of Equality}\end{array}$$

$$3.5 + x = 7.5 \qquad \text{Simplify.}$$

$$\underline{-\ 3.5 \qquad\quad -\ 3.5} \qquad \text{Subtraction Property of Equality}$$

$$x = 4 \qquad \text{Simplify.}$$

Check You run $2 + 1.5 + 4 = 7.5$ miles in 5 days. So, the mean number of miles run per day is $\frac{7.5}{5} = 1.5$. ✓

So, you need to run 4 miles on Friday.

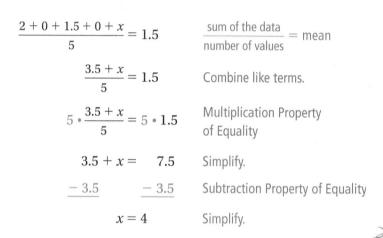

 Self-Assessment for Problem Solving

Solve each exercise. Then rate your understanding of the success criteria in your journal.

Day	Action Figures
Monday	55
Tuesday	45
Wednesday	53
Thursday	44
Friday	x

17. Find the number x of action figures that a small business needs to produce on Friday so that the mean number of action figures produced per day is 50.

18. **DIG DEEPER!** A hard drive is 80% full and has 12,000 MB of free space. One minute of video uses 60 MB of storage. How many minutes of video should be deleted so that the hard drive is 75% full?

19. A teacher spends $354 on costumes and microphones for six cast members in a play. Each cast member receives a costume that costs $38 and a microphone that costs c. What did the teacher spend on each microphone? Justify your answer.

Laurie's Notes

EXAMPLE 4

- Ask a volunteer to read the problem. Then ask another volunteer to interpret the problem. If the student cannot interpret the problem, ask them to read the problem again and ask a third student to explain it.
- You may need to review *mean* with students.
- Discuss the information displayed in the table and write the equation.
- ❓ "Is it equivalent to write $\frac{x + 3.5}{5} = 1.5$ instead of $\frac{3.5 + x}{5} = 1.5$? Explain." Yes, addition is commutative.
- **FYI:** It may be helpful to write the third step with parentheses: $5\left(\frac{3.5 + x}{5}\right)$.
- **MP4 Model with Mathematics:** Ask students to explain the impact of trying to achieve a mean of 1.5 miles run per day when you ran 0 miles on two of the days.
- **Note:** This is a classic question. When all of the data are known except for one, what is needed in order to achieve a particular average? Students often ask this in the context of wanting to know what they have to score on a test to achieve a certain average.

✔ Self-Assessment for Problem Solving

- Allow time in class for students to practice using the problem-solving plan. Remember, some students may only be able to complete the first step.
- Divide students into three groups. Assign each group one of Exercises 17–19. The groups may choose to subdivide into smaller groups, but they should work with the assigned problem. Students need to read and interpret the problem. Each group should write a verbal model or make a plan to solve the problem. Select two members of each group to present their verbal model or plan to the class.
- Students should solve the problems independently and then have their neighbors check their work.
- ◉ **Thumbs Up:** Have students indicate their understanding of the success criteria.

The Success Criteria Self-Assessment chart can be found in the *Student Journal* or online at *BigIdeasMath.com*.

Closure

- Solve $8x + 9 - 4x = 25$. Check your solution. $x = 4$

Extra Example 4
You have scored 7, 10, 8, and 9 on four quizzes. Find the score you need on the fifth quiz so that your mean score is 8. $\frac{x + 7 + 10 + 8 + 9}{5} = 8$; 6

Self-Assessment
for Problem Solving

17. 53 action figures

18. 50 min

19. $21;
$$6(38) + 6c = 354$$
$$228 + 6c = 354$$
$$6c = 126$$
$$c = 21$$

Learning Target

Write and solve multi-step equations.

Success Criteria

- Apply properties to produce equivalent equations.
- Solve multi-step equations.
- Use multi-step equations to model and solve real-life problems.

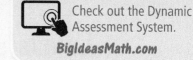

 **Review & Refresh**

1. $y = -5$

2. $h = 8.2$

3. $n = -2\frac{1}{2}$

4. $m = \frac{1}{3}$

5. $-\frac{1}{5}$

6. $3\frac{41}{50}$

7. $-\frac{227}{500}$

8. $-\frac{1}{8}$

 Concepts, Skills, & Problem Solving

9. $20°, 24°, 136°$;
$20 + (y - 10) + 4y = 180$,
$y = 34$

10. $37.5°, 67.5°, 75°$;
$x + (x + 30) + 2x = 180$,
$x = 37.5$

11. $x = 3$

12. $c = 0.5$

13. $x = 2$

14. $n = 2$

15. $x = -2$

16. $h = -9$

17. $v = 2$

18. $x = -\frac{2}{9}$

19. $d = 2$

20. $x = -6$

21. no; Your friend did not distribute the -2 properly.

22. yes; The solution is correct.

23. 20 watches

Assignment Guide and Concept Check

Scaffold assignments to support all students in their learning progression. The suggested assignments are a starting point. Continue to assign additional exercises and revisit with spaced practice to move every student toward proficiency.

Level	Assignment 1	Assignment 2
Emerging	2, 4, 6, 9, 11, 13, 15, 17, 19, 21, 22	12, 14, 16, 18, 20, 23, 24, 25, 30
Proficient	2, 4, 6, 10, 12, 14, 16, 18, 20, 21, 22	23, 24, 25, 26, 27, 28, 29, 30
Advanced	2, 4, 6, 10, 12, 14, 16, 18, 20, 21, 22	24, 25, 26, 27, 28, 29, 30

- Assignment 1 is for use after students complete the Self-Assessment for Concepts & Skills.
- Assignment 2 is for use after students complete the Self-Assessment for Problem Solving.
- The red exercises can be used as a concept check.

Review & Refresh Prior Skills

Exercises 1 and 2 Solving Equations Using Addition or Subtraction
Exercises 3 and 4 Solving Equations Using Multiplication or Division
Exercises 5–8 Writing a Decimal as a Fraction or Mixed Number

Common Errors

- **Exercises 13–16 and 18–20** When combining like terms, students may square the variable. Remind students that $x^2 = x \cdot x$, and in these exercises they are not multiplying the variables. Remind students that when adding and subtracting variables, they perform the addition or subtraction on the coefficient of the variable.
- **Exercises 17–20** When using the Distributive Property, students may forget to distribute to all the values within the parentheses. Remind students that they need to distribute to all the values and encourage them to draw arrows showing the distribution, if needed.

? Go to **BigIdeasMath.com** to get HELP with solving the exercises.

▶ Review & Refresh

Solve the equation.

1. $y + 8 = 3$

2. $h - 1 = 7.2$

3. $5 = -2n$

4. $-3.3m = -1.1$

Write the decimal as a fraction or mixed number in simplest form.

5. -0.2

6. 3.82

7. -0.454

8. -0.125

▶▶ Concepts, Skills, & Problem Solving

FINDING ANGLE MEASURES **Find each angle measure in the figure. Use equations to justify your answers.** (See Exploration 1, p. 11.)

9.

10.

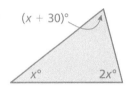

SOLVING AN EQUATION **Solve the equation. Check your solution.**

11. $10x + 2 = 32$

12. $19 - 4c = 17$

13. $5x + 2x + 4 = 18$

14. $2 = -9n + 22 - n$

15. $1.1x + 1.2x - 5.4 = -10$

16. $\dfrac{2}{3}h - \dfrac{1}{3}h + 11 = 8$

17. $6(5 - 8v) + 12 = -54$

18. $21(2 - x) + 12x = 44$

19. $8.5 = 6.5(2d - 3) + d$

20. $-\dfrac{1}{4}(x + 2) + 5 = -x$

MP YOU BE THE TEACHER **Your friend solves the equation. Is your friend correct? Explain your reasoning.**

21.

$-2(7 - y) + 4 = -4$
$-14 - 2y + 4 = -4$
$-10 - 2y = -4$
$-2y = 6$
$y = -3$

22.

$3(y - 1) + 8 = 11$
$3y - 3 + 8 = 11$
$3y + 5 = 11$
$3y = 6$
$y = 2$

23. **MP STRUCTURE** The cost C (in dollars) of making n watches is represented by $C = 15n + 85$. How many watches are made when the cost is $385?

24. **MP** **MODELING REAL LIFE** The height of the house is 26 feet. What is the height x of each story?

6 ft

x

x

25. **MP** **MODELING REAL LIFE** After the addition of an acid, a solution has a volume of 90 milliliters. The volume of the solution is 3 milliliters greater than 3 times the volume of the solution before the acid was added. What was the original volume of the solution?

26. **MP** **PROBLEM SOLVING** A grocer prepares free samples of a salad to give out during the day. By lunchtime, the grocer has given out 5 fewer than half the total number of samples. How many samples did the grocer prepare if she gives out 50 samples before lunch?

27. **GEOMETRY** What is the length of the missing base of the trapezoid?

3 in.

Area = 21 in.^{2}

8 in.

28. **MP** **MODELING REAL LIFE** You order two servings of pancakes and a fruit cup. The cost of the fruit cup is \$1.50. You leave a 15% tip. Your total bill is \$11.50. How much does one serving of pancakes cost?

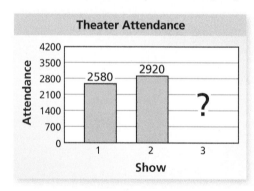

Theater Attendance

2580	2920	?

Attendance — 0, 700, 1400, 2100, 2800, 3500, 4200

Show — 1, 2, 3

29. **MP** **PROBLEM SOLVING** How many people must attend the third show so that the average attendance per show is 3000?

30. **DIG DEEPER!** Divers in a competition are scored by an international panel of judges. The highest and the lowest scores are dropped. The total of the remaining scores is multiplied by the degree of difficulty of the dive. This product is multiplied by 0.6 to determine the final score.

    a. A diver's final score is 77.7. What is the degree of difficulty of the dive?

Judge	Russia	China	Mexico	Germany	Italy	Japan	Brazil
Score	7.5	8.0	6.5	8.5	7.0	7.5	7.0

    b. **CRITICAL THINKING** The degree of difficulty of a dive is 4.0. The diver's final score is 97.2. Judges award half or whole points from 0 to 10. What scores could the judges have given the diver?

Common Errors

- **Exercise 28** Students may struggle with writing the equation for this problem because of the tip that is added to the total. Encourage students to write an expression for the cost of the food and then add the tip.

Mini-Assessment

Solve the equation. Check your solution.

1. $18 = 5a - 2a + 3$ $a = 5$

2. $2(4 - 2w) - 8 = -4$ $w = 1$

3. $2.3y + 4.4y - 3.7 = 16.4$ $y = 3$

4. $\frac{3}{4}z + \frac{1}{4}z + 6 = 5$ $z = -1$

5 The perimeter of the picture is 36 inches. What is the height of the picture?

x in.

8 in.

10 in.

Concepts, Skills, & Problem Solving

24. 10 ft

25. 29 mL

26. 110 samples

27. 6 in.

28. $4.25

29. 3500 people

30. a. 3.5

  b. *Sample answer:* 8.0, 7.5, 8.0, 8.0, 9.0, 8.5, 8.0

Section Resources

Surface Level	Deep Level
Resources by Chapter • Extra Practice • Reteach • Puzzle Time Student Journal • Self-Assessment • Practice Differentiating the Lesson Tutorial Videos Skills Review Handbook Skills Trainer	Resources by Chapter • Enrichment and Extension Graphic Organizers Dynamic Assessment System • Section Practice
Transfer Level	
Dynamic Assessment System • Mid-Chapter Quiz	Assessment Book • Mid-Chapter Quiz

Learning Target

Write and solve equations with variables on both sides.

Success Criteria

- Explain how to solve an equation with variables on both sides.
- Determine whether an equation has one solution, no solution, or infinitely many solutions.
- Use equations with variables on both sides to model and solve real-life problems.

Warm Up

Cumulative, vocabulary, and prerequisite skills practice opportunities are available in the *Resources by Chapter* or at *BigIdeasMath.com*.

ELL Support

Remind students that in an equation, a variable is often represented by a letter. The word *variable* is related to the word *vary*. Point out that *vary* and *very* are two different words. *Vary* means "change" and *very* is used to intensify the meaning of a word. If something is a variable, it can change. You may want to review the parts of speech: *vary* (verb, an action) and a *variable* (noun, a name for something).

Exploration 1

a. See Additional Answers.

b. See Additional Answers.

c. *Sample answer:* The equations have variables on both sides of the equal sign; To solve, collect the variable terms on one side of the equation and the constant terms on the other side.

Laurie's Notes

STATE STANDARDS
8.EE.C.7a, 8.EE.C.7b

Preparing to Teach

- **MP6 Attend to Precision:** Mathematically proficient students try to communicate precisely with others. In the exploration, students will work with vocabulary related to measurement.

Motivate

? "What balances with the cylinder? Explain."

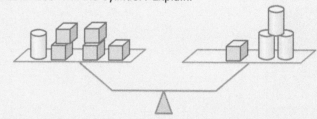

2 cubes; If you remove 1 cube and 1 cylinder from each side, 2 cylinders balance with 4 cubes. So, 1 cylinder would balance with 2 cubes.

- This balance problem is equivalent to $x + 5 = 3x + 1$, where x is a cylinder and the whole numbers represent cubes. This is an example of an equation with variables on both sides, the type students will solve today.
- **MP2 Reason Abstractly and Quantitatively:** You can also model the problem using algebra tiles. Replace the cylinders with x-tiles and the cubes with unit tiles.

Exploration 1

- In this exploration, students will write equations with variables on both sides and then discover how to solve them.
- Discuss with students the general concept of what it means to measure the attributes of a two-dimensional figure. What type of units are used to measure perimeter and area? Linear units are used for perimeter and square units are used for area.
- **MP6 Attend to Precision:** Be sure to make it clear that the directions are saying that perimeter and area are not the same, but their values are equal. For example, a square that measures 4 centimeters on each edge has a perimeter of 16 centimeters and an area of 16 square centimeters. The value (16) is the same, but the units of measure are not.

? Before students begin, ask a few review questions.
  - "How do you find the perimeter P and the area A of a rectangle with length ℓ and width w?" $P = 2\ell + 2w$ and $A = \ell w$
  - "How do you find the perimeter and the area of a composite figure?" Listen for students' understanding that perimeter is the sum of all of the sides, and the area is found in parts and then added together.
- For the yellow figure, students will obtain $0 = 4$ when solving for x. They may think they did something wrong. Ask students what this means before sharing that there is no solution where the perimeter and area have the same value.
- Have a few groups share their work for part (a) at the board.

? "How do you find the surface area S and volume V of a rectangular prism with length ℓ, width w, and height h?" $S = 2\ell w + 2\ell h + 2wh$ and $V = \ell wh$
- Have a few groups share their work for part (b) at the board.

1.3 Solving Equations with Variables on Both Sides

Learning Target: Write and solve equations with variables on both sides.

Success Criteria:
- I can explain how to solve an equation with variables on both sides.
- I can determine whether an equation has one solution, no solution, or infinitely many solutions.
- I can use equations with variables on both sides to model and solve real-life problems.

EXPLORATION 1

Finding Missing Measures in Figures

Work with a partner.

a. If possible, find the value of x so that the value of the perimeter (in feet) is equal to the value of the area (in square feet) for each figure. Use an equation to justify your answer.

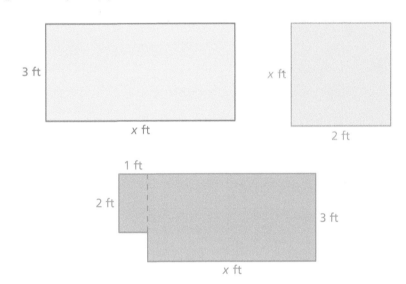

Math Practice

Use Operations
What properties do you need to use to solve for x in each figure?

b. If possible, find the value of y so that the value of the surface area (in square inches) is equal to the value of the volume (in cubic inches) for each figure. Use an equation to justify your answer.

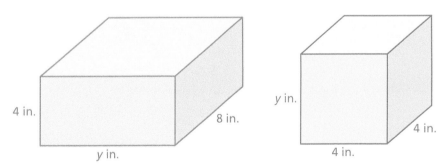

c. How are the equations you used in parts (a) and (b) different from equations used in previous sections? Explain how to solve this type of equation.

1.3 Lesson

 **Key Idea**

Solving Equations with Variables on Both Sides
To solve equations with variables on both sides, collect the variable terms on one side and the constant terms on the other side.

EXAMPLE 1 **Solving an Equation with Variables on Both Sides**

Solve $15 - 2x = -7x$. Check your solution.

$15 - 2x = -7x$	Write the equation.
Undo the subtraction. → $\underline{+ 2x \quad + 2x}$	Addition Property of Equality
$15 = -5x$	Simplify.
Undo the multiplication. → $\dfrac{15}{-5} = \dfrac{-5x}{-5}$	Division Property of Equality
$-3 = x$	Simplify.

Check
$$15 - 2x = -7x$$
$$15 - 2(-3) \stackrel{?}{=} -7(-3)$$
$$21 = 21 \checkmark$$

▶ The solution is $x = -3$.

Try It Solve the equation. Check your solution.

1. $-3x = 2x + 20$

2. $2.5y + 6 = 4.5y - 1$

EXAMPLE 2 **Using the Distributive Property to Solve an Equation**

Solve $-2(x - 5) = 6(2 - 0.5x)$.

$-2(x - 5) = 6(2 - 0.5x)$	Write the equation.
$-2x + 10 = 12 - 3x$	Distributive Property
Undo the subtraction. → $\underline{+ 3x \qquad\qquad + 3x}$	Addition Property of Equality
$x + 10 = \quad 12$	Simplify.
Undo the addition. → $\underline{- 10 \quad - 10}$	Subtraction Property of Equality
$x = 2$	Simplify.

▶ The solution is $x = 2$.

Try It Solve the equation. Check your solution.

3. $6(4 - z) = 2z$

4. $5(w - 2) = -2(1.5w + 5)$

Laurie's Notes

Scaffolding Instruction

- In the exploration, students developed an intuitive understanding of solving equations with variables on both sides. Now they will solve equations with variables on both sides by using properties of equality and collecting variable terms on one side. The equations can have one solution, no solution, or infinitely many solutions.
- **Emerging:** Students struggle to solve equations with variables on both sides of the equal sign. They need guided instruction for the examples and plenty of practice in class.
- **Proficient:** Students can solve equations with variables on both sides. They should complete Try It Exercises 4, 6, and 8 before proceeding to Example 5 and the Self-Assessment exercises.

Key Idea

- **?** "In the expression $5x - 2 - 9x + y + 4$, what are the variable terms? the constant terms?" $5x$, $-9x$, and y; -2 and 4
- **Common Error:** Students may forget to include the sign of the variable term.
- **Teaching Tip:** After working through the examples as shown, you could solve the equations or ask students to solve the equations with the variable on the other side. This will help students see that it does not matter which side the variable is on.

EXAMPLE 1

- Notice that a constant is on the left side only. For this reason, it makes sense to solve for the variable term on the right side of the equation. It is possible to solve for the variable term on the left side of the equation, but finding the solution involves an extra step. Show students this approach as well, and point out that it gives the same solution.

Try It

- **Whiteboards:** Ask students to solve the problems and show their work.

EXAMPLE 2

- **Teaching Tip:** Before distributing on the left side, rewrite the inside expression as $x + (-5)$ (add the opposite). Students are likely to recognize that they are multiplying $(-2)(-5)$ to get a product of 10.
- **FYI:** Solve for the variable on the side of the equation where the coefficient is the greatest. The coefficient of the variable term will be positive, a condition that generally renders fewer mistakes.
- **?** "Is there another way to solve this equation? Explain." yes; *Sample answer:* Divide both sides by -2 to get $x - 5 = -3(2 - 0.5x)$. Distribute -3 to get $x - 5 = -6 + 1.5x$. Add 6 to both sides to get $x + 1 = 1.5x$. Subtract x from both sides to get $1 = 0.5x$. Divide both sides by 0.5 to get $2 = x$.

Try It

- **Whiteboards:** Ask students to solve the problems and show their work.

Scaffold instruction to support all students in their learning. Learning is individualized and you may want to group students differently as they move in and out of these levels with each skill and concept. Student self-assessment and feedback help guide your instructional decisions about how and when to layer support for all students to become proficient learners.

Extra Example 1

Solve $r = -5r + 18$. Check your solution. $r = 3$

Try It

1. $x = -4$
2. $y = 3.5$
3. $z = 3$
4. $w = 0$

Extra Example 2

Solve $6\left(1 + \frac{1}{2}x\right) = 2(x + 1)$. Check your solution. $x = -4$

Laurie's Notes

Discuss

? Ask a few questions about equation solving:
- "Does every equation have a solution?" no
- "Does every equation have just one solution?" no
- "Is it possible for an equation to have two solutions?" yes Students may say no, but using the third example below will convince them otherwise. They will study these types of equations in Chapter 9.
- Share some common equations and discuss the number of solutions:
  $x + 2 = 7$ one solution, 5
  $x + 2 = x + 7$ no solution
  $x^2 = 4$ two solutions, 2 and −2
  $x + 2 = x + 2$ infinitely many solutions
- Explain that in Examples 3 and 4, students will investigate equations that have no solution or infinitely many solutions. Assure students that they will use the same techniques for solving equations as before.

EXAMPLE 3

- **Teaching Tip:** Instead of telling students when an equation has no solution, work through the example and ask students about the "solution" $3 = −7$.
- Work through the problem as shown and then by first collecting the constant terms on one side of the equation. Show that the solution is the same both ways.
- For the final step, write $3 \neq −7$ to emphasize that there is no solution.
- **MP7 Look for and Make Use of Structure:** It may not be necessary to completely solve the equation. Students should notice that the same quantity, $4x$, is being subtracted from different numbers, 3 and −7. They should reason that the two sides of the equation can never be equal, so there is no solution.

? "How do you know when an equation has no solution?" Solve the equation normally and if you end up with a false statement, the equation has no solution.

Try It

- Have students use *Think-Pair-Share* as they solve these problems.

EXAMPLE 4

- **Teaching Tip:** Instead of telling students when an equation has infinitely many solutions, work through the example and ask students about the "solution" $4 = 4$.
- To check the solution, ask volunteers to choose several values for x.
- Substitute these values into the original equation and show that they all result in true statements.
- **MP3 Construct Viable Arguments and Critique the Reasoning of Others:** Ask for a volunteer to explain what it means when the expressions on both sides of the equal sign are the same. Have other students critique their reasoning.

Try It

- Have students use *Think-Pair-Share* as they solve these problems.

Extra Example 3

Solve $3x − 5 = 7 + 3x$. no solution

Try It

5. no solution

6. no solution

Extra Example 4

Solve $\frac{1}{4}(8x − 12) = 2x − 3$.

infinitely many solutions

ELL Support

After demonstrating Examples 3 and 4, have students work in groups to discuss and complete Try It Exercises 5–8. Provide guiding questions: What properties are useful? How are they applied? Is there one solution, no solution, or infinitely many solutions? Expect students to perform according to their language levels.

Beginner: Write out each step of the process.

Intermediate: Discuss the problem using simple sentences.

Advanced: Use detailed sentences and help guide discussion.

Try It

7. infinitely many solutions

8. infinitely many solutions

Some equations do not have one solution. Equations can also have no solution or infinitely many solutions.

When solving an equation that has no solution, you will obtain an equivalent equation that is not true for any value of the variable, such as $0 = 2$.

EXAMPLE 3 **Solving an Equation with No Solution**

Solve $3 - 4x = -7 - 4x$.

$$3 - 4x = -7 - 4x \qquad \text{Write the equation.}$$

$$\underline{+\ 4x} \qquad \underline{+\ 4x} \qquad \text{Addition Property of Equality}$$

$$3 = -7 \quad \text{✗} \qquad \text{Simplify.}$$

▶ The equation $3 = -7$ is never true. So, the equation has no solution.

Try It **Solve the equation.**

5. $2x + 1 = 2x - 1$

6. $6(5 - 2v) = -4(3v + 1)$

When solving an equation that has infinitely many solutions, you will obtain an equivalent equation that is true for all values of the variable, such as $-5 = -5$.

EXAMPLE 4 **Solving an Equation with Infinitely Many Solutions**

Solve $6x + 4 = 4\left(\dfrac{3}{2}x + 1\right)$.

Check Choose any value of x, such as $x = 2$.

$$6x + 4 = 4\left(\frac{3}{2}x + 1\right)$$

$$6(2) + 4 \stackrel{?}{=} 4\left[\frac{3}{2}(2) + 1\right]$$

$$12 + 4 \stackrel{?}{=} 4(3 + 1)$$

$$16 = 16 \ ✓$$

$$6x + 4 = 4\left(\frac{3}{2}x + 1\right) \qquad \text{Write the equation.}$$

$$6x + 4 = \quad 6x + 4 \qquad \text{Distributive Property}$$

$$\underline{-\ 6x} \qquad \underline{-\ 6x} \qquad \text{Subtraction Property of Equality}$$

$$4 = 4 \qquad \text{Simplify.}$$

▶ The equation $4 = 4$ is always true. So, the equation has infinitely many solutions.

Try It **Solve the equation.**

7. $\dfrac{1}{2}(6t - 4) = 3t - 2$

8. $\dfrac{1}{3}(2b + 9) = \dfrac{2}{3}\left(b + \dfrac{9}{2}\right)$

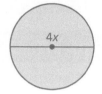

EXAMPLE 5 **Writing and Solving an Equation**

The circles are identical. What is the area of each circle?

    A. 2   **B.** 4

    C. 16π **D.** 64π

The radius of the green circle is $x + 2$ and the radius of the purple circle is $\dfrac{4x}{2} = 2x$. The circles are identical, so the radius of each circle is the same. Write and solve an equation to find the value of x.

$$
\begin{array}{ll}
x + 2 = \ 2x & \text{Write an equation. The radii are equal.} \\[4pt]
\underline{\ -x \qquad\quad -x\ } & \text{Subtraction Property of Equality} \\[4pt]
\qquad 2 = x & \text{Simplify.}
\end{array}
$$

When $x = 2$, the radius of each circle is 4 and the area of each circle is $\pi r^2 = \pi (4)^2 = 16\pi$.

▷ So, the correct answer is **C.**

Try It

9. **WHAT IF?** The diameter of the purple circle is $3x$. What is the area of each circle?

Self-Assessment *for Concepts & Skills*

Solve each exercise. Then rate your understanding of the success criteria in your journal.

10. **OPEN-ENDED** Write an equation with variables on both sides that has a single solution of -1. Explain how to solve your equation.

MP STRUCTURE Without solving, determine whether the equation has one solution, no solution, or infinitely many solutions. Justify your answer.

11. $3(x - 1) = -3$ 12. $6x + 6 = 6(x + 1)$ 13. $z + 1 = z + 6$

SOLVING AN EQUATION Solve the equation. Check your solution, if possible.

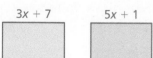

14. $-7x = x + 24$ 15. $8(3 - z) = 4z$ 16. $2(t - 3) = 2t - 6$

17. **WRITING AND SOLVING AN EQUATION** The squares are identical. What is the area of each square?

Laurie's Notes

EXAMPLE 5

- "Define diameter and radius of a circle." Diameter is the distance across a circle through its center. Radius is half the diameter.
- Remind students that the plural form of radius is *radii*.
- Write and solve the equation as shown.
- This example reviews the formula for the area of a circle. You might also ask about the formula for the circumference of a circle. $C = 2\pi r$

Try It

- Have students work in pairs to discuss and solve the problem. Then select several students to share with the class.

✓ Self-Assessment for Concepts & Skills

- **Neighbor Check:** Have students work independently and then have their neighbors check their work. Have students discuss any discrepancies.

⦿ Ask students to give an example of an equation that has:
 a. no solution. *Sample answer:* $x + 5 = x + 2$
 b. one solution. *Sample answer:* $x + 5 = 2x + 3$
 c. infinitely many solutions. *Sample answer:* $4x + 12 = 2(2x + 6)$

ELL Support

Proceed as described in Laurie's Notes, but allow students to work in pairs for extra support. Then have two pairs check each other's work. Check answers for Exercises 11–13 by asking students to hold up 1 finger for one solution, no fingers for no solution, and 5 fingers for infinitely many solutions. Have students display their solutions for Exercises 14–17 on whiteboards for your review

The Success Criteria Self-Assessment chart can be found in the *Student Journal* or online at *BigIdeasMath.com*.

Extra Example 5
The legs of the right triangle have the same length. What is the area of the triangle?

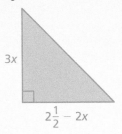

$3x$

$2\frac{1}{2} - 2x$

A. $\frac{1}{8}$ square unit

B. $\frac{1}{4}$ square unit

C. $1\frac{1}{8}$ square units

D. $2\frac{1}{4}$ square units

C

Try It

9. 36π

Self-Assessment
for Concepts & Skills

10. *Sample answer:*
 $2x + 4 = 3x + 5$; Collect the variable terms on one side of the equation by subtracting $2x$ from each side. Collect the constant terms on the other side of the equation by subtracting 5 from each side. The solution is $x = -1$.

11. one solution; *Sample answer:* There is only one value of x for which $3(x - 1) = -3$.

12. infinitely many solutions; *Sample answer:* $6x + 6 = 6(x + 1)$ for any value of x.

13. no solution; *Sample answer:* $z + 1$ is never equal to $z + 6$.

14. $x = -3$ 15. $z = 2$

16. infinitely many solutions

17. 256 units^2

Extra Example 6

A boat travels 3 hours downstream at r miles per hour. On the return trip, the boat travels 5 miles per hour slower and takes 4 hours. What is the distance the boat travels each way? 60 mi

Self-Assessment
for Problem Solving

18. $1100

19. a. no; $6x + 4 = 8x$, $x = 2$. It would take 2 hours for your friend to pass you. Both would have traveled 16 miles, which is longer than the 10-mile trail.

   b. yes; $7x + 5 = 17x$, $x = \dfrac{1}{2}$. It would take $\dfrac{1}{2}$ hour for your friend to pass you. Both would have traveled 8.5 miles, which is less than the 10-mile trail.

Learning Target

Write and solve equations with variables on both sides.

Success Criteria

- Explain how to solve an equation with variables on both sides.
- Determine whether an equation has one solution, no solution, or infinitely many solutions.
- Use equations with variables on both sides to model and solve real-life problems.

EXAMPLE 6

- Ask a volunteer to read the problem.
- ? "What do you know about the distance the boat travels upstream and the distance the boat travels on the return trip?" They are the same.
- ? "What do you know about the speeds of the boat in both directions?" The speed of the boat is 2 miles per hour faster on the return trip. "Why?" The current goes with the boat when it travels downstream, increasing the speed.
- ? "How can you write the speed of the boat on the return trip?" $(x + 2)$ miles per hour
- ? "How do you find the distance traveled d when you know the rate r and time t?" $d = rt$
- ? "If you travel 40 miles per hour for 2 hours, how far will you go?" 80 miles
  "If you travel 40 miles per hour for a half-hour, how far will you go?" 20 miles
- ? "How far do you travel at x miles per hour for 3 hours?" $3x$ miles
- Students need to read the time from the map. The rates for each direction are x and $(x + 2)$.
- Write and solve the equation as shown.
- Remind students to re-read the question to make sure they have answered it.
- Have students check the answer by using the return trip rate:
  $\dfrac{12\ \text{mi}}{1\ \cancel{h}} \times 2.5\ \cancel{h} = 30$ miles on the return trip.

✅ Self-Assessment for Problem Solving

- Students may benefit from trying the exercises independently and then working with peers to refine their work. It is important to provide time in class for problem solving, so that students become comfortable with the problem-solving plan.

- **Think-Pair-Share:** Students should read each exercise independently and then work in pairs to solve the exercises. Have each pair compare their answers with another pair and discuss any discrepancies.

The Success Criteria Self-Assessment chart can be found in the *Student Journal* or online at *BigIdeasMath.com*.

Closure

◉ Describe how to solve the equation from the Motivate: $x + 5 = 3x + 1$.
Sample answer: Subtract x from both sides, subtract 1 from both sides, and then divide both sides by 2.

EXAMPLE 6 **Modeling Real Life**

A boat travels x miles per hour upstream on the Mississippi River. On the return trip, the boat travels 2 miles per hour faster. How far does the boat travel upstream?

The boat travels the same distance upstream as on the return trip. The speed of the boat on the return trip is $(x + 2)$ miles per hour. Write and solve an equation to find the distance upstream.

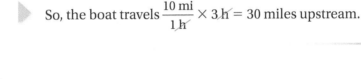

$$x(3) = (x + 2)(2.5) \quad \text{Write an equation.}$$
$$3x = 2.5x + 5 \quad \text{Distributive Property}$$
$$\underline{-2.5x} \quad \underline{-2.5x} \quad \text{Subtraction Property of Equality}$$
$$0.5x = 5 \quad \text{Simplify.}$$
$$\frac{0.5x}{0.5} = \frac{5}{0.5} \quad \text{Division Property of Equality}$$
$$x = 10 \quad \text{Simplify.}$$

The boat travels 10 miles per hour for 3 hours upstream.

▶ So, the boat travels $\dfrac{10 \text{ mi}}{1 \text{ h}} \times 3 \text{ h} = 30$ miles upstream.

Self-Assessment for Problem Solving

Solve each exercise. Then rate your understanding of the success criteria in your journal.

18. Your cousin renews his apartment lease and pays a new monthly rent. His new rent is calculated by applying a discount of $50 to his original rent and then applying a 10% increase to the discounted amount. What was your cousin's original monthly rent when his new rent is 5% greater?

19. **DIG DEEPER!** You and your friend race on a trail that is 10 miles long. In each situation, does your friend pass you before the end of the trail? Justify your answer.

    a. You have a four-mile head start and jog at 6 miles per hour. Your friend bikes at 8 miles per hour.

    b. You have a five-mile head start and run at 7 miles per hour. Your friend bikes at 17 miles per hour.

? Go to *BigIdeasMath.com* to get HELP with solving the exercises.

▶ Review & Refresh

Solve the equation. Check your solution.

1. $-9z + 2 = 11$

2. $-3n - 4n - 17 = 25$

3. $-2(x + 3) + 5x = -39$

4. $-15 + 7.5(2d - 1) = 7.5$

Find the volume of the solid.

5.
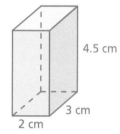
4.5 cm
3 cm
2 cm

6.
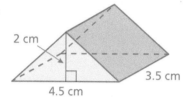
2 cm
3.5 cm
4.5 cm

7.
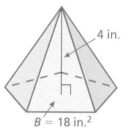
4 in.
$B = 18$ in.^{2}

▶▶ Concepts, Skills, & Problem Solving

FINDING MISSING MEASURES IN FIGURES **If possible, find the value of x so that the value of the surface area (in square inches) is equal to the value of the volume (in cubic inches). Use an equation to justify your answer.** (See Exploration 1, p. 17.)

8.
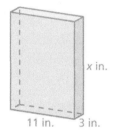
x in.
11 in.   3 in.

9.
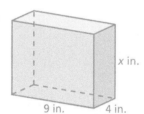
x in.
9 in.   4 in.

10.
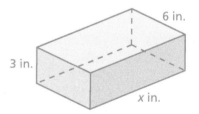
6 in.
3 in.
x in.

SOLVING AN EQUATION **Solve the equation. Check your solution.**

11. $m - 4 = 2m$

12. $3k - 1 = 7k + 2$

13. $6x = 5x + 22$

14. $-24 - 8p = 4p$

15. $12(2w - 3) = 6w$

16. $2(n - 3) = 4n + 1$

17. $2(4z - 1) = 3(z + 2)$

18. $0.1x = 0.2(x + 2)$

19. $\frac{1}{6}d + \frac{2}{3} = \frac{1}{4}(d - 2)$

20. **MP YOU BE THE TEACHER** Your friend solves the equation shown. Is your friend correct? Explain your reasoning.

$$3x - 4 = 2x + 1$$
$$3x - 4 - 2x = 2x + 1 - 2x$$
$$x - 4 = 1$$
$$x - 4 + 4 = 1 - 4$$
$$x = -3$$

Assignment Guide and Concept Check

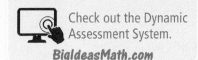

Scaffold assignments to support all students in their learning progression. The suggested assignments are a starting point. Continue to assign additional exercises and revisit with spaced practice to move every student toward proficiency.

Level	Assignment 1	Assignment 2
Emerging	4, 5, 8, 11, 13, 15, 17, 19, 20, 23, 25, 27, 34	21, 28, 31, 33, 35, 36, 37, 39, 44
Proficient	4, 6, 9, 12, 14, 16, 17, 19, 20, 22, 24, 26, 34	28, 29, 32, 35, 36, 37, 38, 40, 42, 44, 45, 46, 47
Advanced	4, 7, 10, 12, 14, 16, 17, 19, 20, 22, 24, 29, 34	32, 33, 35, 37, 38, 41, 42, 43, 44, 45, 46, 48, 49

- Assignment 1 is for use after students complete the Self-Assessment for Concepts & Skills.
- Assignment 2 is for use after students complete the Self-Assessment for Problem Solving.
- The red exercises can be used as a concept check.

Review & Refresh Prior Skills

Exercises 1–4 Solving an Equation
Exercises 5 and 6 Finding the Volume of a Prism
Exercise 7 Finding the Volume of a Pyramid

Common Errors

- **Exercises 11–19** Students may perform the same operation that they are trying to undo instead of the inverse operation when trying to get the variable or constant terms on the same side. Remind students that whenever a variable or constant term is moved from one side of the equal sign to the other, the inverse operation is used.
- **Exercises 15–19** When using the Distributive Property, students may forget to distribute to all the values within the parentheses. Remind students that they need to distribute to all the values and encourage them to draw arrows showing the distribution, if needed.

▶ Review & Refresh

1. $z = -1$
2. $n = -6$
3. $x = -11$
4. $d = 2$
5. 27 cm^3
6. 15.75 cm^3
7. 24 in.^3

▶ Concepts, Skills, & Problem Solving

8. $x = 13.2$; $28x + 66 = 33x$, $x = 13.2$
9. $x = 7.2$; $26x + 72 = 36x$, $x = 7.2$
10. not possible; $18x + 36 = 18x$, $36 \neq 0$
11. $m = -4$
12. $k = -0.75$
13. $x = 22$
14. $p = -2$
15. $w = 2$
16. $n = -3.5$
17. $z = 1.6$
18. $x = -4$
19. $d = 14$
20. no; The 4 should have been added to the right side.

Concepts, Skills, & Problem Solving

21. $20 + 0.5m = 30 + 0.25m$; 40 mi

22. no solution

23. $x = \dfrac{1}{3}$

24. infinitely many solutions

25. $x = 0$

26. infinitely many solutions

27. $x = 6$

28. no solution

29. $x = 2$

30. no solution

31. infinitely many solutions

32. no solution

33. infinitely many solutions

34. no; When the equation is $0 = 0$, it means it is true for all values of n, not just 0. So, the equation has infinitely many solutions.

35. *Sample answer:* $8x + 2 = 8x$; The number $8x$ cannot be equal to 2 more than itself.

36. It's never the same. Your neighbor's total cost will always be $75 more than your total cost.

37. The total number of crusts made by the pizza parlor is always twice the total number of crusts made by the diner.

38. no; $2x + 5.2$ can never equal $2x + 6.2$.

Common Errors

- **Exercises 22, 24, 26, 28, and 30–33** Students may end up with an equivalent equation such as $6 = 0$ or $3x + 15 = 3x + 15$ and get confused about how to state the final answer. Remind students that an equation can have no solution or infinitely many solutions.

- **Exercises 24, 26, 29, 31, and 33** When using the Distributive Property, students may forget to distribute to all the values within the parentheses. Remind students that they need to distribute to all the values and encourage them to draw arrows showing the distribution, if needed.

- **Exercise 25** Students may end up with an equivalent equation such as $0.5x = 0$ and not know how to proceed to a final answer. Remind students that dividing 0 by a nonzero number is permissible and gives a result of 0. Encourage students to check their solutions. The solution $x = 0$ checks in this equation.

- **Exercise 29** Students may be confused about the meaning of the negative sign outside the parentheses. Remind students that it means -1 times the quantity in the parentheses, and they can make this substitution in a solution step if it helps them see how to arrive at a solution.

- **Exercise 32** Students may combine like terms on the left side of the equation incorrectly, ending up with $14x$ instead of $6x$. Remind students to consider the signs of the variable terms.

21.  **MP MODELING REAL LIFE** Write and solve an equation to find the number of miles you must drive to have the same cost for each of the car rentals.

$20 plus $0.50 per mile $30 plus $0.25 per mile

SOLVING AN EQUATION Solve the equation. Check your solution, if possible.

22. $x + 6 = x$

23. $3x - 1 = 1 - 3x$

24. $3x + 15 = 3(x + 5)$

25. $4x - 9 = 3.5x - 9$

26. $\frac{1}{3}(9x + 3) = 3x + 1$

27. $5x - 7 = 4x - 1$

28. $\frac{1}{2}x + \frac{1}{2}x = x + 1$

29. $2x + 4 = -(-7x + 6)$

30. $5.5 - x = -4.5 - x$

31. $-3(2x - 3) = -6x + 9$

32. $10x - \frac{8}{3} - 4x = 6x$

33. $6(7x + 7) = 7(6x + 6)$

34. **MP YOU BE THE TEACHER** Your friend solves the equation shown. Is your friend correct? Explain your reasoning.

$$-4(2n - 3) = 12 - 8n$$
$$-8n + 12 = 12 - 8n$$
$$-8n = -8n$$
$$0 = 0$$
The solution is $n = 0$.

35. **OPEN-ENDED** Write an equation with variables on both sides that has no solution. Explain why it has no solution.

36. **MP MODELING REAL LIFE** A cable television provider charges $75 for installation and $39.96 per month for a basic entertainment package. A satellite television provider offers free installation and charges $13.32 per month for service for each television. Your neighbor subscribes to the cable provider the same month you subscribe to the satellite provider. After how many months is your neighbor's total cost the same as your total cost when you own three televisions?

37. **MP MODELING REAL LIFE** A pizza parlor makes 52 pizza crusts the first week of summer and 180 pizza crusts each subsequent week. A diner makes 26 pizza crusts the first week of summer and 90 pizza crusts each subsequent week. In how many weeks will the total number of pizza crusts made by the pizza parlor be twice the total number of pizza crusts made by the diner?

38. **MP PRECISION** Is the triangle an equilateral triangle? Justify your answer.

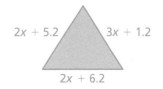

2x + 5.2   3x + 1.2

2x + 6.2

GEOMETRY Find the perimeter of the regular polygon.

39.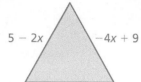
$5 - 2x$ $-4x + 9$

40.
$3(x - 1)$
$5x - 6$

41.
$x + 7$
$\frac{4}{3}x - \frac{1}{3}$

42. **MP** **PRECISION** The cost of mailing a DVD in an envelope using Company B is equal to the cost of mailing a DVD in a box using Company A. What is the weight of the DVD with its packing material? Round your answer to the nearest hundredth.

Packing Material	Company A	Company B
Box	$2.25	$2.50 per lb	$8.50 per lb
Envelope	$1.10	$2.50 per lb	$8.50 per lb

43. **WRITING** Would you solve the equation $0.25x + 7 = \frac{1}{3}x - 8$ using fractions or decimals? Explain.

44. **MP** **NUMBER SENSE** The weight of an object is equal to $\frac{3}{4}$ of its own weight plus $\frac{3}{4}$ of a pound. How much does the object weigh? Explain.

45. **MP** **STRUCTURE** Fill in the blanks in three different ways to create an equation that has one solution, no solution, and infinitely many solutions.

$$7x + 3x + 10 = -2\left(\boxed{} x + \boxed{} \right)$$

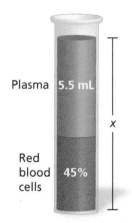
Plasma 5.5 mL
x
Red blood cells 45%

46. **MP** **MODELING REAL LIFE** The volume of red blood cells in a blood sample is equal to the total volume of the sample minus the volume of plasma. What is the total volume x of blood drawn?

47. **MP** **PROBLEM SOLVING** One serving of oatmeal provides 16% of the fiber you need daily. You must get the remaining 21 grams of fiber from other sources. How many grams of fiber should you consume daily? Justify your answer.

48. **DIG DEEPER!** The floor of a six-foot-wide hallway is painted as shown, using equal amounts of white and black paint.

a. How long is the hallway?

b. Can this same hallway be painted with the same pattern, but using twice as much black paint as white paint? Explain.

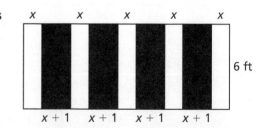
x x x x x
6 ft
$x + 1$ $x + 1$ $x + 1$ $x + 1$

49. **MP** **PRECISION** Consider the equation $c = ax - bx$, where a, b, and c are whole numbers. Which of the following result in values of a, b, and c so that the original equation has exactly one solution? Justify your answer.

$a - b = 1, c = 0$ $a = b, c \neq 0$ $a = b, c = 0$ $a \neq b, c = 0$

Mini-Assessment

Solve the equation. Check your solution, if possible.

1. $n - 4 = 3n + 6$ $n = -5$

2. $0.3(w + 10) = 1.8w$ $w = 2$

3. $-3x + 15 = 3(5 - x)$ infinitely many solutions

4. $\frac{1}{2}(4x + 14) = 2(x - 7)$ no solution

5. The perimeter of the rectangle is equal to the perimeter of the square. What are the side lengths of each figure?

$3x + 1$
$5x - 3$
$2x$
$4x + 2$

square: 7 units by 7 units
rectangle: 4 units by 10 units

Section Resources

Concepts, Skills, & Problem Solving

39. 3 units

40. 7.5 units

41. 232 units

42. about 0.19 lb

43. fractions; $\frac{1}{3}$ written as a decimal is repeating.

44. 3 lb;
$$w = \frac{3}{4}w + \frac{3}{4}$$
$$\frac{1}{4}w = \frac{3}{4}$$
$$w = 3$$

45. *Sample answer:* one solution:
$7x + 3x + 10 = -2(7x + 4)$
no solution:
$7x + 3x + 10 = -2(-5x + 4)$
infinitely many solutions:
$7x + 3x + 10 = -2(-5x + (-5))$

46. 10 mL

47. 25 g;
$$x = 21 + 0.16x$$
$$0.84x = 21$$
$$x = 25$$

48. **a.** 40 ft

b. no;
2 (white area) = black area
$$2[5(6x)] = 4[6(x + 1)]$$
$$60x = 24x + 24$$
$$36x = 24$$
$$x = \frac{2}{3}$$
$$5x + 4(x + 1) \stackrel{?}{=} 40$$
$$5\left(\frac{2}{3}\right) + 4\left(\frac{2}{3} + 1\right) \stackrel{?}{=} 40$$
$$10 \neq 40$$

49. See Additional Answers.

Learning Target

Solve literal equations for given variables and convert temperatures.

Success Criteria

- Use properties of equality to rewrite literal equations.
- Use a formula to convert temperatures.

Warm Up

Cumulative, vocabulary, and prerequisite skills practice opportunities are available in the *Resources by Chapter* or at *BigIdeasMath.com*.

ELL Support

Students may be familiar with the word *formula* from everyday life as it refers to milk for babies or a category of racecar (Formula 1). Remind them that in math the word *formula* refers to a rule that is expressed using symbols. Explain that formulas are used to find perimeters, areas, and volumes of figures, as well as many other measurements.

Exploration 1

a. See Additional Answers.

b. rectangle: $\ell = \dfrac{P - 2w}{2}$; Subtract $2w$ from each side of the equation $P = 2\ell + 2w$. Then divide each side by 2.

   rectangular prism: $\ell = \dfrac{S - 2wh}{2w + 2h}$; Subtract $2wh$ from each side of the equation $S = 2\ell w + 2\ell h + 2wh$. Factor out ℓ from each term on the right side. Divide each side of the equation by $(2w + 2h)$.

c. parallelogram: $h = 7$ m; rectangle: $\ell = 5.5$ in.; triangle: $h = 8$ in.; orange rectangular prism: $\ell = 6$ m; yellow rectangular prism: $h = 5$ in.

T-25

Laurie's Notes

Preparing to Teach

- **MP8 Look for and Express Regularity in Repeated Reasoning**: Mathematically proficient students look for shortcuts for solving problems, such as solving a literal equation for a specified variable.

Motivate

- **Preparation:** Make a set of formula cards. My set is a collection of five cards for each shape: the labeled diagram, the two measurements, and the two formulas being found.

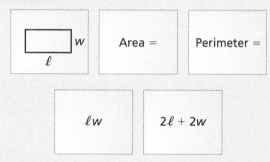

- Depending upon the number of students in your class, use some or all of the cards. Pass out the cards and have students form groups matching all 5 cards for the shape.
- When all of the matches have been made, ask each group to read their formulas aloud.
- You may also need to review the formulas for the volume of a rectangular prism. Students will learn more volume formulas in Chapter 10.

Exploration 1

- If time is a factor, you may want to skip the parallelogram and/or rectangle.
- Solving **literal equations** can be one of the most challenging skills for students. Model a problem, such as solving $A = \ell w$ for width. Make sure students understand that they are solving the formula for a different variable.
- The reason for solving for the variable is that the equation can be used for the width of any rectangle given the area and length, not just one specific problem. It is a general solution that can be reused.
- Fractional coefficients can also be a challenge, so model an additional problem, such as solving $A = \dfrac{1}{2}xy$ for *y*. First, multiply both sides by 2. Then divide both sides by *x*.
- **Teaching Tip:** After 2 or more groups have correctly written a formula for a parallelogram, have a volunteer write the solution on the board for the other groups to see.
- For the triangle, suggest students start by multiplying both sides by the reciprocal of $\dfrac{1}{2}$.
- **Teaching Tip:** In part (c), you may find that students are substituting the known values of the variables in the original formula and then solving the equation, instead of substituting the known values in the new formula.

1.4 Rewriting Equations and Formulas

Learning Target: Solve literal equations for given variables and convert temperatures.

Success Criteria:
- I can use properties of equality to rewrite literal equations.
- I can use a formula to convert temperatures.

EXPLORATION 1

Rewriting Formulas

Work with a partner.

Math Practice

Find General Methods

When does it make more sense to use the formulas you wrote in part (a) than the original area and volume formulas?

a. Write a formula for the height h of each figure. Explain your method.

- A parallelogram with area A and base b
- A rectangular prism with volume V, length ℓ, and width w
- A triangle with area A and base b

b. Write a formula for the length ℓ of each figure. Explain your method.

- A rectangle with perimeter P and width w
- A rectangular prism with surface area S, width w, and height h

c. Use your formulas in parts (a) and (b) to find the missing dimension of each figure.

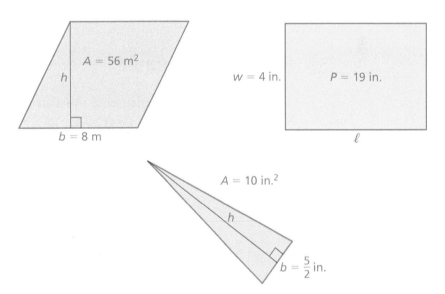

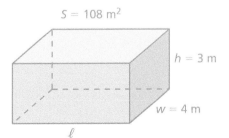

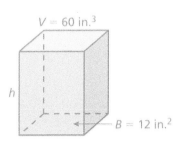

1.4 Lesson

Key Vocabulary 🔊
literal equation, *p. 26*

An equation that has two or more variables is called a **literal equation**. To rewrite a literal equation, solve for one variable in terms of the other variable(s).

EXAMPLE 1 **Rewriting an Equation**

Solve the equation $2y + 5x = 6$ for y.

$$2y + 5x = 6 \qquad \text{Write the equation.}$$

Undo the addition. ⟶ $2y + 5x - 5x = 6 - 5x \qquad$ Subtraction Property of Equality

$$2y = 6 - 5x \qquad \text{Simplify.}$$

Undo the multiplication. ⟶ $\dfrac{2y}{2} = \dfrac{6 - 5x}{2} \qquad$ Division Property of Equality

$$y = 3 - \frac{5}{2}x \qquad \text{Simplify.}$$

Try It Solve the equation for y.

1. $5y - x = 10$ **2.** $4x - 4y = 1$ **3.** $12 = 6x + 3y$

EXAMPLE 2 **Rewriting a Formula**

The formula for the surface area S of a cone is $S = \pi r^2 + \pi r \ell$. Solve the formula for the slant height ℓ.

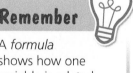

Remember

A *formula* shows how one variable is related to one or more other variables. A formula is a type of literal equation.

$$S = \pi r^2 + \pi r \ell \qquad \text{Write the formula.}$$

$$S - \pi r^2 = \pi r^2 - \pi r^2 + \pi r \ell \qquad \text{Subtraction Property of Equality}$$

$$S - \pi r^2 = \pi r \ell \qquad \text{Simplify.}$$

$$\frac{S - \pi r^2}{\pi r} = \frac{\pi r \ell}{\pi r} \qquad \text{Division Property of Equality}$$

$$\frac{S - \pi r^2}{\pi r} = \ell \qquad \text{Simplify.}$$

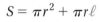

Try It Solve the formula for the red variable.

4. Area of rectangle: $A = bh$ **5.** Simple interest: $I = Prt$

6. Surface area of cylinder: $S = 2\pi r^2 + 2\pi rh$

Laurie's Notes

Scaffolding Instruction

- Students explored rewriting geometric formulas to solve for different variables. Now they will use the same process to rewrite literal equations.
- **Emerging:** Students struggle with equations containing more than one variable. They will benefit from additional practice and guided instruction.
- **Proficient:** Students can rewrite formulas and literal equations. They should complete Try It Exercises 6 and 7 before the Self-Assessment exercises.

Discuss

- Go over the definition for a literal equation and what it means to rewrite it.

EXAMPLE 1

- **Teaching Tip:** To remind students which variable they are solving for, make y a different color when solving.
- **?** "Can 6 and $5x$ be combined? Explain." No, they are not like terms.
- Point out that instead of dividing by 2, students could multiply by $\frac{1}{2}$ and then use the Distributive Property.
- **MP7 Look for and Make Use of Structure:** Simplifying the last step is not obvious to all students. The expression $\frac{6 - 5x}{2}$ is a fraction with two terms in the numerator. You subtract the numerators and keep the same denominator. For example: $\frac{5 - 3}{7} = \frac{5}{7} - \frac{3}{7}$ and $\frac{6 - 5x}{2} = \frac{6}{2} - \frac{5x}{2} = 3 - \frac{5}{2}x$.

Try It

- Spend sufficient time on these problems. Students will encounter many equations in which they need to rewrite y in terms of x.
- Notice in Exercise 2 that the coefficient of y is -4. Suggest students first rewrite the equation as $4x + (-4)y = 1$.

EXAMPLE 2

- Explain that the slant height of a cone is the distance from the vertex to the outer edge of the base, similar to the slant height of a pyramid.
- **Teaching Tip:** Highlight the variable ℓ in red as shown in the textbook. Discuss the idea that everything except the variable ℓ must be moved to the left side of the equation using properties of equality.
- **MP7 Look for and Make Use of Structure:** Structurally, the formula has the form $A = B + Cx$. It can be solved by subtracting B from both sides and then dividing both sides by C.
- **?** "The term πr^2 is added to the term $\pi r \ell$. How do you move it to the left side of the equation?" Subtract πr^2 from each side of the equation.
- Discuss the technique of dividing by πr in one step, instead of dividing by π and then dividing by r.

Try It

- **Think-Pair-Share:** Students should read each exercise independently and then work in pairs to solve the exercises. Have each pair compare their answers with another pair and discuss any discrepancies.

Scaffold instruction to support all students in their learning. Learning is individualized and you may want to group students differently as they move in and out of these levels with each skill and concept. Student self-assessment and feedback help guide your instructional decisions about how and when to layer support for all students to become proficient learners.

Extra Example 1

Solve the equation $-2x - 3y = 6$ for y.

$y = -\frac{2}{3}x - 2$

Try It

1. $y = 2 + \frac{1}{5}x$ 2. $y = x - \frac{1}{4}$

3. $y = 4 - 2x$ 4. $b = \frac{A}{h}$

5. $P = \frac{I}{rt}$

6. $h = \frac{S - 2\pi r^2}{2\pi r}$

Extra Example 2

The formula for the surface area S of a square pyramid is $S = x^2 + 2x\ell$. Solve the formula for the slant height ℓ.

$\ell = \frac{S - x^2}{2x}$

ELL Support

After demonstrating Examples 1 and 2, have students work in pairs to discuss and complete Try It Exercises 1–6. Provide guiding questions: What properties are useful? How are they applied? Can the solution be simplified? Expect students to perform according to their language levels.

Beginner: Write out each step of the process.

Intermediate: Discuss the problem using simple sentences.

Advanced: Use detailed sentences and help guide discussion.

Key Idea

- Write the formula for converting from degrees Fahrenheit to degrees Celsius.
- Remind students that they have seen capital letters as variables before. A variable is just a symbol that represents a value and it can be lowercase or uppercase, as long as you are consistent!
- Explain that you use this formula if you know the temperature in degrees Fahrenheit and you want to find the temperature in degrees Celsius.

? "You are traveling abroad, and the temperature is always stated in degrees Celsius. How can you figure out the temperature in degrees Fahrenheit, with which you are more familiar?" Students may recognize that you will want to have a different conversion formula that allows you to substitute for C and calculate F.

EXAMPLE 3

? "What is the reciprocal of $\frac{5}{9}$?" $\frac{9}{5}$

- Remind students that multiplying by the reciprocal $\frac{9}{5}$ is more efficient than dividing by the fraction $\frac{5}{9}$.

Try It

- **Neighbor Check:** Have students work independently and then have their neighbors check their work. Have students discuss any discrepancies.

✓ Self-Assessment for Concepts & Skills

- Students should solve the problems independently and then check with their neighbors.
- In Exercise 9, have volunteers demonstrate how to solve for y in each answer choice.
- ◉ Write the equation $3x + 2y - z = 6$ on the board. Tell students to solve the equation for x, for y, and for z. $x = -\frac{2}{3}y + \frac{1}{3}z + 2$; $y = -\frac{3}{2}x + \frac{1}{2}z + 3$; $z = 3x + 2y - 6$ When students finish, they should discuss their rewritten equations with a partner. Ask volunteers to share with the class.

ELL Support

Allow students to work in pairs for extra support and to practice language. Ask pairs to display their answers to Exercise 8 for your review. In Exercise 9, have two pairs alternate demonstrating to each other how to solve for y in each answer choice. Then review the answers as a class.

The Success Criteria Self-Assessment chart can be found in the *Student Journal* or online at *BigIdeasMath.com*.

Extra Example 3

Solve the temperature formula
$F = \frac{9}{5}C + 32$ for C. $C = \frac{5}{9}(F - 32)$

Try It

7. $C = \frac{5}{9}(F - 32)$;

$$F = \frac{9}{5}C + 32$$

$$F - 32 = \frac{9}{5}C$$

$$\frac{5}{9}(F - 32) = C$$

Self-Assessment
for Concepts & Skills

8. $r = \dfrac{C}{2\pi}$

9. Solve $2y - 4x = 6$ for y.;
    $y = 2x + 3$; $y = 2x - 3$

 **Key Idea**

Temperature Conversion

A formula for converting from degrees Fahrenheit F to degrees Celsius C is

$$C = \frac{5}{9}(F - 32).$$

EXAMPLE 3 **Rewriting the Temperature Formula**

Solve the temperature formula for F.

$C = \frac{5}{9}(F - 32)$	Write the temperature formula.
Use the reciprocal. $\quad \frac{9}{5} \cdot C = \frac{9}{5} \cdot \frac{5}{9}(F - 32)$	Multiplication Property of Equality
$\frac{9}{5}C = F - 32$	Simplify.
Undo the subtraction. $\quad \frac{9}{5}C + 32 = F - 32 + 32$	Addition Property of Equality
$\frac{9}{5}C + 32 = F$	Simplify.

▸ The rewritten formula is $F = \frac{9}{5}C + 32$.

Try It

7. Solve the formula $F = \frac{9}{5}C + 32$ for C. Justify your answer.

 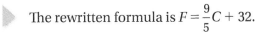 **Self-Assessment** *for Concepts & Skills*

Solve each exercise. Then rate your understanding of the success criteria in your journal.

8. **REWRITING A FORMULA** The formula for the circumference of a circle is $C = 2\pi r$. Solve the formula for r.

9. **DIFFERENT WORDS, SAME QUESTION** Which is different? Find "both" answers.

Solve $4x = 6 + 2y$ for y.	Solve $6 = 4x - 2y$ for y.
Solve $2y - 4x = -6$ for y.	Solve $2y - 4x = 6$ for y.

EXAMPLE 4 **Modeling Real Life**

Which has the greater temperature?

Understand the problem.

You are given the temperature of the Sun in degrees Fahrenheit and the temperature of lightning in degrees Celsius. You are asked which temperature is greater.

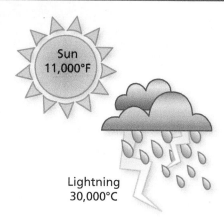
Sun
11,000°F

Lightning
30,000°C

Make a plan.

Convert the Celsius temperature to Fahrenheit. Then compare the temperatures.

Solve and check.

$$F = \frac{9}{5}C + 32$$ Write the rewritten formula from Example 3.

$$= \frac{9}{5}(30{,}000) + 32$$ Substitute 30,000 for C.

$$= 54{,}032$$ Simplify.

▷ Because $54{,}032°F > 11{,}000°F$, lightning has the greater temperature.

Another Method Compare the temperatures in degrees Celsius.

When $F = 11{,}000$, $C = \frac{5}{9}(F - 32) = \frac{5}{9}(11{,}000 - 32) \approx 6093$.

Because $30{,}000°C > 6093°C$, lightning has the greater temperature. ✓

 Self-Assessment for Problem Solving

Solve each exercise. Then rate your understanding of the success criteria in your journal.

10. Room temperature is considered to be 70°F. The temperature outside is currently 23°C. Is this greater than or less than room temperature?

11. A bird flies at a top speed of 20,000 meters per hour. The bird flies 30,000 meters without stopping.

    a. For how many hours did the bird fly if it flew at top speed?

    b. In part (a), did you rewrite a formula to find the number of hours the bird flew, or did you use another approach? Explain.

12. A ball pit is in the shape of a cylinder with a lateral surface area of 245 square feet. The diameter of the ball pit is 312 inches. What is the height of the ball pit? Justify your answer.

Laurie's Notes

EXAMPLE 4

- **FYI:** The graphic on the right provides information about the temperature of the surface of the sun and the temperature of a lightning bolt. The two temperatures use different scales.
- ? "How can you compare two temperatures that are in different scales?" Convert one of the temperatures.
- Use a Four Square to work through the problem-solving plan with students.

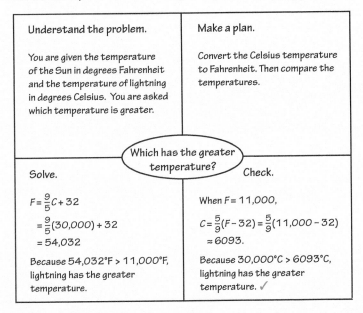

Understand the problem.	Make a plan.
You are given the temperature of the Sun in degrees Fahrenheit and the temperature of lightning in degrees Celsius. You are asked which temperature is greater.	Convert the Celsius temperature to Fahrenheit. Then compare the temperatures.

Which has the greater temperature?

Solve.	Check.
$F = \frac{9}{5}C + 32$ $= \frac{9}{5}(30,000) + 32$ $= 54,032$ Because 54,032°F > 11,000°F, lightning has the greater temperature.	When $F = 11,000$, $C = \frac{5}{9}(F-32) = \frac{5}{9}(11,000 - 32)$ ≈ 6093. Because 30,000°C > 6093°C, lightning has the greater temperature. ✓

- ? "How do you multiply $\frac{9}{5}$ times 30,000?" Students may recall that you can simplify before multiplying. Five divides into 30,000 six thousand times, so $6000 \times 9 = 54,000$.
- ? **Extension:** "Approximately how many times hotter is a lightning bolt than the surface of the sun?" 5 times This is a *cool* fact for students to know!

✓ Self-Assessment *for Problem Solving*

- Encourage students to use a Four Square to complete these exercises. Until students become comfortable with the problem-solving plan, they may only be ready to complete the first square.
- Work through Exercise 10 with students. Ask guiding questions and encourage discussion as you complete a Four Square.
- Have students work in pairs and use a Four Square to complete Exercise 11.
- Review the meaning of lateral surface area with students. Then have them work independently and use a Four Square to complete Exercise 12.

The Success Criteria Self-Assessment chart can be found in the *Student Journal* or online at *BigIdeasMath.com*.

Closure

- Solve $2x + 4y = 11$ for y. $y = -\frac{1}{2}x + \frac{11}{4}$

Extra Example 4

Which temperature is greater, 400°F or 200°C? 400°F

Self-Assessment
for Problem Solving

10. greater than

11. **a.** 1.5 h

    b. Check students' work.

12. about 3 ft; $d = 312$ in. $= 26$ ft, so $r = 13$ ft.

    $S = 2\pi r h$,

    $h = \dfrac{S}{2\pi r} = \dfrac{245}{2\pi(13)} \approx 3$

Learning Target

Solve literal equations for given variables and convert temperatures.

Success Criteria

- Use properties of equality to rewrite literal equations.
- Use a formula to convert temperatures.

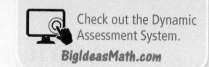
▶ Review & Refresh

1. $x = -5$

2. $z = 6$

3. no solution

4. infinitely many solutions

5. 12 mi per h

6. $1.70 per oz

7. 1.5 lb per crate

▶▶ Concepts, Skills, & Problem Solving

8. $h = \dfrac{2A}{b}$; 6 mm

9. $h = \dfrac{V}{B}$; 6 in.

10. no; The equation only contains 1 variable.

11. yes; The equation contains 2 variables.

12. yes; The equation contains 3 variables.

13. $y = 4 - \dfrac{1}{3}x$

14. $y = 35 - 15x$

15. $y = \dfrac{2}{3} - \dfrac{4}{9}x$

16. $y = \dfrac{7}{2}x - \dfrac{\pi}{2}$

17. $y = 3x - 1.5$

18. $y = \dfrac{4}{3} + \dfrac{1}{4}x$

19. no; When $2x$ is subtracted from each side of the equation, the result should be $-y = -2x + 5$.

20. $t = \dfrac{d}{r}$

21. $m = \dfrac{e}{c^2}$

22. $C = R - P$

23. $a = P - b - c$

24. $V = \dfrac{Bh}{3}$

25. $V = \dfrac{m}{D}$

Assignment Guide and Concept Check

Scaffold assignments to support all students in their learning progression. The suggested assignments are a starting point. Continue to assign additional exercises and revisit with spaced practice to move every student toward proficiency.

Level	Assignment 1	Assignment 2
Emerging	4, 6, 8, 10, 12, 13, 15, 19, 20, 22	16, 18, 21, 23, 25, 26, 27, 28, 32
Proficient	4, 6, 9, 10, 12, 14, 16, 19, 21, 23	18, 25, 26, 27, 28, 29, 30
Advanced	4, 6, 9, 10, 12, 16, 18, 19, 23, 25	27, 28, 29, 30, 31, 32

- Assignment 1 is for use after students complete the Self-Assessment for Concepts & Skills.
- Assignment 2 is for use after students complete the Self-Assessment for Problem Solving.
- The red exercises can be used as a concept check.

Review & Refresh Prior Skills

Exercises 1–4 Solving an Equation with Variables on Both Sides
Exercises 5–7 Finding Unit Rates

◻ Common Errors

- **Exercises 13–18** Students may solve the equation for the wrong variable. Remind students that they are solving the equation for y. Encourage them to make y a different color when solving so that it is easy to remember that they are solving for y.
- **Exercises 13–18 and 20–25** Students may be unsure about how to solve the literal equation or formula for the specified variable. Point out that they should work through the order of operations *backwards*, using inverse operations to isolate the variable.

1.4 Practice

 Go to **BigIdeasMath.com** to get HELP with solving the exercises.

▶ Review & Refresh

Solve the equation. Check your solution, if possible.

1. $-2x = x + 15$
2. $4(z - 3) = 2z$
3. $x - 8 = x - 1$
4. $5(4 + t) = 5t + 20$

Find the unit rate.

5. 60 miles in 5 hours
6. $8.50 : 5 ounces
7. 9 pounds per 6 crates

▶ Concepts, Skills, & Problem Solving

REWRITING FORMULAS Solve the formula for the height of the figure. Then use the new formula to find the height. (See Exploration 1, p. 25.)

8. $A = \dfrac{1}{2}bh$

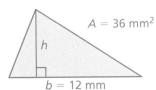

$A = 36$ mm²
h
$b = 12$ mm

9. $V = Bh$

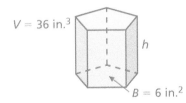

$V = 36$ in.³
h
$B = 6$ in.²

IDENTIFYING LITERAL EQUATIONS Is the equation a literal equation? Explain.

10. $y = 4$
11. $t + 8y = 7$
12. $z = 4x + 9y$

REWRITING AN EQUATION Solve the equation for y.

13. $\dfrac{1}{3}x + y = 4$
14. $3x + \dfrac{1}{5}y = 7$
15. $6 = 4x + 9y$
16. $\pi = 7x - 2y$
17. $4.2x - 1.4y = 2.1$
18. $6y - 1.5x = 8$

19. **MP YOU BE THE TEACHER** Your friend rewrites the equation $2x - y = 5$. Is your friend correct? Explain your reasoning.

> $2x - y = 5$
> $y = -2x + 5$

REWRITING A FORMULA Solve the formula for the red variable.

20. $d = rt$
21. $e = mc^2$
22. $R - C = P$
23. $P = a + b + c$
24. $B = 3\dfrac{V}{h}$
25. $D = \dfrac{m}{V}$

26. **(MP) MODELING REAL LIFE** The formula $K = C + 273.15$ converts temperatures from degrees Celsius C to Kelvin K.

    a. Convert 200 degrees Celsius to Kelvin.

    b. Solve the formula for C.

    c. Convert 300 Kelvin to degrees Celsius.

27. **(MP) PROBLEM SOLVING** The formula for simple interest is $I = Prt$.

    a. Solve the formula for t.

    b. Use the new formula to find the value of t in the table.

I	$75
P	$500
r	5%
t	

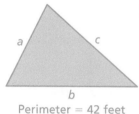

28. **GEOMETRY** Use the triangle shown.

    a. Write a formula for the perimeter P of the triangle.

    b. Solve the formula for b.

    c. Use the new formula to find b when a is 10 feet and c is 17 feet.

Perimeter = 42 feet

29. **(MP) REASONING** The formula $K = \dfrac{5}{9}(F - 32) + 273.15$ converts temperatures from degrees Fahrenheit F to Kelvin K.

    a. Solve the formula for F.

    b. The freezing point of helium is 0.95 Kelvin. What is this temperature in degrees Fahrenheit?

    c. The temperature of dry ice is $-78.5°C$. Which is colder, dry ice or liquid nitrogen?

30. **(MP) MODELING REAL LIFE** In which city is the water temperature higher?

31. **GEOMETRY** The volume of a square pyramid with a height of 30 feet is 360 cubic feet. What are the side lengths of the base? Justify your answer.

32. **DIG DEEPER!** The Navy Pier Ferris Wheel in Chicago has a circumference that is 56% of the circumference of the first Ferris wheel built in 1893.

    a. What is the radius of the Navy Pier Ferris Wheel?

    b. What was the radius of the first Ferris wheel?

    c. The first Ferris wheel took 9 minutes to make a complete revolution. How fast was the wheel moving?

C = 439.6 ft

Mini-Assessment

Solve the equation for _y_.

1. $2x - y = 4$ $y = 2x - 4$

2. $5 = \frac{1}{4}x + 2y$ $y = -\frac{1}{8}x + \frac{5}{2}$

Solve the formula for the red variable.

3. $d = rt$ $r = \frac{d}{t}$

4. $A = \frac{1}{2}bh$ $b = \frac{2A}{h}$

5. The temperature in Portland, Oregon, is 37°F. The temperature in Mobile, Alabama, is 22°C. In which city is the temperature higher?   Mobile, Alabama

Section Resources

Surface Level	Deep Level
Resources by Chapter • Extra Practice • Reteach • Puzzle Time Student Journal • Self-Assessment • Practice Differentiating the Lesson Tutorial Videos Skills Review Handbook Skills Trainer	Resources by Chapter • Enrichment and Extension Graphic Organizers Dynamic Assessment System • Section Practice
Transfer Level	
Dynamic Assessment System • End-of-Chapter Quiz	Assessment Book • End-of-Chapter Quiz

Concepts, Skills, & Problem Solving

26. **a.** 473.15 K

   b. $C = K - 273.15$

   c. 26.85°C

27. **a.** $t = \frac{I}{Pr}$

   b. 3 yr

28. **a.** $P = a + b + c$

   b. $b = P - a - c$

   c. 15 ft

29. **a.** $F = 32 + \frac{9}{5}(K - 273.15)$

   b. $-457.96°F$

   c. liquid nitrogen

30. Portland

31. 6 ft; $V = \frac{Bh}{3}$,

   $B = \frac{3V}{h} = \frac{3(360)}{30} = 36$. Because B is the area of the square base, the side lengths of the base are 6 feet.

32. **a.** 70 ft

   b. 125 ft

   c. about 87.2 ft per min

Skills Needed

Exercise 1

- Solving Equations Using Multiplication or Division
- Using the Percent Equation

Exercise 2

- Finding the Volume of a Prism
- Rewriting a Formula

ELL Support

Students with limited language may find visual support strategies more helpful than others. Emphasize the strategies that are most beneficial: draw a diagram, sketch a graph or number line, and make a table.

Using the Problem-Solving Plan

1. 12 h;
$$0.5x = 4.5$$
$$x = 9$$
$$\text{original}(0.75) = 9$$
$$\text{original} = 12$$

2. 5.5 cm; $V = Bh$,
$$h = \frac{V}{B} = \frac{132}{\frac{1}{2}(8)(6)} = \frac{132}{24} = 5.5$$

Performance Task

The *STEAM Video Performance Task* provides the opportunity for additional enrichment and greater depth of knowledge as students explore the mathematics of the chapter within a context tied to the chapter STEAM Video. The performance task and a detailed scoring rubric are provided at *BigIdeasMath.com*.

Scaffolding Instruction

- The goal of this lesson is to help students become more comfortable with problem solving. These exercises combine solving equations with prior skills from other courses. The solution for Exercise 1 is worked out below, to help you guide students through the problem-solving plan. Use the remaining class time to have students work on the other exercise.
- **Emerging:** The goal for these students is to feel comfortable with the problem-solving plan. Allow students to work in pairs to write the beginning steps of the problem-solving plan for Exercise 2. Keep in mind that some students may only be ready to do the first step.
- **Proficient:** Students may be able to work independently or in pairs to complete Exercise 2.
- Visit each pair to review their plan. Ask students to describe their plans.

▶ Using the Problem-Solving Plan

Exercise 1

⇨ **Understand the problem.** You know how long a cell phone battery lasts when it is charged to 50% of its capacity. You also know that the battery life of the phone is 75% of its original battery life. You are asked to find the original battery life of the phone.

⇨ **Make a plan.** First, find the battery life of the one-year-old cell phone. Then, use this information to write and solve an equation for the original battery life of the phone.

⇨ **Solve and check.** Use the plan to solve the problem. Then check your solution.

- Find the battery life of the one-year-old cell phone.

$$a = p\% \cdot w$$
$$4\frac{1}{2} = 0.50 \cdot w$$
$$4.5 = 0.5w$$
$$\frac{4.5}{0.5} = \frac{0.5w}{0.5}$$
$$9 = w$$

So, the battery life of the one-year-old cell phone is 9 hours.

- Write and solve an equation for the original battery life of the phone.

$$a = p\% \cdot w$$
$$9 = 0.75 \cdot w$$
$$9 = 0.75w$$
$$\frac{9}{0.75} = \frac{0.75w}{0.75}$$
$$12 = w$$

So, the original battery life of the cell phone is 12 hours.

- **Check:** Verify that the battery life of the one-year-old cell phone is 75% of its original battery life.

$$\text{percent} = \frac{\text{one-year-old battery life}}{\text{original battery life}} = \frac{9}{12} = 0.75, \text{ or } 75\% \checkmark$$

Connecting Concepts

Problem-Solving Strategies

Using an appropriate strategy will help you make sense of problems as you study the mathematics in this course. You can use the following strategies to solve problems that you encounter.

- Use a verbal model.
- Draw a diagram.
- Write an equation.
- Solve a simpler problem.
- Sketch a graph or number line.
- Make a table.
- Make a list.
- Break the problem into parts.

▶ *Using the Problem-Solving Plan*

1. The battery life of a one-year-old cell phone is 75% of its original battery life. When the battery is charged to 50% of its capacity, it dies after $4\frac{1}{2}$ hours. Find the original battery life of the phone. Justify your answer.

Understand the problem. You know how long a cell phone battery lasts when it is charged to 50% of its capacity. You also know that the battery life of the phone is 75% of its original battery life. You are asked to find the original battery life of the phone.

Make a plan. First, find the battery life of the one-year-old cell phone. Then use this information to write and solve an equation for the original battery life of the phone.

Solve and check. Use the plan to solve the problem. Then check your solution.

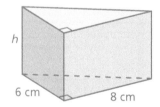

h

6 cm   8 cm

2. The triangular prism shown has a volume of 132 cubic centimeters. Find the height of the prism. Justify your answer.

Performance Task

Target Heart Rates

At the beginning of this chapter, you watched a STEAM Video called "Training for a Half Marathon." You are now ready to complete the performance task related to this video, available at *BigIdeasMath.com*. Be sure to use the problem-solving plan as you work through the performance task.

▶ Review Vocabulary

Write the definition and give an example of the vocabulary term.

literal equation, *p. 26*

▶ Graphic Organizers

You can use an **Information Frame** to help organize and remember a concept. Here is an example of an Information Frame for *solving equations with variables on both sides*.

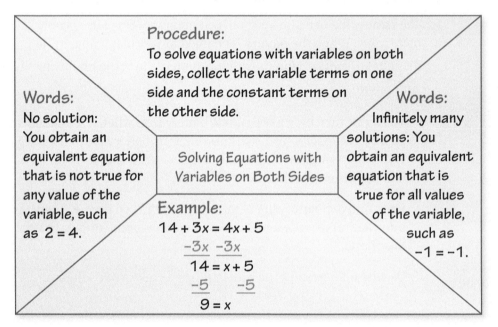

Procedure:
To solve equations with variables on both sides, collect the variable terms on one side and the constant terms on the other side.

Words:
No solution: You obtain an equivalent equation that is not true for any value of the variable, such as $2 = 4$.

Solving Equations with Variables on Both Sides

Words:
Infinitely many solutions: You obtain an equivalent equation that is true for all values of the variable, such as $-1 = -1$.

Example:
$$14 + 3x = 4x + 5$$
$$\underline{-3x \quad -3x}$$
$$14 = x + 5$$
$$\underline{-5 \qquad -5}$$
$$9 = x$$

Choose and complete a graphic organizer to help you study the concept.

1. solving simple equations using addition

2. solving simple equations using subtraction

3. solving simple equations using multiplication

4. solving simple equations using division

5. inverse operations

6. literal equation

"I finished my Information Frame about Romulus and Remus. What did Romulus and Remus say to their mommy?"

Review Vocabulary

- As a review of the chapter vocabulary, have students revisit the vocabulary section in their *Student Journals* to fill in any missing definitions and record examples of each term.

Graphic Organizers

Sample answers:

1.
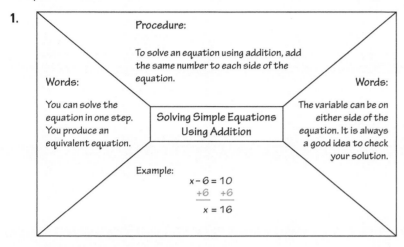

2.
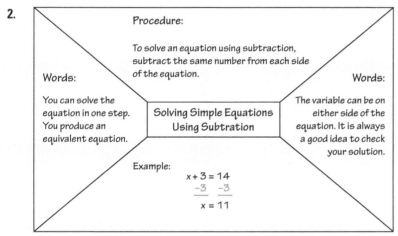

3.
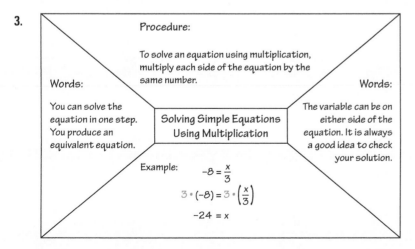

4–6. Answers at *BigIdeasMath.com*.

List of Organizers

Available at *BigIdeasMath.com*
Definition and Example Chart
Example and Non-Example Chart
Four Square
Information Frame
Summary Triangle

About this Organizer

An **Information Frame** can be used to help students organize and remember concepts. Students write the concept in the middle rectangle. Then students write related categories in the spaces around the rectangle. Related categories may include: words, numbers, algebra, example, definition, non-example, visual, procedure, details, or vocabulary. Students can place their Information Frames on note cards to use as a quick study reference.

1. $y = -19$

2. $n = -8$

3. $t = 12\pi$

4. $v = 8.1$

5. $w = -4$

6. $x = -\dfrac{1}{4}$

7. $\dfrac{41}{200}x = 357;\ 1741°C$

8. *Sample answer:* $x - 2 = 7$

9. both are correct; *Sample answer:* Dividing by $\dfrac{2}{5}$ is the same as multiplying by its reciprocal, $\dfrac{5}{2}$.

10. $x + 10 = 55;\ x = 45$

11. 12 in.

✓ Chapter Self-Assessment

The Success Criteria Self-Assessment chart can be found in the *Student Journal* or online at *BigIdeasMath.com.*

ELL Support

Allow students to work in pairs to complete the first section of the Chapter Self-Assessment. Once pairs have finished, check for understanding by asking pairs to display their solutions and equations on whiteboards for your review. Have each pair discuss their explanation for Exercise 9 with another pair and reach an agreement for the answer. Monitor discussions and provide support. Use similar techniques to check the remaining sections of the Chapter Self-Assessment.

Common Errors

- **Exercises 1–6** Students may perform the same operation that they are trying to undo instead of the inverse operation. Remind students that they must use an inverse operation to undo an operation. Also, remind students to check their solutions in the original equation.

Chapter Self-Assessment

As you complete the exercises, use the scale below to rate your understanding of the success criteria in your journal.

1	2	3	4
I do not understand.	I can do it with help.	I can do it on my own.	I can teach someone else.

1.1 Solving Simple Equations *(pp. 3–10)*

Learning Target: Write and solve one-step equations.

Solve the equation. Check your solution.

1. $y + 8 = -11$

2. $3.2 = -0.4n$

3. $-\dfrac{t}{4} = -3\pi$

4. $v - \left| 2.4 \right| = 5.7$

5. $-6 = -2 + w$

6. $x - \dfrac{2}{3} = -\dfrac{11}{12}$

7. The *boiling point* of a liquid is the temperature at which the liquid becomes a gas. The boiling point of mercury is about $\dfrac{41}{200}$ of the boiling point of lead. Write and solve an equation to find the boiling point of lead.

Boiling point of mercury

8. Write an equation that you can use the Addition Property of Equality to solve.

9. To solve $\dfrac{2}{5}x = 14$, you multiply both sides of the equation by $\dfrac{5}{2}$. Your friend divides both sides of the equation by $\dfrac{2}{5}$. Who is correct? Explain.

10. Write and solve an equation to find the value of x.

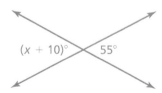

11. The circumference C of a circle is 24π inches. Use the formula $C = 2\pi r$ to find the radius r of the circle.

1.2 Solving Multi-Step Equations (pp. 11–16)

Learning Target: Write and solve multi-step equations.

Solve the equation. Check your solution.

12. $3n + 12 = 30$

13. $2(3 - p) - 17 = 41$

14. $-14x + 28 + 6x = -44$

15. $1.06(12.95 + x) = 31.27$

16. The sum of the angle measures of a quadrilateral is $360°$. Find the value of x. Then find the angle measures of the quadrilateral.

17. The equation $P = 2.5m + 35$ represents the price P (in dollars) of a bracelet, where m is the cost of the materials (in dollars). The price of a bracelet is $115. What is the cost of the materials?

18. A 455-foot fence encloses a pasture. What is the length of each side of the pasture?

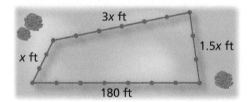

1.3 Solving Equations with Variables on Both Sides (pp. 17–24)

Learning Target: Write and solve equations with variables on both sides.

Solve the equation. Check your solution, if possible.

19. $3(x - 4) = -2(4 - x)$

20. $4 - 5k = -8 - 5k$

21. $5m - 1 = 4m + 5$

22. $3(5p - 3) = 5(p - 1)$

23. $0.4n + 0.1 = 0.5(n + 4)$

24. $7t + 3 = 8 + 7t$

25. $\frac{1}{5}(15b - 7) = 3b - 9$

26. $\frac{1}{6}(12z - 18) = 2z - 3$

27. The side lengths of an isosceles triangle are $(3x + 1)$ inches, $(4x + 5)$ inches, and $(2x + 7)$ inches. Find the perimeters of two possible triangles.

Common Errors

- **Exercises 13, 15, 19, 22, 23, 25, and 26** When using the Distributive Property, students may forget to distribute to all the values within the parentheses. Remind students that they need to distribute to all the values and encourage them to draw arrows showing the distribution, if needed.
- **Exercises 19–26** Students may perform the same operation that they are trying to undo instead of the inverse operation when trying to get the variable or constant terms on the same side. Remind students that whenever a variable or constant term is moved from one side of the equal sign to the other, the inverse operation is used.
- **Exercises 20 and 24–26** Students may end up with an equivalent equation such as $4 = -8$ or $2z - 3 = 2z - 3$ and get confused about how to state the final answer. Remind students that an equation can have no solution or infinitely many solutions.

12. $n = 6$
13. $p = -26$
14. $x = 9$
15. $x = 16.55$
16. $120; 60°, 120°, 120°, 60°$
17. \$32
18. 50 ft, 150 ft, 75 ft, 180 ft
19. $x = 4$
20. no solution
21. $m = 6$
22. $p = 0.4$
23. $n = -19$
24. no solution
25. no solution
26. infinitely many solutions
27. 22 in. and 67 in.

28. 15 mi

29. The amount in the checking account is always twice the amount in the savings account.

30. $y = -\dfrac{1}{6}x + \dfrac{4}{3}$

31. $y = 30x - 45$

32. $y = -\dfrac{1}{2}x + 2$

33. a. $K = \dfrac{5}{9}(F - 32) + 273.15$

   b. about 388.71 K

34. a. $A = \dfrac{1}{2}h(b_1 + b_2)$

   b. $h = \dfrac{2A}{b_1 + b_2}$

   c. 6 cm

35. $\dfrac{y - b}{m} = x$

36. a. $h = \dfrac{V}{\pi r^2}$

   b. 3.84 in.

Common Errors

- **Exercises 30–32** Students may solve the equation for the wrong variable. Remind students that they are solving the equation for *y*. Encourage them to make *y* a different color when solving so that it is easy to remember that they are solving for *y*.

- **Exercises 30–36** Students may be unsure about how to solve the literal equation or formula for the specified variable. Point out that they should work through the order of operations *backwards*, using inverse operations to isolate the variable.

Chapter Resources

Surface Level	Deep Level

Resources by Chapter
  • Extra Practice
  • Reteach
  • Puzzle Time
Student Journal
  • Practice
  • Chapter Self-Assessment
Differentiating the Lesson
Tutorial Videos
Skills Review Handbook
Skills Trainer
Game Library
	Resources by Chapter
	  • Enrichment and Extension
	Graphic Organizers
	Game Library

Transfer Level	

STEAM Video
Dynamic Assessment System
  • Chapter Test
	Assessment Book
	  • Chapter Tests A and B
	  • Alternative Assessment
	  • STEAM Performance Task

28. A shuttle company charges $3.25 plus $0.55 per mile. A taxi company charges $2.50 plus $0.60 per mile. After how many miles will both companies charge the same amount?

29. You begin the year with $25 in a savings account and $50 in a checking account. Each week you deposit $5 into the savings account and $10 into the checking account. In how many weeks is the amount in the checking account twice the amount in the savings account?

1.4 Rewriting Equations and Formulas (pp. 25–30)

Learning Target: Solve literal equations for given variables and convert temperatures.

Solve the equation for y.

30. $6y + x = 8$

31. $10x - \dfrac{1}{3}y = 15$

32. $20 = 5x + 10y$

33. The formula $F = \dfrac{9}{5}(K - 273.15) + 32$ converts a temperature from Kelvin K to Fahrenheit F.

   a. Solve the formula for K.

   b. Convert 240°F to Kelvin. Round your answer to the nearest hundredth.

34. Use the trapezoid shown.

   a. Write the formula for the area A of a trapezoid.

   b. Solve the formula for h.

   c. Use the new formula to find the height h of the trapezoid.

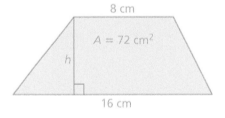

35. The equation for a line in slope-intercept form is $y = mx + b$. Solve the equation for x.

36. The formula for the volume of a cylinder is $V = \pi r^2 h$, where r is the radius of the circular base and h is the height of the cylinder.

   a. Solve the formula for h.

   b. Use the new formula to find the height of the cylinder.

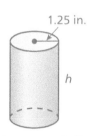

Volume = 6π in.³

Solve the equation. Check your solution, if possible.

1. $4 + y = 9.5$

2. $-\dfrac{x}{9} = -8$

3. $z - \dfrac{2}{3} = \dfrac{1}{8}$

4. $15 = 9 - 3a$

5. $4(b + 5) - 9 = -7$

6. $9j - 8 = 8 + 9j$

7. $3.8n - 13 = 1.4n + 5$

8. $9(8d - 5) + 13 = 12d - 2$

9. $\dfrac{1}{4}t + 4 = \dfrac{3}{4}(t + 8)$

10. The sum of the angle measures of a triangle is 180°. Find the value of x. Then find the angle measures of the triangle.

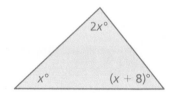

11. A formula for the perimeter of a rectangle is $P = 2\ell + 2w$.

   a. Solve the formula for w.

   b. Use the new formula to find the width w (in meters) of a rectangle with a perimeter of 2 meters and a length of 40 centimeters.

12. Solve $0.5 = 0.4y - 0.25x$ for y.

13. Your basketball team wins a game by 13 points. The opposing team scores 72 points. Explain how to find your team's score.

14. You are biking at a speed of 18 miles per hour. You are 3 miles behind your friend, who is biking at a speed of 12 miles per hour. Write and solve an equation to find the amount of time it takes for you to catch up to your friend.

15. Two scientists are measuring the temperatures of lava. One scientist records a temperature of 1725°F. The other scientist records a temperature of 950°C. Which is the greater temperature?

16. Your profit for mowing lawns this week is $24. You are paid $8 per hour and you paid $40 for gas for the lawn mower. How many hours did you work this week?

Practice Test Item References

Practice Test Questions	Section to Review
1, 2, 3, 13	1.1
4, 5, 10, 16	1.2
6, 7, 8, 9, 14	1.3
11, 12, 15	1.4

Test-Taking Strategies

Remind students to quickly look over the entire test before they start so that they can budget their time. They should not spend too much time on any single problem. Urge students to try to work on a part of each problem, because partial credit is better than no credit. When working with equations, students need to write all numbers and variables clearly, line up terms in each step, and not crowd their work. Teach students to use the **Stop** and **Think** strategy before answering. **Stop** and carefully read the problem and **Think** about what the answer should look like.

Common Errors

- **Exercises 1–9** Students may perform the same operation that they are trying to undo instead of the inverse operation. Remind students that they must use an inverse operation to undo an operation. Also, remind students to check their solutions in the original equation.
- **Exercises 5, 8, and 9** When using the Distributive Property, students may forget to distribute to all the values within the parentheses. Remind students that they need to distribute to all the values and encourage them to draw arrows showing the distribution, if needed.
- **Exercise 6** Students may end up with an equivalent equation such as $-8 = 8$ and get confused about how to state the final answer. Remind students that an equation can have no solution or infinitely many solutions.
- **Exercise 10** When combining like terms, students may change the exponent of the variable. For example, they may write the sum $2x + x + (x + 8)$ as $4x^3 + 8$. Remind students that when adding and subtracting variables, they perform the addition or subtraction on the coefficient of the variable.
- **Exercises 11 and 12** Students may be unsure about how to solve the formula or literal equation for the specified variable. Point out that they should work through the order of operations *backwards*, using inverse operations to isolate the variable.
- **Exercise 12** Students may solve the equation for the wrong variable. Remind students that they are solving the equation for y. Encourage them to make y a different color when solving so that it is easy to remember that they are solving for y.

Test-Taking Strategies

Available at *BigIdeasMath.com*
After Answering Easy Questions, Relax
Answer Easy Questions First
Estimate the Answer
Read All Choices before Answering
Read Question before Answering
Solve Directly or Eliminate Choices
Solve Problem before Looking at Choices
Use Intelligent Guessing
Work Backwards

About this Strategy

When taking a multiple-choice test, be sure to read each question carefully and thoroughly. Before answering a question, determine exactly what is being asked, then eliminate the wrong answers and select the best choice.

Cumulative Practice

1. A
2. F
3. B
4. 12
5. G

Item Analysis

1. **A.** Correct answer

   B. The student subtracts 4 from 32 instead of dividing by 4.

   C. The student adds 4 to 32 instead of dividing by 4.

   D. The student multiplies 32 by 4 instead of dividing by 4.

2. **F.** Correct answer

   G. The student adds 3 to 39 instead of subtracting 3 from 39 and then performs the division correctly.

   H. The student subtracts 3 from 39, but then subtracts 2 from 36 instead of dividing 36 by 2.

   I. The student subtracts 3 from 39, but then multiplies 2 by 36 instead of dividing 36 by 2.

3. **A.** The student makes an operation error when solving for the variable.

   B. Correct answer

   C. The student makes an operation error when solving for the variable.

   D. The student makes an operation error when solving for the variable.

4. **Gridded Response:** Correct answer: 12

   Common error: The student correctly determines that $x = 3$, but states 3 as the final answer without finding the side lengths of the square.

5. **F.** The student multiplies r by d and moves t to the other side of the equal sign instead of dividing d by r.

   G. Correct answer

   H. The student subtracts r from d instead of dividing d by r.

   I. The student divides r by d and moves t to the other side of the equal sign instead of dividing d by r.

Cumulative Practice

1. Which value of x makes the equation true?

   $$4x = 32$$

   A. 8

   C. 36

   B. 28

   D. 128

Test-Taking Strategy

Solve Directly or Eliminate Choices

When a cat wakes up, it's grumpy for x hours, where $2x - 5x = x - 4$. What's x?

Ⓐ 0 Ⓑ 1 Ⓒ 2 Ⓓ -3

Don't talk to me until I've had my morning milk.

"You can eliminate A and D. Then, solve directly to determine that the correct answer is B."

2. A taxi ride costs $3 plus $2 for each mile driven. You spend $39 on a taxi. This can be modeled by the equation $2m + 3 = 39$, where m represents the number of miles driven. How long was your taxi ride?

   F. 18 mi

   H. 34 mi

   G. 21 mi

   I. 72 mi

3. Which of the following equations has exactly one solution?

   A. $\frac{2}{3}(x + 6) = \frac{2}{3}x + 4$

   B. $\frac{3}{7}y + 13 = 13 - \frac{3}{7}y$

   C. $\frac{4}{5}\left(n + \frac{1}{3}\right) = \frac{4}{5}n + \frac{1}{3}$

   D. $\frac{7}{8}\left(2t + \frac{1}{8}\right) = \frac{7}{4}t$

4. The perimeter of the square is equal to the perimeter of the triangle. What are the side lengths of the square?

   $7x - 2$ $7x - 2$

   $3x + 3$ $2x + 4$

5. The formula $d = rt$ relates distance, rate, and time. Solve the formula for t.

   F. $t = dr$

   H. $t = d - r$

   G. $t = \dfrac{d}{r}$

   I. $t = \dfrac{r}{d}$

6. What is a possible first step to solve the equation $3x + 5 = 2(x + 7)$?

    A. Combine $3x$ and 5.   **B.** Multiply x by 2 and 7 by 2.

    C. Subtract x from $3x$.   **D.** Subtract 5 from 7.

7. You work as a sales representative. You earn $400 per week plus 5% of your total sales for the week.

    Part A Last week, you had total sales of $5000. Find your total earnings. Show your work.

    Part B One week, you earned $1350. Let s represent your total sales that week. Write an equation that you can use to find s.

    Part C Using your equation from Part B, find s. Show all steps clearly.

8. In 10 years, your aunt will be 39 years old. Let m represent your aunt's age today. Which equation can you use to find m?

    F. $m = 39 + 10$ **G.** $m - 10 = 39$

    H. $m + 10 = 39$ **I.** $10m = 39$

9. Which value of y makes the equation $3y + 8 = 7y + 11$ true?

    A. -4.75 **B.** -0.75

    C. 0.75 **D.** 4.75

10. What is the value of x?

    F. 23

    G. 39

    H. 58

    I. 68

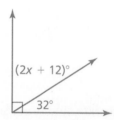

Item Analysis (continued)

6. **A.** The student incorrectly thinks that $3x$ and 5 are like terms.

   B. Correct answer

   C. The student does not realize that the Distributive Property must first be used to multiply 2 by $(x + 7)$.

   D. The student does not realize that the Distributive Property must first be used to multiply 2 by $(x + 7)$.

7. **4 points** The student's work and explanations demonstrate a thorough understanding of evaluating expressions, writing equations, and solving equations. In Part A, the student correctly finds the total earnings, $650. In Part B, the student correctly writes an equation equivalent to $0.05s + 400 = 1350$. In Part C, the student correctly solves the equation to find $s = \$19,000$. The student provides accurate work with clear and complete explanations.

   3 points The student's work and explanations demonstrate an essential but less than thorough understanding of evaluating expressions, writing equations, and solving equations. For example, the student writes a correct equation but makes an arithmetic error in Part C.

   2 points The student's work and explanations demonstrate a partial but limited understanding of evaluating expressions, writing equations, and solving equations. For example, the student completes Part A correctly, but the equation in Part B may be written incorrectly. Alternatively, a correct equation could be written in Part B, but Part C might display misunderstanding of how to proceed.

   1 point The student's work and explanations demonstrate a very limited understanding of evaluating expressions, writing equations, and solving equations.

   0 points The student provides no response, a completely incorrect or incomprehensible response, or a response that demonstrates insufficient understanding of evaluating expressions, writing equations, and solving equations.

8. **F.** The student misunderstands the problem and decides to add the two numbers together.

   G. The student understands that m and 39 are 10 apart but chooses subtraction instead of addition to relate them.

   H. Correct answer

   I. The student mistakes $10m$ for $10 + m$.

9. **A.** The student adds 11 to 8 instead of subtracting and incorrectly thinks $7y - 3y = -4y$ instead of $4y$.

   B. Correct answer

   C. The student subtracts 11 from 8 but incorrectly thinks $7y - 3y = -4y$ instead of $4y$.

   D. The student adds 11 to 8 instead of subtracting.

10. **F.** Correct answer

    G. The student solves $2x + 12 = 90$ instead of $(2x + 12) + 32 = 90$.

    H. The student finds the missing angle measure instead of the value of x.

    I. The student solves $(2x + 12) + 32 = 180$ instead of $(2x + 12) + 32 = 90$.

Cumulative Practice

6. B

7. *Part A* $650

   Part B $0.05s + 400 = 1350$

   Part C $19,000

8. H

9. B

10. F

11. 14

12. B

13. I

14. A

Item Analysis (continued)

11. Gridded Response: Correct answer: 14

Common error: The student adds 35 and 175 to get 210 and then divides by 10 to get 21.

12. A. The student finds x.

   B. Correct answer

   C. The student solves $5x = 180$ and uses $3x°$ as the greatest angle measure.

   D. The student solves $5x = 180 + 50$ and uses $3x°$ as the greatest angle measure.

13. F. The student distributes correctly but incorrectly thinks that $-7 + 18 = -11$ instead of 11 and gets $2x = -11$.

   G. The student does not distribute the left side of the equation correctly and gets $6x - 3 = 4x - 7$.

   H. The student adds $4x$ to $6x$ instead of subtracting and gets $10x = 11$.

   I. Correct answer

14. A. Correct answer

   B. The student incorrectly uses the fact that there are 4 items on one side and 2 on the other to get the ratio $\frac{2}{4} = \frac{1}{2}$.

   C. The student incorrectly uses the fact that there are 4 items on one side and 2 on the other to get the ratio $\frac{2}{4} = \frac{1}{2}$ and then misinterprets the order of the ratio.

   D. The student finds the correct ratio of $\frac{1}{3}$ but misinterprets the order of the ratio.

11. You have already saved $35 for a new cell phone. You need $175 to buy the cell phone. You think you can save $10 per week. At this rate, how many more weeks will you need to save money before you can buy the new cell phone?

12. What is the greatest angle measure in the triangle?

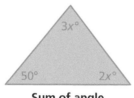

Sum of angle measures: 180°

A. 26°

B. 78°

C. 108°

D. 138°

13. Which value of x makes the equation $6(x - 3) = 4x - 7$ true?

F. −5.5

G. −2

H. 1.1

I. 5.5

14. The drawing below shows equal weights on two sides of a balance scale.

What can you conclude from the drawing?

A. A mug weighs one-third as much as a trophy.

B. A mug weighs one-half as much as a trophy.

C. A mug weighs twice as much as a trophy.

D. A mug weighs three times as much as a trophy.

2 Transformations

Chapter Learning Target:
Understand transformations.

Chapter Success Criteria:
- ☐ I can identify a translation.
- ☐ I can describe a transformation.
- ☑ I can describe a sequence of rigid motions between two congruent figures.
- ☑ I can solve real-life problems involving transformations.

STEAM Video: "Shadow Puppets"

Laurie's Notes

Chapter 2 Overview

The concepts of congruence and similarity are introduced through the study of transformations. Informally, a transformation changes one figure into another. If a figure and a resulting image are *congruent*, the transformation is rigid. A non-rigid transformation produces an image that is *similar* to the original figure.

Students' prior knowledge of transformations may involve the language of *slides*, *flips*, and *turns*. These terms suggest that two-dimensional figures have been manipulated and often students will talk of motions. The challenge for students is in visualizing the result of a transformation, the image. This is particularly true of rotations and reflections. To help students develop these important spatial skills, use transparent paper or patty paper (thin tissue paper used by delis and bakeries). Students can trace the figure and move it (translate, rotate, or reflect) according to the definition of the particular transformation.

The first three lessons present translations, reflections, and rotations. In the coordinate plane to the right, the blue triangles (the images) are congruent to the red triangle (the original figure). Students observe patterns when they investigate the coordinates of figures resulting from a transformation.

In the coordinate plane, the green triangle (the image) is similar to the red triangle (the original figure). The green triangle is a dilation with respect to the origin with a scale factor of 0.5. Dilations, as well as all transformations, can be demonstrated using geometry software available at *BigIdeasMath.com.*

The chapter ends with a lesson on perimeter and area of similar figures. Understanding the difference between perimeters (linear measurements) of similar figures and areas (square measurements) of similar figures takes time. Students need to investigate simple figures. When you double the side lengths of a square, the perimeter is double and the area is quadruple as the diagram shows. This is true for circles as well, but not as obvious to see. Students need time to develop this understanding.

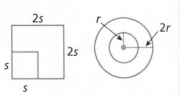

Note: In Chapter 4, students will use similar triangles to explain why the slope is the same between any two distinct points on a non-vertical line in the coordinate plane. Similarity of figures is developed through transformations, so Chapters 2 and 3 must precede Chapter 4.

Suggested Pacing

Chapter Opener	1 Day
Section 1	2 Days
Section 2	2 Days
Section 3	2 Days
Section 4	2 Days
Section 5	2 Days
Section 6	2 Days
Section 7	2 Days
Connecting Concepts	1 Day
Chapter Review	1 Day
Chapter Test	1 Day
Total Chapter 2	18 Days
Year-to-Date	31 Days

Chapter Learning Target
Understand transformations.

Chapter Success Criteria
- Identify a translation.
- Describe a transformation.
- Describe a sequence of rigid motions between two congruent figures.
- Solve real-life problems involving transformations.

Chapter 2 Learning Targets and Success Criteria

Section	Learning Target	Success Criteria
2.1 Translations	Translate figures in the coordinate plane.	• Identify a translation. • Find the coordinates of a translated figure. • Use coordinates to translate a figure.
2.2 Reflections	Reflect figures in the coordinate plane.	• Identify a reflection. • Find the coordinates of a figure reflected in an axis. • Use coordinates to reflect a figure in the *x*- or *y*-axis.
2.3 Rotations	Rotate figures in the coordinate plane.	• Identify a rotation. • Find the coordinates of a figure rotated about the origin. • Use coordinates to rotate a figure about the origin.
2.4 Congruent Figures	Understand the concept of congruent figures.	• Identify congruent figures. • Describe a sequence of rigid motions between two congruent figures.
2.5 Dilations	Dilate figures in the coordinate plane.	• Identify a dilation. • Find the coordinates of a figure dilated with respect to the origin. • Use coordinates to dilate a figure with respect to the origin.
2.6 Similar Figures	Understand the concept of similar figures.	• Identify similar figures. • Describe a similarity transformation between two similar figures.
2.7 Perimeters and Areas of Similar Figures	Find perimeters and areas of similar figures.	• Use corresponding side lengths to compare perimeters of similar figures. • Use corresponding side lengths to compare areas of similar figures. • Use similar figures to solve real-life problems involving perimeter and area.

Progressions

Through the Grades

Grade 7	Grade 8	High School
• Find unit rates associated with ratios of fractions, areas, and other quantities in like or different units. • Represent proportional relationships with equations. • Use proportionality to solve multistep ratio problems. • Use scale drawings to compute actual lengths and areas and reproduce a scale drawing at a different scale. • Draw geometric shapes with given conditions, focusing on triangles.	• Verify the properties of translations, reflections, and rotations. • Understand that figures are congruent (or similar) when they can be related by a sequence of translations, reflections, and rotations (and dilations). Describe a sequence that exhibits congruence (or similarity) between two figures. • Describe translations, reflections, rotations, and dilations using coordinates.	• Translate, reflect, stretch, and shrink graphs of functions, and combine transformations of graphs of functions. • Identify lines of symmetry and rotational symmetry. • Describe and perform congruence transformations and similarity transformations. • Identify and use corresponding parts. • Use SAS, SSS, HL, ASA, and AAS to prove two triangles congruent. • Use the AA, SSS, and SAS Similarity Theorems to prove triangles are similar.

Through the Chapter

Standard	2.1	2.2	2.3	2.4	2.5	2.6	2.7
8.G.A.1 Verify experimentally the properties of rotations, reflections, and translations: lines are taken to lines, and line segments to line segments of the same length; angles are taken to angles of the same measure; and parallel lines are taken to parallel lines.	●	●	★				
8.G.A.2 Understand that a two-dimensional figure is congruent to another if the second can be obtained from the first by a sequence of rotations, reflections, and translations; given two congruent figures, describe a sequence that exhibits the congruence between them.				★			
8.G.A.3 Describe the effect of dilations, translations, rotations, and reflections on two-dimensional figures using coordinates.	●	●	●		★		
8.G.A.4 Understand that a two-dimensional figure is similar to another if the second can be obtained from the first by a sequence of rotations, reflections, translations, and dilations; given two similar two-dimensional figures, describe a sequence that exhibits the similarity between them.						★	■

Key

▲ = preparing ★ = complete
● = learning ■ = extending

Laurie's Notes

STEAM Video

1. translation; *Sample answer:* A translation will slide the pig from the floor to the window.

2. *Sample answer:* Move the pig puppet away from the light source.

Performance Task

Sample answer: The puppeteer might use a reflection to show the kite moving in the opposite direction.

Mathematical Practices

Students have opportunities to develop aspects of the mathematical practices throughout the chapter. Here are some examples.

1. **Make Sense of Problems and Persevere in Solving Them**
   2.5 Math Practice note, *p. 69*

2. **Reason Abstractly and Quantitatively**
   2.5 Exercise 36, *p. 76*

3. **Construct Viable Arguments and Critique the Reasoning of Others**
   2.3 Exercise 19, *p. 61*

4. **Model with Mathematics**
   2.6 Exercise 12, *p. 82*

5. **Use Appropriate Tools Strategically**
   2.1 Math Practice note, *p. 43*

6. **Attend to Precision**
   2.4 Math Practice note, *p. 63*

7. **Look for and Make Use of Structure**
   2.7 Exercise 18, *p. 88*

8. **Look for and Express Regularity in Repeated Reasoning**
   2.7 Exercise 21, *p. 88*

STEAM Video

Before the Video

- To introduce the STEAM Video, read aloud the first paragraph of Shadow Puppets and discuss the question with your students.
- ? "How else can a puppet be controlled?"

During the Video

- The video shows Robert and Tory discussing shadow puppetry.
- ? Pause the video at 0:53 and ask, "How does a shadow puppeteer manipulate a puppet?" using transformations
- Watch the remainder of the video.

After the Video

- ? "What four types of transformations did Robert and Tory discuss?" translations, rotations, dilations, and reflections
- ? "Which transformation can make an image larger or smaller?" a dilation
- Have students work with a partner to answer Questions 1 and 2.
- As students discuss and answer the questions, listen for a basic understanding of transformations.

Performance Task

- Use this information to spark students' interest and promote thinking about real-life problems.
- ? Ask, "When might a puppeteer want to use a reflection?"
- After completing the chapter, students will have gained the knowledge needed to complete "Master Puppeteer."

Shadow Puppets

Some puppets are controlled using strings or wires. How else can a puppet be controlled?

Watch the STEAM Video "Shadow Puppets." Then answer the following questions.

1. Tory and Robert are using a light source to display puppets on a screen. Tory wants to show the pig jumping from the floor to the window. Should she use a *translation*, *reflection*, *rotation*, or *dilation*? Explain.

2. How can Tory show the pig getting smaller as it jumps out the window?

Master Puppeteer

After completing this chapter, you will be able to use the concepts you learned to answer the questions in the *STEAM Video Performance Task.* You will be given the coordinates of a kite being used by a puppeteer.

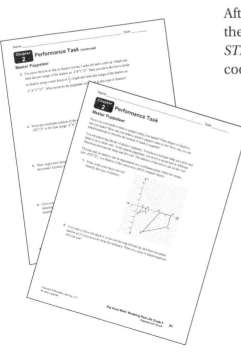

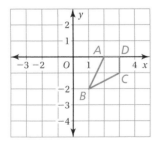

You will be asked to identify transformations for given movements of the kite. When might a puppeteer want to use a reflection?

Getting Ready for Chapter 2

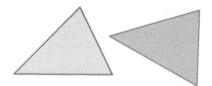

Congruent (same size and shape)

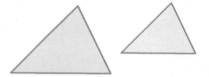

Not Congruent (same shape but not same size)

1. **Work with a partner. Form each triangle on a geoboard.**

   * Which of the triangles are congruent to the triangle at the right?
   * Measure the sides of each triangle with a ruler. Record your results in a table.
   * Write a conclusion about the side lengths of triangles that are congruent.

   a.

   b.
   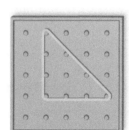

   c.

   d.

   e.
   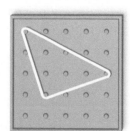

   f.
   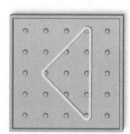

Vocabulary

The following vocabulary terms are defined in this chapter. Think about what the terms might mean and record your thoughts.

translation	rotation	dilation
reflection	rigid motion	similar figures

Laurie's Notes

Check out the digital flash cards.
BigIdeasMath.com

Chapter Exploration

- **Teaching Tip:** If this is the first time your students have used geoboards, give them time to explore and play. I hand out the geoboards with two rubber bands arranged vertically and two arranged horizontally, and students are to return them the same way. If your geoboards are a different size than the 5×5 shown, don't worry. Your students will adjust. Also, you can use geoboard dot paper in place of geoboards.
- **Common Misconception:** Measuring between two pins horizontally or vertically is *not* the same as measuring across a diagonal. The distance between two diagonal pins is longer.
- Have students use their rulers to measure each side in millimeters. Recommend that they try to measure from the center of one pin to the center of another pin.
- Students with good spatial skills may be able to rotate or reflect some triangles, so they may not want to measure each side. Encourage students to leave the triangles in the orientations given and measure each side.
- Depending upon the accuracy of their measurements, students may believe that all of the triangles are congruent.
- The yellow triangle has two congruent sides. The triangles in parts (b) and (f) also have two congruent sides but they are not congruent to the yellow triangle.
- Have students share their results and observations. If they use vocabulary such as *isosceles* or *scalene* to describe the triangles, ask them to explain what these words mean. None of the triangles are equilateral.

Vocabulary

- These terms represent some of the vocabulary that students will encounter in Chapter 2. Discuss the terms as a class.
- Where have students heard the term *reflection* outside of a math classroom? In what contexts? Students may not be able to write the actual definition, but they may write phrases associated with a *reflection*.
- Allowing students to discuss these terms now will prepare them for understanding the terms as they are presented in the chapter.
- When students encounter a new definition, encourage them to write in their *Student Journals*. They will revisit these definitions during the Chapter Review.

ELL Support

Discuss the meaning of the chapter title by writing *trans/form/ation* on the board with slashes as shown and reviewing its word parts. Explain that the prefix *trans-* means "across" or "beyond" and the root word *form* means "shape." The suffix *-ation* makes the word into a noun—it names the action. When you transform a figure, you change its location, orientation, and/or size. You can slide, flip, turn, enlarge, or reduce a figure to perform a transformation.

Topics for Review

- Area
- Clockwise and Counterclockwise
- Congruent Angles
- Congruent Sides
- Drawing a Polygon in the Coordinate Plane
- Horizontal and Vertical Lines
- Lines of Symmetry
- Perimeter
- Proportion
- Quadrants
- Ratio
- Right Angle

Chapter Exploration

1. a and e; *Sample answer:*

	Side 1	Side 2	Side 3
Given triangle	126 mm	126 mm	180 mm
a	126 mm	126 mm	180 mm
b	120 mm	120 mm	170 mm
c	165 mm	126 mm	200 mm
d	165 mm	126 mm	200 mm
e	126 mm	126 mm	180 mm
f	115 mm	115 mm	160 mm

Corresponding sides of congruent triangles have the same length.

Learning Target

Translate figures in the coordinate plane.

Success Criteria

- Identify a translation.
- Find the coordinates of a translated figure.
- Use coordinates to translate a figure.

Warm Up

Cumulative, vocabulary, and prerequisite skills practice opportunities are available in the *Resources by Chapter* or at *BigIdeasMath.com*.

ELL Support

Students may be familiar with the word *translation* as it applies to languages. When you do not understand a different language, someone may perform a translation for you. That person understands the language you do not know and changes it into the language that you do know. In math, the word *translation* is used to mean something different and very specific. A translation is a transformation of a figure. The figure slides but does not turn. Every point of the figure moves the same distance and in the same direction.

Exploration 1

a. Check students' work.

b. See Additional Answers.

c. Point *B*: 1 unit right and 2 units up; Point *C*: 3 units left and 4 units up; Point *D*: 2 units left and 3 units up; Point *E*: 4 units right and 1 unit down

d. $(x + a, y + b)$

T-43

Laurie's Notes

STATE STANDARDS
COMMON CORE 8.G.A.1a, 8.G.A.1b, 8.G.A.1c, 8.G.A.3

Preparing to Teach

- In previous courses, students plotted points in the coordinate plane. Now they will experiment with figures in a coordinate plane to verify properties of translations.
- **MP3 Construct Viable Arguments and Critique the Reasoning of Others:** As students manipulate geometric shapes, they develop spatial reasoning and make conjectures. Mathematically proficient students explore the truth of their conjectures by considering all cases.

Motivate

- **Whole Class Activity:** Model translations by having all students stand in an open area facing the same direction. Give directions such as: two steps right; three steps backward, etc. They should step backward or sideways as needed without turning their torso to keep their orientation.
- **The Meaning of a Word:** To *translate* a figure, you slide it to a new location in the plane. All points in the figure move the same distance and direction. The size, shape, and orientation of the figure do not change.
- Model a translation on the overhead (or document camera) by sliding a transparency with a shape or design on it.
- To help students develop spatial skills, have them explore transformations by moving and manipulating pattern blocks and designs traced on tracing paper or transparencies.

Exploration 1

- **Note:** This exploration can be completed using geometry software available at *BigIdeasMath.com*, transparent paper, patty paper, or transparencies. Any of these tools allow students to manipulate figures and develop an understanding of properties of a translation.
- If transparent paper is used, then students may need to measure lengths of segments and find measures of angles by hand, or they may understand intuitively that the original figure and its copy are identical.
- Point out the use of "prime" notation in the figure. If *A* is the original point, then the translated point will be *A'*. If the original figure is triangle *ABC*, then the translated figure will be triangle *A'B'C'*.
- In part (a), students can use words to describe the new location. For example, "The copy is 5 units right and 3 units up from the original."
- In part (b), students should realize that the figure is the same size and shape. If necessary, they can measure the sides and angles to verify their conjectures.
- In part (d), encourage students to identify the ordered pair $(x + a, y + b)$. Students may think that this ordered pair only describes points moved in positive directions.

? "Do these coordinates describe the location of the point if it is moved to the left and down? Explain." Yes, *a* and *b* would be negative.

2.1 Translations

Learning Target: Translate figures in the coordinate plane.

Success Criteria:
- I can identify a translation.
- I can find the coordinates of a translated figure.
- I can use coordinates to translate a figure.

EXPLORATION 1

Sliding Figures

Work with a partner.

a. For each figure below, draw the figure in a coordinate plane. Then copy the figure onto a piece of transparent paper and slide the copy to a new location in the coordinate plane. Describe the location of the copy compared to the location of the original.

- point
- line segment
- line

- triangle
- rectangle

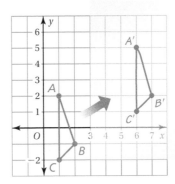

Math Practice

Recognize Usefulness of Tools

How does using transparencies help you compare each figure and its copy?

b. When you slide figures, what do you notice about sides, angles, and parallel lines?

c. Describe the location of each point below compared to the point $A(x, y)$.

$$B(x + 1, y + 2) \qquad C(x - 3, y + 4)$$

$$D(x - 2, y + 3) \qquad E(x + 4, y - 1)$$

d. You copy a point with coordinates (x, y) and slide it horizontally a units and vertically b units. What are the coordinates of the copy?

Key Vocabulary
transformation, *p. 44*
image, *p. 44*
translation, *p. 44*

A **transformation** changes a figure into another figure. The new figure is called the **image**.

A **translation** is a transformation in which a figure *slides* but does not turn. Every point of the figure moves the same distance and in the same direction.

EXAMPLE 1 **Identifying a Translation**

Tell whether the blue figure is a translation of the red figure.

a.

b.

The red figure *slides* to form the blue figure.

▷ So, the blue figure is a translation of the red figure.

The red figure *turns* to form the blue figure.

▷ So, the blue figure is *not* a translation of the red figure.

Try It **Tell whether the blue figure is a translation of the red figure.**

1.

2.

🔑 Key Idea

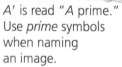
Reading

A′ is read "*A* prime."
Use *prime* symbols when naming an image.

$A \rightarrow A'$
$B \rightarrow B'$
$C \rightarrow C'$

Translations in the Coordinate Plane

Words To translate a figure *a* units horizontally and *b* units vertically in a coordinate plane, add *a* to the *x*-coordinates and *b* to the *y*-coordinates of the vertices.

Positive values of *a* and *b* represent translations up and right. Negative values of *a* and *b* represent translations down and left.

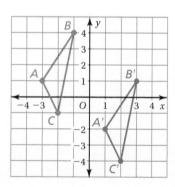

Algebra $(x, y) \rightarrow (x + a, y + b)$

In a translation, the original figure and its image are identical.

Laurie's Notes

Scaffolding Instruction

- Students explored translations by manipulating figures using transparent paper or geometry software. Now they will use their visual skills to work with translations in the coordinate plane.
- **Emerging:** Student may be able to translate a figure but struggle with naming the new coordinates (with or without physically moving the figure). They will benefit from guided instruction for the examples and Key Idea.
- **Proficient:** Students intuitively understand what happens to the coordinates of a figure when it is translated. They should review the definitions before proceeding to the Self-Assessment exercises.
- For all of the examples, you can use transparencies to copy the original figure and show that you can slide the transparency to create the image. This will help students visually understand the translation. It will also show why the side lengths and angle measures are preserved.

Discuss

- Discuss the introductory vocabulary: transformation, image, and translation.
- Point out the difference between a transformation and a translation. A translation is a transformation, but a transformation may not be a translation. Students will study other transformations in this chapter.
- Relate a translation to the Motivate activity when each student would move (slide) the same distance in the same direction.

EXAMPLE 1

- **Common Misconception:** The translation does not need to be in a horizontal or vertical direction. It can also be in a diagonal direction.
- Students generally have little difficulty identifying translations.

Try It

- **Think-Pair-Share:** Students should read each exercise independently and then work in pairs to solve the exercises. Have each pair compare their answers with another pair and discuss any discrepancies.
- For any exercises that are translations, ask students to describe the direction of the translation.

Key Idea

- Write the Key Idea, using the language of A and A' (A prime) as you identify the coordinates of the original figure (A, B, C) and its image (A', B', C').
- In this example, red triangle ABC is the original figure and blue triangle $A'B'C'$ is the translated image.
- Use a third color to draw the translation arrow from A to A'.
- "How was vertex A translated to vertex A'?" It moved 4 units right and 3 units down.
- Remind students that for two figures to be *identical*, they must be the same size and shape.

Scaffold instruction to support all students in their learning. Learning is individualized and you may want to group students differently as they move in and out of these levels with each skill and concept. Student self-assessment and feedback help guide your instructional decisions about how and when to layer support for all students to become proficient learners.

Extra Example 1

Tell whether the blue figure is a translation of the red figure.

a.

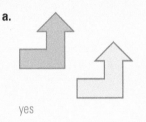

yes

b.

no

ELL Support

After demonstrating Example 1, have students work in pairs to discuss and solve Try It Exercises 1 and 2. Have one student ask another, "Is this a translation? Why?" Have students alternate roles.

Beginner: Answer using *yes, no*, or a gesture.

Intermediate: Explain using a phrase or a simple sentence.

Advanced: Explain using a detailed sentence.

Try It

1. no
2. yes

Extra Example 2

Translate the red triangle 2 units right and 5 units up. What are the coordinates of the image?

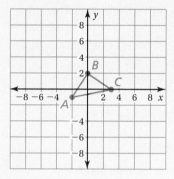

$A'(0, 4)$, $B'(2, 7)$, $C'(5, 5)$

Try It

3. $A'(-6, 3)$, $B'(-2, 7)$, $C'(-3, 4)$

Formative Assessment Tip

Talk Moves

This technique helps facilitate classroom discussion. Prompt students to answer a question and provide adequate *Wait Time* for students to respond. After a student shares an answer, repeat the answer to emphasize and clarify what the student said. Leave room for the student to agree, disagree, or elaborate by saying, "So you are saying _____. Do I have that right?" Then ask a student to restate what another student has said to ensure that students are listening carefully. Continue asking students to evaluate, critique, and use the responses and strategies discussed.

Self-Assessment
for Concepts & Skills

4. no   5. yes

6. $A'(-3, 0)$, $B'(-1, 4)$, $C'(2, 2)$

EXAMPLE 2

- Work through Method 1 as shown.
- Draw triangle *ABC* and label the vertices on a transparency. Slide the transparency 3 units to the right and 3 units down.
- Alternatively, you can model the translation on an interactive whiteboard. Draw triangle *ABC*. Copy triangle *ABC* and slide the copy to the new position.
- After the result of the translation has been drawn, you can draw arrows from *A* to *A'*, *B* to *B'*, and *C* to *C'*. The resulting figure appears to be a 3-D diagram of a triangular prism.
- Explain that translating the triangle on a diagonal is equivalent to translating the triangle horizontally and then vertically. The two steps focus on what happens to each of the coordinates in an ordered pair.
- **?** "Is the blue triangle the same size and shape as the red triangle?" yes
- Reinforce the concept of same size and shape by talking about the lengths of corresponding sides, the measures of the corresponding angles, and the perimeters and areas of the two triangles.
- Work through Method 2 as shown.
- **?** "If a figure is translated in the coordinate plane 3 units right, what will change, the *x*-coordinate or the *y*-coordinate?" *x*-coordinate
- **?** "If a figure is translated in the coordinate plane 3 units down, what will change, the *x*-coordinate or the *y*-coordinate?" *y*-coordinate
- **MP8 Look for and Express Regularity in Repeated Reasoning:** Use an alternate color to draw attention to the repeated pattern (adding 3 and subtracting 3) that occurs with each ordered pair.
- **?** "Are the coordinates of the image the same as the coordinates of the blue triangle?" yes

Try It

- Students should work in pairs.

✅ Self-Assessment for Concepts & Skills

- **Neighbor Check:** Have students work independently and then have their neighbors check their work. Have students discuss any discrepancies.
- ⊙ **Talk Moves:** Working in pairs, students should take turns explaining what a translation means and how to find the coordinates of a translated figure. Circulate and encourage students to utilize *Talk Moves* in their discussions. Then ask several students to share with the class.

ELL Support

Allow students to work in pairs for extra support and to practice language. Check answers to Exercises 4 and 5 by having students indicate *yes* or *no* using a thumbs up or down signal. Have each pair display their coordinates for Exercise 6 on a whiteboard for your review.

The Success Criteria Self-Assessment chart can be found in the *Student Journal* or online at *BigIdeasMath.com*.

EXAMPLE 2 **Translating a Figure in the Coordinate Plane**

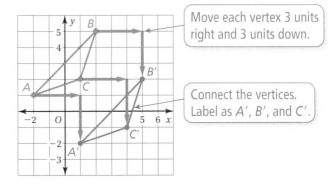

Translate the red triangle 3 units right and 3 units down. What are the coordinates of the image?

Method 1: Use a coordinate plane. Move each vertex 3 units right and 3 units down.

> Move each vertex 3 units right and 3 units down.

> Connect the vertices. Label as A', B', and C'.

▶ The coordinates of the image are $A'(1, -2)$, $B'(5, 2)$, and $C'(4, -1)$.

Method 2: Use coordinates. Add 3 to the x-coordinates of the vertices and add -3, or subtract 3, from the y-coordinates of the vertices.

$$A(-2, 1) \rightarrow A'(-2 + 3, 1 - 3) \rightarrow A'(1, -2)$$
$$B(2, 5) \longrightarrow B'(2 + 3, 5 - 3) \longrightarrow B'(5, 2)$$
$$C(1, 2) \longrightarrow C'(1 + 3, 2 - 3) \longrightarrow C'(4, -1)$$

▶ The coordinates of the image are $A'(1, -2)$, $B'(5, 2)$, and $C'(4, -1)$.

Try It

3. **WHAT IF?** The red triangle is translated 4 units left and 2 units up. What are the coordinates of the image?

Self-Assessment *for Concepts & Skills*

Solve each exercise. Then rate your understanding of the success criteria in your journal.

IDENTIFYING A TRANSLATION Tell whether the blue figure is a translation of the red figure.

4.

5.

6. **TRANSLATING A FIGURE** The vertices of a triangle are $A(-2, -2)$, $B(0, 2)$, and $C(3, 0)$. Translate the triangle 1 unit left and 2 units up. What are the coordinates of the image?

EXAMPLE 3 **Modeling Real Life**

A landscaper represents a park using a coordinate plane. He draws a square with vertices $A(1, -2)$, $B(3, -2)$, $C(3, -4)$, and $D(1, -4)$ to represent the location of a new fountain. City officials want to move the fountain 4 units left and 6 units up. Find the coordinates of the image. Then draw the original figure and the image in a coordinate plane.

Understand the problem.

You are given the coordinates for the vertices of a fountain. You are asked to find the coordinates after a translation 4 units left and 6 units up, and then graph the original figure and its image in a coordinate plane.

Make a plan.

Use the coordinates of the original figure to calculate the coordinates of the image after the translation. Then graph each figure in a coordinate plane.

Solve and check.

To find the coordinates of the image, subtract 4 from each x-coordinate and add 6 to each y-coordinate.

$$(x, y) \longrightarrow (x - 4, y + 6)$$

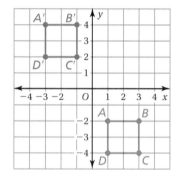

Check Counting grid lines in the graph shows that each vertex of the image is translated 4 units left and 6 units up. ✓

$A(1, -2) \longrightarrow A'(1 - 4, -2 + 6) \longrightarrow A'(-3, 4)$

$B(3, -2) \longrightarrow B'(3 - 4, -2 + 6) \longrightarrow B'(-1, 4)$

$C(3, -4) \longrightarrow C'(3 - 4, -4 + 6) \longrightarrow C'(-1, 2)$

$D(1, -4) \longrightarrow D'(1 - 4, -4 + 6) \longrightarrow D'(-3, 2)$

▷ The coordinates of the image are $A'(-3, 4)$, $B'(-1, 4)$, $C'(-1, 2)$, and $D'(-3, 2)$.

Self-Assessment for Problem Solving

Solve each exercise. Then rate your understanding of the success criteria in your journal.

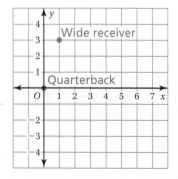

7. A neighborhood planner uses a coordinate plane to design a new neighborhood. The coordinates $A(1, -1)$, $B(1, -2)$, and $C(2, -1)$ represent House A, House B, and House C. The planner decides to place a playground centered at the origin, and moves the houses to make space. House A is now located at $A'(3, -4)$. What are the new coordinates of House B and House C when each house is moved using the same translation? Justify your answer.

8. The locations of a quarterback and a wide receiver on a football field are represented in a coordinate plane. The quarterback throws the football to the point $(6, -2)$. Use a translation to describe a path the wide receiver can take to catch the pass.

Laurie's Notes

EXAMPLE 3

- Select a student to read the problem and another to explain it.
- Work through the problem-solving plan as shown.
- **MP8 Look for and Express Regularity in Repeated Reasoning:** Use an alternate color to draw attention to the repeated pattern (subtracting 4 and adding 6) that occurs with each ordered pair.
- Draw the original figure and the image in a coordinate plane.
- "In which quadrant is the original square?" Quadrant IV
- "In which quadrant is the image?" Quadrant II
- "Is the blue square the same size and shape as the red square?" yes
- Have students use transparencies to verify the coordinates of the translation.
- Discuss the Check note.

✓ Self-Assessment for Problem Solving

- The goal for all students is to feel comfortable with the problem-solving plan. It is important for students to problem-solve in class, where they may receive support from you and their peers. Keep in mind that some students may only be ready for the first step.
- Students should work in pairs and complete the problem-solving plan for each exercise.

The Success Criteria Self-Assessment chart can be found in the *Student Journal* or online at *BigIdeasMath.com*.

Closure

- Draw a right triangle in Quadrant II. Translate the triangle so that the image is in Quadrant IV. Describe the translation.

Extra Example 3

A designer represents a playground using a coordinate plane. She draws a rectangle with vertices $A(1, 4)$, $B(3, 4)$, $C(3, 1)$, and $D(1, 1)$ to represent the current location of a sandbox. The designer wants to move the sandbox 3 units left and 4 units down. Find the coordinates of the image. Then draw the original figure and the image in a coordinate plane.

$A'(-2, 0)$, $B'(0, 0)$, $C'(0, -3)$, $D'(-2, -3)$

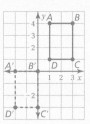

Self-Assessment
for Problem Solving

7. House B: $B'(3, -5)$,
   House C: $C'(4, -4)$; The translation for House A is $(x, y) \rightarrow (x + 2, y - 3)$.
   $B(1, -2) \rightarrow B'(1 + 2, -2 - 3)$
   $\rightarrow B'(3, -5)$
   $C(2, -1) \rightarrow C'(2 + 2, -1 - 3)$
   $\rightarrow C'(4, -4)$

8. 5 units right and 5 units down

Learning Target

Translate figures in the coordinate plane.

Success Criteria

- Identify a translation.
- Find the coordinates of a translated figure.
- Use coordinates to translate a figure.

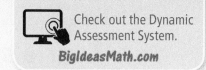

Review & Refresh

1. $y = -6x + 12$

2. $y = -\frac{1}{3}x + 3$

3. $y = -\frac{1}{6}x + 4$ 4. B

Concepts, Skills, & Problem Solving

5. 6 units right and 3 units down

6. 5 units left and 2 units down

7. yes   8. no   9. no

10. yes   11. yes   12. no

13.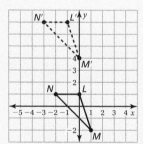

14.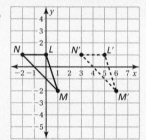

15.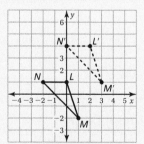

16.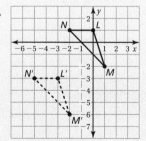

17. no; The translations for the
x- and y-coordinates were
reversed.

Assignment Guide and Concept Check

Scaffold assignments to support all students in their learning progression. The suggested assignments are a starting point. Continue to assign additional exercises and revisit with spaced practice to move every student toward proficiency.

Level	Assignment 1	Assignment 2
Emerging	3, 4, 5, 7, 9, 11, 13, 15, 17, 18, 20	8, 10, 12, 14, 16, 19, 21, 22, 23, 24
Proficient	3, 4, 6, 8, 10, 12, 14, 16, 17, 18, 20	19, 21, 22, 23, 24
Advanced	3, 4, 6, 8, 10, 12, 14, 16, 17, 19, 21	22, 23, 24, 25, 26

- Assignment 1 is for use after students complete the Self-Assessment for Concepts & Skills.
- Assignment 2 is for use after students complete the Self-Assessment for Problem Solving.
- The red exercises can be used as a concept check.

Review & Refresh Prior Skills
Exercises 1–3 Rewriting an Equation
Exercise 4 Finding Interest Earned

Common Errors

- **Exercise 12** Students may forget that the objects must be the same size to be a translation. Remind them that the size stays the same. Tell students that when the size is different, it is a scale drawing.
- **Exercises 13–16** Students may translate the figure in the wrong direction or mix up the units for the translation. Tell students to draw the original figure on graph paper. Also, tell students to write the direction of the translation using arrows to show the movement left, right, up, or down.

2.1 Practice

? Go to *BigIdeasMath.com* to get HELP with solving the exercises.

▶ Review & Refresh

Solve the equation for *y*.

1. $6x + y = 12$

2. $9 = x + 3y$

3. $\frac{1}{3}x + 2y = 8$

4. You put $550 in an account that earns 4.4% simple interest per year. How much interest do you earn in 6 months?

    A. $1.21   **B.** $12.10   **C.** $121.00   **D.** $145.20

▶▶ Concepts, Skills, & Problem Solving

DESCRIBING RELATIONSHIPS **For each figure, describe the location of the blue figure relative to the location of the red figure.** (See Exploration 1, p. 43.)

5.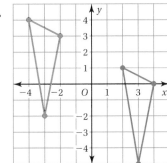

6.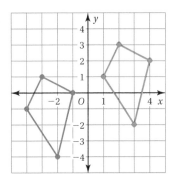

IDENTIFYING A TRANSLATION **Tell whether the blue figure is a translation of the red figure.**

7.

8.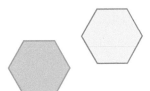

9.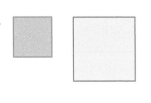

10.

11.

12.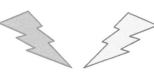

TRANSLATING A FIGURE **The vertices of a triangle are $L(0, 1)$, $M(1, -2)$, and $N(-2, 1)$. Draw the figure and its image after the translation.**

13. 1 unit left and 6 units up

14. 5 units right

15. $(x + 2, y + 3)$

16. $(x - 3, y - 4)$

17. **MP YOU BE THE TEACHER** Your friend translates point *A* 2 units down and 1 unit right. Is your friend correct? Explain your reasoning.

> $A(3, 1) \rightarrow A'(3 - 2, 1 + 1) \rightarrow A'(1, 2)$
>
> The translated point is $A'(1, 2)$.

18. **TRANSLATING A FIGURE**
    Translate the triangle 4 units right
    and 3 units down. What are the
    coordinates of the image?

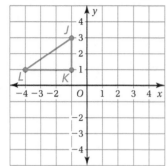

19. **TRANSLATING A FIGURE**
    Translate the figure 2 units left
    and 4 units down. What are the
    coordinates of the image?

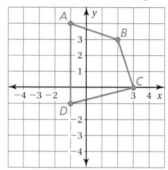

DESCRIBING A TRANSLATION Describe the translation of the point to its image.

20. $(3, -2) \longrightarrow (1, 0)$

21. $(-8, -4) \longrightarrow (-3, 5)$

22. **MP REASONING** You can click and drag an icon on a computer's desktop.
    Is this an example of a translation? Explain.

23. **MP MODELING REAL LIFE** The proposed location for a new oil platform is
    represented in a coordinate plane by a rectangle with vertices $A(1, -3)$,
    $B(1, 4)$, $C(4, 4)$, and $D(4, -3)$. An inspector recommends moving the oil
    platform 4 units right and 2 units down. Find the coordinates of the image.
    Then draw the original figure and the image in the coordinate plane.

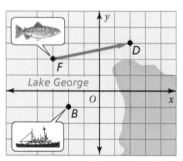

24. **MP PROBLEM SOLVING** A school of fish translates from
    point F to point D.

    a. Describe the translation of the school of fish.

    b. Can the fishing boat make the same translation?
       Explain.

    c. Describe a translation the fishing boat could make
       to get to point D.

25. **MP REASONING** The vertices of a triangle are $A(0, -3)$, $B(2, -1)$, and $C(3, -3)$. You
    translate the triangle 5 units right and 2 units down. Then you translate the image
    3 units left and 8 units down. Is the original triangle identical to the final image?
    Explain your reasoning.

26. **DIG DEEPER!** In chess, a knight can move only in
    an L-shaped pattern:
    - *two* vertical squares, then *one* horizontal square;
    - *two* horizontal squares, then *one* vertical square;
    - *one* vertical square, then *two* horizontal squares; or
    - *one* horizontal square, then *two* vertical squares.

    Write a series of translations to move the knight
    from g8 to g5.

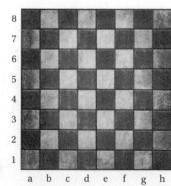

Common Errors

- **Exercises 18 and 19** Students may translate the figure in the wrong direction or mix up the units for the translation. Tell students to redraw the original figure on graph paper. Also, tell students to write the direction of the translation using arrows to show the movement left, right, up, or down.
- **Exercises 20 and 21** Students may struggle to find the translation. Encourage students to plot the points in a coordinate plane and count the change left, right, up, or down.

Mini-Assessment

The vertices of a triangle are $A(1, 3)$, $B(4, 3)$, and $C(3, 0)$. Draw the figure and its image after the translation.

1. 2 units left and 3 units down

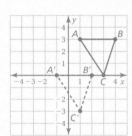

2. $(x + 1, y + 2)$

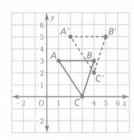

3. Describe a translation of the helicopter from point A to point B.

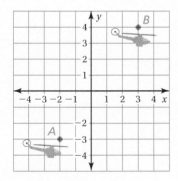

5 units right and 7 units up

Section Resources

Surface Level	Deep Level
Resources by Chapter • Extra Practice • Reteach • Puzzle Time Student Journal • Self-Assessment • Practice Differentiating the Lesson Tutorial Videos Skills Review Handbook Skills Trainer	Resources by Chapter • Enrichment and Extension Graphic Organizers Dynamic Assessment System • Section Practice

 Concepts, Skills, & Problem Solving

18. $J'(3, 0)$, $K'(3, -2)$, $L'(0, -2)$

19. $A'(-3, 0)$, $B'(0, -1)$, $C'(1, -4)$, $D'(-3, -5)$

20. 2 units left and 2 units up

21. 5 units right and 9 units up

22. yes; The figure slides.

23. $A'(5, -5)$, $B'(5, 2)$, $C'(8, 2)$, $D'(8, -5)$

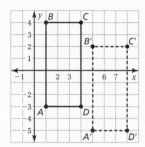

24. **a.** 5 units right and 1 unit up

   b. no; It would hit the island.

   c. 4 units up and 4 units right

25. yes; *Sample answer:* You can write one translation to get from the original triangle to the final triangle, which is $(x + 2, y - 10)$. So, the triangles are identical.

26. *Sample answer:* (1) Move 1 unit right to h8, then 2 units down to h6.
   (2) Move 2 units left to f6, then 1 unit up to f7.
   (3) Move 2 units down to f5, then 1 unit right to g5.

Learning Target

Reflect figures in the coordinate plane.

Success Criteria

- Identify a reflection.
- Find the coordinates of a figure reflected in an axis.
- Use coordinates to reflect a figure in the *x*- or *y*-axis.

Warm Up

Cumulative, vocabulary, and prerequisite skills practice opportunities are available in the *Resources by Chapter* or at *BigIdeasMath.com*.

ELL Support

Ask students how they might use the word *reflection*. If they are unfamiliar with the word, describe a reflection in a mirror or pool of water. If possible, demonstrate a reflection with a hand mirror. Explain that a reflection is another type of transformation in math. Ask them what they think it might be. Then have them confirm or revise their guesses as they work through the lesson.

Exploration 1

a. Check students' work.

b. The sides have the same length in the image as in the original figure, the angle measures are the same in the figures, and parallel lines are still parallel.

c. Point *B*: reflection in *y*-axis; Point *C*: reflection in *x*-axis; Point *D*: reflection in the *x*-axis and in the *y*-axis

d. $(x, -y)$

e. $(-x, y)$

Laurie's Notes

STATE STANDARDS
8.G.A.1a, 8.G.A.1b,
8.G.A.1c, 8.G.A.3

Preparing to Teach

- Students know how to plot points in the coordinate plane. They have also worked with lines of symmetry in a previous course. Now they will experiment with figures in a coordinate plane to verify properties of reflections.
- **MP3 Construct Viable Arguments and Critique the Reasoning of Others:** As students manipulate geometric shapes, they make conjectures and develop spatial reasoning. Mathematically proficient students explore the truth of their conjectures by considering all cases.

Motivate

- When students were younger, they probably folded a piece of paper in half, drew a figure on one side, such as half of a heart, and then cut it out to make a symmetric figure.
- **?** "What is the fold line called?" *a line of symmetry*
- **?** Write the word *MOM* on a transparency and ask a few questions.
  - "What is special about this word?" Listen for ideas about **reflection**.
  - "Describe the result when the word is reflected in the red line." MOM
  - "Describe the result when the word is reflected in the green line." WOW

- **?** "Can you think of other words that behave in a similar fashion?" *Sample answers:* YAM/MAY (reflected in a vertical line) and OHIO (reflected in a horizontal line)

Exploration 1

- Students will need transparent paper or transparencies, as in the previous section. Alternatively, they could use geometry software available at *BigIdeasMath.com*.
- Students should recognize that a figure retains its original size and shape after it is reflected. If they do not intuitively understand that the original figure and its copy are identical, have students use rulers and protractors to verify segment lengths and angle measures.
- **Popsicle Sticks:** Select students to explain what they did in part (a) and what happened, using *Talk Moves*. See the Formative Assessment Tip on page T-50 for a description of *Popsicle Sticks*.
- In part (b), the focus should be on the fact that the sides have the same length in the image as in the original figure, the angle measures are the same in both figures, and the parallel lines are still parallel.
- Students should use coordinate notation in parts (d) and (e).

2.2 Reflections

Learning Target: Reflect figures in the coordinate plane.

Success Criteria:
- I can identify a reflection.
- I can find the coordinates of a figure reflected in an axis.
- I can use coordinates to reflect a figure in the *x*- or *y*-axis.

EXPLORATION 1

Reflecting Figures

Work with a partner.

a. For each figure below, draw the figure in the coordinate plane. Then copy the axes and the figure onto a piece of transparent paper. Flip the transparent paper and align the origin and the axes with the coordinate plane. For each pair of figures, describe the line of symmetry.

- point
- line segment
- line
- triangle
- rectangle

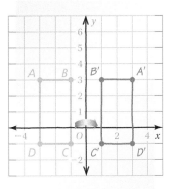

b. When you reflect figures, what do you notice about sides, angles, and parallel lines?

Math Practice

Look for Structure

How can you show that the image of a figure reflected in the coordinate plane is identical to the original figure?

---

c. Describe the relationship between each point below and the point $A(4, 7)$ in terms of reflections.

$$B(-4, 7) \qquad C(4, -7) \qquad D(-4, -7)$$

d. A point with coordinates (x, y) is reflected in the *x*-axis. What are the coordinates of the image?

e. Repeat part (d) when the point is reflected in the *y*-axis.

Key Vocabulary 🔊))
reflection, p. 50
line of reflection,
   p. 50

A **reflection**, or *flip*, is a transformation in which a figure is reflected in a line called the **line of reflection**. A reflection creates a mirror image of the original figure.

Line of reflection

Flip

EXAMPLE 1   Identifying Reflections

Tell whether the blue figure is a reflection of the red figure.

a.

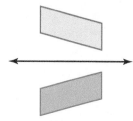

The red figure can be *flipped* to form the blue figure.

▶ So, the blue figure is a reflection of the red figure.

b.

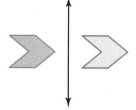

If the red figure were *flipped*, it would point to the left.

▶ So, the blue figure is *not* a reflection of the red figure.

Try It   **Tell whether the blue figure is a reflection of the red figure.**

1.

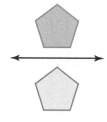

2.

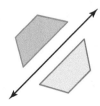

🔑 Key Idea

Reflections in the Coordinate Plane

Words   To reflect a figure in the *x*-axis, take the opposite of the *y*-coordinate.

To reflect a figure in the *y*-axis, take the opposite of the *x*-coordinate.

Algebra   Reflection in *x*-axis: $(x, y) \rightarrow (x, -y)$

Reflection in *y*-axis: $(x, y) \rightarrow (-x, y)$

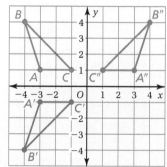

In a reflection, the original figure and its image are identical.

🔊)) Multi-Language Glossary at *BigIdeasMath.com*

Laurie's Notes

Scaffolding Instruction

- Students explored reflections using transparent paper or technology. Now they will continue to use their visual skills to identify reflections and draw reflections in the coordinate plane.
- **Emerging:** Students may be able to identify reflections, but they struggle to identify the coordinates of the image. They will benefit from guided instruction for the examples and Key Idea.
- **Proficient:** Students understand the connection between reflections and changes in coordinates. They should review the Key Idea and then proceed to the Self-Assessment exercises.

Discuss

- Discuss the introductory vocabulary: **reflection** (flip) and **line of reflection**.
- Relate lines of reflection to the red and green lines in the Motivate activity.
- **Note:** All of the lines of reflection in this section are horizontal or vertical, but tell students that lines of reflection can be slanted (oblique).

EXAMPLE 1

- **Common Error:** Students may say part (b) is a reflection because the shapes remain the same size and the orientation is the same. It is actually a translation.
- Offer transparent paper to students who struggle with spatial reasoning.

Try It

- **Think-Pair-Share:** Students should read each exercise independently and then work in pairs to solve the exercises. Have each pair compare their answers with another pair and discuss any discrepancies.

Key Idea

- Write the Key Idea, using the language of A and A' as you identify the coordinates of the original figure (A, B, C) and its image (A', B', C') reflected in the x-axis. The reflection of triangle ABC in the y-axis is the image, triangle A'', B'', C''. Note that you read A'' as "A double prime."
- Discuss how the coordinates change when you reflect a figure in each axis.
- **MP6 Attend to Precision:** Students may think $(x, -y)$ means there is a positive x-coordinate and a negative y-coordinate. Read the ordered pair as (x, the opposite of y) and explain that when y is negative, $-y$ is positive. Have students read the ordered pair this way also.

ELL Support

After demonstrating Example 1, have students work in pairs to discuss and solve Try It Exercises 1 and 2. Have one student ask another, "Is this a reflection? Why?" Have students alternate roles.

Beginner: Answer using *yes*, *no*, or a gesture.

Intermediate: Explain using a phrase or a simple sentence.

Advanced: Explain using a detailed sentence.

Extra Example 1

Tell whether the blue figure is a reflection of the red figure.

a.

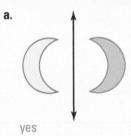

yes

b.

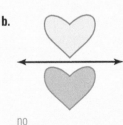

no

Try It

1. no   2. yes

Laurie's Notes

Extra Example 2

The vertices of a parallelogram are $A(-1, -1)$, $B(2, -1)$, $C(4, -3)$, and $D(1, -3)$. Draw the figure and its reflection in (a) the x-axis and (b) the y-axis. What are the coordinates of the image?

a.

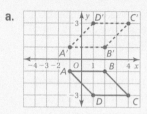

$A'(-1, 1)$, $B'(2, 1)$, $C'(4, 3)$, $D'(1, 3)$

b.

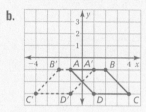

$A'(1, -1)$, $B'(-2, -1)$, $C'(-4, -3)$, $D'(-1, -3)$

Try It

3. See Additional Answers.

ELL Support

Allow students to work in pairs for extra support and to practice language. Have each pair display their coordinates for Exercise 4 on a whiteboard for your review. Have two pairs form a group and discuss their answers for Exercise 5. The two groups must come to an agreement if their ideas differ. Monitor discussions and provide support.

Self-Assessment
for Concepts & Skills

4. See Additional Answers.

5. the third one; It is not a reflection.

EXAMPLE 2

- Draw triangle *ABC* and label the vertices.
- ? "Which is the *x*-axis?" the horizontal axis
- You want to reflect the triangle from above the *x*-axis to below the *x*-axis. Be sure students understand the difference between a reflection and a translation.
- Work through part (a) as shown.
- ? "Is the blue triangle the same size and shape as the red triangle?" yes
- Reinforce the concept of same size and shape by talking about the lengths of corresponding sides, the measures of the corresponding angles, and the perimeters and areas of the two triangles.
- Write the ordered pairs for the vertices of each triangle.

$A(1, 1)$	$B(1, 4)$	$C(3, 4)$
$A'(1, -1)$	$B'(1, -4)$	$C'(3, -4)$

Discuss the Another Method note and refer back to the Key Idea. Tell students that when you reflect a point in the *x*-axis, the point and its image have the same *x*-coordinates, and the *y*-coordinates are opposites.

- Work through part (b) as shown.
- ? "Is the blue triangle the same size and shape as the red triangle?" yes
- Write the ordered pairs for the vertices of each triangle.

$A(1, 1)$	$B(1, 4)$	$C(3, 4)$
$A'(-1, 1)$	$B'(-1, 4)$	$C'(-3, 4)$

Refer back to the Key Idea. Tell students that when you reflect a point in the *y*-axis, the point and its image have the same *y*-coordinates, and the *x*-coordinates are opposites.

Try It

- **Neighbor Check:** Have students work independently and then have their neighbors check their work. Have students discuss any discrepancies.
- **Common Error:** In part (a), students may reflect the rectangle over side *BC*. Remind them that they are reflecting the rectangle in the *x*-axis, so side *B'C'* should be the same distance from the *x*-axis as side *BC* but on the opposite side. In part (b), students may reflect the rectangle over side *CD*. Remind them that they are reflecting the rectangle in the *y*-axis, so side *C'D'* should be the same distance from the *y*-axis as side *CD* but on the opposite side.

✔ Self-Assessment for Concepts & Skills

- ⊙ Use *Popsicle Sticks* to select students to explain how to:
    a. identify a reflection,
    b. find the coordinates of a figure reflected in an axis, and
    c. use coordinates to reflect a figure in the *x*-axis or *y*-axis.
- Students should solve the exercises independently.
- Use *Popsicle Sticks* to solicit explanations for Exercise 5.

The Success Criteria Self-Assessment chart can be found in the *Student Journal* or online at *BigIdeasMath.com*.

EXAMPLE 2 **Reflecting Figures**

The vertices of a triangle are $A(1, 1)$, $B(1, 4)$, and $C(3, 4)$. Draw the figure and its reflection in (a) the *x*-axis and (b) the *y*-axis. What are the coordinates of the image?

Another Method
Take the opposite of each *y*-coordinate. The *x*-coordinates do not change.

$A(1, 1) \rightarrow A'(1, -1)$
$B(1, 4) \rightarrow B'(1, -4)$
$C(3, 4) \rightarrow C'(3, -4)$ ✓

a. Point *A* is 1 unit above the *x*-axis, so plot A' 1 unit below the *x*-axis. Points *B* and *C* are 4 units above the *x*-axis, so plot B' and C' 4 units below the *x*-axis.

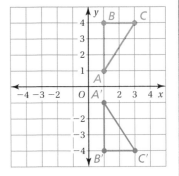

▷ The coordinates of the image are $A'(1, -1)$, $B'(1, -4)$, and $C'(3, -4)$.

b. Points *A* and *B* are 1 unit to the right of the *y*-axis, so plot A' and B' 1 unit to the left of the *y*-axis. Point *C* is 3 units to the right of the *y*-axis, so plot C' 3 units to the left of the *y*-axis.

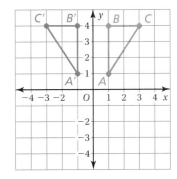

▷ The coordinates of the image are $A'(-1, 1)$, $B'(-1, 4)$, and $C'(-3, 4)$.

Try It

3. The vertices of a rectangle are $A(-4, -3)$, $B(-4, -1)$, $C(-1, -1)$, and $D(-1, -3)$. Draw the figure and its reflection in (a) the *x*-axis and (b) the *y*-axis.

Self-Assessment for Concepts & Skills

Solve each exercise. Then rate your understanding of the success criteria in your journal.

4. REFLECTING A FIGURE The vertices of a triangle are $J(-3, -5)$, $K(-2, 2)$, and $L(1, -4)$. Draw the figure and its reflection in (a) the *x*-axis and (b) the *y*-axis.

5. WHICH ONE DOESN'T BELONG? Which transformation does *not* belong with the other three? Explain your reasoning.

EXAMPLE 3 **Modeling Real Life**

A graphic artist designs a T-shirt using a pentagon with vertices $P(0, 0)$, $Q(-2, 0)$, $R(-1, 3)$, $S(-4, 3)$, and $T(0, 7)$. The artist reflects the pentagon in the y-axis to create the design. Find the coordinates of the reflected image. Then draw the design in the coordinate plane.

The pentagon is reflected in the y-axis. To find the coordinates of the reflected image, take the opposite of each x-coordinate. The y-coordinates do not change.

$(x, y) \longrightarrow (-x, y)$

$P(0, 0) \longrightarrow P'(0, 0)$

$Q(-2, 0) \longrightarrow Q'(2, 0)$

$R(-1, 3) \longrightarrow R'(1, 3)$

$S(-4, 3) \longrightarrow S'(4, 3)$

$T(0, 7) \longrightarrow T'(0, 7)$

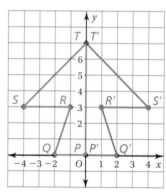

▷ The coordinates of the reflected image are $P'(0, 0)$, $Q'(2, 0)$, $R'(1, 3)$, $S'(4, 3)$, and $T'(0, 7)$.

Self-Assessment for Problem Solving

Solve each exercise. Then rate your understanding of the success criteria in your journal.

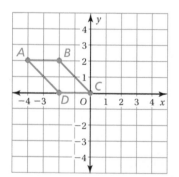

6. You design a logo using the figure shown at the left. You want both the x-axis and the y-axis to be lines of reflection. Describe how to use reflections to complete the design. Then draw the logo in the coordinate plane.

7. **DIG DEEPER!** You hit the golf ball along the path shown, so that its final location is a reflection in the y-axis of its starting location.

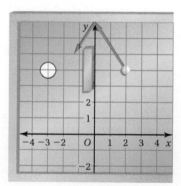

a. Does the golf ball land in the hole? Explain.

b. Your friend tries the shot from the same starting location. He bounces the ball off the wall at the point $(-0.5, 7)$ so that its path is a reflection. Does the golf ball land in the hole?

Laurie's Notes

EXAMPLE 3

- Ask a volunteer to read the problem. Then ask another volunteer to explain what the problem is asking.
- ❓ "Why might a graphic artist want to use a reflection to create a design?" *Sample answer:* To make sure the design is symmetric.
- ❓ "When you reflect a point in the *y*-axis which coordinate do you change?" the *x*-coordinate
- Write each coordinate of the pentagon and its corresponding reflected point.
- Graph both pentagons in the same coordinate plane to create the design.
- **Extension:** Find the area of the figure. 25 square units

✔ Self-Assessment for Problem Solving

- Allow time in class for students to practice using the problem-solving plan. Remember, some students may only be able to complete the first step.
- **MP4 Model with Mathematics:** In Exercise 7, students use reflections to determine the path of a golf ball. Encourage students to reason about what the reflections mean in the context of the problem.
- Students should work through the problem-solving plan independently.
- Discuss each exercise. Select several students to share their answers and reasoning.

The Success Criteria Self-Assessment chart can be found in the *Student Journal* or online at *BigIdeasMath.com*.

Closure

- Draw a right triangle in Quadrant II. Draw its reflection in (a) the *x*-axis and (b) the *y*-axis.

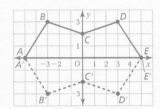
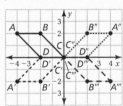

Learning Target

Reflect figures in the coordinate plane.

Success Criteria

- Identify a reflection.
- Find the coordinates of a figure reflected in an axis.
- Use coordinates to reflect a figure in the *x*- or *y*-axis.

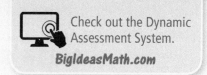

Review & Refresh

1–4. See Additional Answers.

5. neither

6. complementary

7. neither

8. B

Concepts, Skills, & Problem Solving

9. reflection in the *x*-axis

10. reflection in the *x*-axis and in the *y*-axis

11. reflection in the *y*-axis

12. no   13. yes

14. yes   15. no

16. yes   17. no

18.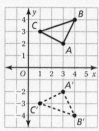

$A'(3, -2), B'(4, -4), C'(1, -3)$

19.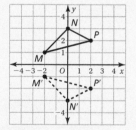

$M'(-2, -1), N'(0, -3),$
$P'(2, -2)$

20.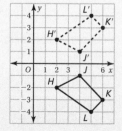

$H'(2, 2), J'(4, 1), K'(6, 3),$
$L'(5, 4)$

21. See Additional Answers.

Assignment Guide and Concept Check

Scaffold assignments to support all students in their learning progression. The suggested assignments are a starting point. Continue to assign additional exercises and revisit with spaced practice to move every student toward proficiency.

Level	Assignment 1	Assignment 2
Emerging	2, 4, 7, 8, 9, 13, 15, 17, 18, 22, 26, 27	12, 14, 16, 20, 24, 29, 31, 32, 33, 34
Proficient	2, 4, 7, 8, 10, 12, 14, 16, 18, 20, 22, 26, 28	24, 30, 31, 32, 33, 34
Advanced	2, 4, 7, 8, 11, 12, 17, 19, 21, 22, 24, 26, 28	30, 31, 32, 33, 34, 35

- Assignment 1 is for use after students complete the Self-Assessment for Concepts & Skills.
- Assignment 2 is for use after students complete the Self-Assessment for Problem Solving.
- The red exercises can be used as a concept check.

Review & Refresh Prior Skills

Exercises 1–4 Translating a Figure
Exercises 5–7 Identifying Complementary and Supplementary Angles
Exercise 8 Using the Percent Proportion or Using the Percent Equation

Common Errors

- **Exercises 12–17** Students may struggle with the visual and think that a translation is actually a reflection. Give students transparent paper to copy the objects and then fold the paper to see if the vertices line up.
- **Exercises 18–21** Students may reflect in the incorrect axis. Remind students that when they reflect a point in the *x*-axis, the point and its image have the same *x*-coordinates, and the *y*-coordinates are opposites.

? Go to *BigIdeasMath.com* to get HELP with solving the exercises.

▶ Review & Refresh

The vertices of a quadrilateral are $P(-1, -1)$, $Q(0, 4)$, $R(3, 1)$, and $S(1, -2)$. Draw the figure and its image after the translation.

1. 7 units down

2. 3 units left and 2 units up

3. $(x + 4, y - 1)$

4. $(x - 5, y - 6)$

Tell whether the angles are *complementary*, *supplementary*, or *neither*.

5.
$108°$ $82°$

6.
$47°$ $43°$

7.
$38°$ $62°$

8. 36 is 75% of what number?

   A. 27   **B.** 48   **C.** 54   **D.** 63

▶▶ Concepts, Skills, & Problem Solving

DESCRIBING RELATIONSHIPS Describe the relationship between the given point and the point $A(5, 3)$ in terms of reflections. (See Exploration 1, p. 49.)

9. $B(5, -3)$

10. $C(-5, -3)$

11. $D(-5, 3)$

IDENTIFYING A REFLECTION Tell whether the blue figure is a reflection of the red figure.

12.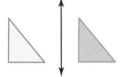

13.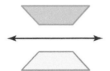

14.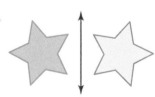

15.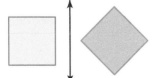

16.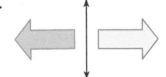

17.

REFLECTING FIGURES Draw the figure and its reflection in the x-axis. Identify the coordinates of the image.

18. $A(3, 2)$, $B(4, 4)$, $C(1, 3)$

19. $M(-2, 1)$, $N(0, 3)$, $P(2, 2)$

20. $H(2, -2)$, $J(4, -1)$, $K(6, -3)$, $L(5, -4)$

21. $D(-2, -5)$, $E(0, -1)$, $F(2, -1)$, $G(0, -5)$

REFLECTING FIGURES Draw the figure and its reflection in the *y*-axis. Identify the coordinates of the image.

22. $Q(-4, 2), R(-2, 4), S(-1, 1)$

23. $T(4, -2), U(4, 2), V(6, -2)$

24. $W(2, -1), X(5, -2), Y(5, -5), Z(2, -4)$

25. $J(2, 2), K(7, 4), L(9, -2), M(3, -1)$

26. **MP REASONING** Which letters look the same when reflected in the line?

A B C D E F G H I J K L M N O P Q R S T U V W X Y Z

MP STRUCTURE The coordinates of a point and its image after a reflection are given. Identify the line of reflection.

27. $(2, -2) \rightarrow (2, 2)$

28. $(-4, 1) \rightarrow (4, 1)$

29. $(-2, -5) \rightarrow (4, -5)$

30. $(-3, -4) \rightarrow (-3, 0)$

TRANSFORMING FIGURES Find the coordinates of the figure after the transformations.

31. Translate the triangle 1 unit right and 5 units down. Then reflect the image in the *y*-axis.

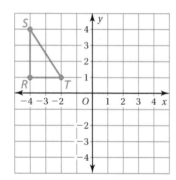

32. Reflect the trapezoid in the *x*-axis. Then translate the image 2 units left and 3 units up.

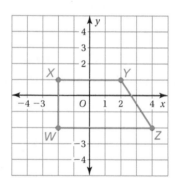

33. **MP REASONING** In Exercises 31 and 32, is the original figure identical to the final image? Explain.

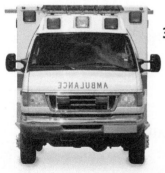

34. **CRITICAL THINKING** Hold a mirror to the left side of the photo of the vehicle.

    a. What word do you see in the mirror?

    b. Why do you think it is written that way on the front of the vehicle?

35. **DIG DEEPER!** Reflect the triangle in the line $y = x$. How are the *x*- and *y*-coordinates of the image related to the *x*- and *y*-coordinates of the original triangle?

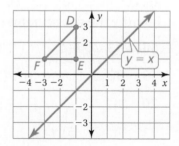

Common Errors

- **Exercises 22–25** Students may reflect in the incorrect axis. Remind students that when they reflect a point in the *y*-axis, the point and its image have the same *y*-coordinates, and the *x*-coordinates are opposites.
- **Exercise 26** Students may need to copy the alphabet and fold their paper on the line to see which letters look the same.

A B C D E F G H I J K L M N O P Q R S T U V W X Y Z

∀ B C D E F G H I J K L M N O P Q R S T U V W X Y Z

Mini-Assessment

1. The vertices of a triangle are $A(-4, -2)$, $B(4, -1)$, and $C(1, -6)$. Draw the figure and its reflection in the *x*-axis. Identify the coordinates of the image.

   $A'(-4, 2)$, $B'(4, 1)$, $C'(1, 6)$

   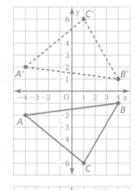

2. The vertices of a triangle are $A(-2, 4)$, $B(-4, 2)$, and $C(-1, -1)$. Draw the figure and its reflection in the *y*-axis. Identify the coordinates of the image.

   $A'(2, 4)$, $B'(4, 2)$, $C'(1, -1)$

   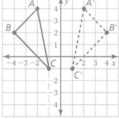

3. Will the letter E look the same when reflected in the *y*-axis? no

   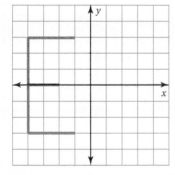

Section Resources

Surface Level	Deep Level
Resources by Chapter • Extra Practice • Reteach • Puzzle Time Student Journal • Self-Assessment • Practice Differentiating the Lesson Tutorial Videos Skills Review Handbook Skills Trainer	Resources by Chapter • Enrichment and Extension Graphic Organizers Dynamic Assessment System • Section Practice

Concepts, Skills, & Problem Solving

22.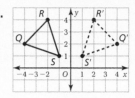

    $Q'(4, 2)$, $R'(2, 4)$, $S'(1, 1)$

23.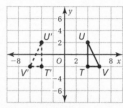

    $T'(-4, -2)$, $U'(-4, 2)$, $V'(-6, -2)$

24. See Additional Answers.

25. See Additional Answers.

26. B, C, D, E, H, I, K, O, X

27. *x*-axis   28. *y*-axis

29. $x = 1$ 30. $y = -2$

31. $R''(3, -4)$, $S''(3, -1)$, $T''(1, -4)$

32. $W''(-4, 5)$, $X''(-4, 2)$, $Y''(0, 2)$, $Z''(2, 5)$

33. yes; *Sample answer:* Translations and reflections produce images that are identical to the original figure.

34. a. AMBULANCE

    b. The word "AMBULANCE" is written that way so that when the ambulance comes up behind a car, the word will look correct in the car's rear-view mirror.

35.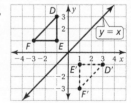

    The *x*-coordinate and *y*-coordinate for each point are switched in the image.

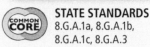
STATE STANDARDS
8.G.A.1a, 8.G.A.1b,
8.G.A.1c, 8.G.A.3

Learning Target

Rotate figures in the coordinate plane.

Success Criteria

- Identify a rotation.
- Find the coordinates of a figure rotated about the origin.
- Use coordinates to rotate a figure about the origin.

Warm Up

Cumulative, vocabulary, and prerequisite skills practice opportunities are available in the *Resources by Chapter* or at *BigIdeasMath.com*.

ELL Support

Ask students to think of a science class and consider how they might use the word *rotation*. They may apply it to planetary motion or the movement of wheels. If they are unfamiliar with the word, you could demonstrate it with a wheel of a toy car. Point out that the wheel moves around an axis, or a single point in the center of the wheel. Explain that a rotation is another type of transformation in math. Ask students to guess what it might be. Then have them confirm or revise their ideas as they work through the lesson.

Laurie's Notes

Preparing to Teach

- Students have worked with translations and reflections in the coordinate plane. Now they will explore rotations.
- **MP3 Construct Viable Arguments and Critique the Reasoning of Others**: As students manipulate geometric shapes, they develop spatial reasoning and make conjectures. Mathematically proficient students explore the truth of their conjectures by considering all possible cases.

Motivate

- **Time to Play:** *Name Five Twice.* In this game, students will name things that rotate: the first five objects rotate about a point in the center of the object (like a wheel) and the next five objects rotate about a point not in the center of the object (like a windshield wiper). Give students time to work with partners to generate two lists of five.

  Example 1: car tire, Ferris wheel, merry-go-round, dial on a
  combination lock

  Example 2: windshield wiper, lever—as on a mechanical arm or wrench
- **FYI:** Rotation is generally the most challenging transformation for students to visualize.

Exploration 1

- This exploration can be completed using geometry software available at *BigIdeasMath.com*. The software provides opportunities for students to rotate many different points in the coordinate plane to find the pattern.
- **MP5 Use Appropriate Tools Strategically:** If the exploration is done with transparent paper or patty paper, it might be helpful to create a "spinner" to help students rotate the points. Draw the figure in a coordinate plane that will remain stationary. Trace the axes and the figure onto the transparent paper. Then use a paperclip to poke a small hole through the origin.

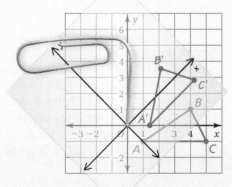

- After students have finished the exploration, ask them to share their results. If necessary, prompt them to explain their reasoning.
- In part (d), students should use coordinate notation. This may be more challenging than writing coordinates for translations and reflections.

Exploration 1

a. Check students' work.

b. The sides have the same length in the image as in the original figure, the angle measures are the same in the figures, and parallel lines are still parallel.

c. See Additional Answers.

d. $P'(-y, x)$; $P'(-x, -y)$; $P'(y, -x)$

2.3 Rotations

Learning Target: Rotate figures in the coordinate plane.

Success Criteria:
- I can identify a rotation.
- I can find the coordinates of a figure rotated about the origin.
- I can use coordinates to rotate a figure about the origin.

EXPLORATION 1

Rotating Figures

Work with a partner.

a. For each figure below, draw the figure in the coordinate plane. Then copy the axes and the figure onto a piece of transparent paper. Turn the transparent paper and align the origin and the axes with the coordinate plane. For each pair of figures, describe the angle of rotation.

- point
- line segment
- line

- triangle
- rectangle

Math Practice

Explain the Meaning

What does it mean to rotate a figure about the origin?

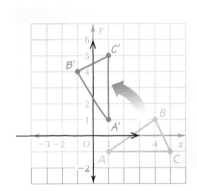

b. When you rotate figures, what do you notice about sides, angles, and parallel lines?

c. Describe the relationship between each point below and the point $A(3, 6)$ in terms of rotations.

$$B(-3, -6) \qquad C(6, -3) \qquad D(-6, 3)$$

d. What are the coordinates of a point $P(x, y)$ after a rotation 90° counterclockwise about the origin? 180°? 270°?

2.3 Lesson

Key Vocabulary 🔊
rotation, *p. 56*
center of rotation, *p. 56*
angle of rotation, *p. 56*

A **rotation**, or *turn*, is a transformation in which a figure is rotated about a point called the **center of rotation**. The number of degrees a figure rotates is the **angle of rotation**.

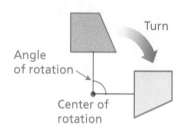

Turn

Angle of rotation

Center of rotation

EXAMPLE 1   **Identifying a Rotation**

You must rotate the puzzle piece 270° clockwise about point *P* to fit it into a puzzle. Which piece fits in the puzzle as shown?

•*P*

A.   **B.**   **C.**   **D.**

Rotate the puzzle piece 270° clockwise about point *P*.

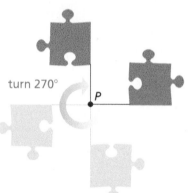

turn 270°

P

> When rotating figures, it may help to sketch the rotation in several steps, as shown in Example 1.

▷ So, the correct answer is **C**.

Try It **Tell whether the blue figure is a rotation of the red figure about the origin. If so, give the angle and direction of rotation.**

1.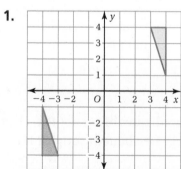

2.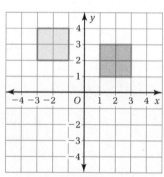

Laurie's Notes

Scaffolding Instruction

- Students explored and sketched rotations. Now they will use their visual skills to draw rotations in the coordinate plane.
- **Emerging:** Students may struggle to visualize rotations without the use of transparent paper or technology. They will benefit from practice and guided instruction for the definitions, examples, and Key Idea.
- **Proficient:** Students can identify a rotation, find the coordinates of a figure rotated about the origin, and use coordinates to rotate a figure about the origin. They should work through Example 3 and Try It Exercise 6 before proceeding to the Self-Assessment exercises.
- For all of the examples, you can use transparencies to copy the original figure and show that you can rotate the transparency to create the image. This will help students visually understand the rotation. It will also show why the side lengths and angle measures are preserved.

Discuss

- Use a marker to make two sizeable dots, one at the tip of your middle finger and one at the base of your palm. Anchor your elbow on a level surface. Wave at the class so that your elbow is the pivot.
- **?** Do a "wave" of 90°, by starting in the horizontal position and "waving" to the vertical position.
  - "Through how many degrees did I wave my hand?" 90°
  - "Did my elbow move?" no
  - "Did the two points move the same distance?" no "If not, which point moved farther?" The point on the tip of the middle finger moved farther.
- Relate this motion to that of a windshield wiper. The farther a point on the wiper is from the point of **rotation**, the farther it travels.
- The rotation is hard to visualize because the **center of rotation** is generally not attached to the shape being rotated. Your hand is connected to your forearm, which is connected to your elbow, so the "wave" is easier to see as a rotation. When a diagram only shows the original figure and the image, it is harder to see the **angle of rotation**.

EXAMPLE 1

- Model a rotation of 270° clockwise using a transparency with an arrow pointing to the right. Lightly place your finger on the middle to act as the center of rotation. Turn the transparency 90° clockwise, 3 times, stopping each time for students to see where the arrow is pointing. After 270° the arrow will be pointing up.
- Students should notice that the rotation does not alter the size or shape of the figure.

Try It

- After completing the exercises, students can use transparent paper and paperclips to rotate the red figure about the origin to check their answers.

Scaffold instruction to support all students in their learning. Learning is individualized and you may want to group students differently as they move in and out of these levels with each skill and concept. Student self-assessment and feedback help guide your instructional decisions about how and when to layer support for all students to become proficient learners.

Extra Example 1

Which figure is rotated 180° clockwise about point *P*?

A.   B.

C.   D.

B

Try It

1. yes; 180° clockwise or counterclockwise

2. no

Laurie's Notes

Key Idea

- Point out the push-pin note and explain that counterclockwise is considered the standard direction of rotation in math. Have students try some examples using coordinates, transparent paper, and paperclips.

Formative Assessment Tip

Turn and Talk

This technique allows all students in the class to have a voice. Using a three-foot voice, students turn and talk to their partners about a problem or discuss a question. There may be different roles that I ask partners to assume, so I refer to Partner A and Partner B. In discussing a procedure or explaining an answer, I might ask Partner A to talk uninterrupted for a fixed period of time. Then Partner B might be asked to repeat back what he or she heard, or to ask a question about what has been shared. Example: "*Turn and Talk*, so that Partner A explains how to rotate a point 90° counterclockwise about the origin." It is important to establish norms: three-foot voices should be expected when students are doing partner work. Discuss with students the difference between *authentic listening* and just being quiet while your partner is speaking.

EXAMPLE 2

- Many students will need transparent paper for this example. They need to see where the trapezoid rotates before they can plot the ordered pairs.
- Draw the trapezoid and label the vertices.
- **Common Error:** Students may rotate the trapezoid about vertex Z instead of rotating about the origin.
- **Teaching Strategy:** Remind students that when rotating a figure 180°, what was on the top will rotate to the bottom, and vice versa. Model this by holding a sheet of paper and rotating it 180°.
- **Turn and Talk:** Have students discuss the push-pin note.

Try It

- Students should complete these exercises without using transparent paper. Then have them compare their coordinates with their neighbors and use transparent paper and paperclips to resolve any discrepancies.

ELL Support

After demonstrating Example 2, have students work in pairs to discuss and solve Try It Exercises 3–5. Have one student ask another, "What are the coordinates of the image?" Have students alternate roles.

Beginner: State the coordinates.

Intermediate: Describe the coordinates of the image using simple sentences such as, "J prime is four, four."

Advanced: Describe the coordinates using detailed sentences such as, "The coordinates of point J prime are four, four."

Extra Example 2

The vertices of a triangle are $A(-4, 1)$, $B(-1, 6)$, and $C(-1, 1)$. Rotate the triangle 270° counterclockwise about the origin. What are the coordinates of the image?

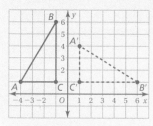

$A'(1, 4)$, $B'(6, 1)$, $C'(1, 1)$

Try It

3. $J'(4, 4)$, $K'(4, -2)$, $L'(1, 0)$, $M'(2, 3)$

4. $P'(-2, -3)$, $Q'(-1, 6)$, $R'(5, -1)$

5. $A'(3, -5)$, $B'(-1, -4)$, $C'(-1, -1)$

You can use coordinate rules to find the coordinates of a point after a rotation of 90°, 180°, or 270° about the origin.

 **Key Idea**

Rotations in the Coordinate Plane

When a point (x, y) is rotated counterclockwise about the origin, the following are true.

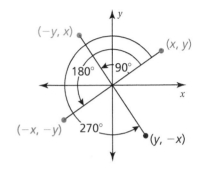

- For a rotation of 90°, $(x, y) \rightarrow (-y, x)$.
- For a rotation of 180°, $(x, y) \rightarrow (-x, -y)$.
- For a rotation of 270°, $(x, y) \rightarrow (y, -x)$.

In a rotation, the original figure and its image are identical.

A counterclockwise rotation of $n°$ is the same as a clockwise rotation of $(360 - n)°$. Similarly, a clockwise rotation of $n°$ is the same as a counterclockwise rotation of $(360 - n)°$.

EXAMPLE 2 **Rotating a Figure**

The vertices of a trapezoid are $W(-4, 2)$, $X(-3, 4)$, $Y(-1, 4)$, and $Z(-1, 2)$. Rotate the trapezoid 180° about the origin. What are the coordinates of the image?

A point (x, y) rotated 180° about the origin results in an image with coordinates $(-x, -y)$.

$$(x, y) \longrightarrow (-x, -y)$$

$$W(-4, 2) \longrightarrow W'(4, -2)$$
$$X(-3, 4) \longrightarrow X'(3, -4)$$
$$Y(-1, 4) \longrightarrow Y'(1, -4)$$
$$Z(-1, 2) \longrightarrow Z'(1, -2)$$

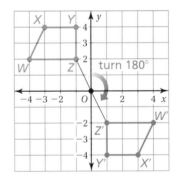

Math Practice

Build Arguments
Explain why you do not need to specify direction when rotating a figure 180°.

The coordinates of the image are $W'(4, -2)$, $X'(3, -4)$, $Y'(1, -4)$, and $Z'(1, -2)$.

Try It The vertices of a figure are given. Rotate the figure as described. Find the coordinates of the image.

3. $J(-4, -4)$, $K(-4, 2)$, $L(-1, 0)$, $M(-2, -3)$; 180° about the origin

4. $P(-3, 2)$, $Q(6, 1)$, $R(-1, -5)$; 90° counterclockwise about the origin

5. $A(5, 3)$, $B(4, -1)$, $C(1, -1)$; 90° clockwise about the origin

EXAMPLE 3 **Using More Than One Transformation**

The vertices of a rectangle are $A(-3, -3)$, $B(1, -3)$, $C(1, -5)$, and $D(-3, -5)$. Rotate the rectangle 90° clockwise about the origin, and then reflect it in the y-axis. What are the coordinates of the image?

Common Error

Be sure to pay attention to whether a rotation is clockwise or counterclockwise.

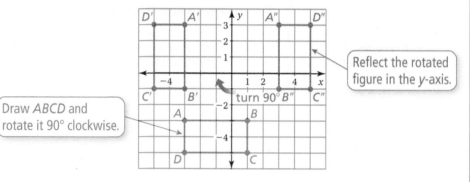

Draw *ABCD* and rotate it 90° clockwise.

Reflect the rotated figure in the y-axis.

▶ The coordinates of the image are $A''(3, 3)$, $B''(3, -1)$, $C''(5, -1)$, and $D''(5, 3)$.

Try It

6. The vertices of a triangle are $P(-1, 2)$, $Q(-1, 0)$, and $R(2, 0)$. Rotate the triangle 180° about the origin, and then reflect it in the x-axis. What are the coordinates of the image?

Self-Assessment for Concepts & Skills

Solve each exercise. Then rate your understanding of the success criteria in your journal.

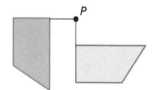

7. **IDENTIFYING A ROTATION** Tell whether the blue figure is a rotation of the red figure about point *P*. If so, give the angle and direction of rotation.

8. **DIFFERENT WORDS, SAME QUESTION** Which is different? Find "both" answers.

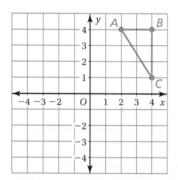

What are the coordinates of the image after a 90° clockwise rotation about the origin?

What are the coordinates of the image after a 270° clockwise rotation about the origin?

What are the coordinates of the image after turning the figure 90° to the right about the origin?

What are the coordinates of the image after a 270° counterclockwise rotation about the origin?

Laurie's Notes

EXAMPLE 3

- This example involves two transformations. First the rectangle is rotated and then it is reflected. Work slowly and carefully through this example. Transparent paper and paperclips will be helpful for many students.

- ? "Can you visualize where the image will be after the two transformations?" Answers will vary.

- Graph the original rectangle *ABCD.*

- ? "Does it matter whether you rotate the rectangle 90° clockwise or 90°counterclockwise?" yes

- To construct the image after the rotation, draw the segment *OB,* where *O* represents a point at the origin. Next locate vertex *B'* by drawing segment *OB'* so that the measure of ∠*BOB'* is 90° and segments *OB* and *OB'* are the same length. After you locate vertex *B'*, the remaining vertices should be relatively easy to locate.

- Reflect rectangle *A'B'C'D'* in the *y*-axis to obtain rectangle *A"B"C"D".*

- **Common Error:** Because the reflection resembles a translation, students may label the vertices of rectangle *A"B"C"D"* incorrectly. Watch for this.

- ? **MP3 Construct Viable Arguments and Critique the Reasoning of Others:** "Are rectangles *ABCD* and *A"B"C"D"* the same size? Explain." Yes, because in both rotations and reflections the original figure and its image are the same size.

- **MP6 Attend to Precision:** If time allows, ask students whether the order in which you perform the transformations matters. (The answer is yes.) Have them thoroughly explain their reasoning.

Try It

- **Think-Pair-Share:** Students should read the exercise independently and then work in pairs to solve the exercise. Have each pair compare their answer with another pair and discuss any discrepancies.

✓ Self-Assessment for Concepts & Skills

- Students should work independently on these exercises.
- **Popsicle Sticks:** Solicit explanations for Exercise 8.
- ◉ **Thumbs Up:** Ask students to indicate their understanding of rotations.

ELL Support

Allow students to work in pairs for extra support and to practice language. Check answers to Exercise 7 by having students indicate *yes* or *no* using a thumbs up or down signal. Then have each pair write the angle and direction of rotation on a whiteboard to hold up for your review. Have two pairs form a group to discuss their answers for Exercise 8. Monitor discussions and provide support. Have two groups present their explanations for one of the two answers and discuss as a class.

The Success Criteria Self-Assessment chart can be found in the *Student Journal* or online at *BigIdeasMath.com.*

The vertices of a rectangle are *A*(−1, 1), *B*(−4, 1), *C*(−4, 5), and *D*(−1, 5). Rotate the rectangle 90° clockwise about the origin, and then reflect it in the *y*-axis. What are the coordinates of the image?

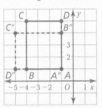

A"(−1, 1), *B"*(−1, 4), *C"*(−5, 4), *D"*(−5, 1)

Try It

6. *P"*(1, 2), *Q"*(1, 0), *R"*(−2, 0)

Self-Assessment
for Concepts & Skills

7. yes; 90° counterclockwise

8. What are the coordinates of the image after a 270° clockwise rotation about the origin?; *A'*(−4, 2), *B'*(−4, 4), *C'*(−1, 4); *A'*(4, −2), *B'*(4, −4), *C'*(1, −4)

Extra Example 4

A Ferris wheel is represented in a coordinate plane with the center of the Ferris wheel at the origin. You and two friends sit at $A(3, -4)$, $B(5, 0)$, and $C(3, 4)$. The Ferris wheel rotates $90°$ clockwise about the center of the Ferris wheel. What are your new locations?

$A'(-4, -3)$, $B'(0, -5)$, $C'(4, -3)$

Self-Assessment
for Problem Solving

9. $(-1, 0)$, $(-1, 1)$, $(0, 1)$, $(0, 2)$, $(1, 2)$, $(1, -1)$, $(0, -1)$, $(0, 0)$; The red game piece is rotated $270°$ counterclockwise about the origin, so $(x, y) \rightarrow (y, -x)$.

10. HELLO; Rotate the image $90°$ counterclockwise.

EXAMPLE 4

- Ask a volunteer to read the problem. Give students time to come up with an answer. Ask volunteers to share their answers with the class.
- Use transparencies to demonstrate the rotation.

✓ Self-Assessment for Problem Solving

- Students may benefit from trying the exercises independently and then working with peers to refine their work. It is important to provide time in class for problem solving, so that students become comfortable with the problem-solving plan.
- **Neighbor Check:** Have students work independently and then have their neighbors check their work. Have students discuss any discrepancies.

The Success Criteria Self-Assessment chart can be found in the *Student Journal* or online at *BigIdeasMath.com*.

Closure

- Draw a right triangle in Quadrant II. Reflect the triangle in the *x*-axis, and then rotate it $90°$ clockwise about the origin.

Learning Target

Rotate figures in the coordinate plane.

Success Criteria

- Identify a rotation.
- Find the coordinates of a figure rotated about the origin.
- Use coordinates to rotate a figure about the origin.

EXAMPLE 4 **Modeling Real Life**

A carousel is represented in a coordinate plane with the center of the carousel at the origin. You and three friends sit at $A(-4, -4)$, $B(-3, 0)$, $C(-1, -2)$, and $D(-2, -3)$. At the end of the ride, your positions have rotated 270° clockwise about the center of the carousel. What are your locations at the end of the ride?

A rotation of 270° clockwise about the origin is the same as a rotation of 90° counterclockwise about the origin. Use coordinate rules to find the locations after a rotation of 90° counterclockwise about the origin.

A point (x, y) rotated 90° counterclockwise about the origin results in an image with coordinates $(-y, x)$.

$$(x, y) \longrightarrow (-y, x)$$

$$A(-4, -4) \longrightarrow A'(4, -4)$$
$$B(-3, 0) \longrightarrow B'(0, -3)$$
$$C(-1, -2) \longrightarrow C'(2, -1)$$
$$D(-2, -3) \longrightarrow D'(3, -2)$$

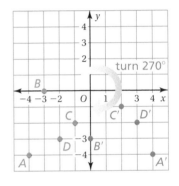

Your locations at the end of the ride are $A'(4, -4)$, $B'(0, -3)$, $C'(2, -1)$, and $D'(3, -2)$.

 Self-Assessment *for Problem Solving*

Solve each exercise. Then rate your understanding of the success criteria in your journal.

9. You move the red game piece to the indicated location using a rotation about the origin, followed by a translation. What are the coordinates of the vertices of the game piece after the rotation? Justify your answer.

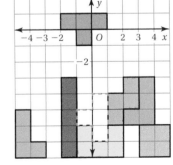

10. **DIG DEEPER!** *Skytyping* is a technique that airplanes use to write messages in the sky. The coordinate plane shows a message typed in the sky over a city, where the positive y-axis represents north. What does the message say? How can you transform the message so that it is read from north to south?

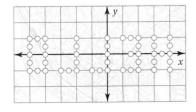

Go to **BigIdeasMath.com** to get HELP with solving the exercises.

▶Review & Refresh

Tell whether the blue figure is a reflection of the red figure.

1.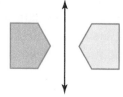

2.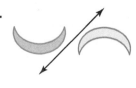

Find the circumference of the object. Use 3.14 or $\frac{22}{7}$ for π.

3.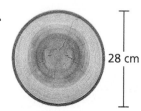

28 cm

4.

11.4 in.

5.

0.5 ft

▶▶ Concepts, Skills, & Problem Solving

DESCRIBING RELATIONSHIPS Describe the relationship between the given point and the point $A(2, 7)$ in terms of rotations. (See Exploration 1, p. 55.)

6. $B(7, -2)$ **7.** $C(-7, 2)$ **8.** $D(-2, -7)$

IDENTIFYING A ROTATION Tell whether the blue figure is a rotation of the red figure about the origin. If so, give the angle and direction of rotation.

9.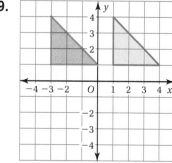

10.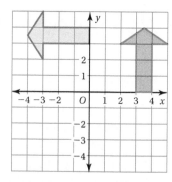

11.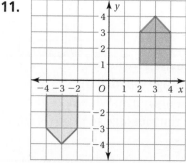

12.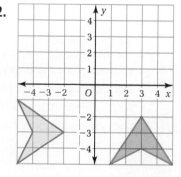

Assignment Guide and Concept Check

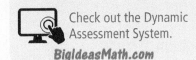

Check out the Dynamic Assessment System.
BigIdeasMath.com

Scaffold assignments to support all students in their learning progression. The suggested assignments are a starting point. Continue to assign additional exercises and revisit with spaced practice to move every student toward proficiency.

Level	Assignment 1	Assignment 2
Emerging	2, 5, 6, 9, 11, 13, 15, 17, 19, 24	14, 16, 18, 20, 21, 25, 26, 27, 29, 33
Proficient	2, 5, 7, 9, 12, 14, 16, 18, 19, 24	20, 22, 25, 26, 27, 28, 30, 31, 33
Advanced	2, 5, 8, 9, 12, 14, 16, 18, 19, 24	20, 23, 25, 27, 28, 30, 32, 33, 34

- Assignment 1 is for use after students complete the Self-Assessment for Concepts & Skills.
- Assignment 2 is for use after students complete the Self-Assessment for Problem Solving.
- The red exercises can be used as a concept check.

Review & Refresh Prior Skills

Exercises 1 and 2 Identifying a Reflection
Exercises 3–5 Finding a Circumference

Common Errors

- **Exercises 9–12** Students with minimal spatial skills may not be able to tell whether a figure is rotated. Give them transparent paper and have them copy the red figure and rotate it.

Review & Refresh

1. yes
2. no
3. about 88 cm
4. about 35.796 in.
5. about 3.14 ft

Concepts, Skills, & Problem Solving

6. rotation of 270° counterclockwise about the origin
7. rotation of 90° counterclockwise about the origin
8. rotation of 180° counterclockwise about the origin
9. no
10. yes; 90° counterclockwise
11. yes; 180° clockwise or counterclockwise
12. yes; 90° clockwise

Concepts, Skills, & Problem Solving

13. $A'(2, 2)$, $B'(1, 4)$, $C'(3, 4)$, $D'(4, 2)$

14. $F'(-1, -2)$, $G'(-3, -5)$, $H'(-3, -2)$

15. $J'(1, 4)$, $K'(1, 2)$, $L'(-3, 4)$

16. $P'(-4, -3)$, $Q'(-4, -1)$, $R'(-1, -2)$, $S'(-1, -4)$

17. $W'(-2, 6)$, $X'(-2, 2)$, $Y'(-6, 2)$, $Z'(-6, 5)$

18. $A'(1, 1)$, $B'(6, 5)$, $C'(6, 1)$

19. no; Your friend found the coordinates of the image after a rotation 90° counterclockwise, not clockwise.

20. Free Spin

21. yes; The figure only needs to rotate 120° to produce an identical image.

22. no; The figure needs to rotate 360° to produce an identical image.

23. yes; The figure only needs to rotate 180° to produce an identical image.

24. $R''(2, 1)$, $S''(-1, 7)$, $T''(2, 7)$

25. $J''(4, 4)$, $K''(3, 4)$, $L''(1, 1)$, $M''(4, 1)$

Common Errors

- **Exercises 13–18** Students may rotate the figure in the wrong direction. Remind them what clockwise and counterclockwise mean. It may be helpful for students to graph the figure and draw an arrow on the graph in the direction of the rotation.

ROTATING A FIGURE The vertices of a figure are given. Rotate the figure as described. Find the coordinates of the image.

13. $A(2, -2), B(4, -1), C(4, -3), D(2, -4)$
   90° counterclockwise about the origin

14. $F(1, 2), G(3, 5), H(3, 2)$
   180° about the origin

15. $J(-4, 1), K(-2, 1), L(-4, -3)$
   90° clockwise about the origin

16. $P(-3, 4), Q(-1, 4), R(-2, 1), S(-4, 1)$
   270° clockwise about the origin

17. $W(-6, -2), X(-2, -2), Y(-2, -6), Z(-5, -6)$
   270° counterclockwise about the origin

18. $A(1, -1), B(5, -6), C(1, -6)$
   90° counterclockwise about the origin

19. (MP) **YOU BE THE TEACHER** The vertices of a triangle are $A(4, 4)$, $B(1, -2)$, and $C(-3, 0)$. Your friend finds the coordinates of the image after a rotation 90° clockwise about the origin. Is your friend correct? Explain your reasoning.

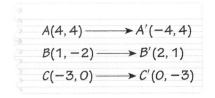

20. (MP) **PROBLEM SOLVING** A game show contestant spins the prize wheel shown. The arrow remains in a fixed position while the wheel rotates. The wheel stops spinning, resulting in an image that is a rotation 270° clockwise about the center of the wheel. What is the result?

(MP) **PATTERNS** A figure has *rotational symmetry* if a rotation of 180° or less produces an image that fits exactly on the original figure. Determine whether the figure has rotational symmetry. Explain your reasoning.

21.

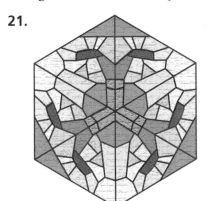

22.

23.

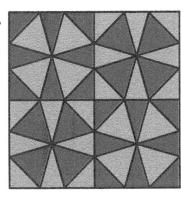

USING MORE THAN ONE TRANSFORMATION The vertices of a figure are given. Find the coordinates of the image after the transformations given.

24. $R(-7, -5), S(-1, -2), T(-1, -5)$
   Rotate 90° counterclockwise about the origin. Then translate 3 units left and 8 units up.

25. $J(-4, 4), K(-3, 4), L(-1, 1), M(-4, 1)$
   Reflect in the *x*-axis, and then rotate 180° about the origin.

CRITICAL THINKING Describe two different sequences of transformations in which the blue figure is the image of the red figure.

26.

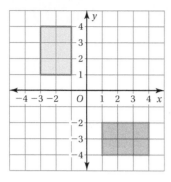

27.

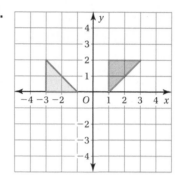

28. (MP) **REASONING** A trapezoid has vertices $A(-6, -2)$, $B(-3, -2)$, $C(-1, -4)$, and $D(-6, -4)$.

    a. Rotate the trapezoid 180° about the origin. What are the coordinates of the image?

    b. Describe a way to obtain the same image without using rotations.

ROTATING A FIGURE The vertices of a figure are given. Rotate the figure as described. Find the coordinates of the image.

29. $D(2, 1)$, $E(2, -2)$, $F(-1, 4)$
90° counterclockwise about vertex D

30. $L(-4, -3)$, $M(-1, -1)$, $N(2, -2)$
180° about vertex M

31. $W(-5, 0)$, $X(-1, 4)$, $Y(3, -1)$, $Z(0, -4)$
270° counterclockwise about vertex W

32. $D(-3, -4)$, $E(-5, 2)$, $F(1, -1)$, $G(3, -7)$
270° clockwise about vertex E

33. (MP) **LOGIC** You want to find the treasure located on the map at ✕. You are located at ●. The following transformations will lead you to the treasure, but they are not in the correct order. Find the correct order. Use each transformation exactly once.

- Rotate 180° about the origin.
- Reflect in the y-axis.
- Rotate 90° counterclockwise about the origin.
- Translate 1 unit right and 1 unit up.

34. **DIG DEEPER!** You rotate a triangle 90° counterclockwise about the origin. Then you translate its image 1 unit left and 2 units down. The vertices of the final image are $(-5, 0)$, $(-2, 2)$, and $(-2, -1)$. What are the vertices of the original triangle?

Common Errors

- **Exercises 29–32** Students may rotate the figure about the origin instead of the indicated vertex. Remind students to read the problem carefully to determine what is being asked.

Mini-Assessment

Tell whether the blue figure is a rotation of the red figure about the origin. If so, give the angle and direction of the rotation.

1.

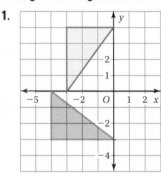

yes; 90° clockwise rotation

2.

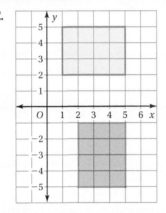

yes; 90° counterclockwise rotation

The vertices of a figure are given. Rotate the figure as described. Find the coordinates of the image.

3. $L(3, 2)$, $M(1, 1)$, $N(1, 5)$
90° counterclockwise about the origin
$L'(-2, 3)$, $M'(-1, 1)$, $N'(-5, 1)$

4. $T(2, 5)$, $U(5, 4)$, $V(6, 1)$, $W(2, 1)$
180° about the origin
$T'(-2, -5)$, $U'(-5, -4)$, $V'(-6, -1)$, $W'(-2, -1)$

Section Resources

Surface Level	Deep Level
Resources by Chapter • Extra Practice • Reteach • Puzzle Time Student Journal • Self-Assessment • Practice Differentiating the Lesson Tutorial Videos Skills Review Handbook Skills Trainer	Resources by Chapter • Enrichment and Extension Graphic Organizers Dynamic Assessment System • Section Practice

Concepts, Skills, & Problem Solving

26. *Sample answer:* Rotate 90° counterclockwise about the origin and then translate 5 units left; Rotate 90° clockwise about the origin and then translate 1 unit right and 5 units up.

27. *Sample answer:* Rotate 90° counterclockwise about the origin and then translate 1 unit left and 1 unit down; Reflect in the *x*-axis and then translate 4 units left and 2 units up.

28. **a.** $A'(6, 2)$, $B'(3, 2)$, $C'(1, 4)$, $D'(6, 4)$

   b. Reflect the trapezoid in the *x*-axis and then in the *y*-axis, or reflect the trapezoid in the *y*-axis and then in the *x*-axis.

29. $D'(2, 1)$, $E'(5, 1)$, $F'(-1, -2)$

30. $L'(2, 1)$, $M'(-1, -1)$, $N'(-4, 0)$

31. $W'(-5, 0)$, $X'(-1, -4)$, $Y'(-6, -8)$, $Z'(-9, -5)$

32. $D'(1, 4)$, $E'(-5, 2)$, $F'(-2, 8)$, $G'(4, 10)$

33. (1) Rotate 180° about the origin.
   (2) Rotate 90° counterclockwise about the origin.
   (3) Reflect in the *y*-axis.
   (4) Translate 1 unit right and 1 unit up.

34. $(2, 4)$, $(4, 1)$, $(1, 1)$

Learning Target

Understand the concept of congruent figures.

Success Criteria

- Identify congruent figures.
- Describe a sequence of rigid motions between two congruent figures.

Warm Up

Cumulative, vocabulary, and prerequisite skills practice opportunities are available in the *Resources by Chapter* or at *BigIdeasMath.com*.

ELL Support

Ask students if they remember the meaning of congruent angles. Remind them that congruent angles are angles with the same measure. Explain that if one figure can be obtained from another by translations, reflections, and/or rotations, then the figures are congruent. Cut a two-dimensional figure out of paper. Trace the figure on the board. Move the paper figure left, right, up, and down. Reflect and rotate the figure. Explain that the figures are congruent, no matter their locations or orientations.

Laurie's Notes

Preparing to Teach

- Throughout the chapter, students have recognized that translations, rotations, and reflections produce images that are the same size and shape as the original figure. Students will use these transformations as they study congruent figures.

Motivate

- **?** "What word is used to describe figures that have the same size and shape?" congruent
- Display a variety of objects such as templates, stencils, rubber stamps, and cookie cutters.
- **?** "What do all of these objects have in common?" They can be used to create figures that are congruent to one another.
- **?** "Can you think of other things that can be used to create **congruent figures**?" *Sample answers:* computer graphics program, clay molds
- **?** "What are some congruent items that you use every day?" *Sample answers:* dinner plates from the same set, notebook paper, tissues

Exploration 1

- **Note:** Transparent paper is required for this exploration. Students may also want to use paperclips, as in the previous section. Alternatively, geometry software is available at *BigIdeasMath.com*.
- Before students begin part (c), explain that obtaining one figure from another can be thought of as "mapping" one figure onto another or matching the figures up.
- As students identify the figures that can be obtained using transformations, they should make a list of the transformations they use.
- Have volunteers demonstrate their transformations using an interactive whiteboard or document camera.
- For part (c), have pairs *Turn and Talk* to discuss their ideas with another pair. Remind them to use three-foot voices.
- **Popsicle Sticks:** Select students to share their reasoning for parts (b) and (c) with the class.

Exploration 1

a. Check students' work.

b. Triangle *ABC* and Triangle *DEF*, Triangle *GHJ* and Triangle *LMN*; Figure *ABCD* and Figure *FGHJ*; *Sample answer:* In each pair of figures, one figure can be obtained from the other using transformations.

c. yes; Translations, reflections, and rotations each produce identical figures, so a sequence of these transformations will do the same.

2.4 Congruent Figures

Learning Target: Understand the concept of congruent figures.

Success Criteria:
- I can identify congruent figures.
- I can describe a sequence of rigid motions between two congruent figures.

EXPLORATION 1

Transforming Figures

Work with a partner.

a. For each pair of figures whose vertices are given below, draw the figures in a coordinate plane. Then copy one of the figures onto a piece of transparent paper. Use transformations to try to obtain one of the figures from the other figure.

- $A(-5, 1), B(-5, -4), C(-2, -4)$ and $D(1, 4), E(1, -1), F(-2, -1)$

- $G(1, 2), H(2, -6), J(5, 0)$ and $L(-1, -2), M(-2, 6), N(-5, 0)$

- $P(0, 0), Q(2, 2), R(4, -2)$ and $X(0, 0), Y(3, 3), Z(6, -3)$

- $A(0, 4), B(3, 8), C(6, 4), D(3, 0)$ and $F(-4, -3), G(-8, 0), H(-4, 3), J(0, 0)$

- $P(-2, 1), Q(-1, -2), R(1, -2), S(1, 1)$ and $W(7, 1), X(5, -2), Y(3, -2), Z(3, 1)$

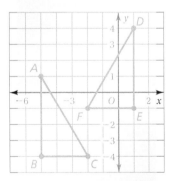

Math Practice

Communicate Precisely

When you can use translations, reflections, and rotations to obtain one figure from another, what do you know about the side lengths and angle measures of the figures?

b. Which pairs of figures in part (a) are identical? Explain your reasoning.

c. Figure A and Figure B are identical. Do you think there must be a sequence of transformations that obtains Figure A from Figure B? Explain your reasoning.

2.4 Lesson

Key Vocabulary
rigid motion, *p. 64*
congruent figures,
  p. 64
congruent angles,
  p. 64
congruent sides,
  p. 64

A **rigid motion** is a transformation that preserves length and angle measure. Translations, reflections, and rotations are rigid motions.

  Key Idea

Congruent Figures

Two figures are **congruent figures** when one can be obtained from the other by a sequence of rigid motions. Congruent figures have the same size and the same shape. Angles with the same measure are called **congruent angles**. Sides with the same measure are **congruent sides**.

The triangles below are congruent.

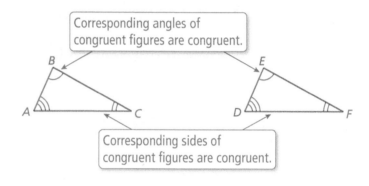

Reading

The symbol △ means *triangle*. The symbol ≅ means *is congruent to*. In the Key Idea,

△*ABC* ≅ △*DEF*.

In diagrams, matching arcs indicate congruent angles.

Sides

$\overline{AB} \cong \overline{DE}, \overline{BC} \cong \overline{EF}, \overline{AC} \cong \overline{DF}$

Angles

$\angle A \cong \angle D, \angle B \cong \angle E, \angle C \cong \angle F$

EXAMPLE 1 **Identifying Congruent Figures**

Identify any congruent figures in the coordinate plane.

△*DEF* is a translation 1 unit left and 5 units down of △*MNP*. So, △*DEF* and △*MNP* are congruent.

△*ABC* is a reflection in the *x*-axis of △*JKL*. So, △*ABC* and △*JKL* are congruent.

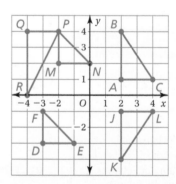

Common Error

When writing a congruence statement, make sure to list the vertices of the figures in the correct order.

Try It

1. A triangle has vertices *X*(0, 4), *Y*(4, 4), and *Z*(4, 2). Is △*XYZ* congruent to any of the triangles in Example 1? Explain.

Laurie's Notes

Scaffolding Instruction

- Students used transformations to explore congruent figures. They will now use the definition for congruent figures to determine whether two figures are congruent.
- **Emerging:** Students may struggle with using transformations to identify congruent figures. They will benefit from additional practice and guided instruction.
- **Proficient:** Students can use rigid motions to obtain and identify congruent figures. They should review the Key Idea for the definitions for congruent figures, congruent angles, and congruent sides before proceeding to the Self-Assessment exercises.

Key Idea

- ❓ "What do you think preserving length and angle measure means?" The size and shape of the figure does not change.
- **Note:** If you use rigid motions on a set of parallel lines, then the lines will remain parallel.
- ❓ "Why do you think rigid motions are also called *congruence transformations*?" Because a figure obtained by a sequence of rigid motions is congruent to the original figure.
- Explain to students that the notation $\overline{AB}$ means side AB.
- The use of the three different colors helps to identify the corresponding sides and angles of the triangles.
- ❓ "What are the corresponding sides in the given triangles?" $\overline{AB}$ and $\overline{DE}$, $\overline{BC}$ and $\overline{EF}$, $\overline{AC}$ and $\overline{DF}$
- ❓ "What are the corresponding angles in the given triangles?" $\angle A$ and $\angle D$, $\angle B$ and $\angle E$, $\angle C$ and $\angle F$
- Point out the Reading note and explain that when you name congruent triangles, the corresponding angles are listed in the same order.

EXAMPLE 1

- Work through the example as shown. Make sure students understand the transformations that are used from one figure to the other.
- ❓ "Is $\triangle DEF \cong \triangle MPN$? Explain." Yes, you can rotate $\triangle MPN$ 90° clockwise about the origin, reflect it in the x-axis, and translate it 5 units left and 1 unit down to obtain $\triangle DEF$.
- Point out that $\triangle DEF$ is congruent to both $\triangle MNP$ and $\triangle MPN$ because they are isosceles triangles.
- ❓ "Is $\triangle QRP \cong \triangle JKL$? Explain." No, $\overline{QR}$ is 4 units long and the corresponding side, $\overline{JK}$, is 3 units long.
- ❓ "Is $\triangle QRP \cong \triangle ABC$? Explain." No, $\overline{QR}$ is 4 units long and the corresponding side, $\overline{AB}$, is 3 units long.
- ❓ "Is $\triangle ABC \cong \triangle JKL$? Explain." Yes, you can reflect $\triangle JKL$ in the x-axis to obtain $\triangle ABC$.

Try It

- Students should work with a partner.

Scaffold instruction to support all students in their learning. Learning is individualized and you may want to group students differently as they move in and out of these levels with each skill and concept. Student self-assessment and feedback help guide your instructional decisions about how and when to layer support for all students to become proficient learners.

Extra Example 1

A triangle has vertices $G(-3, -1)$, $H(-3, -4)$, and $I(-5, -1)$. Identify any congruent figures in the coordinate plane in Example 1. $\triangle ABC$ and $\triangle JKL$

ELL Support

After demonstrating Example 1, have students work in groups to discuss and complete Try It Exercise 1. Expect students to perform according to their language levels.

Beginner: Name the triangle.

Intermediate: Discuss the problem using phrases or simple sentences.

Advanced: Use detailed sentences and help guide discussion.

Try It

1. yes; $\triangle XYZ \cong \triangle RQP$ because $\triangle XYZ$ is a 270° counterclockwise rotation about the origin of $\triangle RQP$.

Extra Example 2

The red figure is congruent to the blue figure. Describe a sequence of rigid motions between the figures.

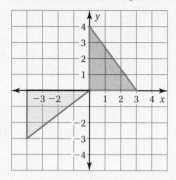

Sample answer: Rotate the red figure 90° clockwise about the origin and then translate the image 4 units left.

Try It

2. *Sample answer:* Rotate the red figure 90° clockwise about the origin and then translate the image 4 units right and 1 unit up.

Self-Assessment
for Concepts & Skills

3. **a.** Rectangle *ABCD* and Rectangle *KLMJ*

   b. no; There is no sequence of rigid motions between Rectangle *WXYZ* and any of the other three rectangles.

4. *Sample answer:* Rotate the red figure 180° about the origin and then translate the image 1 unit left.

5. *Sample answer:* Rotate the blue figure 90° clockwise about the origin and then translate the image 3 units right and 1 unit down.

EXAMPLE 2

- Ask a volunteer to read the problem. Give students time to come up with an answer. Ask volunteers to share and demonstrate their answers using transparent paper.
- There are many correct sequences of rigid motions, including sequences that go from the blue figure to the red figure. Ask volunteers to share some other possibilities.
- **Extension:** "Is there a single transformation to get from the red figure to the blue figure? Explain." Yes, a 90° counterclockwise rotation about the point $(-2, 2)$. Students may need a hint to consider moving the center of rotation.

Try It

- Students should work with a partner. Select a volunteer to share and demonstrate his or her answer using transparent paper.

✓ Self-Assessment *for Concepts & Skills*

- **Think-Pair-Share:** Students should read each exercise independently and then work in pairs to complete the exercises. Select pairs to explain and demonstrate their answers to the class.
- ◉ Have students use *Thumbs Up* to indicate their understanding of: (a) identifying congruent figures and (b) describing a sequence of rigid motions between two congruent figures.

ELL Support

Allow students to work in pairs for extra support and to practice language. Have each pair display their answer to Exercise 3(a) on a whiteboard for your review. Check answers to Exercise 3(b) by having students indicate *yes* or *no* using a thumbs up or down signal. Have two pairs form a group to discuss and refine their explanations or descriptions for Exercises 3(b), 4, and 5. Then have each group present their answers to another group. The two groups must reach an agreement if their ideas differ. Monitor discussions and provide support.

The Success Criteria Self-Assessment chart can be found in the *Student Journal* or online at *BigIdeasMath.com*.

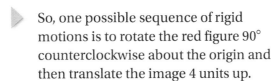

EXAMPLE 2 — Describing a Sequence of Rigid Motions

The red figure is congruent to the blue figure. Describe a sequence of rigid motions between the figures.

The orientations of the figures are different. You can rotate the red figure 90° to match the orientation of the blue figure.

After rotating the red figure, you can translate its image to the blue figure.

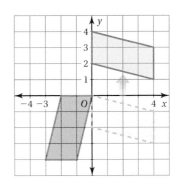

▸ So, one possible sequence of rigid motions is to rotate the red figure 90° counterclockwise about the origin and then translate the image 4 units up.

Try It

2. Describe a different sequence of rigid motions between the figures.

Self-Assessment *for Concepts & Skills*

Solve each exercise. Then rate your understanding of the success criteria in your journal.

3. **IDENTIFYING CONGRUENT FIGURES** Use the coordinate plane shown.

   a. Identify any congruent figures.

   b. A rectangle has vertices $W(-4, -1)$, $X(-4, 2)$, $Y(-1, 2)$, and $Z(-1, -1)$. Is Rectangle $WXYZ$ congruent to any of the rectangles in the coordinate plane? Explain.

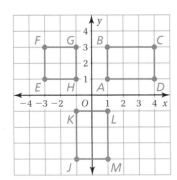

RIGID MOTIONS **The red figure is congruent to the blue figure. Describe a sequence of rigid motions between the figures.**

4.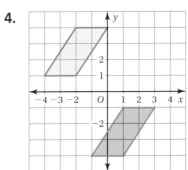

5.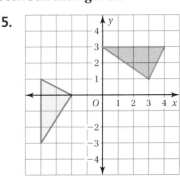

EXAMPLE 3 **Modeling Real Life**

You can use the buttons shown at the left to transform objects in a computer program. You can rotate objects 90° in either direction and reflect objects in a horizontal or vertical line. How can you transform the emoji as shown below?

Original

Image

When you rotate the emoji 90° counterclockwise, the tongue is in the wrong place. Reflect the emoji in a horizontal line to move the tongue to the correct location.

▶ To transform the emoji as shown, you can use a 90° counterclockwise rotation followed by a reflection in a horizontal line.

Self-Assessment for Problem Solving

Solve each exercise. Then rate your understanding of the success criteria in your journal.

6. In the coordinate plane at the left, each grid line represents 50 feet. Each figure represents a pasture.

a. Are the figures congruent? Use rigid motions to justify your answer.

b. How many feet of fencing do you need to enclose each pasture?

7. A home decorator uses a computer to design a floor tile. How can the decorator transform the tile as shown?

Original   Image

Laurie's Notes

EXAMPLE 3

- Ask a volunteer to read the problem. Then ask students what type of rigid motion each button in the computer program represents. 90° clockwise rotation, 90° counterclockwise rotation, reflection in the *y*-axis, reflection in the *x*-axis

- Have students work in pairs to answer the question. Then have each pair compare their answers with another pair. Remind students that there may be more than one correct answer.

- Ask several volunteers to share their sequences of rigid motions with the class. Ask other students to evaluate each sequence.

 Self-Assessment *for Problem Solving*

- Encourage students to use a Four Square to complete these exercises. Until students become comfortable with the problem-solving plan, they may only be ready to complete the first square.

- Students should solve the problems independently and then work with a partner to resolve any discrepancies. While students are working, circulate and check their Four Squares.

The Success Criteria Self-Assessment chart can be found in the *Student Journal* or online at *BigIdeasMath.com*.

Formative Assessment Tip

One-Minute Card

This technique provides a quick assessment of students' understanding of a concept. Write a short prompt on the board and allow 1 minute for students to consider the prompt. Give each student an index card and allow 1 minute for students to write their responses. When time is up, collect the cards and review the responses. The next day, spend a few minutes discussing any misconceptions or exceptional responses.

Closure

- **One-Minute Card:** $\triangle XYZ \cong \triangle ABC$. Name the corresponding sides and corresponding angles. $\overline{XY}$ and $\overline{AB}$, $\overline{YZ}$ and $\overline{BC}$, $\overline{XZ}$ and $\overline{AC}$; $\angle X$ and $\angle A$, $\angle Y$ and $\angle B$, $\angle Z$ and $\angle C$

- Collect the cards as students leave. Begin the next class with a discussion of any misunderstandings.

Extra Example 3

You can use the buttons shown in Example 3 to transform objects in a computer program. You can rotate objects 90° in either direction and reflect objects in a horizontal or vertical line. How can you transform the cloud as shown below?

Original   Image

90° clockwise rotation followed by a reflection in a vertical line.

Self-Assessment
for Problem Solving

6. **a.** no; *Sample answer:* Reflecting the blue figure about the *y*-axis and then translating the image 4 units down shows that the two figures are not the same size and shape.

   b. blue figure: 600 ft, red figure: 600 ft

7. *Sample answer:* Use a reflection in a vertical line followed by a 90° counterclockwise rotation.

Learning Target

Understand the concept of congruent figures.

Success Criteria

- Identify congruent figures.
- Describe a sequence of rigid motions between two congruent figures.

Review & Refresh

1. $A'(-3, 1)$, $B'(-5, 2)$, $C'(-5, 3)$, $D'(-3, 2)$

2. $F'(2, -1)$, $G'(1, -3)$, $H'(-3, -1)$

3. $4(n - 8)$

4. $3(w + 22)$

5. $2(y - 9)$

Concepts, Skills, & Problem Solving

6. no

7. yes

8. Figure *ABCDE* and Figure *FKJHG*

9. Figure *EFGH* and Figure *BCDA*

10. *Sample answer:* Rotate the red figure 90° clockwise about the origin and then translate the image 1 unit left and 1 unit down.

11. *Sample answer:* Rotate the red figure 180° about the origin and then translate the image 1 unit right and 1 unit down.

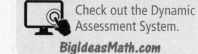
Assignment Guide and Concept Check

Scaffold assignments to support all students in their learning progression. The suggested assignments are a starting point. Continue to assign additional exercises and revisit with spaced practice to move every student toward proficiency.

Level	Assignment 1	Assignment 2
Emerging	1, 5, 6, 9, 11, 12, 13	8, 10, 14, 15, 16, 17
Proficient	1, 5, 7, 8, 9, 10, 11, 12, 13	14, 15, 16, 17
Advanced	1, 5, 7, 8, 9, 10, 11, 12, 14	15, 16, 17, 18

- Assignment 1 is for use after students complete the Self-Assessment for Concepts & Skills.
- Assignment 2 is for use after students complete the Self-Assessment for Problem Solving.
- The red exercises can be used as a concept check.

Review & Refresh Prior Skills

Exercises 1 and 2 Rotating a Figure
Exercises 3–5 Factoring Out the GCF

2.4 Practice

Go to **BigIdeasMath.com** to get HELP with solving the exercises.

▶ Review & Refresh

The vertices of a figure are given. Rotate the figure as described. Find the coordinates of the image.

1. $A(1, 3), B(2, 5), C(3, 5), D(2, 3)$
   90° counterclockwise about the origin

2. $F(-2, 1), G(-1, 3), H(3, 1)$
   180° about the origin

Factor the expression using the greatest common factor.

3. $4n - 32$

4. $3w + 66$

5. $2y - 18$

▶ Concepts, Skills, & Problem Solving

TRANSFORMING FIGURES The vertices of a pair of figures are given. Determine whether the figures are identical. (See Exploration 1, p. 63.)

6. $G(0, 0), H(3, 2), J(1, -2)$ and $L(-1, 0), M(2, 2), N(0, -3)$

7. $A(-2, -1), B(-2, 2), C(-1, 1), D(-1, -2)$ and $F(-2, 0), G(-1, 1), H(2, 1), J(1, 0)$

IDENTIFYING CONGRUENT FIGURES Identify any congruent figures in the coordinate plane.

8.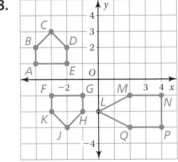

9.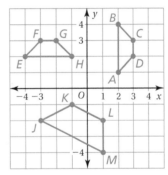

DESCRIBING A SEQUENCE OF RIGID MOTIONS The red figure is congruent to the blue figure. Describe a sequence of rigid motions between the figures.

10.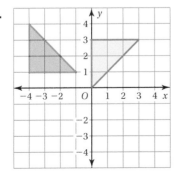

11.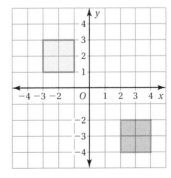

12. **MP YOU BE THE TEACHER** Your friend describes a sequence of rigid motions between the figures. Is your friend correct? Explain your reasoning.

Reflect the red figure in the x-axis, and then translate it left 5 units.

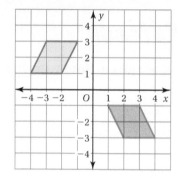

NAMING CORRESPONDING PARTS The figures are congruent. Name the corresponding angles and the corresponding sides.

13.

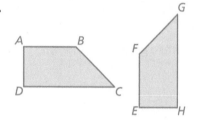

14.

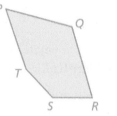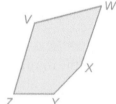

15. **MP MODELING REAL LIFE** You use a computer program to transform an emoji. How can you transform the emoji as shown?

Original   Image

16. **CRITICAL THINKING** Two figures are congruent. Are the areas of the two figures the same? the perimeters? Explain your reasoning.

17. **DIG DEEPER!** The houses are identical.

   a. What is the length of side *LM*?

   b. Which angle of *JKLMN* corresponds to ∠*D*?

   c. Side *AB* is congruent to side *AE*. What is the length of side *AB*? What is the perimeter of *ABCDE*?

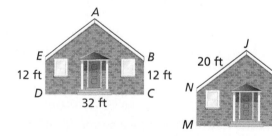

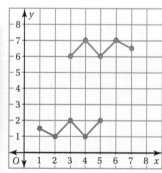

18. **MP REASONING** Two constellations are represented by the figures in the coordinate plane shown. Are the figures congruent? Justify your answer.

Common Errors

- **Exercises 13 and 14** Students may forget to write the angle symbol with the name and/or the segment notation. Remind students that A is a point and $\angle A$ is the angle. Tell students that AB without the segment bar is the measure of side AB.
- **Exercise 17** In part (b), students may have difficulty determining the corresponding angle. Point out that the fronts of the houses form congruent figures and remind students that corresponding angles in congruent figures have matching positions.

Mini-Assessment

1. Identify any congruent figures in the coordinate plane.

   Rectangle *ABCD* and Rectangle *EFGH*

   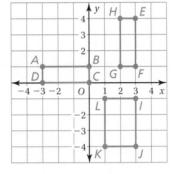

2. The red figure is congruent to the blue figure. Describe a sequence of rigid motions between the figures.

   Sample answer: Rotate the red figure 90° clockwise about the origin and then translate the image 2 units left and 1 unit up.

   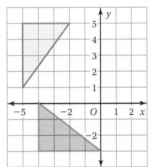

Section Resources

Surface Level	Deep Level
Resources by Chapter • Extra Practice • Reteach • Puzzle Time Student Journal • Self-Assessment • Practice Differentiating the Lesson Tutorial Videos Skills Review Handbook Skills Trainer	Resources by Chapter • Enrichment and Extension Graphic Organizers Dynamic Assessment System • Section Practice
Transfer Level	
Dynamic Assessment System • Mid-Chapter Quiz	Assessment Book • Mid-Chapter Quiz

Concepts, Skills, & Problem Solving

12. yes; The blue figure is obtained from the red figure by the sequence of rigid motions described.

13. $\angle A$ and $\angle E$, $\angle B$ and $\angle F$, $\angle C$ and $\angle G$, $\angle D$ and $\angle H$; $\overline{AB}$ and $\overline{EF}$, $\overline{BC}$ and $\overline{FG}$, $\overline{CD}$ and $\overline{GH}$, $\overline{DA}$ and $\overline{HE}$

14. $\angle P$ and $\angle W$, $\angle Q$ and $\angle V$, $\angle R$ and $\angle Z$, $\angle S$ and $\angle Y$, $\angle T$ and $\angle X$; $\overline{PQ}$ and $\overline{WV}$, $\overline{QR}$ and $\overline{VZ}$, $\overline{RS}$ and $\overline{ZY}$, $\overline{ST}$ and $\overline{YX}$, $\overline{TP}$ and $\overline{XW}$

15. *Sample answer:* Use a reflection in a vertical line followed by a 90° clockwise rotation.

16. yes; yes; Congruent figures have the same size and shape.

17. **a.** 32 ft

    b. $\angle M$

    c. 20 ft; 96 ft

18. yes; *Sample answer:* Rotate the blue figure 180° about the origin and then translate the image 8 units right and 8 units up to obtain the red figure.

Learning Target

Dilate figures in the coordinate plane.

Success Criteria

- Identify a dilation.
- Find the coordinates of a figure dilated with respect to the origin.
- Use coordinates to dilate a figure with respect to the origin.

Warm Up

Cumulative, vocabulary, and prerequisite skills practice opportunities are available in the *Resources by Chapter* or at *BigIdeasMath.com*.

ELL Support

Ask students if they have had their eyes checked and have them describe their experiences. If no one mentions dilation, describe the process of putting drops in your eyes to make your pupils larger, so that a doctor can better examine your eyes. Then ask students what they think dilation means in the context of transformations.

Laurie's Notes

STATE STANDARDS
8.G.A.3

Preparing to Teach

- In the previous course, students worked with scale drawings. Now they will progress from scale drawings to describing dilations in terms of coordinates. Change in scale will now be understood in terms of dilations.

Motivate

- Cut a rectangle out of heavy card stock. Use a flashlight to cast a shadow of the rectangle onto a wall.
- ? "Are the two figures congruent? Explain." No, they are the same shape, but not the same size.
- Vary the distance between the bulb of the flashlight and the rectangle. Be sure to hold the figure parallel to the wall and the flashlight perpendicular to the wall. Discuss how this changes the shadow.
- ? "Is the shadow always the same shape as the original figure?" yes

Discuss

- ? "Did the size or shape of the figures change when you performed a translation, reflection, or rotation?" no
- ? "At an eye appointment, the optometrist dilates your pupils. What does it mean to dilate your pupils?" enlarge your pupils
- ? "Does the shape of your pupil change when it is dilated?" no
- Tell students that there is a fourth type of transformation called a **dilation**.

Exploration 1

- This exploration is best completed using geometry software, which is available at *BigIdeasMath.com*. If this is not possible, students can use the sample provided in part (a).
- Remind students of their previous work with scale drawings. Scale drawings are the same shape as the actual object, but *not* the same size. In the previous course, students determined the **scale factor** (or the constant of proportionality) by finding the value of the ratio of a dimension in the scale drawing to the corresponding dimension of the actual object.
- In the sample, $\overline{AB}$ is 1 unit long and $\overline{A'B'}$ is 3 units long. So, the scale factor is $\frac{3}{1}$ or 3. Triangle $A'B'C'$ has a scale factor of 3 when compared to Triangle ABC.
- **Popsicle Sticks:** After pairs have discussed parts (b)–(d), solicit responses for each part.
- ? "When dilating a polygon, the side lengths may change, but the figures have the same shape. What can you conclude about the angles?" The angles remain the same size.
- ? **Extension:** "In part (c), do the dilations result in an *enlargement* or a *reduction* of the original figure? Explain." *B* and *C* result in enlargements because the scale factors are greater than 1. *D* results in a reduction because the scale factor is a positive number less than 1.

Exploration 1

a. Check students' work.

b. Corresponding side lengths of the figures are proportional; Corresponding angles of the figures are congruent.

c. Point *B*: dilation with respect to the origin by a scale factor of 3;
Point *C*: dilation with respect to the origin by a scale factor of 5;
Point *D*: dilation with respect to the origin by a scale factor of 0.5

d. $P'(kx, ky)$

2.5 Dilations

Learning Target: Dilate figures in the coordinate plane.

Success Criteria:
- I can identify a dilation.
- I can find the coordinates of a figure dilated with respect to the origin.
- I can use coordinates to dilate a figure with respect to the origin.

The Meaning of a Word ▷ Dilate

When you have your eyes checked, the optometrist sometimes **dilates** one or both of the pupils of your eyes.

EXPLORATION 1

Dilating a Polygon

Work with a partner. Use geometry software.

Math Practice

Consider Similar Problems
How does your previous work with scale drawings help you understand the concept of dilations?

a. Draw a polygon in the coordinate plane. Then *dilate* the polygon with respect to the origin. Describe the scale factor of the image.

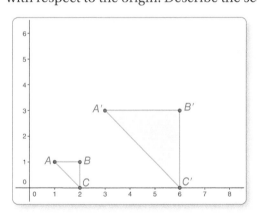

Available at BigIdeasMath.com.

Sample

Points
$A(1, 1)$
$B(2, 1)$
$C(2, 0)$

Segments
$AB = 1$
$BC = 1$
$AC = 1.41$

Angles
$m\angle A = 45°$
$m\angle B = 90°$
$m\angle C = 45°$

b. Compare the image and the original polygon in part (a). What do you notice about the sides? the angles?

c. Describe the relationship between each point below and the point $A(x, y)$ in terms of dilations.

$$B(3x, 3y) \qquad C(5x, 5y) \qquad D(0.5x, 0.5y)$$

d. What are the coordinates of a point $P(x, y)$ after a dilation with respect to the origin by a scale factor of k?

2.5 Lesson

A **dilation** is a transformation in which a figure is made larger or smaller with respect to a point called the **center of dilation**. In a dilation, the angles of the image and the original figure are congruent.

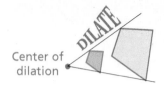

Center of dilation

A scale drawing is an example of a dilation.

EXAMPLE 1 Identifying a Dilation

Key Vocabulary
dilation, *p. 70*
center of dilation, *p. 70*
scale factor, *p. 70*

Tell whether the blue figure is a dilation of the red figure.

a.

Lines connecting corresponding vertices meet at a point.

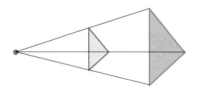

So, the blue figure is a dilation of the red figure.

b.

The figures have the same size and shape. The red figure *slides* to form the blue figure.

So, the blue figure is *not* a dilation of the red figure. It is a translation.

Try It **Tell whether the blue figure is a dilation of the red figure.**

1.

2.

In a dilation, the value of the ratio of the side lengths of the image to the corresponding side lengths of the original figure is the **scale factor** of the dilation.

 Key Idea

Dilations in the Coordinate Plane

Words   To dilate a figure with respect to the origin, multiply the coordinates of each vertex by the scale factor *k*.

Algebra $(x, y) \rightarrow (kx, ky)$

- When $k > 1$, the dilation is an enlargement.
- When $k > 0$ and $k < 1$, the dilation is a reduction.

In this course, when the center of dilation is not specified, it is the origin.

Laurie's Notes

Scaffolding Instruction

- Students have explored dilating polygons in the coordinate plane. Now they will continue working with dilations.
- **Emerging:** Students understand that a dilation results in a larger or smaller figure, but they may struggle with the details of how to determine the scale factor or draw the new figure. They will benefit from guided instruction for the examples and Key Idea.
- **Proficient:** Students can draw figures using dilations and a scale factor. They should review the definitions and Key Idea before proceeding to Example 4. Then have students check their understanding with the Self-Assessment exercises.

Discuss

- Explain what a dilation and the center of a dilation are, based on the Motivate activity.

EXAMPLE 1

- It is important to draw the line segments connecting the corresponding vertices. It enables you to locate the center of dilation.
- **Extension:** In part (a), if the blue triangle was rotated, you would not have a dilation. The triangles would still be similar, but there would not be a center of dilation.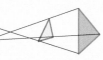
- In part (b), segments connecting corresponding vertices are parallel.

Try It

- **Popsicle Sticks:** Solicit explanations for each exercise.

Key Idea

- Write the Key Idea, including the example in the coordinate plane.
- **Write:** scale factor = side length of image : side length of original
- Put numbers on the vertical sides of the triangles in Example 1(a) to approximate the lengths, such as 4 (blue) and 8 (red). The blue triangle is reduced by an approximate scale factor of $4 : 8$ or $\frac{1}{2}$.
- **?** "Can the red triangle in Example 1(a) be a dilation of the blue triangle?" Yes, it is an enlargement of the blue triangle.
- Discuss the difference between a scale factor for an enlargement , $k > 1$, and a scale factor for a reduction, $k > 0$ and $k < 1$.
- **?** "What do you think the image would look like if $k = 1$?" The two figures would be congruent and there would be no center of dilation. Explain that although dilation with a scale factor of 1 does not have a center of dilation, it is still technically a dilation.
- Point out the push-pin note. Emphasize that in a dilation the shape and angles measures do not change, but the size may change.
- **Note:** In this course, negative scale factors will not be addressed because they involve reflections.

Extra Example 1

Tell whether the blue figure is a dilation of the red figure.

a.

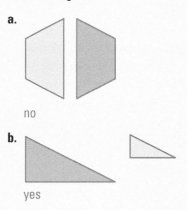

no

b.

yes

Try It

1. no
2. yes

Extra Example 2

The vertices of a triangle are $D(1, 4)$, $E(1, 1)$, and $F(3,1)$. Draw the image after a dilation with a scale factor of 2. Identify the type of dilation.

enlargement

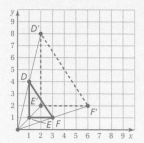

Try It

3. $A'(2, 6)$, $B'(4, 6)$, $C'(4, 2)$

Extra Example 3

The vertices of a rectangle are $J(-4, 2)$, $K(4, 2)$, $L(4, -2)$, and $M(-4, -2)$. Draw the image after a dilation with a scale factor of 0.5. Identify the type of dilation.

reduction

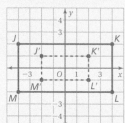

Try It

4. $W'(-1, -1.5)$, $X'(-1, 2)$, $Y'(1, 2)$, $Z'(1, -1.5)$

Laurie's Notes

EXAMPLE 2

- Work through the example.
- Use color to identify the two different triangles and their vertices.
- Note that the two triangles are similar. $\overline{AB}$ is horizontal and its image, $\overline{A'B'}$, is horizontal. $\overline{BC}$ is vertical and its image, $\overline{B'C'}$, is vertical. $\overline{AC}$ and its image, $\overline{A'C'}$, are parallel.
- Refer to the push-pin note. Students could also measure the length of each of the distances from O to A', O to B', and O to C'. These lengths should be 3 times the lengths of O to A, O to B, and O to C.
- **MP3 Construct Viable Arguments and Critique the Reasoning of Others**: Ask the following questions.
  - ❓ "How do you think the perimeters of the two triangles compare? Explain." Because the two triangles are similar with a scale factor of 3, the perimeter of the larger triangle is 3 times the perimeter of the smaller triangle.
  - ❓ "How do you think the areas of the two triangles compare? Explain." The area of the larger triangle is the square of the scale factor, or $3^2 = 9$ times greater than the area of the smaller triangle.

Try It

- Students can make a table to record the original coordinates and those of the dilation.
- Students should draw the triangle and its image after the dilation. Ask volunteers to share their drawings.

EXAMPLE 3

- Work through the example.
- Use color to identify the two different rectangles and their vertices.
- ❓ "What is the product of a positive integer and a negative integer?" a negative integer
- ❓ "Where is the center of dilation?" the origin $(0, 0)$
- **MP6 Attend to Precision**: Ask the following questions.
  - ❓ "How do you think the perimeters of the two rectangles compare? Explain." Because the two rectangles are similar with a scale factor of 0.5, the perimeter of the smaller rectangle is $\frac{1}{2}$ the perimeter of the larger rectangle.
  - ❓ "How do you think the areas of the two rectangles compare? Explain." The area of the smaller rectangle is the square of the scale factor, or $\left(\frac{1}{2}\right)^2 = \frac{1}{4}$ times the area of the larger rectangle.

Try It

- Students can make a table to record the original coordinates and those of the dilation.
- Students should draw the rectangle and its image after the dilation. Ask volunteers to share their drawings.

EXAMPLE 2 **Dilating a Figure**

The vertices of a triangle are $A(1, 3)$, $B(2, 3)$, and $C(2, 1)$. Draw the image after a dilation with a scale factor of 3. Identify the type of dilation.

Multiply each x- and y-coordinate by the scale factor 3.

Math Practice

Use a Graph
Check your answer by drawing a line from the origin through each vertex of the original figure. The vertices of the image should lie on these lines.

$$(x, y) \longrightarrow (3x, 3y)$$

$A(1, 3) \longrightarrow A'(3 \cdot 1, 3 \cdot 3) \longrightarrow A'(3, 9)$

$B(2, 3) \longrightarrow B'(3 \cdot 2, 3 \cdot 3) \longrightarrow B'(6, 9)$

$C(2, 1) \longrightarrow C'(3 \cdot 2, 3 \cdot 1) \longrightarrow C'(6, 3)$

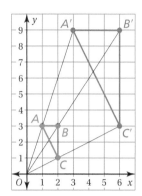

▶ The image is shown at the right. The dilation is an *enlargement* because the scale factor is greater than 1.

Try It

3. **WHAT IF?** Triangle ABC is dilated by a scale factor of 2. What are the coordinates of the image?

EXAMPLE 3 **Dilating a Figure**

The vertices of a rectangle are $W(-4, -6)$, $X(-4, 8)$, $Y(4, 8)$, and $Z(4, -6)$. Draw the image after a dilation with a scale factor of 0.5. Identify the type of dilation.

Multiply each x- and y-coordinate by the scale factor 0.5.

$$(x, y) \longrightarrow (0.5x, 0.5y)$$

$W(-4, -6) \longrightarrow W'(0.5 \cdot (-4), 0.5 \cdot (-6)) \longrightarrow W'(-2, -3)$

$X(-4, 8) \longrightarrow X'(0.5 \cdot (-4), 0.5 \cdot 8) \longrightarrow X'(-2, 4)$

$Y(4, 8) \longrightarrow Y'(0.5 \cdot 4, 0.5 \cdot 8) \longrightarrow Y'(2, 4)$

$Z(4, -6) \longrightarrow Z'(0.5 \cdot 4, 0.5 \cdot (-6)) \longrightarrow Z'(2, -3)$

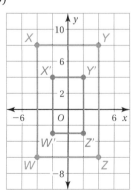

▶ The image is shown at the right. The dilation is a *reduction* because the scale factor is greater than 0 and less than 1.

Try It

4. **WHAT IF?** Rectangle $WXYZ$ is dilated by a scale factor of $\frac{1}{4}$. What are the coordinates of the image?

EXAMPLE 4 **Using More than One Transformation**

The vertices of a trapezoid are $A(-2, -1)$, $B(-1, 1)$, $C(0, 1)$, and $D(0, -1)$. Dilate the trapezoid using a scale factor of 2. Then translate it 6 units right and 2 units up. What are the coordinates of the image?

Draw *ABCD*. Then dilate it with respect to the origin using a scale factor of 2.

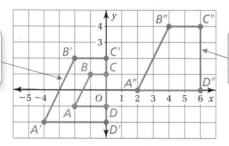

Translate the dilated figure 6 units right and 2 units up.

▷ The coordinates of the image are $A''(2, 0)$, $B''(4, 4)$, $C''(6, 4)$, and $D''(6, 0)$.

Try It

5. **WHAT IF?** Trapezoid *ABCD* is dilated using a scale factor of 3, and then rotated 180° about the origin. What are the coordinates of the image?

Self-Assessment for Concepts & Skills

Solve each exercise. Then rate your understanding of the success criteria in your journal.

IDENTIFYING A DILATION **Tell whether the blue figure is a dilation of the red figure.**

6.

7.

8. **DILATING A FIGURE** The vertices of a rectangle are $J(4, 8)$, $K(12, 8)$, $L(12, 4)$, and $M(4, 4)$. Draw the image after a dilation with a scale factor of $\frac{1}{4}$. Identify the type of dilation.

9. **VOCABULARY** How is a dilation different from other transformations?

Laurie's Notes

EXAMPLE 4

- The legs of the original trapezoid are not congruent, and there is a right angle. Both of these attributes will help students with orientation questions.
- Plot the original trapezoid. Say that you will perform two transformations.
- ? "How will a dilation with a scale factor of 2 change the trapezoid?" It will double the size of the trapezoid.
- ? "What will a translation do to the dilated trapezoid?" It will shift the trapezoid to another location.
- Set up a table to organize the vertices and then draw each trapezoid.

Vertices of *ABCD*	Vertices of *A′B′C′D′*	Vertices of *A″B″C″D″*
$A(-2, -1)$	$A'(-4, -2)$	$A''(2, 0)$
$B(-1, 1)$	$B'(-2, 2)$	$B''(4, 4)$
$C(0, 1)$	$C'(0, 2)$	$C''(6, 4)$
$D(0, -1)$	$D'(0, -2)$	$D''(6, 0)$

- ? "How is each pair of trapezoids related?" *ABCD* and *A′B′C′D′* are similar; *A′B′C′D′* and *A″B″C″D″* are congruent; *ABCD* and *A″B″C″D″* are similar.
- ? "When is a figure and its image after a sequence of transformations congruent? similar?" When there are translation(s), reflection(s), and/or rotation(s) and no dilations with a scale factor other than 1; When a dilation with a scale factor other than 1 is involved.

Try It

- Students should set up a table to organize the vertices and then draw each trapezoid. Ask volunteers to share their coordinates and drawings.

✓ Self-Assessment for Concepts & Skills

- **Neighbor Check:** Have students work independently and then have their neighbors check their work. Have students discuss any discrepancies.
- ◉ **Always-Sometimes-Never:** Pose the following conjectures to students. Use *Popsicle Sticks* to solicit explanations.
    a. If an image is larger or smaller than its original figure, then the image is a dilation. sometimes; There must be a center of dilation.
    b. If a figure is a dilation of another figure, then the ratios of the corresponding sides are equivalent. always
    c. Dilations with a scale factor of 1 result in congruent figures. always

ELL Support

Allow students to work in pairs for extra support and to practice language. Check answers to Exercises 6 and 7 by having students indicate *yes* or *no* using a thumbs up or down signal. For Exercise 8, have each pair write the vertices of the image and the type of dilation on a whiteboard to hold up for your review. Have two pairs form a group to discuss Exercise 9 and then review each group's explanation as a class.

The Success Criteria Self-Assessment chart can be found in the *Student Journal* or online at *BigIdeasMath.com*.

Extra Example 4

The vertices of a trapezoid are $A(-4, 0)$, $B(-2, 4)$, $C(2, 4)$, and D(6, 0). Dilate the trapezoid using a scale factor of 0.5. Then translate it 2 units right and 3 units down. What are the coordinates of the image?

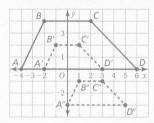

$A''(0, -3)$, $B''(1, -1)$, $C''(3, -1)$, $D''(5, -3)$

Try It

5. $A''(6, 3)$, $B''(3, -3)$, $C''(0, -3)$, $D''(0, 3)$

Formative Assessment Tip

Always-Sometimes-Never True (AT-ST-NT)

This strategy is useful in assessing whether students overgeneralize or under generalize a particular concept. When answering, a student should be asked to justify his or her answer and other students listening should critique the reasoning. *AT-ST-NT* statements help students practice the habit of checking validity when a statement (or conjecture) is made. Are there different cases that need to be checked? Is there a counterexample that would show the conjecture to be false? To develop these statements for a lesson, consider the common errors or misconceptions that students have relating to the success criteria of the lesson. Allow private think time before students share their thinking with partners or the whole class.

Self-Assessment
for Concepts & Skills

6. yes   7. no

8–9. See Additional Answers.

A national park is mapped on a coordinate plane, where each grid line represents 1 kilometer. The park has vertices $X(0, 0)$, $Y(3, 4)$, and $Z(5, 0)$. An expansion of the park can be represented by a dilation with a scale factor of 2.5. How much does the area of the national park increase? 52.5 km²

EXAMPLE 5

- Ask a volunteer to read the problem and another student to interpret it.
- Work through the example as shown.
- **Another Method:** Students might remember that the area of a dilated figure is the square of the scale factor times the area of the original figure. In this case, the scale factor is 1.5, so the area of the refuge with the expansion is $(1.5)^2$ or 2.25 times the original area. The area of the original refuge is $\frac{1}{2}(4)(3) = 6$ square miles. The area of the refuge with the expansion will be $2.25(6) = 13.5$ square miles. So, the increase in area will be $13.5 - 6 = 7.5$ square miles.

Self-Assessment
for Problem Solving

10. 3; *Sample answer:* If the length and width each increase by a factor of 3, the area increases by a factor of 9.

11. $(0, 0)$, $(0, 60)$, $(80, 60)$, $(80, 0)$; the scale; Each unit should represent 3 feet.

✓ Self-Assessment for Problem Solving

- The goal for all students is to feel comfortable with the problem-solving plan. It is important for students to problem-solve in class, where they may receive support from you and their peers. Keep in mind that some students may only be ready for the first step.

- Students should work in pairs to make a plan for each problem. Circulate while students make their plans and help clarify any misunderstandings before they solve the problems.

The Success Criteria Self-Assessment chart can be found in the *Student Journal* or online at *BigIdeasMath.com*.

Closure

- The vertices of a triangle are $T(-2, 3)$, $R(3, 2)$, and $S(3, 1)$. Draw the triangle and its image after a dilation with a scale factor of 2. What are the coordinates of $\triangle T'R'S'$?

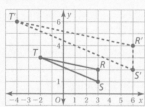

$T'(-4, 6)$, $R'(6, 4)$, and $S'(6, 2)$

Learning Target
Dilate figures in the coordinate plane.

Success Criteria
- Identify a dilation.
- Find the coordinates of a figure dilated with respect to the origin.
- Use coordinates to dilate a figure with respect to the origin.

EXAMPLE 5 **Modeling Real Life**

A wildlife refuge is mapped on a coordinate plane, where each grid line represents 1 mile. The refuge has vertices $J(0, 0)$, $K(1, 3)$, and $L(4, 0)$. An expansion of the refuge can be represented by a dilation with a scale factor of 1.5. How much does the area of the wildlife refuge increase?

Multiply each x- and y-coordinate by the scale factor 1.5. Then find the area of each figure.

$$(x, y) \longrightarrow (1.5x, 1.5y)$$

$$J(0, 0) \longrightarrow J'(1.5 \cdot 0, 1.5 \cdot 0) \longrightarrow J'(0, 0)$$

$$K(1, 3) \longrightarrow K'(1.5 \cdot 1, 1.5 \cdot 3) \longrightarrow K'(1.5, 4.5)$$

$$L(4, 0) \longrightarrow L'(1.5 \cdot 4, 1.5 \cdot 0) \longrightarrow L'(6, 0)$$

The original figure is a triangle with a base of 4 miles and a height of 3 miles. The image has a base of 6 miles and a height of 4.5 miles. Use the formula for the area of a triangle to find the areas of the original figure and the image.

Original Figure		*Image*
$A = \dfrac{1}{2}bh$	Write the formula.	$A = \dfrac{1}{2}bh$
$= \dfrac{1}{2}(4)(3)$	Substitute for b and h.	$= \dfrac{1}{2}(6)(4.5)$
$= 6$	Simplify.	$= 13.5$

▷ So, the area of the wildlife refuge increases $13.5 - 6 = 7.5$ square miles.

 Self-Assessment for Problem Solving

Solve each exercise. Then rate your understanding of the success criteria in your journal.

10. A photograph is dilated to fit in a frame, so that its area after the dilation is 9 times greater than the area of the original photograph. What is the scale factor of the dilation? Explain.

11. **DIG DEEPER!** The location of a water treatment plant is mapped using a coordinate plane, where each unit represents 1 foot. The plant has vertices $(0, 0)$, $(0, 180)$, $(240, 180)$, and $(240, 0)$. You dilate the figure with a scale factor of $\dfrac{1}{3}$. What are the coordinates of the image? What do you need to change so that the image accurately represents the location of the plant? Explain your reasoning.

Go to *BigIdeasMath.com* to get HELP with solving the exercises.

 Review & Refresh

The red figure is congruent to the blue figure. Describe a sequence of rigid motions between the figures.

1.

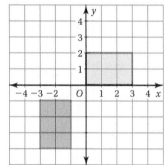

2.

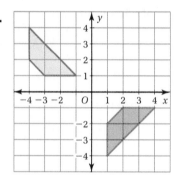

Tell whether the ratios form a proportion.

3. $3:5$ and $15:20$　　　**4.** 2 to 3 and 12 to 18　　　**5.** $7:28$ and $12:48$

Concepts, Skills, & Problem Solving

DESCRIBING RELATIONSHIPS Describe the relationship between the given point and the point $A(8, 12)$ in terms of dilations. (See Exploration 1, p. 69.)

6. $B(16, 24)$　　　**7.** $C(2, 3)$　　　**8.** $D(6, 9)$

IDENTIFYING A DILATION Tell whether the blue figure is a dilation of the red figure.

9.

10.

11.

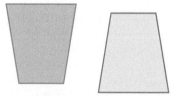

12.

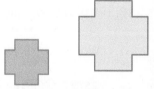

13.

14.

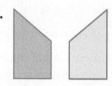

Assignment Guide and Concept Check

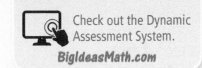
Scaffold assignments to support all students in their learning progression. The suggested assignments are a starting point. Continue to assign additional exercises and revisit with spaced practice to move every student toward proficiency.

Level	Assignment 1	Assignment 2
Emerging	2, 5, 6, 9, 11, 13, 15, 16, 21, 23	10, 12, 14, 19, 20, 24, 25, 26, 29, 31
Proficient	2, 5, 7, 10, 12, 14, 16, 19, 20, 21, 22, 25	17, 26, 27, 29, 30, 31, 32, 33, 34, 36, 37
Advanced	2, 5, 8, 10, 12, 14, 17, 19, 20, 21, 22, 25	27, 28, 29, 30, 31, 32, 33, 35, 36, 37, 38

- Assignment 1 is for use after students complete the Self-Assessment for Concepts & Skills.
- Assignment 2 is for use after students complete the Self-Assessment for Problem Solving.
- The red exercises can be used as a concept check.

Review & Refresh Prior Skills

Exercises 1 and 2   Describing a Sequence of Rigid Motions
Exercises 3–5   Determining Whether Ratios Form a Proportion

Common Errors

- **Exercises 9–14** Students may think that a figure with the same shape as another is a dilation. Remind them that a transformation is a dilation when the lines connecting corresponding vertices meet at a point (except when the figures are congruent).

▶ Review & Refresh

1. *Sample answer:* Rotate the blue figure 90° counterclockwise about the origin and then translate the image 1 unit left and 4 units down.

2. *Sample answer:* Reflect the blue figure in the *x*-axis and then translate the image 5 units right.

3. no

4. yes

5. yes

▶ Concepts, Skills, & Problem Solving

6. dilation with respect to the origin by a scale factor of 2

7. dilation with respect to the origin by a scale factor of $\frac{1}{4}$

8. dilation with respect to the origin by a scale factor of $\frac{3}{4}$

9. yes

10. yes

11. no

12. yes

13. yes

14. no

15. See Additional Answers.

16.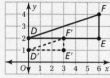

reduction

17. See Additional Answers.

18.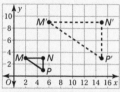

enlargement

19.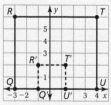

reduction

20.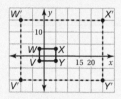

enlargement

21. yes; Each x- and y-coordinate was multiplied by the scale factor 2.

22. enlargement; 2

23. reduction; $\frac{1}{4}$

24. enlargement; $\frac{3}{2}$

25. reduction; $\frac{1}{2}$

26. $A''(10, 6)$, $B''(4, 6)$, $C''(4, 2)$, $D''(10, 2)$

27. $F''(-6, 0)$, $G''(-2, 2)$, $H''(-2, 0)$

28. $J''(3, -3)$, $K''(12, -9)$, $L''(3, -15)$

❗ **Common Errors**

- **Exercises 15–20** Students may confuse the image of a dilation with the original figure when both are drawn in the same coordinate plane. Remind students to pay attention to the prime notation when determining the dilation.

- **Exercises 22–25** Students may indicate the wrong type of dilation and give the reciprocal of the scale factor. Remind students that you multiply each coordinate of the original figure by the scale factor to obtain the corresponding image coordinate.

DILATING A FIGURE The vertices of a figure are given. Draw the figure and its image after a dilation with the given scale factor. Identify the type of dilation.

15. $A(1, 1), B(1, 4), C(3, 1); k = 4$

16. $D(0, 2), E(6, 2), F(6, 4); k = 0.5$

17. $G(-2, -2), H(-2, 6), J(2, 6); k = 0.25$

18. $M(2, 3), N(5, 3), P(5, 1); k = 3$

19. $Q(-3, 0), R(-3, 6), T(4, 6), U(4, 0); k = \dfrac{1}{3}$

20. $V(-2, -2), W(-2, 3), X(5, 3), Y(5, -2); k = 5$

21. **MP YOU BE THE TEACHER** Your friend finds the coordinates of the image of $\triangle ABC$ after a dilation with a scale factor of 2. Is your friend correct? Explain your reasoning.

$A(2, 5) \longrightarrow A'(2 \cdot 2, 2 \cdot 5) \longrightarrow A'(4, 10)$
$B(2, 0) \longrightarrow B'(2 \cdot 2, 2 \cdot 0) \longrightarrow B'(4, 0)$
$C(4, 0) \longrightarrow C'(2 \cdot 4, 2 \cdot 0) \longrightarrow C'(8, 0)$

FINDING A SCALE FACTOR The blue figure is a dilation of the red figure. Identify the type of dilation and find the scale factor.

22.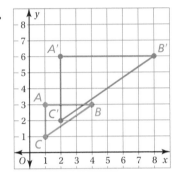

23.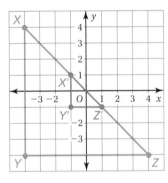

24.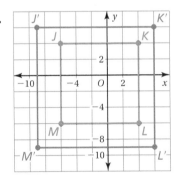

25.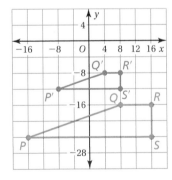

USING MORE THAN ONE TRANSFORMATION The vertices of a figure are given. Find the coordinates of the image after the transformations given.

26. $A(-5, 3), B(-2, 3), C(-2, 1), D(-5, 1)$

Reflect in the y-axis. Then dilate using a scale factor of 2.

27. $F(-9, -9), G(-3, -6), H(-3, -9)$

Dilate using a scale factor of $\dfrac{2}{3}$. Then translate 6 units up.

28. $J(1, 1), K(3, 4), L(5, 1)$

Rotate 90° clockwise about the origin. Then dilate using a scale factor of 3.

29. **MP LOGIC** You can use a flashlight and a shadow puppet (your hands) to project shadows on the wall.

    a. Identify the type of dilation.

    b. What does the flashlight represent?

    c. The length of the ears on the shadow puppet is 3 inches. The length of the ears on the shadow is 4 inches. What is the scale factor?

    d. Describe what happens as the shadow puppet moves closer to the flashlight. How does this affect the scale factor?

30. **MP REASONING** A triangle is dilated using a scale factor of 3. The image is then dilated using a scale factor of $\frac{1}{2}$. What scale factor can you use to dilate the original triangle to obtain the final image? Explain.

CRITICAL THINKING The coordinate notation shows how the coordinates of a figure are related to the coordinates of its image after transformations. What are the transformations? Are the figure and its image congruent? Explain.

31. $(x, y) \rightarrow (2x + 4, 2y - 3)$ 32. $(x, y) \rightarrow (-x - 1, y - 2)$ 33. $(x, y) \rightarrow \left(\frac{1}{3}x, -\frac{1}{3}y\right)$

MP STRUCTURE The blue figure is a transformation of the red figure. Use coordinate notation to describe the transformation. Explain your reasoning.

34.

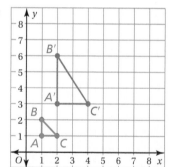

35.

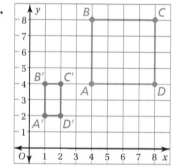

36. **MP NUMBER SENSE** You dilate a figure using a scale factor of 2, and then translate it 3 units right. Your friend translates the same figure 3 units right and then dilates it using a scale factor of 2. Are the images congruent? Explain.

37. **MP PROBLEM SOLVING** The vertices of a trapezoid are $A(-2, 3)$, $B(2, 3)$, $C(5, -2)$, and $D(-2, -2)$. Dilate the trapezoid with respect to vertex A using a scale factor of 2. What are the coordinates of the image? Explain the method you used.

38. **DIG DEEPER!** A figure is dilated using a scale factor of -1. How can you obtain the image without using a dilation? Explain your reasoning.

Mini-Assessment

1. Tell whether the blue figure is a dilation of the red figure.

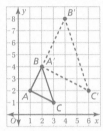

no

2. The vertices of a triangle are $A(1, 2)$, $B(2, 4)$, and $C(3, 1)$. Draw the triangle and its image after a dilation with a scale factor of 2. Identify the type of dilation.

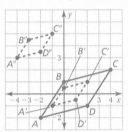

enlargement

3. The vertices of a quadrilateral are $A(-2, -2)$, $B(0, 1)$, $C(4, 2)$, and $D(2, -1)$. Dilate the quadrilateral using a scale factor of 0.5. Then translate it 3 units left and 4 units up. What are the coordinates of the image?

$A''(-4, 3)$, $B''(-3, 4.5)$, $C''(-1, 5)$, $D''(-2, 3.5)$

Section Resources

Surface Level	Deep Level
Resources by Chapter • Extra Practice • Reteach • Puzzle Time Student Journal • Self-Assessment • Practice Differentiating the Lesson Tutorial Videos Skills Review Handbook Skills Trainer	Resources by Chapter • Enrichment and Extension Graphic Organizers Dynamic Assessment System • Section Practice

Concepts, Skills, & Problem Solving

29. **a.** enlargement

    b. center of dilation

    c. $\dfrac{4}{3}$

    d. The shadow on the wall becomes larger; The scale factor becomes larger.

30. $\dfrac{3}{2}$; Multiply the two scale factors.

31. The transformations are a dilation with a scale factor of 2 and then a translation of 4 units right and 3 units down; no; The dilation does not produce a congruent figure, so the final image is not congruent.

32. See Additional Answers.

33. The transformations are a dilation with a scale factor of $\dfrac{1}{3}$ and then a reflection in the x-axis; no; The dilation does not produce a congruent figure, so the final image is not congruent.

34. $(x, y) \rightarrow (2x, 3y)$; Each x-coordinate is multiplied by 2 and each y-coordinate is multiplied by 3.

35. See Additional Answers.

36. yes; *Sample answer:* The angle measures are preserved in each sequence of transformations, and the side lengths of both final images are double the side lengths of the original figure.

37. $A'(-2, 3)$, $B'(6, 3)$, $C'(12, -7)$, $D'(-2, -7)$; Check students' work.

38. reflect the figure in both axes or rotate 180° about the origin; A dilation using a scale factor of -1 results in $(x, y) \rightarrow (-x, -y)$. A reflection in both axes or a rotation of 180° about the origin results in the same coordinates, $(x, y) \rightarrow (-x, -y)$.

Laurie's Notes

COMMON CORE STATE STANDARDS
8.G.A.4

Learning Target

Understand the concept of similar figures.

Success Criteria

- Identify similar figures.
- Describe a similarity transformation between two similar figures.

Warm Up

Cumulative, vocabulary, and prerequisite skills practice opportunities are available in the *Resources by Chapter* or at *BigIdeasMath.com*.

ELL Support

Discuss the meaning of the word *similar*. Have students express their understanding of its meaning from everyday life. Does it mean one thing is exactly the same as another? How might they be the same or different? Have students consider their understanding of the word *similar* as they learn about similarity transformations and think about how the math definition for *similar* may differ from its use in everyday life.

Exploration 1

a. Check students' work.

b. yes; △*GHJ* is a proportional drawing of △*ABC*. △*LMN* is a proportional drawing of △*DEF*. Rectangle *ABCD* is a proportional drawing of Rectangle *FGHJ*.

c. yes; Rigid motions produce congruent figures, and dilations produce scale drawings of figures. So, a sequence of these transformations will also produce scale drawings of figures.

Preparing to Teach

- Students have worked with translations, reflections, rotations, and dilations. Now they will use these transformations to describe a similarity transformation between two similar figures.
- **MP6 Attend to Precision:** Students should use precise vocabulary to communicate their thinking to others. In working with similar figures, they should be able to state which transformations can be used to obtain one figure from another and why.

Motivate

- Place an item under a document camera or on an overhead projector, such as an index card, school ID, or other rectangular item. Ask questions about the actual item and its projected image.
- ? "How does the actual item compare to its projection?" Listen for: "They look alike," "They have the same shape," "They are similar," or "One is a dilation of the other."
- Place a different-shaped item under the document camera or on the overhead.
- ? "There are two items and two projected images. Which projection goes with which item? How do you know?" Listen for students to say the items are the same shape but different sizes.
- ? "Where are similar figures found in everyday life?" *Sample answers:* model cars, model planes, pictures on a TV

Formative Assessment Tip

Wait Time

Wait Time is the interval between a question being posed and a student (or teacher) response. Silence can be uncomfortable in a classroom, but research has shown that increasing *Wait Time* increases class participation and answers become more detailed. For complex, higher-order thinking questions, increased *Wait Time* is necessary. With increased participation, you will learn more about your students' progress and learning.

Exploration 1

- This exploration is best completed using geometry software, which is available at *BigIdeasMath.com*. It can be completed using transparent paper, but the dilation will be difficult.
- If time is a concern, you could divide students into 5 groups and assign each group one pair of figures in part (a). Then have volunteers from each group demonstrate the transformations needed to obtain one figure from the other.
- As students discuss parts (b) and (c), it is important to provide *Wait Time* before soliciting responses. Use *Popsicle Sticks* to select students to share their ideas, as this encourages all students to be prepared to answer the questions.

2.6 Similar Figures

Learning Target: Understand the concept of similar figures.

Success Criteria:
- I can identify similar figures.
- I can describe a similarity transformation between two similar figures.

EXPLORATION 1

Transforming Figures

Work with a partner. Use geometry software.

a. For each pair of figures whose vertices are given below, draw the figures in a coordinate plane. Use dilations and rigid motions to try to obtain one of the figures from the other figure.

- $A(-3, 6)$, $B(0, -3)$, $C(3, 6)$ and $G(-1, 2)$, $H(0, -1)$, $J(1, 2)$

- $D(0, 0)$, $E(3, 0)$, $F(3, 3)$ and $L(0, 0)$, $M(0, 6)$, $N(-6, 6)$

- $P(1, 0)$, $Q(4, 2)$, $R(7, 0)$ and $X(-1, 0)$, $Y(-4, 6)$, $Z(-7, 0)$

- $A(-3, 2)$, $B(-1, 2)$, $C(-1, -1)$, $D(-3, -1)$ and $F(6, 4)$, $G(2, 4)$, $H(2, -2)$, $J(6, -2)$

- $P(-2, 2)$, $Q(-1, -1)$, $R(1, -1)$, $S(2, 2)$ and $W(2, 8)$, $X(3, 3)$, $Y(7, 3)$, $Z(8, 8)$

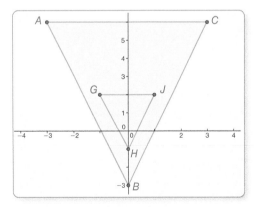

Available at BigIdeasMath.com.

Math Practice

Interpret Results

When you need a dilation to obtain one figure from another, what does it tell you about the side lengths and angle measures of the figures?

b. Is a scale drawing represented by any of the pairs of figures in part (a)? Explain your reasoning.

c. Figure A is a scale drawing of Figure B. Do you think there must be a sequence of transformations that obtains Figure A from Figure B? Explain your reasoning.

Dilations do not preserve length, so dilations are not rigid motions. A **similarity transformation** is a dilation or a sequence of dilations and rigid motions.

 Key Idea

Similar Figures

Two figures are **similar figures** when one can be obtained from the other by a similarity transformation. Similar figures have the same shape but not necessarily the same size. The triangles below are similar.

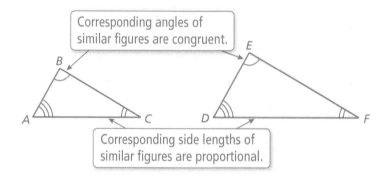

Corresponding angles of similar figures are congruent.

Corresponding side lengths of similar figures are proportional.

Reading

The symbol ~ means *is similar to*.
In the Key Idea,
$\triangle ABC \sim \triangle DEF$.

Side Lengths	*Angles*
$\dfrac{AB}{DE} = \dfrac{BC}{EF} = \dfrac{AC}{DF}$	$\angle A \cong \angle D, \angle B \cong \angle E, \angle C \cong \angle F$

EXAMPLE 1 Identifying Similar Figures

Determine whether $\triangle ABC$ and $\triangle JKL$ are similar.

Compare the coordinates of the vertices.

$$A(0, 3) \longrightarrow A'(2 \cdot 0, 2 \cdot 3) \longrightarrow J(0, 6)$$

$$B(3, 3) \longrightarrow B'(2 \cdot 3, 2 \cdot 3) \longrightarrow K(6, 6)$$

$$C(3, 0) \longrightarrow C'(2 \cdot 3, 2 \cdot 0) \longrightarrow L(6, 0)$$

$\triangle JKL$ is a dilation of $\triangle ABC$ using a scale factor of 2.

So, $\triangle ABC$ and $\triangle JKL$ are similar.

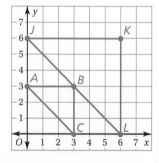

Common Error

When writing a similarity statement, make sure to list the vertices of the figures in the correct order.

Try It

1. A triangle has vertices $D(0, 4)$, $E(5, 4)$, and $F(5, 0)$. Is $\triangle DEF$ similar to $\triangle ABC$ and $\triangle JKL$ in Example 1? Explain.

🔊 Multi-Language Glossary at *BigIdeasMath.com*

Laurie's Notes

Scaffolding Instruction

- Students explored similarity transformations. Now they will use the formal definition for similar figures to identify similar figures and describe a similarity transformation.
- **Emerging:** Students may struggle with the use of transformations to identify similar figures. They will benefit from guided instruction for the Key Idea and examples.
- **Proficient:** Students can identify similar figures using transformations. They can also describe a similarity transformation between two similar figures. These students should review the definitions and Key Idea before proceeding to the Self-Assessment exercises.

Discuss

- Discuss the definition for a similarity transformation. Make sure students understand that similarity transformations are not restricted to rigid motions.
- ❓ "Do you think congruence transformations can only include rigid motions? Explain." Yes, congruent figures are the same size and shape so they cannot be dilated by a scale factor other than 1.

Key Idea

- Discuss the Reading note about the tilde symbol ~ that denotes similarity. Remind students that the order in which the vertices of the triangle are written identifies how the sides and angles correspond.
- ❓ "What is the difference between similar figures and congruent figures?" Congruent figures must have the same size and shape. Similar figures have the same shape but not necessarily the same size.
- **Representation:** Point out the color-coding, which should help students see the corresponding parts.
- Take your time in this section. There is a great deal of vocabulary, symbols, representations, *and* the fundamental concept of similarity. Give students time to ask questions and think about all that is being presented.

EXAMPLE 1

- When comparing the coordinates, suggest that students write a coordinate from the first triangle, leave space, and then write the corresponding coordinate from the second triangle. Then they can look for the relationship between the points to determine the scale factor and fill in the middle space.

Try It

- Students should work independently and then share with the class.

Scaffold instruction to support all students in their learning. Learning is individualized and you may want to group students differently as they move in and out of these levels with each skill and concept. Student self-assessment and feedback help guide your instructional decisions about how and when to layer support for all students to become proficient learners.

Extra Example 1

Determine whether $\triangle MNP$ and $\triangle XYZ$ are similar.

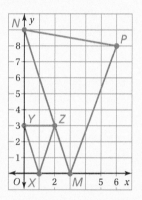

not similar

Try It

1. no; There is no similarity transformation between $\triangle DEF$ and $\triangle ABC$ or $\triangle DEF$ and $\triangle JKL$.

Laurie's Notes

Extra Example 2

The red figure is similar to the blue figure. Describe a similarity transformation between the figures.

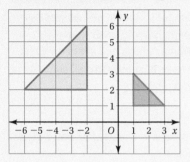

Sample answer: Dilate the red figure with respect to the origin using a scale factor of 2 and then reflect the image in the *y*-axis.

Try It

2. yes; *Sample answer:* The order in which the transformations are performed does not change the result.

Self-Assessment

for Concepts & Skills

3. no; There is no similarity transformation between Rectangle *ABCD* and Rectangle *EFGH*.

4. *Sample answer:* Dilate the red figure using a scale factor of 2 and then translate the image 10 units left and 8 units down.

EXAMPLE 2

- After reading the problem, allow time for students to study the graph. They should recognize that a dilation is involved.
- **?** Ask, "Which pair of corresponding sides should you use to find the scale factor?" Any pair of corresponding sides could be used, but the easiest would be the two vertical sides or the two horizontal sides.
- After determining that the scale factor is $\frac{1}{2}$, have students compare the coordinates of the red figure to the coordinates of its image after a dilation with a scale factor of $\frac{1}{2}$. Students should graph the dilated figure before reflecting the image.
- Alternatively, students could describe a similarity transformation in which the red figure is the image of the blue figure. For example, one possible similarity transformation is to dilate the blue figure with respect to the origin using a scale factor of 2 and then reflect the image in the *x*-axis.

Try It

- Students should work independently. Encourage them to compare the coordinates of the vertices.

✔ Self-Assessment for Concepts & Skills

- Students should work independently on these exercises, showing their work. Then have each student share with a partner.
- ◉ **One-Minute Card:** To determine the similarity transformation between two similar figures, I must… find a scale factor and check for reflections, translations, or rotations.

ELL Support

Allow students to work in pairs for extra support. Then have two pairs compare their answers. Monitor discussions and provide support as needed. Review the answers as a class.

The Success Criteria Self-Assessment chart can be found in the *Student Journal* or online at *BigIdeasMath.com*.

EXAMPLE 2 **Describing a Similarity Transformation**

The red figure is similar to the blue figure. Describe a similarity transformation between the figures.

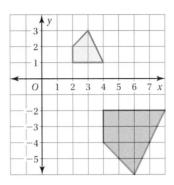

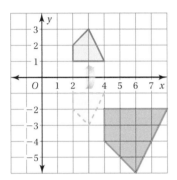

By comparing corresponding side lengths, you can see that the blue figure is one-half the size of the red figure. So, begin by dilating the red figure with respect to the origin using a scale factor of $\frac{1}{2}$.

After dilating the red figure, you need to reflect the figure in the x-axis.

So, one possible similarity transformation is to dilate the red figure with respect to the origin using a scale factor of $\frac{1}{2}$ and then reflect the image in the x-axis.

Try It

2. Can you reflect the red figure first, and then perform the dilation to obtain the blue figure? Explain.

Self-Assessment for Concepts & Skills

Solve each exercise. Then rate your understanding of the success criteria in your journal.

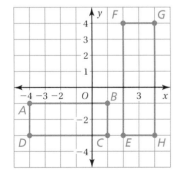

3. **IDENTIFYING SIMILAR FIGURES** In the coordinate plane at the left, determine whether Rectangle *ABCD* is similar to Rectangle *EFGH*. Explain your reasoning.

4. **SIMILARITY TRANSFORMATION** The red triangle is similar to the blue triangle. Describe a similarity transformation between the figures.

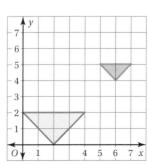

EXAMPLE 3 **Modeling Real Life**

An artist draws a replica of a painting that is on a remaining piece of the Berlin Wall. The painting includes a red trapezoid. The shorter base of the similar trapezoid in the replica is 3.75 inches. What is the height h of the trapezoid in the replica?

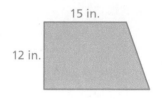

15 in.

12 in.

Painting

3.75 in.

h

Replica

Because the trapezoids are similar, corresponding side lengths are proportional. So, the ratios 3.75 : 15 and h : 12 are equivalent. Use the values of the ratios to write and solve a proportion to find h.

$$\frac{3.75}{15} = \frac{h}{12}$$ Write a proportion.

$$12 \cdot \frac{3.75}{15} = 12 \cdot \frac{h}{12}$$ Multiplication Property of Equality

$$3 = h$$ Simplify.

▷ So, the height of the trapezoid in the replica is 3 inches.

Another Method The replica is a scale drawing of the painting with a scale factor of $\frac{3.75}{15} = \frac{1}{4}$. So, the height of the trapezoid in the replica is $\frac{1}{4}$ the height of the trapezoid in the painting, $\frac{1}{4}(12) = 3$ inches. ✓

Self-Assessment for Problem Solving

Solve each exercise. Then rate your understanding of the success criteria in your journal.

5. A medical supplier sells gauze in large and small rectangular sheets. A large sheet has a length of 9 inches and an area of 45 square inches. A small sheet has a length of 4 inches and a width of 3 inches. Are the sheets similar? Justify your answer.

6. The sail on a souvenir boat is similar in shape to the sail on a sailboat. The sail on the sailboat is in the shape of a right triangle with a base of 9 feet and a height of 24 feet. The height of the souvenir's sail is 3 inches. What is the base of the souvenir's sail?

7. DIG DEEPER! A coordinate plane is used to represent a cheerleading formation. The vertices of the formation are $A(-4, 4)$, $B(0, 8)$, $C(4, 4)$, and $D(0, 6)$. A choreographer creates a new formation similar to the original formation. Three vertices of the new formation are $J(-2, -2)$, $K(0, -4)$, and $L(2, -2)$. What is the location of the fourth vertex? Explain.

Laurie's Notes

EXAMPLE 3

- Ask a volunteer to read the problem.
- Share some information about the Berlin Wall.
  - It was built to keep East Germans from escaping to West Germany.
  - East German crews began tearing up streets and spreading barbed wire at midnight on August 13, 1961. By morning, the border with West Germany was closed. This is how the Berlin Wall began.
  - The wall was over a hundred miles long and went through four major changes. The final version of the Berlin Wall was 12 feet tall.
  - The Berlin Wall symbolized the boundary between communism and democracy until it was torn down in 1989.
  - Thierry Noir is one of the artists who turned the Berlin wall into the world's longest painting canvas. He wanted to "demystify" the wall with his bright-colored paintings.
- Ask a second volunteer to interpret the problem. Students could complete a Four Square to help them work through the problem-solving plan.
- Draw the two trapezoids, one representing the trapezoid in the painting and one representing the trapezoid in the replica. Label the known dimensions.
- **?** "What is the height of each of the trapezoids?" 12 inches and *h* inches
- **?** "The trapezoid in the actual painting has a side of length 15 inches. What is the length of the corresponding side in the replica?" 3.75 inches
- Remind students that because there is a scale factor they know that the corresponding sides are proportional.
- Set up and solve the proportion.
- **MP6 Attend to Precision:** State the solution with the correct units.

✓ Self-Assessment for Problem Solving

- Allow time in class for students to practice using the problem-solving plan. Remember, some students may only be able to complete the first step.
- Each student should work through the problem-solving plan for each exercise independently and then check with a neighbor to discuss any discrepancies.

The Success Criteria Self-Assessment chart can be found in the *Student Journal* or online at *BigIdeasMath.com*.

Closure

- Explain why congruent figures must be similar, but similar figures do not have to be congruent.

Extra Example 3

The artist draws a larger replica of the painting in Example 3. The shorter base of the similar trapezoid is 10 inches. What is the height *h* of this trapezoid? 8 in.

Self-Assessment
for Problem Solving

5. no; Corresponding side lengths are not proportional.

6. 1.125 in.

7. $(0, -3)$; Points A, B, C are dilated using a scale factor of $\frac{1}{2}$ and then reflected in the x-axis to obtain points J, K, and L.
   So, $(x, y) \rightarrow \left(\frac{1}{2}x, -\frac{1}{2}y \right)$.

Learning Target

Understand the concept of similar figures.

Success Criteria

- Identify similar figures.
- Describe a similarity transformation between two similar figures.

Review & Refresh

1. no   2. yes

3. C

Concepts, Skills, & Problem Solving

4. yes   5. no

6. yes; *Sample answer:* Rectangle *ABCD* is a dilation of Rectangle *EFGH* using a scale factor of 2.

7. no; There is no similarity transformation between △*ABC* and △*JKL*.

8.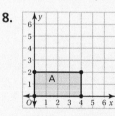

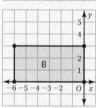

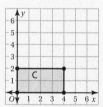

A, B, and C; *Sample answer:* A and C are congruent, so they are also similar. Obtain B from either A or C by dilating the rectangle using a scale factor of $\frac{3}{2}$ and then translating the image 6 units left.

9. See Additional Answers for graphs.

A and B; *Sample answer:* Obtain B from A by dilating A using a scale factor of $\frac{3}{2}$ and then translating the image 7 units right and 1 unit up.

Assignment Guide and Concept Check

Scaffold assignments to support all students in their learning progression. The suggested assignments are a starting point. Continue to assign additional exercises and revisit with spaced practice to move every student toward proficiency.

Level	Assignment 1	Assignment 2
Emerging	1, 2, 3, 4, 5, 6, 7, 8, 10	9, 11, 12, 16, 18
Proficient	1, 2, 3, 4, 5, 6, 7, 8, 9, 10, 11	12, 13, 14, 15, 16, 18
Advanced	1, 2, 3, 4, 5, 6, 7, 8, 9, 10, 11	13, 14, 15, 16, 17, 18

- Assignment 1 is for use after students complete the Self-Assessment for Concepts & Skills.
- Assignment 2 is for use after students complete the Self-Assessment for Problem Solving.
- The red exercises can be used as a concept check.

Review & Refresh Prior Skills

Exercises 1 and 2 Identifying a Dilation
Exercise 3 Rewriting a Formula

2.6 Practice

Go to **BigIdeasMath.com** to get
HELP with solving the exercises.

▶ Review & Refresh

Tell whether the blue figure is a dilation of the red figure.

1.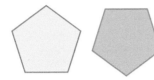

2.

3. You solve the equation $S = \ell w + 2wh$ for w. Which equation is correct?

   A. $w = \dfrac{S - \ell}{2h}$

   B. $w = \dfrac{S - 2h}{\ell}$

   C. $w = \dfrac{S}{\ell + 2h}$

   D. $w = S - \ell - 2h$

▶▶ Concepts, Skills, & Problem Solving

TRANSFORMING FIGURES **The vertices of a pair of figures are given. Determine whether a scale drawing is represented by the pair of figures.** (See Exploration 1, p. 77.)

4. $A(-8, -2)$, $B(-4, 2)$, $C(-4, -2)$ and $G(2, -1)$, $H(4, -1)$, $J(2, -3)$

5. $A(0, 3)$, $B(3, 4)$, $C(5, 3)$, $D(3, 2)$ and $F(-4, 4)$, $G(-1, 5)$, $H(5, 3)$, $J(3, 2)$

IDENTIFYING SIMILAR FIGURES **Determine whether the figures are similar. Explain your reasoning.**

6.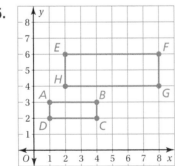

7.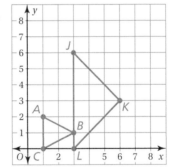

IDENTIFYING SIMILAR FIGURES **Draw the figures with the given vertices in a coordinate plane. Which figures are similar? Explain your reasoning.**

8. Rectangle A: $(0, 0), (4, 0), (4, 2), (0, 2)$
   Rectangle B: $(0, 0), (-6, 0), (-6, 3), (0, 3)$
   Rectangle C: $(0, 0), (4, 0), (4, 2), (0, 2)$

9. Figure A: $(-4, 2), (-2, 2), (-2, 0), (-4, 0)$
   Figure B: $(1, 4), (4, 4), (4, 1), (1, 1)$
   Figure C: $(2, -1), (5, -1), (5, -3), (2, -3)$

DESCRIBING A SIMILARITY TRANSFORMATION The red figure is similar to the blue figure. Describe a similarity transformation between the figures.

10.

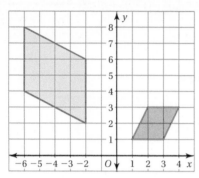

11.

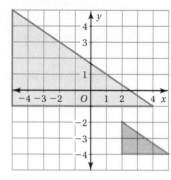

12. **MP** **MODELING REAL LIFE** A barrier in the shape of a rectangle is used to retain oil spills. On a blueprint, a similar barrier is 9 inches long and 2 inches wide. The width of the actual barrier is 1.2 miles. What is the length of the actual barrier?

13. **MP** **LOGIC** Are the following figures *always*, *sometimes*, or *never* similar? Explain.

    a. two triangles   **b.** two squares   **c.** two rectangles

14. **CRITICAL THINKING** Can you draw two quadrilaterals each having two 130° angles and two 50° angles that are *not* similar? Justify your answer.

15. **MP** **REASONING** The sign is rectangular.

    a. You increase each side length by 20%. Is the new sign similar to the original? Explain your reasoning.

    b. You increase each side length by 6 inches. Is the new sign similar to the original? Explain your reasoning.

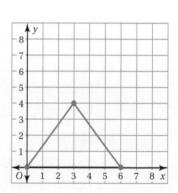

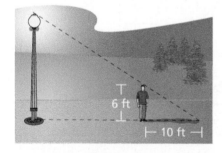

16. **DIG DEEPER!** A person standing 20 feet from a streetlight casts a shadow as shown. How many times taller is the streetlight than the person? Assume the triangles are similar.

17. **GEOMETRY** Use a ruler to draw two different isosceles triangles similar to the one shown. Measure the heights of each triangle.

    a. Are the ratios of the corresponding heights equivalent to the ratios of the corresponding side lengths?

    b. Do you think this is true for all similar triangles? Explain.

18. **CRITICAL THINKING** Given $\triangle ABC \sim \triangle DEF$ and $\triangle DEF \sim \triangle JKL$, is $\triangle ABC \sim \triangle JKL$? Justify your answer.

Mini-Assessment

1. Determine whether the figures are similar. Explain your reasoning.

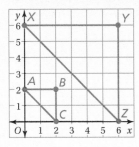

yes; *Sample answer:* △*XYZ* is a dilation of △*ABC* using a scale factor of 3.

2. The red figure is similar to the blue figure. Describe a similarity transformation between the figures.

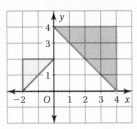

Sample answer: Dilate the red figure with respect to the origin using a scale factor of 0.5 and then reflect the image in the *y*-axis.

Section Resources

Surface Level	Deep Level
Resources by Chapter • Extra Practice • Reteach • Puzzle Time Student Journal • Self-Assessment • Practice Differentiating the Lesson Tutorial Videos Skills Review Handbook Skills Trainer	Resources by Chapter • Enrichment and Extension Graphic Organizers Dynamic Assessment System • Section Practice

Concepts, Skills, & Problem Solving

10. *Sample answer:* Rotate the red figure 90° counterclockwise about the origin and then dilate the image using a scale factor of 2.

11. *Sample answer:* Dilate the red figure using a scale factor of 3 and then translate the image 11 units left and 11 units up.

12. 5.4 mi

13. a. sometimes; They are similar only when corresponding side lengths are proportional and corresponding angles are congruent.

    b. always; All angles are congruent and all sides are proportional.

    c. sometimes; Corresponding angles are always congruent, but corresponding side lengths are not always proportional.

14. See Additional Answers.

15. a. yes; *Sample answer:* The new sign is a dilation of the original sign using a scale factor of 1.2.

    b. no; *Sample answer:* Because the length and width are different, adding 6 to each side length does not produce an equivalent ratio. So, corresponding side lengths are not proportional.

16. 3 times

17. a. yes

    b. yes; The ratios are equivalent because the heights are multiplied by the same amount as the sides.

18. See Additional Answers.

Learning Target

Find perimeters and areas of similar figures.

Success Criteria

- Use corresponding side lengths to compare perimeters of similar figures.
- Use corresponding side lengths to compare areas of similar figures.
- Use similar figures to solve real-life problems involving perimeter and area.

Warm Up

Cumulative, vocabulary, and prerequisite skills practice opportunities are available in the *Resources by Chapter* or at *BigIdeasMath.com.*

ELL Support

Review the terms *area* and *perimeter*. Discuss the multiple meanings of the word *area*. In everyday life, area refers to a space or region. Remind students that in math the word *area* has a very specific meaning. It is the amount of surface covered by a figure. Area is measured in square units. Remind students that perimeter is the distance around a figure. The prefix *peri-* means "around" and the root word *meter* means "measure." So, when you find the perimeter of a figure, you are measuring the distance around the figure.

Laurie's Notes

Preparing to Teach

- Students should understand the concept of similar figures. Now they will extend their understanding to find perimeters and areas of similar figures.
- **MP8 Look for and Express Regularity in Repeated Reasoning:** Students will investigate how perimeters and areas of similar figures are related by finding a pattern.

Motivate

- **Story Time:** Tell students that your neighbor's lawn is twice the size of your lawn. In other words, it is twice as long and twice as wide. If it takes you one-half hour to mow your lawn, about how long does it take your neighbor to mow his lawn? Have students write their answers in their notes. Students will revisit these answers in the Closure.

Exploration 1

- Review the meanings of perimeter and area.
- To complete this exploration, students can use geometry software available at *BigIdeasMath.com*.
- Alternatively, students could use 2 × 1 pattern blocks to build the rectangles instead of drawing in a coordinate plane. For example, if the scale factor is 2, students could use four 2 × 1 pattern blocks.
- Students can continue to add blocks for each scale factor. Make sure they add blocks in both directions.
- **Common Error:** Students may construct ▯ for a scale factor of 3 instead of ▯.
- As students complete the table for perimeter, they should begin to recognize a pattern. Students may simply say that the perimeter increases by 6 each time. Make sure they relate the pattern to the perimeter of the original figure and the scale factor.
- Select several students to share their responses to part (b). Encourage students to use *Accountable Language Stems* to discuss any discrepancies. See page T-84 for a description of *Accountable Language Stems*.
- **MP7 Look for and Make Use of Structure:** In part (c), students may struggle to find the pattern. Ask them how the area of the original figure and the scale factor can be used to find the areas of the dilated figures.
- **Teaching Tip:** It may be easier for students to recognize the pattern for area if they use 1 × 1 pattern blocks.

Exploration 1

a. See Additional Answers.

b. The value of the ratio of the perimeters is equal to the value of the ratio of the corresponding side lengths.

c–e. See Additional Answers.

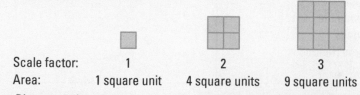

Scale factor:	1	2	3
Area:	1 square unit	4 square units	9 square units

- Discuss students' answers and reasoning for parts (d) and (e). Use *Accountable Language Stems* to encourage students to explain their answers.

2.7 Perimeters and Areas of Similar Figures

Learning Target: Find perimeters and areas of similar figures.

Success Criteria:
- I can use corresponding side lengths to compare perimeters of similar figures.
- I can use corresponding side lengths to compare areas of similar figures.
- I can use similar figures to solve real-life problems involving perimeter and area.

EXPLORATION 1

Comparing Similar Figures

MP CHOOSE TOOLS Work with a partner. Draw a rectangle in the coordinate plane.

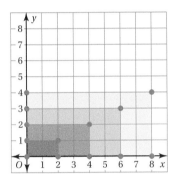

a. Dilate your rectangle using each indicated scale factor k. Then complete the table for the perimeter P of each rectangle. Describe the pattern.

Original Side Lengths	$k = 2$	$k = 3$	$k = 4$	$k = 5$	$k = 6$
$P =$					

b. **MP REPEATED REASONING** Compare the ratios of the perimeters to the ratios of the corresponding side lengths. What do you notice?

c. Repeat part (a) to complete the table for the area A of each rectangle. Describe the pattern.

Original Side Lengths	$k = 2$	$k = 3$	$k = 4$	$k = 5$	$k = 6$
$A =$					

d. **MP REPEATED REASONING** Compare the ratios of the areas to the ratios of the corresponding side lengths. What do you notice?

e. The rectangles shown are similar. You know the perimeter and the area of the red rectangle and a pair of corresponding side lengths. How can you find the perimeter of the blue rectangle? the area of the blue rectangle?

Math Practice

Look for Patterns

How can you use the pattern in part (c) to find the area of the rectangle after a dilation using any scale factor?

🔑 Key Idea

Perimeters of Similar Figures

When two figures are similar, the value of the ratio of their perimeters is equal to the value of the ratio of their corresponding side lengths.

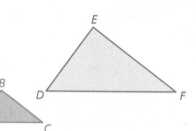

$$\frac{\text{Perimeter of } \triangle ABC}{\text{Perimeter of } \triangle DEF} = \frac{AB}{DE} = \frac{BC}{EF} = \frac{AC}{DF}$$

EXAMPLE 1 **Comparing Perimeters of Similar Figures**

Find the value of the ratio (red to blue) of the perimeters of the similar rectangles.

You can think of the red rectangle as a scale drawing of the blue rectangle, where the ratio of the side lengths is the scale, and the value of the ratio is the scale factor.

$$\frac{\text{Perimeter of red rectangle}}{\text{Perimeter of blue rectangle}} = \frac{4}{6} = \frac{2}{3}$$

▶ The value of the ratio of the perimeters is $\frac{2}{3}$.

Try It

1. The height of Figure A is 9 feet. The height of a similar Figure B is 15 feet. What is the value of the ratio of the perimeter of A to the perimeter of B?

🔑 Key Idea

Areas of Similar Figures

When two figures are similar, the value of the ratio of their areas is equal to the *square* of the value of the ratio of their corresponding side lengths.

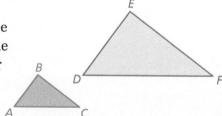

$$\frac{\text{Area of } \triangle ABC}{\text{Area of } \triangle DEF} = \left(\frac{AB}{DE}\right)^2 = \left(\frac{BC}{EF}\right)^2 = \left(\frac{AC}{DF}\right)^2$$

Laurie's Notes

Scaffolding Instruction

- In the exploration, students used patterns to investigate how changes in dimensions of similar figures affect the perimeter and area. They will now use these relationships to solve problems.
- **Emerging:** Students may struggle to extend the patterns beyond the figures in the exploration. They will benefit from guided instruction.
- **Proficient:** Students recognize the patterns and can extend them. They should review the Key Ideas before proceeding to Example 2 and the Self-Assessment exercises.

Key Idea

- ? "How do you identify similar triangles?" Corresponding side lengths are proportional and corresponding angles are congruent.
- Write some side lengths on the two triangles, such as 3-4-5 and 6-8-10.
- "Find the two perimeters and show that they have the same ratio as the corresponding sides." 12 units and 24 units; 12 : 24 → 1 : 2.

EXAMPLE 1

- ? "What is the ratio of the corresponding sides?" 4 : 6 or 2 : 3 The ratio of the perimeters is also 2 : 3.
- ? **MP1 Make Sense of Problems and Persevere in Solving Them:** "Why do you not need to know both dimensions of one of the rectangles to find the ratio of the perimeters?" The rectangles are similar, so only one pair of corresponding sides is necessary.

Try It

- Select several students to explain their reasoning.

ELL Support

After demonstrating Example 1, have students work in pairs to discuss and complete Try It Exercise 1. Provide guiding questions: What is the relationship between the heights of similar figures and their perimeters? Can you simplify your answer? Expect students to perform according to their language levels.

Beginner: Write out the process.

Intermediate: Discuss the process using simple sentences.

Advanced: Use detailed sentences and help guide discussion.

Key Idea

- **Representation:** Draw two triangles whose corresponding sides appear to have a ratio of 1 : 2.

- ? "If the corresponding sides have a ratio of 1 : 2, then what will the ratio of the areas be?" 1 : 4 You can use pattern blocks to show this relationship.
- **MP2 Reason Abstractly and Quantitatively:** There are 4 copies of the smaller triangle inside the larger triangle. In other words, the larger triangle has an area 4 times greater than the area of the smaller triangle.

Extra Example 1

Find the value of the ratio (red to blue) of the perimeters of the similar trapezoids.

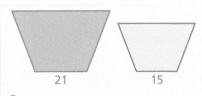

21   15

$\frac{7}{5}$

Try It

1. $\frac{3}{5}$

Extra Example 2

Find the value of the ratio (red to blue) of the areas of the similar parallelograms.

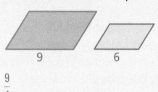

9   6

$\dfrac{9}{4}$

Try It

2. $\dfrac{64}{49}$

Self-Assessment
for Concepts & Skills

3. $\dfrac{9}{7}$

4. $\dfrac{4}{5}$

5. $\dfrac{9}{4}$

6. $\dfrac{16}{225}$

EXAMPLE 2

- As with Example 1, only one pair of corresponding sides is given. The actual areas cannot be computed. Students must use the relationship stated in the Key Idea.
- Remind students that $\left(\dfrac{3}{5}\right)^2$ means $\left(\dfrac{3}{5}\right)\left(\dfrac{3}{5}\right) = \dfrac{9}{25}$.

Try It

- Have students work in pairs.

✔ Self-Assessment for Concepts & Skills

- **Neighbor Check:** Have students work independently and then have their neighbors check their work. Have students discuss any discrepancies.
- ◉ **Thumbs Up:** Ask students to indicate their understanding of finding perimeters and areas of similar figures. Then ask several students that indicate "I get it" to explain their understanding.

ELL Support

Allow students to work in pairs for extra support and to practice language. Then have each pair display their answers on a whiteboard for your review.

The Success Criteria Self-Assessment chart can be found in the *Student Journal* or online at *BigIdeasMath.com*.

EXAMPLE 2 **Comparing Areas of Similar Figures**

Find the value of the ratio (red to blue) of the areas of the similar triangles.

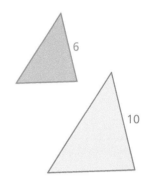

$$\frac{\text{Area of red triangle}}{\text{Area of blue triangle}} = \left(\frac{6}{10}\right)^2$$

$$= \left(\frac{3}{5}\right)^2$$

$$= \frac{9}{25}$$

▷ The value of the ratio of the areas is $\frac{9}{25}$.

Math Practice

Specify Units
Does the value of the ratio of the areas change when the side lengths are measured in inches? feet? Explain your reasoning.

Try It

2. The base of Triangle P is 8 meters. The base of a similar Triangle Q is 7 meters. What is the value of the ratio of the area of P to the area of Q?

Self-Assessment for Concepts & Skills

Solve each exercise. Then rate your understanding of the success criteria in your journal.

COMPARING PERIMETERS OF SIMILAR FIGURES Find the value of the ratio (red to blue) of the perimeters of the similar figures.

3.

4.

COMPARING AREAS OF SIMILAR FIGURES Find the value of the ratio (red to blue) of the areas of the similar figures.

5.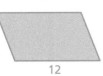

6.

EXAMPLE 3 **Modeling Real Life**

A swimming pool is similar in shape to a volleyball court. Find the perimeter P and the area A of the pool.

The rectangular pool and the court are similar. So, use the ratio of corresponding side lengths to write and solve proportions to find the perimeter and the area of the pool.

18 yd

10 yd

Area = 200 yd²
Perimeter = 60 yd

Perimeter

$$\frac{\text{Perimeter of court}}{\text{Perimeter of pool}} = \frac{\text{Width of court}}{\text{Width of pool}}$$

$$\frac{60}{P} = \frac{10}{18}$$

$$1080 = 10P$$

$$108 = P$$

Area

$$\frac{\text{Area of court}}{\text{Area of pool}} = \left(\frac{\text{Width of court}}{\text{Width of pool}}\right)^2$$

$$\frac{200}{A} = \left(\frac{10}{18}\right)^2$$

$$\frac{200}{A} = \frac{100}{324}$$

$$64{,}800 = 100A$$

$$648 = A$$

▷ So, the perimeter of the pool is 108 yards, and the area is 648 square yards.

Self-Assessment for Problem Solving

Solve each exercise. Then rate your understanding of the success criteria in your journal.

7. Two similar triangular regions are prepared for development.

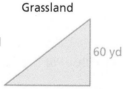

Grassland Perimeter = 240 yd
Grassland Area = 2400 yd²

Grassland   60 yd

Forest   45 yd

   a. It costs $6 per foot to install fencing. How much does it cost to surround the forest with a fence?

   b. The cost to prepare 1 square yard of grassland is $15 and the cost to prepare 1 square yard of forest is $25. Which region costs more to prepare? Justify your answer.

8. **DIG DEEPER!** You buy a new television with a screen similar in shape to your old television screen, but with an area four times greater. The size of a television screen is often described using the distance between opposite corners of the screen. Your old television has a 30-inch screen. What is the size of your new television screen? Explain.

Laurie's Notes

EXAMPLE 3

- Ask a volunteer to read the problem.
- ❓ "What information do you know?" one side length in each object, the area and perimeter of the volleyball court, and the objects are similar
- ❓ "Are the sides whose lengths are given corresponding sides?" yes
- **MP1 Make Sense of Problems and Persevere in Solving Them:** Give students time to think about solution strategies. There are many different strategies, and it is important for students to come up with an entry point that makes sense to them.
- One strategy, which makes use of the Key Ideas, is given in the solution.
- Another strategy is to find the length ℓ of the volleyball court by solving $2(10) + 2\ell = 60$ for ℓ and then set up a proportion to find the length of the pool. From there, you can find the area and perimeter of the pool.
- Discuss any other strategies that students might suggest. Ask students which strategy they prefer.
- **MP6 Attend to Precision:** Make sure students include the correct units in their answers.

✔ Self-Assessment for Problem Solving

- Students may benefit from trying the exercises independently and then working with peers to refine their work. It is important to provide time in class for problem solving, so that students become comfortable with the problem-solving plan.
- **Think-Pair-Share:** Allow time for students to work independently, using the problem-solving plan. Then have each student compare strategies with a partner. Have each pair compare their answers with another pair and discuss any discrepancies

The Success Criteria Self-Assessment chart can be found in the *Student Journal* or online at *BigIdeasMath.com*.

Closure

- Return to the question in the Motivate. Your neighbor's lawn is twice the size of your lawn, meaning twice as long and twice as wide. You both mow your lawns at the same rate. If it takes you one-half hour to mow your lawn, about how long does it take your neighbor to mow his lawn? Explain your reasoning.
  2 hours; Because the dimensions of your neighbor's lawn are double the dimensions of your lawn, the ratio of the width of your neighbor's lawn to the width of your lawn is 2 : 1. The area of your neighbor's lawn is $\left(\frac{2}{1}\right)^2 = \frac{4}{1}$ times the area of your lawn, so it should take your neighbor 4 times longer to mow his lawn, or $4\left(\frac{1}{2}\right) = 2$ hours.
- ❓ **Discuss:** "How does this answer compare to your original answer?" Answers will vary.

Extra Example 3
In Example 3, the width of the pool is 22 yards. Find the perimeter P and the area A of the pool. 132 yd; 968 yd^2

Self-Assessment
for Problem Solving

7. **a.** $3240

   b. grassland;
   $$\frac{2400}{A} = \left(\frac{60}{45}\right)^2$$
   $$1350 = A$$
   Forest:
   $$1350 \text{ yd}^2 \cdot \frac{\$25}{1 \text{ yd}^2} = \$33{,}750$$
   Grassland:
   $$2400 \text{ yd}^2 \cdot \frac{\$15}{1 \text{ yd}^2} = \$36{,}000$$

8. 60 in.; The value of the ratio of the areas is $4 = (2)^2$. So, the value of the ratio of screen sizes is 2.

Learning Target

Find perimeters and areas of similar figures.

Success Criteria

- Use corresponding side lengths to compare perimeters of similar figures.
- Use corresponding side lengths to compare areas of similar figures.
- Use similar figures to solve real-life problems involving perimeter and area.

▶ Review & Refresh

1. *Sample answer:* Dilate the red figure using a scale factor of 3 and then reflect the image in the *y*-axis.

2. *Sample answer:* Dilate the red figure using a scale factor of $\frac{1}{2}$ and then rotate the image 90° clockwise about the origin.

3. 144 cm^2

4. 7.5 in.^{2}

5. 35 km^2

▶ Concepts, Skills, & Problem Solving

6. 3; 9

7. $\frac{1}{2}, \frac{1}{4}$

8. $\frac{11}{6}, \frac{121}{36}$

9. $\frac{5}{8}, \frac{25}{64}$

10. $\frac{4}{7}, \frac{16}{49}$

11. $\frac{14}{9}, \frac{196}{81}$

Assignment Guide and Concept Check

Scaffold assignments to support all students in their learning progression. The suggested assignments are a starting point. Continue to assign additional exercises and revisit with spaced practice to move every student toward proficiency.

Level	Assignment 1	Assignment 2
Emerging	2, 3, 4, 5, 6, 7, 8, 9, 10, 11	12, 13, 14, 15, 16, 20
Proficient	2, 3, 4, 5, 6, 7, 8, 9, 10, 11	12, 13, 14, 15, 16, 17, 18, 20
Advanced	2, 3, 4, 5, 6, 7, 8, 9, 10, 11	13, 14, 15, 17, 18, 19, 20, 21

- Assignment 1 is for use after students complete the Self-Assessment for Concepts & Skills.
- Assignment 2 is for use after students complete the Self-Assessment for Problem Solving.
- The red exercises can be used as a concept check.

Review & Refresh Prior Skills

Exercises 1 and 2 Describing a Similarity Transformation
Exercise 3 Finding the Area of a Parallelogram
Exercise 4 Finding the Area of a Triangle
Exercise 5 Finding the Area of a Trapezoid

Common Errors

- **Exercises 8–11** Students may find the reciprocals of the values of the ratios. For example, they may find the value of the ratio of blue to red instead of red to blue. Remind students to read the directions carefully.
- **Exercises 8–11** When finding the value of the ratio of the areas, students may forget to square the value of the ratio of the corresponding side lengths. Remind them that the value of the ratio of the areas is equal to the *square* of the value of the ratio of the corresponding side lengths.

Go to *BigIdeasMath.com* to get HELP with solving the exercises.

▶ Review & Refresh

The red figure is similar to the blue figure. Describe a similarity transformation between the figures.

1.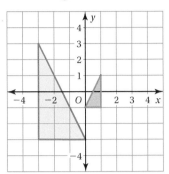

2.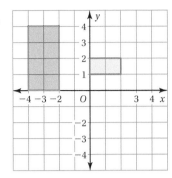

Find the area of the figure.

3.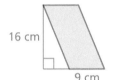

4.

5.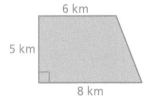

▶▶ Concepts, Skills, & Problem Solving

COMPARING SIMILAR FIGURES Dilate the figure using the indicated scale factor k. What is the value of the ratio (new to original) of the perimeters? the areas? (See Exploration 1, p. 83.)

6. a triangle with vertices $(0, 0)$, $(0, 2)$, and $(2, 0)$; $k = 3$

7. a square with vertices $(0, 0)$, $(0, 4)$, $(4, 4)$, and $(4, 0)$; $k = 0.5$

PERIMETERS AND AREAS OF SIMILAR FIGURES Find the values of the ratios (red to blue) of the perimeters and areas of the similar figures.

8.

9.

10.

11.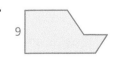

USING SIMILAR FIGURES **The figures are similar. Find *x*.**

12. The ratio of the perimeters is 7 : 10.

13. The ratio of the perimeters is 8 : 5.

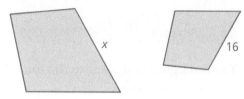

14. **COMPARING AREAS** The playing surfaces of two foosball tables are similar. The ratio of the corresponding side lengths is 10 : 7. What is the ratio of the areas?

15. **CRITICAL THINKING** The ratio of the side length of Square A to the side length of Square B is 4 : 9. The side length of Square A is 12 yards. What is the perimeter of Square B?

16. **MP** **MODELING REAL LIFE** The cost of the piece of fabric shown is $1.31. What would you expect to pay for a similar piece of fabric that is 18 inches by 42 inches?

17. **MP** **PROBLEM SOLVING** A scale model of a merry-go-round and the actual merry-go-round are similar.

a. How many times greater is the base area of the actual merry-go-round than the base area of the scale model? Explain.

b. What is the base area of the actual merry-go-round in square feet?

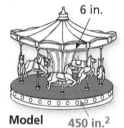

Model 450 in.²

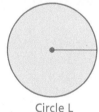

18. **MP** **STRUCTURE** The circumference of Circle K is π. The circumference of Circle L is 4π. What is the value of the ratio of their circumferences? of their radii? of their areas?

19. **GEOMETRY** A triangle with an area of 10 square meters has a base of 4 meters. A similar triangle has an area of 90 square meters. What is the height of the larger triangle?

20. **MP** **PROBLEM SOLVING** You need two bottles of fertilizer to treat the flower garden shown. How many bottles do you need to treat a similar garden with a perimeter of 105 feet?

21. **MP** **REPEATED REASONING** Three square mirrors are used for a light reflection experiment. The ratio of the side length of Mirror A to the side length of Mirror B is 5 : 6. The ratio of the area of Mirror B to the area of Mirror C is 16 : 25. The perimeter of Mirror C is 280 centimeters. What is the area of Mirror A? Justify your answer.

Mini-Assessment

Find the values of the ratios (red to blue) of the perimeters and areas of the similar figures.

1.

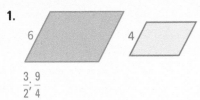

$\frac{3}{2}; \frac{9}{4}$

2.

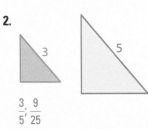

$\frac{3}{5}; \frac{9}{25}$

3. The ratio of the corresponding side lengths of two similar cell phones is 3 : 4. The perimeter of the smaller phone is 9 inches. What is the perimeter of the larger phone? 12 in.

Section Resources

Surface Level	Deep Level
Resources by Chapter • Extra Practice • Reteach • Puzzle Time Student Journal • Self-Assessment • Practice Differentiating the Lesson Tutorial Videos Skills Review Handbook Skills Trainer	Resources by Chapter • Enrichment and Extension Graphic Organizers Dynamic Assessment System • Section Practice
Transfer Level	
Dynamic Assessment System • End-of-Chapter Quiz	Assessment Book • End-of-Chapter Quiz

Concepts, Skills, & Problem Solving

12. 8.4

13. 25.6

14. 100 : 49

15. 108 yd

16. $5.24

17. a. 400 times greater; The value of the ratio of the corresponding lengths is $\frac{120 \text{ in.}}{6 \text{ in.}} = \frac{20}{1}$.
So, the value of the ratio of the areas is $\left(\frac{20}{1}\right)^2 = \frac{400}{1}$.

    b. 1250 ft^2

18. $\frac{1}{4}; \frac{1}{4}; \frac{1}{16}$

19. 15 m

20. 12.5 bottles

21. $2177.\overline{7}$ cm^2; *Sample answer:* The side length of Mirror C is $280 \div 4 = 70$ cm. So, the area of Mirror C is 4900 cm^2.

$$\frac{\text{Area of Mirror B}}{4900} = \frac{16}{25}$$

Area of Mirror B = 3136 cm^2

$$\frac{\text{Area of Mirror A}}{3136} = \left(\frac{5}{6}\right)^2$$

Area of Mirror A = $2177.\overline{7}$ cm^2

Skills Needed

Exercise 1

- Comparing Areas of Similar Figures
- Solving a Proportion
- Using a Scale

Exercise 2

- Describing a Translation
- Finding a Percent of Change
- Solving an Equation

Exercise 3

- Comparing Similar Figures
- Finding a Circumference

ELL Support

In Exercise 2, clarify that the use of the word *plane* refers to the coordinate plane, *not* a mode of transportation. Because the problem refers to a ship, students may see the word *plane* and think of an airplane.

Using the Problem-Solving Plan

1. 2500 ft^2

2. $(x, y) \rightarrow (x + 16, y + 24)$;
   Ship A: $A'(36, 54)$,
   Ship B: $B'(56, 64)$,
   Ship C: $C'(66, 54)$

3. 5.5; For the dilated circle,
   $C = 22\pi$ inches,
   so $r = 11$ inches.

   $\dfrac{\text{Radius of dilated circle}}{\text{Radius of original circle}} = \dfrac{11}{2} = 5.5$

Performance Task

The *STEAM Video Performance Task* provides the opportunity for additional enrichment and greater depth of knowledge as students explore the mathematics of the chapter within a context tied to the chapter STEAM Video. The performance task and a detailed scoring rubric are provided at *BigIdeasMath.com*.

Laurie's Notes

Scaffolding Instruction

- The goal of this lesson is to help students become more comfortable with problem solving. These exercises combine transformations with prior skills from other courses. The solution for Exercise 1 is worked out below, to help you guide students through the problem-solving plan. Use the remaining class time to have students work on the other exercises.
- **Emerging:** The goal for these students is to feel comfortable with the problem-solving plan. Allow students to work in pairs to write the beginning steps of the problem-solving plan for Exercise 2. Keep in mind that some students may only be ready to do the first step.
- **Proficient:** Students may be able to work independently or in pairs to complete Exercises 2 and 3.
- Visit each pair to review their plan for each problem. Ask students to describe their plans.

▶ *Using the Problem-Solving Plan*

Exercise 1

⟹ **Understand the problem.** You know the scale of the drawing and the area of the helipad in the drawing. You are asked to find the area of the actual helipad.

⟹ **Make a plan.** A scale drawing is similar to the actual object. So, use the scale 1 ft : 20 ft and the ratio $6.25 \text{ ft}^2 : A \text{ ft}^2$ to write and solve a proportion that represents the area A of the actual helipad.

⟹ **Solve and check.** Use the plan to solve the problem. Then check your solution.

- Write and solve a proportion that represents the area A of the actual helipad.

$$\left(\frac{\text{Distance in drawing}}{\text{Actual distance}}\right)^2 = \frac{\text{Area in drawing}}{\text{Actual area}}$$

$$\left(\frac{1}{20}\right)^2 = \frac{6.25}{A}$$

$$\frac{1}{400} = \frac{6.25}{A}$$

$$A = 2500$$

So, the area of the actual helipad is 2500 square feet.

- **Check:** Verify that the value of the ratio of the areas is equal to the square of the value of the ratio of the distances.

$$\frac{\text{Area in drawing}}{\text{Actual area}} = \frac{6.25}{2500} = 0.0025$$

$$\left(\frac{\text{Distance in drawing}}{\text{Actual distance}}\right)^2 = \frac{1}{400} = 0.0025 \checkmark$$

Connecting Concepts

Using the Problem-Solving Plan

1. A scale drawing of a helipad uses a scale of 1 ft : 20 ft. The scale drawing has an area of 6.25 square feet. What is the area of the actual helipad?

 Understand the problem.

You know the scale of the drawing and the area of the helipad in the drawing. You are asked to find the area of the actual helipad.

Make a plan.

A scale drawing is similar to the actual object. So, use the scale 1 ft : 20 ft and the ratio 6.25 ft^2 : A ft^2 to write and solve a proportion that represents the area A of the actual helipad.

Solve and check.

Use the plan to solve the problem. Then check your solution.

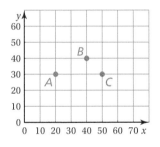

2. The locations of three cargo ships are shown in the coordinate plane. Each ship travels at the same speed in the same direction. After 1 hour, the x- and y-coordinates of Ship A increase 80%. Use a translation to describe the change in the locations of the ships. Then find the new coordinates of each ship.

3. All circles are similar. A circle with a radius of 2 inches is dilated, resulting in a circle with a circumference of 22π inches. What is the scale factor? Justify your answer.

Performance Task

Master Puppeteer

At the beginning of this chapter, you watched a STEAM Video called "Shadow Puppets." You are now ready to complete the performance task related to this video, available at *BigIdeasMath.com*. Be sure to use the problem-solving plan as you work through the performance task.

? Go to *BigIdeasMath.com* to download blank graphic organizers.

▶ Review Vocabulary

Write the definition and give an example of each vocabulary term.

transformation, *p. 44*
image, *p. 44*
translation, *p. 44*
reflection, *p. 50*
line of reflection, *p. 50*
rotation, *p. 56*

center of rotation, *p. 56*
angle of rotation, *p. 56*
rigid motion, *p. 64*
congruent figures, *p. 64*
congruent angles, *p. 64*
congruent sides, *p. 64*

dilation, *p. 70*
center of dilation, *p. 70*
scale factor, *p. 70*
similarity transformation, *p. 78*
similar figures, *p. 78*

▶ Graphic Organizers

You can use a **Summary Triangle** to explain a concept. Here is an example of a Summary Triangle for *translating a figure*.

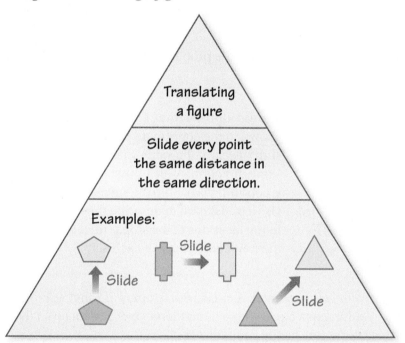

Choose and complete a graphic organizer to help you study the concept.

1. reflecting a figure
2. rotating a figure
3. congruent figures
4. dilating a figure
5. similar figures
6. perimeters of similar figures
7. areas of similar figures

"I hope my owner sees my Summary Triangle.
I just can't seem to learn 'roll over.'"

Review Vocabulary

- As a review of the chapter vocabulary, have students revisit the vocabulary section in their *Student Journals* to fill in any missing definitions and record examples of each term.

Graphic Organizers

Sample answers:

1.

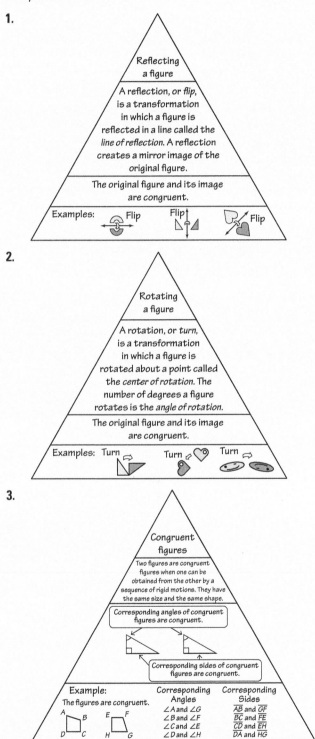

4–7. Answers at *BigIdeasMath.com*.

List of Organizers

Available at *BigIdeasMath.com*
Definition and Example Chart
Example and Non-Example Chart
Four Square
Information Frame
Summary Triangle

About this Organizer

A **Summary Triangle** can be used to explain a concept. Typically, the Summary Triangle is divided into 3 or 4 parts. Students write related categories in the middle part(s). Related categories may include: procedure, explanation, description, definition, theorem, or formula. In the bottom part, students write an example to illustrate the concept. A Summary Triangle can be used as an assessment tool, in which students complete the missing parts. Students may also place their Summary Triangles on note cards to use as a quick study reference.

1. no

2. yes

3.

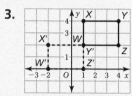

4.

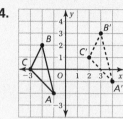

5. 3 lockers right and 1 locker down

6. $A'(-1, 4)$, $B'(2, 2)$, $C'(0, 0)$

7. 6 units right and 4 units down

✓ Chapter Self-Assessment

The Success Criteria Self-Assessment chart can be found in the *Student Journal* or online at *BigIdeasMath.com*.

ELL Support

Allow students to work in pairs to complete the first section of the Chapter Self-Assessment. Once pairs have finished, check for understanding by asking for and reviewing answers. For Exercises 1 and 2, have students use a thumbs up to answer *yes* and a thumbs down to answer *no*. Provide graph paper for Exercises 3 and 4. Ask students to hold up their drawings for your review. For Exercise 6, have each pair display their coordinates on a whiteboard for your review. Have two pairs discuss their descriptions for Exercises 5 and 7 and reach an agreement on the answers. Monitor discussions and provide support. Use similar techniques to check the remaining sections of the Chapter Self-Assessment.

Common Errors

- **Exercise 1** Students may forget that the objects must be the same size to be a translation. Remind them that the size stays the same. Tell students that when the size is different, it is a scale drawing.
- **Exercises 3, 4, and 6** Students may translate the figure in the wrong direction or mix up the units for the translation. Tell students to draw the original figure on graph paper. Also, tell students to write the direction of the translation using arrows to show the movement left, right, up, or down.

Chapter Self-Assessment

As you complete the exercises, use the scale below to rate your understanding of the success criteria in your journal.

1	2	3	4
I do not understand.	I can do it with help.	I can do it on my own.	I can teach someone else.

2.1 Translations (pp. 43–48)

Learning Target: Translate figures in the coordinate plane.

Tell whether the blue figure is a translation of the red figure.

1.

2.

3. The vertices of a quadrilateral are $W(1, 2)$, $X(1, 4)$, $Y(4, 4)$, and $Z(4, 2)$. Draw the figure and its image after a translation 3 units left and 2 units down.

4. The vertices of a triangle are $A(-1, -2)$, $B(-2, 2)$, and $C(-3, 0)$. Draw the figure and its image after a translation 5 units right and 1 unit up.

5. Your locker number is 20 and your friend's locker number is 33. Describe the location of your friend's locker relative to the location of your locker.

6. Translate the triangle 4 units left and 1 unit down. What are the coordinates of the image?

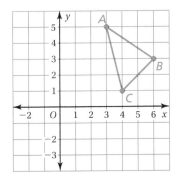

7. Describe a translation of the airplane from point A to point B.

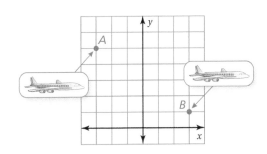

2.2 Reflections *(pp. 49–54)*

Learning Target: Reflect figures in the coordinate plane.

Tell whether the blue figure is a reflection of the red figure.

8. 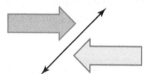 **9.** 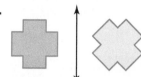 **10.**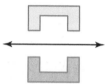

Draw the figure and its reflection in (a) the *x*-axis and (b) the *y*-axis. Identify the coordinates of the image.

11. $A(2, 0), B(1, 5), C(4, 3)$

12. $D(-5, -5), E(-5, 0), F(-2, -2), G(-2, -5)$

13. The vertices of a rectangle are $E(-1, 1), F(-1, 3), G(-5, 3),$ and $H(-5, 1)$. Find the coordinates of the figure after reflecting in the *x*-axis, and then translating 3 units right.

The coordinates of a point and its image after a reflection are given. Identify the line of reflection.

14. $(-1, -3) \longrightarrow (1, -3)$

15. $(2, 1) \longrightarrow (2, -1)$

16. You perform an experiment involving angles of refraction with a laser pen. You point a laser pen from point *L* at a mirror along the red path and the image is a reflection in the *y*-axis.

   a. Does the light reach a cat at point *C*? Explain.

   b. You bounce the light off the top mirror so its path is a reflection. What line of reflection is needed for the light to reach the cat?

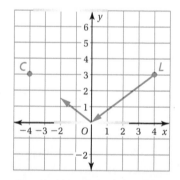

2.3 Rotations *(pp. 55–62)*

Learning Target: Rotate figures in the coordinate plane.

Tell whether the blue figure is a rotation of the red figure about the origin. If so, give the angle and the direction of rotation.

17. 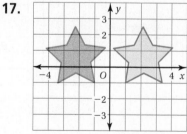 **18.**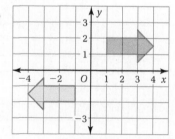

Common Errors

- **Exercises 11 and 12** Students may reflect the image obtained in part (a) to answer part (b). Point out that the directions are asking for a reflection of the *original* figure in each part of the exercise.
- **Exercises 11–13** Students may confuse reflection in the *x*-axis with reflection in the *y*-axis (and vice versa). Have students label the axes in their drawings so it is clearer which way to reflect.
- **Exercises 17 and 18** Students with minimal spatial skills may not be able to tell whether a figure is rotated. Give them transparent paper and have them copy the red figure and rotate it.

8. no

9. no

10. yes

11. a.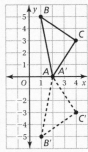

   $A'(2, 0), B'(1, -5), C'(4, -3)$

   b.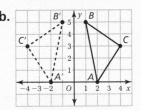

   $A'(-2, 0), B'(-1, 5),$
   $C'(-4, 3)$

12. a.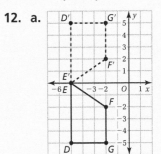

   $D'(-5, 5), E'(-5, 0),$
   $F'(-2, 2), G'(-2, 5)$

   b. See Additional Answers.

13. $E'(2, -1), F'(2, -3), G'(-2, -3),$
   $H'(-2, -1)$

14. *y*-axis

15. *x*-axis

16. a. yes; The coordinates of the image are $L'(-4, 3)$, which is point C.

   b. *y*-axis

17. no

18. yes; 180° counterclockwise or clockwise

Chapter Self-Assessment

19. $A'(4, -2)$, $B'(2, -2)$, $C'(3, -4)$

20. $A'(-2, -4)$, $B'(-2, -2)$, $C'(-4, -3)$

21. $(-4, 7)$ and $(6, -5)$

22. $\triangle ABC$ and $\triangle EDC$, $\triangle GHF$ and $\triangle JKI$

23. Square *ABCD* and Square *EFGH*, Rectangle *RSTU* and Rectangle *IJKL*

24. *Sample answer:* Rotate the blue figure 90° clockwise about the origin and then translate the image 5 units right.

25. *Sample answer:* Reflect the blue figure in the *y*-axis and then translate the image 2 units up.

26. $\angle A$ and $\angle K$, $\angle B$ and $\angle L$, $\angle C$ and $\angle M$; $\overline{AB}$ and $\overline{KL}$, $\overline{BC}$ and $\overline{LM}$, $\overline{AC}$ and $\overline{KM}$

27. **a.** 3 ft

b. $\angle T$

c. 20 ft

Common Errors

- **Exercises 19 and 20** Students with minimal spatial skills may not be able to tell how to rotate a figure. Give them transparent paper and have them copy the figure and rotate it.
- **Exercise 26** Students may forget to write the angle symbol with the name and/or the segment notation. Remind students that *A* is a point and $\angle A$ is the angle. Tell students that *AB* without the segment bar is the measure of side *AB*.
- **Exercise 27** Students may forget to include units in their answers to parts (a) and (c). Remind them that the units must be included to make their answers complete.

The vertices of a triangle are $A(-4, 2)$, $B(-2, 2)$, and $C(-3, 4)$. Rotate the triangle as described. Find the coordinates of the image.

19. 180° about the origin

20. 270° clockwise about the origin

21. A bicycle wheel is represented in a coordinate plane with the center of the wheel at the origin. Reflectors are placed on the bicycle wheel at points $(7, 4)$ and $(-5, -6)$. After a bike ride, the reflectors have rotated 90° counterclockwise about the origin. What are the locations of the reflectors at the end of the bike ride?

2.4 Congruent Figures *(pp. 63–68)*

Learning Target: Understand the concept of congruent figures.

Identify any congruent figures in the coordinate plane.

22.

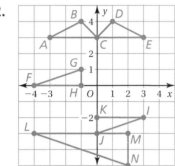

23.

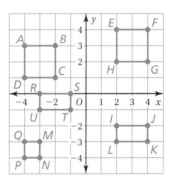

The red figure is congruent to the blue figure. Describe a sequence of rigid motions between the figures.

24.

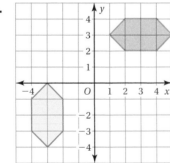

25.

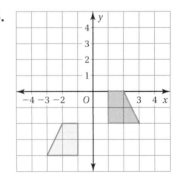

26. The figures are congruent. Name the corresponding angles and the corresponding sides.

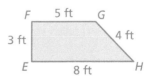

27. Trapezoids *EFGH* and *QRST* are congruent.

   a. What is the length of side *QR*?

   b. Which angle in *QRST* corresponds to ∠*H*?

   c. What is the perimeter of *QRST*?

2.5 Dilations *(pp. 69–76)*

Learning Target: Dilate figures in the coordinate plane.

Tell whether the blue figure is a dilation of the red figure.

28.

29.

The vertices of a figure are given. Draw the figure and its image after a dilation with the given scale factor. Identify the type of dilation.

30. $P(-3, -2)$, $Q(-3, 0)$, $R(0, 0)$; $k = 4$

31. $B(3, 3)$, $C(3, 6)$, $D(6, 6)$, $E(6, 3)$; $k = \dfrac{1}{3}$

32. The blue figure is a dilation of the red figure. Identify the type of dilation and find the scale factor.

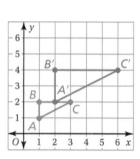

33. The vertices of a rectangle are $Q(-6, 2)$, $R(6, 2)$, $S(6, -4)$, and $T(-6, -4)$. Dilate the rectangle with respect to the origin using a scale factor of $\dfrac{3}{2}$. Then translate it 5 units right and 1 unit down. What are the coordinates of the image?

2.6 Similar Figures *(pp. 77–82)*

Learning Target: Understand the concept of similar figures.

34. Determine whether the two figures are similar. Explain your reasoning.

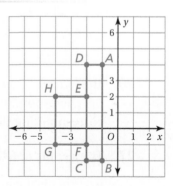

35. Draw figures with the given vertices in a coordinate plane. Which figures are similar? Explain your reasoning.

Triangle A: $(-4, 4)$, $(-2, 4)$, $(-2, 0)$

Triangle B: $(-2, 2)$, $(-1, 2)$, $(-1, 0)$

Triangle C: $(6, 6)$, $(3, 6)$, $(3, 0)$

Common Errors

- **Exercises 28 and 29** Students may think that a figure with the same shape as another is a dilation. Remind them that a transformation is a dilation when the lines connecting corresponding vertices meet at a point (except when the figures are congruent).
- **Exercises 30–33** Students may confuse the image of a dilation with the original figure when both are drawn in the same coordinate plane. Remind students to pay attention to the prime notation when determining the dilation.
- **Exercise 32** Students may indicate the wrong type of dilation and give the reciprocal of the scale factor. Remind students that you multiply each coordinate of the original figure by the scale factor to obtain the corresponding image coordinate.

28. no

29. yes

30.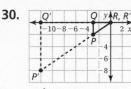

enlargement

31.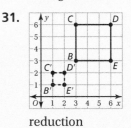

reduction

32. enlargement; 2

33. $Q''(-4, 2)$, $R''(14, 2)$, $S''(14, -7)$, $T''(-4, -7)$

34. no; There is no similarity transformation between Rectangle $ABCD$ and Rectangle $EFGH$.

35.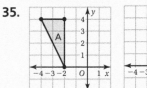

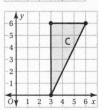

A, B, and C; *Sample answer:* Obtain B from A by dilating A using a scale factor of $\frac{1}{2}$.

Obtain C from B by dilating B using a scale factor of 3 and then reflecting the image in the y-axis.

36. 10 in.

37. 9 cm

38. $\dfrac{3}{4}$; $\dfrac{9}{16}$

39. $\dfrac{7}{4}$; $\dfrac{49}{16}$

40. 16.8

41. 7.2

42. 9 : 16

43. 36 in.^{2}

44. 300 in.^{2}

Common Errors

- **Exercises 36 and 37** Students may write the proportion incorrectly. For example, for Exercise 36 they may write $\dfrac{14}{20} = \dfrac{x}{7}$ instead of $\dfrac{14}{20} = \dfrac{7}{x}$. Remind students that the lengths of the corresponding sides should both be in the numerator or the denominator, or the side lengths of the larger shape or smaller shape should be in the numerators and the corresponding side lengths of the other shape should be in the denominators.

- **Exercises 38 and 39** Students may find the reciprocals of the values of the ratios. For example, they may find the value of the ratio of blue to red instead of red to blue. Remind students to read the directions carefully.

- **Exercises 38, 39, and 42** When finding the value of the ratio of the areas, students may forget to square the value of the ratio of the corresponding side lengths. Remind them that the value of the ratio of the areas is equal to the *square* of the value of the ratio of the corresponding side lengths.

Chapter Resources

Surface Level	Deep Level
Resources by Chapter • Extra Practice • Reteach • Puzzle Time Student Journal • Practice • Chapter Self-Assessment Differentiating the Lesson Tutorial Videos Skills Review Handbook Skills Trainer Game Library	Resources by Chapter • Enrichment and Extension Graphic Organizers Game Library
Transfer Level	
STEAM Video Dynamic Assessment System • Chapter Test	Assessment Book • Chapter Tests A and B • Alternative Assessment • STEAM Performance Task

The figures are similar. Find x.

36.

37.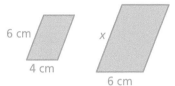

2.7 Perimeters and Areas of Similar Figures (pp. 83–88)

Learning Target: Find perimeters and areas of similar figures.

Find the values of the ratios (red to blue) of the perimeters and areas of the similar figures.

38.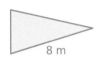

39.

The figures are similar. Find x.

40. The ratio of the perimeters is 5 : 7.

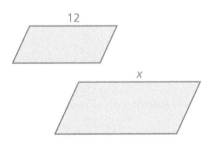

41. The ratio of the perimeters is 6 : 5.

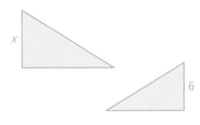

42. Two photos are similar. The ratio of the corresponding side lengths is 3 : 4. What is the ratio of the areas?

43. The ratio of side lengths of Square A to Square B is 2 : 3. The perimeter of Square A is 16 inches. What is the area of Square B?

44. The TV screen is similar to the computer screen. What is the area of the TV screen?

12 in.

Area = 108 in.²

20 in.

Triangles *ABC* and *DEF* are congruent.

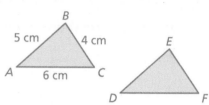

1. Which angle of *DEF* corresponds to $\angle C$?

2. What is the perimeter of *DEF*?

Tell whether the blue figure is a *translation*, *reflection*, *rotation*, or *dilation* of the red figure.

3.

4.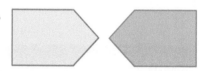

5.

6.

The vertices of a triangle are $A(2, 5)$, $B(1, 2)$, and $C(3, 1)$. Find the coordinates of the image after the transformations given.

7. Reflect in the *y*-axis.

8. Rotate 90° clockwise about the origin.

9. Reflect in the *x*-axis, and then rotate 90° counterclockwise about the origin.

10. Dilate with respect to the origin using a scale factor of 2. Then translate 2 units left and 1 unit up.

11. In a coordinate plane, draw Rectangle A: $(-4, 4)$, $(0, 4)$, $(0, 2)$, $(-4, 2)$; Rectangle B: $(-2, 2)$, $(0, 2)$, $(0, 1)$, $(-2, 1)$; and Rectangle C: $(-6, 6)$, $(0, 6)$, $(0, 3)$, $(-6, 3)$. Which figures are similar? Explain your reasoning.

12. Translate a point (x, y) 3 units left and 5 units up. Then translate the image 5 units right and 2 units up. What are the coordinates of the point after the translations?

13. The two figures are similar. (a) Find the value of *x*. (b) Find the values of the ratios (red to blue) of the perimeters and of the areas.

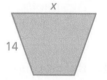

14. A wide-screen television measures 36 inches by 54 inches. A movie theater screen measures 42 feet by 63 feet. Are the screens similar? Explain.

15. You want to use the rectangular piece of fabric shown to make a pair of curtains for your window. Name the types of congruent shapes you can make with one straight cut. Draw an example of each type.

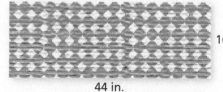

16 in.

44 in.

Practice Test Item References

Practice Test Questions	Section to Review
5, 12	2.1
4, 7	2.2
6, 8, 9	2.3
1, 2, 15	2.4
3, 10	2.5
11, 14	2.6
13	2.7

Test-Taking Strategies

Remind students to quickly look over the entire test before they start so that they can budget their time. On this test, it is very important for students to **Stop** and **Think**. When students hurry on a test involving transformations, they may end up with incorrect coordinates of transformed figures. Encourage students to work carefully and deliberately.

 **Common Errors**

- **Exercises 3–6** Students may confuse the terms *translation*, *reflection*, *rotation*, and *dilation*. Review these terms prior to the test.
- **Exercise 7** Students may reflect the triangle in the incorrect axis. Remind students that when they reflect a point in the *y*-axis, the point and its image have the same *y*-coordinates, and the *x*-coordinates are opposites.
- **Exercises 8 and 9** Students may rotate the triangle in the wrong direction. Remind them what clockwise and counterclockwise mean. It may be helpful for students to graph the figure and draw an arrow on the graph in the direction of the rotation.
- **Exercise 9** Students may reflect the triangle in the incorrect axis. Remind students that when they reflect a point in the *x*-axis, the point and its image have the same *x*-coordinates, and the *y*-coordinates are opposites.
- **Exercise 12** Students may translate the figure in the wrong direction or mix up the units for the translation. Tell students to draw the original figure on graph paper. Also, tell students to write the direction of the translation using arrows to show the movement left, right, up, or down.
- **Exercise 13** In part (b), students may find the reciprocals of the ratios. For example, they may find the ratio of blue to red instead of red to blue. Remind students to read the directions carefully.
- **Exercise 13** When finding the ratio of the areas in part (b), students may forget to square the ratio of the corresponding side lengths. Remind them that the ratio of the areas is equal to the *square* of the ratio of the corresponding side lengths.

1. $\angle F$

2. 15 cm

3. dilation

4. reflection

5. translation

6. rotation

7. $A'(-2, 5)$, $B'(-1, 2)$, $C'(-3, 1)$

8. $A'(5, -2)$, $B'(2, -1)$, $C'(1, -3)$

9. $A''(5, 2)$, $B''(2, 1)$, $C''(1, 3)$

10. $A''(2, 11)$, $B''(0, 5)$, $C''(4, 3)$

11. See Additional Answers for graphs.

    A, B, and C; *Sample answer:* Obtain B from A by dilating A using a scale factor of $\frac{1}{2}$. Obtain C from B by dilating B using a scale factor of 3.

12. $(x + 2, y + 7)$

13. **a.** 17.5   **b.** $\frac{7}{4}$; $\frac{49}{16}$

14. yes; Because both screens are rectangles, the corresponding angle measures are congruent. Corresponding side lengths are proportional.

15. 2 rectangles

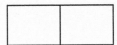

2 right triangles

2 right trapezoids

T-96

After Answering Easy Questions, Relax
Answer Easy Questions First
Estimate the Answer
Read All Choices before Answering
Read Question before Answering
Solve Directly or Eliminate Choices
Solve Problem before Looking at Choices
Use Intelligent Guessing
Work Backwards

About this Strategy

When taking a timed test, it is often best to skim the test and answer the easy questions first. Read each question carefully and thoroughly. Be careful that you record your answer in the correct position on the answer sheet.

Cumulative Practice

1. 270
2. D
3. I
4. C
5. G

Item Analysis

1. **Gridded Response:** Correct answer: 270

   Common error: The student confuses a rotation of 90° with a rotation of 180° and thinks that a 90° clockwise rotation has the same result as a 90° counterclockwise rotation, getting an answer of 90.

2. **A.** The student makes an operation error.

   B. The student makes an operation error.

   C. The student makes an operation error.

   D. Correct answer

3. **F.** The student does not apply inverse operations in the correct order.

   G. The student adds 3 to each side instead of dividing each side by -3.

   H. The student multiplies each side by -3 instead of dividing each side by -3.

   I. Correct answer

4. **A.** The student multiplies 12 by $\frac{3}{4}$ instead of $\frac{4}{3}$.

   B. The student subtracts $\frac{3}{4}$ from 12 instead of multiplying 12 by $\frac{4}{3}$.

   C. Correct answer

   D. The student multiplies 12 by 4 instead of $\frac{4}{3}$.

5. **F.** The student only translates the triangle 3 units right.

   G. Correct answer

   H. The student only translates the triangle 2 units down.

   I. The student translates the triangle 2 units right and 3 units down.

Cumulative Practice

1. A clockwise rotation of 90° is equivalent to a counterclockwise rotation of how many degrees?

2. The formula $K = C + 273.15$ converts temperatures from degrees Celsius C to Kelvin K. Which of the following formulas is *not* correct?

   A. $K - C = 273.15$

   B. $C = K - 273.15$

   C. $C - K = -273.15$

   D. $C = K + 273.15$

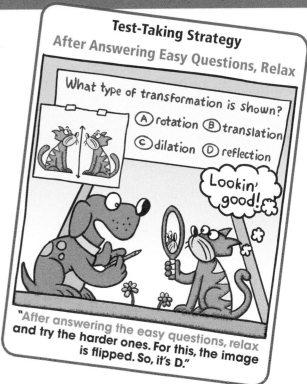

Test-Taking Strategy
After Answering Easy Questions, Relax

What type of transformation is shown?
Ⓐ rotation Ⓑ translation
Ⓒ dilation Ⓓ reflection

Lookin' good!

"After answering the easy questions, relax and try the harder ones. For this, the image is flipped. So, it's D."

3. You want to solve the equation $-3(x + 2) = 12x$. What should you do first?

   F. Subtract 2 from each side.

   G. Add 3 to each side.

   H. Multiply each side by -3.

   I. Divide each side by -3.

4. Which value of x makes the equation $\frac{3}{4}x = 12$ true?

   A. 9

   B. $11\frac{1}{4}$

   C. 16

   D. 48

5. A triangle is graphed in the coordinate plane. What are the coordinates of the image after a translation 3 units right and 2 units down?

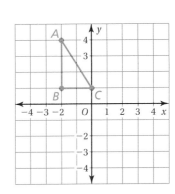

   F. $A'(1, 4), B'(1, 1), C'(3, 1)$

   G. $A'(1, 2), B'(1, -1), C'(3, -1)$

   H. $A'(-2, 2), B'(-2, -1), C'(0, -1)$

   I. $A'(0, 1), B'(0, -2), C'(2, -2)$

6. Your friend solved the equation in the box shown. What should your friend do to correct the error that he made?

A. Add $\frac{2}{5}$ to each side to get $-\frac{x}{3} = -\frac{1}{15}$.

B. Multiply each side by -3 to get $x + \frac{2}{5} = \frac{7}{5}$.

C. Multiply each side by -3 to get $x = 2\frac{3}{5}$.

D. Subtract $\frac{2}{5}$ from each side to get $-\frac{x}{3} = -\frac{5}{10}$.

$$-\frac{x}{3} + \frac{2}{5} = -\frac{7}{15}$$

$$-\frac{x}{3} + \frac{2}{5} - \frac{2}{5} = -\frac{7}{15} - \frac{2}{5}$$

$$-\frac{x}{3} = -\frac{13}{15}$$

$$3 \cdot \left(-\frac{x}{3}\right) = 3 \cdot \left(-\frac{13}{15}\right)$$

$$x = -2\frac{3}{5}$$

7. Your teacher dilates the rectangle using a scale factor of $\frac{1}{2}$.

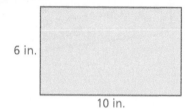

6 in.

10 in.

What is the area of the dilated rectangle in square inches?

8. Your cousin earns \$9.25 an hour at work. Last week she earned \$222.00 How many hours did she work last week?

F. $\frac{1}{24}$ hour

G. 22 hours

H. 24 hours

I. 212.75 hours

9. Triangle *EFG* is a dilation of Triangle *HIJ*.

Which proportion is *not* true for Triangle *EFG* and Triangle *HIJ*?

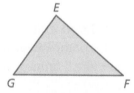

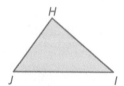

A. $\dfrac{EF}{FG} = \dfrac{HI}{IJ}$

B. $\dfrac{EG}{HI} = \dfrac{FG}{IJ}$

C. $\dfrac{GE}{EF} = \dfrac{JH}{HI}$

D. $\dfrac{EF}{HI} = \dfrac{GE}{JH}$

Item Analysis (continued)

6. A. The student adds $\frac{2}{5}$ to each side instead of subtracting $\frac{2}{5}$.

B. The student performs an order of operations error by not subtracting $\frac{2}{5}$ from each side first.

C. Correct answer

D. The student subtracts the numerators and denominators to get $-\frac{7-2}{15-5} = -\frac{5}{10}$ instead of finding a common denominator before subtracting.

7. Gridded Response: Correct answer: 15

Common error: The student finds half the area of the original rectangle, getting an answer of 30.

8. F. The student sets up the equation $9.25h = 222.00$ but divides 9.25 by 222.00 instead of dividing each side of the equation by 9.25.

G. The student uses estimation and finds $220 \div 10 = 22$.

H. Correct answer

I. The student sets up the equation $9.25h = 222.00$ but subtracts 9.25 from each side of the equation instead of dividing each side by 9.25.

9. A. The student chooses a proportion that correctly represents a relationship between pairs of corresponding sides of the triangles.

B. Correct answer

C. The student chooses a proportion that correctly represents a relationship between pairs of corresponding sides of the triangles.

D. The student chooses a proportion that correctly represents a relationship between pairs of corresponding sides of the triangles.

6. C

7. 15

8. H

9. B

Item Analysis (continued)

10. F

11. *Part A* translation up

Part B dilation with a scale

factor of $\frac{1}{4}$

Part C 2

12. A

10. **F.** Correct answer

G. The student translates the reflected triangle in the opposite direction.

H. The student reflects the red triangle in the incorrect axis.

I. The student incorrectly thinks that rotating the red triangle 90° clockwise about the origin will map it onto the blue triangle.

11. **2 points** The student's work and explanations demonstrate a thorough understanding of working with transformations. In Part A, the student correctly describes the transformation as a translation up. In Part B, the student correctly describes the transformation as a dilation with a scale factor of $\frac{1}{4}$ (reduction). In Part C, the student correctly determines the scale factor is 2. The student provides clear and complete work and explanations.

1 point The student's work and explanations demonstrate a partial but limited understanding of working with transformations. The student provides some correct work and/or explanation.

0 points The student provides no response, a completely incorrect or incomprehensible response, or a response that demonstrates insufficient understanding of working with transformations.

12. **A.** Correct answer

B. The student reflects the rectangle in the *x*-axis instead of the *y*-axis.

C. The student rotates the rectangle 90° clockwise instead reflecting it in the *y*-axis.

D. The student thinks reflecting the rectangle in the *y*-axis causes it to end up where it started.

10. The red figure is congruent to the blue figure. Which of the following is a sequence of rigid motions between the figures?

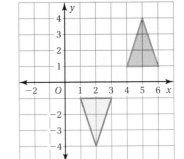

F. Reflect the red triangle in the *x*-axis, and then translate it 3 units left.

G. Reflect the red triangle in the *x*-axis, and then translate it 3 units right.

H. Reflect the red triangle in the *y*-axis, and then translate it 3 units left.

I. Rotate the red triangle 90° clockwise about the origin.

11. Several transformations are used to create the pattern.

Part A   Describe the transformation of Triangle *GLM* to Triangle *DGH*.

Part B   Describe the transformation of Triangle *ALQ* to Triangle *GLM*.

Part C   Triangle *DFN* is a dilation of Triangle *GHM*. Find the scale factor.

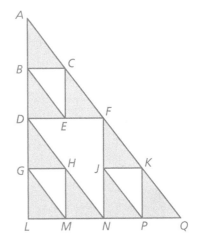

12. A rectangle is graphed in the coordinate plane.

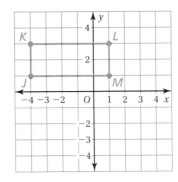

What are the coordinates of the image after a reflection in the *y*-axis?

A. $J'(4, 1), K'(4, 3), L'(-1, 3), M'(-1, 1)$

B. $J'(-4, -1), K'(-4, -3), L'(1, -3), M'(1, -1)$

C. $J'(1, 4), K'(3, 4), L'(3, -1), M'(1, -1)$

D. $J'(-4, 1), K'(-4, 3), L'(1, 3), M'(1, 1)$

3 Angles and Triangles

Chapter Learning Target:
Understand angles.

Chapter Success Criteria:
- I can identify angle relationships.
- I can find angle measurements.
- I can compare angles.
- I can apply angle relationships to solve real-life problems.

STEAM Video: "Honeycombs"

Laurie's Notes

Chapter 3 Overview

This chapter provides many opportunities for students to complete hands-on investigations. Developing conceptual understanding versus learning rules and vocabulary remains the goal.

Students have prior knowledge of angles, triangles, and polygons. They should be familiar with how angles are measured, and that polygons have the same number of angles as sides. Their vocabulary may not be precise, but their understanding will be jogged with partner interactions during the explorations.

The first lesson explores the angles formed when two lines are intersected by a transversal. If the lines are parallel, then certain pairs of angles are congruent. If the lines are not parallel, then those angle pairs are not congruent but their names remain the same. For example, students may think that corresponding angles are always congruent and if they are not congruent, then they are no longer referred to as corresponding angles. This is a common misconception.

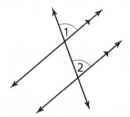
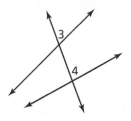

The second lesson focuses on properties of interior and exterior angles of triangles. Students may already know that the sum of the interior angle measures of a triangle is 180°, but they cannot tell you why this is true. It is a fact they recall. Students should complete a hands-on exploration, where they *see* how the three angles form a straight angle. This exploration is quick, yet powerful. Understanding this big idea about the angle sum of a triangle is necessary for deriving the formula for the angle sum of a polygon in the third lesson.

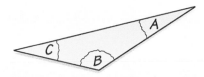

In the last lesson, students explore special properties of similar triangles and use similar triangles to find missing measures. The concept of *indirect measurement* is introduced, which offers many opportunities for real-life modeling. When determining whether two triangles are similar, encourage students to think back to the dilations they studied in the previous chapter.

Chapter Opener	1 Day
Section 1	2 Days
Section 2	2 Days
Section 3	2 Days
Section 4	2 Days
Connecting Concepts	1 Day
Chapter Review	1 Day
Chapter Test	1 Day
Total Chapter 3	12 Days
Year-to-Date	43 Days

Chapter Learning Target
Understand angles.

Chapter Success Criteria
- ◼ Identify angle relationships.
- ◻ Find angle measurements.
- ◼ Compare angles.
- ◼ Apply angle relationships to solve real-life problems.

Chapter 3 Learning Targets and Success Criteria

Section	Learning Target	Success Criteria
3.1 Parallel Lines and Transversals	Find missing angle measures created by the intersections of lines.	• Identify congruent angles when a transversal intersects parallel lines. • Find angle measures when a transversal intersects parallel lines.
3.2 Angles of Triangles	Understand properties of interior and exterior angles of triangles.	• Use equations to find missing angle measures of triangles. • Use interior and exterior angles of a triangle to solve real-life problems.
3.3 Angles of Polygons	Find interior angle measures of polygons.	• Explain how to find the sum of the interior angle measures of a polygon. • Use an equation to find an interior angle measure of a polygon. • Find the interior angle measures of a regular polygon.
3.4 Using Similar Triangles	Use similar triangles to find missing measures.	• Use angle measures to determine whether triangles are similar. • Use similar triangles to solve real-life problems.

Progressions

Through the Grades

Grade 7	Grade 8	High School
• Use proportionality to solve multistep ratio problems. • Use facts about supplementary, complementary, vertical, and adjacent angles.	• Demonstrate that the sum of the interior angle measures of a triangle is 180° and apply this fact to find the unknown measures of angles and the sums of the angle measures of polygons. Classify and determine the measures of angles created when parallel lines are cut by a transversal. Use similar triangles to solve problems that include height and distance.	• Identify planes, pairs of angles formed by transversals, parallel lines, and perpendicular lines. • Prove theorems about parallel lines and about perpendicular lines. • Decide whether polygons are similar. • Use the AA, SSS, and SAS Similarity Theorems to prove triangles are similar. • Use the Triangle Proportionality Theorem and other proportionality theorems. • Use similarity criteria to solve problems about lengths, perimeters, and areas.

Through the Chapter

Standard	3.1	3.2	3.3	3.4
8.G.A.5 Use informal arguments to establish facts about the angle sum and exterior angle of triangles, about the angles created when parallel lines are cut by a transversal, and the angle-angle criterion for similarity of triangles.	●	●	■	★

Key

▲ = preparing   ★ = complete
● = learning   ■ = extending

Laurie's Notes

STEAM Video

1. $1260°$

2. *Sample answer:* about 420 mm^3; Divide the hexagon into 6 equilateral triangles, each with a base of 4 mm and a height of about 3.5 mm.

$$\text{Area of hexagon} \approx 6\left[\frac{1}{2}(4)(3.5)\right]$$
$$= 42 \text{ mm}^2$$

$$\text{Volume of cell} \approx 42 \cdot 10$$
$$= 420 \text{ mm}^3$$

Performance Task

Sample answer: snakes, fish

Mathematical Practices

Students have opportunities to develop aspects of the mathematical practices throughout the chapter. Here are some examples.

1. **Make Sense of Problems and Persevere in Solving Them**
   3.2 Math Practice note, *p. 112*

2. **Reason Abstractly and Quantitatively**
   3.2 Exercise 20, *p. 116*

3. **Construct Viable Arguments and Critique the Reasoning of Others**
   3.4 Math Practice note, *p. 124*

4. **Model with Mathematics**
   3.3 Exercise 21, *p. 122*

5. **Use Appropriate Tools Strategically**
   3.1 Exercise 6, *p. 108*

6. **Attend to Precision**
   3.1 Math Practice note, *p. 103*

7. **Look for and Make Use of Structure**
   3.4 Exercise 15, *p. 128*

8. **Look for and Express Regularity in Repeated Reasoning**
   3.3 Exploration 1g, *p. 117*

STEAM Video

Before the Video
- To introduce the STEAM Video, read aloud the first paragraph of Honeycombs and discuss the question with your students.
- ❓ "Why might bees use this shape?"

During the Video
- The video shows Tony and Enid discussing bees and the shape of a honeycomb.
- ❓ Pause the video at 1:50 and ask, "What are the three regular polygons that produce regular tilings?" square, equilateral triangle, and regular hexagon
- Watch the remainder of the video.

After the Video
- ❓ "Why are hexagonal tilings the best shape for a honeycomb?" They require less wax and work for the bees.
- Have students work with a partner to answer Questions 1 and 2.
- **Common Error:** Students may count all of the triangles in the figure (36) and multiply by 180°. Remind students to find the sum of the interior angle measures of the yellow outline.
- As students discuss and answer the questions, listen for understanding of finding the sum of interior angle measures.

Performance Task

- Use this information to spark students' interest and promote thinking about real-life problems.
- ❓ Ask, "What other animals have features that resemble geometric shapes?"
- After completing the chapter, students will have gained the knowledge needed to complete "Turtle Shells."

STEAM Video

Honeycombs

Each cell in a honeycomb is in the shape of a regular hexagon. Why might bees use this shape?

Watch the STEAM Video "Honeycombs." Then answer the following questions.

1. Enid and Tony show regular tilings made out of squares, equilateral triangles, and regular hexagons. What is the sum of the interior angle measures of the tiling made from equilateral triangles, outlined below in yellow?

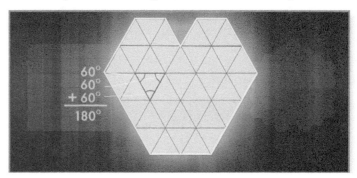

2. The cells in a honeycomb use a tiling pattern of the regular hexagon shown. A cell is 10 millimeters deep. About how much honey can one cell hold? Explain.

4 mm

Performance Task

Turtle Shells

After completing this chapter, you will be able to use the concepts you learned to answer the questions in the *STEAM Video Performance Task*. You will be given angle measures of shapes seen on a turtle shell.

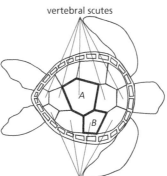

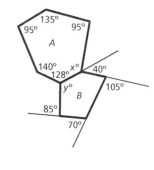

You will be asked to find angle sums and missing angle measures. What other animals have features that resemble geometric shapes?

Getting Ready for Chapter 3

Chapter Exploration

When an object is **transverse**, it is lying or extending across something. In the drawing, the fallen tree lying across the railroad track is transverse to the track.

1. Work with a partner.

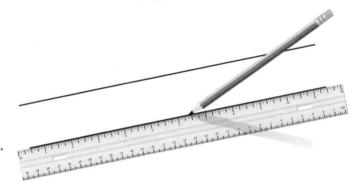

- Discuss what it means for two lines to be parallel. Decide on a strategy for drawing parallel lines. Then draw two parallel lines.

- Draw a third line that intersects the parallel lines. This line is called a *transversal*.

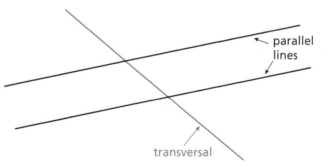

parallel lines

transversal

a. How many angles are formed by the parallel lines and the transversal? Label each angle.

b. Which of these angles have equal measures? Explain your reasoning.

Vocabulary

The following vocabulary terms are defined in this chapter. Think about what the terms might mean and record your thoughts.

transversal   exterior angles of a polygon
interior angles of a polygon   regular polygon

Laurie's Notes

Chapter Exploration

- **MP5 Use Appropriate Tools Strategically:** Mathematically proficient students use appropriate tools to gain an understanding of a new concept or to solve a problem. Rules, protractors, and transparent paper are useful in the exploration.
- Discuss the meaning of the word *transverse*. Give examples, such as a path that cuts through a field or a street that cuts through the downtown area of a city.
- Ask students to give examples of parallel lines in real life, where the lines are
  - functional (as with railroad tracks or lanes of a highway)
  - aesthetic (on clothing)
  - coincidentally parallel (the edge of a table and a pencil).
- Students will likely create parallel lines by tracing opposite edges of a rigid object they believe has parallel edges, such as a ruler or an index card. There are other methods. Ask students to share their methods and give explanations as to why the lines are parallel.
- Students will use protractors to measure the angles formed. If transparent paper is available, some students may simply trace one acute angle and an obtuse angle and slide the transparent paper.

Vocabulary

- These terms represent some of the vocabulary that students will encounter in Chapter 3. Discuss the terms as a class.
- Where have students heard the term *regular polygon* outside of a math classroom? In what contexts? Students may not be able to write the actual definition, but they may write phrases associated with *regular polygon*.
- Allowing students to discuss these terms now will prepare them for understanding the terms as they are presented in the chapter.
- When students encounter a new definition, encourage them to write in their *Student Journals*. They will revisit these definitions during the Chapter Review.

ELL Support

Point out that the title of this chapter is *Angles and Triangles*. Write the words *angle* and *angel* on the board. Say each word and have students repeat them. If necessary, explain the meaning of each. Point to and say "angle," then have students draw a representation of the word and hold it up for your review. Erase the words. Say "angel" and have students write the word and hold it up for your review. Do the same with *angle*.

Topics for Review

- Adjacent Angles
- Complementary Angles
- Similar Triangles
- Solving Multi-Step Equations
- Solving Proportions
- Supplementary Angles
- Vertical Angles

Chapter Exploration

1. **a.** 8; *Sample answer:*

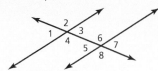

   b. *Sample answer:* $\angle 2$, $\angle 4$, $\angle 6$, and $\angle 8$ have equal measures. $\angle 1$, $\angle 3$, $\angle 5$, and $\angle 7$ have equal measures. $\angle 2$ and $\angle 4$, $\angle 6$ and $\angle 8$, $\angle 1$ and $\angle 3$, and $\angle 5$ and $\angle 7$ are vertical angles. Vertical angles have the same measure. Using a protractor, you can determine that the following angles have equal measures: $\angle 1$ and $\angle 5$, $\angle 2$ and $\angle 6$, $\angle 3$ and $\angle 7$, and $\angle 4$ and $\angle 8$.

Laurie's Notes

Preparing to Teach

- Students worked with transformations and congruent figures in the previous chapter. Now they will make conjectures about angles created by parallel lines and transversals.
- **MP5 Use Appropriate Tools Strategically:** There are many appropriate tools that mathematically proficient students may use to gain an understanding of a new concept or to solve a problem. Several tools could be useful in the exploration. Students might use technology, transparencies, or paper and pencil. To measure angles it will be helpful for students to have protractors.

Motivate

- **Preparation:** Make a model to help discuss the big ideas of this lesson. Cut 3 strips of card stock; punch holes in the middle of two strips and punch two holes in the third strip. Attach the strips using brass fasteners.

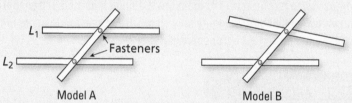

Model A   Model B

- Place the model under a document camera or on an overhead. Show students that the pieces are moveable by transforming from Model A to Model B.
- Focus students' attention on the connection between the four angles on L_1 and the four angles on L_2. Pairs of vertical angles will always be congruent whether or not L_1 and L_2 are parallel.
- Place the model under the document camera or on the overhead and encourage students to point to the angles that they think are congruent. Use Models A and B.

Exploration 1

- Students should use the geometry software available at *BigIdeasMath.com*. Lines *A* and *B* will be given. If you chose to use different software, students will need to draw the lines so that they are nearly parallel.
- This exploration can also be completed using paper, a pencil, and a protractor. You may want students to begin with parallel lines, measure the angles, and then see what happens when a rotation causes the lines to be nonparallel.
- In part (b), students should recognize several congruent angles. They know vertical angles are congruent and they can use protractors to measure the others. They have not yet studied corresponding angles, interior angles, or exterior angles. Ask students about some of these angles so that they see that the angles are close in measure, but not exact because the lines are nonparallel.
- Once students have parallel lines in part (c), they will see many more pairs of congruent angles.
- For parts (c) and (d), it might be easier for students to see that the angles are congruent if they use technology or transparencies to translate the angles.

Exploration 1

a. no; If you extend line *A* and line *B*, they will intersect.

b. The vertical angles are congruent.

c. Line *A* and line *B* are parallel.

d. yes

e. When a line intersects two parallel lines, the angles created by the intersection of the line and the first parallel line are congruent to the corresponding angles created by the intersection of the line and the second parallel line.

3.1 Parallel Lines and Transversals

Learning Target: Find missing angle measures created by the intersections of lines.

Success Criteria:
- I can identify congruent angles when a transversal intersects parallel lines.
- I can find angle measures when a transversal intersects parallel lines.

EXPLORATION 1

Exploring Intersections of Lines

Work with a partner. Use geometry software and the lines *A* and *B* shown.

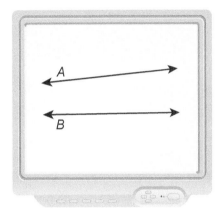

Math Practice

Use Clear Definitions

What does it mean for two lines to be parallel? How does this help you answer the question in part (a)?

a. Are line *A* and line *B* parallel? Explain your reasoning.

b. Draw a line *C* that intersects both line *A* and line *B*. What do you notice about the measures of the angles that are created?

c. Rotate line *A* or line *B* until the angles created by the intersection of line *A* and line *C* are congruent to the angles created by the intersection of line *B* and line *C*. What do you notice about line *A* and line *B*?

d. Rotate line *C* to create different angle measures. Are the angles that were congruent in part (c) still congruent?

e. Make a conjecture about the measures of the angles created when a line intersects two parallel lines.

3.1 Lesson

Key Vocabulary
transversal, p. 104
interior angles, p. 105
exterior angles, p. 105

Lines in the same plane that do not intersect are called *parallel lines*. Lines that intersect at right angles are called *perpendicular lines*.

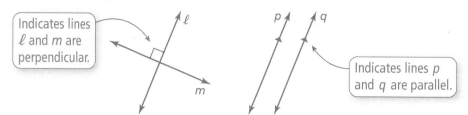

Indicates lines ℓ and *m* are perpendicular.

Indicates lines *p* and *q* are parallel.

A line that intersects two or more lines is called a **transversal**. When parallel lines are cut by a transversal, several pairs of congruent angles are formed.

 Key Idea

Corresponding angles lie on the same side of the transversal in corresponding positions.

Corresponding Angles

When a transversal intersects parallel lines, corresponding angles are congruent.

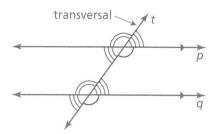

Corresponding angles

EXAMPLE 1 Finding Angle Measures

Use the figure to find the measures of (a) ∠1 and (b) ∠2.

a. ∠1 and the 110° angle are corresponding angles formed by a transversal intersecting parallel lines. The angles are congruent.

▶ So, the measure of ∠1 is 110°.

b. ∠1 and ∠2 are supplementary.

$$∠1 + ∠2 = 180°$$ Definition of supplementary angles
$$110° + ∠2 = 180°$$ Substitute 110° for ∠1.
$$∠2 = 70°$$ Subtract 110° from each side.

▶ So, the measure of ∠2 is 70°.

Try It Use the figure to find the measure of the angle. Explain your reasoning.

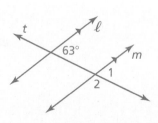

1. ∠1

2. ∠2

Laurie's Notes

Scaffolding Instruction

- Students explored angles formed when parallel lines are intersected by a transversal. Now they will formalize their conjectures and find the measures of many types of angles formed when parallel lines are cut by a transversal.
- **Emerging:** Students struggle with the names and measurements of the different types of angles. They need guided instruction for the Key Ideas and examples.
- **Proficient:** Students intuitively understand which angles are congruent when parallel lines are cut by a transversal. They should review the definitions and Key Ideas before completing the Self-Assessment exercises.
- **Note:** There is a great deal of vocabulary in this section, so students need plenty of practice. It is also important *not* to always draw the parallel lines in the same orientation, particularly horizontal and vertical.

Discuss

- Write the informal definitions of parallel lines and perpendicular lines. Draw examples of each and discuss the notation used in the diagram.
- Write the definition of **transversal**. Explain that a line that intersects two or more lines is called a transversal even if the lines are *not* parallel. Only when the lines are parallel are the pairs of angles in this lesson congruent.

Key Idea

- Write the Key Idea. Identify the corresponding angles which are color-coded in the diagram.
- Mention the push-pin note. Students may ask what is meant by *corresponding positions*. Tell them that corresponding angles are both above or below the parallel lines (when in horizontal position) and on the same side of the transversal (left or right).
- As in the exploration, students can use rigid motions to show that the angles are congruent when the lines are parallel. Refer back to the exploration as you discuss the Key Ideas in this lesson. Point out that corresponding angles were *not* congruent when the lines were nonparallel.
- **MP6 Attend to Precision:** In a formal geometry course, the rules in the Key Ideas of this lesson would be stated in if-then (conditional) form. Discuss this with students.

EXAMPLE 1

- ❓ "Are the lines parallel? Explain." Yes, the blue arrows indicate parallel lines.
- ❓ "What are supplementary angles?" Two angles whose measures have a sum of 180°.
- **Note:** In this course, $m\angle$ notation is not used in the equations, which helps students avoid confusing the measure of an angle with slope. In the equations, students can think of $\angle 1$ as referring to *the measure of angle 1*. In high school, students will use $m\angle 1$, but you could choose to introduce this notation now.

Try It

- Students should write their answers on whiteboards. Have volunteers explain their reasoning.

Scaffold instruction to support all students in their learning. Learning is individualized and you may want to group students differently as they move in and out of these levels with each skill and concept. Student self-assessment and feedback help guide your instructional decisions about how and when to layer support for all students to become proficient learners.

Extra Example 1

Use the figure to find the measures of (a) $\angle 1$ and (b) $\angle 2$.

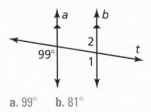

a. 99°   b. 81°

Try It

1. 63°; $\angle 1$ and the given angle are corresponding angles.

2. 117°; $\angle 1$ and $\angle 2$ are supplementary.

Extra Example 2

Use the figure to find the measures of the numbered angles.

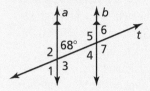

$\angle 1 = 68°$, $\angle 2 = 112°$, $\angle 3 = 112°$,
$\angle 4 = 68°$, $\angle 5 = 112°$, $\angle 6 = 68°$,
$\angle 7 = 112°$

Try It

3. $\angle 1 = 121°$, $\angle 2 = 59°$,
   $\angle 3 = 121°$, $\angle 4 = 121°$,
   $\angle 5 = 59°$, $\angle 6 = 121°$,
   $\angle 7 = 59°$

EXAMPLE 2

- Draw the figure on the board.
- "Can you find the measures of all the angles if you only know one angle?" Students may not know the answer at this point, but by the end of this example, they will see that they can.
- **MP8 Look for and Express Regularity in Repeated Reasoning:** If you know any angle measure when a transversal intersects two parallel lines, then you can use vertical, supplementary, and corresponding angles to find all seven of the other measures.
- Once angles 1, 2, and 3 are found, you can use corresponding angles to find the remaining four angles. To help students visualize the corresponding angles, draw the figure on a transparency and cut the transparency in half. Lay the given angle and angles 1, 2, and 3 over angles 4, 5, 6, and 7 to show that they are congruent corresponding angles.

Try It

- Ask students to explain their reasoning. For example, students may say that angle 2 is vertical to the angle that measures 59° and angles 2 and 7 are corresponding angles, so angle 7 also measures 59°.

ELL Support

After demonstrating Example 2, have students work in groups to discuss and solve Try It Exercise 3. Provide guiding questions: Which angle measure is known? Which angles are congruent? Which angles are supplementary? What are the measures of all the angles?

Beginner: Answer the guiding questions using numbers or single words.

Intermediate: Answer using phrases or simple sentences.

Advanced: Answer using detailed sentences and help guide discussion.

Discuss

- Use the figure to talk about interior angles and exterior angles.
- Identify the four angles that are interior (between the two parallel lines) and the four angles that are exterior (outside the two parallel lines).
- "Are there pairs of interior angles that appear congruent?" yes "Which pairs?" $\angle 3$ and $\angle 6$, $\angle 4$ and $\angle 5$
- "Are there pairs of exterior angles that appear congruent?" yes "Which pairs?" $\angle 1$ and $\angle 8$, $\angle 2$ and $\angle 7$
- "Why are $\angle 4$ and $\angle 5$ congruent?" *Sample answer:* $\angle 2$ and $\angle 4$ are supplementary, as are $\angle 5$ and $\angle 6$. So, $\angle 2 + \angle 4 = \angle 5 + \angle 6$. $\angle 2$ and $\angle 6$ are corresponding angles, so they have the same measure. Because $\angle 2 = \angle 6$, you can substitute $\angle 6$ for $\angle 2$, so $\angle 6 + \angle 4 = \angle 5 + \angle 6$. Then subtract $\angle 6$ from both sides to get $\angle 4 = \angle 5$. So, $\angle 4$ and $\angle 5$ are congruent.
- Similarly, you can explain why other pairs of angles are congruent.

Key Ideas

- Write the Key Ideas. Identify the angles which are marked congruent in the diagrams. Mention the push-pin note.

EXAMPLE 2

Using Corresponding Angles

Use the figure to find the measures of the numbered angles.

∠1: ∠1 and the 75° angle are vertical angles. They are congruent.

So, the measure of ∠1 is 75°.

∠2 and ∠3: The 75° angle is supplementary to both ∠2 and ∠3.

$$75° + ∠2 = 180°$$ Definition of supplementary angles

$$∠2 = 105°$$ Subtract 75° from each side.

So, the measures of ∠2 and ∠3 are 105°.

∠4, ∠5, ∠6, and ∠7: Corresponding angles are congruent because they are formed by a transversal intersecting parallel lines. So, the measures of ∠4 and ∠6 are 75°, and the measures of ∠5 and ∠7 are 105°.

Try It

3. Use the figure to find the measures of the numbered angles.

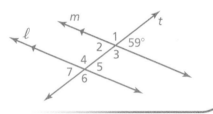

When two parallel lines are cut by a transversal, four **interior angles** are formed on the inside of the parallel lines and four **exterior angles** are formed on the outside of the parallel lines.

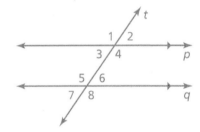

∠3, ∠4, ∠5, and ∠6 are interior angles.

∠1, ∠2, ∠7, and ∠8 are exterior angles.

🔑 Key Ideas

Alternate interior angles and alternate exterior angles lie on opposite sides of the transversal.

Alternate Interior Angles and Alternate Exterior Angles

When a transversal intersects parallel lines, alternate interior angles are congruent and alternate exterior angles are congruent.

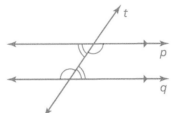

Alternate interior angles

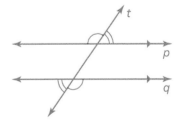

Alternate exterior angles

EXAMPLE 3 **Identifying Angle Relationships**

The photo shows a portion of an airport. Describe the relationship between each pair of angles.

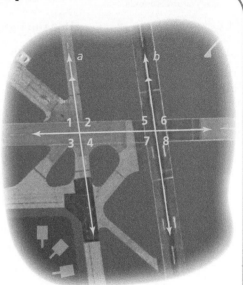

a. ∠3 and ∠6

∠3 and ∠6 are alternate exterior angles formed by a transversal intersecting parallel lines.

▷ So, ∠3 is congruent to ∠6.

b. ∠2 and ∠7

∠2 and ∠7 are alternate interior angles formed by a transversal intersecting parallel lines.

▷ So, ∠2 is congruent to ∠7.

Try It In Example 3, the measure of ∠4 is 84°. Find the measure of the angle. Explain your reasoning.

4. ∠3   **5.** ∠5   **6.** ∠6

Self-Assessment for *Concepts & Skills*

Solve each exercise. Then rate your understanding of the success criteria in your journal.

FINDING ANGLE MEASURES Use the figure to find the measures of the numbered angles.

7.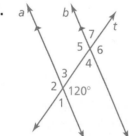

8.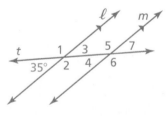

9. WHICH ONE DOESN'T BELONG? Which angle measure does *not* belong with the other three? Explain your reasoning.

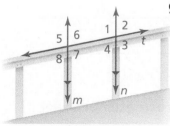

the measure of ∠2	the measure of ∠5
the measure of ∠6	the measure of ∠8

Laurie's Notes

EXAMPLE 3

? *"Are lines a and b parallel? Explain."* Yes, the yellow arrows indicate parallel lines.

- Work through the explanation as shown. This example helps students identify alternate interior and alternate exterior angles.

Try It

- Draw the diagram on the board. When students have finished, ask volunteers to record their answers in the diagram on the board and explain their reasoning.
- In Exercise 6, students can say $\angle 6 = 96°$ because of alternate exterior angles *or* because it is the supplement of $\angle 8$.

Formative Assessment Tip

Which One Doesn't Belong

This technique is one that you should be quite familiar with because it is often used in the Self-Assessment for Concepts & Skills exercises! Students are presented with four expressions, quantities, images, or words and asked which one does not belong with the other three. They are also expected to give a reason for their choice, which can be quite informative.

Used at the end of instruction, *Which One Doesn't Belong* informs you as to how students have conceptualized and made connections in their learning. Used at the beginning of a lesson, this technique can inform you about what knowledge students already have about the topic.

✓ Self-Assessment for Concepts & Skills

- Students should work on the problems independently.
- **Which One Doesn't Belong:** It is very important that students can explain their choices in Exercise 9. Select several students to share their reasoning
- ◉ Draw a set of parallel lines with a transversal on the board. Number each of the angles. Use *Popsicle Sticks* to select students to identify pairs of vertical, corresponding, alternate interior, and alternate exterior angles.

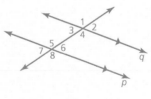

ELL Support

Allow students to work in pairs for extra support. For Exercises 7 and 8, ask for the measure of each angle and have pairs display their answers on whiteboards for your review. Have two pairs form a group to discuss their answers to Exercise 9. Monitor discussions and provide support. Then discuss as a class.

The Success Criteria Self-Assessment chart can be found in the *Student Journal* or online at *BigIdeasMath.com*.

Extra Example 3

Describe the relationship between each pair of angles.

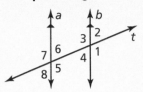

a. $\angle 1$ and $\angle 7$ $\angle 1$ and $\angle 7$ are alternate exterior angles formed by a transversal intersecting parallel lines. So, $\angle 1$ is congruent to $\angle 7$.

b. $\angle 3$ and $\angle 5$ $\angle 3$ and $\angle 5$ are alternate interior angles formed by a transversal intersecting parallel lines. So, $\angle 3$ is congruent to $\angle 5$.

Try It

4. $96°$; $\angle 3$ and $\angle 4$ are supplementary.

5. $84°$; $\angle 5$ and $\angle 4$ are alternate interior angles.

6. $96°$; *Sample answer:* $\angle 5$ and $\angle 6$ are supplementary.

Self-Assessment
for Concepts & Skills

7. $\angle 1 = 60°$, $\angle 2 = 120°$, $\angle 3 = 60°$, $\angle 4 = 60°$, $\angle 5 = 120°$, $\angle 6 = 120°$, $\angle 7 = 60°$

8. $\angle 1 = 145°$, $\angle 2 = 145°$, $\angle 3 = 35°$, $\angle 4 = 35°$, $\angle 5 = 145°$, $\angle 6 = 145°$, $\angle 7 = 35°$

9. the measure of $\angle 5$; The other three measures are equal.

Laurie's Notes

Extra Example 4

The ramp has a 16° incline. At what angles do you need to attach a rail to two parallel posts so that the rail is parallel to the incline of the ramp?

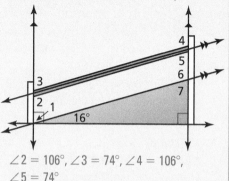

$\angle 2 = 106°$, $\angle 3 = 74°$, $\angle 4 = 106°$, $\angle 5 = 74°$

Self-Assessment
for Problem Solving

10. 20; *Sample answer:* Because the lines are parallel, the $a°$ angle and the angle adjacent to the $a°$ angle also form a right angle. Using alternate interior angles, the measure of the angle adjacent to the $a°$ angle is 70°. So, $a + 70 = 90$, and $a = 20$.

11. 73°

Learning Target

Find missing angle measures created by the intersections of lines.

Success Criteria

- Identify congruent angles when a transversal intersects parallel lines.
- Find angle measures when a transversal intersects parallel lines.

EXAMPLE 4

- Ask a volunteer to read the problem and another to explain what the problem is asking.
- Students could complete a Four Square as you work through the problem-solving plan.
- Work through the solution as shown.
- **?** "Is there another way to solve this problem? Explain." yes; *Sample answer:* You could use $\angle 2$ and $\angle 3$ instead of $\angle 4$ and $\angle 5$. There are many other ways to solve this problem. Some students may suggest using the sum of the angles in a triangle to find the measure of $\angle 2$. This idea will be formally developed in the next section.
- Remind students to make sure that they answer the question and check their answers for reasonableness.
- Point out that you would only need to find one of the angle measures if you were actually hanging the rail. Once you place the rail using one of the angles, the other angles will fall into place because the posts are parallel.

✔ Self-Assessment for Problem Solving

- Encourage students to use a Four Square to complete these exercises. Until students become comfortable with the problem-solving plan, they may only be ready to complete the first square.
- **Neighbor Check:** Have students work independently to complete their Four Squares and then have their neighbors check their work. Have students discuss any discrepancies.
- **⊙ Thumbs Up:** Have students indicate their understanding of each success criterion.

The Success Criteria Self-Assessment chart can be found in the *Student Journal* or online at *BigIdeasMath.com*.

Closure

- Find the measure of each angle. Explain your reasoning.

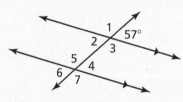

$\angle 1 = 123°$, $\angle 2 = 57°$, $\angle 3 = 123°$, $\angle 4 = 57°$, $\angle 5 = 123°$, $\angle 6 = 57°$, $\angle 7 = 123°$; Explanations will vary.

EXAMPLE 4   Modeling Real Life

The stairs have a 45° incline. At what angles do you need to attach a rail to two parallel posts so that the rail is parallel to the incline of the steps?

Use angle relationships to find the measures of ∠4, ∠5, ∠6, and ∠7 that make the rail parallel to the incline of the steps.

∠1: The 45° angle is complementary to ∠1.

$$45° + ∠1 = 90° \qquad \text{Definition of complementary angles}$$
$$∠1 = 45° \qquad \text{Subtract 45° from each side.}$$

∠5: ∠1 and ∠5 are congruent because they are corresponding angles formed by a transversal intersecting parallel lines.

So, the measure of ∠5 is 45°.

∠4: ∠4 and ∠5 are supplementary.

$$∠4 + ∠5 = 180° \qquad \text{Definition of supplementary angles}$$
$$∠4 + 45° = 180° \qquad \text{Substitute 45° for ∠5.}$$
$$∠4 = 135° \qquad \text{Subtract 45° from each side.}$$

∠6 and ∠7: Using alternate interior angles, the measure of ∠6 is 45° and the measure of ∠7 is 135°.

▶ You need to attach the rail so that the measures of ∠5 and ∠6 are 45° and the measures of ∠4 and ∠7 are 135°.

Self-Assessment for Problem Solving

Solve each exercise. Then rate your understanding of the success criteria in your journal.

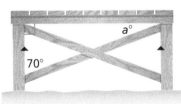

10. A cross section of a pier is shown. Find the value of *a*. Justify your answer.

11. The *head tube angle* of a bike determines how easy the bike is to steer. A bike frame with angle approximations is shown. What is the head tube angle of the bike?

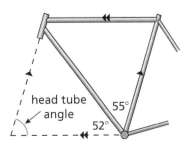

? Go to *BigIdeasMath.com* to get HELP with solving the exercises.

▶ Review & Refresh

Find the values of the ratios (red to blue) of the perimeters and areas of the similar figures.

1.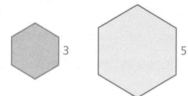

2.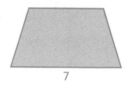

Evaluate the expression.

3. $4 + 3^2$

4. $5(2)^2 - 6$

5. $11 + (-7)^2 - 9$

▶ Concepts, Skills, & Problem Solving

MP **USING TOOLS** Use a protractor to determine whether lines a and b are parallel. (See Exploration 1, p. 103.)

6.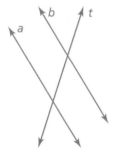

7.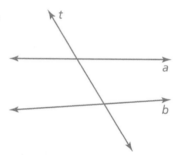

FINDING ANGLE MEASURES Use the figure to find the measures of the numbered angles. Explain your reasoning.

8.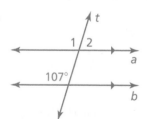

9.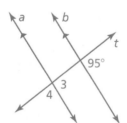

10.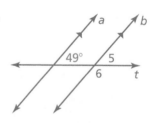

11. **MP** **YOU BE THE TEACHER** Your friend describes a relationship between the angles shown. Is your friend correct? Explain your reasoning.

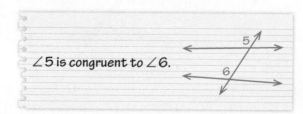

∠5 is congruent to ∠6.

Assignment Guide and Concept Check

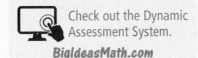

Check out the Dynamic Assessment System.
BigIdeasMath.com

Scaffold assignments to support all students in their learning progression. The suggested assignments are a starting point. Continue to assign additional exercises and revisit with spaced practice to move every student toward proficiency.

Level	Assignment 1	Assignment 2
Emerging	2, 5, 6, 7, 9, 11, 15, 17, 19, 21	8, 10, 12, 13, 14, 16, 22, 23, 27, 28, 29, 30
Proficient	2, 5, 6, 7, 8, 10, 11, 14, 15, 18, 20, 22	23, 24, 25, 26, 27, 28, 29, 30, 31
Advanced	2, 5, 6, 7, 10, 11, 14, 15, 18, 20, 22, 26	23, 24, 25, 27, 29, 30, 31, 32

- Assignment 1 is for use after students complete the Self-Assessment for Concepts & Skills.
- Assignment 2 is for use after students complete the Self-Assessment for Problem Solving.
- The red exercises can be used as a concept check.

Review & Refresh Prior Skills

Exercises 1 and 2 Perimeters and Areas of Similar Figures
Exercises 3–5 Evaluating Expressions

Common Errors

- **Exercises 8–10** Students may mix up some of the definitions for congruent angles and find incorrect angle measures. Encourage students to look at the Key Ideas and color-code the figure they are given to determine what angles are congruent.

 **Review & Refresh**

1. $\dfrac{3}{5}; \dfrac{9}{25}$

2. $\dfrac{7}{6}; \dfrac{49}{36}$

3. 13

4. 14

5. 51

Concepts, Skills, & Problem Solving

6. yes

7. no

8. $\angle 1 = 107°$; $\angle 1$ and the given angle are corresponding angles. $\angle 2 = 73°$; $\angle 1$ and $\angle 2$ are supplementary.

9. $\angle 3 = 95°$; $\angle 3$ and the given angle are corresponding angles. $\angle 4 = 85°$; $\angle 3$ and $\angle 4$ are supplementary.

10. $\angle 5 = 49°$; $\angle 5$ and the given angle are corresponding angles. $\angle 6 = 131°$; $\angle 5$ and $\angle 6$ are supplementary.

11. no; The two lines are not parallel, so $\angle 5 \neq \angle 6$.

Concepts, Skills, & Problem Solving

12. 60°; ∠1 and ∠2 are corresponding angles.

13. *Sample answer:* Railroad tracks are parallel, and the out of bounds lines on a football field are parallel.

14. ∠1 = 61°, ∠2 = 119°, ∠3 = 61°, ∠4 = 119°, ∠5 = 119°, ∠6 = 61°, ∠7 = 119°

15. ∠1 = 81°, ∠2 = 99°, ∠3 = 81°, ∠4 = 99°, ∠5 = 81°, ∠6 = 99°, ∠7 = 81°

16. ∠1 = ∠2 = ∠3 = ∠4 = ∠5 = ∠6 = ∠7 = 90°

17. 56°; *Sample answer:* ∠1 and ∠8 are corresponding angles and ∠8 and ∠4 are supplementary.

18. 132°; *Sample answer:* ∠2 and ∠4 are alternate interior angles and ∠4 and ∠3 are supplementary.

19. 55°; ∠4 and ∠2 are alternate interior angles.

20. 120°; ∠6 and ∠8 are alternate exterior angles.

21. 129.5°; *Sample answer:* ∠7 and ∠5 are alternate exterior angles and ∠5 and ∠6 are supplementary.

22. 61.3°; *Sample answer:* ∠3 and ∠1 are alternate interior angles and ∠1 and ∠2 are supplementary.

23. 40°

24. yes; yes; Exterior angles that lie on the same side of a transversal are supplementary. Interior angles that lie on the same side of a transversal are supplementary.

25. Perpendicular lines form 90° angles.

Common Errors

- **Exercise 12** Students may not realize that the line in front of the cars is the transversal. Remind them that lines are infinite and can be extended. Draw a diagram of the parallel parking spaces to help students visualize that ∠1 and ∠2 are corresponding angles.

- **Exercises 14–16** Students may not understand alternate interior and alternate exterior angles and say that an exterior angle is congruent to the alternate interior angle. For example, in Exercise 14, a student may say the measure of ∠2 is 61°. Use corresponding angles to show that this is not true.

- **Exercises 17–22** Students may use some of the definitions for congruent angles incorrectly in finding the angle measure of the unknown angle. Review the definitions and give an example with an adequate explanation of how to find the missing angle.

12. **MP PROBLEM SOLVING** The painted lines that separate parking spaces are parallel. The measure of ∠1 is 60°. What is the measure of ∠2? Explain.

13. **OPEN-ENDED** Describe two real-life situations that use parallel lines.

USING CORRESPONDING ANGLES Use the figure to find the measures of the numbered angles.

14.

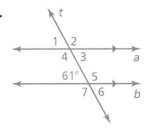

15.

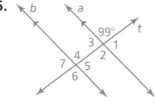

16.

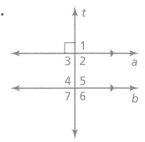

USING CORRESPONDING ANGLES Complete the statement. Explain your reasoning.

17. If the measure of ∠1 = 124°, then the measure of ∠4 = ____.

18. If the measure of ∠2 = 48°, then the measure of ∠3 = ____.

19. If the measure of ∠4 = 55°, then the measure of ∠2 = ____.

20. If the measure of ∠6 = 120°, then the measure of ∠8 = ____.

21. If the measure of ∠7 = 50.5°, then the measure of ∠6 = ____.

22. If the measure of ∠3 = 118.7°, then the measure of ∠2 = ____.

23. **MP MODELING REAL LIFE** A rainbow forms when sunlight reflects off raindrops at different angles. For blue light, the measure of ∠2 is 40°. What is the measure of ∠1?

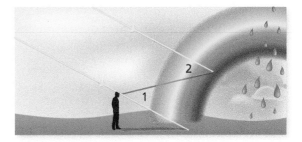

24. **MP REASONING** Is there a relationship between exterior angles that lie on the same side of a transversal? interior angles that lie on the same side of a transversal? Explain.

25. **MP REASONING** When a transversal is perpendicular to two parallel lines, all the angles formed measure 90°. Explain why.

26. **MP REASONING** Two horizontal lines are cut by a transversal. What is the least number of angle measures you need to know to find the measure of every angle? Explain your reasoning.

27. **MP LOGIC** Describe two ways you can show that ∠1 is congruent to ∠7.

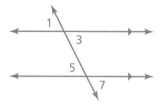

FINDING A VALUE Find the value of *x*.

28.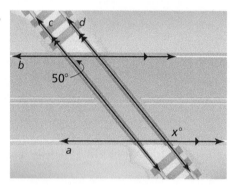

29.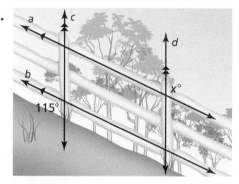

30. **PROJECT** Trace line *p* and line *t* on a piece of paper. Label ∠1. Move the paper so that ∠1 aligns with ∠8. Describe the transformations that you used to show that ∠1 is congruent to ∠8.

31. **OPEN-ENDED** Refer to the figure.

a. Do the horizontal lines appear to be parallel? Explain.

b. Draw your own optical illusion using parallel lines.

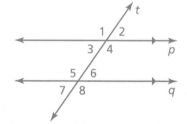

32. **DIG DEEPER!** The figure shows the angles used to make a shot on an air hockey table.

a. Find the value of *x*.

b. How does the angle the puck hits the edge of the table relate to the angle it leaves the edge of the table?

Common Errors

- **Exercises 28 and 29** Students may only see one set of parallel lines and think that they cannot find the measure of the missing angle. Point out the small arrows that denote that two lines are parallel. Encourage students to find the measure of an angle that is near the missing angle and then rotate the figure to help them visualize how to solve for the missing angle.

Mini-Assessment

Use the figure to find the measures of the numbered angles.

1.

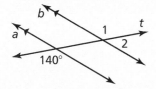

$\angle 1 = 140°$; $\angle 2 = 40°$

2.

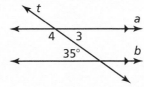

$\angle 3 = 35°$; $\angle 4 = 145°$

3.

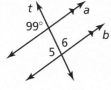

$\angle 5 = 99°$; $\angle 6 = 81°$

4.

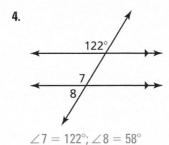

$\angle 7 = 122°$; $\angle 8 = 58°$

26. one angle measure; Three of the angles are congruent to that angle, and the other four angles are supplementary to that angle.

27. *Sample answer:* 1) $\angle 1$ and $\angle 7$ are congruent because they are alternate exterior angles. 2) $\angle 1$ and $\angle 5$ are congruent because they are corresponding angles. $\angle 5$ and $\angle 7$ are congruent because they are vertical angles. So, $\angle 1$ and $\angle 7$ are congruent.

28. 130

29. 115

30. *Sample answer:* Rotate 180° about the intersection point of line p and line t and then translate down along line t.

31. **a.** no; They look like they are spreading apart.

    b. Check students' work.

32. **a.** 64

    b. The angles are congruent.

Section Resources

Surface Level	Deep Level
Resources by Chapter • Extra Practice • Reteach • Puzzle Time Student Journal • Self-Assessment • Practice Differentiating the Lesson Tutorial Videos Skills Review Handbook Skills Trainer	Resources by Chapter • Enrichment and Extension Graphic Organizers Dynamic Assessment System • Section Practice

Learning Target

Understand properties of interior and exterior angles of triangles.

Success Criteria

- Use equations to find missing angle measures of triangles.
- Use interior and exterior angles of a triangle to solve real-life problems.

Warm Up

Cumulative, vocabulary, and prerequisite skills practice opportunities are available in the *Resources by Chapter* or at *BigIdeasMath.com*.

ELL Support

Write the words *interior* and *exterior* on the board. Explain that these words are opposites. Ask students if they recognize a word within these words. If necessary, direct them to the prefix *in-* by underlining it. Then underline the prefix *ex-* and ask if they know another word with this prefix. Guide them to identify *exit* and explain that an *exit* shows the way out of a room or building. Then ask them to guess what each word may mean and use the synonyms *inside* and *outside* if students are unable to guess.

Exploration 1

a. The sum of the interior angle measures of a triangle is 180°.

b. The measure of an exterior angle of a triangle is equal to the sum of the measures of the two nonadjacent interior angles.

Exploration 2

See Additional Answers.

Laurie's Notes

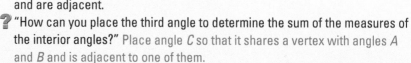

Preparing to Teach

- **MP3 Construct Viable Arguments and Critique the Reasoning of Others:** Mathematically proficient students are able to make conjectures and construct arguments to explain their reasoning.

Motivate

- Divide students into teams of three. Give them 3 minutes to make a list of as many words as they can that begin with the prefix *tri-*.
- Some examples are: triangle, triathlon, tricycle, triangulate, trilogy, and trio.
- Provide dictionaries if needed. The goal is to show that *tri-* is a common prefix.

Exploration 1

- Students can use geometry software available at *BigIdeasMath.com* and/or they can complete the following hands-on exploration.
- Cut out a variety of triangles. The sides of the triangles must be straight.
- Give one triangle to each student. Tell students to label the **interior angles** *A*, *B*, and *C*.
- Have students carefully tear off the three corners of the triangle and arrange angles *A* and *B* so that they share a vertex and are adjacent.

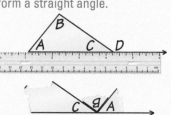

- ❓ "How can you place the third angle to determine the sum of the measures of the interior angles?" Place angle *C* so that it shares a vertex with angles *A* and *B* and is adjacent to one of them.
- ❓ "What is the sum? Explain." 180°; The angles form a straight angle.
- Part (b) may take more time than part (a). Give students another triangle and have them label the interior angles *A*, *B*, and *C*.
- Have students place the triangle on a piece of paper and extend one side to form **exterior angle** *D*.
- Have students tear off the corners that are not adjacent to the exterior angle and arrange them to fill the exterior angle.
- ❓ "What does this tell you about the measure of exterior angle *D*?" $\angle D = \angle A + \angle B$

Exploration 2

- Point out that angle *F* is an obtuse angle formed by lines *t* and *m*.
- **MP6 Attend to Precision:** You want to hear students make statements based upon evidence. Instead of, "Angles *C* and *E* are the same measure because they look it," students should say, "Angles *C* and *E* are the same measure because lines *m* and *n* are parallel and angles *C* and *E* are alternate interior angles."
- Students should connect angles *B*, *D*, and *E* to the three angles they placed about a point in Exploration 1(a). They should connect angles *G*, *B*, and *C* to the three angles they compared in Exploration 1(b). Now students are asked to *justify* their conclusions.

3.2 Angles of Triangles

Learning Target: Understand properties of interior and exterior angles of triangles.

Success Criteria:
- I can use equations to find missing angle measures of triangles.
- I can use interior and exterior angles of a triangle to solve real-life problems.

EXPLORATION 1

Exploring Interior and Exterior Angles of Triangles

Work with a partner.

a. Draw several triangles using geometry software. What can you conclude about the sums of the angle measures?

b. You can extend one side of a triangle to form an *exterior angle*, as shown.

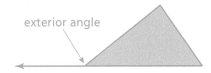

exterior angle

Use geometry software to draw a triangle and an exterior angle. Compare the measure of the exterior angle with the measures of the interior angles. Repeat this process for several different triangles. What can you conclude?

EXPLORATION 2

Using Parallel Lines and Transversals

Work with a partner. Describe what is shown in the figure below. Then use what you know about parallel lines and transversals to justify your conclusions in Exploration 1.

Math Practice

Look for Structure
Which angle labeled in the diagram is an exterior angle of △*ABC*?

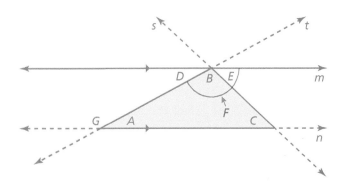

The angles inside a polygon are called **interior angles**. When the sides of a polygon are extended, other angles are formed. The angles outside the polygon that are adjacent to the interior angles are called **exterior angles**.

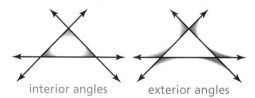

interior angles   exterior angles

Key Idea

Interior Angle Measures of a Triangle

Words The sum of the interior angle measures of a triangle is 180°.

Algebra $x + y + z = 180$

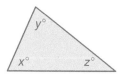

EXAMPLE 1 Using Interior Angle Measures

Find the measures of the interior angles of each triangle.

a.

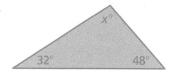

$$x + 32 + 48 = 180$$
$$x + 80 = 180$$
$$x = 100$$

▶ So, the measures of the interior angles are 100°, 48°, and 32°.

b.

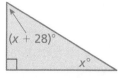

$$x + (x + 28) + 90 = 180$$
$$2x + 118 = 180$$
$$2x = 62$$
$$x = 31$$

▶ So, the measures of the interior angles are $(31 + 28)° = 59°$, 31°, and 90°.

Try It Find the measures of the interior angles of the triangle.

1.

2.

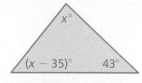

     Multi-Language Glossary at BigIdeasMath.com

Laurie's Notes

Scaffolding Instruction

- Students explored sums of the angle measures of triangles and exterior angle measures of triangles. Now they will use properties of interior and exterior angles of triangles to find missing angle measures.
- **Emerging:** Students understand that the sum of the angle measures of a triangle is 180°, but they need more practice using equations to find missing angle measures. They will benefit from guided instruction for the Key Ideas and examples.
- **Proficient:** Students understand properties of interior and exterior angles of triangles. They can use these properties to find the missing angle measures of triangles. These students should proceed to the Self-Assessment exercises.

Discuss

- Discuss **interior angles** and **exterior angles** of a triangle.
- ❓ "How many exterior angles does each triangle have?" 6 (2 at each vertex)
- Have students draw a triangle, extend the sides, and mark each of the exterior angles.
- ❓ "What is the relationship between the two exterior angles at each vertex?" They are congruent because they are vertical angles.

Key Idea

- The property is written with variables to suggest that you can solve an equation to find the third angle measure when you know the other two angle measures. This is also called the *Triangle Sum Theorem*.
- ❓ "What type of angles are the remaining angles of a right triangle? a triangle with an obtuse angle?" acute; acute
- ❓ "Do you think an obtuse triangle could have a right angle? Explain." No, the sum of the angle measures would be greater than 180°.

EXAMPLE 1

- Emphasize that students should show all the steps. Some students may argue that all they need to do is add the angle measures and subtract from 180. Remind them that they are practicing a *process*, one that works when the three angle measures are given as algebraic expressions, such as $(x + 10)°$, $(x + 20)°$, and $(x + 30)°$.

Try It

- Have students solve the problems on whiteboards. Remind them to show all of their work.

Extra Example 1

Find the measures of the interior angles of each triangle.

a.

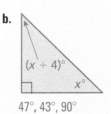

107°, 42°, 31°

b.

$(x + 4)°$ $x°$

47°, 43°, 90°

ELL Support

After demonstrating Example 1, have students work in pairs to discuss and solve Try It Exercises 1 and 2. Have one student ask another, "What angle measure(s) do you know? What is the value of *x*? What is the measure of the unknown angle(s)?" Have students alternate roles.

Beginner: Answer using numbers.

Intermediate: Answer using phrases or simple sentences such as, "Two angles are eighty-one and twenty-five degrees."

Advanced: Explain using detailed sentences such as, "I know that two angles have measures of eighty-one and twenty-five degrees, which is a total of one hundred six degrees."

Try It

1. 25°, 74°, 81°
2. 43°, 51°, 86°

Extra Example 2

Find the measure of the exterior angle.

a.

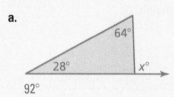

b.

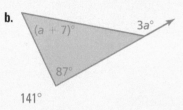

Try It

3. 70°

Self-Assessment
for Concepts & Skills

4. 2; When the sides are extended, 2 angles are formed that are adjacent to the interior angle.

5. 115

6. 105

Key Idea

- This is also called the *Exterior Angle Theorem*, and the two nonadjacent interior angles are also called the *remote interior angles*.

- **?** "If one of the interior angles of a triangle is acute, what do you know about the exterior angle at that vertex?" It is obtuse and a supplement of the acute angle.

- **?** "Can an exterior angle of a triangle be acute? Explain." Yes, if the adjacent interior angle is obtuse.

EXAMPLE 2

- **?** "How do you find the measure of the exterior angle in part (a)?" The exterior angle will be the sum of the two remote interior angles, so 36° + 72°.

- **MP2 Reason Abstractly and Quantitatively:** "Explain two different ways to find the measure of the third angle of the triangle." Use the Triangle Sum Theorem or find the supplement of the exterior angle.

- The problem in part (b) involves writing an equation versus doing mental math.

- Use the Exterior Angle Theorem to write the equation. Solve the equation as shown.

- **Common Error:** Students will solve for the variable *a* correctly and forget to answer the question asked, meaning they forget to substitute the value of *a* into the expression for the exterior angle.

Try It

- Have students solve the problems on whiteboards. Remind them to show all of their work.

Formative Assessment Tip

Fist of Five

This technique asks students to indicate the extent to which they understand a concept or procedure. Students hold 1 to 5 fingers in front of their chests, where 5 fingers represent mastery and 1 finger signifies uncertainty. This strategy can be a quick way for students to communicate where their learning is with respect to a specific success criterion.

✓ Self-Assessment *for Concepts & Skills*

- **Neighbor Check:** Have students complete the exercises independently and then have their neighbors check their work. Have students discuss any discrepancies.

- ◉ **Fist of Five:** Ask students to indicate their understanding of the first success criterion.

The Success Criteria Self-Assessment chart can be found in the *Student Journal* or online at *BigIdeasMath.com*.

 **Key Idea**

Exterior Angle Measures of a Triangle

Words The measure of an exterior angle of a triangle is equal to the sum of the measures of the two nonadjacent interior angles.

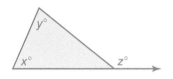

Algebra $z = x + y$

EXAMPLE 2 **Finding Exterior Angle Measures**

Find the measure of the exterior angle.

Each vertex has a pair of congruent exterior angles. However, it is common to show only one exterior angle at each vertex.

a.

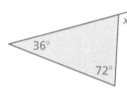

$x = 36 + 72$

$x = 108$

▶ So, the measure of the exterior angle is 108°.

b.

$2a = (a - 5) + 80$

$2a = a + 75$

$a = 75$

▶ So, the measure of the exterior angle is $2(75)° = 150°$.

Try It

3. Find the measure of the exterior angle of the triangle at the left.

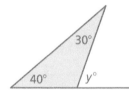 **Self-Assessment** *for Concepts & Skills*

Solve each exercise. Then rate your understanding of the success criteria in your journal.

4. **VOCABULARY** How many exterior angles does a triangle have at each vertex? Explain.

FINDING ANGLE MEASURES Find the value of x.

5.

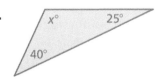

6.

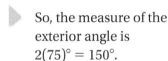

EXAMPLE 3 **Modeling Real Life**

An airplane leaves Miami and travels around the Bermuda Triangle as shown in the diagram. What is the measure of the interior angle at Miami?

Understand the problem.

You are given expressions representing the interior angle measures of the Bermuda Triangle. You are asked to find the measure of the interior angle at Miami.

Make a plan.

Use what you know about interior angle measures of triangles to write and solve an equation for x.

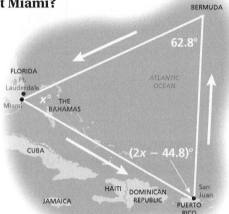

Solve and check.

$x + (2x - 44.8) + 62.8 = 180$	Write an equation.
$3x + 18 = 180$	Combine like terms.
$3x = 162$	Subtract 18 from each side.
$x = 54$	Divide each side by 3.

Check

$$x + (2x - 44.8) + 62.8 = 180$$
$$54 + [2(54) - 44.8] + 62.8 \overset{?}{=} 180$$
$$54 + 63.2 + 62.8 \overset{?}{=} 180$$
$$180 = 180 ✓$$

▷ So, the measure of the interior angle at Miami is 54°.

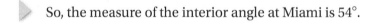

 Self-Assessment for Problem Solving

Solve each exercise. Then rate your understanding of the success criteria in your journal.

7. The *Historic Triangle* in Virginia connects Jamestown, Williamsburg, and Yorktown. The interior angle at Williamsburg is 120°. The interior angle at Jamestown is twice the measure of the interior angle at Yorktown. Find the measures of the interior angles at Jamestown and Yorktown. Explain your reasoning.

8. A helicopter travels from point C to point A to perform a medical supply drop. The helicopter then needs to land at point B. How many degrees should the helicopter turn at point A to travel towards point B? Justify your answer.

Laurie's Notes

EXAMPLE 3

- Ask a volunteer to read the problem aloud.
- Add a little interest by sharing information from the Department of the Navy website, *history.navy.mil*. The *Bermuda Triangle* is an imaginary area located off the southeastern Atlantic coast of the U.S. where a supposedly high incidence of unexplained disappearances of ships and aircraft occurs. The vertices of the triangle are Bermuda; Miami, Florida; and San Juan, Puerto Rico.
- Set up the equation and work through the problem as shown.
- This is a good review of equation solving and work with decimals.

✓ Self-Assessment for Problem Solving

- The goal for all students is to feel comfortable with the problem-solving plan. It is important for students to problem-solve in class, where they may receive support from you and their peers.
- **Think-Pair-Share:** Allow time for students to work independently, using a Four Square for each. Then have each student compare solutions with a partner. Have each pair compare their answers with another pair and discuss any discrepancies.
- **MP4 Model with Mathematics:** In Exercise 7, encourage students to draw a triangle to model the situation.
- ⦿ **Fist of Five:** Ask students to indicate their understanding of the second success criterion.

The Success Criteria Self-Assessment chart can be found in the *Student Journal* or online at *BigIdeasMath.com*.

Closure

- Find the measures of the interior angles of each triangle.

a.

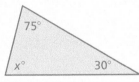

75°, 75°, 30°

b.

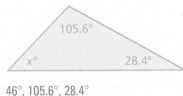

46°, 105.6°, 28.4°

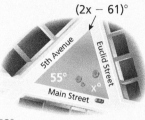

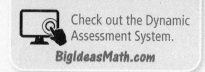
 Review & Refresh

1. 82°; ∠2 and the given angle are alternate exterior angles.

2. 82°; *Sample answer:* ∠6 and the given angle are vertical angles.

3. 82°; *Sample answer:* ∠4 and the given angle are corresponding angles.

4. 98°; *Sample answer:* ∠4 and ∠1 are supplementary.

5. 1, 2, 3

6. 2 ways

Concepts, Skills, & Problem Solving

7. ∠A = 30°, ∠B = 105°, ∠C = 45°, ∠D = 150°, ∠E = 75°, ∠F = 105°, ∠G = 30°

8. no; *Sample answer:* ∠F is not formed by extending a side of the triangle.

9. 30°, 60°, 90°

10. 40°, 65°, 75°

11. 35°, 45°, 100°

12. 25°, 45°, 110°

13. 44°, 48°, 88°

14. 48°, 59°, 73°

Assignment Guide and Concept Check

Scaffold assignments to support all students in their learning progression. The suggested assignments are a starting point. Continue to assign additional exercises and revisit with spaced practice to move every student toward proficiency.

Level	Assignment 1	Assignment 2
Emerging	1, 2, 3, 4, 5, 6, 7, 8, 9, 11, 13, 15	10, 12, 14, 16, 17, 18, 19, 20, 21, 23
Proficient	1, 2, 3, 4, 5, 6, 7, 8, 10, 12, 14, 15, 16	17, 18, 19, 20, 21, 22, 23, 24, 25
Advanced	1, 2, 3, 4, 5, 6, 7, 8, 10, 12, 14, 16, 17	18, 19, 20, 21, 22, 23, 24, 25, 26

- Assignment 1 is for use after students complete the Self-Assessment for Concepts & Skills.
- Assignment 2 is for use after students complete the Self-Assessment for Problem Solving.
- The red exercises can be used as a concept check.

Review & Refresh Prior Skills

Exercises 1–4   Finding Angle Measures
Exercises 5 and 6   Identifying Outcomes

Common Errors

- **Exercises 12–14** Students may forget to combine like terms when solving for x. Remind them that because there are two variables on the same side of the equal sign, they should start by combining like terms.
- **Exercises 12–14** Students may solve for the variable but forget to find the measures of the angles. Remind them to read the directions carefully and to answer the question.

3.2 Practice

Go to **BigIdeasMath.com** to get
HELP with solving the exercises.

▶ Review & Refresh

**Use the figure to find the measure of the angle.
Explain your reasoning.**

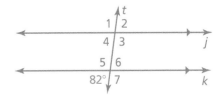

1. ∠2

2. ∠6

3. ∠4

4. ∠1

You spin the spinner shown.

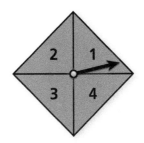

5. What are the favorable outcomes
of spinning a number less than 4?

6. In how many ways can spinning an
odd number occur?

▶▶ Concepts, Skills, & Problem Solving

USING PARALLEL LINES AND TRANSVERSALS **Consider the figure below.**
(See Exploration 2, p. 111.)

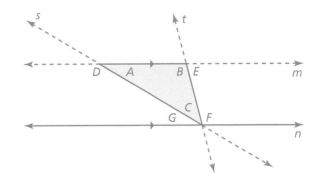

7. Use a protractor to find
the measures of the
labeled angles.

8. Is ∠F an exterior angle of
Triangle *ABC*? Justify your
answer.

USING INTERIOR ANGLE MEASURES **Find the measures of the interior angles of the triangle.**

9.

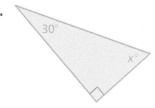

10.

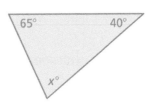

11.

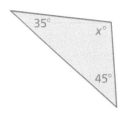

12.

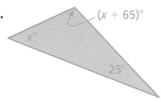

13.

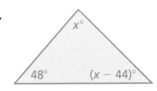

14.

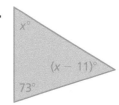

FINDING EXTERIOR ANGLE MEASURES **Find the measure of the exterior angle.**

15.
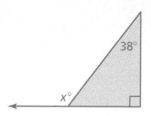

16.
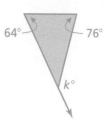

17.
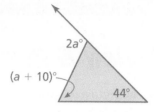

18. **MP MODELING REAL LIFE** A tornado is located between city hall and a cell phone tower and is heading towards the cell phone tower. By what angle does the tornado's direction need to change so that it passes over the radar station instead? Justify your answer.

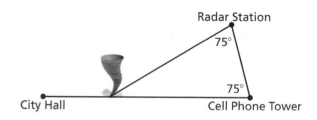

19. **MP YOU BE THE TEACHER** Your friend finds the measure of the exterior angle shown. Is your friend correct? Explain your reasoning.

$(3x - 6) + x + 30 = 180$

$4x + 24 = 180$

$x = 39$

The exterior angle is $(3(39) - 6)° = 111°$.

20. **MP REASONING** The ratio of the interior angle measures of a triangle is $2 : 3 : 5$. What are the angle measures?

21. **MP PROBLEM SOLVING** The support for a window air-conditioning unit forms a triangle and an exterior angle. What is the measure of the exterior angle?

22. **MP REASONING** A triangle has an exterior angle with a measure of $120°$. Can you determine the measures of the interior angles? Explain.

ANGLES OF TRIANGLES **Determine whether the statement is *always, sometimes, or never* true. Explain your reasoning.**

23. Given three angle measures, you can construct a triangle.

24. The acute interior angles of a right triangle are complementary.

25. A triangle has more than one vertex with an acute exterior angle.

26. **DIG DEEPER!** Using the figure at the right, write an equation that represents z in terms of x and y.

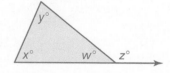

Common Errors

- **Exercises 17 and 21** Students may solve for the variable but forget to find the measure of the exterior angle. Remind them to read the directions carefully and to answer the question.
- **Exercise 21** Students may forget to combine like terms when solving for *x*. Remind them that because there are two variables on the same side of the equal sign, they should start by combining like terms.

Mini-Assessment

Find the measures of the interior angles.

1.

63°, 54°, 63°

2.

60°, 60°, 60°

3.

30°, 90°, 60°

Find the measure of the exterior angle.

4.

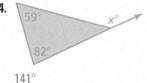

141°

5.

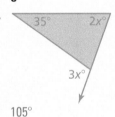

105°

Section Resources

Surface Level	Deep Level
Resources by Chapter • Extra Practice • Reteach • Puzzle Time Student Journal • Self-Assessment • Practice Differentiating the Lesson Tutorial Videos Skills Review Handbook Skills Trainer	Resources by Chapter • Enrichment and Extension Graphic Organizers Dynamic Assessment System • Section Practice
Transfer Level	
Dynamic Assessment System • Mid-Chapter Quiz	Assessment Book • Mid-Chapter Quiz

15. 128°

16. 140°

17. 108°

18. 30°;
$$x + 75 + 75 = 180$$
$$x = 30$$

19. no; The measure of the exterior angle is equal to the sum of the measures of the two nonadjacent interior angles. The sum of all three angles is not 180°.

20. 36°, 54°, 90°

21. 126°

22. no; The two nonadjacent interior angles could be any two angles that sum to 120°.

23. sometimes; The sum of the angle measures must equal 180°.

24. always; Because the sum of the interior angle measures must equal 180° and one of the interior angles is 90°, the other two interior angles must sum to 90°.

25. never; If a triangle had more than one vertex with an acute exterior angle, then it would have to have more than one obtuse interior angle, which is impossible.

26. $z = x + y$

Learning Target

Find interior angle measures of polygons.

Success Criteria

- Explain how to find the sum of the interior angle measures of a polygon.
- Use an equation to find an interior angle measure of a polygon.
- Find the interior angle measures of a regular polygon.

Warm Up

Cumulative, vocabulary, and prerequisite skills practice opportunities are available in the *Resources by Chapter* or at *BigIdeasMath.com*.

ELL Support

Explain that a polygon is a figure with three or more angles. Triangles and rectangles are examples of polygons. The word *polygon* comes from the Greek and Latin languages and literally means "many angles." The prefix *poly-* means "many" and the root *-gon* refers to angles. Ask students to draw a polygon and hold it up for your review.

Exploration 1

a. 360°

b. 540°

c. 720°

d. 900°

e. 1080°

f. 1260°

g. See Additional Answers.

Laurie's Notes

STATE STANDARDS
Applying 8.G.A.5

Preparing to Teach

- In the previous lesson, students found interior angle measures of triangles. Now they will extend their understanding to polygons. If your standards do not require finding interior angle measures of polygons, you may skip this lesson and proceed to the next.
- **MP8 Look for and Express Regularity in Repeated Reasoning:** In making sense of how to find the sum of the interior angles of a polygon, students will repeat a strategy, each time with a polygon having one more side than previously.

Motivate

- **?** "How many of you are looking forward to getting your driver's license?"
- Tell them that they will likely be tested on road signs.
- Draw several shapes and ask students if they know the names of the shapes and what they are used for on highway signs.

Exploration 1

- You may need to guide students through part (a) with the quadrilateral.
- Students recognize that the diagonal divides the quadrilateral into two triangles and that each triangle has interior angle measures that sum to 180°. The confusion is that the two triangles have a total of 6 angles and the quadrilateral has only 4 angles. Help students recognize that the diagonal divides two angles of the quadrilateral.

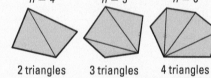

2 triangles   3 triangles   4 triangles

- The approach taken for the remaining polygons is slightly different. All of the diagonals are drawn from one vertex, forming triangles inside the polygon.
- **MP8 Look for and Express Regularity in Repeated Reasoning:** Students will use repeated reasoning as they explore the remaining polygons: the pentagon has 3 interior triangles so 3 × 180°, the hexagon has 4 interior triangles so 4 × 180°, and so on.
- **Common Error:** Students may draw diagonals that result in overlapping triangles. Tell them to draw the diagonals from a common vertex.
- **MP3 Construct Viable Arguments and Critique the Reasoning of Others:** Some students may conjecture that the number of triangles is two less than the number of sides in the polygon. Other students may just notice that the sum of the interior angle measures is increasing by 180° each time.
- **Connection:** Students who snowboard or skateboard will recognize the number pattern quickly. They know the multiples of 180° well.
- The table helps to organize the data. This also will help students make the connection between the number of sides and the number of triangles formed.
- **?** **Extension:** "How can you find the interior angle sum for a polygon with 12 sides?" *Sample answer:* Substitute 12 for *n* in the equation $S = (n - 2) \cdot 180°$, then solve for *S*.

3.3 Angles of Polygons

Learning Target: Find interior angle measures of polygons.

Success Criteria:
- I can explain how to find the sum of the interior angle measures of a polygon.
- I can use an equation to find an interior angle measure of a polygon.
- I can find the interior angle measures of a regular polygon.

EXPLORATION 1

Exploring Interior Angles of Polygons

Work with a partner. In parts (a)–(f), use what you know about the interior angle measures of triangles to find the sum of the interior angle measures of each figure.

Math Practice

View as Components

How does dividing the figure into triangles help you find the sum of the interior angle measures?

a.

b.

c.
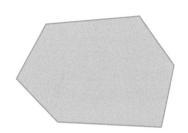

d.

e.

f.

g. **REPEATED REASONING** Use your results in parts (a)–(f) to complete the table. Then write an equation that represents the sum S of the interior angle measures of a polygon with n sides.

Number of Sides, n	3	4	5	6	7	8	9
Number of Triangles							
Interior Angle Sum, S							

3.3 Lesson

Key Vocabulary
regular polygon,
p. 120

A *polygon* is a closed plane figure made up of three or more line segments that intersect only at their endpoints.

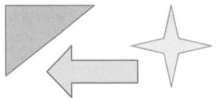

Polygons   **Not polygons**

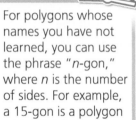 **Reading**

For polygons whose names you have not learned, you can use the phrase "*n*-gon," where *n* is the number of sides. For example, a 15-gon is a polygon with 15 sides.

🔑 Key Idea

Interior Angle Measures of a Polygon

The sum S of the interior angle measures of a polygon with n sides is

$$S = (n - 2) \cdot 180°.$$

EXAMPLE 1 ## Finding the Sum of Interior Angle Measures

Find the sum of the interior angle measures of the school crossing sign.

The sign is in the shape of a pentagon. It has 5 sides.

$S = (n - 2) \cdot 180°$	Write the formula.
$\quad = (5 - 2) \cdot 180°$	Substitute 5 for *n*.
$\quad = 3 \cdot 180°$	Subtract.
$\quad = 540°$	Multiply.

▸ The sum of the interior angle measures is 540°.

Try It **Find the sum of the interior angle measures of the green polygon.**

1.

2.

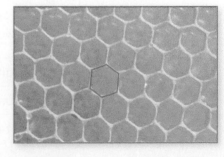

🔊 Multi-Language Glossary at *BigIdeasMath.com*

Laurie's Notes

Scaffolding Instruction

- Students explored finding the sum of the interior angle measures of a polygon and wrote an equation to represent the sum. They will now use a formula to find the sums of interior angle measures of polygons.
- **Emerging:** Students may have difficulty drawing the triangles in a polygon to represent the sum of the interior angle measures. Provide guided instruction for the Key Idea and examples.
- **Proficient:** Students can find the sum of interior angle measures of polygons. They should proceed to Example 2 to develop an understanding of using an equation to find an interior angle measure of a polygon. Example 3 will help them understand how to find the interior angle measures of a **regular polygon**. After reviewing both examples, students can check their understanding using the Self-Assessment exercises.

Discuss

- Write the definition for a *polygon*. Draw examples of figures which are and are not polygons. Students should be able to explain why some are not polygons.
- In all of the samples shown, the interior is shaded. The polygon is the figure formed by the line segments. The polygonal region contains the interior of the polygon.

Key Idea

- Write the Key Idea. This is the same equation that students wrote in the exploration. This form highlights the fact that the sum is a multiple of 180°.
- **Teaching Strategy:** The formula is not something students should just memorize. They need to see the relationship between the triangles and the formula.

EXAMPLE 1

- Review the names of common polygons: triangle (3), quadrilateral (4), pentagon (5), hexagon (6), heptagon (7), octagon (8), nonagon (9), and decagon (10). It is also common to say *n*-gon and replace *n* with 9 to talk about a 9-sided polygon.

Try It

- **Think-Pair-Share:** Students should read each exercise independently and then work in pairs to solve the exercises. Have each pair compare their answers with another pair and discuss any discrepancies.
- ❓ "What are the names of the polygons in Exercises 1 and 2?" 7-gon or heptagon; hexagon

Scaffold instruction to support all students in their learning. Learning is individualized and you may want to group students differently as they move in and out of these levels with each skill and concept. Student self-assessment and feedback help guide your instructional decisions about how and when to layer support for all students to become proficient learners.

Teaching Strategy

The exploration helps students understand the origin of the formula for the sum of the interior angle measures of a polygon. Often, students just want to memorize and apply a formula. If students memorize and then forget the formula, they are lost. If they understand how the formula was derived, they can recreate it. When finding the sum of the interior angle measures of a polygon, students should visualize or draw the diagonals and then multiply the number of triangles by 180°.

Extra Example 1

Find the sum of the interior angle measures of the stop sign.

1080°

Try It

1. 900°
2. 720°

Laurie's Notes

Extra Example 2

Find the value of *x*.

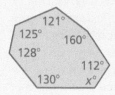

121°
125°
160°
128°
112°
130°   *x*°

124

Try It

3. 105

4. 75

Self-Assessment
for Concepts & Skills

5. *Sample answer:* Subtract 2 from the number of sides the polygon has and multiply that value by 180°.

6. 360°

7. 70

8. 155

EXAMPLE 2

- **Connection:** This example integrates equation solving with finding a missing angle.
- ? "How many sides does the polygon have?" 7
- ? "How do you find the sum of the interior angle measures of a 7-gon?" Solve $S = (7 - 2) \cdot 180°$.
- Once the sum is known, write and solve the equation as shown. Caution students to be careful with their arithmetic.

Try It

- **MP1 Make Sense of Problems and Persevere in Solving Them:** Students should check with their neighbors to make sure they are setting up the equation correctly. Each problem has two parts: determining the sum of the interior angle measures and then writing the equation to solve for the missing angle.
- In Exercise 4, remind students that the symbol for a right angle means the angle measures 90°.

✓ Self-Assessment for Concepts & Skills

- **Think-Pair-Share:** Students should read each exercise independently and then work in pairs to solve the exercises. Have each pair compare their answers with another pair and discuss any discrepancies.
- ⊙ **Fist of Five:** Ask students to indicate their understanding of the first and second success criterion. Then select students to explain each one.

ELL Support

Proceed as described in Laurie's Notes. Have each pair display their answers for Exercises 6–8 on a whiteboard for your review.

The Success Criteria Self-Assessment chart can be found in the *Student Journal* or online at *BigIdeasMath.com*.

EXAMPLE 2 **Finding an Interior Angle Measure of a Polygon**

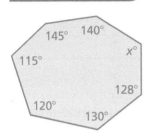

Find the value of x.

Step 1: The polygon has 7 sides. Find the sum of the interior angle measures.

$$S = (n - 2) \cdot 180°$$ Write the formula.

$$= (7 - 2) \cdot 180°$$ Substitute 7 for *n*.

$$= 900°$$ Simplify. The sum of the interior angle measures is 900°.

Step 2: Write and solve an equation.

$$140 + 145 + 115 + 120 + 130 + 128 + x = 900$$
$$778 + x = 900$$
$$x = 122$$

▷   The value of *x* is 122.

Try It **Find the value of x.**

3.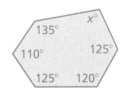

4.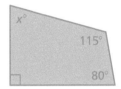

Self-Assessment *for Concepts & Skills*

Solve each exercise. Then rate your understanding of the success criteria in your journal.

5. **WRITING** Explain how to find the sum of the interior measures of a polygon.

6. **FINDING THE SUM OF INTERIOR ANGLE MEASURES** Find the sum of the interior angle measures of the green polygon.

FINDING AN INTERIOR ANGLE MEASURE **Find the value of x.**

7.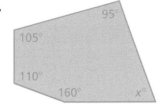

8.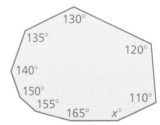

In a **regular polygon**, all the sides are congruent, and all the interior angles are congruent.

Modeling Real Life

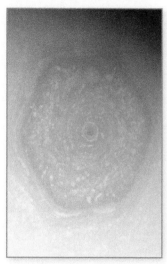

A cloud system discovered on Saturn is in the approximate shape of a regular hexagon. Find the measure of each interior angle of the hexagon.

A hexagon has 6 sides. Use the formula to find the sum of the interior angle measures.

$S = (n - 2) \cdot 180°$ Write the formula.

$= (6 - 2) \cdot 180°$ Substitute 6 for n.

$= 720°$ Simplify. The sum of the interior angle measures is 720°.

In a regular polygon, each interior angle is congruent. So, divide the sum of the interior angle measures by the number of interior angles, 6.

$720° \div 6 = 120°$

The measure of each interior angle is 120°.

The hexagon is about 15,000 miles across. Approximately four Earths can fit inside it.

Self-Assessment for Problem Solving

Solve each exercise. Then rate your understanding of the success criteria in your journal.

9. A company installs an octagonal swimming pool.

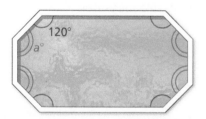

     a. Find the value of a for the pool shown at the left.

     b. The company installs a different pool that is also in the shape of an octagon. The second pool has twice the length and one-third the width of the first pool. Are the sums of the interior angles of the pools different? Justify your answer.

10. **DIG DEEPER!** A *Bronze Star Medal* is shown.

     a. How many interior angles are there?

     b. What is the sum of the interior angle measures?

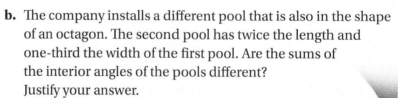

Laurie's Notes

Discuss

- Review the definition for a **regular polygon**. Point out to students that squares and equilateral triangles are examples of regular polygons.

EXAMPLE 3

- Ask a student to read the problem aloud.
- Have students write down what the problem is asking and what information they need to know.
- Discuss their responses and guide them in making a plan.
- A regular hexagon has 6 congruent angles. If the angle measures of a hexagon sum to 720° and the 6 angles are congruent, it should make sense to students why they divide 720° by 6.
- You can show a video of the cloud system from the website *jpl.nasa.gov*.

✓ Self-Assessment for Problem Solving

- Allow time in class for students to practice using the problem-solving plan. Remember, some students may only be able to complete the first step.
- Students should make a plan for each of the problems independently. Then have each student discuss his or her plans with a partner before solving the problems independently.
- ⊙ **Fist of Five:** Ask students to indicate their understanding of the third success criterion.

The Success Criteria Self-Assessment chart can be found in the *Student Journal* or online at *BigIdeasMath.com*.

Closure

- A pentagon has two interior right angles and the other three interior angles are all congruent. What is the measure of one of the three congruent angles? 120°

Extra Example 3

A cloud system is in the approximate shape of a regular polygon with 12 sides. Find the measure of each interior angle of the polygon. 150°

Self-Assessment
for Problem Solving

9. **a.** 150

   b. no; The sum of the interior angles of any octagon is 1080°.

10. **a.** 10 angles

    b. 1440°

Learning Target

Find interior angle measures of polygons.

Success Criteria

- Explain how to find the sum of the interior angle measures of a polygon.
- Use an equation to find an interior angle measure of a polygon.
- Find the interior angle measures of a regular polygon.

Review & Refresh

1. 60
2. 45
3. 113
4. $x = 9$
5. $x = 2$
6. $x = 3$

Concepts, Skills, & Problem Solving

7. 360°
8. 1260°
9. 540°
10. 360°
11. 1080°
12. 1260°
13. no; The right side of the formula should be $(n - 2) \cdot 180°$, not $n \cdot 180°$.
14. 43
15. 135
16. 90

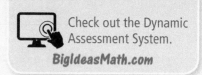
Assignment Guide and Concept Check

Scaffold assignments to support all students in their learning progression. The suggested assignments are a starting point. Continue to assign additional exercises and revisit with spaced practice to move every student toward proficiency.

Level	Assignment 1	Assignment 2
Emerging	2, 3, 6, 7, 8, 9, 10, 11, 12, 13, 14	15, 16, 17, 18, 19, 20, 21, 24
Proficient	2, 3, 6, 7, 8, 9, 10, 12, 13, 14, 15, 16	17, 18, 19, 20, 21, 22, 23, 24, 27
Advanced	2, 3, 6, 7, 8, 9, 10, 12, 13, 14, 15, 16	18, 19, 20, 21, 22, 23, 25, 26, 27

- Assignment 1 is for use after students complete the Self-Assessment for Concepts & Skills.
- Assignment 2 is for use after students complete the Self-Assessment for Problem Solving.
- The red exercises can be used as a concept check.

Review & Refresh Prior Skills

Exercises 1 and 2 Using Interior Angle Measures
Exercise 3 Finding Exterior Angle Measures
Exercises 4–6 Solving a Proportion

Common Errors

- **Exercises 7–9** Students may struggle dividing the polygon into triangles. Encourage them to trace the polygon in pen in their notebooks and then to draw triangles with a pencil so that they can erase lines if necessary.
- **Exercises 10–12** Students may forget to subtract 2 from the number of sides when using the formula to find the sum of the interior angle measures. Remind students of the formula and encourage them to write the formula before substituting the number of sides.
- **Exercises 14–16** Students may forget to include one or more of the given angles when writing an equation for the missing angles. For example, in Exercise 15, students may write $4x = 720$. Remind students to include all of the angles. Encourage them to write the equation and then count the number of terms to make sure that there is the same number of terms as angles before simplifying.

3.3 Practice

Go to *BigIdeasMath.com* to get HELP with solving the exercises.

▶ Review & Refresh

Find the value of *x*.

1.

2.

3.

Solve the proportion.

4. $\dfrac{x}{12} = \dfrac{3}{4}$

5. $\dfrac{14}{21} = \dfrac{x}{3}$

6. $\dfrac{9}{x} = \dfrac{6}{2}$

▶▶ Concepts, Skills, & Problem Solving

EXPLORING INTERIOR ANGLES OF POLYGONS **Use triangles to find the sum of the interior angle measures of the polygon.** (See Exploration 1, p. 117.)

7.

8.

9.

FINDING THE SUM OF INTERIOR ANGLE MEASURES **Find the sum of the interior angle measures of the polygon.**

10.

11.

12.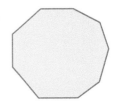

13. **(MP) YOU BE THE TEACHER** Your friend finds the sum of the interior angle measures of a 13-gon. Is your friend correct? Explain your reasoning.

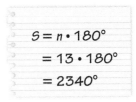

$$S = n \cdot 180°$$
$$= 13 \cdot 180°$$
$$= 2340°$$

FINDING AN INTERIOR ANGLE MEASURE **Find the value of *x*.**

14.

15.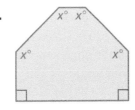

16.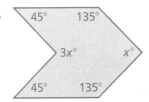

FINDING A MEASURE Find the measure of each interior angle of the regular polygon.

17.

18.

19.

20. (MP) **YOU BE THE TEACHER** Your friend finds the measure of each interior angle of a regular 20-gon. Is your friend correct? Explain your reasoning.

$$S = (n - 2) \cdot 180°$$
$$= (20 - 2) \cdot 180°$$
$$= 18 \cdot 180°$$
$$= 3240°$$
$$3240° \div 18 = 180°$$
The measure of each interior angle is 180°.

21. (MP) **MODELING REAL LIFE** A fire hydrant bolt is in the shape of a regular pentagon.

   a. What is the measure of each interior angle?

   b. **RESEARCH** Why are fire hydrants made this way?

22. (MP) **PROBLEM SOLVING** The interior angles of a regular polygon each measure 165°. How many sides does the polygon have?

23. (MP) **STRUCTURE** A molecule can be represented by a polygon with interior angles that each measure 120°. What polygon represents the molecule? Does the polygon have to be regular? Justify your answers.

24. (MP) **PROBLEM SOLVING** The border of a Susan B. Anthony dollar is in the shape of a regular polygon.

   a. How many sides does the polygon have?

   b. What is the measure of each interior angle of the border? Round your answer to the nearest degree.

25. (MP) **REASONING** The center of the stained glass window is in the shape of a regular polygon. What are the measures of the interior angles of the green triangle?

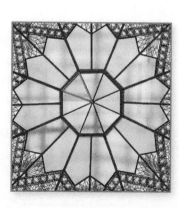

26. **GEOMETRY** Draw a pentagon that has two right interior angles, two 45° interior angles, and one 270° interior angle.

27. **DIG DEEPER!** The floor of a gazebo is in the shape of a heptagon, a seven-sided polygon. Four of the interior angles measure $x°$. The sum of these four angles is 540°. The other interior angles have equal measures. Find the measures of all the interior angles.

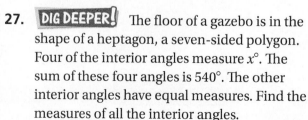

 Common Errors

- **Exercises 17–19** Students may find the sum of the interior angle measures of the regular polygon but forget to divide by the number of angles to find the measure of *each* interior angle. Remind students that they are finding the measure of *one* angle. Because all the angles are congruent (by the definition of a regular polygon), they can divide the sum of the interior angle measures by the number of angles.

Mini-Assessment

Find the sum of the interior angle measures of the polygon.

1.

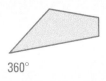

360°

2.

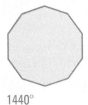

1440°

3. Find the value of *x*.

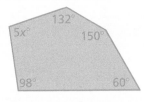

20

4. Find the measure of each interior angle of a 16-gon. 157.5°

Section Resources

Surface Level	Deep Level
Resources by Chapter • Extra Practice • Reteach • Puzzle Time Student Journal • Self-Assessment • Practice Differentiating the Lesson Tutorial Videos Skills Review Handbook Skills Trainer	Resources by Chapter • Enrichment and Extension Graphic Organizers Dynamic Assessment System • Section Practice

 Concepts, Skills, & Problem Solving

17. 60°

18. 140°

19. 150°

20. no; The sum of the interior angle measures should have been divided by the number of interior angles, 20.

21. a. 108°

 b. *Sample answer:* to deter people from tampering with fire hydrants, because most wrenches are hexagonal

22. 24 sides

23. hexagon;
number of interior angles
 = number of sides
 = n
$120 \cdot n = (n - 2) \cdot 180$
 $n = 6$;
no; *Sample answer:* The sides do not have to be the same length.

24. a. 11 sides

 b. 147°

25. 45°, 67.5°, 67.5°

26. *Sample answer:*

27. 135°, 135°, 135°, 135°, 120°, 120°, 120°

STATE STANDARDS
8.G.A.5

COMMON CORE

Learning Target

Use similar triangles to find missing measures.

Success Criteria

- Use angle measures to determine whether triangles are similar.
- Use similar triangles to solve real-life problems.

Warm Up

Cumulative, vocabulary, and prerequisite skills practice opportunities are available in the *Resources by Chapter* or at *BigIdeasMath.com*.

ELL Support

Write the word *similar* on the board, say it, and have students repeat. Ask them what it means and have them describe or provide as many synonyms as possible. You could suggest words such as *same*, *alike*, and *related*. Then review the mathematical definition for the phrase *similar triangles*.

Exploration 1

a–b. no; yes; The triangles are not congruent because they are not the same size. The triangles are similar because the second triangle is a dilation of the first triangle.

c. Two triangles that have two pairs of congruent angles are similar.

Exploration 2

See Additional Answers.

Laurie's Notes
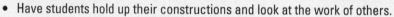

Preparing to Teach

- **MP5 Use Appropriate Tools Strategically:** Similar triangles can be investigated using geometry software or a protractor and a ruler. Mathematically proficient students consider the available tools when solving a mathematics problem.

Motivate

- Ask students to work with partners to construct a triangle with side lengths of 4 inches, 5 inches, and 6 inches. Each pair will need 2 rulers, a protractor, and a piece of paper.
- Without a compass, they will need to work together, using both rulers to locate the third vertex.
- Have students measure the angles in the triangle they constructed.

6 in.

- Have students hold up their constructions and look at the work of others.
- Discuss the results; namely, that all of the triangles are congruent.
- ❓ Ask, "What is the difference between similar triangles and congruent triangles?" Congruent triangles must have the same size and shape. Similar triangles have the same shape but not necessarily the same size.

Exploration 1

- Geometry software is available at *BigIdeasMath.com*. Alternatively, the exploration can be completed using paper, a pencil, and a protractor.
- The length of $\overline{BC}$ is not specified.
- Students can use the measure function to find the measure of angle *A* in each triangle. Students can also measure sides to see that corresponding sides are proportional.

Exploration 2

- **Teaching Tip:** This is a fun exploration for students to conduct themselves, if time and weather permit. Each pair will need a measuring tape. Take students outside (near a flag pole) to measure their heights and shadows. They also need to measure the shadow of the flag pole.
- ❓ "Is your shadow shorter at noon or 5 P.M.? Explain." noon; The Sun is overhead, not at a lower position in the sky.
- ❓ "Do adjacent objects of different heights cast the same length shadow? Explain." No, taller objects cast longer shadows.
- The triangles are similar because they both have a right angle and the parallel rays of the Sun are at the same angle to the ground.
- Discuss students' methods for solving the problem. They may use their conjectures from Exploration 1 or a dilation to show that the triangles are similar. Then students can set up a proportion to find the height of the flag pole.

3.4 Using Similar Triangles

Learning Target: Use similar triangles to find missing measures.

Success Criteria:
- I can use angle measures to determine whether triangles are similar.
- I can use similar triangles to solve real-life problems.

EXPLORATION 1

Drawing Triangles Given Two Angle Measures

Work with a partner. Use geometry software.

a. Draw a triangle that has a 50° angle and a 30° angle. Then draw a triangle that is either larger or smaller that has the same two angle measures. Are the triangles congruent? similar? Explain your reasoning.

b. Choose any two angle measures whose sum is less than 180°. Repeat part (a) using the angle measures you chose.

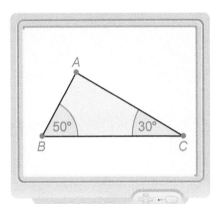

c. Compare your results in parts (a) and (b) with other pairs of students. Make a conjecture about two triangles that have two pairs of congruent angles.

EXPLORATION 2

Using Indirect Measurement

Work with a partner. Use the fact that two rays from the Sun are parallel to make a plan for how to find the height of the flagpole. Explain your reasoning.

Math Practice

Make Sense of Quantities

What do you know about the sides of similar triangles?

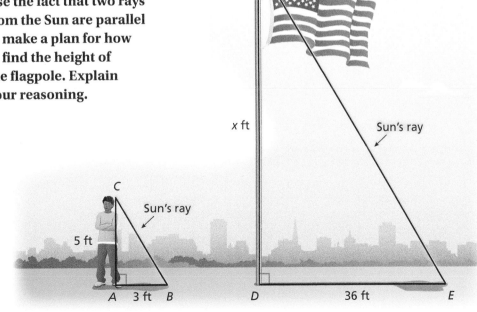

Key Vocabulary 🔊
indirect measurement,
p. 126

🔑 Key Idea

Angles of Similar Triangles

Words When two angles in one triangle are congruent to two angles in another triangle, the third angles are also congruent and the triangles are similar.

Example

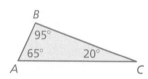
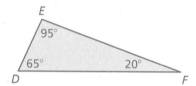

Triangle *ABC* is similar to Triangle *DEF*: △*ABC* ~ △*DEF*.

EXAMPLE 1 ## Identifying Similar Triangles

Tell whether the triangles are similar. Explain.

a.

The triangles have two pairs of congruent angles.

▷ So, the third angles are congruent, and the triangles are similar.

Math Practice

Build Arguments
Explain why you only need to know that two pairs of angles are congruent to know that two triangles are similar.

b.

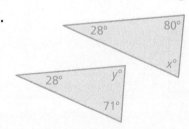

Write and solve an equation to find *x*.

$$x + 90 + 42 = 180$$
$$x + 132 = 180$$
$$x = 48$$

The triangles do not have two pairs of congruent angles.

▷ So, the triangles are not similar.

Try It **Tell whether the triangles are similar. Explain.**

1.

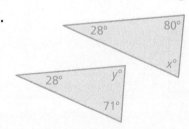

2.

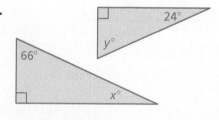

🔊 Multi-Language Glossary at *BigIdeasMath.com*

Laurie's Notes

Scaffolding Instruction

- Students explored special properties of similar triangles. Now they will use similar triangles to solve real-life problems.
- **Emerging:** Students may be able to use angle measures to determine whether triangles are similar, but they might have difficulty finding missing side lengths. They will benefit from guided instruction for the Key Idea and examples.
- **Proficient:** Students understand and can use properties of similar triangles to solve problems. They should review the Key Idea before proceeding to the Self-Assessment exercises.

Key Idea

- Write the informal definition (same shape, not necessarily the same size), and draw examples of similar triangles.
- ? "What is the formal definition of similar triangles?" Two triangles are similar when one can be obtained from the other by a similarity transformation.
- Write the Key Idea.
- Make sure students understand that there are two parts stated in the Key Idea. When you have two angles in one triangle congruent to two angles in another triangle, then:
  (1) the third angles are congruent.
  (2) the two triangles are similar.

EXAMPLE 1

- Draw the two triangles and label the given information. Ask students to solve for the missing angle measure of each triangle.
- ? "Are the triangles in part (a) similar? Explain." Yes, the triangles have two pairs of congruent angles.
- ? "What type of triangles are in part (b)?" Both are right triangles.
- ? "Are the triangles similar? Explain." No, solving for the missing angles, the triangles only have one pair of congruent angles. So, the triangles are not similar.
- ? "Do you need to solve for y? Explain." No, once you solve for x, you know that the triangles do not have two pairs of congruent angles.

Try It

- **Think-Pair-Share:** Students should read each exercise independently and then work in pairs to solve the exercises. Have each pair compare their answers with another pair and discuss any discrepancies.

ELL Support

After demonstrating Example 1, have students work in groups to discuss and complete Try It Exercises 1 and 2. Expect students to perform according to their language levels.

Beginner: Write and solve an equation (if necessary), and state *yes* or *no*.

Intermediate: Explain using phrases or simple sentences.

Advanced: Explain using detailed sentences and help guide discussion.

Scaffold instruction to support all students in their learning. Learning is individualized and you may want to group students differently as they move in and out of these levels with each skill and concept. Student self-assessment and feedback help guide your instructional decisions about how and when to layer support for all students to become proficient learners.

Extra Example 1

Tell whether the triangles are similar. Explain.

a.

no; The triangles do not have two pairs of congruent angles.

b.

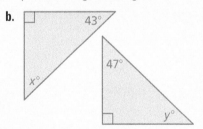

yes; The triangles have two pairs of congruent angles.

Try It

1. no; The triangles do not have the same angle measures.

2. yes; The triangles have the same angle measures, 90°, 66°, and 24°.

Extra Example 2

Can you determine whether △ABC and △EDC are similar? Explain.

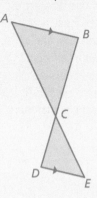

yes; *Sample answer:* ∠ACB and ∠ECD are vertical angles, so they are congruent. $\overline{AB}$ and $\overline{DE}$ are parallel, and each is intersected by $\overline{AE}$. So, ∠A and ∠E are congruent alternate interior angles. Because two angles in △ABC are congruent to two angles in △EDC, the triangles are similar.

Try It

3. no; You cannot determine that two pairs of angles are congruent from the given information.

Self-Assessment
for Concepts & Skills

4. yes; The triangles have the same angle measures, 63°, 63°, and 54°.

5. Are △PQR and △TSR the same size and shape?; no; yes

EXAMPLE 2

- Give students time to read the problem and investigate the diagram.
- Make sure students understand that each side of the triangles is part of an infinite line, so parallel lines and transversal properties from Section 3.1 apply.
- Work through the problem as shown.
- **Extension:** Have students measure the sides (to the nearest 0.5 centimeter) of each triangle and verify that the ratios of corresponding side lengths are equivalent.

$$\frac{JK}{JM} = \frac{KL}{MN} = \frac{JL}{JN}$$

Try It

- Have students work with a partner. Select several pairs to share their explanations with the class.

✓ Self-Assessment for Concepts & Skills

- **Neighbor Check:** Have students complete the exercises independently and then have their neighbors check their work. Have students discuss any discrepancies.

- ⊙ Have students use *Thumbs Up* to indicate their understanding of how to determine if two triangles are similar. Select several students to share with the class.

ELL Support

Allow students to work in pairs for extra support and to practice language. Check for understanding of Exercise 4 by having students indicate whether the triangles are similar using a thumbs up for *yes* or a thumbs down for *no*. Then have two pairs form a group to discuss and refine their explanations for Exercises 4 and 5. The two pairs must reach an agreement if their ideas differ. Monitor discussions and provide support.

The Success Criteria Self-Assessment chart can be found in the *Student Journal* or online at *BigIdeasMath.com*.

EXAMPLE 2 **Identifying Similar Triangles**

Can you determine whether △*JKL* and △*JMN* are similar? Explain.

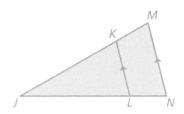

Side *KL* and side *MN* are parallel, and each is intersected by side *JN*. So, ∠*JLK* and ∠*N* are congruent corresponding angles. Each triangle also shares ∠*J*.

> Because two angles in △*JKL* are congruent to two angles in △*JMN*, the third angles are also congruent and the triangles are similar.

You can also use corresponding angles to show that ∠*JKL* is congruent to ∠*M*.

Try It

3. Can you determine whether △*PQR* and △*TSR* are similar? Explain.

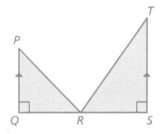

 Self-Assessment *for Concepts & Skills*

Solve each exercise. Then rate your understanding of the success criteria in your journal.

4. **IDENTIFYING SIMILAR TRIANGLES**
   Tell whether the triangles are similar. Explain.

5. **DIFFERENT WORDS, SAME QUESTION** Which is different? Find "both" answers.

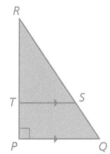

Are △*PQR* and △*TSR* similar?

Are △*PQR* and △*TSR* the same size and shape?

Is △*PQR* a dilation of △*TSR*?

Is △*PQR* a scale drawing of △*TSR*?

Indirect measurement uses similar figures to find a missing measure when it is difficult to find directly.

EXAMPLE 3 **Modeling Real Life**

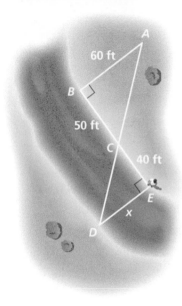

You plan to cross a river and want to know how far it is to the other side. You take measurements on your side of the river and make the drawing shown. What is the distance x across the river?

Notice that $\angle B$ and $\angle E$ are right angles, so they are congruent. $\angle ACB$ and $\angle DCE$ are vertical angles, so they are congruent. Because two angles in $\triangle ABC$ are congruent to two angles in $\triangle DEC$, the third angles are also congruent and the triangles are similar.

Ratios of corresponding side lengths in similar triangles are equivalent. So, the ratios $x:60$ and $40:50$ are equivalent. Write and solve a proportion to find x.

$$\frac{x}{60} = \frac{40}{50} \qquad \text{Write a proportion.}$$

$$60 \cdot \frac{x}{60} = 60 \cdot \frac{40}{50} \qquad \text{Multiplication Property of Equality}$$

$$x = 48 \qquad \text{Simplify.}$$

▷ So, the distance across the river is 48 feet.

Self-Assessment for Problem Solving

Solve each exercise. Then rate your understanding of the success criteria in your journal.

6. Engineers plan to construct an aqueduct to transport water from the top of a ridge to farmland. A portion of the project is complete. Find the length of the entire aqueduct.

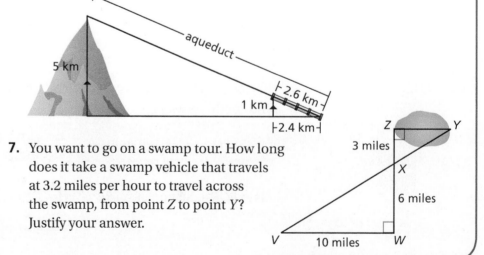

5 km

aqueduct

2.6 km

1 km

2.4 km

7. You want to go on a swamp tour. How long does it take a swamp vehicle that travels at 3.2 miles per hour to travel across the swamp, from point Z to point Y? Justify your answer.

Z Y

3 miles

X

6 miles

V 10 miles W

Laurie's Notes

Discuss

- **Indirect measurement** is used when you want to know the measurement of some length (or angle) and you cannot measure the object directly. In the exploration, students used indirect measurement to find the height of the flag pole.

EXAMPLE 3

- Ask a volunteer to read the problem. Make a rough sketch of the diagram.
- "What do you know about the angles in either triangle?" $\angle B$ and $\angle E$ are right angles. The vertical angles are congruent. Mark the congruent angles.
- "What do you know about the third angle in each triangle? Explain." They are congruent; When two angles in one triangle are congruent to two angles in another triangle, the third angles are also congruent.
- **MP7 Look for and Make Use of Structure:** Because the triangles are similar, the corresponding sides will have the same ratio. Setting up the ratios is challenging for students. Talk about the sides in terms of being the shorter leg of the right triangle and the longer leg of the right triangle. This should help students use the structure of the triangles to set up the ratios.
- Use the Multiplication Property of Equality or the Cross Products Property to solve. Check the reasonableness of the answer.

✓ Self-Assessment for Problem Solving

- Allow time in class for students to practice using the problem-solving plan. Remember, some students may only be able to complete the first step.
- ◉ Have students use *Thumbs Up* to indicate their understanding of how to use similar triangles to solve real-life problems.

The Success Criteria Self-Assessment chart can be found in the *Student Journal* or online at *BigIdeasMath.com*.

Formative Assessment Tip

Exit Ticket

This technique asks students to respond to a question at the end of a lesson, activity, or learning experience. The *Exit Ticket* allows you to collect evidence of student learning. I cut scrap paper into smaller pieces so that "exit tickets" can be distributed quickly to students.

The *Exit Ticket* is helpful in planning instruction. During the class there may be students you have not heard from. They may not have raised their hands or they may have been less vocal when working with partners. The *Exit Ticket* helps you gauge the ability of all students to answer a particular type of question. Collect the *Exit Tickets* and use the responses to inform subsequent instruction.

Closure

- **Exit Ticket:** Are the two triangles similar? Explain.

  yes; The triangles have two pairs of congruent angles.

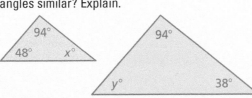

Extra Example 3

You plan to cross a river and want to know how far it is to the other side. You take measurements on your side of the river and make the drawing shown. What is the distance across the river?

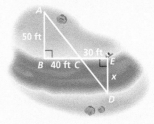

37.5 ft

Self-Assessment
for Problem Solving

6. 13 km

7. 1.5625 h or 93 min 45 sec;

$$\frac{10}{x} = \frac{6}{3}$$

$$x = 5$$

$$\frac{5 \text{ mi}}{3.2 \text{ mi/h}} = 1.5625 \text{ h}$$

Learning Target

Use similar triangles to find missing measures.

Success Criteria

- Use angle measures to determine whether triangles are similar.
- Use similar triangles to solve real-life problems.

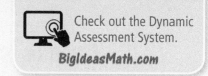

Review & Refresh

1. $135°$
2. $144°$
3. $160°$
4. $y = -4.5$
5. $x = 6$
6. $p = -14$

Concepts, Skills, & Problem Solving

7–8. When two angles in one triangle are congruent to two angles in another triangle, the third angles are also congruent and triangles are similar.

9. yes; The triangles have two pairs of congruent angles.

10. no; The triangles do not have the same angle measures.

11. no; The triangles do not have the same angle measures.

12. yes; The triangles have the same angle measures, $81°$, $51°$, and $48°$.

13. the leftmost and rightmost; They both are right triangles with two $45°$ angles.

Assignment Guide and Concept Check

Scaffold assignments to support all students in their learning progression. The suggested assignments are a starting point. Continue to assign additional exercises and revisit with spaced practice to move every student toward proficiency.

Level	Assignment 1	Assignment 2
Emerging	3, 4, 6, 7, 9, 11, 13, 15, 17	10, 12, 14, 16, 18, 19, 20, 22
Proficient	3, 4, 6, 8, 9, 11, 13, 15, 17	10, 12, 14, 16, 18, 19, 20, 22
Advanced	3, 4, 6, 8, 10, 12, 13, 15, 17	14, 16, 18, 19, 20, 21, 22, 23

- Assignment 1 is for use after students complete the Self-Assessment for Concepts & Skills.
- Assignment 2 is for use after students complete the Self-Assessment for Problem Solving.
- The red exercises can be used as a concept check.

Review & Refresh Prior Skills

Exercises 1–3 Finding an Angle Measure
Exercise 4 Solving Equations Using Addition or Subtraction
Exercises 5 and 6 Solving Equations Using Multiplication or Division

Common Errors

- **Exercises 9–12** Students may find the missing angle measure for one of the triangles and then make a decision about the similarity of the triangles. While it is possible to use this method, encourage them to find the missing angles of both triangles to verify that they are correct.

3.4 Practice

 Go to *BigIdeasMath.com* to get HELP with solving the exercises.

▶ Review & Refresh

Find the measure of each interior angle of the regular polygon.

1. octagon

2. decagon

3. 18-gon

Solve the equation. Check your solution.

4. $3.5 + y = -1$

5. $9x = 54$

6. $-4 = \dfrac{2}{7}p$

▶▶ Concepts, Skills, & Problem Solving

CREATING SIMILAR TRIANGLES **Draw a triangle that is either larger or smaller than the one given and has two of the same angle measures. Explain why the new triangle is similar to the original triangle.** (See Exploration 1, p. 123.)

7.

8.
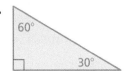

IDENTIFYING SIMILAR TRIANGLES **Tell whether the triangles are similar. Explain.**

9.
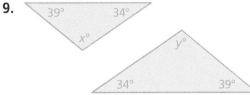

10.

11.
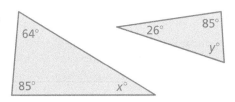

12.
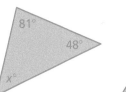

13. GEOMETRY Which of the rulers are similar in shape? Explain.

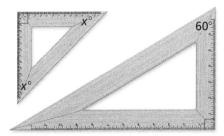
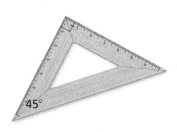

MP STRUCTURE Tell whether the triangles are similar. Explain.

14.

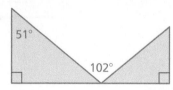

51°
102°

15.

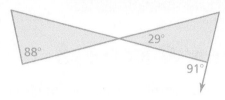

88°
29°
91°

IDENTIFYING SIMILAR TRIANGLES Can you determine whether the triangles are similar? Explain.

16. △*PQS* and △*RQS*

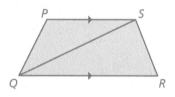

P
S
Q
R

17. △*ABC* and △*EDC*

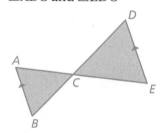

D
A
C
E
B

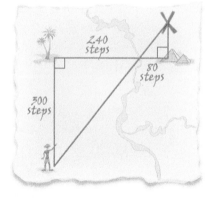

50 ft
5 ft
1.5 ft
d
Not drawn to scale

18. **MP PROBLEM SOLVING** A water sample must be taken from water at least 20 feet deep. Find the depth of the water 50 feet from shore. Is this an appropriate location for a water sample?

19. **MP MODELING REAL LIFE** A map shows the number of steps you must take to get to a treasure. However, the map is old, and the last dimension is unreadable. Explain why the triangles are similar. How many steps do you take from the pyramids to the treasure?

240 steps
80 steps
300 steps

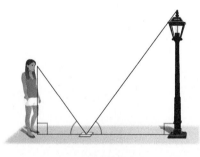

20. **MP PROBLEM SOLVING** A person who is 6 feet tall casts a 3-foot-long shadow. A nearby pine tree casts a 15-foot-long shadow. What is the height *h* of the pine tree?

21. **OPEN-ENDED** You place a mirror on the ground 6 feet from the lamppost. You move back 3 feet and see the top of the lamppost in the mirror. What is the height of the lamppost?

22. **DIG DEEPER!** In each of two right triangles, one angle measure is two times another angle measure. Can you determine that the triangles are similar? Explain your reasoning.

23. **GEOMETRY** In the diagram, $\overline{BG}$, $\overline{CF}$, and $\overline{DE}$ are parallel. The length of $\overline{BD}$ is 6.32 feet, and the length of $\overline{DE}$ is 6 feet. Name all pairs of similar triangles in the diagram. Then find the lengths of $\overline{BG}$ and $\overline{CF}$.

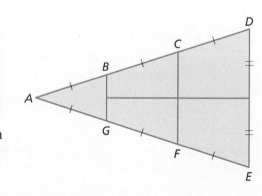

A
B
C
D
G
F
E

Mini-Assessment

Tell whether the triangles are similar. Explain.

1.

yes; The triangles have two pairs of congruent angles.

2.

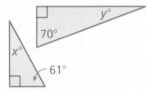

no; The triangles do not have two pairs of congruent angles.

3.

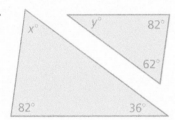

yes; The triangles have two pairs of congruent angles.

4. A person that is 5 feet tall casts a 3-foot-long shadow. A nearby telephone pole casts a 12-foot-long shadow. What is the height h of the telephone pole?
20 ft

Section Resources

Surface Level	Deep Level
Resources by Chapter • Extra Practice • Reteach • Puzzle Time Student Journal • Self-Assessment • Practice Differentiating the Lesson Tutorial Videos Skills Review Handbook Skills Trainer	Resources by Chapter • Enrichment and Extension Graphic Organizers Dynamic Assessment System • Section Practice
Transfer Level	
Dynamic Assessment System • End-of-Chapter Quiz	Assessment Book • End-of-Chapter Quiz

Concepts, Skills, & Problem Solving

14. yes; The triangles have the same angle measures, 90°, 51°, and 39°.

15. no; The triangles do not have the same angle measures.

16. no; You cannot determine that two pairs of angles are congruent from the given information.

17. yes; *Sample answer:* $\angle ACB$ and $\angle ECD$ are vertical angles, and $\angle B$ and $\angle D$ are congruent alternate interior angles.

18. 15 ft; no

19. Because the triangles have a pair of vertical angles and a pair of right angles, the triangles have the same interior angle measures; 100 steps

20. 30 ft

21. Check students' work.

22. no; One triangle could have angle measures of 30°, 60°, 90° and the other triangle could have angle measures of 45°, 45°, 90°.

23. $\triangle ABG \sim \triangle ACF$, $\triangle ABG \sim \triangle ADE$, $\triangle ACF \sim \triangle ADE$; 2 ft; 4 ft

Skills Needed

Exercise 1
- Finding the Area of a Triangle
- Identifying Similar Triangles
- Solving a Proportion
- Using Similar Figures

Exercise 2
- Rotating a Figure
- Using Corresponding Angles

ELL Support

Discuss the concept of a dog park, as it may not be common in other cultures. Ask students to share their experiences of using parks, if they have any. You may also want to discuss the multiple meanings of the word *park*, as a verb or a noun.

Using the Problem-Solving Plan

1. Small dogs: 857.5 m²;
   Large dogs: 1662.5 m²

2.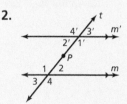

   a. $\angle 1 \cong \angle 1'$ and $\angle 2 \cong \angle 2'$ because a rotation produces an identical angle.

   b. $\angle 3 \cong \angle 3'$ and $\angle 4 \cong \angle 4'$ because a rotation produces an identical angle.

   c. See Additional Answers.

Performance Task

The *STEAM Video Performance Task* provides the opportunity for additional enrichment and greater depth of knowledge as students explore the mathematics of the chapter within a context tied to the chapter STEAM Video. The performance task and a detailed scoring rubric are provided at *BigIdeasMath.com*.

Scaffolding Instruction

- The goal of this lesson is to help students become more comfortable with problem solving. These exercises combine concepts of angles and triangles with prior skills from other chapters and courses. The solution for Exercise 1 is worked out below, to help you guide students through the problem-solving plan. Use the remaining class time to have students work on Exercise 2.
- **Emerging:** The goal for these students is to feel comfortable with the problem-solving plan. Allow students to work in pairs to write the beginning steps of the problem-solving plan for Exercise 2. Keep in mind that some students may only be ready to do the first step.
- **Proficient:** Students may be able to work independently or in pairs to complete Exercise 2.
- Visit each pair to review their plan. Ask students to describe their plans.

▶ Using the Problem-Solving Plan

Exercise 1

➡ **Understand the problem.** You know two dimensions of a dog park and the ratio of the perimeter of the small dog section to the perimeter of the entire park. You are asked to find the area of each section.

➡ **Make a plan.** Verify that the small triangle and the large triangle are similar. Then use the ratio of the perimeters to find the base or the height of each triangle and calculate the areas.

➡ **Solve and check.** Use the plan to solve the problem. Then check your solution.

- Verify that the small triangle and the large triangle are similar. Each triangle has a right angle and shares an angle. Because two angles in the small triangle are congruent to two angles in the large triangle, the third angles are also congruent and the triangles are similar.

- Find the base or the height of each triangle.

$$\frac{\text{Perimeter of small triangle}}{\text{Perimeter of large triangle}} = \frac{\text{Height of small triangle}}{\text{Height of large triangle}}$$

$$\frac{\text{Perimeter of small triangle}}{\text{Perimeter of large triangle}} = \frac{\text{Base of small triangle}}{\text{Base of large triangle}}$$

$$\frac{7}{12} = \frac{h}{60} \qquad\qquad \frac{7}{12} = \frac{49}{b}$$
$$420 = 12h \qquad\qquad 7b = 588$$
$$35\text{ m} = h \qquad\qquad b = 84\text{ m}$$

- Calculate the areas.

$$A(\text{small triangle}) = 0.5bh \qquad A(\text{large triangle}) = 0.5bh$$
$$= 0.5(49)(35) \qquad\qquad = 0.5(84)(60)$$
$$= 857.5\text{ m}^2 \qquad\qquad = 2520\text{ m}^2$$

So, the area of the small dog section is 857.5 square meters and the area of the large dog section is $2520 - 857.5 = 1662.5$ square meters.

- **Check:** Verify that the value of the ratio of the areas is equal to the square of the value of the ratio of the perimeters.

$$\frac{\text{Area of small triangle}}{\text{Area of large triangle}} = \frac{857.5}{2520} \approx 0.34$$

$$\left(\frac{\text{Perimeter of small triangle}}{\text{Perimeter of large triangle}}\right)^2 = \left(\frac{7}{12}\right)^2 = \frac{49}{144} \approx 0.34 \checkmark$$

Connecting Concepts

Using the Problem-Solving Plan

1. A dog park is divided into sections for large and small dogs. The ratio of the perimeter of the small dog section to the perimeter of the entire dog park is 7 : 12. Find the area of each section.

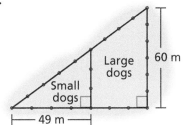

Understand the problem.

You know two dimensions of a dog park and the **ratio** of the perimeter of the small dog section to the perimeter of the entire park. You are asked to find the area of each section.

Make a plan.

Verify that the small triangle and the large triangle are similar. Then use the ratio of the perimeters to find the base or the height of each triangle and calculate the areas.

Solve and check.

Use the plan to solve the problem. Then check your solution.

2. You rotate lines m and t 180° about point P. The image of line m is parallel to the original line. Use the diagram to show that when a transversal intersects parallel lines, each of the following pairs of angles are congruent. Explain your reasoning.

   a. alternate interior angles

   b. alternate exterior angles

   c. corresponding angles

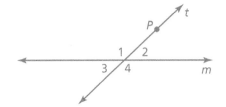

Performance Task

Turtle Shells

At the beginning of this chapter, you watched a STEAM Video called "Honeycombs." You are now ready to complete the performance task related to this video, available at *BigIdeasMath.com*. Be sure to use the problem-solving plan as you work through the performance task.

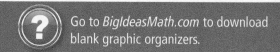

▶ Review Vocabulary

Write the definition and give an example of each vocabulary term.

transversal, *p. 104*
interior angles, *p. 105*
exterior angles, *p. 105*

interior angles of a polygon, *p. 112*
exterior angles of a polygon, *p. 112*

regular polygon, *p. 120*
indirect measurement, *p. 126*

▶ Graphic Organizers

You can use an **Example and Non-Example Chart** to list examples and non-examples of a concept. Here is an Example and Non-Example Chart for *transversals*.

Transversals

Examples	Non-Examples
p ↖ ↗ *q* *r* line *p*, line *q*, line *r*	↗*a* ↗*b* ↗*c* line *a*, line *b*, line *c*
a↗ *b*↗ *c* *d* line *a*, line *b*, line *c*, line *d*	↗*t* *p* line *p*, line *t*

Choose and complete a graphic organizer to help you study the concept.

1. interior angles formed by parallel lines and a transversal

2. exterior angles formed by parallel lines and a transversal

3. interior angles of a triangle

4. exterior angles of a triangle

5. polygons

6. similar triangles

"**What do you think of my Example & Non-Example Chart for popular cat toys?**"

Review Vocabulary

- As a review of the chapter vocabulary, have students revisit the vocabulary section in their *Student Journals* to fill in any missing definitions and record examples of each term.

Graphic Organizers

Sample answers:

1.

Interior Angles Formed by
Parallel Pines and a Transversal

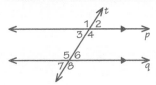

Examples	Non-Examples
∠3	∠1
∠4	∠2
∠5	∠7
∠6	∠8

2.

Exterior Angles Formed by
Parallel Lines and a Transversal

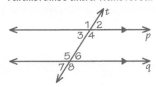

Examples	Non-Examples
∠1	∠3
∠2	∠4
∠7	∠5
∠8	∠6

3.

Interior Angles of a Triangle

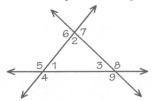

Examples	Non-Examples
∠1	∠4
∠2	∠5
∠3	∠6
	∠7
	∠8
	∠9

4–6. Answers at *BigIdeasMath.com.*

List of Organizers

Available at *BigIdeasMath.com*
Definition and Example Chart
Example and Non-Example Chart
Four Square
Information Frame
Summary Triangle

About this Organizer

An **Example and Non-Example Chart** can be used to list examples and non-examples of a concept. Students write examples of the concept in the left column and non-examples in the right column. This organizer can be used to assess students' understanding of two concepts that have subtle, but important differences. Blank Example and Non-Example Charts can be included on tests or quizzes for this purpose.

1. 140°; ∠8 and the given angle are alternate exterior angles.

2. 140°; *Sample answer:* ∠8 and ∠5 are vertical angles.

3. 40°; *Sample answer:* ∠8 and ∠7 are supplementary.

4. 40°; *Sample answer:* ∠2 and the given angle are supplementary.

5. 40°; *Sample answer:* ∠7 and ∠6 are vertical angles.

6. 123°; ∠1 and ∠7 are alternate exterior angles.

7. 122°; *Sample answer:* ∠2 and ∠8 are alternate interior angles and ∠8 and ∠5 are supplementary.

8. 119°; ∠5 and ∠3 are alternate interior angles.

9. 60°; ∠4 and ∠6 are alternate exterior angles.

10. ∠2 and ∠8 are congruent.

11. ∠1 = 108°, ∠2 = 108°; *Sample answer:* Using alternate interior angles, the measure of the adjacent angle below ∠1 is 72°. This angle is supplementary to both ∠1 and ∠2.

✓ *Chapter Self-Assessment*

The Success Criteria Self-Assessment chart can be found in the *Student Journal* or online at *BigIdeasMath.com*.

ELL Support

Allow students to work in pairs to complete the first section of the Chapter Self-Assessment. Once pairs have finished, check for understanding by having each pair display their answers on a whiteboard for your review. Have two pairs present their explanations to each other. Monitor discussions and provide support. Use similar techniques to check the remaining sections of the Chapter Self-Assessment. You may want to discuss some of the exercises as a class.

Common Errors

- **Exercises 1–5** Students may mix up some of the definitions for congruent angles and find incorrect angle measures. Encourage students to color-code the figure they are given to determine what angles are congruent.
- **Exercises 1–5** Students may not understand alternate interior and alternate exterior angles and say that an exterior angle is congruent to the alternate interior angle. Use corresponding angles to show that this is not necessarily true.
- **Exercises 6–10** Students may use some of the definitions for congruent angles incorrectly in finding the angle measure of the unknown angle or describing the relationship. Review the definitions.

▶ Chapter Self-Assessment

As you complete the exercises, use the scale below to rate your understanding of the success criteria in your journal.

1	**2**	**3**	**4**
I do not understand.	I can do it with help.	I can do it on my own.	I can teach someone else.

3.1 Parallel Lines and Transversals *(pp. 103–110)*

Learning Target: Find missing angle measures created by the intersections of lines.

Use the figure to find the measure of the angle. Explain your reasoning.

1. ∠8

2. ∠5

3. ∠7

4. ∠2

5. ∠6

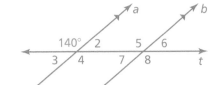

Complete the statement. Explain your reasoning.

6. If the measure of ∠1 = 123°, then the measure of ∠7 = ▢ .

7. If the measure of ∠2 = 58°, then the measure of ∠5 = ▢ .

8. If the measure of ∠5 = 119°, then the measure of ∠3 = ▢ .

9. If the measure of ∠4 = 60°, then the measure of ∠6 = ▢ .

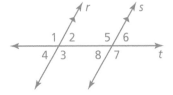

10. In Exercises 6–9, describe the relationship between ∠2 and ∠8.

11. In a park, a bike path and a horse riding path are parallel. In one part of the park, a hiking trail intersects the two paths. Find the measures of ∠1 and ∠2. Explain your reasoning.

3.2 Angles of Triangles (pp. 111–116)

Learning Target: Understand properties of interior and exterior angles of triangles.

Find the measures of the interior angles of the triangle.

12.

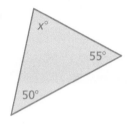

13.

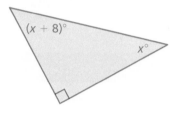

Find the measure of the exterior angle.

14.

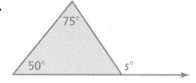

15.

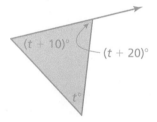

16. What is the measure of each interior angle of an equilateral triangle? Explain.

17. You draw the Leo constellation. You notice that the three stars Denebola, Zosma, and Chertan form a triangle. In your drawing, you find the measure of the interior angle at Denebola is 30° and the measure of the interior angle of the triangle at Zosma is 56°. What is the measure of the interior angle of the triangle at Chertan?

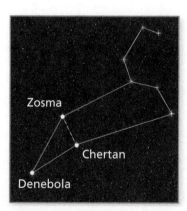

3.3 Angles of Polygons (pp. 117–122)

Learning Target: Find interior angle measures of polygons.

Find the sum of the interior angle measures of the polygon.

18.

19.

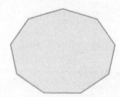

Common Errors

- **Exercises 13 and 15** Students may forget to combine like terms when solving for the variable. Remind them that because there are two variables on the same side of the equal sign, they should start by combining like terms.
- **Exercises 13 and 15** Students may solve for the variable but forget to find the measures of the interior angles or the measure of the exterior angle. Remind them to read the directions carefully and to answer the question.
- **Exercises 18 and 19** Students may forget to subtract 2 from the number of sides when using the formula to find the sum of the interior angle measures. Remind students of the formula and encourage them to write the formula before substituting the number of sides.

12. $50°, 55°, 75°$

13. $41°, 49°, 90°$

14. $125°$

15. $110°$

16. $60°$; In an equilateral triangle, all angles are congruent. So, $x + x + x = 180$ and $x = 60$.

17. $94°$

18. $1980°$

19. $1260°$

20. 77

21. 110

22. 113

23. 135°

24. yes; The triangles have the same angle measures, 90°, 68°, and 22°.

25. yes; The triangles have the same angle measures, 100°, 50°, and 30°.

26. no; The triangles do not have the same angle measures.

27. yes; The triangles have a pair of vertical angles and two pairs of congruent alternate interior angles.

28. 30 ft

Common Errors

- **Exercises 20–22** Students may forget to include one or more of the given angles when writing an equation for the missing angles. Remind students to include all of the angles. Encourage them to write the equation and then count the number of terms to make sure that there is the same number of terms as angles before simplifying.

- **Exercise 23** Students may find the sum of the interior angle measures of the regular polygon but forget to divide by the number of angles to find the measure of *each* interior angle. Remind students that they are finding the measure of *one* angle. Because all the angles are congruent (by the definition of a regular polygon), they can divide the sum of the interior angle measures by the number of angles.

- **Exercises 24–26** Students may find the missing angle measure for one of the triangles and then make a decision about the similarity of the triangles. While it is possible to use this method, encourage them to find the missing angles of both triangles to verify that they are correct.

Chapter Resources

Surface Level	Deep Level
Resources by Chapter • Extra Practice • Reteach • Puzzle Time Student Journal • Practice • Chapter Self-Assessment Differentiating the Lesson Tutorial Videos Skills Review Handbook Skills Trainer Game Library	Resources by Chapter • Enrichment and Extension Graphic Organizers Game Library
Transfer Level	
STEAM Video Dynamic Assessment System • Chapter Test	Assessment Book • Chapter Tests A and B • Alternative Assessment • STEAM Performance Task

Find the value of x.

20.

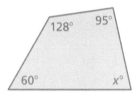

21.

22.

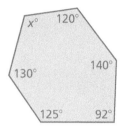

23. Find the measure of each interior angle of the regular polygon.

3.4 Using Similar Triangles *(pp. 123–128)*

Learning Target: Use similar triangles to find missing measures.

Tell whether the triangles are similar. Explain.

24.

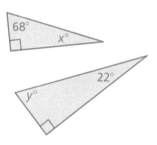

25.

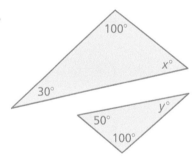

26.

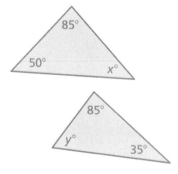

27.

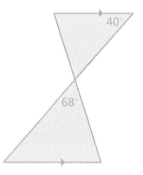

28. A person who is 5 feet tall casts a shadow that is 4 feet long. A nearby building casts a shadow that is 24 feet long. What is the height of the building?

Use the figure to find the measure of the angle. Explain your reasoning.

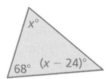

1. $\angle 7$

2. $\angle 6$

3. $\angle 4$

4. $\angle 5$

5. Find the value of x.

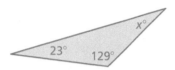

6. Find the measures of the interior angles.

7. Find the measure of the exterior angle.

8. Find the sum of the interior angle measures of the border of the coin.

9. Find the value of x.

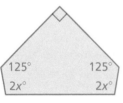

10. Find the measure of each interior angle of the regular polygon.

Tell whether the triangles are similar. Explain.

11.

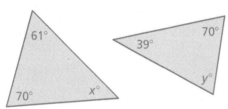

12.

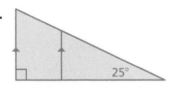

13. Describe two ways you can find the measure of $\angle 5$.

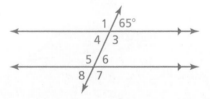

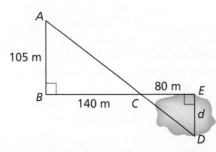

14. You swim 3.6 kilometers per hour. How long (in minutes) will it take you to swim the distance d across the pond?

Practice Test Item References

Practice Test Questions	Section to Review
1, 2, 3, 4, 13	3.1
5, 6, 7	3.2
8, 9, 10	3.3
11, 12, 14	3.4

Test-Taking Strategies

Remind students to quickly look over the entire test before they start so that they can budget their time. Students should jot down the formula for the sum of the interior angle measures of a polygon on the back of the test before they begin. Have them use the **Stop** and **Think** strategy before they write their answers.

Common Errors

- **Exercises 1–4** Students may mix up some of the definitions for congruent angles and find incorrect angle measures. Encourage students to color-code the figure they are given to determine what angles are congruent.
- **Exercises 1–4** Students may not understand alternate interior and alternate exterior angles and say that an exterior angle is congruent to the alternate interior angle. Use corresponding angles to show that this is not true.
- **Exercise 6** Students may solve for the variable but forget to find the measures of the angles. Remind them to read the directions carefully and to answer the question.
- **Exercises 6 and 9** Students may forget to combine like terms when solving for x. Remind them that because there are two variables on the same side of the equal sign, they should start by combining like terms.
- **Exercise 8** Students may forget to subtract 2 from the number of sides when using the formula to find the sum of the interior angle measures. Remind students of the formula and encourage them to write the formula before substituting the number of sides.
- **Exercise 9** Students may forget to include one or more of the given angles when writing an equation for the missing angles. Remind students to include all of the angles. Encourage them to write the equation and then count the number of terms to make sure that there is the same number of terms as angles before simplifying.
- **Exercise 10** Students may find the sum of the interior angle measures of the regular polygon but forget to divide by the number of angles to find the measure of *each* interior angle. Remind students that they are finding the measure of *one* angle. Because all the angles are congruent (by the definition of a regular polygon), they can divide the sum of the interior angle measures by the number of angles.

1. $47°$; $\angle 7$ and the given angle are alternate exterior angles.

2. $47°$; *Sample answer:* $\angle 6$ and the given angle are corresponding angles.

3. $133°$; $\angle 4$ and the given angle are supplementary.

4. $133°$; *Sample answer:* $\angle 4$ and $\angle 5$ are alternate interior angles.

5. 28

6. $44°, 68°, 68°$

7. $130°$

8. $900°$

9. 50

10. $120°$

11. no; The triangles do not have the same angle measures.

12. yes; The triangles share a $25°$ angle and have two pairs of congruent corresponding angles.

13. *Sample answer:* 1) The given angle and $\angle 3$ are supplementary, so $\angle 3 = 115°$. $\angle 3$ and $\angle 5$ are alternate interior angles, so $\angle 3 = \angle 5 = 115°$.

    2) The given angle and $\angle 8$ are alternate exterior angles, so $\angle 8 = 65°$. $\angle 5$ and $\angle 8$ are supplementary, so $\angle 5 = 115°$.

14. 1 min

After Answering Easy Questions, Relax
Answer Easy Questions First
Estimate the Answer
Read All Choices before Answering
Read Question before Answering
Solve Directly or Eliminate Choices
Solve Problem before Looking at Choices
Use Intelligent Guessing
Work Backwards

About this Strategy

When taking a multiple-choice test, be sure to read each question carefully and thoroughly. Sometimes it is easier to solve the problem and then look for the answer among the choices.

Cumulative Practice

1. 147

2. B

3. I

4. C

Item Analysis

1. **Gridded Response:** Correct answer: 147

   Common error: The student divides 180 by 11 and gets 16.

2. **A.** The student incorrectly combines $11 + 1.6t$ to get $12.6t$.

   B. Correct answer

   C. The student performs an order of operations error by not subtracting 11 from each side first.

   D. The student correctly subtracts 11 from each side of the equation but then subtracts 1.6 from the left side instead of dividing by 1.6.

3. **F.** The student subtracts 20 from the right side instead of adding 20.

   G. The student does not distribute the 5 to the second term in $(x - 4)$.

   H. The student adds $3x$ to the left side instead of subtracting $3x$.

   I. Correct answer

4. **A.** The student does not correctly match corresponding side lengths and solves the proportion $\dfrac{PQ}{QR} = \dfrac{US}{ST}$.

   B. The student does not correctly match corresponding side lengths and solves the proportion $\dfrac{PQ}{QR} = \dfrac{TU}{ST}$.

   C. Correct answer

   D. The student does not correctly match corresponding side lengths and solves the proportion $\dfrac{PQ}{QR} = \dfrac{ST}{US}$.

3 Cumulative Practice

1. The border of a Canadian one-dollar coin is shaped like an 11-sided regular polygon. The shape was chosen to help visually impaired people identify the coin. How many degrees are in each interior angle along the border? Round your answer to the nearest degree.

2. A public utility charges its residential customers for natural gas based on the number of therms used each month. The formula shows how the monthly cost C in dollars is related to the number t of therms used.

   $$C = 11 + 1.6t$$

   Solve this formula for t.

   A. $t = \dfrac{C}{12.6}$

   B. $t = \dfrac{C - 11}{1.6}$

   C. $t = \dfrac{C}{1.6} - 11$

   D. $t = C - 12.6$

Test-Taking Strategy

Solve Problem Before Looking at Choices

Could someone scratch my base angles?

Your ears are isosceles triangles with base angles of 70°. Find the top angle.

(A) 30°   (B) 35°   (C) 40°   (D) 45°

"Solve the problem before looking at the choices. You know $180 - 2(70) = 40$. So, the answer is C."

3. What is the value of x?

   $$5(x - 4) = 3x$$

   F. -10

   G. 2

   H. $2\dfrac{1}{2}$

   I. 10

4. In the figures, $\triangle PQR$ is similar to $\triangle STU$. What is the value of x?

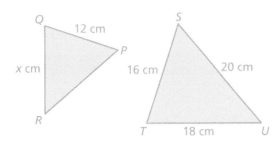

   A. 9.6

   B. $10\dfrac{2}{3}$

   C. 13.5

   D. 15

5. What is the value of x?

6. Your friend was solving an equation in the box shown.

$$-\frac{2}{5}(10x - 15) = -30$$

$$10x - 15 = -30\left(-\frac{2}{5}\right)$$

$$10x - 15 = 12$$

$$10x - 15 + 15 = 12 + 15$$

$$10x = 27$$

$$\frac{10x}{10} = \frac{27}{10}$$

$$x = \frac{27}{10}$$

What should your friend do to correct the error that she made?

F. Multiply both sides by $-\frac{5}{2}$ instead of $-\frac{2}{5}$.

G. Multiply both sides by $\frac{2}{5}$ instead of $-\frac{2}{5}$.

H. Distribute $-\frac{2}{5}$ to get $-4x - 6$.

I. Add 15 to -30.

Item Analysis (continued)

5. Gridded Response: Correct answer: 55

Common error: The student thinks the angles are congruent and gets 125.

6. **F.** Correct answer

    G. The student thinks that multiplying by $\frac{2}{5}$ is the inverse operation of multiplying by $-\frac{2}{5}$.

    H. The student does not distribute the negative sign to the second term.

    I. The student makes an order of operations error by not multiplying both sides by $-\frac{5}{2}$ first.

5. 55

6. F

7. B

8. *Part A* $S = (n - 2) \cdot 180°$

Part B $80°$

Part C

The sum of the interior angle measures of a triangle is 180°. Because the pentagon can be divided into three triangles, the sum of the angle measures of a pentagon is
$180° + 180° + 180° = 540°$
or
$$(n - 2) \cdot 180° = (5 - 2) \cdot 180°$$
$$= 3 \cdot 180°$$
$$= 540°.$$

Item Analysis (continued)

7. **A.** The student reflects the figure in the *x*-axis instead of the *y*-axis.

   B. Correct answer

   C. The student translates the figure 7 units right instead of reflecting it in the *y*-axis.

   D. The student translates the figure 6 units up instead of reflecting it in the *y*-axis.

8. **4 points** The student's work and explanations demonstrate a thorough understanding of writing and applying the angle sum formula for polygons, as well as how it relates to the fact that there are 180° in a triangle. In Part A, the student correctly writes the formula $S = (n - 2) \cdot 180°$. In Part B, the student correctly finds that the fourth angle measures 80°. In Part C, the student correctly explains the connection between the algebraic and geometric representations of the angle sum formula. The student provides accurate work with clear and complete explanations.

   3 points The student's work and explanations demonstrate an essential but less than thorough understanding of writing and applying the angle sum formula for polygons, as well as how it relates to the fact that there are 180° in a triangle. For example, Parts A and B may be completed fully and clearly, but Part C may lack a full explanation.

   2 points The student's work and explanations demonstrate a partial but limited understanding of writing and applying the angle sum formula for polygons, as well as how it relates to the fact that there are 180° in a triangle. The formula in Part A should be properly stated, but Part B may show an error in application and Part C may lack any explanation.

   1 point The student's work and explanations demonstrate a very limited understanding of writing and applying the angle sum formula for polygons, as well as how it relates to the fact that there are 180° in a triangle.

   0 points The student provides no response, a completely incorrect or incomprehensible response, or a response that demonstrates insufficient understanding of writing and applying the angle sum formula for polygons, as well as how it relates to the fact that there are 180° in a triangle.

7. In the coordinate plane below, △XYZ is plotted and its vertices are labeled.

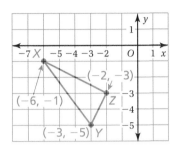

Which of the following shows △X′Y′Z′, the image of △XYZ after it is reflected in the y-axis?

A.

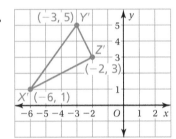

B.

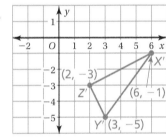

C.

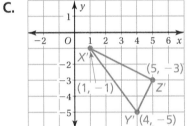

D.

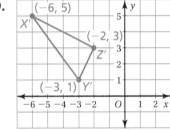

8. The sum S of the interior angle measures of a polygon with n sides can be found by using a formula.

Part A Write the formula.

Part B A quadrilateral has angles measuring 100°, 90°, and 90°. Find the measure of its fourth angle. Show your work and explain your reasoning.

Part C The sum of the measures of the angles of the pentagon shown is 540°. Divide the pentagon into triangles to show why this must be true. Show your work and explain your reasoning.

4 Graphing and Writing Linear Equations

Chapter Learning Target:
Understand graphing linear equations.

Chapter Success Criteria:
- ◻ I can identify key features of a graph.
- ◻ I can explain the meaning of different forms of linear equations.
- ◼ I can interpret the slope and intercepts of a line.
- ◼ I can create graphs of linear equations.

STEAM Video: "Hurricane!"

Laurie's Notes

Chapter 4 Overview

In the previous course, students solved two-step equations and inequalities using rational numbers. This included writing equations from a given context. Earlier in this course, students solved multi-step equations and rewrote equations and formulas. This work introduced students to equations with more than one variable, which is a foundational concept for this chapter.

The chapter begins with graphing linear equations, equations whose graphs are lines. The equations describe a relationship between two variables, such as the amount of time and the depth of snow. Contextual problems help students make sense of and interpret graphical representations. Making a table of values is the intermediate step between the equation and the graph. Multiple representations (algebraic, numeric, and graphic) help students to recognize different mathematical features of the same problem. Be sure to refer to each representation as you progress through the chapter to help students see the connections between them.

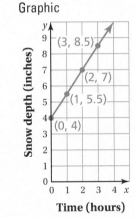

Algebraic
$y = 1.5x + 4$

Numeric

x	y
0	4
1	5.5
2	7
3	8.5

Graphic

The slope of a line is introduced and a connection to proportional relationships is made. The remainder of the chapter is about writing and graphing linear equations in various forms: slope-intercept, standard, and point-slope.

Students often ask, "Why do we need so many forms?" It is because the information you know about the relationship between two variables is not always the same! Understanding that all of the forms can be rewritten as another form allows you to write a model that represents a given relationship.

Throughout the chapter, students will apply their understanding of equality and solving equations in new ways. Solving for y in each equation below may seem different to students. What does it mean to solve for a variable? How do you solve equations? Help students understand how the process is the same for both equations.

$$3 + y = -7 \qquad\qquad 3x + y = -7$$
$$\underline{-3 \quad\quad -3} \qquad\qquad \underline{-3x \quad\quad -3x}$$
$$y = -7 - 3 \qquad\qquad y = -7 - 3x$$
$$y = -10 \qquad\qquad y = -3x - 7$$

Note: In Chapter 4, students will use similar triangles to explain why the slope is the same between any two distinct points on a non-vertical line in the coordinate plane. Similarity of figures is developed through transformations, so Chapters 2 and 3 must precede Chapter 4.

Suggested Pacing

Chapter Opener	1 Day
Section 1	2 Days
Section 2	2 Days
Section 3	2 Days
Section 4	2 Days
Section 5	2 Days
Section 6	2 Days
Section 7	2 Days
Connecting Concepts	1 Day
Chapter Review	1 Day
Chapter Test	1 Day
Total Chapter 4	18 Days
Year-to-Date	61 Days

Chapter Learning Target

Understand graphing linear equations.

Chapter Success Criteria

- Identify key features of a graph.
- Explain the meaning of different forms of linear equations.
- Interpret the slope and intercepts of a line.
- Create graphs of linear equations.

Chapter 4 Learning Targets and Success Criteria

Section	Learning Target	Success Criteria
4.1 Graphing Linear Equations	Graph linear equations.	• Create a table of values and write ordered pairs given a linear equation. • Plot ordered pairs to create a graph of a linear equation. • Use a graph of a linear equation to solve a real-life problem.
4.2 Slope of a Line	Find and interpret the slope of a line.	• Explain the meaning of slope. • Find the slope of a line. • Interpret the slope of a line in a real-life problem.
4.3 Graphing Proportional Relationships	Graph proportional relationships.	• Graph an equation that represents a proportional relationship. • Write an equation that represents a proportional relationship. • Use graphs to compare proportional relationships.
4.4 Graphing Linear Equations in Slope-Intercept Form	Graph linear equations in slope-intercept form.	• Identify the slope and y-intercept of a line given an equation. • Rewrite a linear equation in slope-intercept form. • Use the slope and y-intercept to graph linear equations.
4.5 Graphing Linear Equations in Standard Form	Graph linear equations in standard form.	• Rewrite the standard form of a linear equation in slope-intercept form. • Find intercepts of linear equations written in standard form. • Use intercepts to graph linear equations.
4.6 Writing Equations in Slope-Intercept Form	Write equations of lines in slope-intercept form.	• Find the slope and the y-intercept of a line. • Use the slope and the y-intercept to write an equation of a line. • Write equations in slope-intercept form to solve real-life problems.
4.7 Writing Equations in Point-Slope Form	Write equations of lines in point-slope form.	• Use a point on a line and the slope to write an equation of the line. • Use any two points to write an equation of a line. • Write equations in point-slope form to solve real-life problems.

Progressions

Through the Grades		
Grade 7	**Grade 8**	**High School**
• Identify the constant of proportionality in tables, graphs, equations, diagrams, and verbal descriptions. • Represent proportional relationships with equations.	• Graph and compare proportional relationships, interpreting the unit rate as the slope. • Use similar triangles to explain why the slope is the same between any two points on a line. Derive $y = mx$ and $y = mx + b$. • Interpret the rate of change and the initial value of a function.	• Find the slope of a line and use it to write a linear equation in slope-intercept form. • Solve systems of linear equations by graphing, by substitution, and by elimination. • Graph and write systems of linear inequalities. • Identify linear functions, using graphs, tables, and equations. • Identify, write, and use linear equations in slope-intercept form and point-slope form. • Identify, write, and use equations for parallel and perpendicular lines. • Solve real-life problems using function notation, linear equations, slopes, and y-intercepts.

Through the Chapter							
Standard	**4.1**	**4.2**	**4.3**	**4.4**	**4.5**	**4.6**	**4.7**
8.EE.B.5 Graph proportional relationships, interpreting the unit rate as the slope of the graph. Compare two different proportional relationships represented in different ways.	▲		★				
8.EE.B.6 Use similar triangles to explain why the slope m is the same between any two distinct points on a non-vertical line in the coordinate plane; derive the equation $y = mx$ for a line through the origin and the equation $y = mx + b$ for a line intercepting the vertical axis at b.		●	●	★	■		
8.F.B.4 Construct a function to model a linear relationship between two quantities. Determine the rate of change and initial value of the function from a description of a relationship or from two (x, y) values, including reading these from a table or from a graph. Interpret the rate of change and initial value of a linear function in terms of the situation it models, and in terms of its graph or a table of values.						●	●

Key

▲ = preparing   ★ = complete
● = learning   ■ = extending

1. a. *Sample answer:* The wind speed will be greater than 50 miles per hour.

b. *Sample answer:* The distance from the eye of the hurricane is greater than 140 miles away.

c. *Sample answer:*

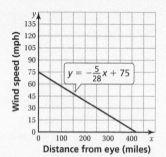

2. *Sample answer:* The storm weakens in intensity over land.

Performance Task

Sample answer: The stronger the winds, the more damage that can occur. This prediction can help residents prepare their homes.

Mathematical Practices

Students have opportunities to develop aspects of the mathematical practices throughout the chapter. Here are some examples.

1. **Make Sense of Problems and Persevere in Solving Them**
   4.6 Math Practice note, *p. 173*

2. **Reason Abstractly and Quantitatively**
   4.3 Exercise 17, *p. 160*

3. **Construct Viable Arguments and Critique the Reasoning of Others**
   4.2 Exercise 22, *p. 153*

4. **Model with Mathematics**
   4.5 Exercise 23, *p. 172*

5. **Use Appropriate Tools Strategically**
   4.7 Math Practice note, *p. 179*

6. **Attend to Precision**
   4.4 Exercise 31, *p. 166*

7. **Look for and Make Use of Structure**
   4.2 Exercise 40, *p. 154*

8. **Look for and Express Regularity in Repeated Reasoning**
   4.4 Math Practice note, *p. 163*

STEAM Video

Before the Video

- To introduce the STEAM Video, read aloud the first paragraph of Hurricane! and discuss the question with your students.
- **?** "How can you prepare your home for a hurricane?"

During the Video

- The video shows Robert and Tory discussing hurricanes.
- **?** Pause the video at 1:23 and ask, "What is a hurricane?" a tropical cyclone
- **?** "What is the relatively calm area in the center of the hurricane called?" the eye of the hurricane
- Watch the remainder of the video.

After the Video

- Ask several students to restate the hurricane safety tips that Robert and Tory discussed.
- Have students work with a partner to answer Questions 1 and 2.
- As students discuss and answer the questions, listen for understanding of the linear relationships that represent the wind speeds of a hurricane.

Performance Task

- Use this information to spark students' interest and promote thinking about real-life problems.
- **?** Ask, "Why is it helpful to predict how strong the winds of a hurricane will become?"
- After completing the chapter, students will have gained the knowledge needed to complete "Anatomy of a Hurricane."

Hurricane!

A hurricane is a storm with violent winds. How can you prepare your home for a hurricane?

Watch the STEAM Video "Hurricane!" Then answer the following questions.

Wind Speed

1. Robert says that the closer you are to the eye of a hurricane, the stronger the winds become. The wind speed on an island is 50 miles per hour when the eye of a hurricane is 140 miles away.

   a. Describe the wind speed on the island when the eye of the hurricane is 100 miles away.

   b. Describe the distance of the island from the eye of the hurricane when the wind speed on the island is 25 miles per hour.

   c. Sketch a line that could represent the wind speed y (in miles per hour) on the island when the eye of the hurricane is x miles away from the island.

2. A storm dissipates as it travels over land. What does this mean?

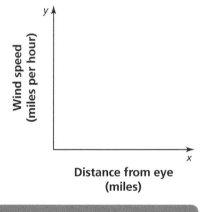

Distance from eye (miles)

Anatomy of a Hurricane

After completing this chapter, you will be able to use the concepts you learned to answer the questions in the *STEAM Video Performance Task*. You will be given information about the atmospheric pressure inside a hurricane.

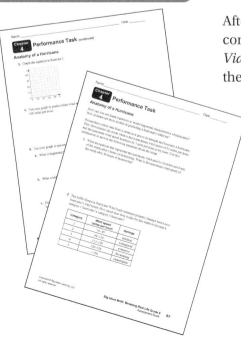

Time, x (hours)	Atmospheric Pressure, y (millibars)
18	1008
36	999
84	975

You will be asked to use a model to find the strength of a hurricane after x hours of monitoring. Why is it helpful to predict how strong the winds of a hurricane will become?

Getting Ready for Chapter

Chapter Exploration

1. **Work with a partner.**

   a. Use the equation $y = \frac{1}{2}x + 1$ to complete the table. (Choose any two x-values and find the y-values.)

   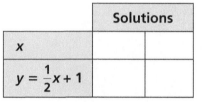

	Solutions	
x		
$y = \frac{1}{2}x + 1$		

   b. Write the two ordered pairs given by the table. These are called *solutions* of the equation.

   c. **MP PRECISION** Plot the two solutions. Draw a line *exactly* through the points.

   d. Find a different point on the line. Check that this point is a solution of the equation $y = \frac{1}{2}x + 1$.

   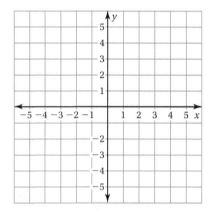

   e. **MP LOGIC** Do you think it is true that *any* point on the line is a solution of the equation $y = \frac{1}{2}x + 1$? Explain.

   f. Choose five additional x-values for the table below. (Choose both positive and negative x-values.) Plot the five corresponding solutions. Does each point lie on the line?

	Solutions				
x					
$y = \frac{1}{2}x + 1$					

   g. **MP LOGIC** Do you think it is true that any solution of the equation $y = \frac{1}{2}x + 1$ is a point on the line? Explain.

   h. Why do you think $y = ax + b$ is called a *linear equation*?

Vocabulary

The following vocabulary terms are defined in this chapter. Think about what each term might mean and record your thoughts.

linear equation   slope y-intercept

solution of a linear equation x-intercept

Laurie's Notes

Check out the digital flash cards.
BigIdeasMath.com

Chapter Exploration

- In previous courses, students plotted ordered pairs from a table. Now they will use a table of values and a graph to model a linear equation. Using multiple representations of linear equations deepens students' understanding and supports learning.
- Some students will recognize right away that if they substitute an even number for *x*, the *y*-coordinate will not be a fraction. It is likely that students will only try positive *x*-values. Encourage them to try negative values of *x*.
- In part (d), suggest that students consider only those ordered pairs that appear to be lattice points, meaning the *x*- and *y*-coordinates are integers.
- **MP3 Construct Viable Arguments and Critique the Reasoning of Others:** Listen and discuss student responses to the generalizations in parts (e) and (g).
- Point out that the question in part (g) is the converse of the question in part (e).
- **Big Idea:** The goal of this exploration is for students to recognize and understand two related, but different, ideas. (1) *All* solutions of a linear equation lie on the same line. (2) *All* points on the line are solutions of the equation.

Vocabulary

- These terms represent some of the vocabulary that students will encounter in Chapter 4. Discuss the terms as a class.
- Where have students heard the term *slope* outside of a math classroom? In what contexts? Students may not be able to write the actual definition, but they may write phrases associated with *slope*.
- Allowing students to discuss these terms now will prepare them for understanding the terms as they are presented in the chapter.
- When students encounter a new definition, encourage them to write in their *Student Journals*. They will revisit these definitions during the Chapter Review.

ELL Support

Write the word *linear* on the board. Ask students if they recognize a word contained within it. Underline *line*. If students do not know the word *line*, draw a line using a straight edge (a ruler) to guide you. Point and say, "line." Explain that the word *linear* describes something related to a line. In this chapter, equations whose graphs are lines will be discussed. Explain that a strategy for guessing the meaning of a word they do not know is to look for a word they already know within the unknown word.

Topics for Review

- Evaluating Expressions
- Exponents
- Order of Operations
- Parallel Lines
- Plotting Points
- Proportional Relationships
- Similar Triangles
- Slope
- Unit Rate

Chapter Exploration

1. a. *Sample answer:*

	Solution Points	
x	-2	2
$y = \dfrac{1}{2}x + 1$	0	2

b. *Sample answer:* $(-2, 0)$, $(2, 2)$

c. *Sample answer:*

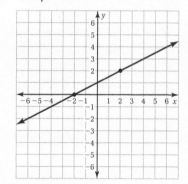

d. *Sample answer:*
Choose $(0, 1)$.

$$y = \frac{1}{2}x + 1$$

$$1 \overset{?}{=} \frac{1}{2}(0) + 1$$

$$1 = 1 \checkmark$$

e. yes; Because the line is the graph of the equation, all points on the line are solution points.

f. See Additional Answers.

g. yes; The graph of the equation is the set of all solutions to the equation. So, each of these solutions falls on the line.

h. The graph of an equation of this form is a line.

COMMON CORE STATE STANDARDS
Preparing for 8.EE.B.5

Learning Target

Graph linear equations.

Success Criteria

- Create a table of values and write ordered pairs given a linear equation.
- Plot ordered pairs to create a graph of a linear equation.
- Use a graph of a linear equation to solve a real-life problem.

Warm Up

Cumulative, vocabulary, and prerequisite skills practice opportunities are available in the *Resources by Chapter* or at *BigIdeasMath.com*.

ELL Support

Point out that the success criteria include creating a table of values. Students may be familiar with the word *table* as a piece of furniture. Explain that in a math context, a table is a type of chart. Point to the table on page 142 to provide visual support.

Exploration 1

a.

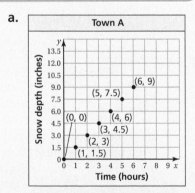

Town A

b–c. See Additional Answers.

d. *Sample answer:* At midnight, Town D has the most snow (8 in.) and Town A has the least snow (0 in.). At 6 A.M., Town C has the most snow (15 in.) and Town D has the least snow (8 in.).

T-141

Laurie's Notes

Preparing to Teach

- In previous courses, students used tables of values to show proportional relationships. In this lesson, they will use a table of values to create a graph of a **linear equation**. Plotting points to graph equations prepares students to graph proportional relationships and derive the general form, $y = mx$.
- **MP4 Model with Mathematics:** Using multiple representations of linear equations to represent a real-life problem deepens students' understanding and supports learning.
- At this point, it is acceptable for students to draw a line through discrete data points to help them solve a problem. They will determine whether non-integer values or negative values are valid in various contexts; however, the terms *discrete* and *continuous* are not used at this time.

Motivate

- To review creating and using ordered pairs, play a game of coordinate BINGO.
- Distribute small coordinate planes to students. They should plot ten ordered pairs, where the *x*- and *y*-coordinates are integers between −4 and 4.
- Generate a random ordered pair in the coordinate plane. Write the integers from −4 to 4 on slips of paper and place them in a bag. Draw and replace two slips of paper to generate the ordered pair and write it on the board.
- Each time you record a new ordered pair, students check to see if it is one of their 10 ordered pairs. If it is, the student puts an X over the point. The goal is to be the first person with three Xs. A student who calls "BINGO" reads the three ordered pairs for you to check against your list.
- ? "Are there ordered pairs that are not on lattice points, meaning the *x*- or *y*-coordinate is not an integer? Explain." Yes, it is possible for an ordered pair to be $\left(3\frac{1}{2}, \frac{1}{2}\right)$. Plot the examples that students suggest.

Exploration 1

- **FYI:** The amount of snowfall a town receives may cause a school cancellation.
- ? "How can you organize the data for the graph?" Use a table in which *x* represents the time after midnight and *y* represents the amount of snowfall.
- ? "What ordered pair is associated with midnight for Town A?" (0, 0)
- Students should create a table and plot the points for Town A.
- ? "What ordered pair is associated with midnight for Town B?" (0, 4)
- Students should create a table and plot the points for Town B in the same coordinate plane they used for part (a). Using a different color for each town will make it easier for students to compare the graphs.
- ? "What does the equation for Town D ($y = 8$) indicate?" Town D started with 8 inches of snow on the ground but received no snow after midnight.
- Graph both equations for Towns C and D in the same plane as Towns A and B.
- In part (d), students should compare the rates as well as the initial amounts. They should see how these are represented by differences in the graphs. You may want to bring up proportionality, if students do not. The relationship between time and snowfall for Town A is proportional, but the others are not.

4.1 Graphing Linear Equations

Learning Target: Graph linear equations.

Success Criteria:
- I can create a table of values and write ordered pairs given a linear equation.
- I can plot ordered pairs to create a graph of a linear equation.
- I can use a graph of a linear equation to solve a real-life problem.

EXPLORATION 1

Creating Graphs

Work with a partner. It starts snowing at midnight in Town A and Town B. The snow falls at a rate of 1.5 inches per hour.

a. In Town A, there is no snow on the ground at midnight. How deep is the snow at each hour between midnight and 6 A.M.? Make a graph that represents this situation.

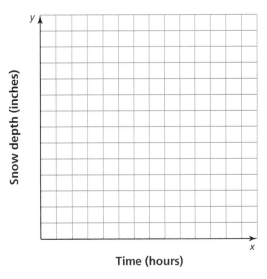

Snow depth (inches)

Time (hours)

b. Repeat part (a) for Town B, which has 4 inches of snow on the ground at midnight.

c. The equations below represent the depth y (in inches) of snow x hours after midnight in Town C and Town D. Graph each equation.

Town C   **Town D**

$y = 2x + 3$ $y = 8$

Math Practice

Use a Graph

How can you use each graph to find the rate of snowfall? the depth of the snow when it begins to fall?

d. Use your graphs to compare the snowfall in each town.

4.1 Lesson

 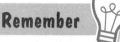
 Key Idea

Linear Equations

A **linear equation** is an equation whose graph is a line. The points on the line are **solutions** of the equation.

You can use a graph to show the solutions of a linear equation. The graph below represents the equation $y = x + 1$.

Remember

An ordered pair (x, y) is used to locate a point in a coordinate plane.

x	y	(x, y)
−1	0	(−1, 0)
0	1	(0, 1)
2	3	(2, 3)

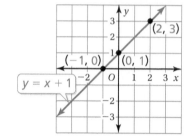

EXAMPLE 1 **Graphing a Linear Equation**

Graph $y = -2x + 1$.

Step 1: Make a table of values.

x	y = −2x + 1	y	(x, y)
−1	y = −2(−1) + 1	3	(−1, 3)
0	y = −2(0) + 1	1	(0, 1)
2	y = −2(2) + 1	−3	(2, −3)

Step 2: Plot the ordered pairs.

Step 3: Draw a line through the points.

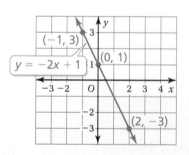

Try It **Graph the linear equation.**

1. $y = 3x$ **2.** $y = -2x - 1$ **3.** $y = -\dfrac{1}{2}x + 2$

Laurie's Notes

Scaffolding Instruction

- Students reviewed creating ordered pairs and plotting them in a coordinate plane. They will continue to graph linear equations, making a connection between the points in the graph and the solutions to the equation.
- **Emerging:** Students are able to create and plot ordered pairs but have difficulty connecting the ordered pairs to solutions of the equation. They need guided instruction for the Key Ideas and examples.
- **Proficient:** Students can plot ordered pairs to create a graph of a linear equation. They should review the Key Ideas before proceeding to the Self-Assessment exercises.

Key Idea

- Define linear equation and solutions of a linear equation.
- Note the use of color in the table. The equation used is a simple equation that helps students focus on the representation of the solutions as ordered pairs. The y-coordinate is always 1 greater than the x-coordinate, just as the equation states.

EXAMPLE 1

- As a quick review, ask a volunteer to review the rules for integer multiplication. If the factors have the same sign, the product is positive. If the factors have different signs, the product is negative.
- Write the four-column table. Take the time to show how the x-coordinate is being substituted in the second column. The number in blue is the only quantity that varies (variable); the other quantities are always the same (constant). Values from the first and third columns form the ordered pair.
- **?** "From the graph, can you estimate the solution when $x = \frac{1}{2}$? Verify your answer by solving the equation when $x = \frac{1}{2}$." yes; $\left(\frac{1}{2}, 0\right)$
- **MP5 Use Appropriate Tools Strategically:** Students can use graphing calculators to check their answers. Plan to spend some time teaching them how to use their calculators. It will be time well spent.

Try It

- **Neighbor Check:** Have students graph the equations independently and then have their neighbors check their work. Have students discuss any discrepancies. See the Teaching Strategy for more information.

ELL Support

After demonstrating Example 1, have students work in groups to discuss and complete Try It Exercises 1–3. Provide graph paper and list the steps: (1) Make a table of values, (2) Plot the ordered pairs, and (3) Draw a line through the points. Expect students to perform according to their language levels.

Beginner: Complete each step by making a table and plotting ordered pairs.

Intermediate: Use phrases or simple sentences.

Advanced: Use detailed sentences and help guide discussion.

Extra Example 1
Graph $y = \frac{1}{2}x - 3$

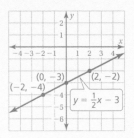

Teaching Strategy

Neighbor Check is a quick way for students to assess their work. It is important that discussions are not, "What do you have? Okay, I'll put that down." Students need to learn how to properly discuss their methods and solutions with their peers. They should explain how they arrived at their answers and work together to find methods and solutions that both students understand. Make it clear that *Neighbor Check* is *not* permission to copy answers. To help ensure that students do not copy their neighbors' work, you can call on students to explain their solutions to the class.

Try It

1.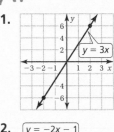

2.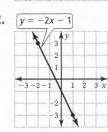

3.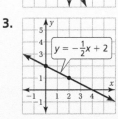

Extra Example 2

a. Graph $y = 4$.

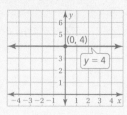

b. Graph $x = -1$.

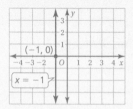

Try It

4.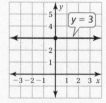

5–7. See Additional Answers.

ELL Support

Allow students to complete the Self-Assessment for Concepts & Skills exercises in pairs for extra support. Ask pairs to display their graphs for your review. Have two pairs form a group to discuss their explanations for Exercise 12. Monitor discussions and provide support as needed.

Self-Assessment
for Concepts & Skills

8.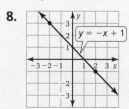

9–11. See Additional Answers.

12. $y = x^2 + 6$; It is not a linear equation.

Laurie's Notes

Key Idea

- Students are sometimes confused by the equations $y = b$ and $x = a$.
- Explain to students that a and b can equal any number.
- **Teaching Tip:** Another way to discuss the equation $y = b$ is to say that "y always equals a certain number, while x can equal anything." For example, if $y = -4$, the table of values may look like this:

x	-1	0	1	2
y	-4	-4	-4	-4

- **Teaching Tip:** Another way to discuss the equation $x = a$ is to say that "x always equals a certain number, while y can equal anything." For example, if $x = -2$, the table of values may look like this:

x	-2	-2	-2	-2
y	-1	0	1	2

EXAMPLE 2

- Have students create a table of values for $y = -3$.
- "What points are on the line $y = -3$?" *Sample answer:* $(5, -3)$, or anything of the form $(x, -3)$
- "If the graph of an equation is a vertical line, what do you know about the ordered pairs?" The x-values will remain the same while the y-values change.
- Have students create a table of values for $x = 2$.
- "What points are on the line $x = 2$?" *Sample answer:* $(2, -3)$, or anything of the form $(2, y)$
- "If the graph of an equation is a horizontal line, what do you know about the ordered pairs?" The y-values will remain the same while the x-values change.

Try It

- Ask volunteers to share their graphs at the board.
- Students may ask how to graph $x = -4$ on their calculators. To create a graph using a graphing calculator, the equation must begin with "$y = .$" So, vertical lines cannot be graphed on a calculator.

✓ Self-Assessment *for Concepts & Skills*

- **Neighbor Check:** Have students complete the exercises independently and then have their neighbors check their work. Have students discuss any discrepancies.

- If a few students are struggling, address them individually while others are working on the exercises. If several students are struggling, address the whole class.

- ⊙ Ask students to use *Thumbs Up* to indicate their understanding of creating a table of values, writing ordered pairs, and plotting them to create a graph of a linear equation.

The Success Criteria Self-Assessment chart can be found in the *Student Journal* or online at *BigIdeasMath.com*.

 **Key Idea**

Every point that is a solution of $y = b$ has a y-coordinate of b. These points lie on a horizontal line through $(0, b)$. You can use similar reasoning to understand why the graph of $x = a$ is a vertical line through $(a, 0)$.

Graphing Horizontal and Vertical Lines

The graph of $y = b$ is a horizontal line passing through $(0, b)$.

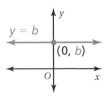

The graph of $x = a$ is a vertical line passing through $(a, 0)$.

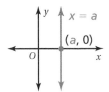

EXAMPLE 2 **Graphing a Horizontal Line and a Vertical Line**

a. **Graph $y = -3$.**

The graph of $y = -3$ is a horizontal line passing through $(0, -3)$. Draw a horizontal line through this point.

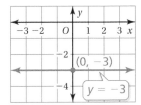

b. **Graph $x = 2$.**

The graph of $x = 2$ is a vertical line passing through $(2, 0)$. Draw a vertical line through this point.

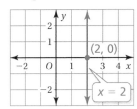

Try It **Graph the linear equation.**

4. $y = 3$ 5. $y = -1.5$ 6. $x = -4$ 7. $x = \dfrac{1}{2}$

 Self-Assessment for Concepts & Skills

Solve each exercise. Then rate your understanding of the success criteria in your journal.

GRAPHING A LINEAR EQUATION **Graph the linear equation.**

8. $y = -x + 1$

9. $y = 0.8x - 2$

10. $x = 2.5$

11. $y = \dfrac{2}{3}$

12. **WHICH ONE DOESN'T BELONG?** Which equation does *not* belong with the other three? Explain your reasoning.

| $y = x - 2$ | $4x + 3 = y$ | $y = x^2 + 6$ | $x + 5 = y$ |

EXAMPLE 3 **Modeling Real Life**

A tropical storm becomes a hurricane when wind speeds are at least 74 miles per hour.

The wind speed y (in miles per hour) of a tropical storm is $y = 2x + 66$, where x is the number of hours after the storm enters the Gulf of Mexico. When does the storm become a hurricane?

Use a graph to find the time it takes for the storm to become a hurricane. Make a table of values. Plot the ordered pairs and draw a line through the points.

x	$y = 2x + 66$	y	(x, y)
0	$y = 2(0) + 66$	66	$(0, 66)$
1	$y = 2(1) + 66$	68	$(1, 68)$
2	$y = 2(2) + 66$	70	$(2, 70)$
3	$y = 2(3) + 66$	72	$(3, 72)$

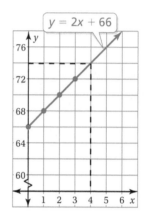

Math Practice

Use Equations
How else can you use the equation $y = 2x + 66$ to help you determine when the storm becomes a hurricane?

From the graph, you can see that $y = 74$ when $x = 4$.

▷ So, the storm becomes a hurricane 4 hours after it enters the Gulf of Mexico.

 Self-Assessment for Problem Solving

Solve each exercise. Then rate your understanding of the success criteria in your journal.

13. A game show contestant earns y dollars for completing a puzzle in x minutes. This situation is represented by the equation $y = -250x + 5000$. How long did a contestant who earned $500 take to complete the puzzle? Justify your answer.

14. The total cost y (in dollars) to join a cheerleading team and attend x competitions is represented by the equation $y = 10x + 50$.

　a. Graph the linear equation.

　b. You have $75 to spend. How many competitions can you attend?

15. The seating capacity y for a banquet hall is represented by $y = 8x + 56$, where x is the number of extra tables you need. How many extra tables do you need to double the original seating capacity?

Laurie's Notes

EXAMPLE 3

- **FYI:** During a wild April storm in 1934, a wind gust of 231 miles per hour (372 kilometers per hour) pushed across the summit of Mount Washington in New Hampshire.
- Ask a volunteer to read the problem aloud. Then ask another volunteer to explain the problem. If necessary, have another student re-read the problem.
- ❓ "What are you asked to find?" the time it takes for the storm to become a hurricane
- ❓ "How will you know when the storm becomes a hurricane? When the wind speed is at least 74 miles per hour.
- ❓ "What does x represent in the problem?" x = number of hours after the storm enters the Gulf of Mexico "What does y represent?" y = wind speed
- Work through the problem using a four-column table to generate solutions of the equation.
- Note that the y-coordinate is much greater than the x-coordinate. For this reason, a broken vertical axis is used. Students should *not* scale the y-axis beginning at 0.
- ❓ "Why are only non-negative numbers substituted for x?" Because x represents the number of hours after the storm enters the Gulf of Mexico, you do not know if the equation makes sense for x-values before that.
- Note that the ordered pairs are all located in Quadrant I because x is non-negative. Even though this restriction is not stated explicitly, you know from reading the description of x that it needs to be non-negative.
- Help students to understand they can answer the question by reading the graph. Starting with a y-value of 74 on the y-axis, trace horizontally until you reach the graph of the line, and then trace straight down (vertically) to the x-axis. The x-coordinate is 4.
- Students may also realize that they can answer the question by finding x when $y = 74$ by extending the table of values.

✅ Self-Assessment for Problem Solving

- The goal for all students is to feel comfortable with the problem-solving plan. It is important for students to problem-solve in class, where they may receive support from you and their peers. Keep in mind that some students may only be ready for the first step.
- **Neighbor Check:** Have students complete the exercises independently and then have their neighbors check their work. Have students discuss any discrepancies.
- Ask volunteers to share their work at the board.

The Success Criteria Self-Assessment chart can be found in the *Student Journal* or online at *BigIdeasMath.com*.

Closure

- **Exit Ticket:** Explain how you know if an equation is linear. *Sample answer:* The graph of the equation is a line.

Extra Example 3

The cost y (in dollars) for making friendship bracelets is $y = 0.5x + 2$, where x is the number of bracelets. How many bracelets can be made for $10? 16 bracelets

Self-Assessment
for Problem Solving

13. 18 min; $500 = -250x + 5000$, so $x = 18$.

14. a.

y = 10x + 50

b. 2 competitions

15. 7 tables

Learning Target

Graph linear equations.

Success Criteria

- Create a table of values and write ordered pairs given a linear equation.
- Plot ordered pairs to create a graph of a linear equation.
- Use a graph of a linear equation to solve a real-life problem.

Review & Refresh

1. yes; The triangles have the same angle measures, 95°, 46°, and 39°.

2. no; The triangles do not have the same angle measures.

3. 2 units right and 4 units up

4. 10 units left and 10 units down

5. 13 units left and 5 units up

Concepts, Skills, & Problem Solving

6–9. See Additional Answers.

10.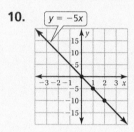
$y = -5x$

11. See Additional Answers.

12.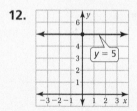
$y = 5$

13.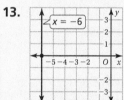
$x = -6$

14.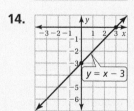
$y = x - 3$

15.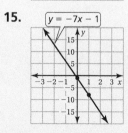
$y = -7x - 1$

16–23. See Additional Answers.

T-145

Assignment Guide and Concept Check

Scaffold assignments to support all students in their learning progression. The suggested assignments are a starting point. Continue to assign additional exercises and revisit with spaced practice to move every student toward proficiency.

Level	Assignment 1	Assignment 2
Emerging	2, 5, 6, 8, 11, 12, 13, 15, 22	16, 17, 19, 21, 23, 24, 25, 29, 32
Proficient	2, 5, 6, 9, 10, 12, 14, 16, 22	18, 20, 23, 24, 25, 26, 29, 30, 31, 32
Advanced	2, 5, 6, 9, 14, 16, 18, 20, 22	24, 27, 28, 29, 30, 31, 32, 33

- Assignment 1 is for use after students complete the Self-Assessment for Concepts & Skills.
- Assignment 2 is for use after students complete the Self-Assessment for Problem Solving.
- The red exercises can be used as a concept check.

Review & Refresh Prior Skills

Exercises 1 and 2 Identifying Similar Triangles
Exercises 3–5 Describing a Translation

Common Errors

- **Exercises 10–21** Students may make calculation errors when solving for ordered pairs. If they only find two ordered pairs for the graph, they may not recognize their mistakes. Encourage students to find at least three ordered pairs when drawing a graph.
- **Exercises 12, 18, and 19** Students may draw a vertical line through points on the x-axis. Remind them that the graph of the equation is a horizontal line. Ask students to identify the y-coordinate for several x-coordinates. For example, "What is the y-coordinate for $x = 5$? $x = 6$? $x = -4$?" Students should answer with the same y-coordinate each time.
- **Exercises 13, 20, and 21** Students may draw a horizontal line through points on the y-axis. Remind them that the graph of the equation is a vertical line. Ask students to identify the x-coordinate for several y-coordinates. For example, "What is the x-coordinate for $y = 3$? $y = -1$? $y = 0$?" Students should answer with the same x-coordinate each time.

4.1 Practice

 Go to *BigIdeasMath.com* to get HELP with solving the exercises.

▶ Review & Refresh

Tell whether the triangles are similar. Explain.

1.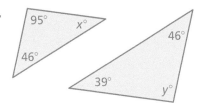

2.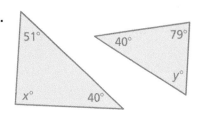

Describe the translation of the point to its image.

3. $(1, -4) \rightarrow (3, 0)$ **4.** $(6, 4) \rightarrow (-4, -6)$ **5.** $(4, -2) \rightarrow (-9, 3)$

▶ Concepts, Skills, & Problem Solving

CREATING GRAPHS **Make a graph of the situation.** (See Exploration 1, p. 141.)

6. The equation $y = -2x + 8$ represents the amount y (in fluid ounces) of dish detergent in a bottle after x days of use.

7. The equation $y = 15x + 20$ represents the cost y (in dollars) of a gym membership after x months.

MP **PRECISION** **Copy and complete the table with two solutions. Plot the ordered pairs and draw the graph of the linear equation. Use the graph to find a third solution of the equation.**

8.

x		
$y = 3x - 1$		

9.

x		
$y = \frac{1}{3}x + 2$		

GRAPHING A LINEAR EQUATION **Graph the linear equation.**

10. $y = -5x$ **11.** $y = 9x$ **12.** $y = 5$ **13.** $x = -6$

14. $y = x - 3$ **15.** $y = -7x - 1$ **16.** $y = -\frac{x}{3} + 4$ **17.** $y = 0.75x - 0.5$

18. $y = -\frac{2}{3}$ **19.** $y = 6.75$ **20.** $x = -0.5$ **21.** $x = \frac{1}{4}$

22. **MP** **YOU BE THE TEACHER** Your friend graphs the equation $y = 4$. Is your friend correct? Explain your reasoning.

23. **MP** **MODELING REAL LIFE** The equation $y = 20$ represents the cost y (in dollars) for sending x text messages in a month. Graph the linear equation. What does the graph tell you about your texting plan?

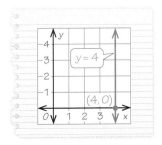

24. **MP MODELING REAL LIFE** The equation $y = 2x + 3$ represents the cost y (in dollars) of mailing a package that weighs x pounds.

    a. Use a graph to estimate how much it costs to mail the package.

    b. Use the equation to find exactly how much it costs to mail the package.

SOLVING A LINEAR EQUATION Solve for y. Then graph the linear equation.

25. $y - 3x = 1$

26. $5x + 2y = 4$

27. $-\dfrac{1}{3}y + 4x = 3$

28. $x + 0.5y = 1.5$

29. **MP MODELING REAL LIFE** The depth y (in inches) of a lake after x years is represented by the equation $y = 0.2x + 42$. How much does the depth of the lake increase in four years? Use a graph to justify your answer.

30. **MP MODELING REAL LIFE** The amount y (in dollars) of money in your savings account after x months is represented by the equation $y = 12.5x + 100$.

    a. Graph the linear equation.

    b. How many months will it take you to save a total of $237.50?

31. **MP PROBLEM SOLVING** The radius y (in millimeters) of a chemical spill after x days is represented by the equation $y = 6x + 50$.

    a. Graph the linear equation.

    b. The leak is noticed after two weeks. What is the area of the leak when it is noticed? Justify your answer.

32. **GEOMETRY** The sum S of the interior angle measures of a polygon with n sides is $S = (n - 2) \cdot 180°$.

    a. Plot four points (n, S) that satisfy the equation. Is the equation a linear equation? Explain your reasoning.

    b. Does the value $n = 3.5$ make sense in the context of the problem? Explain your reasoning.

33. **DIG DEEPER!** One second of video on your cell phone uses the same amount of memory as two pictures. Your cell phone can store 2500 pictures.

    a. Create a graph that represents the number y of pictures your cell phone can store when you take x seconds of video.

    b. How many pictures can your cell phone store in addition to a video that is one minute and thirty seconds long?

Common Errors

- **Exercises 25–28** Students may make mistakes in solving for y, such as using the same operation instead of the opposite operation. Remind students to use inverse operations to isolate y.

Mini-Assessment

1. Graph $y = \frac{1}{2}x - 2$.

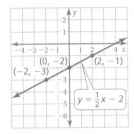

2. The amount y (in dollars) of money in your savings account after x months is represented by the equation $y = 20x + 100$.

a. Graph the linear equation.

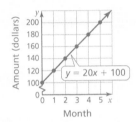

b. How many months will it take you to save a total of $200? 5 months

Section Resources

Surface Level	Deep Level
Resources by Chapter • Extra Practice • Reteach • Puzzle Time Student Journal • Self-Assessment • Practice Differentiating the Lesson Tutorial Videos Skills Review Handbook Skills Trainer	Resources by Chapter • Enrichment and Extension Graphic Organizers Dynamic Assessment System • Section Practice

Concepts, Skills, & Problem Solving

24. a. about $5

b. $5.25

25. $y = 3x + 1$

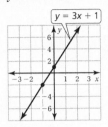

26. $y = -\frac{5}{2}x + 2$

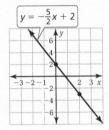

27. $y = 12x - 9$

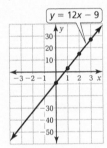

28. $y = -2x + 3$

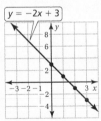

29. 0.8 in.;

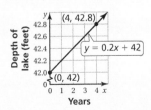

30–33. See Additional Answers.

Learning Target

Find and interpret the slope of a line.

Success Criteria

- Explain the meaning of slope.
- Find the slope of a line.
- Interpret the slope of a line in a real-life problem.

Warm Up

Cumulative, vocabulary, and prerequisite skills practice opportunities are available in the *Resources by Chapter* or at *BigIdeasMath.com*.

ELL Support

Explain that math provides a technical definition of *slope*. In everyday life, people often think of slope as a slant. Draw a line to clearly demonstrate its meaning. If students are familiar with ski slopes, use that as an example. Explain that a slope can be described by its rise and run. In everyday life, *rise* means "go up," as demonstrated by a sunrise or waking and rising. The rise of a slope describes how high the line goes up between two points. Students may know the word *run*. If not, pantomime it. The run of a slope describes how far the line goes horizontally between two points.

Exploration 1

a. Check students' work.

b. Check students' work. Because the two lines are a constant distance apart from each other, the steepness of each line is the same.

Exploration 2

a–c. See Additional Answers.

Laurie's Notes

Preparing to Teach

- Students should know the relationship between corresponding sides of similar triangles. Now they will use this relationship to explore slopes of lines.
- **MP1 Make Sense of Problems and Persevere in Solving Them:** The goal is for students to use different pairs of points on a line to find the line's slope. Drawing arrow diagrams will help students to visualize the *slope triangles*. Students should recognize the triangles are similar and proportions can be formed.

Motivate

- ❓ "How many of you have been on a roller coaster?"
- Discuss with students what makes one roller coaster more thrilling than another. Students will usually describe how quickly the coaster drops or the steepness of the hill. This is similar to the *change in y* of a line when finding the **slope**.

Exploration 1

- After completing the exploration, ask several students to draw their lines on the board.
- ❓ "What makes one line steeper than another?" *Sample answer:* how high the line goes up compared to the horizontal distance
- ❓ "What things do you encounter in your everyday life that may or may not be steep?" *Sample answers:* stairs, ski slopes, mountain roads
- ❓ "Which type of stairs would you prefer to climb? Why?" Answers may vary.

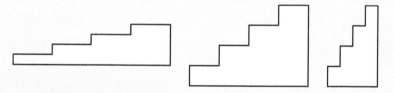

Exploration 2

- In part (a), check to see that students have located the points correctly. Encourage students to choose lattice points, meaning the *x*- and *y*-coordinates are integers.
- In part (b), students should use what they know about parallel lines and transversals to conclude that the triangles are similar.
- Have pairs compare their triangles with other pairs, so they realize that they can pick any two points on the line and construct a right triangle that is similar to the one shown.
- In part (c), lead students to the conclusion that the ratio of the side lengths, which gives the slope, is the same regardless of which points are used to draw the slope triangles.

4.2 Slope of a Line

Learning Target: Find and interpret the slope of a line.

Success Criteria:
- I can explain the meaning of slope.
- I can find the slope of a line.
- I can interpret the slope of a line in a real-life problem.

EXPLORATION 1

Measuring the Steepness of a Line

Work with a partner. Draw any nonvertical line in a coordinate plane.

a. Develop a way to measure the *steepness* of the line. Compare your method with other pairs.

b. Draw a line that is parallel to your line. What can you determine about the steepness of each line? Explain your reasoning.

EXPLORATION 2

Using Right Triangles

Work with a partner. Use the figure shown.

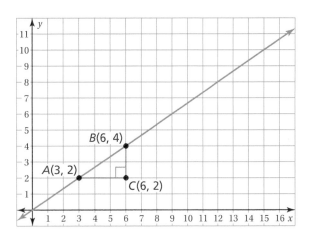

a. △ABC is a right triangle formed by drawing a horizontal line segment from point A and a vertical line segment from point B. Use this method to draw another right triangle, △DEF, with its longest side on the line.

b. What can you conclude about the two triangles in part (a)? Justify your conclusion. Compare your results with other pairs.

c. Based on your conclusions in part (b), what is true about $\frac{BC}{AC}$ and the corresponding measure in △DEF? Explain your reasoning. What do these values tell you about the line?

Math Practice

Construct Arguments

Do your answers to parts (b) and (c) change when you draw △DEF in a different location in part (a)? Explain.

Key Vocabulary
slope, p. 148
rise, p. 148
run, p. 148

Key Idea

Slope

The **slope** m of a line is the value of the ratio of the change in y (the **rise**) to the change in x (the **run**) between any two points, (x_1, y_1) and (x_2, y_2), on the line. The slope of a line is a measure of the steepness of the line.

$$m = \frac{\text{rise}}{\text{run}}$$

$$= \frac{\text{change in } y}{\text{change in } x}$$

$$= \frac{y_2 - y_1}{x_2 - x_1}$$

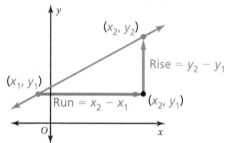

Reading

In the slope formula, x_1 is read as "x sub one," and y_2 is read as "y sub two." The numbers 1 and 2 in x_1 and y_2 are called *subscripts*.

Lines with positive slopes rise from left to right.

Lines with negative slopes fall from left to right.

EXAMPLE 1 **Finding Slopes of Lines**

Describe the slope of each line. Then find each slope.

a.

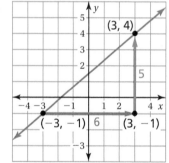

b.

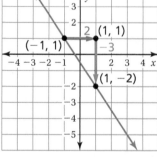

The methods in parts (a) and (b) show that you can find the slope of a line by using the graph or by using a formula.

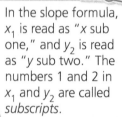

The line rises from left to right. So, the slope is positive. Use the graph to find the rise and the run of the line.

$$m = \frac{\text{rise}}{\text{run}}$$

$$= \frac{5}{6}$$

The line falls from left to right. So, the slope is negative. Use the coordinates $(x_1, y_1) = (-1, 1)$ and $(x_2, y_2) = (1, -2)$ to find the slope.

$$m = \frac{y_2 - y_1}{x_2 - x_1}$$

$$= \frac{-2 - 1}{1 - (-1)}$$

$$= \frac{-3}{2}, \text{ or } -\frac{3}{2}$$

Laurie's Notes

Scaffolding Instruction

- Students explored slopes of lines. They will now use more formal definitions to find slopes using graphs, tables, and formulas.
- **Emerging:** Students understand that some lines are steeper than others, but they may struggle with the fact that the slope of a line is constant and how to find it. They need guided instruction for the Key Ideas and examples.
- **Proficient:** Students understand that the slope of a line is determined by the ratio of the vertical change to the horizontal change between any two points. They also understand that parallel lines have the same slope. These students should review the Key Ideas and the Summary before proceeding to the Self-Assessment exercises.

Key Idea

- Write the Key Idea. Define slope of a line.
- Tell students that it is traditional to use *m* to represent slope. They will also see this in future mathematics courses. Students may ask why *m* is used. There does not seem to be agreement about this among mathematicians. In fact, some countries use different letters.
- Note the use of color in the definition and on the graph. The *change in y* and the *vertical change arrow* are both red. The *change in x* and the *horizontal change arrow* are both blue.
- Explain that it is common to refer to the triangle formed by the line and the change in *x* and change in *y* arrows as a *slope triangle*.
- Discuss the difference in positive and negative slopes.
- Remind students that graphs are read from left to right.
- Explain to students that in addition to finding the **rise** and the **run** graphically, they can also subtract coordinates to find the rise and the run.
- Go over the Reading note, so students understand how to read variables with subscripts.

EXAMPLE 1

- **MP1 Make Sense of Problems and Persevere in Solving Them:** Drawing the arrow diagrams will help students visualize the *slope triangle*.
- Students often ask if they can move in the *y*-direction first, followed by the *x*-direction. The answer is *yes*. Demonstrate this on either graph.
  - In part (a), start at $(-3, -1)$ and move up 5 units in the *y*-direction and then to the right 6 units in the *x*-direction. You will end at $(3, 4)$.
  - In part (b), start at $(-1, 1)$ and move down 3 units in the *y*-direction and then to the right 2 units in the *x*-direction. You will end at $(1, -2)$.
- **Discuss:** When finding the slope, you can label either point as (x_1, y_1) and the other point as (x_2, y_2). The labeling of the ordered pairs is arbitrary.

Scaffold instruction to support all students in their learning. Learning is individualized and you may want to group students differently as they move in and out of these levels with each skill and concept. Student self-assessment and feedback help guide your instructional decisions about how and when to layer support for all students to become proficient learners.

Extra Example 1

Describe the slope of each line. Then find each slope.

a.

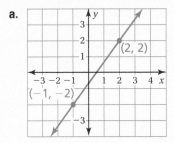

The line rises from left to right, so the slope is positive; $\frac{4}{3}$

b.

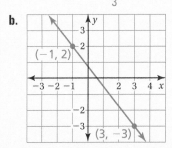

The line falls from left to right, so the slope is negative; $-\frac{5}{4}$

Try It

1. $-\dfrac{1}{5}$ 2. $\dfrac{1}{3}$

Extra Example 2

Find the slope of each line.

a.

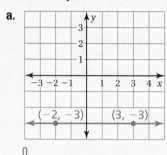

0

b.

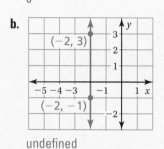

undefined

Try It

3. 0 4. undefined

Laurie's Notes

Try It

- Have students use whiteboards to find each slope. Ask them to show their work so you can quickly evaluate their understanding.
- **Common Error:** Students may confuse the slope ratio, saying, "slope is run over rise." Tell students that they must "rise up" before they can "run," so slope is rise over run.

EXAMPLE 2

- ❓ "How does a slope of $\dfrac{1}{2}$ compare to a slope of $\dfrac{1}{5}$? Describe the lines." A slope of $\dfrac{1}{2}$ runs 2 units for every 1 unit it rises. A slope of $\dfrac{1}{5}$ runs 5 units for each 1 unit it rises. A slope of $\dfrac{1}{5}$ is not as steep.

- ❓ "What would a slope of $\dfrac{1}{10}$ look like?" A slope of $\dfrac{1}{10}$ is less steep than a slope of $\dfrac{1}{5}$, so it is almost flat.

- ❓ "How steep do you think a horizontal line is?" Listen for students to describe a horizontal line as having no rise. In part (a), they will see it has a slope of 0.

- This progression of questions is to help students visualize that as slopes of lines get less steep, the lines approach a horizontal line.

- Work through part (a). There is no change in y. So, the change in y is 0.

- In part (b), ask a series of questions similar to part (a).

- ❓ "How does a slope of $\dfrac{9}{2}$ compare to a slope of $\dfrac{3}{2}$? Describe the lines." A slope of $\dfrac{9}{2}$ runs 2 units for every 9 units it rises. A slope of $\dfrac{3}{2}$ runs 2 units for every 3 units it rises. A slope of $\dfrac{9}{2}$ is steeper.

- ❓ "What would a slope of 10 look like?" A slope of 10 is steeper than a slope of $\dfrac{9}{2}$, so it is almost vertical.

- ❓ "How steep do you think a vertical line is?" Listen for students to describe a vertical line as having a slope of infinity.

- Work through part (b). There is no change in x. So, the change in x is 0. Because division by zero is undefined, the slope of the line is undefined.

Try It

- Students should solve the problems on whiteboards. Discuss any discrepancies as a class.

Summary

- Students have computed the slopes of several lines. Have students discuss the Summary by working with a partner to provide an example of each type of slope.

Try It Find the slope of the line.

1.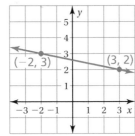

2.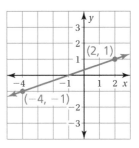

EXAMPLE 2 **Finding Slopes of Horizontal and Vertical Lines**

Find the slope of each line.

a.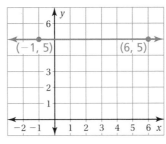

$$m = \frac{y_2 - y_1}{x_2 - x_1}$$

$$= \frac{5 - 5}{6 - (-1)}$$

$$= \frac{0}{7}, \text{ or } 0$$

▶ The slope is 0.

b.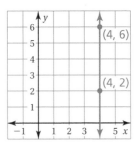

$$m = \frac{y_2 - y_1}{x_2 - x_1}$$

$$= \frac{6 - 2}{4 - 4}$$

$$= \frac{4}{0} \ \textbf{✗}$$

▶ Division by zero is undefined. So, the slope is undefined.

 The slope of every horizontal line is 0. The slope of every vertical line is undefined.

Try It Find the slope of the line through the given points.

3. $(1, -2), (7, -2)$

4. $(-3, -3), (-3, -5)$

🔑 Summary

Slope

Positive Slope

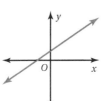

The line rises from left to right.

Negative Slope

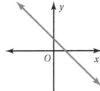

The line falls from left to right.

Slope of 0

The line is horizontal.

Undefined Slope

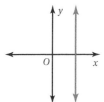

The line is vertical.

 **Key Idea**

Parallel Lines and Slope

Lines in the same plane that do not intersect are parallel lines. Nonvertical parallel lines have the same slope.

All vertical lines are parallel.

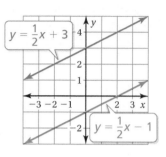

EXAMPLE 3 **Identifying Parallel Lines**

Which lines are parallel? How do you know?

Find the slope of each line.

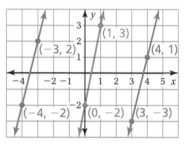

Blue Line	Red Line	Green Line
$m = \dfrac{y_2 - y_1}{x_2 - x_1}$	$m = \dfrac{y_2 - y_1}{x_2 - x_1}$	$m = \dfrac{y_2 - y_1}{x_2 - x_1}$
$= \dfrac{-2 - 2}{-4 - (-3)}$	$= \dfrac{-2 - 3}{0 - 1}$	$= \dfrac{-3 - 1}{3 - 4}$
$= \dfrac{-4}{-1}$, or 4	$= \dfrac{-5}{-1}$, or 5	$= \dfrac{-4}{-1}$, or 4

The slopes of the blue and green lines are 4. The slope of the red line is 5.

▷ The blue and green lines have the same slope, so they are parallel.

Try It

5. **WHAT IF?** The blue line passes through $(-4, -3)$ and $(-3, 2)$. Are any of the lines parallel? Explain.

 Self-Assessment *for Concepts & Skills*

Solve each exercise. Then rate your understanding of the success criteria in your journal.

6. **VOCABULARY** What does it mean for a line to have a slope of 4?

FINDING THE SLOPE OF A LINE **Find the slope of the line through the given points.**

7. $(1, -1), (6, 2)$

8. $(2, -3), (5, -3)$

9. **FINDING SLOPE** Are the lines parallel? Explain your reasoning.

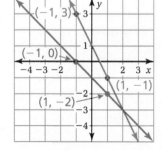

Laurie's Notes

Key Idea

- Write the Key Idea on the board.
- Model what a slope of $\frac{1}{2}$ means. Start at a point on the line and run 2 units for each unit you rise. Repeat for each line.

EXAMPLE 3

- **?** "How do you compute the slope for each line?" Students should use rise over run language, along with the formal definition, $\frac{y_2 - y_1}{x_2 - x_1}$.
- Remind students that either point can be labeled as (x_1, y_1), as long as they are consistent in both the numerator and denominator.
- Work through the example. Students may look quickly and believe that all of the lines are parallel. They should compute the slope of each line to prove which lines are parallel.

Try It

- **Turn and Talk:** After completing the exercise, have students compare strategies and answers with partners.

✓ Self-Assessment for Concepts & Skills

- ◉ Use *Popsicle Sticks* to solicit responses to the questions:
  - What does *slope* mean?
  - How do you find the slope of a line?
- **Neighbor Check:** Have students complete the exercises independently and then have their neighbors check their work. Have students discuss any discrepancies.

ELL Support

Allow students to work in pairs for extra support. Have each pair display their answers for Exercises 7 and 8 on a whiteboard for your review. Have two pairs form a group to discuss and answer Exercises 6 and 9. Then have each group present their answers to another group. The two groups must reach an agreement if their ideas differ. Monitor discussions and provide support.

The Success Criteria Self-Assessment chart can be found in the *Student Journal* or online at *BigIdeasMath.com*.

Extra Example 3

Which lines are parallel? How do you know?

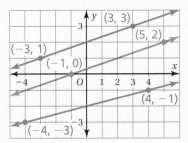

blue and red; Both lines have a slope of $\frac{1}{3}$.

Try It

5. yes; *Sample answer:* Because the slopes of the blue and red lines are both equal to 5, these two lines are parallel.

Self-Assessment
for Concepts & Skills

6. The line rises 4 units for every 1 unit it runs.

7. $\frac{3}{5}$

8. 0

9. no; Because the slopes of the lines are not the same, the lines are not parallel.

Extra Example 4

The table shows your distance y (in miles) from your school x minutes after you leave. The points in the table lie on a line. Find and interpret the slope of the line.

x	1	6	11	16
y	1	4	7	10

$\frac{3}{5}$; The distance between you and your school increases 3 miles every 5 minutes, or $\frac{3}{5}$ mile every minute.

Self-Assessment
for Problem Solving

10. $\frac{1}{2}$; Your hair grows $\frac{1}{2}$ inch every month; 8 months

11. $14; *Sample answer:* Using the two points and the slope formula,
$$m = \frac{120 - 92}{5 - 3} = \frac{28}{2} = 14.$$

12. See Additional Answers.

Formative Assessment Tip

Sentence Summary

This technique asks students to write a single sentence to describe what they have learned about a topic. You may ask students to summarize new information, make a comparison, or describe a problem and solution. Give students time to reflect before writing. Discourage responses like, "I learned how to subtract." *Sentence Summary* gives you a quick glimpse into each student's level of understanding of the material.

Learning Target

Find and interpret the slope of a line.

Success Criteria

• Explain the meaning of slope.
• Find the slope of a line.
• Interpret the slope of a line in a real-life problem.

EXAMPLE 4

? "What do you notice about the x-values and the y-values?" The x-values are increasing by 3 and the y-values are decreasing by 2.

• **Connection:** Show the changes in x and y from each column to the next (i.e., $+3$, $+3$, $+3$ on the top and -2, -2, -2 on the bottom). Ask students to use the table and graph to determine if x and y represent a proportional relationship. They are not proportional.

• Compute the slope between any two points in the table.

Using (1, 8) and (4, 6): $m = \dfrac{y_2 - y_1}{x_2 - x_1} = \dfrac{6 - 8}{4 - 1} = -\dfrac{2}{3}$.

Using (1, 8) and (7, 4): $m = \dfrac{y_2 - y_1}{x_2 - x_1} = \dfrac{4 - 8}{7 - 1} = -\dfrac{2}{3}$.

• Remind students about the exploration, where they found that the slope is the same regardless of which two points are selected. The slope triangles that are formed are similar.

? "The line has a negative slope. What do you notice about the line?" The line falls from left to right.

? "What word can you use to represent a negative slope?" decrease

• Interpret the slope of the line.

✔ Self-Assessment for Problem Solving

• Allow time in class for students to practice using the problem-solving plan. Remember, some students may only be able to complete the first step.

• Ask students to write their plans for each problem. Discuss the plans of several students as a class.

• **Neighbor Check:** Have students complete the exercises independently and then have their neighbors check their work. Have students discuss any discrepancies.

⊙ Have students use *Thumbs Up* to indicate their understanding of the third success criterion.

The Success Criteria Self-Assessment chart can be found in the *Student Journal* or online at *BigIdeasMath.com*.

Closure

• **Sentence Summary:** Give each student an index card. Ask students to write about what they have learned about (a) slopes of horizontal lines and (b) slopes of vertical lines. Allow time for students to reflect and discourage responses like, "I learned how to find the slope." Use these responses to plan your instruction for the next day.

EXAMPLE 4 **Modeling Real Life**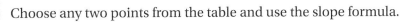

The table shows the distance y (in miles) of a space probe from a comet x minutes after it begins its approach. The points in the table lie on a line. Find and interpret the slope of the line.

x	1	4	7	10
y	8	6	4	2

Choose any two points from the table and use the slope formula.

Use the points $(x_1, y_1) = (1, 8)$ and $(x_2, y_2) = (4, 6)$.

$$m = \frac{y_2 - y_1}{x_2 - x_1}$$

$$= \frac{6 - 8}{4 - 1}$$

$$= \frac{-2}{3}, \text{ or } -\frac{2}{3}$$

© ESA/Rosetta/MPS for OSIRIS TeamMPS/
UPD/LAM/IAA/SSO/INTA/UPM/DASP/IDA

Check

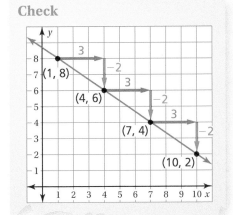

▷ The slope is $-\frac{2}{3}$. So, the distance between the probe and the comet decreases 2 miles every 3 minutes, or $\frac{2}{3}$ mile every minute.

Self-Assessment for Problem Solving

Solve each exercise. Then rate your understanding of the success criteria in your journal.

x	y
1	0.5
2	1
3	1.5
4	2

10. The table shows the lengths y (in inches) of your hair x months after your last haircut. The points in the table lie on a line. Find and interpret the slope of the line. After how many months is your hair 4 inches long?

11. A customer pays an initial fee and a daily fee to rent a snowmobile. The total payment for 3 days is 92 dollars. The total payment for 5 days is 120 dollars. What is the daily fee? Justify your answer.

12. You in-line skate from an elevation of 720 feet to an elevation of 750 feet in 30 minutes. Your friend in-line skates from an elevation of 600 feet to an elevation of 690 feet in one hour. Compare your rates of change in elevation.

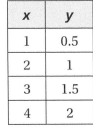

Go to *BigIdeasMath.com* to get HELP with solving the exercises.

▶ Review & Refresh

Graph the linear equation.

1. $y = 4x - 3$

2. $x = -3$

3. $y = 2$

4. $y = \dfrac{3}{2}x - \dfrac{1}{2}$

Find the missing values in the ratio table.

5.

Yards	1		5	7
Feet	3	10		

6.

Miles	0.6		1.8	
Hours	1	2		4

▶▶ Concepts, Skills, & Problem Solving

USING RIGHT TRIANGLES Use the figure shown. (See Exploration 2, p. 147.)

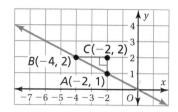

7. Find the slope of the line.

8. Let point *D* be at $(-4, 1)$. Use the sides of $\triangle BDA$ to find the slope of the line.

FINDING THE SLOPE OF A LINE Find the slope of the line.

9.
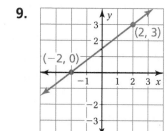

10.
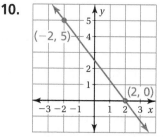

11.
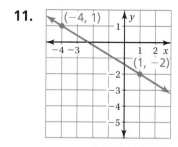

12.
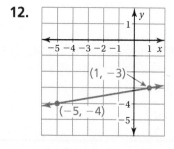

13.
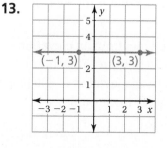

14.
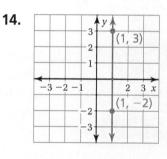

Assignment Guide and Concept Check

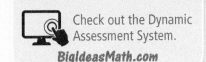
Scaffold assignments to support all students in their learning progression. The suggested assignments are a starting point. Continue to assign additional exercises and revisit with spaced practice to move every student toward proficiency.

Level	Assignment 1	Assignment 2
Emerging	3, 4, 6, 7, 8, 9, 10, 11, 15, 17, 22	13, 14, 16, 20, 21, 23, 25, 28, 30, 32, 36, 38
Proficient	3, 4, 6, 7, 8, 10, 12, 13, 14, 16, 18, 22	20, 21, 23, 24, 26, 27, 29, 30, 32, 34, 36, 37, 38, 39
Advanced	3, 4, 6, 7, 8, 10, 12, 13, 14, 16, 18, 22	20, 21, 24, 27, 29, 31, 34, 36, 37, 38, 39, 40, 41

- Assignment 1 is for use after students complete the Self-Assessment for Concepts & Skills.
- Assignment 2 is for use after students complete the Self-Assessment for Problem Solving.
- The red exercises can be used as a concept check.

Review & Refresh Prior Skills

Exercises 1–4   Graphing a Linear Equation
Exercises 5 and 6   Completing a Ratio Table

Common Errors

- **Exercises 9–14** Students may forget negatives or include them when they are not needed. Remind students that if the line rises from left to right the slope is positive and if the line falls from left to right the slope is negative.
- **Exercises 9–14** Students may find the reciprocal of the slope because they mix up the rise and the run. Remind students that the change in *y* is the numerator and the change in *x* is the denominator.

Review & Refresh

1.
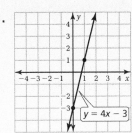
$y = 4x - 3$

2.
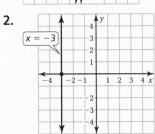
$x = -3$

3.
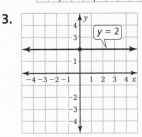
$y = 2$

4.
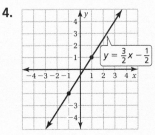
$y = \frac{3}{2}x - \frac{1}{2}$

5.

Yards	1	$3\frac{1}{3}$	5	7
Feet	3	10	15	21

6.

Miles	0.6	1.2	1.8	2.4
Hours	1	2	3	4

Concepts, Skills, & Problem Solving

7. $-\dfrac{1}{2}$ 8. $-\dfrac{1}{2}$

9. $\dfrac{3}{4}$ 10. $-\dfrac{5}{4}$

11. $-\dfrac{3}{5}$ 12. $\dfrac{1}{6}$

13. 0   14. undefined

Concepts, Skills, & Problem Solving

15. 0

16. undefined

17. undefined

18. 2

19. $-\dfrac{11}{6}$

20. 0

21. no; Both lines have the same slope, so the lines are parallel.

22. no; The denominator should be $2 - 4$.

23. blue and red; They both have a slope of -3.

24. red and green; They both have a slope of $\dfrac{4}{3}$.

25. yes; Both lines are horizontal and have a slope of 0.

26. no; $y = 0$ has a slope of 0 and $x = 0$ has an undefined slope.

27. yes; Both lines are vertical and have an undefined slope.

28. 4

29. $\dfrac{2}{5}$

30. $\dfrac{1}{3}$

Common Errors

- **Exercises 15–20** Students may find the reciprocal of the slope because they mix up the rise and the run. Remind students that the change in *y* is the numerator and the change in *x* is the denominator.
- **Exercises 28 and 29** Students may find the change in *x* over the change in *y*. Remind students that slope is the change in *y* over the change in *x*.

FINDING THE SLOPE OF A LINE Find the slope of the line through the given points.

15. $(4, -1), (-2, -1)$

16. $(5, -3), (5, 8)$

17. $(-7, 0), (-7, -6)$

18. $(-3, 1), (-1, 5)$

19. $(10, 4), (4, 15)$

20. $(-3, 6), (2, 6)$

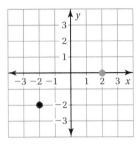

21. **MP REASONING** Draw a line through each point using a slope of $m = \frac{1}{4}$. Do the lines intersect? Explain.

22. **MP YOU BE THE TEACHER** Your friend finds the slope of the line shown. Is your friend correct? Explain your reasoning.

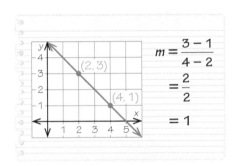

IDENTIFYING PARALLEL LINES Which lines are parallel? How do you know?

23.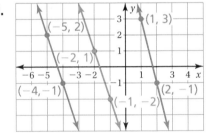

24.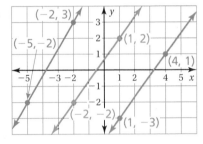

IDENTIFYING PARALLEL LINES Are the given lines parallel? Explain your reasoning.

25. $y = -5, y = 3$

26. $y = 0, x = 0$

27. $x = -4, x = 1$

FINDING SLOPE The points in the table lie on a line. Find the slope of the line.

28.

x	1	3	5	7
y	2	10	18	26

29.

x	-3	2	7	12
y	0	2	4	6

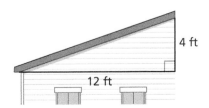

30. **MP MODELING REAL LIFE** Carpenters refer to the slope of a roof as the *pitch* of the roof. Find the pitch of the roof.

31. **PROJECT** The guidelines for a wheelchair ramp suggest that the ratio of the rise to the run be no greater than $1:12$.

     a. **MP CHOOSE TOOLS** Find a wheelchair ramp in your school or neighborhood. Measure its slope. Does the ramp follow the guidelines?

     b. Design a wheelchair ramp that provides access to a building with a front door that is 2.5 feet above the sidewalk. Illustrate your design.

USING AN EQUATION **Use an equation to find the value of k so that the line that passes through the given points has the given slope.**

32. $(1, 3), (5, k); m = 2$

33. $(-2, k), (2, 0); m = -1$

34. $(-4, k), (6, -7); m = -\dfrac{1}{5}$

35. $(4, -4), (k, -1); m = \dfrac{3}{4}$

36. **MP MODELING REAL LIFE** The graph shows the numbers of prescriptions filled over time by a pharmacy.

     a. Find the slope of the line.

     b. Explain the meaning of the slope as a rate of change.

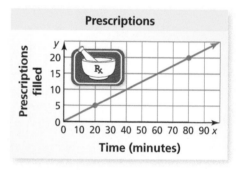

37. **CRITICAL THINKING** Which is steeper: the boat ramp, or a road with a 12% grade? Explain. (*Note:* Road grade is the vertical increase divided by the horizontal distance.)

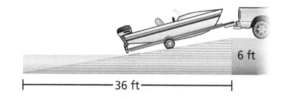

38. **MP REASONING** Do the points $A(-2, -1)$, $B(1, 5)$, and $C(4, 11)$ lie on the same line? Without using a graph, how do you know?

39. **MP PROBLEM SOLVING** A small business earns a profit of $6500 in January and $17,500 in May. What is the rate of change in profit for this time period? Justify your answer.

40. **MP STRUCTURE** Choose two points in the coordinate plane. Use the slope formula to find the slope of the line that passes through the two points. Then find the slope using the formula $\dfrac{y_1 - y_2}{x_1 - x_2}$. Compare your results.

41. **DIG DEEPER!** The top and the bottom of the slide are level with the ground, which has a slope of 0.

     a. What is the slope of the main portion of the slide?

     b. Describe the change in the slope when the bottom of the slide is only 12 inches above the ground. Explain your reasoning.

Mini-Assessment

Find the slope of the line.

1.

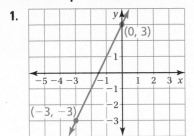

2

2.

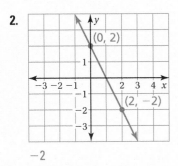

−2

3. Which two lines are parallel? How do you know?

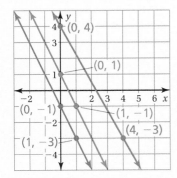

red and blue; Both lines have a slope of −2.

Concepts, Skills, & Problem Solving

31. a. Check students' work.

    b. See Additional Answers.

32. $k = 11$

33. $k = 4$

34. $k = -5$

35. $k = 8$

36. a. $\dfrac{1}{4}$

    b. 1 prescription filled every 4 minutes

37. the boat ramp; It has a 16.67% grade.

38. yes; The slopes are the same between the points.

39. $2750 per month;

$$\frac{17{,}500 - 6500}{5 - 1} = \frac{11{,}000}{4} = 2750$$

40. When you switch the coordinates, the differences in the numerator and denominator are the opposite of the numbers when using the slope formula. You still get the same slope.

41. a. 0.65

    b. The slope increases because the vertical distance for the main portion of the slide increases and the horizontal distance stays the same.

Section Resources

Surface Level	Deep Level

Resources by Chapter
  • Extra Practice
  • Reteach
  • Puzzle Time
Student Journal
  • Self-Assessment
  • Practice
Differentiating the Lesson
Tutorial Videos
Skills Review Handbook
Skills Trainer
	Resources by Chapter
	  • Enrichment and Extension
	Graphic Organizers
	Dynamic Assessment System
	  • Section Practice

Learning Target

Graph proportional relationships.

Success Criteria

- Graph an equation that represents a proportional relationship.
- Write an equation that represents a proportional relationship.
- Use graphs to compare proportional relationships.

Warm Up

Cumulative, vocabulary, and prerequisite skills practice opportunities are available in the *Resources by Chapter* or at *BigIdeasMath.com*.

ELL Support

Point out the heading of Exploration 2, *Deriving an Equation*. Explain that the word *derive* means "figure out." Ask students what other words they might use to explain the word *derive*. Examples may be *get* or *understand*. Suggest that they keep a notebook of synonyms to help expand their knowledge of vocabulary.

Exploration 1

a–b. See Additional Answers.

Exploration 2

a. corresponding side lengths are proportional; *Sample answer:* The corresponding angles of the triangles are congruent, so the triangles are similar.

b. $\dfrac{y-0}{x-0} = \dfrac{m}{1}$; $y = mx$

c. $y = mx$ is the general equation for two quantities x and y that are in a proportional relationship; m represents the slope of the line, constant of proportionality, or unit rate.

T-155

Laurie's Notes

Preparing to Teach

- In previous courses, students determined whether two quantities are proportional. In this chapter, they have graphed linear equations and found slopes of lines. Now students will graph and write an equation that represents a proportional relationship.
- **MP2 Reason Abstractly and Quantitatively:** Mathematically proficient students make sense of the quantities and their relationships in problem situations. To develop this proficiency, students must be asked to interpret the meaning of a slope as a unit rate.

Motivate

- As a warm-up and to connect to prior content, tell students that x and y are in a proportional relationship. Have students complete the ratio table.

Minutes, x	1	2	4	6
Gallons, y	8.5			

- **Construct Viable Arguments and Critique the Reasoning of Others:** Ask volunteers to justify their procedures and explain why their procedures show a proportional relationship.

Exploration 1

- In part (a), students should see how the additive structure in the table relates to the red and blue arrows in the graph, which gives them the rise and run.
- **Common Error:** Students may confuse the slope ratio, saying, "slope is run over rise." Tell students that they must "rise up" before they can "run," so slope is rise over run.
- In part (b), students should use a similar additive structure to create their ratio tables. They should show that there is an increase of y fluid ounces of water for every increase of x fluid ounces of vinegar. So, the slope of the line is $\dfrac{y}{x}$, where y and x are real numbers based on the ratio chosen by students.

Exploration 2

? "What do you know about the two triangles?" *Sample answer:* Their corresponding angles are congruent, so the triangles are similar. If students do not mention similar, lead them to it. The triangles both have right angles and share a common angle at (0, 0), so the third angles must be congruent.

? "When two triangles are similar, what do you know about their side lengths?" Corresponding side lengths are proportional.

- It may not be obvious to students that the vertical side of the smaller triangle has a length of m units and the horizontal side has a length of 1 unit. It may be even less obvious that the vertical side of the larger triangle has a length of y units and the horizontal side has a length of x units.
- Ask students to share their responses for part (c). They should realize that the equation $y = mx$ represents a proportional relationship, where m is the slope.

4.3 Graphing Proportional Relationships

Learning Target: Graph proportional relationships.

Success Criteria:
- I can graph an equation that represents a proportional relationship.
- I can write an equation that represents a proportional relationship.
- I can use graphs to compare proportional relationships.

EXPLORATION 1

Using a Ratio Table to Find Slope

Work with a partner. The graph shows amounts of vinegar and water that can be used to make a cleaning product.

a. Use the graph to make a ratio table relating the quantities. Explain how the slope of the line is represented in the table.

b. Make a ratio table that represents a different ratio of vinegar to water. Use the table to describe the slope of the graph of the new relationship.

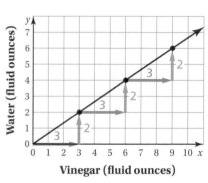

EXPLORATION 2

Deriving an Equation

Work with a partner. Let (x, y) represent any point on the graph of a proportional relationship.

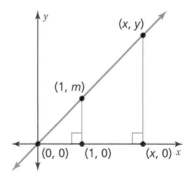

Math Practice

Make a Plan
How can you find the side lengths of the triangles in the graph?

a. Describe the relationship between the corresponding side lengths of the triangles shown in the graph. Explain your reasoning.

b. Use the relationship in part (a) to write an equation relating y, m, and x. Then solve the equation for y.

c. What does your equation in part (b) describe? What does m represent? Explain your reasoning.

Key Idea

Proportional Relationships

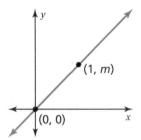

In the equation $y = mx$, m represents the constant of proportionality, the slope, and the unit rate.

Words When two quantities x and y are proportional, the relationship can be represented by the equation $y = mx$, where m is the constant of proportionality.

Graph The graph of $y = mx$ is a line with a slope of m that passes through the origin.

EXAMPLE 1 **Graphing a Proportional Relationship**

The cost y (in dollars) for x ounces of frozen yogurt is represented by $y = 0.5x$. Graph the equation and interpret the slope.

Method 1: Make a table of values.

x	$y = 0.5x$	y	(x, y)
0	$y = 0.5(0)$	0	$(0, 0)$
1	$y = 0.5(1)$	0.5	$(1, 0.5)$
2	$y = 0.5(2)$	1	$(2, 1)$
3	$y = 0.5(3)$	1.5	$(3, 1.5)$

Method 2: Use the slope.

The equation shows that the slope m is 0.5. So, the graph passes through $(0, 0)$ and $(1, 0.5)$.

Plot the ordered pairs and draw a line through the points. Because negative values of x do not make sense in this context, graph in the first quadrant only.

Math Practice

Use a Graph
Why does it make sense to graph the equations in Example 1 in the first quadrant only?

▷ The slope indicates that the unit cost is $0.50 per ounce.

Frozen Yogurt

Try It

1. **WHAT IF?** The cost of frozen yogurt is represented by $y = 0.75x$. Graph the equation and interpret the slope.

Laurie's Notes

Scaffolding Instruction

- Students explored the slopes of proportional relationships. They will now write and graph proportional relationships.
- **Emerging:** Students may struggle to determine the proportional relationship of points in a graph. They will benefit from guided instruction for the Key Idea and examples.
- **Proficient:** Students made the connection between the slope of a line and the constant of proportionality with ease. They should review the Key Idea and complete the Try It exercises before proceeding to the Self-Assessment exercises.

Key Idea

- Write the Key Idea. Draw the graph and discuss the two labeled points.
- Students studied proportional relationships in the previous course. You could choose to introduce terminology of *direct variation*, by saying that proportional quantities vary directly and the equation $y = mx$ is a direct variation equation. It is a special kind of linear equation, one whose graph passes through the origin.
- Discuss the push-pin note to help students connect prior concepts. In the equation $y = mx$, you can think of the coefficient m as the constant of proportionality, the slope, and/or the unit rate.

EXAMPLE 1

- ❓ "Do x and y show a proportional relationship? Explain." Yes, the equation is in the form $y = mx$.
- ❓ "In the context of the problem, can x be negative? Explain." No, x represents ounces of frozen yogurt and cannot be a negative amount.
- Show students how to use the slope of the line and the origin to graph the line. It may help students to think of the slope as $\frac{1}{2}$ rather than 0.5. After drawing the line, show students how to use the slope and any point to find another point.
- Although there are several points shown in the table and the graph, select two to find the slope.
- **MP6 Attend to Precision:** Ask students to interpret the slope of the line. Students should precisely refer to the *unit* cost of $0.50 per ounce of frozen yogurt.

Try It

- **Neighbor Check:** Have students work independently and then have their neighbors check their work. Have students discuss any discrepancies.

ELL Support

After demonstrating Example 1, have students work in groups to discuss and complete Try It Exercise 1. Provide graph paper to each group and ask that students use both methods demonstrated. Expect students to perform according to their language levels.

Beginner: Complete each step by making a table and plotting points.

Intermediate: Use phrases or simple sentences.

Advanced: Use detailed sentences and help guide discussion.

Scaffold instruction to support all students in their learning. Learning is individualized and you may want to group students differently as they move in and out of these levels with each skill and concept. Student self-assessment and feedback help guide your instructional decisions about how and when to layer support for all students to become proficient learners.

Extra Example 1

The cost y (in dollars) to rent x video games is represented by $y = 4x$. Graph the equation and interpret the slope.

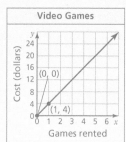

The slope indicates that the unit cost is $4 per video game.

Try It

1.

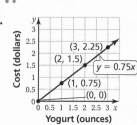

The unit cost is $0.75 per ounce.

Extra Example 2

The daily wage *y* (in dollars) of a factory worker is proportional to the number of parts *x* assembled in a day. A worker who assembles 250 parts in a day earns $75.

a. Write an equation that represents the situation. $y = \frac{3}{10}x$

b. How much does a worker earn who assembles 300 parts in a day? $90

Try It

2. 500 kg

ELL Support

Allow students to complete the Self-Assessment for Concepts & Skills exercises in pairs for extra support. Ask pairs to display their graphs for Exercises 3–5 and answers for Exercise 6 for your review.

Self-Assessment
for Concepts & Skills

3.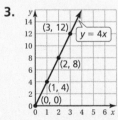

4.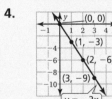

5.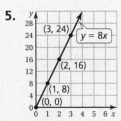

6. See Additional Answers.

EXAMPLE 2

- **FYI:** Titan is Saturn's largest known moon. Titan is larger than our moon and the planet Mercury. Titan has clouds and a thick atmosphere, like some planets. It may rain "gasoline-like" liquids on Titan. You can find more information about Titan at *www.nasa.gov*.
- Ask a volunteer to read the problem aloud. Then ask another volunteer to explain the problem.
- ? "How do you know how to write the ordered pairs?" The first sentence explains how the ordered pairs will be written (weight on Earth, weight on Titan).
- ? "What two ordered pairs do you know?" (0, 0) and (105, 15)
- **MP2 Reason Abstractly and Quantitatively:** In part (a), students should recognize that they know an ordered pair that satisfies the equation $y = mx$. Substitute the *x*- and *y*-values and solve for *m*.
- In part (b), you need to find *x* when *y* is 3.5. Substitute and solve.
- **Connection:** Have students solve part (b) using a ratio table.

Try It

- Students should work in pairs and then share their answers with another pair.

Formative Assessment Tip

Visitor Explanation

This technique simulates what it would look like if a visitor were to enter your classroom during the middle of a lesson or activity. Could your students explain what they are doing and why they are doing it? The learning target and success criteria should have been made known to students at the beginning of the lesson.

Visitor Explanation lets you know whether students understand the learning target or the success criteria related to the lesson. Are students simply following directions or are they aware of the goal for today's lesson? Students are more engaged and their learning improves when the learning target or purpose of the lesson or activity is understood.

This technique is best used when students are actively engaged in an exploration, activity, or problem. It can be done as a *Think-Pair-Share* or as a *Writing Prompt*.

✓ Self-Assessment for Concepts & Skills

- **Think-Pair-Share:** Students should read each exercise independently and then work in pairs to complete the exercises. Then have each pair compare their answers with another pair and discuss any discrepancies.
- ◉ **Visitor Explanation:** Ask, "If a visitor entered the room right now, how would you explain how to graph and write an equation that represents a proportional relationship?" Students should practice explanations with partners. Solicit responses.

The Success Criteria Self-Assessment chart can be found in the *Student Journal* or online at *BigIdeasMath.com*.

EXAMPLE 2   **Writing and Using an Equation**

The weight y of an object on Titan, one of Saturn's moons, is proportional to the weight x of the object on Earth. An object that weighs 105 pounds on Earth would weigh 15 pounds on Titan.

a. Write an equation that represents the situation.

Use the point (105, 15) to find the slope of the line.

$y = mx$	Equation of a proportional relationship
$15 = m(105)$	Substitute 15 for y and 105 for x.
$\dfrac{1}{7} = m$	Simplify.

▶ So, an equation that represents the situation is $y = \dfrac{1}{7}x$.

b. How much would a chunk of ice that weighs 3.5 pounds on Titan weigh on Earth?

$3.5 = \dfrac{1}{7}x$	Substitute 3.5 for y.
$24.5 = x$	Multiply each side by 7.

▶ So, the chunk of ice would weigh 24.5 pounds on Earth.

Math Practice

Interpret Results
Interpret the slope in the context of the problem.

Try It

2. How much would a spacecraft that weighs 3500 kilograms on Earth weigh on Titan?

Self-Assessment *for Concepts & Skills*

Solve each exercise. Then rate your understanding of the success criteria in your journal.

GRAPHING A PROPORTIONAL RELATIONSHIP   **Graph the equation.**

3. $y = 4x$ **4.** $y = -3x$ **5.** $y = 8x$

6. WRITING AND USING AN EQUATION The number y of objects a machine produces is proportional to the time x (in minutes) that the machine runs. The machine produces five objects in four minutes.

a. Write an equation that represents the situation.

b. Graph the equation in part (a) and interpret the slope.

c. How many objects does the machine produce in one hour?

EXAMPLE 3 **Modeling Real Life**

The distance y (in meters) that a four-person ski lift travels in x seconds is represented by the equation $y = 2.5x$. The graph shows the distance that a two-person ski lift travels.

Two-Person Lift

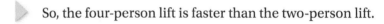

a. **Which ski lift is faster?**

Identify the slope of the graph for each lift. Then interpret each slope as a unit rate.

Four-Person Lift

$$y = 2.5x$$

The slope is 2.5.

The four-person lift travels 2.5 meters per second.

Two-Person Lift

$$\text{slope} = \frac{\text{change in } y}{\text{change in } x}$$

$$= \frac{8}{4} = 2$$

The two-person lift travels 2 meters per second.

So, the four-person lift is faster than the two-person lift.

b. **Graph the equation that represents the four-person lift in the same coordinate plane as the two-person lift. Compare and interpret the steepness of each graph.**

Ski Lift

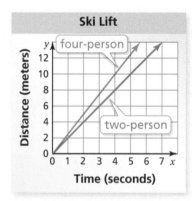

The graph that represents the four-person lift is steeper than the graph that represents the two-person lift. So, the four-person lift is faster.

Self-Assessment for Problem Solving

Solve each exercise. Then rate your understanding of the success criteria in your journal.

Artificial Waterfall

7. The amount y (in liters) of water that flows over a natural waterfall in x seconds is represented by the equation $y = 500x$. The graph shows the number of liters of water that flow over an artificial waterfall. Which waterfall has a greater flow? Justify your answer.

8. The speed of sound in air is 343 meters per second. You see lightning and hear thunder 12 seconds later.

　a. Is there a proportional relationship between the amount of time that passes and your distance from a lightning strike? Explain.

　b. Estimate your distance from the lightning strike.

Laurie's Notes

EXAMPLE 3

- Discuss why these relationships are proportional. For instance, the two-person lift starts at 0 meters, travels 2 meters in 1 second, 4 meters in 2 seconds, 6 meters in 3 seconds, and so on. $\frac{2\,m}{1\,sec} = \frac{4\,m}{2\,sec} = \frac{6\,m}{3\,sec}$.

- Make sure the students recognize the unit labels for each axis. The x-axis represents time (in seconds) and the y-axis represents distance (in meters).

- **Connection:** The question asks which ski lift is faster. Students are looking for the rate, or the speed of each lift. The rate is the slope of the line. For the two-person lift, the slope can be found using the ordered pairs in the graph. For the four-person lift, the slope is given in the equation.

- In part (b), point out that the graphs do not represent the steepness of the lifts, but rather the distance traveled (y-axis) over a period of time (x-axis).

- ❓ "If a vertical line is drawn through the graph in part (b) at $x = 4$, then it will intersect the two lines. What do these points of intersection mean in the context of the problem?" The y-value is the distance traveled by each lift in 4 seconds. The four-person lift travels farther in 4 seconds.

✅ Self-Assessment for Problem Solving

- Students may benefit from trying the exercises independently and then working with peers to refine their work. It is important to provide time in class for problem solving, so that students become comfortable with the problem-solving plan.

- Have students read the problems independently and make a plan for each. Students should discuss their plans with their neighbors before solving independently. Then have students discuss their solutions with their neighbors and resolve any discrepancies.

- ❓ "Why is the answer in Exercise 8(b) an estimate?" *Sample answer:* Because you may not record the exact amount of time between the lightning strike and the thunder.

The Success Criteria Self-Assessment chart can be found in the *Student Journal* or online at *BigIdeasMath.com*.

Closure

- **Exit Ticket:** Refer back to the ratio table in the Motivate with minutes and gallons.
  - **a.** Write an equation that represents this situation. $y = 8.5x$
  - **b.** What is the value of x when y is 85 gallons? Explain. 10; When you substitute 85 for y in $y = 8.5x$ and solve $85 = 8.5x$, you get $x = 10$.

Extra Example 3

At a track meet, the distance y (in meters) traveled by Student A in x seconds is represented by the equation $y = 7x$. The graph shows the distance traveled by Student B.

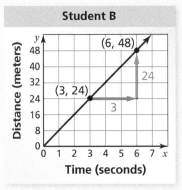

Student B

a. Which student is faster? Student B

b. Graph the equation that represents Student A in the same coordinate plane as Student B. Compare and interpret the steepness of each graph.

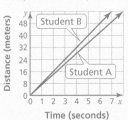

The graph that represents Student B is steeper than the graph that represents Student A. So, Student B is faster than Student A.

Self-Assessment
for Problem Solving

7. See Additional Answers.

8. See Additional Answers.

Learning Target
Graph proportional relationships.

Success Criteria
- Graph an equation that represents a proportional relationship.
- Write an equation that represents a proportional relationship.
- Use graphs to compare proportional relationships.

 **Review & Refresh**

1. 1
2. −2
3. 4
4. $x = 2$
5. $x = \dfrac{23}{18}$
6. $x = -\dfrac{9}{2}$

 Concepts, Skills, & Problem Solving

7.

Water (cups), x	3	6	9
Flour (cups), y	5	10	15

For every increase of 5 cups of flour, there is an increase of 3 cups of water. The slope is $\dfrac{5}{3}$.

8. *Sample answer:*

Water (cups), x	1	2	3
Flour (cups), y	2	4	6

For every increase of 2 cups of flour, there is an increase of 1 cup of water. The slope is 2.

9.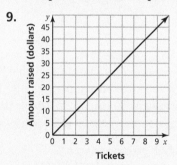

Each ticket costs $5.

10. no; The line does not pass through the origin.

11. yes; The line passes through the origin; $y = 4x$

12. yes; The rate of change in the table is constant and can be used to show that $y = 0$ when $x = 0$; $y = \dfrac{1}{3}x$

13. no; The rate of change in the table is not constant.

Assignment Guide and Concept Check

Scaffold assignments to support all students in their learning progression. The suggested assignments are a starting point. Continue to assign additional exercises and revisit with spaced practice to move every student toward proficiency.

Level	Assignment 1	Assignment 2
Emerging	2, 6, 7, 9, 10, 12	11, 13, 14, 15, 16, 17
Proficient	2, 6, 8, 9, 10, 11, 12, 13	14, 15, 16, 18, 19
Advanced	2, 6, 8, 9, 10, 11, 12, 13	15, 16, 17, 18, 19

- Assignment 1 is for use after students complete the Self-Assessment for Concepts & Skills.
- Assignment 2 is for use after students complete the Self-Assessment for Problem Solving.
- The red exercises can be used as a concept check.

Review & Refresh Prior Skills

Exercises 1–3 Finding the Slope of a Line
Exercises 4–6 Solving an Equation

Common Errors

- **Exercises 10 and 11** Students may think that the slope of each line is 1. Remind students to pay attention to the scales on the axes.

4.3 Practice

? Go to *BigIdeasMath.com* to get HELP with solving the exercises.

▶ **Review & Refresh**

Find the slope of the line.

1.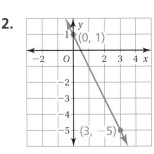

2.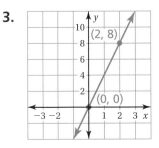

3.

Solve the equation. Check your solution.

4. $2x + 3x = 10$

5. $x + \dfrac{1}{6} = 4 - 2x$

6. $2(1 - x) = 11$

▶▶ **Concepts, Skills, & Problem Solving**

USING EQUIVALENT RATIOS **The graph shows amounts of water and flour that can be used to make dough.** (See Exploration 1, p. 155.)

7. Use the graph to make a ratio table relating the quantities. Explain how the slope of the line is represented in the table.

8. Make a ratio table that represents a different ratio of flour to water. Use the table to describe the slope of the graph of the new relationship.

9. **GRAPHING AN EQUATION** The amount y (in dollars) that you raise by selling x fundraiser tickets is represented by the equation $y = 5x$. Graph the equation and interpret the slope.

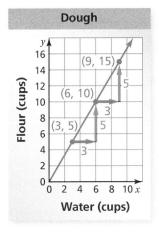

IDENTIFYING PROPORTIONAL RELATIONSHIPS **Tell whether x and y are in a proportional relationship. Explain your reasoning. If so, write an equation that represents the relationship.**

10.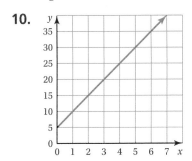

11.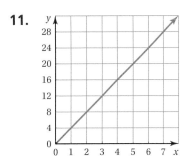

12.

x	3	6	9	12
y	1	2	3	4

13.

x	2	5	8	10
y	4	8	13	23

14. **MP MODELING REAL LIFE** The cost y (in dollars) to rent a kayak is proportional to the number x of hours that you rent the kayak. It costs $27 to rent the kayak for 3 hours.

a. Write an equation that represents the situation.

b. Interpret the slope of the graph of the equation.

c. How much does it cost to rent the kayak for 5 hours? Justify your answer.

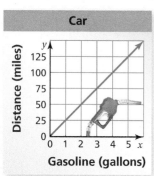

15. **MP MODELING REAL LIFE** The distance y (in miles) that a truck travels on x gallons of gasoline is represented by the equation $y = 18x$. The graph shows the distance that a car travels.

a. Which vehicle gets better gas mileage? Explain how you found your answer.

b. How much farther can the vehicle you chose in part (a) travel on 8 gallons of gasoline?

16. **MP PROBLEM SOLVING** Toenails grow about 13 millimeters per year. The table shows fingernail growth.

Weeks	1	2	3	4
Fingernail Growth (millimeters)	0.7	1.4	2.1	2.8

a. Do fingernails or toenails grow faster? Explain.

b. In the same coordinate plane, graph equations that represent the growth rates of toenails and fingernails. Compare and interpret the steepness of each graph.

17. **MP REASONING** The quantities x and y are in a proportional relationship. What do you know about the ratio of y to x for any point (x, y) on the graph of x and y?

18. **DIG DEEPER!** The graph relates the temperature change y (in degrees Fahrenheit) to the altitude change x (in thousands of feet).

a. Is the relationship proportional? Explain.

b. Write an equation of the line. Interpret the slope.

c. You are at the bottom of a mountain where the temperature is 74°F. The top of the mountain is 5500 feet above you. What is the temperature at the top of the mountain? Justify your answer.

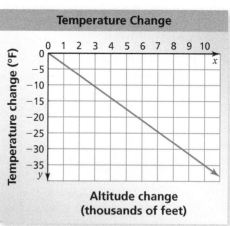

19. **CRITICAL THINKING** Consider the distance equation $d = rt$, where d is the distance (in feet), r is the rate (in feet per second), and t is the time (in seconds). You run for 50 seconds. Are the distance you run and the rate you run at proportional? Use a graph to justify your answer.

Common Errors

- **Exercise 14** Students may switch the *x*- and *y*-values, substituting incorrectly in the equation $y = mx$ when finding the slope. Remind students to make sure they are substituting the correct value for each variable.

Mini-Assessment

A maple tree grows 1.5 feet each year. The table shows the yearly growth for a pine tree.

Time (years)	1	2	3	4
Growth (inches)	12	24	36	48

1. Which tree grows faster? Maple tree

2. Write and graph equations that represent the growth rates of each tree. Compare and interpret the steepness of each graph. Maple tree: $y = 1.5x$; Pine tree: $y = x$

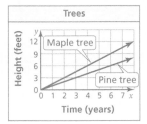

The graph that represents the maple tree is steeper than the graph that represents the pine tree. So, the maple tree grows faster than the pine tree.

Section Resources

Surface Level	Deep Level
Resources by Chapter • Extra Practice • Reteach • Puzzle Time Student Journal • Self-Assessment • Practice Differentiating the Lesson Tutorial Videos Skills Review Handbook Skills Trainer	Resources by Chapter • Enrichment and Extension Graphic Organizers Dynamic Assessment System • Section Practice
Transfer Level	
Dynamic Assessment System • Mid-Chapter Quiz	Assessment Book • Mid-Chapter Quiz

Concepts, Skills, & Problem Solving

14. **a.** $y = 9x$

   b. It costs $9 per hour to rent a kayak.

   c. $45; $y = 9x = 9(5) = 45$

15. **a.** car; *Sample answer:* Compare unit rates. 25 mpg > 18 mpg

   b. 56 mi

16. **a.** fingernails; Fingernails grow about 0.7 millimeter per week and toenails grow about 0.25 millimeter per week.

   b.

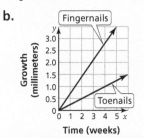

   The graph that represents fingernails is steeper than the graph that represents toenails. So, fingernails grow faster than toenails.

17. it is the same

18. **a.** yes; The line passes through the origin.

   b. $y = -3.5x$; The temperature decreases by 3.5°F for each 1000-foot increase in altitude.

   c. 54.75°F;
   $y = -3.5x = -3.5(5.5)$
   $= -19.25,$
   $74 - 19.25 = 54.75$

19. yes; The equation is $d = 50r$, which represents a proportional relationship.

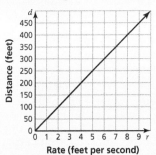

STATE STANDARDS
8.EE.B.6

Learning Target

Graph linear equations in slope-intercept form.

Success Criteria

- Identify the slope and *y*-intercept of a line given an equation.
- Rewrite a linear equation in slope-intercept form.
- Use the slope and *y*-intercept to graph linear equations.

Warm Up

Cumulative, vocabulary, and prerequisite skills practice opportunities are available in the *Resources by Chapter* or at *BigIdeasMath.com*.

ELL Support

Students often confuse the words *intercept* and *intersect*. Write the word *inter/cept* with a slash as shown. Explain that the prefix *inter-* can mean "together." Provide other examples of the prefix using visuals, such as *interlocking* or *intertwine*. Then draw a simple graph with a line crossing (intersecting) the *x*- or *y*-axis and point to the intercept (the point of intersection). Emphasize that understanding the meaning of word parts can help students understand a word they do not know.

Exploration 1

a. *Sample answer:* Because the *y*-value of each point on the line increases by 3 units, you can add 3 to the right side of the equation $y = mx$ to obtain $y = mx + 3$.

b–d. See Additional Answers.

Laurie's Notes

Preparing to Teach

- In the previous section, students derived an equation to represent a proportional relationship. Students will build upon that relationship to derive the slope-intercept form of a linear equation.
- **MP3 Construct Viable Arguments and Critique the Reasoning of Others:** The goal is for students to discover that when equations are written in **slope-intercept form**, the coefficient of the *x*-term is the slope and the constant is the *y*-intercept.

Motivate

- **Preparation:** Make three demonstration cards on paper measuring 8.5×11 inches. The *x*-axis is labeled "Time" and the *y*-axis is labeled "Distance from home." If you plan to use these again next year, laminate them.
- Sample cards A, B, and C are shown.

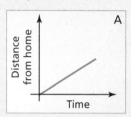
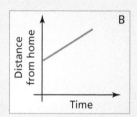
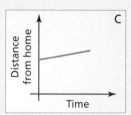

- Ask three students to hold the cards for the class to see.
- ❓ "Consider how the axes are labeled. What does the slope of the line represent?" $\dfrac{\text{change in distance}}{\text{change in time}} = \text{rate}$
- ❓ "What story does each card tell? How are the stories similar and different?" A: you begin at home; B: you travel at the same rate, but you start away from home; C: you start away from home, but you travel at a slower rate

Exploration 1

- To help students understand what happens to the line in part (a), have them draw the original graph on coordinate plane paper. Then use patty paper or transparencies (anything see-through) to trace the line. Then shift the traced line 3 units up. Students should recall that this is called a *translation*.
- ❓ "How are the graphs similar? different?" The triangles are congruent and the lines are parallel; The triangles are located in different positions.
- ❓ "Where does the original line cross the *y*-axis?" (0, 0)
- ❓ "Where does the translated line cross the *y*-axis?" (0, 3)
- Students may think the point (x, y) in the second graph should be $(x, y + 3)$. Remind them that (x, y) represents any point on the graph.
- In part (a), students may calculate the slope using two points or recall that parallel lines have the same slope. They might reason that because the *y*-coordinate of each point on the line increases by *b* units, they can add *b* to the right side of the equation $y = mx$.
- Parts (b) and (c) are similar to the questions asked in Section 4.3 Exploration 2, but with a translated line. Guide students to see that the triangles are similar.
- In part (d), students should end up with $y = mx + b$.

4.4 Graphing Linear Equations in Slope-Intercept Form

Learning Target: Graph linear equations in slope-intercept form.

Success Criteria:
• I can identify the slope and *y*-intercept of a line given an equation.
• I can rewrite a linear equation in slope-intercept form.
• I can use the slope and *y*-intercept to graph linear equations.

EXPLORATION 1

Deriving an Equation

Work with a partner. In the previous section, you learned that the graph of a proportional relationship can be represented by the equation $y = mx$, where m is the constant of proportionality.

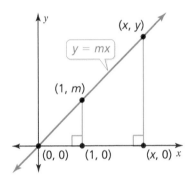

Math Practice

Understand Quantities

How does the meaning of the equation $y = mx$ help you make a conjecture in part (a)?

a. You translate the graph of a proportional relationship 3 units up as shown below. Let (x, y) represent any point on the graph. Make a conjecture about the equation of the line. Explain your reasoning.

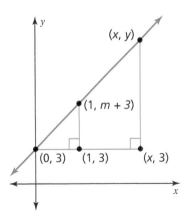

b. Describe the relationship between the corresponding side lengths of the triangles. Explain your reasoning.

c. Use the relationship in part (b) to write an equation relating y, m, and x. Does your equation support your conjecture in part (a)? Explain.

d. You translate the graph of a proportional relationship b units up. Write an equation relating y, m, x, and b. Justify your answer.

Key Ideas

Intercepts

The **x-intercept** of a line is the *x*-coordinate of the point where the line crosses the *x*-axis. It occurs when $y = 0$.

The **y-intercept** of a line is the *y*-coordinate of the point where the line crosses the *y*-axis. It occurs when $x = 0$.

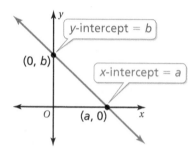

y-intercept = *b*

x-intercept = *a*

(0, *b*)

(*a*, 0)

Slope-Intercept Form

Words A linear equation written in the form $y = mx + b$ is in **slope-intercept form**. The slope of the line is *m*, and the *y*-intercept of the line is *b*.

Algebra $y = mx + b$

slope   *y*-intercept

> Linear equations can, but do not always, pass through the origin. So, proportional relationships are a special type of linear equation in which $b = 0$.

EXAMPLE 1 **Identifying Slopes and *y*-Intercepts**

Find the slope and the *y*-intercept of the graph of each linear equation.

a. $y = -4x - 2$

$y = -4x + (-2)$ Write in slope-intercept form.

▶ The slope is -4, and the *y*-intercept is -2.

b. $y - 5 = \dfrac{3}{2}x$

$y = \dfrac{3}{2}x + 5$ Add 5 to each side.

▶ The slope is $\dfrac{3}{2}$, and the *y*-intercept is 5.

Try It Find the slope and the *y*-intercept of the graph of the linear equation.

1. $y = 3x - 7$

2. $y - 1 = -\dfrac{2}{3}x$

Laurie's Notes

Scaffolding Instruction

- Students have explored the connection between the equation of a line and its graph. Now they will formalize their conjectures about slope-intercept form.
- **Emerging:** Students may be able to find the equation of a line using numerical points but struggle with abstract points, such as $(0, b)$ and $(a, 0)$. These students require more practice and guided instruction for the Key Ideas and examples.
- **Proficient:** Students derived the slope-intercept form of a linear equation with ease. They should review the Key Ideas before completing the Self-Assessment exercises.

Key Ideas

- Write the Key Ideas on the board. Draw the graph and discuss the vocabulary of this lesson: *x-intercept*, *y-intercept*, and **slope-intercept form**.
- Explain to students that the equation must be written with y in terms of x. This means that the equation must be solved for y.
- Discuss the push-pin note that connects to earlier lessons in this chapter.

EXAMPLE 1

- ❓ "What is a linear equation?" an equation whose graph is a line
- Write part (a). This is written in the form $y = mx + b$, enabling students to quickly identify the slope and y-intercept.
- Write part (b).
- ❓ "Is $y - 5 = \frac{3}{2}x$ in slope-intercept form?" no "Can you rewrite it so that it is? Explain." Yes, add 5 to each side of the equation.
- Make sure students understand that you can use the Commutative Property of Addition to write $y = b + mx$ as $y = mx + b$.

Try It

- Have students solve these problems on whiteboards.

Scaffold instruction to support all students in their learning. Learning is individualized and you may want to group students differently as they move in and out of these levels with each skill and concept. Student self-assessment and feedback help guide your instructional decisions about how and when to layer support for all students to become proficient learners.

Extra Example 1

Find the slope and the *y*-intercept of the graph of each linear equation.

a. $y = \frac{3}{4}x - 5$

slope: $\frac{3}{4}$; y-intercept: -5

b. $y + \frac{1}{2} = -6x$

slope: -6; y-intercept: $-\frac{1}{2}$

Try It

1. slope: 3; y-intercept: -7

2. slope: $-\frac{2}{3}$; y-intercept: 1

Graph $y = -\frac{2}{3}x - 2$. Identify the
x-intercept.

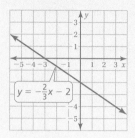

x-intercept: -3

Try It

3.

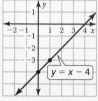

x-intercept: 4

4. $\boxed{y = -\frac{1}{2}x + 1}$

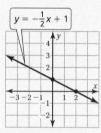

x-intercept: 2

Self-Assessment
for Concepts & Skills

5. a. *Sample answer:* It affects the steepness of the line and whether it rises or falls from left to right.

   b. *Sample answer:* It affects where the graph crosses the y-axis.

6. slope: -1; y-intercept: 0.25

7. slope: $-\frac{3}{4}$; y-intercept: 2

8. See Additional Answers.

9.

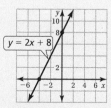

x-intercept: -4

Laurie's Notes

EXAMPLE 2

❓ "How can knowing the slope and y-intercept help you graph a line?" Listen for understanding of what slope and y-intercept mean.

- Remind students that a slope of -3 can be interpreted as $\frac{-3}{1} = \frac{3}{-1}$. Starting at the y-intercept, you can move to the right 1 unit and down 3 units, or to the left 1 unit and up 3 units. In both cases, you land on a point which satisfies the equation.

❓ **MP8 Look for and Express Regularity in Repeated Reasoning:** "In this problem, you used the slope to plot a point that coincidentally landed on the x-axis. How would you find the x-intercept without using a graph?" Set $y = 0$ and solve for x.

Try It

- **Think-Pair-Share:** Students should read each exercise independently and then work in pairs to complete the exercises. Then have each pair compare their answers with another pair and discuss any discrepancies.

✔️ Self-Assessment for Concepts & Skills

- Students should solve the problems independently and then share with a neighbor. Discuss their solutions to Exercise 5 as a class.

- ◎ Have students use *Thumbs Up* to indicate their understanding of each success criterion.

ELL Support

Allow students to work in pairs for extra support and to practice language. Ask pairs to display their answers for Exercises 6 and 7 and their graphs for Exercises 8 and 9 for your review. Monitor discussions and provide support as needed.

The Success Criteria Self-Assessment chart can be found in the *Student Journal* or online at *BigIdeasMath.com*.

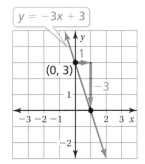

EXAMPLE 2 **Graphing a Linear Equation in Slope-Intercept Form**

Graph $y = -3x + 3$. Identify the x-intercept.

Step 1: Find the slope and the y-intercept.

$$y = -3x + 3$$

slope ⟶   ⟵ y-intercept

Step 2: The y-intercept is 3. So, plot $(0, 3)$.

Step 3: Use the slope to find another point and draw the line.

$$m = \frac{\text{rise}}{\text{run}} = \frac{-3}{1}$$

Plot the point that is 1 unit right and 3 units down from $(0, 3)$. Draw a line through the two points.

> The line crosses the x-axis at $(1, 0)$. So, the x-intercept is 1.

Math Practice

Find General Methods

How can you use substitution to find the x-intercept of a line?

Try It **Graph the linear equation. Identify the x-intercept.**

3. $y = x - 4$

4. $y = -\dfrac{1}{2}x + 1$

Self-Assessment *for Concepts & Skills*

Solve each exercise. Then rate your understanding of the success criteria in your journal.

5. **IN YOUR OWN WORDS** Consider the graph of the equation $y = mx + b$.

    a. How does changing the value of m affect the graph of the equation?

    b. How does changing the value of b affect the graph of the equation?

IDENTIFYING SLOPE AND y-INTERCEPT **Find the slope and the y-intercept of the graph of the linear equation.**

6. $y = -x + 0.25$

7. $y - 2 = -\dfrac{3}{4}x$

GRAPHING A LINEAR EQUATION **Graph the linear equation. Identify the x-intercept.**

8. $y = x - 7$

9. $y = 2x + 8$

EXAMPLE 3 **Modeling Real Life**

The cost *y* (in dollars) of taking a taxi
x miles is represented by the equation
$y = 2.5x + 2$. Graph the equation.
Interpret the *y*-intercept and the slope.

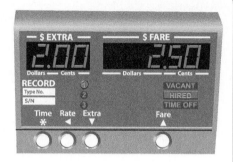

Understand the problem.

You are given an equation that
represents the cost of taking a taxi. You
are asked to graph the equation and
interpret the *y*-intercept and the slope.

Make a plan.

Use the equation to identify the slope and the *y*-intercept. Then graph
the equation and interpret the *y*-intercept and the slope.

Solve and check.

The equation is already written in the form $y = mx + b$. So, the slope
is $2.5 = \dfrac{5}{2}$ and the *y*-intercept is 2. Use the slope and the *y*-intercept to
graph the equation.

Check

Use a graphing calculator to
graph $y = 2.5x + 2$.

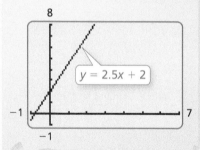

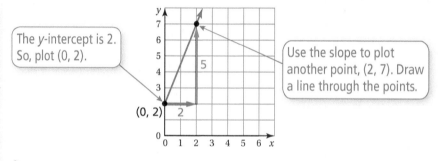

The *y*-intercept is 2.
So, plot (0, 2).

Use the slope to plot
another point, (2, 7). Draw
a line through the points.

The *y*-intercept is 2. So, there is an initial fee of \$2 to take
the taxi. The slope is 2.5. So, the cost per mile is \$2.50.

Self-Assessment for Problem Solving

*Solve each exercise. Then rate your understanding of the success criteria
in your journal.*

10. The height *y* (in feet) of a movable bridge after rising for *x* seconds is
represented by the equation $y = 3x + 16$. Graph the equation. Interpret
the *y*-intercept and slope. How many seconds does it take the bridge to
reach a height of 76 feet? Justify your answer.

11. The number *y* of perfume bottles in storage after *x* months
is represented by the equation $y = -20x + 460$. Graph the
equation. Interpret the *y*-intercept and the slope. In how
many months will there be no perfume bottles left in
storage? Justify your answer.

Laurie's Notes

Teaching Strategy

Explain that a graphing calculator can graph equations that are entered in the equation editor.

Explain how to set the *standard viewing window* (or *standard viewing rectangle*). Because the viewing screen is a rectangle, one unit in the *x*-direction appears longer than one unit in the *y*-direction. When graphing by hand, you generally use a square grid. It is important to point out this distinction to students because they will eventually graph $y = x$, which is a 45° line. It will not appear this way in the standard viewing rectangle on the calculator.

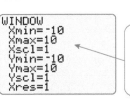

This is the standard viewing window.

EXAMPLE 3

- Write the equation $y = 2.5x + 2$ on the board.
- **?** "What is the slope and what does it mean in the context of this problem?" 2.5; It costs $2.50 for each mile you travel in the taxi.
- **?** "What is the *y*-intercept and what does it mean in the context of this problem?" 2; The initial fee is $2 when you sit down in the taxi.
- **MP2 Reason Abstractly and Quantitatively:** Mathematically proficient students make sense of the quantities and their relationships in problem situations. To develop this proficiency, students must be asked to interpret the meaning of the symbols.
- **MP6 Attend to Precision:** Suggest to students that because the slope is 2.5, any ratio equivalent to 2.5 can also be used, such as $\frac{2.5}{1} = \frac{5}{2}$. Using whole numbers instead of decimals improves the accuracy of graphing.
- Explain that the graph of this equation will only be in Quadrant I because it does not make sense to have a negative number of miles or a negative cost.
- **Teaching Strategy:** Discuss the Check note with students. Explain how to graph a linear equation using a graphing calculator.
  - After the graph of $y = 2.5x + 2$ appears, ask students to verify the slope and the *y*-intercept of the graphs they made.

✔ Self-Assessment for Problem Solving

- Encourage students to use a Four Square to complete these exercises. Until students become comfortable with the problem-solving plan, they may only be ready to complete the first square.

The Success Criteria Self-Assessment chart can be found in the *Student Journal* or online at *BigIdeasMath.com*.

Closure

- **Exit Ticket:** Find the slope and *y*-intercept of $y - 4 = 2x$. slope: 2; *y*-intercept: 4

Extra Example 3

The cost *y* (in dollars) for making *x* friendship bracelets is represented by the equation $y = 0.5x + 2$. Graph the equation. Interpret the *y*-intercept and the slope.

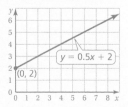

The slope is 0.5. So, the cost per bracelet is $0.50. The *y*-intercept is 2. So, there is an initial cost of $2 to make the bracelets.

Self-Assessment for Problem Solving

10.

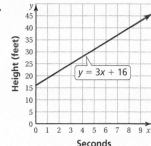

The *y*-intercept is 16. So, the initial height of the bridge is 16 feet. The slope is 3. So, the bridge rises 3 feet per second; 20 seconds;
$76 = 3x + 16$
$60 = 3x$
$20 = x$

11. See Additional Answers.

Learning Target

Graph linear equations in slope-intercept form.

Success Criteria

- Identify the slope and *y*-intercept of a line given an equation.
- Rewrite a linear equation in slope-intercept form.
- Use the slope and *y*-intercept to graph linear equations.

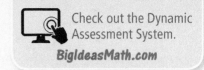
Review & Refresh

1. no; The line does not pass through the origin.

2. yes; The rate of change in the table is constant; $y = -\dfrac{1}{2}x$

3. $y = \dfrac{1}{4}x + \dfrac{1}{2}$ 4. $y = -2x + \dfrac{1}{3}$

5. $y = -\dfrac{4}{5}x - 3$ 6. $y = 2x - 2$

7. $y = -3x - 4$ 8. $y = \dfrac{2}{3}x - 6$

Concepts, Skills, & Problem Solving

9.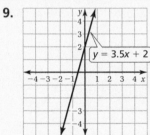
$y = 3.5x + 2$

10.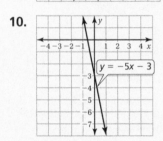
$y = -5x - 3$

11. B; slope: 2; y-intercept: 1

12. A; slope: $\dfrac{1}{3}$; y-intercept: -2

13. C; slope: $-\dfrac{2}{3}$; y-intercept: 1

14. slope: 4; y-intercept: -5

15. slope: -7; y-intercept: 12

16. slope: $-\dfrac{4}{5}$; y-intercept: -2

17. slope: 2.25; y-intercept: 3

18. slope: $\dfrac{4}{3}$; y-intercept: -1

19. slope: $\dfrac{3}{8}$; y-intercept: 6

20. slope: -2; y-intercept: 3.5

21. slope: $-\dfrac{1}{2}$; y-intercept: -5

22. slope: 1.5; y-intercept: 11

23. no; The y-intercept should be -3.

Assignment Guide and Concept Check

Scaffold assignments to support all students in their learning progression. The suggested assignments are a starting point. Continue to assign additional exercises and revisit with spaced practice to move every student toward proficiency.

Level	Assignment 1	Assignment 2
Emerging	2, 7, 8, 9, 11, 12, 13, 14, 15, 16, 23	18, 19, 20, 24, 25, 27, 31, 32, 33
Proficient	2, 7, 8, 10, 11, 12, 13, 17, 18, 19, 23	20, 21, 22, 24, 27, 29, 31, 32, 33
Advanced	2, 7, 8, 10, 11, 12, 13, 20, 21, 22, 23	26, 28, 29, 31, 32, 33, 34

• Assignment 1 is for use after students complete the Self-Assessment for Concepts & Skills.

• Assignment 2 is for use after students complete the Self-Assessment for Problem Solving.

• The red exercises can be used as a concept check.

Review & Refresh Prior Skills

Exercises 1 and 2   Identifying Proportional Relationships
Exercises 3–8   Rewriting an Equation

Common Errors

• **Exercises 14–22** Students may forget to include negatives with the slope and/or y-intercept. Remind students to look at the sign in front of the slope and y-intercept. Also remind students that slope-intercept form is $y = mx + b$. This means that if the linear equation has "minus b," then the y-intercept is negative.

• **Exercises 18–20** Students may identify the opposite y-intercept because they forget to solve for y. Remind students that slope-intercept form has y by itself, so they must solve for y before identifying the slope and y-intercept.

4.4 Practice

? Go to *BigIdeasMath.com* to get
HELP with solving the exercises.

▶ Review & Refresh

Tell whether *x* and *y* are in a proportional relationship. Explain your reasoning.
If so, write an equation that represents the relationship.

1.

x	1	2	3	4
y	6	8	10	12

2.

x	−8	−4	4	8
y	4	2	−2	−4

Solve the equation for *y*.

3. $x = 4y - 2$

4. $3y = -6x + 1$

5. $1 + y = -\dfrac{4}{5}x - 2$

6. $2.5y = 5x - 5$

7. $1.3y + 5.2 = -3.9x$

8. $y - \dfrac{2}{3}x = -6$

▶ Concepts, Skills, & Problem Solving

GRAPHING A LINEAR EQUATION **Graph the equation.** (See Exploration 1, p. 161.)

9. The graph of $y = 3.5x$ is translated up 2 units.

10. The graph of $y = -5x$ is translated down 3 units.

MATCHING EQUATIONS AND GRAPHS **Match the equation with its graph.**
Identify the slope and the *y*-intercept.

11. $y = 2x + 1$

12. $y = \dfrac{1}{3}x - 2$

13. $y = -\dfrac{2}{3}x + 1$

A.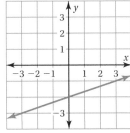

B.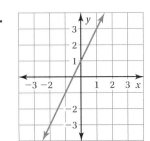

C.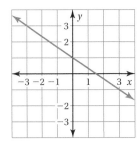

IDENTIFYING SLOPES AND *y*-INTERCEPTS **Find the slope and the**
y-intercept of the graph of the linear equation.

14. $y = 4x - 5$

15. $y = -7x + 12$

16. $y = -\dfrac{4}{5}x - 2$

17. $y = 2.25x + 3$

18. $y + 1 = \dfrac{4}{3}x$

19. $y - 6 = \dfrac{3}{8}x$

20. $y - 3.5 = -2x$

21. $y = -5 - \dfrac{1}{2}x$

22. $y = 11 + 1.5x$

23. **MP YOU BE THE TEACHER** Your friend finds the slope
and *y*-intercept of the graph of the equation $y = 4x - 3$.
Is your friend correct? Explain your reasoning.

> $y = 4x - 3$; The slope is 4
> and the y-intercept is 3.

24. **MP MODELING REAL LIFE** The number y of seasonal allergy shots available at a facility x days after receiving a shipment is represented by $y = -15x + 375$.

    a. Graph the linear equation.

    b. Interpret the slope and the y-intercept.

GRAPHING AN EQUATION **Graph the linear equation. Identify the x-intercept.**

25. $y = x + 3$

26. $y = 4x - 8$

27. $y = -3x + 9$

28. $y = -5x - 5$

29. $y + 14 = -7x$

30. $y = 8 - 2x$

31. **MP PRECISION** You go to a harvest festival and pick apples.

    a. Which equation represents the cost (in dollars) of going to the festival and picking x pounds of apples? Explain.

        | $y = 5x + 0.75$ | $y = 0.75x + 5$ |

    b. Graph the equation you chose in part (a).

You Pick 'Em
Apples $0.75 per lb
Admission: $5

32. **MP REASONING** Without graphing, identify the equations of the lines that are parallel. Explain your reasoning.

| $y = 2x + 4$ | $y = \frac{1}{2}x + 1$ | $y = 2x - 3$ | $y = 2x + 1$ | $y = \frac{1}{2}x + 2$ |

33. **MP PROBLEM SOLVING** A skydiver parachutes to the ground. The height y (in feet) of the skydiver after x seconds is $y = -10x + 3000$.

    a. Graph the linear equation.

    b. Interpret the slope, y-intercept, and x-intercept.

34. **DIG DEEPER!** Six friends create a website. The website earns money by selling banner ads. It costs $120 a month to operate the website.

    a. A banner ad earns $0.005 per click. Write a linear equation that represents the monthly profit after paying operating costs.

    b. Graph the equation in part (a). On the graph, label the number of clicks needed for the friends to start making a profit. Explain.

Common Errors

- **Exercises 25–30** Students may find the y-intercept instead of the x-intercept. Remind students to read the problem carefully to determine what is being asked.
- **Exercises 25–30** Students may use the reciprocal of the slope when graphing and may find an incorrect x-intercept. Remind students that slope is *rise* over *run*, so the numerator represents vertical change, not the horizontal change.

Mini-Assessment

Find the slope and the y-intercept of the graph of the linear equation.

1. $y = 5x - 8$ slope: 5; y-intercept: -8

2. $y - 2 = -\dfrac{3}{4}x$ slope: $-\dfrac{3}{4}$; y-intercept: 2

3. Graph $y = -2x + 4$. Identify the x-intercept.

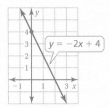

x-intercept: 2

Section Resources

Surface Level	Deep Level
Resources by Chapter • Extra Practice • Reteach • Puzzle Time Student Journal • Self-Assessment • Practice Differentiating the Lesson Tutorial Videos Skills Review Handbook Skills Trainer	Resources by Chapter • Enrichment and Extension Graphic Organizers Dynamic Assessment System • Section Practice

Concepts, Skills, & Problem Solving

24. See Additional Answers.

25.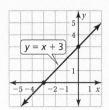

x-intercept: -3

26.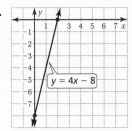

x-intercept: 2

27.

x-intercept: 3

28.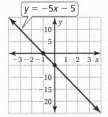

x-intercept: -1

29.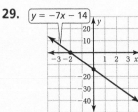

x-intercept: -2

30.

x-intercept: 4

31–34. See Additional Answers.

STATE STANDARDS
Applying 8.EE.B.6

Learning Target

Graph linear equations in standard form.

Success Criteria

- Rewrite the standard form of a linear equation in slope-intercept form.
- Find intercepts of linear equations written in standard form.
- Use intercepts to graph linear equations.

Warm Up

Cumulative, vocabulary, and prerequisite skills practice opportunities are available in the *Resources by Chapter* or at *BigIdeasMath.com*.

ELL Support

Explain that a standard is a norm accepted by all, so that everyone understands the same thing. For example, the metric system is the standard system of measurement used throughout the world. People throughout the world understand a measurement when the metric system is used. There is also a standard form for writing linear equations. Tell students that they will study the standard form of a linear equation in this lesson.

Exploration 1

a. $50; $25; $150; $50x + 25y = 150$

b. 3 fruit trays; 6 vegetable trays; yes; *Sample answer:* These values can be used as the *x*- and *y*-intercepts. Draw a line through the intercepts, (3, 0) and (0, 6).

c. See Additional Answers.

d. the intercepts increase; The equation now becomes $50x + 25y = 200$. The *x*-intercept shifts right 1 unit to the point (4, 0), and the *y*-intercept shifts up 2 units to (8, 0).

Laurie's Notes

Preparing to Teach

- In the previous lesson, students learned to graph linear equations in slope-intercept form. Now students will graph linear equations in a new form, standard form.
- **MP7 Look for and Make Use of Structure:** Mathematically proficient students discern a pattern or structure. Recognizing the equivalence of equations written in different forms requires that students be able to manipulate equations.

Motivate

- **Preparation:** Make a set of equation cards on strips of paper. The equations should all be the same when simplified and need to be written large enough to be read by students sitting at the back of the classroom.
- Sample set: $y = 2x + 1, -2x + y = 1, 2x - y = -1, 4x - 2y = -2$
- Ask 4 students to stand at the front of the room and hold the cards so only they can see the equations.
- As you state an ordered pair, each student holding a card determines whether it is a solution to the equation on the card and if it is, raises his or her hand. If not, they do nothing. State several ordered pairs, four that are solutions and two that are not. Plot all of the points that you state. The four ordered pairs that are solutions will lie on a line.
- ❓ "How many lines can pass through any two points?" one "How many lines can pass through the four solution points?" Students will likely say four; now is the time to discuss the idea of one line written in different forms.
- Have the students holding the cards reveal the equations to the class and read them aloud. Write each of the equations on the board.
- Explain to students that equations can be written in different forms. Today they will explore a new form of a linear equation.

Exploration 1

- Read the problem and part (a). Have students complete the verbal model and write an equation.
- ❓ "If you purchase the greatest number of fruit trays that you can, how many vegetable trays can you buy?" 0 vegetable trays
- Allow time for students to complete parts (b) and (c).
- ❓ "Is every point on your graph a solution to your equation in part (a)?" yes
- ❓ "Is every point on the graph a reasonable solution to the problem? Explain." No, because you cannot buy a portion of a fruit or vegetable tray.
- Have students circle the reasonable solutions on the graph and justify them algebraically. This could lead to a discussion about *discrete* versus *continuous* data.
  - The line represents a continuous data set because it consists of infinite data values. The solutions to the problem represent a discrete data set because it consists of only certain data values.
- Ask volunteers to explain their reasoning in part (d).

4.5 Graphing Linear Equations in Standard Form

Learning Target: Graph linear equations in standard form.

Success Criteria:
- I can rewrite the standard form of a linear equation in slope-intercept form.
- I can find intercepts of linear equations written in standard form.
- I can use intercepts to graph linear equations.

EXPLORATION 1

Using Intercepts

Work with a partner. You spend $150 on fruit trays and vegetable trays for a party.

Fruit Tray: $50

Vegetable Tray: $25

a. You buy x fruit trays and y vegetable trays. Complete the verbal model. Then use the verbal model to write an equation that relates x and y.

$$\frac{\boxed{}}{1 \text{ fruit tray}} \cdot \begin{array}{c}\text{Number} \\ \text{of fruit} \\ \text{trays}\end{array} + \frac{\boxed{}}{1 \text{ vegetable tray}} \cdot \begin{array}{c}\text{Number} \\ \text{of vegetable} \\ \text{trays}\end{array} = \boxed{}$$

b. What is the greatest number of fruit trays that you can buy? vegetable trays? Can you use these numbers to graph your equation from part (a) in the coordinate plane? Explain.

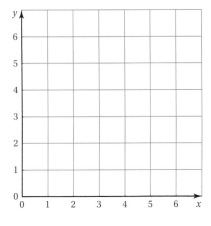

c. Use a graph to determine the different combinations of fruit trays and vegetable trays that you can buy. Justify your answers algebraically.

Math Practice

Make Sense of Quantities
What does the slope of the line represent in this context?

d. You are given an extra $50 to spend. How does this affect the intercepts of your graph in part (c)? Explain your reasoning.

4.5 Lesson

Key Vocabulary
standard form, p. 168

Any linear equation can be written in standard form.

Key Idea

Standard Form of a Linear Equation

The **standard form** of a linear equation is

$$Ax + By = C$$

where A and B are not both zero.

EXAMPLE 1 **Graphing a Linear Equation in Standard Form**

Graph $-2x + 3y = -6$.

Step 1: Write the equation in slope-intercept form.

$$-2x + 3y = -6 \qquad \text{Write the equation.}$$

$$3y = 2x - 6 \qquad \text{Add } 2x \text{ to each side.}$$

$$y = \frac{2}{3}x - 2 \qquad \text{Divide each side by 3.}$$

Step 2: Use the slope and the y-intercept to graph the equation.

$$y = \underset{\text{slope}}{\frac{2}{3}}x + \underset{y\text{-intercept}}{(-2)}$$

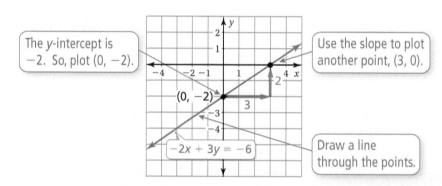

The y-intercept is -2. So, plot $(0, -2)$.

Use the slope to plot another point, $(3, 0)$.

$-2x + 3y = -6$

Draw a line through the points.

Try It **Graph the linear equation.**

1. $x + y = -2$

2. $-\dfrac{1}{2}x + 2y = 6$

3. $-\dfrac{2}{3}x + y = 0$

4. $2x + y = 5$

◄)) Multi-Language Glossary at *BigIdeasMath.com*

Laurie's Notes

Scaffolding Instruction

- Students have explored the graph of an equation written in standard form. They will now formalize the definition of standard form and use it to graph equations.
- **Emerging:** Students may struggle to find and graph the intercepts of an equation and find solutions to an equation from a graph. They will benefit from guided instruction for the Key Idea and examples.
- **Proficient:** Students recognize that the standard form of a linear equation is just another way of writing the equation. They should proceed to the Self-Assessment exercises.

Key Idea

- Define the **standard form** of a linear equation.
- Students may ask why A and B cannot both be zero. Explain that if $A = 0$ and $B = 0$, then the equation would be $0 = C$, which is not the equation of a line.
- **Teaching Tip:** Students are often confused when the standard form is written with parameters A, B, and C. Students see 5 variables. Show examples of equations written in standard form and identify A, B, and C.
- Ask students why they think $Ax + By = C$ is called *standard* form. Students might suggest that the variables are on the left and a constant is on the right.
- Point out the push-pin note. Share with students that although any linear equation can be written in standard form, not all linear equations can be written in slope-intercept form.
- ❓ "Can you think of a linear equation that cannot be written in slope-intercept form?" The equation of any vertical line. For example, $x = 5$.

EXAMPLE 1

- Have students identify A, B, and C. $A = -2$, $B = 3$, and $C = -6$
- ❓ "How do you solve for y?" Add $2x$ to each side, then divide each side by 3.
- Explain that the reason for rewriting the equation in slope-intercept form is so the slope and the y-intercept can be used to graph the equation.
- **Common Error:** Students only divide one of the two terms on the right side of the equation by 3.
- ❓ "Now that the equation is in slope-intercept form, explain how to graph the equation." *Sample answer:* Plot the ordered pair for the y-intercept. To plot another point, start at $(0, -2)$ and move to the right 3 units and up 2 units. Connect these points with a line.
- Substitute additional ordered pairs into the original equation to verify that they are solutions of the equation.

Try It

- Students should work in pairs.

Extra Example 1

Graph $3x - 2y = 2$.

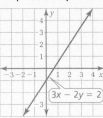

ELL Support

After demonstrating Example 1, have students work in groups to discuss and complete Try It Exercises 1–4. Provide graph paper to each group and list the steps students need to take: (1) Write the equation in slope-intercept form and (2) Use the slope and the y-intercept to graph the equation. If it is helpful, list the actions needed to complete Step 1. Expect students to perform according to their language levels.

Beginner: Complete each step by writing equations and plotting points.

Intermediate: Use phrases or simple sentences.

Advanced: Use detailed sentences and help guide discussion.

Try It

1.

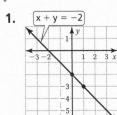

2.

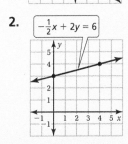

3–4. See Additional Answers.

Extra Example 2

Graph $5x - y = -5$ using intercepts.

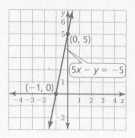

Try It

5–6. See Additional Answers.

Self-Assessment
for Concepts & Skills

7. no; $x - y = 6$

8. no; $\frac{1}{6}x - y = 5$

9. yes

10–14. See Additional Answers.

Discuss

- Write a simple equation in standard form on the board, such as $x + y = 4$. In this example, $A = 1$, $B = 1$, and $C = 4$. Explain to students that this could be solved for y by subtracting x from each side of the equation. Instead, you want to leave the equation as it was written.
- ❓ "Another way to think of this equation is *the sum of two numbers is 4*. Can you name some ordered pairs that would satisfy the equation?" Students should give many, including $(0, 4)$ and $(4, 0)$.
- ❓ "When would you want to graph an equation in standard form instead of rewriting the equation in slope-intercept form?" When it is convenient to substitute 0 for x and y.

EXAMPLE 2

- Write the equation $x + 3y = -3$.
- ❓ "To find the x-intercept, what is the value of y?" 0 "To find the y-intercept, what is the value of x?" 0
- Finish the problem as shown.
- **Big Idea:** When the equation is in standard form, you can plot the points for the two intercepts and then draw the line through them.

Try It

- **Neighbor Check:** Have students graph independently and then have their neighbors check their graphs. Have students discuss any discrepancies.

Formative Assessment Tip

Writing Prompt

This technique asks students to give feedback at the end of the lesson, activity, or learning experience. The *Writing Prompt* allows you to collect feedback in a short period of time (two minutes) on student learning. Used at the end of the class, a *Writing Prompt* is similar to an *Exit Ticket*. The written responses give students time to reflect on their learning, how well they believe they understand the concept or skill, and where they are still uncertain. It is important to share responses with students on the following day and let them know how you have adjusted the lesson based on their responses. Students need to know that you value their feedback and that instruction will be modified accordingly. Students will take the *Writing Prompt* more seriously if it is valued and used.

✅ Self-Assessment for Concepts & Skills

- **Think-Pair-Share:** Students should work independently and then check their answers with their neighbors. Ask several pairs of students to present their graphs for Exercises 11–14 under a document camera or at the board.
- ⊙ **Writing Prompt:** Explain three different methods of graphing a linear equation.
  - Students should include: using a table, using slope-intercept form, and using standard form to plot intercepts. Collect their responses. Use them to clarify any misconceptions at the end of the lesson.

The Success Criteria Self-Assessment chart can be found in the *Student Journal* or online at *BigIdeasMath.com*.

EXAMPLE 2 **Graphing a Linear Equation in Standard Form**

Graph $x + 3y = -3$ **using intercepts.**

Step 1: To find the x-intercept, substitute 0 for y.

$$x + 3y = -3$$
$$x + 3(0) = -3$$
$$x = -3$$

To find the y-intercept, substitute 0 for x.

$$x + 3y = -3$$
$$0 + 3y = -3$$
$$y = -1$$

Step 2: Graph the equation.

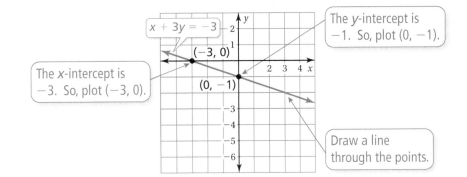

The y-intercept is -1. So, plot $(0, -1)$.

The x-intercept is -3. So, plot $(-3, 0)$.

Draw a line through the points.

Math Practice

Find Entry Points
Given the information in Example 2, how would you write the given equation in slope-intercept form?

Try It **Graph the linear equation using intercepts.**

5. $2x - y = 8$

6. $x + 3y = 6$

Self-Assessment *for Concepts & Skills*

Solve each exercise. Then rate your understanding of the success criteria in your journal.

MP **STRUCTURE** **Determine whether the equation is in standard form. If not, rewrite the equation in standard form.**

7. $y = x - 6$

8. $y - \dfrac{1}{6}x + 5 = 0$

9. $4x + y = 5$

10. **WRITING** Describe two ways to graph the equation $4x + 2y = 6$.

GRAPHING A LINEAR EQUATION **Graph the linear equation.**

11. $4x + y = 5$

12. $\dfrac{1}{3}x + 2y = 8$

13. $5x - y = 10$

14. $x - 3y = 9$

EXAMPLE 3 **Modeling Real Life**

Bananas
$0.60/pound

Apples
$1.50/pound

You have $6 to spend on apples and bananas. The equation $1.5x + 0.6y = 6$ represents this situation, where x is the number of pounds of apples and y is the number of pounds of bananas. Graph the equation. Interpret the intercepts.

Find the intercepts. Then use the intercepts to graph the equation and interpret the intercepts.

x-intercept	y-intercept
$1.5x + 0.6y = 6$	$1.5x + 0.6y = 6$
$1.5x + 0.6(0) = 6$	$1.5(0) + 0.6y = 6$
$x = 4$	$y = 10$

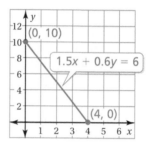

$1.5x + 0.6y = 6$

(0, 10)

(4, 0)

▶ The x-intercept shows that you can buy 4 pounds of apples when you do not buy any bananas. The y-intercept shows that you can buy 10 pounds of bananas when you do not buy any apples.

Self-Assessment for Problem Solving

Solve each exercise. Then rate your understanding of the success criteria in your journal.

15. You have $30 to spend on paint and clay. The equation $2x + 6y = 30$ represents this situation, where x is the number of paint bottles and y is the number of tubs of clay. Graph the equation. Interpret the intercepts. How many bottles of paint can you buy if you buy 3 tubs of clay? Justify your answer.

16. You complete two projects for a class in 60 minutes. The equation $x + y = 60$ represents this situation, where x is the time (in minutes) you spend assembling a birdhouse and y is the time (in minutes) you spend writing a paper.

    a. Graph the equation. Interpret the intercepts.

    b. You spend twice as much time assembling the birdhouse as you do writing the paper. How much time do you spend writing the paper? Justify your answer.

Laurie's Notes

EXAMPLE 3

- Ask a volunteer to read the problem and another to explain it. Then ask probing questions, "What do you know? What do you need to do to solve this problem?"
- Write the equation $1.5x + 0.6y = 6$ on the board.
- ? "What are the intercepts for this equation?" The *x*-intercept is 4 and the *y*-intercept is 10. "What are the ordered pairs for the intercepts?" (4, 0) and (0, 10)
- Interpreting the intercepts is an important step, particularly for real-life applications.
- ? "Why should you only graph in the first quadrant?" Negative values of *x* and *y* are not included in the graph because it does not make sense to have negative pounds of apples and bananas.
- ? "What is the cost of 2 pounds of apples and 5 pounds of bananas?" $6
- ? **MP1 Make Sense of Problems and Persevere in Solving Them:** "In what other ways can you buy $6 worth of apples and bananas?" *Sample answer:* 4 pounds of apples, or 10 pounds of bananas, or some other combination that is a solution. You are helping students make sense of the problem by asking them to interpret the symbolic representation.

✔ Self-Assessment for Problem Solving

- The goal for all students is to feel comfortable with the problem-solving plan. It is important for students to problem-solve in class, where they may receive support from you and their peers. Keep in mind that some students may only be ready for the first step.
- Students should work with a partner to complete the exercises. Select several pairs to explain each problem and their results.

The Success Criteria Self-Assessment chart can be found in the *Student Journal* or online at *BigIdeasMath.com*.

Closure

- Discuss students' responses to the *Writing Prompt* that you collected during the Self-Assessment for Concepts & Skills exercises.

Extra Example 3

You have $2.40 to spend on grapes and bananas. The equation $1.2x + 0.6y = 2.4$ represents this situation, where *x* is the number of pounds of grapes and *y* is the number of pounds of bananas. Graph the equation. Interpret the intercepts.

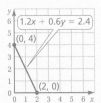

The *x*-intercept shows that you can buy 2 pounds of grapes when you do not buy any bananas. The *y*-intercept shows that you can buy 4 pounds of bananas when you do not buy any grapes.

Self-Assessment
for Problem Solving

15–16. See Additional Answers.

Learning Target

Graph linear equations in standard form.

Success Criteria

- Rewrite the standard form of a linear equation in slope-intercept form.
- Find intercepts of linear equations written in standard form.
- Use intercepts to graph linear equations.

▶ Review & Refresh

1. slope: 1; y-intercept: -1

2. slope: -2; y-intercept: 1

3. slope: $\dfrac{8}{9}$; y-intercept: -8

4. no

5. yes

6. yes

▶ Concepts, Skills, & Problem Solving

7–8. See Additional Answers.

9. $y = -2x + 17$

10. $y = 5x - \dfrac{1}{4}$

11. $y = \dfrac{1}{2}x + 10$

12.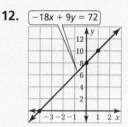
$-18x + 9y = 72$

13.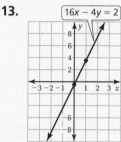
$16x - 4y = 2$

14.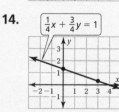
$\dfrac{1}{4}x + \dfrac{3}{4}y = 1$

15. B

16. A

17. C

Assignment Guide and Concept Check

Scaffold assignments to support all students in their learning progression. The suggested assignments are a starting point. Continue to assign additional exercises and revisit with spaced practice to move every student toward proficiency.

Level	Assignment 1	Assignment 2
Emerging	3, 6, 7, 9, 13, 15, 16, 17, 18, 20	11, 12, 14, 19, 23, 24, 27
Proficient	3, 6, 8, 10, 12, 15, 16, 17, 20	11, 14, 19, 22, 23, 24, 25, 26, 27
Advanced	3, 6, 8, 11, 12, 15, 16, 17, 18, 20	14, 22, 23, 24, 25, 26, 27

- Assignment 1 is for use after students complete the Self-Assessment for Concepts & Skills.
- Assignment 2 is for use after students complete the Self-Assessment for Problem Solving.
- The red exercises can be used as a concept check.

Review & Refresh Prior Skills

Exercises 1–3   Identifying Slopes and y-Intercepts
Exercises 4–6   Identifying a Reflection

▯ Common Errors

- **Exercises 9–14** Students may use the same operation instead of the opposite operation when writing the equation in slope-intercept form. Remind students of the rules for solving equations.
- **Exercises 15–17** Students may mix up the x- and y-intercepts. Remind students that the x-intercept is the x-coordinate of where the line crosses the x-axis and the y-intercept is the y-coordinate of where the line crosses the y-axis.

4.5 Practice

? Go to **BigIdeasMath.com** to get
HELP with solving the exercises.

▷ Review & Refresh

Find the slope and the *y*-intercept of the graph of the linear equation.

1. $y = x - 1$

2. $y = -2x + 1$

3. $y = \dfrac{8}{9}x - 8$

Tell whether the blue figure is a reflection of the red figure.

4.
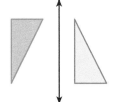

5.
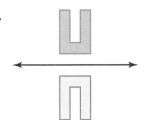

6.
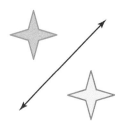

▷▷ Concepts, Skills, & Problem Solving

USING INTERCEPTS **Define two variables for the verbal model. Write an equation in slope-intercept form that relates the variables. Graph the equation using intercepts.** (See Exploration 1, p. 167.)

7. $\dfrac{\$2.00}{\text{pound}} \cdot \text{Pounds of peaches} + \dfrac{\$1.50}{\text{pound}} \cdot \text{Pounds of apples} = \$15$

8. $\dfrac{16 \text{ miles}}{\text{hour}} \cdot \text{Hours biked} + \dfrac{2 \text{ miles}}{\text{hour}} \cdot \text{Hours walked} = 32 \text{ miles}$

REWRITING AN EQUATION **Write the linear equation in slope-intercept form.**

9. $2x + y = 17$

10. $5x - y = \dfrac{1}{4}$

11. $-\dfrac{1}{2}x + y = 10$

GRAPHING AN EQUATION **Graph the linear equation.**

12. $-18x + 9y = 72$

13. $16x - 4y = 2$

14. $\dfrac{1}{4}x + \dfrac{3}{4}y = 1$

MATCHING **Match the equation with its graph.**

15. $15x - 12y = 60$

16. $5x + 4y = 20$

17. $10x + 8y = -40$

A.
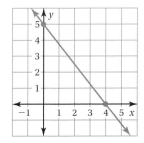

B.
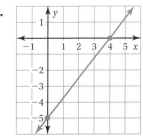

C.
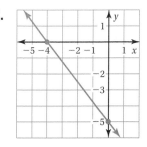

18. **(MP) YOU BE THE TEACHER** Your friend finds the x-intercept of $-2x + 3y = 12$. Is your friend correct? Explain your reasoning.

$$-2x + 3y = 12$$
$$-2(0) + 3y = 12$$
$$3y = 12$$
$$y = 4$$

19. **(MP) MODELING REAL LIFE** A charm bracelet costs $65, plus $25 for each charm. The equation $-25x + y = 65$ represents the cost y (in dollars) of the bracelet, where x is the number of charms.

    a. Graph the equation.

    b. How much does a bracelet with three charms cost?

USING INTERCEPTS TO GRAPH Graph the linear equation using intercepts.

20. $3x - 4y = -12$ 21. $2x + y = 8$ 22. $\frac{1}{3}x - \frac{1}{6}y = -\frac{2}{3}$

23. **(MP) MODELING REAL LIFE** Your cousin has $90 to spend on video games and movies. The equation $30x + 15y = 90$ represents this situation, where x is the number of video games purchased and y is the number of movies purchased. Graph the equation. Interpret the intercepts.

24. **(MP) PROBLEM SOLVING** A group of friends go scuba diving. They rent a boat for x days and scuba gear for y people, represented by the equation $250x + 50y = 1000$.

    a. Graph the equation and interpret the intercepts.

    b. How many friends can go scuba diving if they rent the boat for 1 day? 2 days?

    c. How much money is spent in total?

25. **(MP) MODELING REAL LIFE** You work at a restaurant as a host and a server. You earn $9.45 for each hour you work as a host and $3.78 for each hour you work as a server.

    a. Write an equation in standard form that models your earnings.

    b. Graph the equation.

Basic Information	
Number of hours worked as host:	x
Number of hours worked as server:	y
Earnings for this pay period:	$113.40

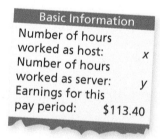

26. **(MP) LOGIC** Does the graph of every linear equation have an x-intercept? Justify your reasoning.

27. **CRITICAL THINKING** For a house call, a veterinarian charges $70, plus $40 per hour.

    a. Write an equation that represents the total fee y (in dollars) the veterinarian charges for a visit lasting x hours.

    b. Find the x-intercept. Does this value make sense in this context? Explain your reasoning.

    c. Graph the equation.

Common Errors

- **Exercises 20–22** Students may mix up the x- and y-intercepts. Remind students that the x-intercept is the x-coordinate of where the line crosses the x-axis and the y-intercept is the y-coordinate of where the line crosses the y-axis.

Mini-Assessment

1. Write $4x + 3y = 9$ in slope-intercept form. $y = -\frac{4}{3}x + 3$

2. Graph $-2x + 4y = 16$ using intercepts.

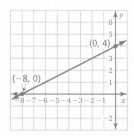

3. You have $12 to spend on pears and oranges. The equation $1.2x + 0.8y = 12$ represents this situation, where x is the number of pounds of pears and y is the number of pounds of oranges. Graph the equation. Interpret the intercepts.

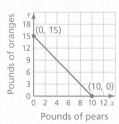

The x-intercept shows that you can buy 10 pounds of pears when you do not buy any oranges. The y-intercept shows that you can buy 15 pounds of oranges when you do not buy any pears.

Section Resources

Surface Level	Deep Level
Resources by Chapter • Extra Practice • Reteach • Puzzle Time Student Journal • Self-Assessment • Practice Differentiating the Lesson Tutorial Videos Skills Review Handbook Skills Trainer	Resources by Chapter • Enrichment and Extension Graphic Organizers Dynamic Assessment System • Section Practice

 Concepts, Skills, & Problem Solving

18. no; They should have let $y = 0$, not $x = 0$.

19. a.
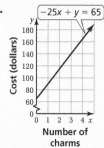
    b. $140

20.
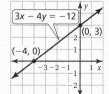

21.
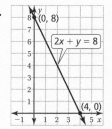

22.
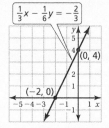

23–25. See Additional Answers.

26. no; Any horizontal line other than $y = 0$ does not have an x-intercept.

27. a. $y = 40x + 70$

    b. x-intercept: $-\frac{7}{4}$; no; You cannot have a negative time.

    c.
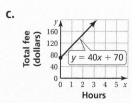

Learning Target

Write equations of lines in slope-intercept form.

Success Criteria

- Find the slope and the y-intercept of a line.
- Use the slope and the y-intercept to write an equation of a line.
- Write equations in slope-intercept form to solve real-life problems.

Warm Up

Cumulative, vocabulary, and prerequisite skills practice opportunities are available in the *Resources by Chapter* or at *BigIdeasMath.com*.

ELL Support

Point out the heading of Exploration 2, *Interpreting the Slope and the y-Intercept*. Students may be familiar with the word *interpret* as it applies to languages. Explain that when you do not understand a different language someone may interpret it for you. That person understands and explains what is being said. When you interpret the slope and y-intercept of a line, you understand and explain their meanings.

Exploration 1

a–b. See Additional Answers.

Exploration 2

a. slope: 50, y-intercept: 100;
The car travels 50 miles per hour and starts 100 miles from Phoenix.

b. $y = 50t + 100$

c. *Sample answer:* Use the equation found in part (b) and substitute 11 for the variable t.

Laurie's Notes

STATE STANDARDS
8.F.B.4

Preparing to Teach

- **MP1 Make Sense of Problems and Persevere in Solving Them:** The goal of this lesson is for students to write equations of lines by first determining the slope and y-intercept from a graph. Visual models help students make sense of the problems and identify important features of lines. Mathematically proficient students are able to interpret the mathematical results in the context of the situation or problem.

Motivate

- If there is sufficient space in your classroom, hallway, or school foyer, make coordinate axes on the floor using masking tape. Use a marker to scale each axis with integers −5 through 5. The axes could also be drawn on the board.
- Take turns having two students hold the ends of a rope to make a line in the coordinate plane while other students observe.
- Here are a series of directions you can give and some follow-up questions. Remind students that slope is rise over run and that the equation of a line in slope-intercept form is $y = mx + b$.

  ❓ Make the line $y = x$. "What is the slope?" 1 "What is the y-intercept?" 0

  ❓ Keep the same slope, but make the y-intercept 2. "What is the equation of this line?" $y = x + 2$

  ❓ Use the y-intercept 2, but make the slope steeper. "What is the slope of this line?" Answers will vary.

  ❓ Keep the same y-intercept, but make the slope $\frac{1}{2}$. "What is the equation of this line?" $y = \frac{1}{2}x + 2$

Exploration 1

❓ "How do you determine the slope of a line drawn in a coordinate plane?" Use two points that are on the graph and find the rise and run between the points.

❓ "Does it matter whether you move left-to-right or right-to-left when you are finding the rise and run? Explain." No, either way the slope will be the same.

- **Teaching Tip:** If you have a student who is color blind, refer to the lines by a number or letter scheme (1, 2, 3 or A, B, C).
- Students may have difficulty writing the equation in slope-intercept form. They think it should be harder to do!
- **Note:** Although $y = \frac{1}{2}x - 2$ is the common way to write the equation of the green line in part (a), $y = \frac{1}{2}x + (-2)$ is also acceptable.
- Ask students to share what they found in common for each trio of lines.

Exploration 2

- If students have difficulty getting started with this real-life problem, remind them to read the labels on the axes and interpret the y-intercept. The car was 100 miles from Phoenix at the beginning of the trip.
- Discuss answers to each part of the problem as a class.

4.6 Writing Equations in Slope-Intercept Form

Learning Target: Write equations of lines in slope-intercept form.

Success Criteria:
- I can find the slope and the *y*-intercept of a line.
- I can use the slope and the *y*-intercept to write an equation of a line.
- I can write equations in slope-intercept form to solve real-life problems.

EXPLORATION 1

Writing Equations of Lines

Work with a partner. For each part, answer the following questions.

- **What are the slopes and the *y*-intercepts of the lines?**
- **What are equations that represent the lines?**
- **What do the lines have in common?**

Math Practice

Analyze Givens

Why are the slope and *y*-intercept enough information to write an equation for a line?

a.

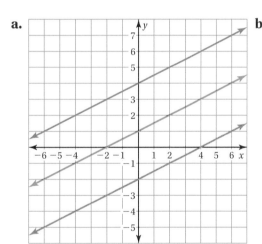

b.

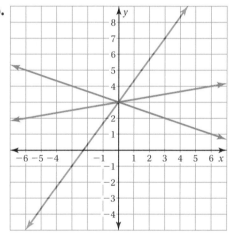

EXPLORATION 2

Interpreting the Slope and the *y*-Intercept

Work with a partner. The graph represents the distance *y* (in miles) of a car from Phoenix after *t* hours of a trip.

a. Find the slope and the *y*-intercept of the line. What do they represent in this situation?

b. Write an equation that represents the graph.

c. How can you determine the distance of the car from Phoenix after 11 hours?

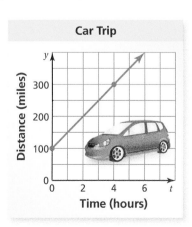

Car Trip

EXAMPLE 1 **Writing Equations in Slope-Intercept Form**

Write an equation in slope-intercept form of the line that passes through the given points.

a.

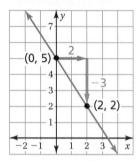

Find the slope and the y-intercept.

$$m = \frac{y_2 - y_1}{x_2 - x_1}$$

$$= \frac{2 - 5}{2 - 0}$$

$$= \frac{-3}{2}, \text{ or } -\frac{3}{2}$$

After writing an equation, check that the given points are solutions of the equation.

Because the line crosses the y-axis at $(0, 5)$, the y-intercept is 5.

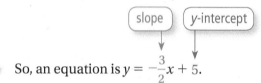

So, an equation is $y = -\frac{3}{2}x + 5$.

b.

x	y
0	−3
3	2
6	7
9	12

Find the slope and the y-intercept. Use the points $(0, -3)$ and $(3, 2)$.

$$m = \frac{y_2 - y_1}{x_2 - x_1}$$

$$= \frac{-3 - 2}{0 - 3}$$

$$= \frac{-5}{-3}, \text{ or } \frac{5}{3}$$

Remember

You can use *any* two points on a line to find slope.

Because $y = -3$ when $x = 0$, the y-intercept is -3.

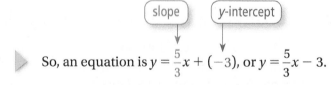

So, an equation is $y = \frac{5}{3}x + (-3)$, or $y = \frac{5}{3}x - 3$.

Try It Write an equation in slope-intercept form of the line that passes through the given points.

1.

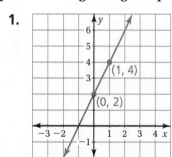

2.

x	y
−3	3
0	−1
3	−5
6	−9

Laurie's Notes

Scaffolding Instruction

- Students have begun to develop an understanding of how to write an equation of a line using its slope and *y*-intercept. Now they will write equations using slopes and *y*-intercepts.
- **Emerging:** Students may mix up rise and run when writing the slope. They will benefit from working through the examples before checking their understanding with the Try It and Self-Assessment exercises.
- **Proficient:** Students can use their prior knowledge of slope and *y*-intercept to write equations in slope-intercept form. They should complete Try It Exercises 3 and 4 before proceeding to the Self-Assessment exercises.

Discuss

- **MP1 Make Sense of Problems and Persevere in Solving Them:** In this lesson, students will make quick visual inspections of linear graphs to approximate the slopes and *y*-intercepts. This approximation is a helpful check when the slope and *y*-intercept are computed.

EXAMPLE 1

- Write the slope-intercept form of an equation, $y = mx + b$. Review with students that the coefficient of the *x*-term is the slope, and the constant *b* is the *y*-intercept. Also, review how to compute slope.
- ❓ "What do you know about the slope of the line in part (a) by inspection? Explain." The slope is negative because the graph falls from left to right.
- Compute the slope.
- ❓ "In part (a), what are the coordinates of the point where the line crosses the *y*-axis?" (0, 5)
- Use the slope and the *y*-intercept to write the equation.
- Work through part (b). Have different groups of students use different pairs of points to show students that no matter which points are selected the slope is the same.
- Remind students to write the more simplified equation $y = \frac{5}{3}x - 3$ instead of $y = \frac{5}{3}x + (-3)$. Stress that while both forms are correct, the simplified version is preferred.

Try It

- Before students begin Exercise 1, they should do a visual inspection to make a note of the sign of the slope and *y*-intercept. Encourage students to draw the slope triangle and label the horizontal and vertical lengths.
- **Neighbor Check:** Have students work independently and then have their neighbors check their work. Have students discuss any discrepancies.

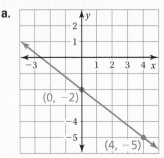

Extra Example 2

Which equation is shown in the graph?

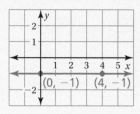

A. $y = -x$ **B.** $y = -1$

C. $y = 4x$ **C.** $y = 4$

B

Try It

3. $y = 5$

4. $y = 1$

EXAMPLE 2

- Make a quick sketch of the graph to reference as you work through the solution.
- When finding the slope, students are often unsure of how to simplify $\frac{0}{3}$. This is a good time to review the difference between $\frac{0}{3}$ and $\frac{3}{0}$.
- **Teaching Tip:** To explain why $\frac{3}{0}$ is undefined, first write the problem $8 \div 4 = 2$ on the board. Then rewrite it as $4\overline{)8}$. To check, multiply the quotient (2) by the divisor (4) and you get the dividend (8). In other words, 2 multiplied by 4 is 8. Do the same thing with $\frac{3}{0}$. Rewrite it using long division, $0\overline{)3}$. What do you multiply 0 by to get 3? There is no quotient, so you say $\frac{3}{0}$ is undefined. You cannot divide by 0.
- **MP7 Look for and Make Use of Structure:** Students do not always recognize that $y = -4$ is written in slope-intercept form, where $m = 0$ and $b = -4$. It helps to write the extra step of $y = (0)x + (-4)$ so students can see that the slope is 0. Students should recognize that $y = -4$ and $y = (0)x + (-4)$ are equivalent.

Try It

- Have students solve the problems on whiteboards.

Formative Assessment Tip

Partner Speaks

This strategy provides the opportunity for students to share their thinking about a problem or concept. Pair students and ask one person to speak. When the speaker is finished, the listener asks for clarification or gives feedback. Then the listener shares this thinking with the whole class.

Thinking through a problem with a partner is less intimidating for many students than sharing it with an entire class. For the listener, he or she needs to pay attention to the thoughts of the speaker and set aside his or her own thinking about the problem. As students are engaged in dialogue, circulate to hear the discussion and gain understanding of how students are thinking about the problem or concept. *Partner Speaks* should not be used for simple, less challenging problems.

ELL Support

Allow students extra support by working on the Self-Assessment for Concepts & Skills exercises in pairs. Check comprehension by having each pair display their equations on a whiteboard for your review.

Self-Assessment
for Concepts & Skills

5. $y = 3x + 2$

6. $y = -3x + 2$

7. $y = -5$

✓ Self-Assessment *for Concepts & Skills*

- **Neighbor Check:** Have students work independently and then have their neighbors check their work. Have students discuss any discrepancies.
- ⦿ **Partner Speaks:** One partner should explain how to write the equation of a line in slope-intercept form using a graph. Then the listener asks for clarification or gives feedback. Ask the listener to describe the explanation given by his or her partner. Partners should reverse roles to explain how to write the equation of a line in slope-intercept form using two ordered pairs.

The Success Criteria Self-Assessment chart can be found in the *Student Journal* or online at *BigIdeasMath.com*.

EXAMPLE 2 **Writing an Equation**

Which equation is shown in the graph?

   A. $y = -4$ **B.** $y = -3$

   C. $y = 0$ **D.** $y = -3x$

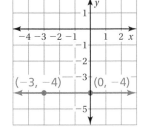

Find the slope and the y-intercept. The line is horizontal, so the change in y is 0.

$$m = \frac{\text{change in } y}{\text{change in } x} = \frac{0}{3} = 0$$

Because the line crosses the y-axis at $(0, -4)$, the y-intercept is -4.

So, the equation is $y = 0x + (-4)$, or $y = -4$.

    The correct answer is **A.**

Remember

The graph of $y = a$ is a horizontal line that passes through $(0, a)$.

Try It **Write an equation of the line that passes through the given points.**

3.

x	−4	0	4
y	5	5	5

4.

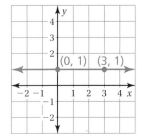

 Self-Assessment *for Concepts & Skills*

Solve each exercise. Then rate your understanding of the success criteria in your journal.

WRITING EQUATIONS IN SLOPE-INTERCEPT FORM **Write an equation in slope-intercept form of the line that passes through the given points.**

5.

x	y
−2	−4
−1	−1
0	2
1	5

6.

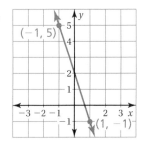

7. WRITING AN EQUATION Write an equation of the line that passes through $(0, -5)$ and $(2, -5)$.

EXAMPLE 3 **Modeling Real Life**

Engineers used tunnel boring machines like the ones shown above to dig an extension of the Metro Gold Line in Los Angeles. The tunnels are 1.7 miles long and 21 feet wide.

Engineers are digging a 3500-foot long tunnel at a constant rate. After 4 months, the engineers still need to dig 1500 feet to finish the project. How much time does it take to complete the tunnel from start to finish?

Write an equation of the line that represents the distance y (in feet) remaining after x months.

When the project starts, the engineers still need to dig 3500 feet, represented by (0, 3500). So, the y-intercept is 3500.

After 4 months, the engineers still need to dig 1500 feet, represented by (4, 1500). Use the points (0, 3500) and (4, 1500) to find the slope.

$$m = \frac{\text{change in } y}{\text{change in } x} = \frac{-2000}{4} = -500$$

So, an equation is $y = -500x + 3500$.

The tunnel is complete when the distance remaining is 0 feet. So, find the value of x when $y = 0$.

$y = -500x + 3500$	Write the equation.
$0 = -500x + 3500$	Substitute 0 for y.
$-3500 = -500x$	Subtract 3500 from each side.
$7 = x$	Divide each side by -500.

▷ It takes 7 months to complete the tunnel from start to finish.

Self-Assessment for Problem Solving

Solve each exercise. Then rate your understanding of the success criteria in your journal.

8. You load boxes onto an empty truck at a constant rate. After 3 hours, there are 100 boxes on the truck. How much longer do you work if you load a total of 120 boxes? Justify your answer.

9. The table shows the amounts y (in tons) of waste left in a landfill after x months of waste relocation. Interpret the slope and the y-intercept of the line that passes through the given points. How many months does it take to empty the landfill? Justify your answer.

x	0	6	12
y	15	12	9

10. A lifetime subscription to a website costs $250. A monthly subscription to the website costs $10 to join and $15 per month. Write equations to represent the costs of each plan. If you want to be a member for one year, which plan is less expensive? Explain.

Laurie's Notes

EXAMPLE 3

- Share some interesting facts about tunnels.
  - The world's longest overland tunnel is a 21-mile-long rail link under the Alps in Switzerland. The tunnel took eight years to build and cost $3.5 billion. It reduces the time trains need to cross between Germany and Italy from 3.5 hours to just under 2 hours.
  - The world's longest underwater tunnel is the Seikan Tunnel in Japan. It is about 33.5 miles long and runs under the Tsugaru Strait. It opened in 1988 and took 17 years to construct.
  - The Channel Tunnel (Chunnel) connects England and France. It is 31 miles long and travels under the English Channel.
- Ask a volunteer to read the problem.
- ❓ **"What do you know?"** Engineers are digging a 3500-foot tunnel. After 4 months, the engineers still need to dig 1500 feet.
- ❓ **"What do you need to find?"** how much time it takes to complete the tunnel
- ❓ **"What does the 3500 feet represent in the equation?"** the y-intercept, (0, 3500)
- ❓ **"Name another point you can use to find the slope."** (4, 1500)
- Finish solving the problem as shown.
- ❓ **Extension:** "If you were to make a graph to represent this situation, which quadrants would you use? Explain." Quadrant 1; Negative values for either distance or months do not make sense in the context of the problem.

✅ Self-Assessment for Problem Solving

- Allow time in class for students to practice using the problem-solving plan. Remember, some students may only be able to complete the first step.
- Students should work independently to make a plan for each problem. Then have students discuss their plans with a partner to clarify any misunderstandings.

The Success Criteria Self-Assessment chart can be found in the *Student Journal* or online at *BigIdeasMath.com*.

Closure

- **Exit Ticket:** What is the slope and y-intercept of the equation $y = 2x + 4$? slope: 2; y-intercept: 4 Write an equation of a line with a slope of 3 and a y-intercept of 1. $y = 3x + 1$

Self-Assessment
for Problem Solving

8. 0.6 h, or 36 min;

$$\frac{100 \text{ boxes}}{3 \text{ h}} = \frac{120 \text{ boxes}}{x \text{ h}}$$

$$100x = 360$$
$$x = 3.6$$
$$3.6 - 3 = 0.6$$

9. See Additional Answers.

10. $y = 250$, $y = 15x + 10$, where y is the total cost and x is the number of months of subscription; monthly subscription; *Sample answer:* The lifetime subscription will cost a flat fee of $250, but the monthly subscription for 1 year (12 months) will cost $15(12) + 10 = 190$, $\$190 < \$250$.

Learning Target

Write equations of lines in slope-intercept form.

Success Criteria

- Find the slope and the y-intercept of a line.
- Use the slope and the y-intercept to write an equation of a line.
- Write equations in slope-intercept form to solve real-life problems.

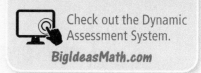

▶ Review & Refresh

1. $y = -4x + 1$

2. $y = x - \dfrac{1}{5}$

3. $y = \dfrac{1}{3}x - \dfrac{7}{2}$

4–7.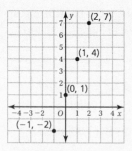

▶▶ Concepts, Skills, & Problem Solving

8. slope: 10; y-intercept: 15; The slope of $10 represents the cost per game. The y-intercept of $15 represents the initial cost to open an account.

9. $y = 10x + 15$

10. *Sample answer:* Substitute 6 for x in the equation $y = 10x + 15$.

11. $y = x + 4$

12. $y = -2x$

13. $y = \dfrac{1}{4}x + 1$

14. $y = -\dfrac{1}{2}x + 1$

15. $y = \dfrac{1}{3}x - 3$

16. $y = -\dfrac{5}{2}x - 1$

17. $y = -2x + 2$

18. $y = 0$

19. $x = 0$

Assignment Guide and Concept Check

Scaffold assignments to support all students in their learning progression. The suggested assignments are a starting point. Continue to assign additional exercises and revisit with spaced practice to move every student toward proficiency.

Level	Assignment 1	Assignment 2
Emerging	3, 5, 6, 8, 9, 10, 11, 12, 14, 15, 17, 19, 20	13, 16, 18, 21, 22, 23, 24
Proficient	3, 5, 6, 8, 9, 10, 12, 13, 15, 16, 18, 19, 20	21, 22, 23, 24, 25
Advanced	3, 5, 6, 8, 9, 10, 12, 13, 15, 16, 18, 19, 20	22, 23, 24, 25, 26

- Assignment 1 is for use after students complete the Self-Assessment for Concepts & Skills.
- Assignment 2 is for use after students complete the Self-Assessment for Problem Solving.
- The red exercises can be used as a concept check.

Review & Refresh Prior Skills

Exercises 1–3 Rewriting an Equation
Exercises 4–7 Plotting Ordered Pairs

Common Errors

- **Exercises 11–13** Students may use the reciprocal of the slope or forget a negative sign when writing the equation. Remind them of the definition for slope. Ask students to predict the sign of the slope based on the rise or fall of the line.
- **Exercises 14–16** Students may use the reciprocal of the slope when writing the equation. Remind students that slope is the value of the ratio of the change in y to the change in x.
- **Exercise 18** Students may write the wrong equation when the slope is zero. For example, instead of $y = 0$, students may write $x = 0$. Ask them what is the rise of the graph (zero) and write this in slope-intercept form with the y-intercept as well, $y = 0x + 0$. Then ask students what happens when a variable (or any number) is multiplied by zero. Rewrite the equation as $y = 0$.

Go to *BigIdeasMath.com* to get
HELP with solving the exercises.

Review & Refresh

Write the linear equation in slope-intercept form.

1. $4x + y = 1$

2. $x - y = \dfrac{1}{5}$

3. $-\dfrac{2}{3}x + 2y = -7$

Plot the ordered pair in a coordinate plane.

4. $(1, 4)$

5. $(-1, -2)$

6. $(0, 1)$

7. $(2, 7)$

Concepts, Skills, & Problem Solving

INTERPRETING THE SLOPE AND THE *y*-INTERCEPT **The graph represents the cost *y* (in dollars) to open an online gaming account and buy *x* games.** (See Exploration 2, p. 173.)

8. Find the slope and the *y*-intercept of the line. What do they represent in this situation?

9. Write an equation that represents the graph.

10. How can you determine the total cost of opening an account and buying 6 games?

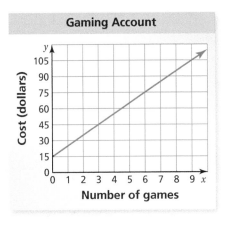

WRITING EQUATIONS IN SLOPE-INTERCEPT FORM Write an equation in slope-intercept form of the line that passes through the given points.

11.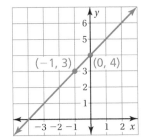

12.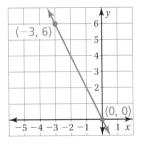

13.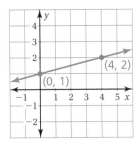

14.

x	y
−2	2
0	1
2	0
4	−1

15.

x	y
−3	−4
0	−3
3	−2
6	−1

16.

x	y
−4	9
−2	4
0	−1
2	−6

WRITING EQUATIONS Write an equation of the line that passes through the given points.

17. $(-1, 4), (0, 2)$

18. $(-1, 0), (0, 0)$

19. $(0, 4), (0, -3)$

20. **MP YOU BE THE TEACHER** Your friend writes an equation of the line shown. Is your friend correct? Explain your reasoning.

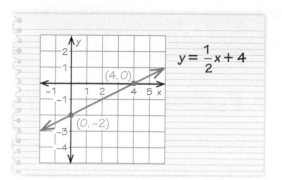

21. **MP MODELING REAL LIFE** A boa constrictor is 18 inches long at birth and grows 8 inches per year. Write an equation in slope-intercept form that represents the length y (in feet) of a boa constrictor that is x years old.

22. **MP MODELING REAL LIFE** The table shows the speeds y (in miles per hour) of a car after x seconds of braking. Write an equation of the line that passes through the points in the table. Interpret the slope and the y-intercept of the line.

x	0	1	2	3
y	70	60	50	40

23. **MP MODELING REAL LIFE** A dentist charges a flat fee for an office visit, plus an additional fee for every tooth removed. The graph shows the total cost y (in dollars) for a patient when the dentist removes x teeth. Interpret the slope and the y-intercept.

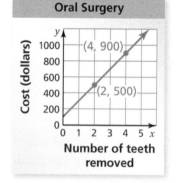

24. **MP MODELING REAL LIFE** One of your friends gives you $10 for a charity walkathon. Another friend gives you an amount per mile. After 5 miles, you have raised $13.50 total. Write an equation that represents the amount y of money you have raised after x miles.

25. **MP PROBLEM SOLVING** You have 500 sheets of notebook paper. After 1 week, you have 72% of the sheets left. You use the same number of sheets each week. Write an equation that represents the number y of sheets remaining after x weeks.

26. **DIG DEEPER!** The palm tree on the left is 10 years old. The palm tree on the right is 8 years old. The trees grow at the same rate.

    a. Estimate the height y (in feet) of each tree.

    b. Plot the two points (x, y), where x is the age of each tree and y is the height of each tree.

    c. What is the rate of growth of the trees?

    d. Write an equation that represents the height of a palm tree in terms of its age.

Mini-Assessment

Write an equation in slope-intercept form of the line that passes through the given points.

1.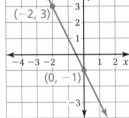

$y = -2x - 1$

2.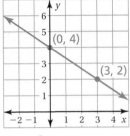

$y = -\frac{2}{3}x + 4$

3. $(-2, 7), (0, 1)$

$y = -3x + 1$

4. $(-6, 4), (3, 4)$

$y = 4$

5.

x	y
−4	−7
−2	−6
0	−5
2	−4

$y = \frac{1}{2}x - 5$

Concepts, Skills, & Problem Solving

20. no; The *x*-intercept was used instead of the *y*-intercept.

21. $y = \frac{2}{3}x + \frac{3}{2}$

22. $y = -10x + 70$; The slope of -10 represents the decrease in car speed, in miles per hour, each second after braking. The *y*-intercept of 70 represents the initial car speed before braking.

23. The slope of 200 represents the additional fee per tooth removal. The *y*-intercept of 100 represents the initial fee for an office visit.

24. $y = 0.7x + 10$

25. $y = -140x + 500$

26. Check students' work.

Section Resources

Surface Level	Deep Level
Resources by Chapter • Extra Practice • Reteach • Puzzle Time Student Journal • Self-Assessment • Practice Differentiating the Lesson Tutorial Videos Skills Review Handbook Skills Trainer	Resources by Chapter • Enrichment and Extension Graphic Organizers Dynamic Assessment System • Section Practice

Learning Target

Write equations of lines in point-slope form.

Success Criteria

- Use a point on a line and the slope to write an equation of the line.
- Use any two points to write an equation of a line.
- Write equations in point-slope form to solve real-life problems.

Warm Up

Cumulative, vocabulary, and prerequisite skills practice opportunities are available in the *Resources by Chapter* or at *BigIdeasMath.com*.

ELL Support

Students may be familiar with the word *point* from different contexts. Examples include the main idea of a discussion, the purpose of an action, a dot, or the act of gesturing with a finger at something. Remind students that in math a point is a location. It has no size, width, or length. It is represented by a small, closed circle.

Exploration 1

a. $m = \dfrac{y - y_1}{x - x_1}$; *Sample answer:* To find the slope of the line, divide the vertical distance of the coordinates by the horizontal distance of the coordinates.

b. $y - y_1 = m(x - x_1)$; This result represents the equation of a line with slope m that passes through the point (x_1, y_1).

Exploration 2

a. See Additional Answers.

b. $A - 175 = 25(t - 4)$
$A = 25t + 75$

Laurie's Notes

Preparing to Teach

- **MP1 Make Sense of Problems and Persevere in Solving Them:** The goal is for students to write equations of lines given a slope and a point. The slope may be stated explicitly or determined from a contextual setting. Students use the slope to graph the line and work backwards to find the y-intercept. There are different approaches students may use as they make sense of the problem.

Motivate

- Hold a piece of ribbon and a pair of scissors in your hands. Snip off a one-foot piece of ribbon. Repeat once or twice more.
- **?** "Do you know how long my ribbon was when I first started?" no
- Your question should prompt students to ask two obvious questions: "How much are you cutting off each time?" and "How many times have you made a cut?" How much you cut off is the slope (-1). How many times you cut the ribbon helps students work backwards to find the length before any cuts were made, which is the y-intercept.

Exploration 1

- **?** "What is the slope of the line that passes through (2, 1) and (3, 5)? Explain." $4;\ m = \dfrac{5 - 1}{3 - 2} = \dfrac{4}{1} = 4$ Tell students that they can use the same reasoning to find the slope of the line that passes through (x_1, y_1) and (x, y).
- In part (b), students may struggle to recognize that the resulting equation $m(x - x_1) = y - y_1$ represents an equation of a line. Have them compare the new equation to the slope-intercept form of a linear equation. They should notice that x and y are the same in each equation.

Exploration 2

- If students do not understand what the slope is, suggest they work backwards and make a table of values.

Month, t	0	1	2	3	4
Balance in Account, A	$75	$100	$125	$150	$175

- Students can use the table to draw the graph.
- Ask a few questions to guide students' understanding:
  - **?** "What is the slope for this problem?" 25 "What point is given?" (4, 175)
  - **?** "Do you have enough information to write an equation?" yes; $A - 175 = 25(t - 4)$, or $A = 25t + 75$ Students may get confused by using t and A instead of x and y. Point out the labels on the graph. If necessary, let them use x and y. Then they can substitute A for y and t for x. When using the point (4, 175) in the equation, tell students to substitute for (x_1, y_1) because the final equation should include x and y.
  - **?** "Why is the slope positive?" You are putting money in the bank, so the balance in your account is growing.
- Take time for students to transform the equation into slope-intercept form. They should interpret the slope and y-intercept in the context of the problem.

4.7 Writing Equations in Point-Slope Form

Learning Target: Write equations of lines in point-slope form.

Success Criteria:
- I can use a point on a line and the slope to write an equation of the line.
- I can use any two points to write an equation of a line.
- I can write equations in point-slope form to solve real-life problems.

EXPLORATION 1

Deriving an Equation

Work with a partner. Let (x_1, y_1) represent a specific point on a line. Let (x, y) represent any other point on the line.

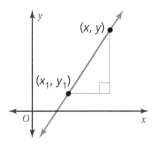

Math Practice

Recognize Usefulness of Tools

How does the graph help you derive an equation?

a. Write an equation that represents the slope m of the line. Explain your reasoning.

b. Multiply each side of your equation in part (a) by the expression in the denominator. What does the resulting equation represent? Explain your reasoning.

EXPLORATION 2

Writing an Equation

Work with a partner.

For 4 months, you saved $25 a month. You now have $175 in your savings account.

a. Draw a graph that shows the balance in your account after t months.

b. Use your result from Exploration 1 to write an equation that represents the balance A after t months.

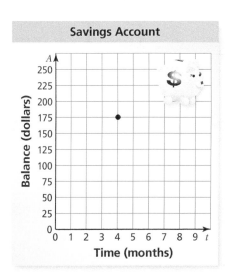

Savings Account

Balance (dollars) / Time (months)

4.7 Lesson

Key Vocabulary 🔊
point-slope form,
p. 180

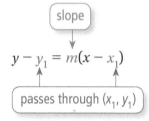 **Key Idea**

Point-Slope Form

Words   A linear equation written in the form $y - y_1 = m(x - x_1)$ is in **point-slope form**. The line passes through the point (x_1, y_1), and the slope of the line is m.

Algebra

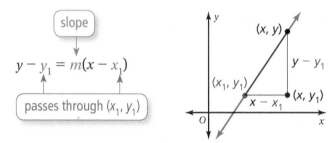

EXAMPLE 1   **Writing an Equation Using a Slope and a Point**

Write an equation in point-slope form of the line that passes through the point $(-6, 1)$ with slope $\dfrac{2}{3}$.

$y - y_1 = m(x - x_1)$	Write the point-slope form.
$y - 1 = \dfrac{2}{3}[x - (-6)]$	Substitute $\dfrac{2}{3}$ for m, -6 for x_1, and 1 for y_1.
$y - 1 = \dfrac{2}{3}(x + 6)$	Simplify.

▶ So, an equation is $y - 1 = \dfrac{2}{3}(x + 6)$.

Check   Check that $(-6, 1)$ is a solution of the equation.

$y - 1 = \dfrac{2}{3}(x + 6)$	Write the equation.
$1 - 1 \stackrel{?}{=} \dfrac{2}{3}(-6 + 6)$	Substitute.
$0 = 0$ ✓	Simplify.

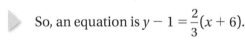

Try It   Write an equation in point-slope form of the line that passes through the given point and has the given slope.

1. $(1, 2)$; $m = -4$ **2.** $(7, 0)$; $m = 1$ **3.** $(-8, -5)$; $m = -\dfrac{3}{4}$

Laurie's Notes

Scaffolding Instruction

- Students developed an intuitive understanding of how to write an equation of a line given the slope and a point. They will continue this work and formalize the process.
- **Emerging:** Students struggle with the use of subscripts and the connection between using the slope formula and an equation for a line. They will benefit from guided instruction for the Key Idea and examples.
- **Proficient:** Students understand the relationship between the three forms of a linear equation. They can use a point on a line and the slope to write an equation of the line. These students should review the Key Idea and Example 2 before they proceed to the Self-Assessment exercises.

Key Idea

- Draw a coordinate plane and graph a point. "How many lines go through this point with a slope of $\frac{1}{2}$?" only one line
- Explain that the **point-slope form** of the equation of a line is equivalent to the slope-intercept form and is the equation of a unique line.
- Write the Key Idea on the board. Use of color is helpful.
- **Teaching Tip:** On a side board, write the formula for slope as $\frac{y - y_1}{x - x_1} = m$ so students are reminded of how point-slope form was derived.
- **MP1 Make Sense of Problems and Persevere in Solving Them:** Although students derived point-slope form in the exploration, they may have lingering questions about the use of subscripts. They might ask why the first point was not labeled (x, y) and the second point (x_1, y_1). The labels are arbitrary, the line could be sloping downward, and the points could be located in any quadrant.
- **Teaching Strategy:** Students need to see the connection between the slope formula and the point-slope form of a linear equation. They should be able to recreate one formula from the other.

EXAMPLE 1

- Write the point-slope form of a linear equation.
- ❓ "What is the slope of the line?" $\frac{2}{3}$ "What point do you know the line passes through?" $(-6, 1)$
- Substitute the known information. Remind students that they are subtracting a negative, so they have $x + 6$ inside the parentheses.
- ❓ "How can you check the reasonableness of your equation?" Students might suggest a quick sketch or rewriting the equation in slope-intercept form to see if the y-intercept makes sense.

Try It

- **Neighbor Check:** Have students work independently and then have their neighbors check their work. Have students discuss any discrepancies.

Teaching Strategy

Whenever possible, encourage students to make sense of problems rather than just memorize and apply a process. As they proceed through their mathematics courses, many processes will be presented. If students simply memorize the processes, they will quickly forget or confuse them. If students understand the basis of a problem, then they can recreate the method as needed.

Extra Example 1

Write the equation in point-slope form of the line that passes through the point $(3, -6)$ with slope $-\frac{4}{3}$.

$y + 6 = -\frac{4}{3}(x - 3)$

ELL Support

After demonstrating Example 1, have students work in pairs to discuss and complete Try It Exercises 1–3. Provide the steps: (1) Write the point-slope form, (2) Substitute, (3) Simplify, and (4) Check that the given point is a solution. Expect students to perform according to their language levels.

Beginner: Use phrases and write out the steps and equations.

Intermediate: Use simple sentences to discuss and state the equations.

Advanced: Use detailed sentences and help guide the discussion.

Try It

1. $y - 2 = -4(x - 1)$
2. $y - 0 = 1(x - 7)$
3. $y + 5 = -\frac{3}{4}(x + 8)$

Extra Example 2

Write an equation in slope-intercept form of the line that passes through the given points.

x	y
−3	0
3	2
6	3

$y = \dfrac{1}{3}x + 1$

Try It

4. $y = -x - 1$

5. $y = -x$

Self-Assessment
for Concepts & Skills

6. $y - 0 = 1(x - 2)$

7. $y + 1 = -\dfrac{1}{3}(x + 3)$

8. $y - 4 = 3(x - 5)$

9. $y = -\dfrac{3}{2}x + \dfrac{11}{2}$

10. Graph the line that passes through the points $(4, 5)$, $(5, 9)$;

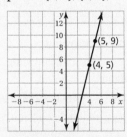

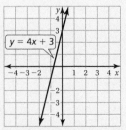

EXAMPLE 2

- Plot the points. Draw the line through the points.
- ? "Is the slope positive or negative?" negative
- ? "How can you find the slope exactly?" Use the slope formula.
- ? "Can you estimate the y-intercept?" Listen for a positive number greater than 4.
- Continue to work through the problem as shown.
- ? "Would you get the same equation if you had used $(5, -2)$ instead of $(2, 4)$?" Students may be unsure.
- Solve the problem again using $(5, -2)$ as shown in the Another Method note.
- Mathematically proficient students can make sense of why any point on the line will result in the same equation.

Try It

- Discuss student solutions. Check that the signs of the numbers are correct.

✓ Self-Assessment for Concepts & Skills

- Students should solve the problems independently. Then have them *Turn and Talk* to discuss their answers. Remind student to use three-foot voices when discussing their reasoning.
- ◉ **Partner Speaks:** Have students take turns explaining the first two success criteria. As you circulate, listen carefully to their discussions. Ask students to share as needed.

ELL Support

Allow students to work in pairs for extra support and to practice language. Check comprehension of Exercises 6–9 by having each pair display their equations on a whiteboard for your review. Have two pairs discuss their answers for Exercise 10. Monitor discussions and provide support.

The Success Criteria Self-Assessment chart can be found in the *Student Journal* or online at *BigIdeasMath.com*.

EXAMPLE 2 **Writing an Equation Using Two Points**

Write an equation in slope-intercept form of the line that passes through the given points.

x	y
−1	10
2	4
5	−2

Find the slope. Use the points $(2, 4)$ and $(5, -2)$.

$$m = \frac{y_2 - y_1}{x_2 - x_1} = \frac{-2 - 4}{5 - 2} = \frac{-6}{3} = -2$$

Then use the slope $m = -2$ and the point $(2, 4)$ to write an equation of the line.

$y - y_1 = m(x - x_1)$	Write the point-slope form.
$y - 4 = -2(x - 2)$	Substitute -2 for m, 2 for x_1, and 4 for y_1.
$y - 4 = -2x + 4$	Distributive Property
$y = -2x + 8$	Write in slope-intercept form.

Math Practice

Build Arguments
Will you obtain the same equation when you use a different pair of points from the table? Explain why or why not.

Try It Write an equation in slope-intercept form of the line that passes through the given points.

4. $(-2, 1), (3, -4)$

5.

x	−5	−3	−1
y	5	3	1

Self-Assessment for Concepts & Skills

Solve each exercise. Then rate your understanding of the success criteria in your journal.

WRITING AN EQUATION Write an equation in point-slope form of the line that passes through the given point and has the given slope.

6. $(2, 0)$; $m = 1$ 7. $(-3, -1)$; $m = -\dfrac{1}{3}$ 8. $(5, 4)$; $m = 3$

x	3	5	7
y	1	−2	−5

9. **WRITING AN EQUATION** Write an equation of the line that passes through the points given in the table.

10. **DIFFERENT WORDS, SAME QUESTION** Which is different? Sketch "both" graphs.

What is the graph of the equation $y = 4x + 3$?

Graph the line that passes through the points $(4, 5)$ and $(5, 9)$.

Graph $y = 4x + 3$.   Graph the linear equation $y - 7 = 4(x - 1)$.

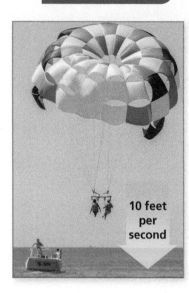

10 feet per second

EXAMPLE 3 **Modeling Real Life**

You finish parasailing and are being pulled back to the boat. After 2 seconds, you are 25 feet above the boat. At what height were you parasailing?

You are 25 feet above the boat after 2 seconds, which can be represented by the point (2, 25). You are being pulled down at a rate of 10 feet per second. So, the slope is -10.

Because you know a point and the slope, use point-slope form to write an equation that represents your height y (in feet) above the boat after x seconds.

$y - y_1 = m(x - x_1)$	Write the point-slope form.
$y - 25 = -10(x - 2)$	Substitute for m, x_1, and y_1.
$y - 25 = -10x + 20$	Distributive Property
$y = -10x + 45$	Write in slope-intercept form.

The height at which you were parasailing is represented by the y-intercept.

▷ So, you were parasailing at a height of 45 feet.

Self-Assessment for Problem Solving

Solve each exercise. Then rate your understanding of the success criteria in your journal.

11. A writer finishes a project that a coworker started at a rate of 3 pages per hour. After 3 hours, 25% of the project is complete.

    a. The project is 200 pages long. Write and graph an equation for the total number y of pages that have been finished after the writer works for x hours.

    b. The writer has a total of 45 hours to finish the project. Will the writer meet the deadline? Explain your reasoning.

12. **DIG DEEPER!** You and your friend begin to run along a path at different constant speeds. After 1 minute, your friend is 45 meters ahead of you. After 3 minutes, your friend is 105 meters ahead of you.

    a. Write and graph an equation for the distance y (in meters) your friend is ahead of you after x minutes. Justify your answer.

    b. Did you and your friend start running from the same spot? Explain your reasoning.

Laurie's Notes

EXAMPLE 3

- Ask a volunteer to read the problem. Select another student to explain the given information. Select another student to explain what the problem is asking.
- ❓ "Have any of you parasailed?" Wait for students to respond. Explain that when parasailing, you want a smooth descent, like an airplane.
- ❓ "What is the slope for this problem?" −10 "How do you know?" The arrow pointing down means the slope is negative.
- ❓ "Can you name a point that satisfies the equation?" (2, 25)
- Write the point-slope form of a linear equation. Substitute the known information.
- Remind students to always check that they have answered the question. In this case, "At what height were you parasailing?"
- **Extension:** Have students determine when you will reach the boat, meaning what is x when $y = 0$.

✓ Self-Assessment for Problem Solving

- Students may benefit from trying the exercises independently and then working with peers to refine their work. It is important to provide time in class for problem solving, so that students become comfortable with the problem-solving plan.
- **Think-Pair-Share:** Students should solve each exercise independently. Then students should compare their answers with a partner and resolve any discrepancies. Then have each pair share their ideas with the class.

The Success Criteria Self-Assessment chart can be found in the *Student Journal* or online at *BigIdeasMath.com*.

Closure

- **Exit Ticket:** Write an equation of the line with a slope of 2 that passes through the point (−1, 4) in point-slope form and slope-intercept form.
  $y − 4 = 2(x + 1)$; $y = 2x + 6$

Extra Example 3
You are pulling down your kite at a rate of 2 feet per second. After 3 seconds, your kite is 54 feet above you. At what height was the kite flying before you began pulling it down? 60 ft

Self-Assessment
for Problem Solving

11. **a.** $y = 3x + 41$

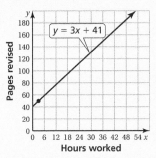

b. no; *Sample answer:* The writer will only finish 176 out of the 200 pages.

12. **a.** See Additional Answers.

b. no; *Sample answer:* When $x = 0$, your friend is 15 meters ahead of you.

Learning Target

Write equations of lines in point-slope form.

Success Criteria

- Use a point on a line and the slope to write an equation of the line.
- Use any two points to write an equation of a line.
- Write equations in point-slope form to solve real-life problems.

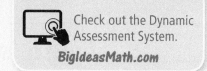

Review & Refresh

1. $y = \frac{1}{2}x + 5$

2. $y = \frac{3}{2}x + 2$

3. no solution

4. $x = \frac{8}{9}$

5. $x = 4$

Concepts, Skills, & Problem Solving

6.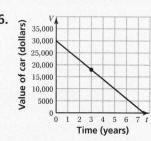

7. $V = -4000t + 30{,}000$

8. $y - 0 = -\frac{2}{3}(x - 3)$

9. $y - 8 = \frac{3}{4}(x - 4)$

10. $y + 3 = 4(x - 1)$

11. $y + 5 = -\frac{1}{7}(x - 7)$

12. $y - 3 = \frac{5}{3}(x - 3)$

13. $y + 4 = -2(x + 1)$

14. $y = 3x + 2$

15. $y = 2x$

16. $y = x + 5$

17. $y = \frac{1}{4}x$

18. $y = -\frac{1}{3}x + 2$

19. $y = x + 1$

20. $V = \frac{2}{25}T + 22$

Assignment Guide and Concept Check

Scaffold assignments to support all students in their learning progression. The suggested assignments are a starting point. Continue to assign additional exercises and revisit with spaced practice to move every student toward proficiency.

Level	Assignment 1	Assignment 2
Emerging	1, 2, 5, 6, 7, 9, 11, 15, 17, 21, 25	10, 12, 16, 18, 20, 22, 24, 27, 28, 29
Proficient	1, 2, 5, 6, 7, 8, 10, 14, 16, 22, 24	12, 18, 20, 23, 26, 27, 28, 29
Advanced	1, 2, 5, 6, 7, 10, 12, 16, 18, 22, 24	23, 26, 27, 28, 29, 30

- Assignment 1 is for use after students complete the Self-Assessment for Concepts & Skills.
- Assignment 2 is for use after students complete the Self-Assessment for Problem Solving.
- The red exercises can be used as a concept check.

Review & Refresh Prior Skills

Exercises 1 and 2 Writing Equations in Slope-Intercept Form

Exercises 3–5 Solving an Equation with Variables on Both Sides

Common Errors

- **Exercises 8–19** Students may forget to include negatives with the slope and coordinates, or they may apply them incorrectly. Remind students that when the coordinates are negative, they will be subtracting a negative after substituting in point-slope form, which results in adding a positive.
- **Exercises 14–19** Students may use the reciprocal of the slope when writing the equation. Remind students that slope is the change in y over the change in x.
- **Exercise 20** Students might have trouble knowing which variable can be compared with x and y and may write the given point backwards. Review what the words *in terms of* mean when writing an equation. In this problem, V could be replaced by y and T could be replaced by x. Remind students to check their equations by substituting the given point and checking that it is a solution of the equation.

? Go to *BigIdeasMath.com* to get HELP with solving the exercises.

▶ ## Review & Refresh

Write an equation in slope-intercept form of the line that passes through the given points.

1.

x	-2	0	2
y	4	5	6

2.

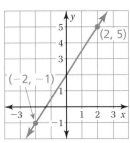

Solve the equation. Check your solution, if possible.

3. $2x + 3 = 2x$

4. $6x - 7 = 1 - 3x$

5. $0.1x - 1 = 1.2x - 5.4$

▶▶ ## Concepts, Skills, & Problem Solving

WRITING AN EQUATION The value of a new car decreases $4000 each year. After 3 years, the car is worth $18,000. (See Exploration 2, p. 179.)

6. Draw a graph that shows the value of the car after t years.

7. Write an equation that represents the value V of the car after t years.

WRITING AN EQUATION Write an equation in point-slope form of the line that passes through the given point and has the given slope.

8. $(3, 0)$; $m = -\dfrac{2}{3}$

9. $(4, 8)$; $m = \dfrac{3}{4}$

10. $(1, -3)$; $m = 4$

11. $(7, -5)$; $m = -\dfrac{1}{7}$

12. $(3, 3)$; $m = \dfrac{5}{3}$

13. $(-1, -4)$; $m = -2$

WRITING AN EQUATION Write an equation in slope-intercept form of the line that passes through the given points.

14. $(-1, -1), (1, 5)$

15. $(2, 4), (3, 6)$

16. $(-2, 3), (2, 7)$

17. $(4, 1), (8, 2)$

18. $(-9, 5), (-3, 3)$

19. $(1, 2), (-2, -1)$

20. **MP** **MODELING REAL LIFE** At 0°C, the volume of a gas is 22 liters. For each degree the temperature T (in degrees Celsius) increases, the volume V (in liters) of the gas increases by $\dfrac{2}{25}$. Write an equation that represents the volume of the gas in terms of the temperature.

WRITING AN EQUATION Write an equation of the line that passes through the given points in any form. Explain your choice of form.

21.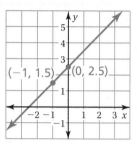

22. (graph with points (2, 3.5) and (1, 1.5))

23. (graph with points (−1, 4.5) and (1, −1.5))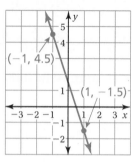

24.

x	y
−1	3.5
1	−0.5
3	−4.5

25.

x	y
−3	−1
0	1
3	3

26.

x	y
−7	6
−3	4
1	2

27. **(MP) REASONING** Write an equation of the line that passes through the point (8, 2) and is parallel to the graph of the equation $y = 4x - 3$.

28. **(MP) MODELING REAL LIFE** The table shows the amount y (in fluid ounces) of carpet cleaner in a tank after x minutes of cleaning.

x	y
5	108
10	88
15	68

  a. Write an equation that represents the amount of cleaner in the tank after x minutes.

  b. How much cleaner is in the tank when the cleaning begins?

  c. After how many minutes is the tank empty? Justify your answer.

Leaning Tower of Pisa

(10.75, 42)

7.75 m

29. **DIG DEEPER!** According to Dolbear's law, you can predict the temperature T (in degrees Fahrenheit) by counting the number x of chirps made by a snowy tree cricket in 1 minute. When the temperature is 50°F, a cricket chirps 40 times in 1 minute. For each rise in temperature of 0.25°F, the cricket makes an additional chirp each minute.

  a. You count 100 chirps in 1 minute. What is the temperature?

  b. The temperature is 96°F. How many chirps do you expect the cricket to make? Justify your answer.

30. **(MP) PROBLEM SOLVING** The Leaning Tower of Pisa in Italy was built between 1173 and 1350.

  a. Write an equation that represents the yellow line.

  b. The tower is 56 meters tall. How far from the center is the top of the tower? Justify your answer.

Mini-Assessment

Write an equation in point-slope form of the line that passes through the given point and has the given slope.

1. $(1, 4)$; $m = 3$ $y - 4 = 3(x - 1)$

2. $(2, -1)$; $m = \dfrac{1}{2}$ $y + 1 = \dfrac{1}{2}(x - 2)$

Write an equation in slope-intercept form of the line that passes through the given points.

3. $(-1, 5)$, $(1, 1)$ $y = -2x + 3$

4. $(-2, -6)$, $(4, 3)$ $y = \dfrac{3}{2}x - 3$

5. You rent a floor sander for $24 per day. You pay $82 for 3 days.

    a. Write an equation that represents your total cost y (in dollars) after x days.
    $y = 24x + 10$

    b. How much is the initial fee to rent the sander? $10

Section Resources

Surface Level	Deep Level

Resources by Chapter
  • Extra Practice
  • Reteach
  • Puzzle Time
Student Journal
  • Self-Assessment
  • Practice
Differentiating the Lesson
Tutorial Videos
Skills Review Handbook
Skills Trainer
	Resources by Chapter
	  • Enrichment and Extension
	Graphic Organizers
	Dynamic Assessment System
	  • Section Practice

Transfer Level	

Dynamic Assessment System
  • End-of-Chapter Quiz
	Assessment Book
	  • End-of-Chapter Quiz

21. *Sample answer:* $y = x + 2.5$; Explanations will vary.

22. *Sample answer:* $y = 2x - 0.5$; Explanations will vary.

23. *Sample answer:* $y = -3x + 1.5$; Explanations will vary.

24. *Sample answer:* $y = -2x + 1.5$; Explanations will vary.

25. *Sample answer:* $y = \dfrac{2}{3}x + 1$; Explanations will vary.

26. *Sample answer:* $y = -\dfrac{1}{2}x + \dfrac{5}{2}$; Explanations will vary.

27. $y = 4x - 30$

28. a. $y = -4x + 128$

    b. 128 fl oz

    c. 32 min;
$$0 = -4x + 128$$
$$4x = 128$$
$$x = 32$$

29. a. $65°F$

    b. 224 chirps;
$$96 = 0.25x + 40$$
$$56 = 0.25x$$
$$224 = x$$

30. a. $y = 14x - 108.5$

    b. 4 m;
$$56 = 14x - 108.5$$
$$164.5 = 14x$$
$$11.75 = x$$
$$11.75 - 7.75 = 4$$

Skills Needed

Exercise 1
- Finding an Original Price
- Graphing a Proportional Relationship

Exercise 2
- Graphing an Equation
- Using Pairs of Angles
- Writing Equations in Slope-Intercept Form

Exercise 3
- Solving an Equation
- Writing Equations in Slope-Intercept Form

ELL Support

Discuss the phrase *on sale*. Explain that this phrase means something is being sold for a lower price than the original price. Compare *on sale* to the phrase *for sale*, which simply means that something is being sold.

Using the Problem-Solving Plan

1. $y = 0.6x$

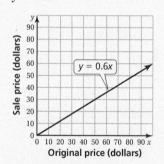

2. See Additional Answers.

3. 4.25 h

Performance Task

The *STEAM Video Performance Task* provides the opportunity for additional enrichment and greater depth of knowledge as students explore the mathematics of the chapter within a context tied to the chapter STEAM Video. The performance task and a detailed scoring rubric are provided at *BigIdeasMath.com*.

Laurie's Notes

Scaffolding Instruction

- The goal of this lesson is to help students become more comfortable with problem solving. These exercises combine graphing and writing linear equations with prior skills from other chapters and courses. The solution for Exercise 1 is worked out below, to help you guide students through the problem-solving plan. Use the remaining class time to have students work on the other exercises.
- **Emerging:** The goal for these students is to feel comfortable with the problem-solving plan. Allow students to work in pairs to write the beginning steps of the problem-solving plan for Exercise 2. Keep in mind that some students may only be ready to do the first step.
- **Proficient:** Students may be able to work independently or in pairs to complete Exercises 2 and 3.
- Visit each pair to review their plan for each problem. Ask students to describe their plans.

▶ Using the Problem-Solving Plan

Exercise 1

Understand the problem. You know the percent discount of items in a retail store. You are asked to write and graph an equation that represents the sale price of an item that has an original price of x dollars.

Make a plan. Selling an item for 40% off is the same as selling an item for 60% of its original price. Use this information to write and graph an equation that represents the situation.

Solve and check. Use the plan to solve the problem. Then check your solution.

- Write an equation that represents the situation.
  $$a = p\% \cdot w$$
  $$y = 0.60 \cdot x$$
  $$y = 0.6x$$

  So, the equation that represents the situation is $y = 0.6x$.

- Graph $y = 0.6x$. The equation represents a proportional relationship and shows that the slope m is 0.6. So, the graph passes through $(0, 0)$ and $(1, 0.6)$. Plot the ordered pairs and draw a line through the points.

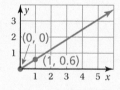

- **Check:** Use a graphing calculator to graph $y = 0.6x$.

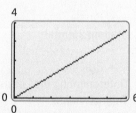

Connecting Concepts

Using the Problem-Solving Plan

1. Every item in a retail store is on sale for 40% off. Write and graph an equation that represents the sale price y of an item that has an original price of x dollars.

 Understand the problem.

You know the percent discount of items in a retail store. You are asked to write and graph an equation that represents the sale price of an item that has an original price of x dollars.

Make a plan.

Selling an item for 40% off is the same as selling an item for 60% of its original price. Use this information to write and graph an equation that represents the situation.

Solve and check.

Use the plan to solve the problem. Then check your solution.

2. Two supplementary angles have angle measures of $x°$ and $y°$. Write and graph an equation that represents the relationship between the measures of the angles.

3. A mechanic charges a diagnostic fee plus an hourly rate. The table shows the numbers of hours worked and the total costs for three customers. A fourth customer pays $285. Find the number of hours that the mechanic worked for the fourth customer.

Hours, x	1	3	5
Cost, y (dollars)	90	210	330

Performance Task

Anatomy of a Hurricane

At the beginning of this chapter, you watched a STEAM Video called "Hurricane!" You are now ready to complete the performance task related to this video, available at *BigIdeasMath.com*. Be sure to use the problem-solving plan as you work through the performance task.

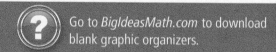
▶ Review Vocabulary

Write the definition and give an example of each vocabulary term.

linear equation, *p. 142*
solution of a linear equation, *p. 142*
slope, *p. 148*

rise, *p. 148*
run, *p. 148*
x-intercept, *p. 162*
y-intercept, *p. 162*

slope-intercept form, *p. 162*
standard form, *p. 168*
point-slope form, *p. 180*

▶ Graphic Organizers

You can use a **Definition and Example Chart** to organize information about a concept. Here is an example of a Definition and Example Chart for the vocabulary term *linear equation*.

> **Linear equation:** an equation whose graph is a line
>
> Example
> $$y = 2x + 1$$
>
> Example
> $$y = 8$$
>
> Example
> $$x = -2$$

Choose and complete a graphic organizer to help you study the concept.

1. slope

2. slope of parallel lines

3. proportional relationship

4. slope-intercept form

5. standard form

6. point-slope form

"Here is my Definition and Example Chart**. Wednesday, Thursday, and Friday (Freya's day) are all named after mythical beings."**

Review Vocabulary

- As a review of the chapter vocabulary, have students revisit the vocabulary section in their *Student Journals* to fill in any missing definitions and record examples of each term.

Graphic Organizers

Sample answers:

1.

Slope: the value of the ratio of the change in y (the rise) to the change in x (the run) between any two points, (x_1, y_1) and (x_2, y_2), on a line

Example

Find the slope of the line through the points $(3, 4)$ and $(5, 8)$.

$m = \dfrac{y_2 - y_1}{x_2 - x_1} = \dfrac{8 - 4}{5 - 3} = \dfrac{4}{2} = 2$

Example

Find the slope of the line through the points $(-1, 6)$ and $(3, 6)$.

$m = \dfrac{y_2 - y_1}{x_2 - x_1} = \dfrac{6 - 6}{3 - (-1)} = \dfrac{0}{4} = 0$

Example

Find the slope of the line through the points $(-2, -4)$ and $(-2, 3)$.

$m = \dfrac{y_2 - y_1}{x_2 - x_1} = \dfrac{3 - (-4)}{-2 - (-2)} = \dfrac{7}{0} = $ undefined

2.

Slope of parallel lines: Nonvertical parallel lines have the same slope. All vertical lines are parallel.

Example

Are the lines $y = 2x - 5$ and $y = 2x + 3$ parallel?
Both lines have a slope of 2, so they are parallel.

Example

Are the lines $y = 3x + 7$ and $3x + y = 2$ parallel?
The line $y = 3x + 7$ has a slope of 3 and the line $3x + y = 2$ has a slope of -3, so they are *not* parallel.

Example

Are the lines $y = 2$ and $x = 2$ parallel?
The line $y = 2$ has a slope of 0 and the line $x = 2$ has an undefined slope, so they are *not* parallel.

3–6. Answers at *BigIdeasMath.com*.

List of Organizers

Available at *BigIdeasMath.com*
Definition and Example Chart
Example and Non-Example Chart
Four Square
Information Frame
Summary Triangle

About this Organizer

A **Definition and Example Chart** can be used to organize information about a concept. Students fill in the top rectangle with a term and its definition or description. Students fill in the rectangles that follow with examples to illustrate the term. Each sample answer shows three examples, but students can show more or fewer examples. Definition and Example Charts are useful for concepts that can be illustrated with more than one type of example.

1.

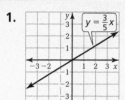

2.

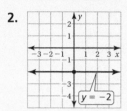

3.

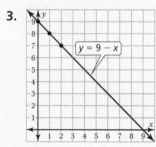

4.

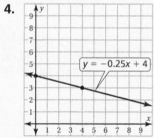

5.

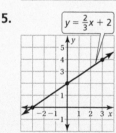

6.

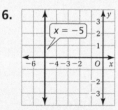

7. a. about $5.75

   b. $5.63

8. See Additional Answers.

9. no; *Sample answer:* The graph
   of $y = x^2$ is not a line.

10. See Additional Answers.

✓ *Chapter Self-Assessment*

The Success Criteria Self-Assessment chart can be found in the
Student Journal or online at *BigIdeasMath.com.*

ELL Support

Allow students to work in pairs to complete the first section of the
Chapter Self-Assessment. Provide graph paper. Once pairs have finished,
check for understanding by asking each pair to display their graphs for
Exercises 1–8 for your review. Have each pair display their answers for
Exercises 7(b) and 8(b) on a whiteboard for your review. Have two pairs
discuss their reasoning in Exercises 9 and 10. Each group should reach an
agreement for their answers. Monitor discussions and provide support.
Use similar techniques to check remaining sections of the Chapter
Self-Assessment.

Common Errors

- **Exercises 1–8** Students may make calculation errors when solving for
  ordered pairs. If they only find two ordered pairs for the graph, they may not
  recognize their mistakes. Encourage students to find at least three ordered
  pairs when drawing a graph.
- **Exercise 2** Students may draw a vertical line through points on the *x*-axis.
  Remind them that the graph of the equation is a horizontal line. Ask students
  to identify the *y*-coordinate for several *x*-coordinates. For example, "What is
  the *y*-coordinate for $x = 5$? $x = 6$? $x = -4$?" Students should answer with
  the same *y*-coordinate each time.
- **Exercise 6** Students may draw a horizontal line through points on the *y*-axis.
  Remind them that the graph of the equation is a vertical line. Ask students
  to identify the *x*-coordinate for several *y*-coordinates. For example, "What is
  the *x*-coordinate for $y = 3$? $y = -1$? $y = 0$?" Students should answer with
  the same *x*-coordinate each time.

Chapter Self-Assessment

As you complete the exercises, use the scale below to rate your understanding of the success criteria in your journal.

1	**2**	**3**	**4**
I do not understand.	I can do it with help.	I can do it on my own.	I can teach someone else.

4.1 Graphing Linear Equations *(pp. 141–146)*

Learning Target: Graph linear equations.

Graph the linear equation.

1. $y = \frac{3}{5}x$

2. $y = -2$

3. $y = 9 - x$

4. $y = -0.25x + 4$

5. $y = \frac{2}{3}x + 2$

6. $x = -5$

7. The equation $y = 0.5x + 3$ represents the cost y (in dollars) of riding in a taxi x miles.

   a. Use a graph to estimate how much it costs to ride 5.25 miles in a taxi.

   b. Use the equation to find exactly how much it costs to ride 5.25 miles in a taxi.

8. The equation $y = 9.5x$ represents the earnings y (in dollars) of an aquarium gift shop employee that works x hours.

   a. Graph the linear equation.

   b. How much does the employee earn for working 40 hours?

9. Is $y = x^2$ a linear equation? Explain your reasoning.

10. The sum S of the exterior angle measures of a polygon with n sides is $S = 360°$.

   a. Plot four points (n, S) that satisfy the equation. Is the equation a linear equation? Explain your reasoning.

   b. Does the value $n = 2$ make sense in the context of the problem? Explain your reasoning.

4.2 Slope of a Line *(pp. 147–154)*

Learning Target: Find and interpret the slope of a line.

Describe the slope of the line. Then find the slope of the line.

11.

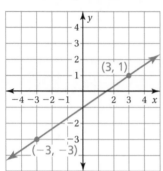

12.

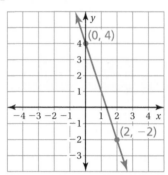

Find the slope of the line through the given points.

13. $(-5, 4), (8, 4)$

14. $(-3, 5), (-3, 1)$

The points in the table lie on a line. Find the slope of the line.

15.

x	0	1	2	3
y	−1	0	1	2

16.

x	−2	0	2	4
y	3	4	5	6

17. How do you know when two lines are parallel? Use an example to justify your answer.

18. Draw a line through the point $(-1, 2)$ that is parallel to the graph of the line in Exercise 11.

4.3 Graphing Proportional Relationships *(pp. 155–160)*

Learning Target: Graph proportional relationships.

Tell whether *x* and *y* are in a proportional relationship. Explain your reasoning. If so, write an equation that represents the relationship.

19.

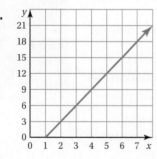

20.

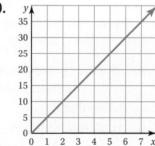

Common Errors

- **Exercises 11 and 12** Students may forget negatives or include them when they are not needed. Remind students that if the line rises from left to right the slope is positive and if the line falls from left to right the slope is negative.
- **Exercises 13–16** Students may find the reciprocal of the slope instead of the slope. Remind students that slope is the change in *y* over the change in *x*.

11. The slope is positive; $\frac{2}{3}$

12. The slope is negative; -3

13. 0

14. undefined

15. 1

16. $\frac{1}{2}$

17. *Sample answer:* Two lines are parallel when they have the same slope but different y-intercepts. The lines $y = 2x + 3$ and $y = 2x - 6$ are parallel with slopes of 2 and y-intercepts of 3 and -6.

18.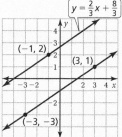

19. no; The line does not pass through the origin.

20. yes; The line passes through the origin; $y = 5x$

21. a. $y = 7.50x$

b. The slope indicates that the unit cost is $7.50 per guest.

c. $75; $7.5(10) = 75$

22.

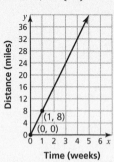

You run 8 miles per week.

23. See Additional Answers.

24. slope: -4; y-intercept: 1

25. slope: $\frac{2}{3}$; y-intercept: -12

26. slope: 0.5; y-intercept: 7

27.

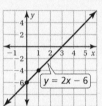

x-intercept: 3

28. See Additional Answers.

29.

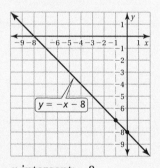

x-intercept: -8

30. See Additional Answers.

31.

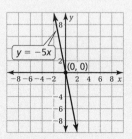

Common Errors

- **Exercises 24–26** Students may forget to include negatives with the slope and/or y-intercept. Remind students to look at the sign in front of the slope and y-intercept. Also remind students that slope-intercept form is $y = mx + b$. This means that if the linear equation has "minus b," then the y-intercept is negative.

- **Exercises 27–29** Students may use the reciprocal of the slope when graphing and may find an incorrect x-intercept. Remind students that slope is *rise* over *run*, so the numerator represents vertical change, not the horizontal change.

21. The cost y (in dollars) to provide food for guests at a dinner party is proportional to the number x of guests attending the party. It costs \$30 to provide food for 4 guests.

   a. Write an equation that represents the situation.

   b. Interpret the slope of the graph of the equation.

   c. How much does it cost to provide food for 10 guests? Justify your answer.

22. The distance y (in miles) you run after x weeks is represented by the equation $y = 8x$. Graph the equation and interpret the slope.

23. You research that hair grows 15 centimeters per year on average. The table shows your friend's hair growth.

Months	1	2	3	4
Hair Growth (centimeters)	1.5	3	4.5	6

   a. Does your friend's hair grow faster than average? Explain.

   b. In the same coordinate plane, graph the average hair growth and the hair growth of your friend. Compare and interpret the steepness of each of the graphs.

4.4 Graphing Linear Equations in Slope-Intercept Form (pp. 161–166)

Learning Target: Graph linear equations in slope-intercept form.

Find the slope and the y-intercept of the graph of the linear equation.

24. $y = -4x + 1$

25. $y = \dfrac{2}{3}x - 12$

26. $y - 7 = 0.5x$

Graph the linear equation. Identify the x-intercept.

27. $y = 2x - 6$

28. $y = -4x + 8$

29. $y = -x - 8$

30. The cost y (in dollars) of one person buying admission to a fair and going on x rides is $y = x + 12$.

   a. Graph the equation.

   b. Interpret the y-intercept and the slope.

31. Graph the linear equation with slope -5 and y-intercept 0.

4.5 Graphing Linear Equations in Standard Form (pp. 167–172)

Learning Target: Graph linear equations in standard form.

Write the linear equation in slope-intercept form.

32. $4x + 2y = -12$

33. $x - y = \frac{1}{4}$

Graph the linear equation.

34. $\frac{1}{4}x + y = 3$

35. $-4x + 2y = 8$

36. $x + 5y = 10$

37. $-\frac{1}{2}x + \frac{1}{8}y = \frac{3}{4}$

38. A dog kennel charges $30 per night to board your dog and $6 for each hour of playtime. The amount of money you spend is given by $30x + 6y = 180$, where x is the number of nights and y is the number of hours of playtime. Graph the equation and interpret the intercepts.

4.6 Writing Equations in Slope-Intercept Form (pp. 173–178)

Learning Target: Write equations of lines in slope-intercept form.

Write an equation in slope-intercept form of the line that passes through the given points.

39.
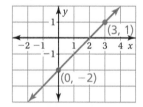

40.
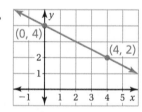

41.

x	y
−2	4
0	1
2	−2
4	−5

42.

x	y
0	−3
1	−1
2	1
3	3

43. Write an equation of the line that passes through $(0, 8)$ and $(6, 8)$.

44. Write an equation of the line that passes through $(0, -5)$ and $(-5, -5)$.

Common Errors

- **Exercises 32–38** Students may use the same operation instead of the opposite operation when writing the equation in slope-intercept form. Remind students of the rules for solving equations.

- **Exercises 32–38** Students may mix up the x- and y-intercepts. Remind students that the x-intercept is the x-coordinate of where the line crosses the x-axis and the y-intercept is the y-coordinate of where the line crosses the y-axis.

- **Exercises 39 and 40** Students may use the reciprocal of the slope or forget a negative sign when writing the equation. Remind them of the definition for slope. Ask students to predict the sign of the slope based on the rise or fall of the line.

- **Exercises 41 and 42** Students may use the reciprocal of the slope when writing the equation. Remind students that slope is the value of the ratio of the change in y to the change in x.

- **Exercises 43 and 44** Students may write the wrong equation when the slope is zero. For example, instead of $y = 8$, students may write $x = 8$. Ask them what is the rise of the graph (zero) and write this in slope-intercept form with the y-intercept as well, $y = 0x + 8$. Then ask students what happens when a variable (or any number) is multiplied by zero. Rewrite the equation as $y = 8$.

32. $y = -2x - 6$ **33.** $y = x - \frac{1}{4}$

34.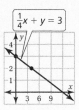

35.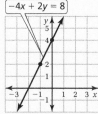

36.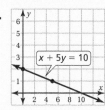

37.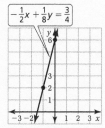

38.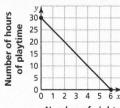

The x-intercept shows that you can board your dog for 6 nights when there are no hours of playtime. The y-intercept shows that you can have 30 hours of playtime for your dog when you do not leave your dog at the kennel for any nights.

39. $y = x - 2$

40. $y = -\frac{1}{2}x + 4$

41. $y = -\frac{3}{2}x + 1$ **42.** $y = 2x - 3$

43. $y = 8$ **44.** $y = -5$

45. $y = \dfrac{1}{2}x + 13$

46. $y - 4 = 3(x - 4)$

47. $y + 8 = -\dfrac{2}{3}(x - 2)$

48. $y = -\dfrac{1}{2}x$

49. $y = 4x - 7$

50. **a.** $y = -200x + 1000$

 b. 1000 ft

 c. 5 min;
$$0 = -200x + 1000$$
$$200x = 1000$$
$$x = 5$$

51. **a.** $y - 214.70 = 29.95(x - 6)$

 b. $35; The equation in slope-intercept form is $y = 29.95x + 35$. The y-intercept represents the installation fee.

52. *Sample answer:* when the slope and a point other than the y-intercept are known; When $(-1, 2)$ and $m = 3$ are given, it requires less steps to write the equation in point-slope form instead of slope-intercept form.

Common Errors

- **Exercises 48–50** Students may use the reciprocal of the slope when writing the equation. Remind students that slope is the change in y over the change in x.

Chapter Resources

Surface Level	Deep Level
Resources by Chapter • Extra Practice • Reteach • Puzzle Time Student Journal • Practice • Chapter Self-Assessment Differentiating the Lesson Tutorial Videos Skills Review Handbook Skills Trainer Game Library	Resources by Chapter • Enrichment and Extension Graphic Organizers Game Library
Transfer Level	
STEAM Video Dynamic Assessment System • Chapter Test	Assessment Book • Chapter Tests A and B • Alternative Assessment • STEAM Performance Task

45. A construction crew is extending a highway sound barrier that is 13 miles long. The crew builds $\frac{1}{2}$ of a mile per week. Write an equation in slope-intercept form that represents the length y (in miles) of the barrier after x weeks.

4.7 Writing Equations in Point-Slope Form (pp. 179–184)

Learning Target: Write equations of lines in point-slope form.

Write an equation in point-slope form of the line that passes through the given point and has the given slope.

46. $(4, 4)$; $m = 3$

47. $(2, -8)$; $m = -\dfrac{2}{3}$

Write an equation in slope-intercept form of the line that passes through the given points.

48. $(-4, 2), (6, -3)$

49.

x	1	2	3
y	-3	1	5

50. The table shows your elevation y (in feet) on a ski slope after x minutes.

x	1	2	3
y	800	600	400

   a. Write an equation that represents your elevation after x minutes.

   b. What is your starting elevation?

   c. After how many minutes do you reach the bottom of the ski slope? Justify your answer.

51. A company offers cable television at $29.95 per month plus a one-time installation fee. The total cost for the first six months of service is $214.70.

   a. Write an equation in point-slope form that represents the total cost you pay for cable television after x months.

   b. How much is the installation fee? Justify your answer.

52. When might it be better to represent an equation in point-slope form rather than slope-intercept form? Use an example to justify your answer.

Practice Test

Find the slope and the y-intercept of the graph of the linear equation.

1. $y = 6x - 5$

2. $y - 1 = 3x + 8.4$

3. $-\dfrac{1}{2}x + 2y = 7$

Graph the linear equation.

4. $y = -\dfrac{1}{2}x - 5$

5. $-3x + 6y = 12$

6. $y = \dfrac{2}{3}x$

7. Which lines are parallel? Explain.

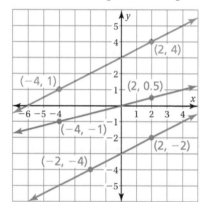

8. The points in the table lie on a line. Find the slope of the line.

x	y
−1	−4
0	−1
1	2
2	5

Write an equation in slope-intercept form of the line that passes through the given points.

9.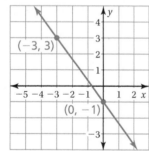

10.

x	y
−2	2
0	2
2	2
4	2

11. Write an equation in point-slope form of the line that passes through $(-4, 1)$ and $(4, 3)$.

12. The number y of new vocabulary words that you learn after x weeks is represented by the equation $y = 15x$.

   a. Graph the equation and interpret the slope.

   b. How many new vocabulary words do you learn after 5 weeks?

   c. How many more vocabulary words do you learn after 6 weeks than after 4 weeks?

13. You used $90 worth of paint for a school float. The amount of money you spend is given by $18x + 15y = 90$, where x is the number of gallons of blue paint and y is the number of gallons of white paint. Graph the equation and interpret the intercepts.

Practice Test Item References

Practice Test Questions	Section to Review
4, 5, 6	4.1
7, 8	4.2
6, 12	4.3
1, 2, 3, 4, 6	4.4
5, 13	4.5
9, 10	4.6
11	4.7

Test-Taking Strategies

Remind students to quickly look over the entire test before they start so that they can budget their time. Students should jot down the formulas for slope-intercept form and point-slope form on the back of their tests before they begin. Have them use the **Stop** and **Think** strategy before they write their answers.

Common Errors

- **Exercises 1–3** Students may forget to include negatives with the slope and/or y-intercept. Remind students to look at the sign in front of the slope and y-intercept. Also remind students that slope-intercept form is $y = mx + b$. This means that if the linear equation has "minus b," then the y-intercept is negative.
- **Exercises 4–6** Students may make calculation errors when solving for ordered pairs. If they only find two ordered pairs for the graph, they may not recognize their mistakes. Encourage students to find at least three ordered pairs when drawing a graph.
- **Exercise 9** Students may write the reciprocal of the slope or forget a negative sign. Remind them of the definition for slope. Ask students to predict the sign of the slope based on the rise or fall of the line.
- **Exercise 10** Students may write the wrong equation when the slope is zero. For example, instead of $y = 2$, students may write $x = 2$. Ask them what is the rise of the graph (zero) and write this in slope-intercept form with the y-intercept as well, $y = 0x + 2$. Then ask students what happens when a variable (or any number) is multiplied by zero. Rewrite the equation as $y = 2$.

1. slope: 6; y-intercept: -5

2. slope: 3; y-intercept: 9.4

3. slope: $\frac{1}{4}$; y-intercept: $\frac{7}{2}$

4.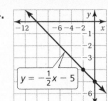

5.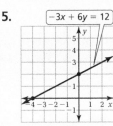

6.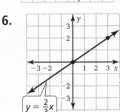

7. The red and green lines are parallel. They both have a slope of $\frac{1}{2}$.

8. 3

9. $y = -\frac{4}{3}x - 1$

10. $y = 2$

11. $y - 3 = \frac{1}{4}(x - 4)$ or

    $y - 1 = \frac{1}{4}(x + 4)$

12. See Additional Answers.

13.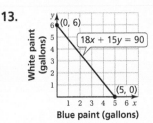

The x-intercept shows that you can buy 5 gallons of blue paint when you do not buy any white paint. The y-intercept shows that you can buy 6 gallons of white paint when you do not buy any blue paint.

Test-Taking Strategies

Available at *BigIdeasMath.com*

After Answering Easy Questions, Relax

Answer Easy Questions First

Estimate the Answer

Read All Choices before Answering

Read Question before Answering

Solve Directly or Eliminate Choices

Solve Problem before Looking at
  Choices

Use Intelligent Guessing

Work Backwards

About this Strategy

When taking a multiple-choice test, be sure to read each question carefully and thoroughly. After reading the question, estimate the answer before trying to solve it.

Cumulative Practice

1. A

2. H

3. C

Item Analysis

1. **A.** Correct answer

   B. The student identifies the slope correctly, but misidentifies the *y*-intercept.

   C. The student identifies the y-intercept correctly, but misidentifies the slope.

   D. The student misidentifies the slope and the *y*-intercept.

2. **F.** The student interchanges the values for *x* and *y*.

   G. The student makes two mistakes with a correct solution (4, 2): assigning a negative value to 2 and interchanging the values for *x* and *y*.

   H. Correct answer

   I. The student makes a mistake with a correct solution (4, 2) and assigns a negative value to 2, forgetting that there is already a minus sign in the equation.

3. **A.** The student reflects the triangle in the *y*-axis.

   B. The student rotates the triangle 180° about the origin.

   C. Correct answer

   D. The student rotates the triangle 90° clockwise about the origin.

4 Cumulative Practice

1. Which equation matches the line shown in the graph?

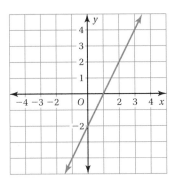

A. $y = 2x - 2$

B. $y = 2x + 1$

C. $y = x - 2$

D. $y = x + 1$

2. Which point lies on the graph of $6x - 5y = 14$?

F. $(-4, -1)$

G. $(-2, 4)$

H. $(-1, -4)$

I. $(4, -2)$

3. You reflect the triangle in the x-axis. What are the coordinates of the image?

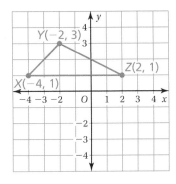

A. $X'(4, 1), Y'(2, 3), Z'(-2, 1)$

B. $X'(4, -1), Y'(2, -3), Z'(-2, -1)$

C. $X'(-4, -1), Y'(-2, -3), Z'(2, -1)$

D. $X'(1, 4), Y'(3, 2), Z'(1, -2)$

4. Which of the following is the equation of a line parallel to the line shown in the graph?

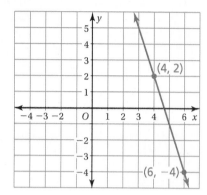

F. $y = 3x - 10$

G. $y = \dfrac{1}{3}x + 12$

H. $y = -3x + 5$

I. $y = -\dfrac{1}{3}x - 18$

5. What is the value of x?

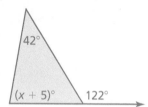

6. An emergency plumber charges $49.00 plus $70.00 per hour of the repair. A bill to repair your sink is $241.50. This can be modeled by $70.00h + 49.00 = 241.50$, where h represents the number of hours for the repair. How many hours did it take to repair your sink?

A. 2.75 hours

B. 3.45 hours

C. 4.15 hours

D. 13,475 hours

7. It costs $40 to rent a car for one day. In addition, the rental agency charges you for each mile driven, as shown in the graph.

Think
Solve
Explain

Part A Determine the slope of the line joining the points on the graph.

Part B Explain what the slope represents.

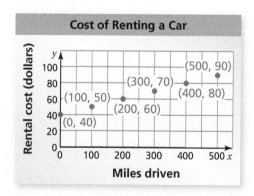

Item Analysis (continued)

4. **F.** The student forgets the negative sign when finding the slope.

   G. The student forgets the negative sign when finding the slope. The student also mixes up rise and run and finds the reciprocal of the slope.

   H. Correct answer

   I. The student mixes up rise and run and finds the reciprocal of the slope.

5. **Gridded Response:** Correct answer: 75

   Common error: The student thinks that the sum of the measures of the exterior angle and two nonadjacent interior angles is equal to 180°. The student writes the equation $(x + 5) + 42 + 122 = 180$ and gets $x = 11$.

6. **A.** Correct answer

   B. The student forgets to subtract 49.00 from each side of the equation and divides 241.50 by 70.00.

   C. The student adds 49.00 to each side of the equation instead of subtracting 49.00 from each side.

   D. The student multiplies each side of the equation by 70.00 instead of dividing each side by 70.00.

7. **2 points** The student's work and explanations demonstrate a thorough understanding of the slope of a line and what it represents. In Part A, the student correctly finds the slope of the line is $\frac{50 - 40}{100 - 0} = \frac{10}{100} = \frac{1}{10} = 0.1$. In Part B, the student correctly states that the slope represents the rental cost per mile driven, $0.10 per mile. The student provides clear and complete work and explanations.

   1 point The student's work and explanations demonstrate a partial but limited understanding of the slope of a line and what it represents. The student provides some correct work and/or explanation. The formula for the slope of a line is misstated, or the student incorrectly states what the slope of the line represents.

   0 points The student provides no response, a completely incorrect or incomprehensible response, or a response that demonstrates insufficient understanding of the slope of a line and what it represents.

4. H

5. 75

6. A

7. *Part A* 0.1

   Part B $0.10 per mile

8. 6

9. F

10. B

11. H

Item Analysis (continued)

8. **Gridded Response:** Correct answer: 6

   Common error: The student correctly adds 5 to each side, but incorrectly adds $2x$ to $4x$ instead of subtracting and gets $x = 2$.

9. **F.** Correct answer

   G. The student reflects the trapezoid in the y-axis.

   H. The student rotates the trapezoid 180° about the origin.

   I. The student rotates the figure 90° counterclockwise about the origin.

10. **A.** The student divides M by 3, but does not divide $(K + 7)$ by 3.

    B. Correct answer

    C. The student divides K by 3, but does not divide 7 by 3.

    D. The student subtracts 7 instead of adding 7 to each side.

11. **F.** The student incorrectly sets up the proportion as $\frac{30}{100} = \frac{d}{12}$ or $\frac{30}{100} = \frac{12}{d}$.

    G. The student incorrectly thinks that the corresponding side lengths are the same length.

    H. Correct answer

    I. The student incorrectly sets up the proportion as $\frac{d}{100} = \frac{30}{12}$ or $\frac{100}{d} = \frac{12}{30}$.

8. What value of x makes the equation true?

$$7 + 2x = 4x - 5$$

9. Trapezoid *KLMN* is graphed in the coordinate plane shown.

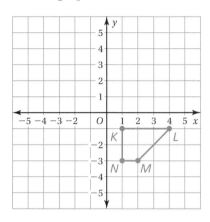

Rotate Trapezoid *KLMN* 90° clockwise about the origin. What are the coordinates of point M', the image of point M after the rotation?

F. $(-3, -2)$ **G.** $(-2, -3)$

H. $(-2, 3)$ **I.** $(3, 2)$

10. Solve the formula $K = 3M - 7$ for M.

A. $M = K + 7$ **B.** $M = \dfrac{K + 7}{3}$

C. $M = \dfrac{K}{3} + 7$ **D.** $M = \dfrac{K - 7}{3}$

11. What is the distance d across the canyon?

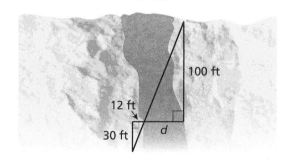

100 ft

12 ft

30 ft

d

F. 3.6 ft   **G.** 12 ft

H. 40 ft   **I.** 250 ft

Systems of Linear Equations

Chapter Learning Target:
Understand systems of linear equations.

Chapter Success Criteria:
- ▢ I can identify a linear equation.
- ▢ I can describe a system of linear equations.
- ◼ I can solve a system of linear equations.
- ◼ I can model solving systems with different numbers of solutions.

STEAM Video: "Gold Alloys"

Laurie's Notes

Chapter 5 Overview

Students have graphed linear equations, solved multi-step equations, and rewritten equations and formulas. These are foundational skills for systems of linear equations.

The chapter begins with solving systems of linear equations by graphing. The equations in a system describe a relationship between two variables, such as the cost of an adult ticket and the cost of a student ticket. Contextual problems help students make sense of and interpret graphical representations.

In the next two sections, students will study algebraic methods of solving systems, substitution and elimination. Continue to relate the solutions to the points of intersection of the graphs of the equations. Students should also be checking their solutions in *both* original equations.

Some of the exercises ask students to choose a method of solving. Students should understand that they can use any of the methods, and that even within a particular method there are different ways to solve a system.

If the system is $y = -2x + 1$ and $3x - y = 4$:

Substitution

$$3x - y = 4$$
$$3x - (-2x + 1) = 4$$
$$3x + 2x - 1 = 4 \qquad y = -2x + 1$$
$$5x - 1 = 4 \qquad y = -2(1) + 1$$
$$5x = 5 \qquad y = -2 + 1$$
$$x = 1 \qquad y = -1$$

So, the solution of the system is $(1, -1)$.

Graphing

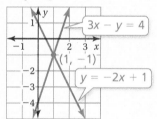

Elimination

Rewrite $y = -2x + 1$ as $2x + y = 1$.

$$2x + y = 1 \qquad y = -2x + 1$$
$$\underline{3x - y = 4} \qquad y = -2(1) + 1$$
$$5x \quad = 5 \qquad y = -2 + 1$$
$$x = 1 \qquad y = -1$$

It is important to ask, "Which method makes sense for the given system?"

System	Which Method Makes Sense?
$y = 3x - 4$ $y = -2x + 1$	Graphing and substitution are good choices because both equations are solved for y.
$y = 2x - 4$ $7x - 2y = 5$	Substitution is a good choice because one equation is solved for y.
$3x - 4y = 15$ $5x + 4y = -7$	Elimination is a good choice because a pair of like terms has the opposite coefficients.

In the last section, students will study special systems of linear equations, where there is no solution because the lines are parallel or there are infinitely many solutions because the lines coincide (are the same).

Chapter Opener	1 Day
Section 1	2 Days
Section 2	2 Days
Section 3	2 Days
Section 4	2 Days
Connecting Concepts	1 Day
Chapter Review	1 Day
Chapter Test	1 Day
Total Chapter 5	12 Days
Year-to-Date	73 Days

Chapter Learning Target

Understand systems of linear equations.

Chapter Success Criteria

- Identify a linear equation.
- Describe a system of linear equations.
- Solve a system of linear equations.
- Model solving systems with different numbers of solutions.

Chapter 5 Learning Targets and Success Criteria

Section	Learning Target	Success Criteria
5.1 Solving Systems of Linear Equations by Graphing	Understand how to solve systems of linear equations by graphing.	• Graph a linear equation. • Find the point where two lines intersect. • Solve a system of linear equations by graphing.
5.2 Solving Systems of Linear Equations by Substitution	Understand how to solve systems of linear equations by substitution.	• Solve a linear equation in two variables for either variable. • Solve a system of linear equations by substitution.
5.3 Solving Systems of Linear Equations by Elimination	Understand how to solve systems of linear equations by elimination.	• Add or subtract equations in a system. • Use the Multiplication Property of Equality to produce equivalent equations. • Solve a system of linear equations by elimination.
5.4 Solving Special Systems of Linear Equations	Solve systems with different numbers of solutions.	• Determine the number of solutions of a system. • Solve a system of linear equations with any number of solutions.

Progressions

Through the Grades		
Grade 7	**Grade 8**	**High School**
• Write, graph, and solve one-step equations. • Solve two-step equations. Compare algebraic solutions to arithmetic solutions.	• Understand that the solution of a system of two linear equations in two variables corresponds to the point of intersection of their graphs. • Solve systems of two linear equations in two variables graphically and algebraically. • Solve real-world mathematical problems leading to systems of two linear equations in two variables.	• Use systems of linear equations and linear inequalities to solve real-life problems. • Solve systems of linear equations by graphing, by substitution, and by elimination. • Solve systems of nonlinear equations by graphing and algebraically. • Approximate solutions of nonlinear systems. • Graph and write systems of linear inequalities.

Through the Chapter				
Standard	**5.1**	**5.2**	**5.3**	**5.4**
8.EE.C.8a Understand that solutions to a system of two linear equations in two variables correspond to points of intersection of their graphs, because points of intersection satisfy both equations simultaneously.	●			★
8.EE.C.8b Solve systems of two linear equations in two variables algebraically, and estimate solutions by graphing the equations. Solve simple cases by inspection.	●	●	●	★
8.EE.C.8c Solve real-world and mathematical problems leading to two linear equations in two variables.	●	●	●	★

Key

▲ = preparing   ★ = complete
● = learning   ■ = extending

Laurie's Notes

STEAM Video

1. a. 37.5%

b. 14.4 karats

2. a. 50%

b. 75%

Performance Task

Sample answer: to provide customers with jewelry in their desired price range

Mathematical Practices

Students have opportunities to develop aspects of the mathematical practices throughout the chapter. Here are some examples.

1. **Make Sense of Problems and Persevere in Solving Them**
   5.3 Math Practice note, *p. 211*

2. **Reason Abstractly and Quantitatively**
   5.2 Exercise 24, *p. 210*

3. **Construct Viable Arguments and Critique the Reasoning of Others**
   5.4 Exercise 22, *p. 224*

4. **Model with Mathematics**
   5.2 Exercise 17, *p. 210*

5. **Use Appropriate Tools Strategically**
   5.1 Math Practice note, *p. 199*

6. **Attend to Precision**
   5.4 Exercise 26, *p. 224*

7. **Look for and Make Use of Structure**
   5.4 Math Practice note, *p. 219*

8. **Look for and Express Regularity in Repeated Reasoning**
   5.2 Exercise 26, *p. 210*

STEAM Video

Before the Video

- To introduce the STEAM Video, read aloud the first paragraph of Gold Alloys and discuss the question with your students.
- ❓ "What are other uses of alloys?"

During the Video

- The video shows Tony and Enid discussing gold dental fillings.
- ❓ Pause the video at 1:02 and ask, "What is an amalgam?" a mixture of metal dust and mercury made at room temperature
- ❓ "What is an alloy?" a mixture of metals melted at high temperature
- Watch the remainder of the video.

After the Video

- ❓ Ask, "What are karats?" a way to measure gold proportions
- ❓ "How many karats are equal to 100% gold?" 24 karats
- Explain that a karat is a measure of the purity of gold and 1 karat is equivalent to $\frac{1}{24}$ part of pure gold in an alloy.
- Have students work with a partner to answer Questions 1 and 2.
- In Question 2(a), some students may reason that because the mixture contains equal parts of 10-karat and 14-karat gold, the resulting alloy is $\frac{10 + 14}{2} =$ 12-karat gold, or 50% gold. Others may find the average karats: $\frac{2(10) + 2(14)}{2 + 2} = \frac{20 + 28}{4} = \frac{48}{4} =$ 12-karat gold, or 50% gold.
- In Questions 2(b), some students may use proportional reasoning and find $\frac{6}{10}(24) + \frac{4}{10}(9) =$ 18-karat gold, or 75% gold. Others may find the average karats: $\frac{6(24) + 4(9)}{6 + 4} = \frac{144 + 36}{10} = \frac{180}{10} =$ 18-karat gold, or 75% gold.
- As students discuss and answer the questions, listen for understanding of using proportional relationships to find a percent gold or number of karats.
- **Note:** Students are not yet ready to solve systems of equations. After completing the chapter, students will make the connection between alloys and systems in the *STEAM Video Performance Task*.

Performance Task

- Use this information to spark students' interest and promote thinking about real-life problems.
- ❓ Ask, "Why might a jeweler need to create a mixture with a specific proportion of gold?"
- After completing the chapter, students will have gained the knowledge needed to complete "Mixing Alloys."

Gold Alloys

An *alloy* is a mixture of different metals melted together at high temperatures. A dental filling is created using a gold alloy. What are other uses of alloys?

Watch the STEAM Video "Gold Alloys." Then answer the following questions.

1. Enid says that the proportion of gold in an alloy can be measured in *karats*. For example, 24 karats represents 100% gold and 18 karats represents 75% gold.

   a. A dental filling is 9 karats. What percent of the filling is gold?

   b. A watch is 60% gold. How many karats is the watch?

2. What percent gold is each described alloy?

   a. A mixture of 2 grams 10-karat gold and 2 grams 14-karat gold

   b. A mixture of 6 grams 24-karat gold and 4 grams 9-karat gold

Mixing Alloys

After completing this chapter, you will be able to use the concepts you learned to answer the questions in the *STEAM Video Performance Task*. You will be given a list of gold alloys available at a jewelry store.

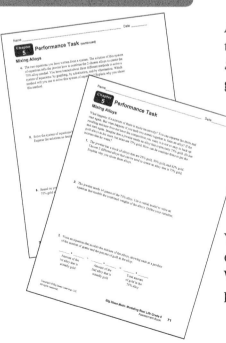

Alloys at Jewelry Store

Alloy 1:   **25% gold**

Alloy 2:   **50% gold**

Alloy 3:   **82% gold**

You will use a *system of equations* to determine the amounts of the given alloys that a jeweler needs to create a new alloy. Why might a jeweler need to create a mixture with a specific proportion of gold?

Getting Ready for Chapter 5

Chapter Exploration

1. **Work with a partner. Your family starts a bed-and-breakfast. You spend $500 fixing up a bedroom to rent. The cost for food and utilities is $10 per night. Your family charges $60 per night to rent the bedroom.**

   a. Write an equation that represents the costs.

Cost, C (in dollars)	=	$10 per night	⋅	Number of nights, x	+	$500

   b. Write an equation that represents the revenue (income).

Revenue, R (in dollars)	=	$60 per night	⋅	Number of nights, x

   c. A set of two (or more) linear equations is called a *system of linear equations*. Write the system of linear equations for this problem.

2. **Work with a partner. Use a graphing calculator to solve the system.**

   $y = 10x + 500$ Equation 1

   $y = 60x$ Equation 2

   a. Enter the equations into your calculator. Then graph the equations. What is an appropriate window?

   b. On your graph, how can you determine which line is the graph of which equation? Label the equations on the graph shown.

   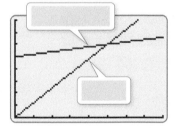

   c. Visually estimate the point of intersection of the graphs.

   d. To find the solution, use the *intersect* feature to find the point of intersection.

   The solution is (☐ , ☐).

Vocabulary

The following vocabulary terms are defined in this chapter. Think about what each term might mean and record your thoughts.

system of linear equations   solution of a system of linear equations

Laurie's Notes

Check out the digital flash cards.
BigIdeasMath.com

Chapter Exploration

- For Exercise 1, discuss what is known about your costs and your income.
- **Financial Literacy:** Do not assume that students are knowledgeable about concepts such as *costs* (fixed and variable) and *revenue* (income). Explain these words as you use them.
- In part (a), point out to students that the units in the verbal model agree. This means that "dollars per night × nights" is equal to dollars. So, the units in the equation are dollars = dollars + dollars.
- Ask a pair of students to share the equations they wrote.
- Discuss the definition for a *system of linear equations*.
- In Exercise 2, remind students that they have used a graphing calculator to graph equations. Now they will enter both equations in the equation editor.
- Discuss how to set an appropriate viewing window.
- **MP2 Reason Abstractly and Quantitatively:** In part (b), students should be able to reason that the steeper graph has the greater slope.
- Students familiar with the *trace* feature of their graphing calculators can use it to answer part (c).
- If students have never used the *intersect* feature of their graphing calculators, then they may need help with part (d).
- **Extension:** If time allows, ask students to name the following.
    - "Name a solution of Equation 1 that is *not* a solution of Equation 2."
      Sample answer: (0, 500)
    - "Name a solution of Equation 2 that is *not* a solution of Equation 1."
      Sample answer: (0, 0)
    - "Name a solution of *both* equations." (10, 600)
    - "Name an ordered pair that is *not* a solution of either equation."
      Sample answer: (10, 10)

Vocabulary

- These terms represent some of the vocabulary that students will encounter in Chapter 5. Discuss the terms as a class.
- Where have students heard the term *system of linear equations* outside of a math classroom? In what contexts? Students may not be able to write the actual definition, but they may write phrases associated with a *system of linear equations*.
- Allowing students to discuss these terms now will prepare them for understanding the terms as they are presented in the chapter.
- When students encounter a new definition, encourage them to write in their *Student Journals*. They will revisit these definitions during the Chapter Review.

Topics for Review

- Combining Like Terms
- Coordinate Plane
- Evaluating Algebraic Expressions
- Graphing Linear Equations
- Opposites
- Ordered Pairs
- Slope-Intercept Form
- Solving Simple and Multi-Step Equations
- Substitution
- Writing Equations

ELL Support

Write the word *system* on the board. Ask students to explain what it means and give an example of a system. Guide students to understand that a system is a complex whole formed by many parts. Explain that a system of linear equations involves more than one linear equation in the same variables and students will learn different strategies for solving systems in this chapter.

Chapter Exploration

1. **a.** $C = 10x + 500$

   b. $R = 60x$

   c. $C = 10x + 500$
      $R = 60x$

2. **a.** *Sample answer:* Xmin = 0,
      Xmax = 16,
      Ymin = 0,
      Ymax = 800

   b. *Sample answer:* Equation 2 has a greater slope and passes through the origin.

   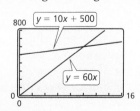

   c. (10, 600)

   d. (10, 600)

Learning Target

Understand how to solve systems of linear equations by graphing.

Success Criteria

- Graph a linear equation.
- Find the point where two lines intersect.
- Solve a system of linear equations by graphing.

Warm Up

Cumulative, vocabulary, and prerequisite skills practice opportunities are available in the *Resources by Chapter* or at *BigIdeasMath.com*.

ELL Support

Explain that graphing is one way to solve a system of linear equations. Ask students what they know about graphing. Explain that the word *graph* comes from the Greek language and refers to writing or drawing. Whenever students see the word *graph*, they should know that it refers to a visual representation of information.

Exploration 1

a. See Additional Answers.

b. 37.5 min; 62.5%; *Sample answer:*
$$\frac{5}{3}x = x + 25$$
$$x = 37.5$$
Headphones: $p = \frac{5}{3}(37.5) = 62.5$
Phone: $p = 37.5 + 25 = 62.5$

c. one, none, or infinitely many; The graphs of two linear equations either intersect at one point (one solution), are parallel and never intersect (no solution), or are the same (infinitely many solutions).

d–e. See Additional Answers.

Laurie's Notes

Preparing to Teach

- Students should know how to graph linear equations in two variables. Now they will begin to solve systems of linear equations by graphing.
- **MP1 Make Sense of Problems and Persevere in Solving Them:** Students will investigate a situation that can be represented by a system of equations. They will have the opportunity to use different approaches to solve the system and discover the form and meaning of the solution. Encourage students to persevere in the different solution approaches.

Motivate

- Write the following "geometric equations" on the board. Explain that each square represents the same quantity, as does each triangle. Have students work with a partner to figure out what the square and triangle represent.

$$\square + \square + \square + \triangle = 47$$
$$\square - \triangle = 1$$

- Ask a pair of students to share their solution and explain how they figured out the answer. $\triangle = 11$, $\square = 12$; Explanations will vary.
- Share with students that this is the type of problem they will be working on throughout Chapter 5.

Exploration 1

- **Big Idea:** The point of intersection of the graphs of the equations is the solution to the problem.
- The equations provide an opportunity for students to review slope and *y*-intercept from Chapter 4.
- **?** "What do you know about these two equations?" Students may say that they represent the battery power each device has after *x* minutes or that the equations are both linear. They may also recognize that the first equation has a slope of $\frac{5}{3}$ and a *y*-intercept of 0, and the second equation has a slope of 1 and a *y*-intercept of 25.
- Make sure students understand what *p* represents. For example, $p = 50$ means that the battery power of the device is 50%.
- Have students complete the table and then answer part (b).
- Allow time for students to think about part (c) before discussing it as a class. If students struggle with part (c), you could have them complete part (d) first. Students should realize that the equations only share one solution.
- The concepts of no solution and infinitely many solutions are presented in Section 5.4, but students can begin to think about these cases now.
  - **?** "Do you think it is possible for two equations to have more than one solution? Explain." Yes, if their graphs are the same line.
  - **?** "Do you think it is possible for two equations to have no solution? Explain." Yes, if the graphs are parallel lines (or never intersect).
- **MP5 Use Appropriate Tools Strategically:** Part (e) is optional, but graphing calculators are used to check answers and solve several exercises throughout this chapter.

5.1 Solving Systems of Linear Equations by Graphing

Learning Target: Understand how to solve systems of linear equations by graphing.

Success Criteria:
- I can graph a linear equation.
- I can find the point where two lines intersect.
- I can solve a system of linear equations by graphing.

EXPLORATION 1

Using a Graph to Solve a Problem

Work with a partner. You charge your headphones and your phone. The equations below represent the battery powers $p\%$ of the devices after x minutes of charging.

$$p = \frac{5}{3}x \qquad \text{Headphones}$$

$$p = x + 25 \qquad \text{Phone}$$

a. You check the battery power of each device every 10 minutes. Copy and complete the table. How do the devices' battery powers compare?

x (minutes)	10	20	30	40	50	60
p (headphones)						
p (phone)						

b. After how much time do the devices have the same battery power? What is the battery power at that time? Justify your answer.

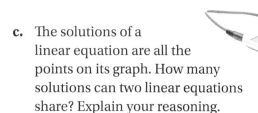

c. The solutions of a linear equation are all the points on its graph. How many solutions can two linear equations share? Explain your reasoning.

Math Practice

Use Technology to Explore

What features of a graphing calculator can you use to check your answers in part (b)?

d. Graph the battery power equations in the same coordinate plane. What do you notice?

e. **MP USING TOOLS** Use a graphing calculator to check your answers in part (b). Explain your method.

Key Vocabulary

system of linear
  equations, *p. 200*
solution of a system of
  linear equations,
  p. 200

A **system of linear equations** is a set of two or more linear equations in the same variables. An example is shown below. A system of linear equations is also called a *linear system*.

$$y = x + 1 \qquad \text{Equation 1}$$
$$y = 2x - 7 \qquad \text{Equation 2}$$

A **solution of a system of linear equations** in two variables is an ordered pair that is a solution of each equation in the system. The solution of a system of linear equations is the point of intersection of the graphs of the equations.

EXAMPLE 1 ## Solving a System of Linear Equations by Graphing

Solve the system by graphing. $\qquad y = 2x + 5 \qquad$ Equation 1

$\qquad\qquad\qquad\qquad\qquad\qquad y = -4x - 1 \qquad$ Equation 2

Graph each equation.

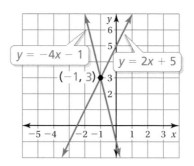

$y = -4x - 1$
$y = 2x + 5$
$(-1, 3)$

Always check that the estimated intersection point is a solution of each equation.

The graphs appear to intersect at $(-1, 3)$. Check that the point is a solution of each equation.

Equation 1	Equation 2
$y = 2x + 5$	$y = -4x - 1$
$3 \stackrel{?}{=} 2(-1) + 5$	$3 \stackrel{?}{=} -4(-1) - 1$
$3 = 3$ ✓	$3 = 3$ ✓

Check

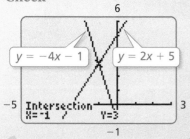

$y = -4x - 1$
$y = 2x + 5$
Intersection
X=-1   Y=3

▶ The solution is $(-1, 3)$.

Try It **Solve the system by graphing.**

1. $y = x - 1$ **2.** $y = -5x + 14$ **3.** $y = x$

$\quad\;\; y = -x + 3$ $y = x - 10$ $y = 2x + 1$

Laurie's Notes

Scaffolding Instruction

- Students explored different approaches to solving a system of equations. Now they will solve systems of linear equations by graphing.
- **Emerging:** Students should be able to substitute values into equations to check a solution, but they need practice graphing systems of linear equations to find the solution. They will benefit from guided instruction for the definitions and examples.
- **Proficient:** Students understand that the point of intersection of the graphs of the equations is the solution of the system of equations. They should review the definitions before proceeding to the Self-Assessment exercises.

Discuss

- Define a **system of linear equations**.
- ❓ "What is a solution of a linear equation in two variables?" an ordered pair that satisfies the equation
- Define a **solution of a system of linear equations**.

EXAMPLE 1

- ❓ Before graphing, ask, "Will the lines intersect? Explain." Yes, the slopes are different.
- Work through the problem as shown.
- This is a great time to review graphing an equation in slope-intercept form. Students may choose different methods of graphing. They may plot the point for the y-intercept and then find a second point on the graph using the slope or make a table of values and plot ordered pairs. Students may find the x- and y-intercepts and plot the ordered pairs. You could assign different methods to students and have them display their graphs to the class to show that each method results in the same graphs.
- ❓ If students choose their methods, ask, "Why did you select the method you did?" Answers will vary.
- ❓ "Should you trust your eyes? What if the solution is actually $(-1.1, 3.2)$?" Checking the solution in the original equations will confirm your estimate. It will also reinforce the need to always check solutions.

Try It

- **Neighbor Check:** Have students work independently and then have their neighbors check their work. Have students discuss any discrepancies.

ELL Support

After demonstrating Example 1, have students work in pairs to discuss and complete Try It Exercises 1–3. Provide graph paper and list the steps students need to take: (1) Graph one equation, (2) Graph the other equation, (3) Estimate the point of intersection, and (4) Check that the point is a solution of each equation. Expect students to perform according to their language levels.

Beginner: Complete each step by graphing and writing.

Intermediate: Use phrases or simple sentences to discuss the process.

Advanced: Use detailed sentences to discuss the process.

Scaffold instruction to support all students in their learning. Learning is individualized and you may want to group students differently as they move in and out of these levels with each skill and concept. Student self-assessment and feedback help guide your instructional decisions about how and when to layer support for all students to become proficient learners.

Extra Example 1

Solve the system by graphing.
$$y = -2x + 2$$
$$y = 3x - 3$$
$(1, 0)$

Try It

1. $(2, 1)$
2. $(4, -6)$
3. $(-1, -1)$

Extra Example 2

Solve the system by graphing.

$3x + 2y = 4$

$y = -3x - 1$

$(-2, 5)$

Try It

4. $(-3, 5)$

5. $(-2, -7)$

6. $(4, -8)$

EXAMPLE 2

- In this example, the second equation is given in standard form instead of slope-intercept form.
- Have students graph both equations in a coordinate plane.
- Students need to decide how they will graph the two equations. You could suggest that students use a method they did not use in Example 1.
- Remind students to check that the point of intersection is a solution of each equation.

Try It

- **Neighbor Check:** Have students work independently and then have their neighbors check their work. Have students discuss any discrepancies.

Formative Assessment Tip

Think-Alouds

This technique is used when you want to hear how well partners comprehend a process involved with solving a problem. It is important to model the process first so that students have a sense of what is expected.

Think-Alouds give students the opportunity to hear the metacognitive processes used by someone who is a proficient problem solver. Hearing someone else describe a process using mathematical language will improve all students' problem-solving abilities.

Use this technique with a multi-step problem. Model using a starter sentence such as: "The problem is asking …," "I can use the strategy of …," "The steps I will use in solving this problem are …," "This problem is similar to …,"or "I can check my answer by …."

You can use *Think-Alouds* for a variety of problem types. Listen for comprehension of skills, concepts, procedures, and precision of language.

Self-Assessment
for Concepts & Skills

7. $(-2, -1)$

8. $(1, 4)$

9. $(-1, 2)$

10. The point of intersection is a solution of each equation in the system.

11. What are the solutions of each equation?; all points on the line $y = -2x + 8$, all points on the line $y = 4x + 2$; $(1, 6)$

✓ Self-Assessment *for Concepts & Skills*

- **Neighbor Check:** Have students work independently and then have their neighbors check their work. Have students discuss any discrepancies.
- ◉ **Think-Alouds:** Say, "I can find the solution of a linear system by …" Ask Partner A to think aloud for Partner B to hear how to find the solution of a linear equation. Then ask Partner B to think aloud for Partner A. Students should include all necessary steps and use precise mathematical language.

ELL Support

Allow students to work in pairs for extra support. Ask pairs to display their graphs for Exercises 7–9 for your review. Have two pairs form a group to discuss their explanations for Exercises 10 and 11. Monitor discussions and provide support as needed. Review explanations as a class.

The Success Criteria Self-Assessment chart can be found in the *Student Journal* or online at *BigIdeasMath.com*.

EXAMPLE 2 **Solving a System of Linear Equations by Graphing**

Solve the system by graphing. $y = 2x - 2$ Equation 1

$-x + 2y = -4$ Equation 2

Graph each equation.

The graphs appear to intersect at $(0, -2)$.
Check that the point is a solution of
each equation.

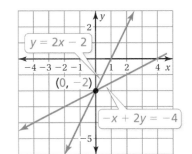

Math Practice

Communicate Precisely

Write a system that has the same solution as the system in Example 2. Explain your method to a classmate.

Equation 1	Equation 2
$y = 2x - 2$	$-x + 2y = -4$
$-2 \overset{?}{=} 2(0) - 2$	$-0 + 2(-2) \overset{?}{=} -4$
$-2 = -2$ ✓	$-4 = -4$ ✓

▶ The solution is $(0, -2)$.

Try It Solve the system by graphing.

4. $y = -4x - 7$

$x + y = 2$

5. $x - y = 5$

$-3x + y = -1$

6. $\dfrac{1}{2}x + y = -6$

$6x + 2y = 8$

 Self-Assessment *for Concepts & Skills*

*Solve each exercise. Then rate your understanding of the success criteria
in your journal.*

SOLVING A SYSTEM OF LINEAR EQUATIONS Solve the system by graphing.

7. $y = x + 1$

$y = 4x + 7$

8. $3x - y = -1$

$y = -x + 5$

9. $x + 2y = 3$

$-x + 3y = 7$

10. **WRITING** Explain why the solution of a system of linear equations is
the point of intersection of their graphs.

11. **DIFFERENT WORDS, SAME QUESTION** Which is different? Find
"both" answers.

$y = -2x + 8$ Equation 1
$y = 4x + 2$ Equation 2

What is the solution
of the system?

At what point do the graphs
of the equations intersect?

What ordered pair makes
both equations true?

What are the solutions
of each equation?

EXAMPLE 3 **Modeling Real Life**

In football, each extra point made is 1 point and each field goal made is 3 points. A kicker makes a total of 8 extra points and field goals in a game and scores 12 points. How many field goals did the kicker make?

Use a verbal model to write a system of linear equations. Let x represent the number of extra points and let y represent the number of field goals.

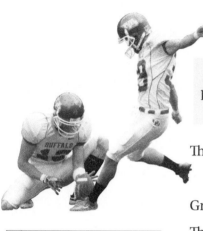

Number of extra points, x	$+$	Number of field goals, y	$=$	Total number of kicks

Points per extra point	$\cdot$	Number of extra points, x	$+$	Points per field goal	$\cdot$	Number of field goals, y	$=$	Total number of points

The system is:

$x + y = 8$ Equation 1

$x + 3y = 12$ Equation 2

Graph each equation.

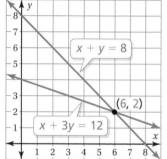

The graphs appear to intersect at $(6, 2)$. Check that the point is a solution of each equation.

Equation 1	Equation 2
$x + y = 8$	$x + 3y = 12$
$6 + 2 \overset{?}{=} 8$	$6 + 3(2) \overset{?}{=} 12$
$8 = 8$ ✓	$12 = 12$ ✓

▷ The solution is $(6, 2)$. So, the kicker made 2 field goals.

Self-Assessment *for Problem Solving*

Solve each exercise. Then rate your understanding of the success criteria in your journal.

12. Your family attends a comic convention. Each autograph costs $20 and each photograph costs $50. Your family buys a total of 5 autographs and photographs for $160. How many photographs does your family buy?

13. **DIG DEEPER!** Two apps on your phone take away points for using your phone at school. You have 140 points on the first app and 80 points on the second app when a school day begins. Each time you check your phone, you lose 10 points on your first app and p points on your second app. After you check your phone ten times, you have the same number of points on each app. Find the value of p.

Laurie's Notes

EXAMPLE 3

- **MP4 Model with Mathematics:** Ask a student to read the problem. Discuss vocabulary as needed. Ask questions to clarify the problem such as, "How many times did the kicker score points? How many of each type of kick was made? How many points were scored on field goals? What do the variables represent in the context of the problem?"

- Students can be careless when defining variables. Be sure students use the definitions from the problem statement: $x =$ the *number* of extra points made and $y =$ the *number* of field goals made.

- This is a great time to review graphing an equation in standard form. One method is to graph the line using the intercepts $(0, y)$ and $(x, 0)$. A second method is to rewrite the equation in slope-intercept form.

 "What is your estimate for the point of intersection?" *Sample answer:* (6, 2)

- Remind students to check the solution in *both* equations.

- If time permits, use a graphing calculator to graph the equations.

✓ Self-Assessment for Problem Solving

- Encourage students to use a Four Square to complete these exercises. Until students become comfortable with the problem-solving plan, they may only be ready to complete the first square.

- Check students' work. Have volunteers explain each problem.

The Success Criteria Self-Assessment chart can be found in the *Student Journal* or online at *BigIdeasMath.com*.

Closure

- **Exit Ticket:** Solve by graphing.

$$y = 2x + 3$$
$$y = -x + 6$$

(1, 5)

Extra Example 3

In Example 3, the kicker makes a total of 6 extra points and field goals in a game and scores 12 points. How many extra points did the kicker make?
3 extra points

Self-Assessment
for Problem Solving

12. 2 photographs

13. 4

Learning Target

Understand how to solve systems of linear equations by graphing.

Success Criteria

- Graph a linear equation.
- Find the point where two lines intersect.
- Solve a system of linear equations by graphing.

T-202

Review & Refresh

1. $y + 4 = 1(x - 3)$

2. $y - 6 = \frac{3}{5}(x - 5)$

3. $y - 0 = -\frac{1}{4}(x - 1)$

4. $c = 8$

5. $y = 4$

6. $x = 11$

Concepts, Skills, & Problem Solving

7. See Additional Answers.

8. 3.5 weeks; 185 tickets

9. $(-1, 7)$

10. $(-5, 1)$

11. $(-4, -3)$

12. $(12, 15)$

13. $(5, 22)$

14. $(8, 1)$

15. $(5, 1.5)$

16. $(1, 3)$

17. $(-6, 2)$

18. no; The solution should be a point (x, y).

Assignment Guide and Concept Check

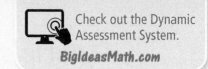
Scaffold assignments to support all students in their learning progression. The suggested assignments are a starting point. Continue to assign additional exercises and revisit with spaced practice to move every student toward proficiency.

Level	Assignment 1	Assignment 2
Emerging	3, 6, 7, 8, 9, 11, 13, 15, 17, 18	10, 12, 14, 16, 19, 20, 24, 26
Proficient	3, 6, 7, 8, 10, 12, 14, 16, 17, 18	19, 20, 21, 22, 23, 24, 26, 27
Advanced	3, 6, 7, 8, 10, 12, 14, 16, 17, 18	20, 21, 22, 23, 24, 25, 26, 27

- Assignment 1 is for use after students complete the Self-Assessment for Concepts & Skills.
- Assignment 2 is for use after students complete the Self-Assessment for Problem Solving.
- The red exercises can be used as a concept check.

Review & Refresh Prior Skills

Exercises 1–3   Writing an Equation in Point-Slope Form
Exercises 4–6   Solving an Equation

Common Errors

- **Exercises 9–14** Students may not show enough of the graph to see where the lines intersect. Encourage them to extend their lines until they intersect.
- **Exercises 15–17** Students may try to visually estimate the point of intersection of the graphs on their graphing calculator screens. Remind them to use the *intersect* feature to estimate the point of intersection.

5.1 Practice

Go to **BigIdeasMath.com** to get HELP with solving the exercises.

▶ Review & Refresh

Write an equation in point-slope form of the line that passes through the given point and has the given slope.

1. $(3, -4)$; $m = 1$

2. $(5, 6)$; $m = \dfrac{3}{5}$

3. $(1, 0)$; $m = -\dfrac{1}{4}$

Solve the equation. Check your solution.

4. $\dfrac{3}{4}c - \dfrac{1}{4}c + 3 = 7$

5. $5(2 - y) + y = -6$

6. $6x - 3(x + 8) = 9$

▶▶ Concepts, Skills, & Problem Solving

USING A GRAPH TO SOLVE A PROBLEM The equations below represent the numbers y of tickets sold after x weeks for two different local music festivals. (See Exploration 1, p. 199.)

$y = 10x + 150$	Country Music Festival
$y = 20x + 115$	Pop Music Festival

7. You check the ticket sales for both festivals each week for 10 weeks. Create a table for the ticket sales each week. How do the festivals' ticket sales compare?

8. After how much time have the same number of tickets been sold for both festivals? What is the number of tickets sold at that time?

SOLVING A SYSTEM OF LINEAR EQUATIONS Solve the system by graphing.

9. $y = 2x + 9$
$y = 6 - x$

10. $y = -x - 4$
$y = \dfrac{3}{5}x + 4$

11. $y = 2x + 5$
$y = \dfrac{1}{2}x - 1$

12. $x + y = 27$
$y = x + 3$

13. $y - x = 17$
$y = 4x + 2$

14. $x - y = 7$
$0.5x + y = 5$

USING A GRAPHING CALCULATOR Use a graphing calculator to solve the system.

15. $2.2x + y = 12.5$
$1.4x - 4y = 1$

16. $2.1x + 4.2y = 14.7$
$-5.7x - 1.9y = -11.4$

17. $-1.1x - 5.5y = -4.4$
$0.8x - 3.2y = -11.2$

18. **MP YOU BE THE TEACHER** Your friend solves the system of linear equations below. Is your friend correct? Explain your reasoning.

$y = 0.5x + 1$ Equation 1
$y = -x + 7$ Equation 2

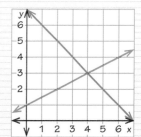

The solution of the linear system is $x = 4$.

19. **MP MODELING REAL LIFE** You have a total of 42 math and science problems for homework. You have 10 more math problems than science problems. How many problems do you have in each subject? Use a system of linear equations to justify your answer.

20. **MP PROBLEM SOLVING** A generator contains 60 gallons of fuel and uses 2.5 gallons per hour. A more efficient power generator contains 40 gallons of fuel and uses 1.5 gallons per hour. After how many hours do the generators have the same amount of fuel? Which generator runs longer? Justify your answers.

21. **MP PROBLEM SOLVING** You and your friend are in a canoe race. Your friend is a half mile in front of you and paddling 3 miles per hour. You are paddling 3.4 miles per hour.

   a. You are 8.5 miles from the finish line. How long will it take you to catch up to your friend?

   b. You both maintain your paddling rates for the remainder of the race. How far ahead of your friend will you be when you cross the finish line?

OPEN-ENDED Write a system of linear equations that fits the description. Use a graph to justify your answer.

22. The solution of the system is a point on the line $y = -9x + 1$.

23. The solution of the system is $(3, -1)$.

24. **DIG DEEPER!** A graph of a system of two linear equations is shown. Write the system of linear equations represented by the graph. What is the solution of the system?

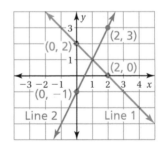

25. **CRITICAL THINKING** Your friend is trying to grow her hair as long as her cousin's hair. The table shows their hair lengths (in inches) in different months.

Month	Friend's Hair (in.)	Cousin's Hair (in.)
March	4	7
August	6.5	9

   a. Write a system of linear equations that represents this situation. Let $x = 1$ represent January.

   b. Will your friend's hair ever be as long as her cousin's hair? If so, in what month?

26. **MP REASONING** Is it possible for a system of two linear equations to have multiple solutions? Explain your reasoning.

27. **GEOMETRY** The length of a rectangle is 8 feet more than its width. The perimeter of the rectangle is 72 feet. Find the width of the rectangle.

Mini-Assessment

Solve the system by graphing.

1. $y = 2x + 6$
$y = -2x - 2$
$(-2, 2)$

2. $y = 3x + 9$
$y = -\frac{1}{4}x - 4$
$(-4, -3)$

3. $2x + y = 4$
$y = x - 5$
$(3, -2)$

4. A wallet contains 23 bills. All the bills are $1 bills and $5 bills. There are 7 more $1 bills than $5 bills. How much money does the wallet contain? $55

Section Resources

Surface Level	Deep Level
Resources by Chapter • Extra Practice • Reteach • Puzzle Time Student Journal • Self-Assessment • Practice Differentiating the Lesson Tutorial Videos Skills Review Handbook Skills Trainer	Resources by Chapter • Enrichment and Extension Graphic Organizers Dynamic Assessment System • Section Practice

Concepts, Skills, & Problem Solving

19. 26 math problems, 16 science problems;
$x + y = 42$
$x = y + 10$
Solution: $(26, 16)$

20. 20 h;
$y = -2.5x + 60$
$y = -1.5x + 40$
Solution: $(20, 10)$;
the more efficient power generator; The x-intercept is greater.

21. **a.** 1.25 h

   b. 0.5 mi

22. *Sample answer:* $y = -9x + 1$
$y = x + 1$

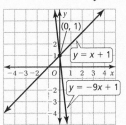

23. *Sample answer:* $y = x - 4$
$y = \frac{1}{3}x - 2$

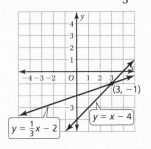

24. $y = 2x - 1$
$y = -x + 2$;
$(1, 1)$

25. **a.** $y = 0.5x + 2.5$
$y = 0.4x + 5.8$

   b. yes; month 33

26. yes; The two linear equations could have the same slope and same y-intercept.

27. 14 ft

Learning Target

Understand how to solve systems of linear equations by substitution.

Success Criteria

- Solve a linear equation in two variables for either variable.
- Solve a system of linear equations by substitution.

Warm Up

Cumulative, vocabulary, and prerequisite skills practice opportunities are available in the *Resources by Chapter* or at *BigIdeasMath.com*.

ELL Support

Ask students what a substitute teacher is. Guide them to understand that it is a teacher who takes the place of another teacher. Explain that when they use substitution to solve, one way to write a value takes the place of another way to write the value. Demonstrate this visually by writing an example of substitution on the board.

Exploration 1

a. System 1: $\mathbb{D} = 2$, $\bigstar = 3$;
   System 2: $\bigcirc = 2$, $\maltese = -1$;
   Answers will vary.

b. $(-1, 4)$; Solve one of the equations for one variable. Substitute the expression for this variable into the other equation and solve for the other variable. Then, substitute this value into one of the original equations and solve for the remaining variable.

Exploration 2

a–b. Check students' work.

Laurie's Notes

STATE STANDARDS
COMMON CORE
8.EE.C.8b, 8.EE.C.8c

Preparing to Teach

- Students should know how to solve linear equations and evaluate expressions at a specified value of the variable. Now they will explore how to solve a system of linear equations by substitution.
- **MP1 Make Sense of Problems and Persevere in Solving Them:** Students will investigate another technique for solving a system of equations. Students have knowledge of systems, solutions of systems, and symbolic manipulation skills. Students will have the opportunity to make different attempts at solving a system. Encourage them to persevere and try different approaches.

Motivate

- Play a game of "Zip, Zap, Zoop," which is a combination of several games.
- **Directions:** Stand in a circle. Count around the circle. When your number is a *multiple* of 4, say, "**Zip**" instead of the number. When your number *contains* a 4, say, "**Zap.**" When your number is *both* a multiple of 4 *and* contains a 4, say, "**Zoop.**"
- The counting will go: 1, 2, 3, zoop, 5, 6, 7, zip, 9, 10, 11, zip, 13, zap, . . .
- Students are *substituting* an expression for a number.
- The faster they count the funnier it becomes!

Exploration 1

- In part (a), students should see that they need to substitute $\mathbb{D} + \mathbb{D} - 1$ for each $\bigstar$ in the Equation 2 in System 1. If they struggle with finding an entry point, give them some hints.
  - Tell them to think about the game they just played, where they replaced certain numbers with words.
  - ❓ Ask, "If $y + 2x = 12$ and $x = 3$, how can you find y?" Substitute 3 for x and solve for y.
  - ❓ Ask, "How could you use a similar method to solve System 1?" Substitute $\mathbb{D} + \mathbb{D} - 1$ for each $\bigstar$ in the Equation 2 and solve for $\mathbb{D}$.
- In System 2, students could solve for either symbol first. Asking students to compare their methods with others will highlight different approaches.
- In part (b), students can solve for either variable first. Select several students to share and compare different methods.

Exploration 2

- Students can struggle with trying to write any equation that passes through a given point. For the example $(3, 4)$, ask students to think about the relationship between the two numbers: x is one less than y, so adding 1 to x is equal to y. This suggests the equation $y = x + 1$. A second equation can be generated by thinking, "You can double the x-value and subtract 2 to get the y-value." This suggests $y = 2x - 2$.
- Take time for students to share their strategies for generating their systems and to solve each other's systems.

5.2 Solving Systems of Linear Equations by Substitution

Learning Target: Understand how to solve systems of linear equations by substitution.

Success Criteria:
• I can solve a linear equation in two variables for either variable.
• I can solve a system of linear equations by substitution.

EXPLORATION 1

Solving Systems Algebraically

Work with a partner.

a. Find the value of each symbol in the systems below. Compare your solution methods with other pairs of students.

System 1:
$$\text{☽} + \text{☽} - 1 = \bigstar \quad \text{Equation 1}$$
$$\text{☽} + \bigstar + \bigstar = 8 \quad \text{Equation 2}$$

System 2:
$$\text{☼} - \text{❄} = 3 \quad \text{Equation 1}$$
$$\text{☼} + \text{❄} = 1 \quad \text{Equation 2}$$

Math Practice

Make a Plan
How does your work in part (a) help you make a plan for solving the system in part (b)?

b. Use a method similar to your method in part (a) to solve the system below. Then explain how to solve a system of linear equations in two variables algebraically.

$$3x + y = 1 \quad \text{Equation 1}$$
$$x - y = -5 \quad \text{Equation 2}$$

EXPLORATION 2

Writing and Solving Systems of Equations

Work with a partner. Roll two number cubes that are different colors. Then write the ordered pair shown by the number cubes.

a. Write a system of linear equations that has your ordered pair as its solution. Explain how you found your system.

b. Exchange systems with another pair of students. Use a method from Exploration 1 to solve the system.

x-value

y-value

Another way to solve a system of linear equations is to use substitution to obtain an equation in one variable. Then solve the resulting equation and substitute to find the value of the other variable.

EXAMPLE 1 **Solving a System of Linear Equations by Substitution**

Solve the system by substitution.

$$y = 2x - 4 \qquad \text{Equation 1}$$
$$7x - 2y = 5 \qquad \text{Equation 2}$$

Step 1: Notice that Equation 1 is solved for y. So, you can substitute $2x - 4$ for y in Equation 2 to obtain an equation in one variable, x. Then solve the equation to find the value of x.

$7x - 2y = 5$	Equation 2
$7x - 2(2x - 4) = 5$	Substitute $2x - 4$ for y.
$7x - 4x + 8 = 5$	Distributive Property
$3x + 8 = 5$	Combine like terms.
$3x = -3$	Subtract 8 from each side.
$x = -1$	Divide each side by 3.

Step 2: Substitute -1 for x in Equation 1 and solve for y.

$y = 2x - 4$	Equation 1
$= 2(-1) - 4$	Substitute -1 for x.
$= -2 - 4$	Multiply.
$= -6$	Subtract.

You can substitute -1 for x in either equation. Using Equation 2,
$$7(-1) - 2y = 5$$
$$-2y = 12$$
$$y = -6.$$

▶ The solution is $(-1, -6)$.

Check

Equation 1
$$y = 2x - 4$$
$$-6 \overset{?}{=} 2(-1) - 4$$
$$-6 = -6 \checkmark$$

Equation 2
$$7x - 2y = 5$$
$$7(-1) - 2(-6) \overset{?}{=} 5$$
$$5 = 5 \checkmark$$

Try It Solve the system by substitution. Check your solution.

1. $y = 2x + 3$
   $y = 5x$

2. $4x + 2y = 0$
   $y = \dfrac{1}{2}x - 5$

3. $x = 5y + 3$
   $2x + 4y = -1$

Laurie's Notes

Scaffolding Instruction

- Students explored how to use substitution to solve a system of equations. They will continue to practice using substitution as a method for solving linear systems.
- Students need to understand that they are expanding their ability to solve linear systems. They know how to solve by graphing but other methods are often more efficient. Substitution is just another tool in their toolkits.
- **Emerging:** Students may struggle with substitution. Students often find the value of one variable but forget to substitute that value to find the value of the other variable. They need more practice solving linear systems using substitution.
- **Proficient:** Students can use substitution to solve linear systems. They should proceed to the Self-Assessment exercises.
- Avoid providing students with a list of steps to follow. That can turn into a procedure rather than a thought process. Also, you should not mandate that students always substitute the first equation into the second. When students look at a system, they should be thinking, "How can I obtain an equation in one variable from this system?" As they learn additional methods for solving systems, they will need to ask themselves, "What is the best way to solve this system?"

EXAMPLE 1

- Write Equation 1 and Equation 2.
- **?** "In what form is Equation 1 written?" slope-intercept form
- **?** "In what form is Equation 2 written?" standard form
- Say, "Equation 1 is already solved for y, so you can substitute the expression $2x - 4$ for y in Equation 2."
- **MP6 Attend to Precision:** Students may get sloppy and say they are "plugging in for y." "Plugging in" is not a mathematical operation or process. It is better to say that they are "substituting for y," so they become familiar with the mathematical terminology they are expected to know.
- **?** After solving for x, ask, "What does $x = -1$ mean in the context of this problem?" The x-coordinate of the solution is -1.
- **?** "How can you find the y-coordinate of the solution?" Substitute -1 for x in one of the original equations and solve for y.
- Check the solution in *both* equations.
- Demonstrate another way to solve the system, perhaps solving Equation 2 for y before substituting. This will help show students why they should stop and think about how they want to approach the problem before solving it.

Try It

- Note that in all of these systems, one of the variables has already been solved for explicitly.

Scaffold instruction to support all students in their learning. Learning is individualized and you may want to group students differently as they move in and out of these levels with each skill and concept. Student self-assessment and feedback help guide your instructional decisions about how and when to layer support for all students to become proficient learners.

Extra Example 1

Solve the system by substitution.
$y = 3x - 4$
$5x - 2y = 10$
$(-2, -10)$

Try It

1. $(1, 5)$
2. $(2, -4)$
3. $\left(\dfrac{1}{2}, -\dfrac{1}{2}\right)$

Solve the system using any method.
$$3y = 2x - 8$$
$$4x + 3y = 7$$
$$(2.5, -1)$$

Try It

4. $(0, 2)$; Explanations will vary.

5–6. See Additional Answers.

Formative Assessment Tip

Quick Write

This technique allows students to write about a process or concept in their own words. Give students 2–4 minutes to respond to a short writing prompt, or sentence stem, relating to the lesson. Then collect the responses and review the information. *Quick Write* not only provides you a quick assessment of your students' level of understanding, but it also helps students become more aware of their own learning.

ELL Support

For the Self-Assessment for Concepts & Skills exercises, allow students to work in pairs. Have pairs display their solutions for Exercises 8–13 on whiteboards for your review. Have two pairs form a group to discuss their explanations for Exercise 7 and their methods for Exercises 11–13.

Self-Assessment
for Concepts & Skills

7. yes; The solution is the same regardless of the method you use.

8. $(6, -2)$ 9. $(8, 3)$

10. $(-4, -1)$

11. $(1, 2)$; Explanations will vary.

12. $(3, 0.5)$; Explanations will vary.

13. See Additional Answers.

Laurie's Notes

EXAMPLE 2

- Write Equation 1 and Equation 2.
- ❓ "Which method would you use to solve this system?" Give sufficient *Wait Time* before soliciting answers. Some students may want to solve Equation 2 for y and then substitute $2x - 5$ for y in Equation 1. Others may suggest solving Equation 2 for x and then substituting $\frac{1}{2}y + 2\frac{1}{2}$ for x in Equation 1. Some may even suggest solving by graphing. Explain that graphing would require solving both equations for y first, which produces equations that are not the most convenient to graph.
- ❓ Discuss and compare the different methods that students suggest. If they do not suggest substituting $y + 5$ for $2x$ in Equation 1, ask, "Are there any terms that appear in both equations?"
- ❓ "Which method is most efficient?" Answers will vary.
- Work through the solution as shown.
- Remind students to check the solution in *both* equations.
- ❓ Ask, "Why is the solution always an ordered pair?" The solution of a system of equations is the point of intersection of the graphs of the equations. Even if students are not graphing the equations, it is important that they relate the solution to the point of intersection.
- ❓ Have students solve the system using the method described in the push-pin note. Then ask, "Which do you prefer?" Answers will vary.
- **Extension:** Write the system on the board.
  $$2x = 2y + 1 \quad \text{Equation 1}$$
  $$4x = 3y + 1 \quad \text{Equation 2}$$
  - ❓ "How would you solve this system using substitution?" Students will likely say to solve for one of the variables first.
  - ❓ "Is there an equivalent equation that could replace Equation 1 that would make it easier to solve the system?" *Sample answer:* $4x = 4y + 2$
  - ❓ "Will the resulting system be equivalent to the original?" yes
  - Solve the system by substituting $4y + 2$ for $4x$ in Equation 2 to get $4y + 2 = 3y + 1$, solve for y, and substitute -1 for y in $2x = 2y + 1$ to solve for x. So, the solution is $\left(-\frac{1}{2}, -1\right)$. This previews some of the thinking that goes on in the next section.

Try It

- **Neighbor Check:** Have students work independently and then have their neighbors check their work. Have students discuss any discrepancies.

✔ Self-Assessment *for Concepts & Skills*

- Check students' work for Exercises 8–13. It is likely that some students will solve for x and others for y. When students have finished, ask two volunteers to demonstrate each method at the board.
- If time is a concern, you may want to skip Exercises 10 and 13.
- ⊙ **Quick Write:** To solve a system of linear equations by substitution…

The Success Criteria Self-Assessment chart can be found in the *Student Journal* or online at *BigIdeasMath.com*.

EXAMPLE 2 **Solving a System of Linear Equations**

Solve the system using any method.

$2x + 3y = -3$	Equation 1
$2x = y + 5$	Equation 2

Step 1: Both equations have a term of $2x$. So, one solution method is to substitute $y + 5$ for $2x$ in Equation 1 and solve to find the value of y.

$2x + 3y = -3$	Equation 1
$y + 5 + 3y = -3$	Substitute $y + 5$ for $2x$.
$4y + 5 = -3$	Combine like terms.
$4y = -8$	Subtract 5 from each side.
$y = -2$	Divide each side by 4.

Step 2: Substitute -2 for y in Equation 2 and solve for x.

$2x = y + 5$	Equation 2
$2x = -2 + 5$	Substitute -2 for y.
$2x = 3$	Add.
$x = 1.5$	Divide each side by 2.

> The solution is $(1.5, -2)$.

Math Practice

Calculate Accurately

Solve the system using a different substitution. Which method do you prefer?

Try It Solve the system. Explain your choice of method.

4. $y = -3x + 2$
   $y = 2$

5. $4y = x$
   $x + 4y = -8$

6. $2x + 2y = 1$
   $-x + 2y = -3$

 Self-Assessment *for Concepts & Skills*

Solve each exercise. Then rate your understanding of the success criteria in your journal.

7. **MP REASONING** Does solving a system of linear equations by graphing give the same solution as solving by substitution? Explain.

SOLVING A SYSTEM OF LINEAR EQUATIONS Solve the system by substitution. Check your solution.

8. $y = x - 8$
   $y = 2x - 14$

9. $x = 2y + 2$
   $2x - 5y = 1$

10. $x - 5y = 1$
   $-2x + 9y = -1$

CHOOSING A SOLUTION METHOD Solve the system. Explain your choice of method.

11. $y = -x + 3$
   $y = 2x$

12. $0.5x + y = 2$
   $0.5x = 1 + y$

13. $x = 5y$
   $y = 22 - 2x$

EXAMPLE 3 **Modeling Real Life**

You are planning a birthday party. You buy a total of 50 turkey burgers and veggie burgers for $90.00. You pay $2.00 per turkey burger and $1.50 per veggie burger. How many of each burger do you buy?

Use a verbal model to write a system of linear equations. Let x represent the number of turkey burgers and let y represent the number of veggie burgers.

Number of turkey burgers, x	$+$	Number of veggie burgers, y	$=$	Total number of burgers

Cost per turkey burger	$\cdot$	Number of turkey burgers, x	$+$	Cost per veggie burger	$\cdot$	Number of veggie burgers, y	$=$	Total cost

The system is: $x + y = 50$ Equation 1

$2x + 1.5y = 90$ Equation 2

Step 1: One solution method is to rewrite Equation 1 as $x = 50 - y$. Then substitute $50 - y$ for x in Equation 2 and solve to find the value of y.

$2x + 1.5y = 90$	Equation 2
$2(50 - y) + 1.5y = 90$	Substitute $50 - y$ for x.
$100 - 2y + 1.5y = 90$	Distributive Property
$-0.5y = -10$	Simplify.
$y = 20$	Divide each side by -0.5.

Check

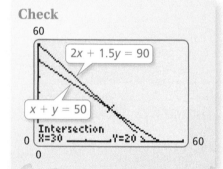

Step 2: Substitute 20 for y in Equation 1 and solve for x.

$x + y = 50$	Equation 1
$x + 20 = 50$	Substitute 20 for y.
$x = 30$	Subtract 20 from each side.

▷ You buy 30 turkey burgers and 20 veggie burgers.

Self-Assessment for Problem Solving

Solve each exercise. Then rate your understanding of the success criteria in your journal.

14. To stock your school store, you buy a total of 25 sweatshirts and hats for $172.50. You pay $8.00 per sweatshirt and $2.50 per hat. How many of each item do you buy?

15. **DIG DEEPER!** The length of a volleyball court is twice its width. The perimeter of the court is 180 feet. Find the area of the volleyball court. Justify your answer.

Laurie's Notes

EXAMPLE 3

❓ MP2 Reason Abstractly and Quantitatively: Ask a student to read the problem. Then ask, "Is it possible that you buy only turkey burgers or only veggie burgers? Explain." No, you spend $90, but 50 turkey burgers would cost $100 and 50 veggie burgers would cost $75.

- Students can be careless when defining variables. Be sure they use:
  - x = number of turkey burgers
  - y = number of veggie burgers

❓ "There are two equations, each with two variables. Can you solve for one of the variables in either equation?" yes

❓ "Is there a choice that might be easier than another? Explain." Yes, it may be easiest to solve for x or y in Equation 1 because both coefficients are 1 and there are no decimals.

- Work through the problem as shown.
- If time permits, solve the system again, solving for y in Step 1. Compare the answers.

❓ "Could this system be solved by graphing?" yes

❓ "Which method is more convenient? Explain." substitution; Graphing would not be as convenient because of the decimal coefficient in Equation 2.

✅ Self-Assessment for Problem Solving

- The goal for all students is to feel comfortable with the problem-solving plan. It is important for students to problem-solve in class, where they may receive support from you and their peers. Keep in mind that some students may only be ready for the first step.
- Have students read the problems and then work with a partner to set up the systems of linear equations. Students should solve the systems independently and check their solutions.

The Success Criteria Self-Assessment chart can be found in the *Student Journal* or online at *BigIdeasMath.com*.

Closure

◉ Discuss students' responses to the *Quick Write* they completed in the Self-Assessment for Concepts & Skills. Encourage students to use *Accountable Language Stems* to clarify any misunderstandings.

Extra Example 3

A weightlifter uses a total of 12 plates to add 260 pounds to a bar. He uses 45-pound plates and 10-pound plates. How many of each plate does he use?
four 45-pound plates
eight 10-pound plates

Self-Assessment
for Problem Solving

14. 20 sweatshirts, 5 hats

15. 1800 ft^2;
$\ell = 2w$
$2\ell + 2w = 180$
$\ell = 60, w = 30$
Area $= \ell w = (60)(30) = 1800$

Learning Target

Understand how to solve systems of linear equations by substitution.

Success Criteria

- Solve a linear equation in two variables for either variable.
- Solve a system of linear equations by substitution.

Review & Refresh

1. $(4, 5)$
2. $(-1, 4)$
3. $(3, -5)$
4. B

Concepts, Skills, & Problem Solving

5. ☽ $= 7$, ★ $= 4$
6. ☼ $= -5$, ❄ $= -3$
7. $(2, -2)$
8. $(6, 17)$
9. $\left(-2, -\dfrac{9}{2}\right)$
10. $(4, 1)$
11. $(-6.5, -3)$
12. $\left(\dfrac{1}{4}, 6\right)$
13. $(-3, -3)$
14. $(4, 2.5)$
15. $(6, -3)$
16. a. $x + y = 64$
    $x = y + 14$

    b. 39 students; 25 students

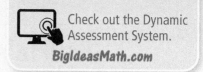

Check out the Dynamic Assessment System.

BigIdeasMath.com

Assignment Guide and Concept Check

Scaffold assignments to support all students in their learning progression. The suggested assignments are a starting point. Continue to assign additional exercises and revisit with spaced practice to move every student toward proficiency.

Level	Assignment 1	Assignment 2
Emerging	3, 4, 5, 7, 9, 11, 13, 15, 19	6, 8, 10, 12, 14, 16, 17, 20, 25
Proficient	3, 4, 6, 8, 10, 12, 14, 19, 20	16, 17, 18, 21, 23, 24, 25
Advanced	3, 4, 6, 8, 10, 12, 14, 20, 21	17, 18, 22, 23, 24, 25, 26

- Assignment 1 is for use after students complete the Self-Assessment for Concepts & Skills.
- Assignment 2 is for use after students complete the Self-Assessment for Problem Solving.
- The red exercises can be used as a concept check.

Review & Refresh Prior Skills

Exercises 1–3 Solving a System of Linear Equations by Graphing
Exercise 4 Finding Angle Measures

Common Errors

- **Exercises 7–15** Students may find one coordinate of the solution and stop. Remind them that the solution of a system of linear equations is a coordinate pair representing both an x-value and a y-value.
- **Exercises 7–15** Students may solve one of the equations for one of the variables and then substitute that expression into the same equation instead of the other equation. For example, in Exercise 11, students might solve the first equation for y, $y = 2x + 10$, and then substitute $2x + 10$ for y in $2x = y - 10$ and get $2x = (2x + 10) - 10$, or $2x = 2x$. Remind students to always substitute the expression into the *other* equation.

5.2 Practice

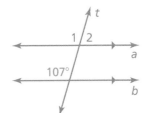

? Go to *BigIdeasMath.com* to get HELP with solving the exercises.

▶ **Review & Refresh**

Solve the system by graphing.

1. $y = 2x - 3$
$y = -x + 9$

2. $6x + y = -2$
$y = -3x + 1$

3. $4x + 2y = 2$
$3x = 4 - y$

4. Use the figure to find the measure of $\angle 2$.

    A. $17°$
    B. $73°$
    C. $83°$
    D. $107°$

▶▶ **Concepts, Skills, & Problem Solving**

SOLVING A SYSTEM ALGEBRAICALLY Find the value of each symbol in the system.
(See Exploration 1, p. 205.)

5. ☽ $+ 1 = $ ★ $+$ ★   Equation 1
    ☽ $= 3 + $ ★   Equation 2

6. ☼ $-$ ❅ $= -2$ Equation 1
    ☼ $-$ ❅ $= 1 + $ ❅   Equation 2

SOLVING A SYSTEM OF LINEAR EQUATIONS Solve the system by substitution. Check your solution.

7. $y = x - 4$
$y = 4x - 10$

8. $y = 2x + 5$
$y = 3x - 1$

9. $x = 2y + 7$
$3x - 2y = 3$

10. $4x - 2y = 14$
$y = \frac{1}{2}x - 1$

11. $2x = y - 10$
$2x + 7 = 2y$

12. $8x - \frac{1}{3}y = 0$
$12x + 3 = y$

13. $y - x = 0$
$2x - 5y = 9$

14. $x + 4y = 14$
$3x + 4y = 22$

15. $-2x - 5y = 3$
$3x + 8y = -6$

16. **MP MODELING REAL LIFE** There are a total of 64 students in a filmmaking club and a yearbook club. The filmmaking club has 14 more students than the yearbook club.

    a. Write a system of linear equations that represents this situation.

    b. How many students are in the filmmaking club? the yearbook club?

17. **MP MODELING REAL LIFE** A drama club earns $1040 from a production by selling 64 adult tickets and 132 student tickets. An adult ticket costs twice as much as a student ticket.

    a. Write a system of linear equations that represents this situation.

    b. What is the cost of each ticket?

18. **OPEN-ENDED** Write a system of linear equations that has the ordered pair $(1, 6)$ as its solution.

CHOOSING A SOLUTION METHOD Solve the system. Explain your choice of method.

19. $y - x = 4$
    $x + y = 6$

20. $0.5x + y = 4$
    $0.5x - y = -1$

21. $y = 2x + 5$
    $y = -3x$

22. **CRITICAL THINKING** A system consists of two different proportional relationships. What is the solution of the system? Justify your answer.

23. **GEOMETRY** The measure of the obtuse angle in the isosceles triangle is two and a half times the measure of one of the acute angles. Write and solve a system of linear equations to find the measure of each angle.

24. **MP NUMBER SENSE** The sum of the digits of a two-digit number is 8. When the digits are reversed, the number increases by 36. Find the original number.

25. **DIG DEEPER!** A hospital employs a total of 77 nurses and doctors. The ratio of nurses to doctors is $9 : 2$. How many nurses are employed at the hospital? How many doctors are employed at the hospital?

26. **MP REPEATED REASONING** A DJ has a total of 1075 dance, rock, and country songs on her system. The dance selection is three times the rock selection. The country selection has 105 more songs than the rock selection. How many songs on the system are dance? rock? country?

Common Errors

- **Exercises 19–21** Students may find one coordinate of the solution and stop. Remind them that the solution of a system of linear equations is a coordinate pair representing both an *x*-value and a *y*-value.

Mini-Assessment

Solve the system of linear equations by substitution. Check your solution.

1. $y = 3x - 2$
   $y = -x + 6$
   $(2, 4)$

2. $2y + 8 = x$
   $8x + y = -21$
   $(-2, -5)$

3. $4x + 3y = 26$
   $2x - 3y = -14$
   $(2, 6)$

4. You spend $56 on food and clothes. You spend $18 more on clothes than on food.

   a. Write a system of linear equations that represents this situation.
   $x + y = 56$
   $y = x + 18$

   b. How much do you spend on each?
   food: $19
   clothes: $37

Section Resources

Surface Level	Deep Level
Resources by Chapter • Extra Practice • Reteach • Puzzle Time Student Journal • Self-Assessment • Practice Differentiating the Lesson Tutorial Videos Skills Review Handbook Skills Trainer	Resources by Chapter • Enrichment and Extension Graphic Organizers Dynamic Assessment System • Section Practice
Transfer Level	
Dynamic Assessment System • Mid-Chapter Quiz	Assessment Book • Mid-Chapter Quiz

 Concepts, Skills, & Problem Solving

17. **a.** $x = 2y$
    $64x + 132y = 1040$

    b. adult tickets: $8, student tickets: $4

18. *Sample answer:* $y = x + 5$
    $y = -2x + 8$

19. $(1, 5)$; Explanations will vary.

20. $(3, 2.5)$; Explanations will vary.

21. $(-1, 3)$; Explanations will vary.

22. $(0, 0)$; *Sample answer:* The graph of any proportional relationship passes through the point $(0, 0)$.

23. $y = 2.5x$
    $2x + y = 180$;
    acute angles: $40°$,
    obtuse angle: $100°$

24. 26

25. 63 nurses; 14 doctors

26. 582 songs; 194 songs; 299 songs

Learning Target

Understand how to solve systems of linear equations by elimination.

Success Criteria

- Add or subtract equations in a system.
- Use the Multiplication Property of Equality to produce equivalent equations.
- Solve a system of linear equations by elimination.

Warm Up

Cumulative, vocabulary, and prerequisite skills practice opportunities are available in the *Resources by Chapter* or at *BigIdeasMath.com*.

ELL Support

Provide students with examples of elimination from everyday life, such as sports teams that lose playoff games or individuals voted off a reality show. If possible, have them provide their own examples. Then ask students how they think elimination is used to solve a system of linear equations. Have students compare their guesses to what they learn about this strategy in the lesson.

Exploration 1

a. Add the equations; no; Adding the equations will only produce an equation in one variable when the equations in the system have one pair of like terms with opposite coefficients.

b. System 1: yes, $(1, -2)$; System 2: no; *Sample answer:* Replace Equation 2 with $6x - 4y = 26$; $(3, -2)$

c. Answers will vary.

Laurie's Notes

STATE STANDARDS
8.EE.C.8b, 8.EE.C.8c

Preparing to Teach

- **MP1 Make Sense of Problems and Persevere in Solving Them:** Students have the prerequisite knowledge for investigating a third technique for solving a system of linear equations. They will use more than one approach. Encourage students to persevere and try to understand why these approaches work.
- There are multiple avenues for solving a system using the elimination technique. Students may solve the system using several different approaches, all of which can lead to the same answer.

Motivate

- Draw a sketch of the two balance scales on the board. Make it clear that the right sides represent 13 pounds of weight and 5 pounds of weight.

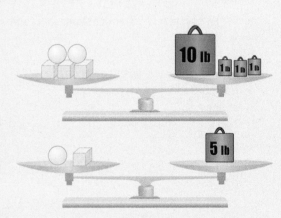

- Have students draw a sketch of a balance scale with 4 cubes and 3 balls on the left and 18 pounds on the right. Relate this to adding equations.
- **?** Ask, "Is this scale balanced? Explain." Yes, if you add equal weights to each side of a balanced scale, then the scale remains balanced.
- Ask students to draw a sketch of a balance scale with 2 cubes and 1 ball on the left and 8 pounds on the right. Relate this to subtracting equations.
- **?** Ask, "Is this scale balanced? Explain." Yes, if you subtract equal weights from both sides of a balanced scale, then the scale remains balanced.

Exploration 1

- The main goal of this exploration is for students to discover that they can add corresponding sides of equations in a system to eliminate a variable and solve the system.
- Allow time for students to examine the original system. Students may recognize this system from Exploration 1 in Section 5.2, but it is good for them to see several methods for solving the same system.
- In part (a), emphasize that students should solve the system using a method other than substitution or graphing.
- If students cannot find an entry point, have them write the system and then write $4x = -4$ below it.
- **?** Ask, "Is there are way to obtain $4x = -4$ from the original system? Explain." Yes, add the two equations together.
- **?** "How do you know that $4x = -4$ is an equivalent equation?" Addition Property of Equality
- In part (b), many students will add the two equations in System 1. Ask some students to subtract and compare the results.
- **?** "How can you obtain an equation in one variable in System 2?" *Sample answer:* Multiply Equation 2 by 2 and then add the two equations together.
- Remind students to write the solution as an ordered pair.

5.3 Solving Systems of Linear Equations by Elimination

Learning Target: Understand how to solve systems of linear equations by elimination.

Success Criteria:
- I can add or subtract equations in a system.
- I can use the Multiplication Property of Equality to produce equivalent equations.
- I can solve a system of linear equations by elimination.

EXPLORATION 1

Solving a System Algebraically

Work with a partner. A student found the value of x in the system using substitution as shown.

$$3x + y = 1 \qquad \text{Equation 1}$$
$$x - y = -5 \qquad \text{Equation 2}$$

Step 1: $\quad 3x + y = 1 \qquad$ Equation 1

$\qquad\quad x + 5 = y \qquad$ Revised Equation 2

Step 2: $\quad 3x + x + 5 = 1 \qquad$ Substitute $x + 5$ for y in Equation 1.

$\qquad\qquad 4x + 5 = 1 \qquad$ Combine like terms.

$\qquad\qquad\quad 4x = -4 \qquad$ Subtract 5 from each side.

$\qquad\qquad\quad\ x = -1 \qquad$ Divide each side by 4.

a. Find another way to obtain the equation $4x = -4$ from the original system. Does your method produce an equation in one variable for any system? Explain.

b. Can you use your method in part (a) to solve each system below? If so, solve the system. If not, replace one of the equations with an equivalent equation that allows you to use your method in part (a). Then solve the system.

$$\text{System 1:} \quad \begin{array}{ll} 2x + 3y = -4 & \text{Equation 1} \\ 2x - 3y = 8 & \text{Equation 2} \end{array}$$

$$\text{System 2:} \quad \begin{array}{ll} x + 4y = -5 & \text{Equation 1} \\ 3x - 2y = 13 & \text{Equation 2} \end{array}$$

Math Practice

Find Entry Points
What do you look for when deciding how to solve a system of equations?

c. Compare your solution methods in part (b) with other pairs of students.

5.3 Lesson

When the equations in a linear system have a pair of like terms with the same or opposite coefficients, you can add or subtract the equations to *eliminate* one of the variables. Then use the resulting equation to solve the system.

EXAMPLE 1 **Solving a System of Linear Equations by Elimination**

Solve the system by elimination.

$$x + 3y = -2 \quad \text{Equation 1}$$
$$x - 3y = 16 \quad \text{Equation 2}$$

Step 1: Notice that the coefficients of the y-terms are opposites. So, you can add the equations to obtain an equation in one variable, x.

$$
\begin{array}{ll}
x + 3y = -2 & \text{Equation 1} \\
\underline{x - 3y = 16} & \text{Equation 2} \\
2x \quad\ \ = 14 & \text{Add the equations.}
\end{array}
$$

Because the coefficients of x are the same, you can also subtract the equations in Step 1.

$$
\begin{array}{l}
x + 3y = -2 \\
\underline{x - 3y = 16} \\
\quad 6y = -18 \\
\text{So, } y = -3.
\end{array}
$$

Step 2: Solve for x.

$$
\begin{array}{ll}
2x = 14 & \text{Equation from Step 1} \\
x = 7 & \text{Divide each side by 2.}
\end{array}
$$

Step 3: Substitute 7 for x in one of the original equations and solve for y.

$$
\begin{array}{ll}
x + 3y = -2 & \text{Equation 1} \\
7 + 3y = -2 & \text{Substitute 7 for } x. \\
3y = -9 & \text{Subtract 7 from each side.} \\
y = -3 & \text{Divide each side by 3.}
\end{array}
$$

▶ The solution is $(7, -3)$.

> **Check**
>
> Equation 1
> $$x + 3y = -2$$
> $$7 + 3(-3) \stackrel{?}{=} -2$$
> $$-2 = -2 \ \checkmark$$
>
> Equation 2
> $$x - 3y = 16$$
> $$7 - 3(-3) \stackrel{?}{=} 16$$
> $$16 = 16 \ \checkmark$$

Try It Solve the system by elimination. Check your solution.

1. $2x - y = 9$
  $4x + y = 21$

2. $-5x + 2y = 13$
  $5x + y = -1$

3. $3x + 4y = -6$
  $7x + 4y = -14$

Laurie's Notes

Scaffolding Instruction

- Students discovered that they can add, subtract, and multiply the equations in a system to eliminate a variable. Now they will solve systems of linear equations by elimination.
- **Emerging:** Students may be able to add equations to eliminate a variable when a pair of like terms has opposite coefficients, but they need more practice solving systems that require additional steps. They will benefit from guided instruction for the examples.
- **Proficient:** Students can solve systems of linear equations by elimination. They should proceed to the Self-Assessment exercises.

Discuss

- Discuss the paragraph at the top of the page with students.
- It may be helpful to show students why you can add (or subtract) corresponding sides of an equation to solve a system.

  Addition Property of Equality: If $a = b$ and $c = d$, then $a + c = b + d$. The first terms on each side of $a + c = b + d$ are equal and the second terms are equal, so the sums must be equal. This is also true for the differences, but it is best explained as an extension of addition.

EXAMPLE 1

- Write Equation 1 and Equation 2.
- ❓ "What are the coefficients of the x-terms?" Both are 1.
- ❓ "What are the coefficients of the y-terms?" 3 and -3
- **Teaching Tip:** Line up like terms vertically so that you can add the terms in each column.
- ❓ "When you add the equations, what is the sum?" $2x = 14$
- ❓ "How can you find the y-coordinate of the solution?" Substitute 7 for x in one of the original equations.
- Check the solution in *both* equations.
- Have students solve the system using substitution. Ask several students to share their work. Select one student who solved Equation 1 for x, $x = -3y - 2$, another who solved Equation 2 for x, $x = 3y + 16$, and yet another who solved one of the equations for $3y$, $3y = -x - 2$ or $3y = x - 16$.
- ❓ Ask, "Which method do you prefer? Why?" Answers will vary.
- **MP3 Construct Viable Arguments and Critique the Reasoning of Others:** Students have solved systems of linear equations by graphing, substitution, and now elimination. They should understand that even within a particular method there are different ways to solve a system. Students should continue to focus on which method makes sense to use when solving a given system. They should choose a method based on the coefficients of the system and the form in which the equations are written. Students should be able to explain why they select a particular method.

Try It

- **Think-Pair-Share:** Students should read each exercise independently and then work in pairs to complete the exercises. Then have each pair compare their answers with another pair and discuss any discrepancies.

Extra Example 1

Solve the system by elimination.

$3x - y = 14$

$-3x + 4y = 16$

$(8, 10)$

Try It

1. $(5, 1)$
2. $(-1, 4)$
3. $(-2, 0)$

Laurie's Notes

Discuss

- Show students that just as they used the Addition Property of Equality to add equations, they may also use the Multiplication Property of Equality (if $a = b$, then $ac = bc$) to change the coefficients before adding or subtracting.

Extra Example 2

Solve the system by elimination.
$3x - 4y = 33$
$4x + 3y = 19$
$(7, -3)$

EXAMPLE 2

- Write Equation 1 and Equation 2.
- ❓ "What do you notice about this system?" Listen for "None of the coefficients of like variable terms are the same or opposite."
- ❓ "Can you think of a way to rewrite the equations so that either the x-terms or the y-terms have coefficients that are the same or opposite?" Multiply each term of one equation by a constant.
- ❓ "If you want to eliminate the x-term, what could you do?" Sample answers: Multiply Equation 2 by -3 and add, or multiply Equation 2 by 3 and subtract.
- First work through the problem using one approach. Then show how the other approach gives the same result in Step 2.
- Although both approaches give you the same solution, sometimes fewer computational errors occur when equations are added rather than subtracted. Some students prefer adding equations.
- **Common Error:** When multiplying through by a constant, be sure that students multiply *every* term by the constant. It helps to use color: $(3)(-2x - 4y) = 14(3)$.
- Remind students that they are using the Distributive Property.
- ❓ Ask, "What if this system had been written this way?"
  $$5y - 6x = 25$$
  $$-2x - 4y = 14$$
  Students should recognize that the like terms are not lined up in the same columns, so one of the equations should be rewritten.
- Remind students that the solution is an ordered pair. Also remind them to check the solution by substitution, by graphing, and/or in both equations.

Try It

- Have students check with their neighbors as they work through the exercises. Remind students to use care when setting up the addition or subtraction. It is very frustrating to check your answer and find out that you made an error at the beginning of your solution process.

Try It

4. $(3, 2)$

5. $(-6, -1)$

6. $(0, 3)$

ELL Support

After demonstrating Example 2, have students work in groups to discuss and complete Try It Exercises 4–6. Provide guiding questions: Which coefficients can you make the same? How can you make them the same? What is the solution? Expect students to perform according to their language levels.

Beginner: Write out the steps.

Intermediate: Use phrases or simple sentences to discuss the process.

Advanced: Use detailed sentences and help guide discussion.

To solve a system by elimination, you may need to multiply one or both equations by a constant so a pair of like terms has the same or opposite coefficients.

EXAMPLE 2 **Solving a System of Linear Equations by Elimination**

Solve the system by elimination.

$$-6x + 5y = 25 \quad \text{Equation 1}$$
$$-2x - 4y = 14 \quad \text{Equation 2}$$

Step 1: Notice that no pairs of like terms have the same or opposite coefficients. One way to solve by elimination is to multiply Equation 2 by 3 so that the x-terms have a coefficient of -6.

Notice that you can also multiply Equation 2 by -3 and then add the equations.

$$-6x + 5y = 25 \qquad\qquad\qquad -6x + 5y = 25 \quad \text{Equation 1}$$
$$-2x - 4y = 14 \;\boxed{\text{Multiply by 3.}}\;\rightarrow\; -6x - 12y = 42 \quad \text{Revised Equation 2}$$

Step 2: Subtract the equations to obtain an equation in one variable, y.

$$
\begin{array}{ll}
-6x + 5y = 25 & \text{Equation 1}\\
\underline{-6x - 12y = 42} & \text{Revised Equation 2}\\
 17y = -17 & \text{Subtract the equations.}
\end{array}
$$

Step 3: Solve for y.

$$
\begin{array}{ll}
17y = -17 & \text{Equation from Step 2}\\
y = -1 & \text{Divide each side by 17.}
\end{array}
$$

Step 4: Substitute -1 for y in one of the original equations and solve for x.

$$
\begin{array}{ll}
-2x - 4y = 14 & \text{Equation 2}\\
-2x - 4(-1) = 14 & \text{Substitute } -1 \text{ for } y.\\
-2x + 4 = 14 & \text{Multiply.}\\
-2x = 10 & \text{Subtract 4 from each side.}\\
x = -5 & \text{Divide each side by } -2.
\end{array}
$$

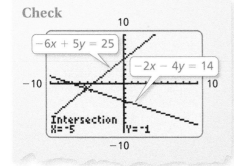

Check

▶ The solution is $(-5, -1)$.

Try It **Solve the system by elimination. Check your solution.**

4. $3x + y = 11$
    $6x + 3y = 24$

5. $4x - 5y = -19$
    $-x - 2y = 8$

6. $5y = 15 - 5x$
    $y = -2x + 3$

EXAMPLE 3 **Choosing a Solution Method**

Which are efficient approaches to solving the system?

$$x - 2y = 6 \qquad \text{Equation 1}$$
$$-x + 4y = 6 \qquad \text{Equation 2}$$

A. Add the equations.

B. Multiply Equation 1 by 2 and subtract the equations.

C. Solve Equation 1 for x and substitute the result in Equation 2.

D. Substitute $-x + 4y$ for 6 in Equation 1.

The methods in Choices A and C result in an equation in one variable, y. You can solve these equations and use the results to find the value of x.

The methods in Choices B and D will not result in an equation in one variable.

 So, Choices A and C are efficient approaches to solving the system.

Try It

7. Change one word in Choice B so that it represents an efficient approach to solving the system.

 ## Self-Assessment *for Concepts & Skills*

Solve each exercise. Then rate your understanding of the success criteria in your journal.

SOLVING A SYSTEM OF LINEAR EQUATIONS Solve the system by elimination. Check your solution.

8. $2x + y = 4$
$\qquad -2x + 2y = 5$

9. $-x + y = 1$
$\qquad -3x + y = 7$

10. $y = -2x + 3$
$\qquad 4x - 5y = 13$

CHOOSING A SOLUTION METHOD Solve the system. Explain your choice of method.

11. $y = 6x - 1$
$\qquad y = 3x - 4$

12. $3x = y + 2$
$\qquad 3x + 2y = 5$

13. $2x - y = 7$
$\qquad x + y = 5$

14. WHICH ONE DOESN'T BELONG? Which system does *not* belong with the other three? Explain your reasoning.

$3x + 3y = 3$	$-2x + y = 6$	$2x + 3y = 11$	$x + y = 5$
$2x - 3y = 7$	$2x - 3y = -10$	$3x - 2y = 10$	$3x - y = 3$

Laurie's Notes

EXAMPLE 3

- Pose the question and allow time for students to consider each answer choice. Have each student write his or her choice(s) on a whiteboard. Use *Popsicle Sticks* to select students to explain and support their choices. If students do not select an answer choice, ask them to explain why.
- Explain that students could still use the equations generated by Choices B and D to solve the system, but they are not as efficient as Choices A and C. Performing these steps will not bring them any closer to solving the system.

Try It

- Each student should discuss the problem with a partner and write the word that he or she would change on a whiteboard. Again, ask students to defend their choices.

✓ Self-Assessment for Concepts & Skills

- Have students solve each exercise independently and then check the solution with their neighbors before moving on to the next exercise.
- ⊙ Have students use *Thumbs Up* to indicate their understanding of how to solve a system of equations by elimination.

ELL Support

Allow students to work in pairs. Have pairs display their solutions for Exercises 8–13 on whiteboards for your review. Have two pairs form a group to discuss their explanations for Exercises 11–14. Then have each group present their explanation for one of the four exercises to the class.

The Success Criteria Self-Assessment chart can be found in the *Student Journal* or online at *BigIdeasMath.com*.

Extra Example 3

Which are efficient approaches to solving the system?

$$x + 3y = 7 \quad \text{Equation 1}$$
$$-2x - 3y = 1 \quad \text{Equation 2}$$

A. Subtract the equations.

B. Add the equations.

C. Solve Equation 1 for x and substitute the result in Equation 2.

D. Multiply Equation 1 by 2 and subtract the equations.

B and C

Try It

7. Change subtract to add.

Self-Assessment
for Concepts & Skills

8. $\left(\dfrac{1}{2}, 3\right)$

9. $(-3, -2)$

10. $(2, -1)$

11. $(-1, -7)$; Explanations will vary.

12. $(1, 1)$; Explanations will vary.

13. $(4, 1)$; Explanations will vary.

14. $2x + 3y = 11$
$3x - 2y = 10$;
You have to use multiplication to solve the system by elimination.

Laurie's Notes

Extra Example 4

Extra Example 4

There are 340 calories in 2 cups of a cereal with 1 cup of milk. There are 570 calories in 3 cups of the cereal with 2 cups of milk. Find the number of calories in 1 cup of the cereal without milk. 110 calories

Self-Assessment
for Problem Solving

15. $600

16. cooking club: $90,
woodshop club: $60

Formative Assessment Tip

Entry Ticket

This technique is similar to *Exit Ticket*. You pose a short problem, or ask a question, at the end of class. Students write their responses on tickets as part of their homework. Students give you their *Entry Tickets* as they enter your class the next day. Because they are short responses, you can read them quickly to decide if you need to answer any questions or clear up any misconceptions.

Learning Target

Understand how to solve systems of linear equations by elimination.

Success Criteria

- Add or subtract equations in a system.
- Use the Multiplication Property of Equality to produce equivalent equations.
- Solve a system of linear equations by elimination.

EXAMPLE 4

- Ask a volunteer to read and summarize the problem: Two people buy different numbers of two types of flowers and pay different amounts.
- Although the problem is asking you to find the cost of each daylily, you need a second variable for the cost of each hosta.
- Discuss the verbal model used to generate each equation.
- **?** "What do you notice about this system of equations that is different than the first three examples?" Listen for "Neither pair of like terms has a coefficient that is a multiple of the other."
- Students should recognize that 24 is the least common multiple of 8 and 3. Work through the problem as shown.
- Discuss alternative approaches to this problem.
  - Multiply Equation 2 by $\frac{8}{3}$ and subtract to eliminate the *x*-terms.
  - Multiply Equation 1 by 4 and Equation 2 by 5 and subtract to eliminate the *y*-terms.
- **Extension:** Find the cost of each hosta. $11 Have students check the solution in both equations.
- **MP8 Look for and Express Regularity in Repeated Reasoning:** Encourage students to look for shortcuts when solving the problem.

✓ *Self-Assessment for Problem Solving*

- Allow time in class for students to practice using the problem-solving plan. Remember, some students may only be able to complete the first step.
- Have each student read Exercise 15 and write a verbal model to represent the situation. Ask volunteers to write their verbal models on the board. Discuss each model and ask students if they have any different verbal models. If so, have them share and discuss their models. Then have students solve each exercise.

The Success Criteria Self-Assessment chart can be found in the *Student Journal* or online at *BigIdeasMath.com*.

Closure

- **Entry Ticket:** Complete the table summarizing the methods for solving systems of linear equations.

Method	When to Use
Graphing (*Lesson 5.1*)	To estimate solutions
Substitution (*Lesson 5.2*)	When one of the variables in one of the equations has a coefficient of 1 or -1
Elimination (*Lesson 5.3*)	When at least 1 pair of like terms has the same or opposite coefficients
Elimination (Multiply First) (*Lesson 5.3*)	When one of the variables cannot be eliminated by adding or subtracting the equations

EXAMPLE 4 **Modeling Real Life**

You buy 8 hostas and 15 daylilies for $193. Your friend buys 3 hostas and 12 daylilies for $117. Find the cost of each daylily.

Use a verbal model to write a system of linear equations. Let x represent the cost of each hosta and let y represent the cost of each daylily.

Number of hostas	$\cdot$	Cost of each hosta, x	$+$	Number of daylilies	$\cdot$	Cost of each daylily, y	$=$	Total cost

The system is:

$8x + 15y = 193$ Equation 1 (You)

$3x + 12y = 117$ Equation 2 (Your friend)

Step 1: One way to find the cost of each daylily is to eliminate the x-terms and solve for y. Multiply Equation 1 by 3 and Equation 2 by 8.

$8x + 15y = 193$ **Multiply by 3.** $24x + 45y = 579$ Revised Equation 1

$3x + 12y = 117$ **Multiply by 8.** $24x + 96y = 936$ Revised Equation 2

Step 2: Subtract the revised equations.

$$24x + 45y = 579 \qquad \text{Revised Equation 1}$$
$$\underline{24x + 96y = 936} \qquad \text{Revised Equation 2}$$
$$-51y = -357 \qquad \text{Subtract the equations.}$$

Step 3: Solving the equation $-51y = -357$ gives $y = 7$.

▶ So, each daylily costs $7.

Math Practice

Maintain Oversight

Do you need to find the value of x in Example 4? Explain your reasoning.

Self-Assessment *for Problem Solving*

Solve each exercise. Then rate your understanding of the success criteria in your journal.

15. A fitness instructor purchases exercise bikes and treadmills for two gyms. For the first gym, 2 exercise bikes and 3 treadmills cost $2200. For the second gym, 3 exercise bikes and 4 treadmills cost $3000. How much does a treadmill cost?

16. **DIG DEEPER!** At your school, cooking club members raise $5 per member for a charity and woodshop club members raise $10 per member for a different charity. The cooking club has three times as many members as the woodshop club. The difference of the number of members in the two clubs is 12 members. How much does each club raise?

Go to *BigIdeasMath.com* to get HELP with solving the exercises.

Review & Refresh

Solve the system by substitution. Check your solution.

1. $x = 5 - y$
$x - y = 3$

2. $x - 5y = 1$
$-x + y = 7$

3. $x + 6y = -2$
$-x = 3y - 10$

The vertices of a triangle are given. Draw the triangle and its image after a dilation with the given scale factor. Identify the type of dilation.

4. $A(-1, 1), B(1, 3), C(3, 1); k = 2$

5. $D(-8, -4), E(-4, 8), F(0, 0); k = 0.5$

Concepts, Skills, & Problem Solving

SOLVING A SYSTEM ALGEBRAICALLY Explain how to obtain the equation $3x = 6$ from the given system. (See Exploration 1, p. 211.)

6. $2x + y = 5$
$x - y = 1$

7. $5x + 2y = 2$
$x + y = -2$

8. $-x + y = -3$
$6x - 3y = 15$

SOLVING A SYSTEM OF LINEAR EQUATIONS Solve the system by elimination. Check your solution.

9. $x + 3y = 5$
$-x - y = -3$

10. $x - 2y = -7$
$3x + 2y = 3$

11. $4x + 3y = -5$
$-x + 3y = -10$

12. $2x + 7y = 1$
$2x - 4y = 12$

13. $2x + 5y = 16$
$3x - 5y = -1$

14. $3x - 2y = 4$
$6x - 2y = -2$

15. **MP YOU BE THE TEACHER**
Your friend solves the system. Is your friend correct? Explain your reasoning.

$5x + 2y = 9$ Equation 1
$3x - 2y = -1$ Equation 2
$2x \quad\quad = 10$
$x = 5$
The solution is $(5, -8)$.

16. **MP MODELING REAL LIFE**
You and your friend are selling raffle tickets for a new laptop. You sell 14 more tickets than your friend sells. Together, you and your friend sell 58 tickets.

a. Write a system of linear equations that represents this situation.

b. How many tickets do each of you sell?

17. **MP MODELING REAL LIFE** You can jog around your block twice and the park once in 10 minutes. You can jog around your block twice and the park 3 times in 22 minutes. Write a system of linear equations that represents this situation. How long does it take you to jog around the park?

Assignment Guide and Concept Check

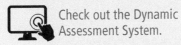
Check out the Dynamic Assessment System.
BigIdeasMath.com

Scaffold assignments to support all students in their learning progression. The suggested assignments are a starting point. Continue to assign additional exercises and revisit with spaced practice to move every student toward proficiency.

Level	Assignment 1	Assignment 2
Emerging	3, 5, 6, 9, 11, 13, 15, 19, 21, 23	14, 16, 17, 20, 24, 25, 27, 29, 37, 38, 41
Proficient	3, 5, 7, 10, 12, 14, 15, 18, 20, 22	16, 17, 24, 26, 28, 30, 31, 33, 34, 36, 37, 38, 41
Advanced	3, 5, 8, 12, 14, 15, 18, 22, 24, 26	28, 30, 32, 34, 35, 36, 37, 38, 39, 40, 41, 42, 43

- Assignment 1 is for use after students complete the Self-Assessment for Concepts & Skills.
- Assignment 2 is for use after students complete the Self-Assessment for Problem Solving.
- The red exercises can be used as a concept check.

Review & Refresh Prior Skills

Exercises 1–3   Solving a System of Linear Equations by Substitution
Exercises 4 and 5   Dilating a Figure

 Common Errors

- **Exercises 9–14** Students may make careless errors. Remind students to line up like terms neatly in columns to avoid confusion about what terms to add or subtract. Also, tell them to take care with subtraction—it may help to change the sign of each term in the equation to be subtracted, so they can just add the terms.
- **Exercise 16** Students may struggle writing an equation to represent "You sell 14 more tickets than your friend sells." Explain that it helps to ask the question, "How does your number of tickets compare to your friend's number of tickets?"

Review & Refresh

1. $(4, 1)$ 2. $(-9, -2)$

3. $(22, -4)$

4.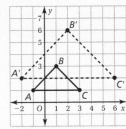

enlargement

5.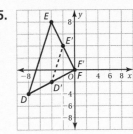

reduction

Concepts, Skills, & Problem Solving

6. Add the equations.

7. Multiply Equation 2 by -2, then add the equations.

8. Multiply Equation 1 by 3, then add the equations.

9. $(2, 1)$

10. $(-1, 3)$

11. $(1, -3)$

12. $(4, -1)$

13. $(3, 2)$

14. $(-2, -5)$

15. no; Your friend should have added the x-terms and the constants, not subtracted them.

16. a. $x + y = 58$
    $x - y = 14$

    b. you: 36 tickets,
    your friend: 22 tickets

17. $2x + y = 10$
    $2x + 3y = 22$;
    6 min

Concepts, Skills, & Problem Solving

18. $(3, 6)$

19. $(5, -1)$

20. $(-2, 1)$

21. $(-2, -1)$

22. $(3, 0)$

23. $(4, 3)$

24. no; Your friend should have multiplied each term in Equation 1 by -5, not just the x-term.

25. $(4, 0)$; Explanations will vary.

26. $(2, -1)$; Explanations will vary.

27. $\left(\dfrac{8}{5}, -\dfrac{4}{5}\right)$; Explanations will vary.

28. $(0, 1)$; Explanations will vary.

29. $\left(-\dfrac{14}{5}, -\dfrac{8}{5}\right)$; Explanations will vary.

30. $\left(\dfrac{1}{8}, 1\right)$; Explanations will vary.

31. *Sample answer:* -4; When $a = -4$, the coefficients of the x-terms are opposites.

32. *Sample answer:* 7; When $a = 7$, the coefficients of the y-terms are opposites.

33. no; The lines are parallel.

34. yes; The lines intersect at $(2, -4)$.

35. $y = 2x$
$y = -\dfrac{1}{3}x + 14$;
Solution: $(6, 12)$

Common Errors

- **Exercises 18–23** Students may make errors in multiplying through the whole equation. Tell them to clearly show what they are multiplying each equation by so they do not forget during the process. Students should check the sign and coefficient of each term after multiplying.
- **Exercise 35** Students may not write a correct system of equations for the situation. Ask them to consider what line each airplane has to follow to fly to the airport.

SOLVING A SYSTEM OF LINEAR EQUATIONS Solve the system by elimination. Check your solution.

18. $2x - y = 0$
$3x - 2y = -3$

19. $x + 4y = 1$
$3x + 5y = 10$

20. $-2x + 3y = 7$
$5x + 8y = -2$

21. $3x + 3 = 3y$
$2x - 6y = 2$

22. $2x - 6 = 4y$
$7y = -3x + 9$

23. $5x = 4y + 8$
$3y = 3x - 3$

24. **(MP) YOU BE THE TEACHER** Your friend solves the system. Is your friend correct? Explain your reasoning.

$x + y = 1$ Equation 1   **Multiply by −5.** $-5x + y = 1$
$5x + 3y = -3$ Equation 2 $\underline{5x + 3y = -3}$
                            $4y = -2$
                            $y = -0.5$

The solution is $(-0.3, -0.5)$.

CHOOSING A SOLUTION METHOD Solve the system. Explain your choice of method.

25. $x + y = 4$
$x - y = 4$

26. $y = x - 3$
$y = -2x + 3$

27. $x + 2y = 0$
$2x - y = 4$

28. $y + 5x = 1$
$5y - x = 5$

29. $2 = x - 3y$
$-2x + y = 4$

30. $8x + 5y = 6$
$8x = 3 - 2y$

(MP) NUMBER SENSE For what value of a might you choose to solve the system by elimination? Explain.

31. $4x - y = 3$
$ax + 10y = 6$

32. $x - 7y = 6$
$-6x + ay = 9$

CRITICAL THINKING Determine whether the line through the first pair of points intersects the line through the second pair of points. Explain.

33. Line 1: $(-2, 1), (2, 7)$
Line 2: $(-4, -1), (0, 5)$

34. Line 1: $(-2, 8), (0, 2)$
Line 2: $(3, -2), (6, 4)$

35. **(MP) REASONING** Two airplanes are flying to the same airport. Their positions are shown in the graph. Write a system of linear equations that represents this situation. Solve the system by elimination to justify your answer.

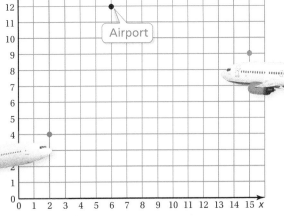

36. **MP MODELING REAL LIFE** A laboratory uses liquid nitrogen tanks of two different sizes. The combined volume of 3 large tanks and 2 small tanks is 24 liters. The combined volume of 2 large tanks and 3 small tanks is 21 liters. What is the volume of each size of tank? Justify your answer.

37. **MP PROBLEM SOLVING** The table shows the numbers of correct answers on a practice standardized test. You score 86 points on the test and your friend scores 76 points. How many points is each type of question worth?

	You	Your Friend
Multiple Choice	23	28
Short Response	10	5

38. **MP LOGIC** You solve a system of equations in which x represents the number of adult memberships sold and y represents the number of student memberships sold. Can $(-6, 24)$ be the solution of the system? Explain your reasoning.

39. **MP PROBLEM SOLVING** The table shows the activities of two tourists at a vacation resort. You want to go parasailing for 1 hour and horseback riding for 2 hours. How much do you expect to pay?

	Parasailing	Horseback Riding	Total Cost
Tourist 1	2 hours	5 hours	$205
Tourist 2	3 hours	3 hours	$240

40. **MP REASONING** Write a system of linear equations containing $2x + y = 0$ and that has the solution $(2, -4)$.

41. **MP REASONING** A metal alloy is a mixture of two or more metals. A jeweler wants to make 8 grams of 18-karat gold, which is 75% gold. The jeweler has an alloy that is 90% gold and an alloy that is 50% gold. How much of each alloy should the jeweler use?

42. **MP PROBLEM SOLVING** It takes a powerboat traveling with the current 30 minutes to go 10 miles. The return trip takes 50 minutes traveling against the current. What is the speed of the current?

43. **DIG DEEPER!** Solve the system of equations by elimination.

$$2x - y + 3z = -1$$
$$x + 2y - 4z = -1$$
$$y - 2z = 0$$

Common Errors

- **Exercise 37** Students may write a system of equations by reading across the table horizontally. Stress that your total number of points is equal to the sum of your points for multiple-choice questions and for short-response questions, which are both listed in the column for "You."

- **Exercise 39** Students may use an incorrect problem-solving strategy. Make sure they realize that they first need to solve for the cost per hour for each activity and then use those rates to answer the question.

- **Exercise 41** Students may not write an equation for the situation using the gold percents. Explain that the total amount of gold contributed by each alloy is equal to the amount of gold in the final mixture. Each amount of gold is given by the percent times the number of grams.

- **Exercise 42** Students may not write a system of equations that represents the problem correctly. Tell them this is an extension of the formula $d = rt$, where the rate is increased or decreased by the speed of the current.

- **Exercise 43** Students may use an incorrect approach. Tell them to look for a way to eliminate two of the variables. This will allow them to solve for the third variable. They can then substitute the value of this variable back into two of the equations to write a new system of two equations in two variables, which they know how to solve.

Mini-Assessment

Solve the system of linear equations by elimination. Check your solution.

1. $5x - 2y = 18$
   $-5x + 3y = -22$
   $(2, -4)$

2. $2x + 4y = 20$
   $-3x + 4y = 30$
   $(-2, 6)$

3. $4x - 2y = 2$
   $7x - 3y = 6$
   $(3, 5)$

4. You have 33 coins consisting of dimes and quarters in a jar. The jar contains a total of $4.95.

   a. Write and solve a system of linear equations that represents this situation.

   $x + y = 33$
   $0.1x + 0.25y = 4.95$

   b. How many of each coin do you have?

   22 dimes and 11 quarters

Section Resources

Surface Level	Deep Level

Resources by Chapter
  • Extra Practice
  • Reteach
  • Puzzle Time
Student Journal
  • Self-Assessment
  • Practice
Differentiating the Lesson
Tutorial Videos
Skills Review Handbook
Skills Trainer
	Resources by Chapter
	  • Enrichment and Extension
	Graphic Organizers
	Dynamic Assessment System
	  • Section Practice

 Concepts, Skills, & Problem Solving

36. large tank: 6 L, small tank: 3 L;
    $3x + 2y = 24$
    $2x + 3y = 21$
    Solution: (6, 3)

37. multiple choice: 2 points each, short response: 4 points each

38. no; You cannot sell -6 memberships.

39. $95

40. *Sample answer:* $2x + y = 0$
    $-2x + y = -8$

41. 90% gold alloy: 5 g, 50% gold alloy: 3 g

42. 4 mi/h

43. $x = -1, y = 2, z = 1$

Learning Target

Solve systems with different numbers of solutions.

Success Criteria

- Determine the number of solutions of a system.
- Solve a system of linear equations with any number of solutions.

Warm Up

Cumulative, vocabulary, and prerequisite skills practice opportunities are available in the *Resources by Chapter* or at *BigIdeasMath.com*.

ELL Support

Write the phrase *break even* on the board. Explain that *break even* is an expression that means something completely different from either of the two words that make it up. Ask students to pay attention to what you are about to read and guess its meaning from the context. Read aloud the introduction and part (b). Lead students to understand that in this context they are trying to recover the money they invest in materials.

Exploration 1

a.
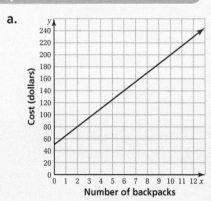

b–d. See Additional Answers.

Laurie's Notes

Preparing to Teach

- **MP1 Make Sense of Problems and Persevere in Solving Them:** Students have learned three techniques for solving a system of linear equations. In this lesson, they will use more than one technique to solve the same system, and in doing so recognize that not all systems have a single solution. Using a variety of strategies helps students make sense of the new possible outcomes for a solution of a system of equations.

Motivate

- If you have an overhead projector or document camera, place 2 pieces of uncooked spaghetti on display (intersecting). Say, "These represent two lines. Right now they are intersecting."
- ❓ "Is there any other relationship they could have?" Listen for parallel (non-intersecting) and a description of coinciding lines (same lines).
- Now place a transparency of a coordinate grid on top of the spaghetti.
- Suggest that lines, when graphed, do not always have to intersect.
- **Management Tip:** I use uncooked spaghetti for many models throughout the year, so I keep a box in my desk.

Exploration 1

- In part (a), students may want to begin by making a table of values and then plotting the ordered pairs.

Backpacks, x	0	1	2	3	4	5	6
Cost (in dollars), y	50	65	80	95	110	125	140

They could also write an equation to represent the cost, $y = 15x + 50$, and then graph using the y-intercept and the slope.

- ❓ In part (b), if students have difficulty finding an entry point, ask, "What does it mean to *break even*?" When you sell enough backpacks to pay for the cost of making the backpacks.
- Students should graph an equation to represent the amount of money you earn for selling the backpacks, $y = 25x$, in the same coordinate plane as the graph for the cost.
- ❓ "Where is the break-even point located?" At the point of intersection of the lines, (5, 125), which is the solution of the system. "What does this mean?" You have to sell 5 backpacks to cover the cost of making the backpacks ($125).
- In part (c), students should graph equations to represent the different selling prices, $y = 20x$ and $y = 15x$.
- ❓ "Can you break even when you sell each backpack for $20? Explain." Yes, but you will have to sell 10 backpacks.
- ❓ "Can you break even when you sell each backpack for $15? Explain." No, if the price is the same as the cost for materials, you will never break even. Make sure students understand that because the lines are parallel, they will never intersect. So, there is no solution of the system of linear equations.
- Discuss part (d) and the Math Practice note as a class.

5.4 Solving Special Systems of Linear Equations

Learning Target: Solve systems with different numbers of solutions.

Success Criteria:
- I can determine the number of solutions of a system.
- I can solve a system of linear equations with any number of solutions.

EXPLORATION 1

Exploring Solutions of Systems

Work with a partner. You spend $50 on a sewing machine to make dog backpacks. Each backpack costs you $15 for materials.

a. Represent the cost y (in dollars) to make x backpacks in the coordinate plane.

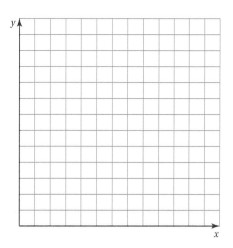

b. You charge $25 per backpack. How many backpacks do you have to sell to *break even*? Use a graph to justify your answer.

c. Can you break even when you sell each backpack for $20? $15? Use graphs to justify your answers.

Math Practice

Look for Structure

How can you use slopes and y-intercepts to determine the number of solutions of a system of linear equations?

d. Explain whether it is possible for a system of linear equations to have the numbers of solutions below.

- no solution

- exactly one solution

- exactly two solutions

- infinitely many solutions

 **5.4 Lesson**

Key Idea

Solutions of Systems of Linear Equations

A system of linear equations can have *one solution*, *no solution*, or *infinitely many solutions*.

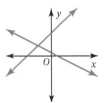

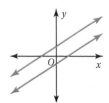

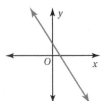

One solution

The lines intersect.
- different slopes

No solution

The lines are parallel.
- same slope
- different y-intercepts

Infinitely many solutions

The lines are the same.
- same slope
- same y-intercept

EXAMPLE 1 ## Solving a System with No Solution

Solve the system using any method. $y = 3x + 1$ Equation 1

$y = 3x - 3$ Equation 2

Method 1: Solve by graphing.

The lines have the same slope, 3, and different y-intercepts, 1 and -3. So, the lines are parallel. Because parallel lines do not intersect, there is no point that is a solution of both equations.

> So, the system has no solution.

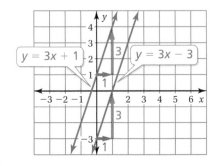

You can also solve by substituting $3x - 3$ for y in Equation 1.

$3x - 3 = 3x + 1$

$-3 = 1$ ✗

The equation $-3 = 1$ is never true. So, the system has no solution.

Method 2: Solve by inspection.

Notice that you can rewrite the system as

$-3x + y = 1$ Revised Equation 1

$-3x + y = -3.$ Revised Equation 2

> The expression $-3x + y$ cannot be equal to 1 and -3 at the same time. So, the system has no solution.

Try It **Solve the system. Explain your choice of method.**

1. $y = -x + 3$
$y = -x + 5$

2. $y = -5x - 2$
$5x + y = 0$

3. $x = 2y + 10$
$2x + 3y = -1$

Laurie's Notes

Scaffolding Instruction

- In the exploration, students explored the graphs of several systems of equations, including a system with no solution. Students will now solve special systems of linear equations.
- **Emerging:** Students may understand that a system of linear equations can have one solution, no solution, or infinitely many solutions, but they may struggle to recognize the different cases. They will benefit from guided instruction for the Key Idea and examples.
- **Proficient:** Students recognize the relationship between the graph of a system of linear equations and the number of solutions. They should review the Key Idea before completing the Self-Assessment exercises.

Key Idea

- Write the Key Idea. Connect this back to the spaghetti used in the Motivate to introduce special systems of linear equations.

EXAMPLE 1

- Ask students to analyze the system and think about how they will approach solving it.
- ❓ "What method would you use to solve this system? Explain." Answers will vary. An argument could be made for any of the methods students have studied, but graphing and substitution are good choices because both equations are solved for y.
- ❓ "How do you graph equations in slope-intercept form?" Plot the point for the y-intercept, use the slope to locate another point, and then draw the line.
- Students should recognize that because the equations have the same slope and different y-intercepts, the lines are parallel. Graphing is a visual check that the lines are parallel.
- **MP1 Make Sense of Problems and Persevere in Solving Them:** Work through Method 2 as shown. Remind students that before starting any problem, they should consider what information is given and which approach makes sense. See the Teaching Strategy.
- ❓ "What if you did not notice that the lines had the same slope and you tried to solve the system algebraically? What do you think will happen?" Students are not likely to have a sense of what will happen.
- **MP7 Look for and Make Use of Structure:** Because both equations are solved for y, substitution is an approach that makes sense. Discuss the push-pin note. Point out that solving the system algebraically leads to a statement $-3 = 1$ that is never true. You can interpret this false statement to mean that the system has no solution, because there are no ordered pairs that satisfy both equations. So, the lines must be parallel.

Try It

- Students may quickly observe that the first two systems have no solution because the slopes are the same but the y-intercepts are different, so the lines are parallel. Make sure students base their answers on sound reasoning.

Teaching Strategy

This is a perfect time to discuss the advantages of analyzing a problem before solving it. Frequently, students just want to start working. This can take up valuable time, particularly when taking a test, and may lead to errors. Method 1 shows students that because the lines have the same slope and different y-intercepts, they are parallel. There will be no solution, no matter which method they choose to solve the system or how much work they do. Encourage students to "look before they leap."

Extra Example 1

Solve the system.
$y = -2x + 5$
$y = -2x + 1$
no solution

ELL Support

After demonstrating Example 1, have students work in groups to discuss and complete Try It Exercises 1–3. Remind students to consider the different strategies they have learned as they attempt to solve each system. Expect students to perform according to their language levels.

Beginner: Write the steps to solve the system or graph the system.

Intermediate: Use simple sentences to contribute to discussion.

Advanced: Use complex sentences and help guide discussion.

Try It

1. no solution; Explanations will vary.

2. no solution; Explanations will vary.

3. $(4, -3)$; Explanations will vary.

Laurie's Notes

Extra Example 2

Solve the system using any method.

$6x + 2y = 10$

$3x + y = 5$

infinitely many solutions

Try It

4. $(0, 3)$; Explanations will vary.

5. no solution; Explanations will vary.

6. infinitely many solutions; Explanations will vary.

Self-Assessment
for Concepts & Skills

7. no solution; The lines have the same slope and different y-intercepts.

8. one solution; The lines have different slopes.

9. infinitely many solutions; The lines are the same.

10. $(3, 0)$; Explanations will vary.

11. infinitely many solutions; Explanations will vary.

12. no solution; Explanations will vary.

13. $\left(-\dfrac{3}{2}, -12\right)$; Explanations will vary.

14. infinitely many solutions; Explanations will vary.

15. $(0, -2)$; Explanations will vary.

EXAMPLE 2

? "What method would you use to solve this system? Explain." Answers will vary. An argument could be made for any of the methods students have studied, but graphing using intercepts and elimination are good choices because both equations are in standard form.

- Divide students into three groups and assign each group a different method of solving: graphing, substitution, or elimination. Each student should solve the system using the assigned method. Select several students to present their solutions to the class. Then ask students which method they prefer and why.

- Point out that solving the system algebraically leads to a statement that is always true, $0 = 0$. You can interpret this identity to mean that the system has infinitely many solutions, because there are infinitely many ordered pairs that satisfy both equations and the lines coincide.

? Have students select any point on the line to substitute into the original system. Then ask, "Were any of your points not a solution?" no If a student says "yes," ask him or her to demonstrate and make sure the point the student chose is on the line.

Try It

- **Think-Pair-Share:** Students should read each exercise independently and then work in pairs to complete the exercises. Then have each pair compare their answers with another pair and discuss any discrepancies.

Self-Assessment for Concepts & Skills

- Have students solve the exercises independently and then check with their neighbors. If time is a concern, you could choose three of Exercises 10–15 for students to complete.

- ◉ **Writing Prompt:** To determine the number of solutions of a system of linear equations . . .

ELL Support

Allow students to work in pairs for extra support and to practice language. Have two pairs compare their explanations for Exercises 7–15 and reach an agreement on each. Monitor discussions and provide support as needed. Then have groups display their answers to Exercises 10–15 on whiteboards for your review.

The Success Criteria Self-Assessment chart can be found in the *Student Journal* or online at *BigIdeasMath.com*.

EXAMPLE 2 **Solving a System with Infinitely Many Solutions**

Solve the system using any method. $x + 2y = 6$ Equation 1

$3x + 6y = 18$ Equation 2

Method 1: Solve by graphing.

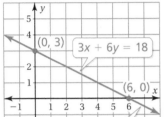

The lines have the same slope, $-\dfrac{1}{2}$, and the same y-intercept, 3.

So, the two equations in the system represent the same line.

▷   All the points on the line are solutions of the system. So, the system has infinitely many solutions.

Method 2: Solve by elimination.

Multiply Equation 1 by 3 and subtract the equations.

$x + 2y = 6$	**Multiply by 3.**	$3x + 6y = 18$	Revised Equation 1
$3x + 6y = 18$		$\underline{3x + 6y = 18}$	Equation 2
		$0 = 0$	Subtract.

The equation $0 = 0$ is always true. You can also see from Revised Equation 1 that the two equations in the system are equivalent.

▷   All the points on the line are solutions of the system. So, the system has infinitely many solutions.

Try It Solve the system. Explain your choice of method.

4. $x + y = 3$
    $x = y - 3$

5. $2x + y = 5$
    $4x + 2y = 0$

6. $2x - 4y = 10$
    $-12x + 24y = -60$

Self-Assessment for Concepts & Skills

Solve each exercise. Then rate your understanding of the success criteria in your journal.

MP STRUCTURE Without graphing or solving, determine the number of solutions of the system. Explain your reasoning.

7. $y = 5x - 9$
    $y = 5x + 9$

8. $y = 6x + 2$
    $y = 3x + 1$

9. $y = 8x - 2$
    $y - 8x = -2$

CHOOSING A METHOD Solve the system. Explain your choice of method.

10. $2x + y = 6$
    $x - y = 3$

11. $4y - 4x = 8$
    $y = x + 2$

12. $5x - 4y = 12$
    $7.5x = 6(y - 1)$

13. $-6x = 9$
    $6x - y = 3$

14. $0.5x + 4y = -11$
    $-1.5x - 12y = 33$

15. $x = y + 2$
    $3x = 6(y + 2)$

Section 5.4   Solving Special Systems of Linear Equations   **221**

EXAMPLE 3 **Modeling Real Life**

You and your friend plant an urban garden. You pay $15.00 for 6 tomato plants and 6 pepper plants. Your friend pays $22.50 for 9 tomato plants and 9 pepper plants. How much does each plant cost?

> *Understand the problem.*

You are given the total costs of two different combinations of tomato plants and pepper plants. You are asked to find the cost of each plant.

> *Make a plan.*

Use a verbal model to write a system of linear equations. Let x represent the cost of each tomato plant and let y represent the cost of each pepper plant. Then solve the system.

> *Solve and check.*

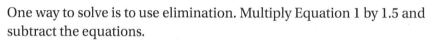

| Number of tomato plants | $\cdot$ | Cost of each tomato plant, x | $+$ | Number of pepper plants | $\cdot$ | Cost of each pepper plant, y | $=$ | Total cost |

The system is: $\quad 6x + 6y = 15 \qquad$ Equation 1 (You)
$\qquad\qquad\qquad 9x + 9y = 22.5 \qquad$ Equation 2 (Your friend)

One way to solve is to use elimination. Multiply Equation 1 by 1.5 and subtract the equations.

$$6x + 6y = 15$$
$$9x + 9y = 22.5$$

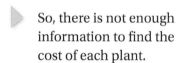 **Multiply by 1.5.**

$$9x + 9y = 22.5 \qquad \text{Revised Equation 1}$$
$$\underline{9x + 9y = 22.5} \qquad \text{Equation 2}$$
$$0 = 0 \qquad\qquad \text{Subtract.}$$

The equation $0 = 0$ is always true. The system has infinitely many solutions.

▷ So, there is not enough information to find the cost of each plant.

> **Look Back** Revised Equation 1 shows that the two equations in the system are equivalent.
> So, the system has infinitely many solutions. ✓

Self-Assessment for Problem Solving

Solve each exercise. Then rate your understanding of the success criteria in your journal.

16. Your friend wants to sell painted rocks. He spends $10.00 on startup costs, and each painted rock costs him $0.75 to make. A store offers to pay your friend's startup costs and buy his painted rocks for $0.75 each. How many painted rocks does your friend need to sell to make a profit?

17. **DIG DEEPER!** The difference in age of two orangutans is 6 years. In 4 years, is it possible for the older orangutan to be twice as old as the younger orangutan? three times as old? Justify your answers.

Laurie's Notes

EXAMPLE 3

- Ask a volunteer to read the problem and another to explain what the problem is asking. If necessary, ask a third student to re-read the problem.
- Students could complete a Four Square as you work through the problem-solving plan.
- Explain that a system with two equivalent equations is essentially one equation, which has infinitely many solutions.
- Note that although the system has infinitely many solutions, they are limited to Quadrant I because the costs of the plants cannot be negative.
- **?** "Why is the question impossible to answer?" Based on the equations, there are infinitely many ways that the plants could be priced. Show students several possibilities.

  If each tomato plant costs $1.50, then each pepper plant costs $1.00.
  If each tomato plant costs $2.00, then each pepper plant costs $0.50.
  If each tomato plant costs $0.75, then each pepper plant costs $1.75.

- **?** **Extension:** "Another friend pays $19.50 for 9 tomato plants and 6 pepper plants. Now can you find the cost?" Yes, each tomato plant costs $1.50 and each pepper plant costs $1.00.

✅ Self-Assessment for Problem Solving

- Students may benefit from trying the exercises independently and then working with peers to refine their work. It is important to provide time in class for problem solving, so that students become comfortable with the problem-solving plan.
- **Think-Pair-Share:** Students should read each exercise independently and then work in pairs to complete the exercises. Then have each pair compare their answers with another pair and discuss any discrepancies.

The Success Criteria Self-Assessment chart can be found in the *Student Journal* or online at *BigIdeasMath.com*.

Closure

- ◉ Discuss students' responses from the *Writing Prompt* in the Self-Assessment for Concepts & Skills.
- **Exit Ticket:** Write a system of equations that has no solution. *Sample answer:* $y = 2x + 4$ and $y = 2x - 6$

Extra Example 3

You and your friend buy school supplies. You pay $12.50 for 6 notebooks and 2 binders. Your friend pays $6.25 for 3 notebooks and 1 binder. How much does each school supply cost? There is not enough information to find the cost of each school supply.

Self-Assessment for Problem Solving

16. Your friend will never make a profit.

17. yes;
    $x - y = 6$
    $x + 4 = 2(y + 4)$
    The solution is $(8, 2)$, which is a possible set of ages.
    no;
    $x - y = 6$
    $x + 4 = 3(y + 4)$
    The solution is $(5, -1)$, and -1 is not a possible age.

Learning Target

Solve systems with different numbers of solutions.

Success Criteria

- Determine the number of solutions of a system.
- Solve a system of linear equations with any number of solutions.

 **Review & Refresh**

1. $(-8, 6)$

2. $(1, 1)$

3. $(2, 1)$

4. $y = 3x$

5. $y = 2x - 3$

6. $y = -\frac{1}{2}x + 2$

 Concepts, Skills, & Problem Solving

7. no solution

8. infinitely many solutions

9. one solution

10. no solution; Explanations will vary.

11. $(-1, -2)$; Explanations will vary.

12. no solution; Explanations will vary.

13. infinitely many solutions; Explanations will vary.

14. infinitely many solutions; Explanations will vary.

15. $(-2.4, -3.5)$; Explanations will vary.

16. no solution; Explanations will vary.

17. $\left(\frac{1}{10}, \frac{9}{10}\right)$; Explanations will vary.

18. infinitely many solutions; Explanations will vary.

19. no; The lines have different y-intercepts, so the system has no solution.

20. no; The lines are parallel, so your pig will always be 3 feet ahead of your friend's pig.

Assignment Guide and Concept Check

Scaffold assignments to support all students in their learning progression. The suggested assignments are a starting point. Continue to assign additional exercises and revisit with spaced practice to move every student toward proficiency.

Level	Assignment 1	Assignment 2
Emerging	3, 6, 7, 11, 13, 15, 17, 19, 21	9, 10, 12, 14, 16, 18, 20, 22, 23, 26
Proficient	3, 6, 8, 12, 14, 16, 17, 18, 19, 21	9, 20, 22, 23, 24, 25, 26
Advanced	3, 6, 9, 12, 14, 16, 17, 18, 19, 21	22, 23, 24, 25, 26, 27, 28

- Assignment 1 is for use after students complete the Self-Assessment for Concepts & Skills.
- Assignment 2 is for use after students complete the Self-Assessment for Problem Solving.
- The red exercises can be used as a concept check.

Review & Refresh Prior Skills

Exercises 1–3 Solving a System of Linear Equations by Elimination
Exercises 4–6 Writing Equations

Common Errors

- **Exercises 7, 8, 10, 12–14, 16, and 18** Students may see that the slope is the same for both equations and immediately say that the system of linear equations has no solution. Remind students that they need to compare the slopes *and* y-intercepts when determining the number of solutions.
- **Exercises 11–18** Students may make calculation errors when solving the equations for y. Encourage students to be careful when solving for y.

5.4 Practice

 ? Go to *BigIdeasMath.com* to get HELP with solving the exercises.

▶ Review & Refresh

Solve the system by elimination. Check your solution.

1. $x + 2y = 4$
   $-x - y = 2$

2. $2x - y = 1$
   $x + 3y - 4 = 0$

3. $3x = -4y + 10$
   $4x + 3y = 11$

Write an equation of the line that passes through the given points.

4. $(0, 0), (2, 6)$

5. $(0, -3), (3, 3)$

6. $(-6, 5), (0, 2)$

▶▶ Concepts, Skills, & Problem Solving

EXPLORING SOLUTIONS OF SYSTEMS Use a graph to determine the number of solutions of the system. (See Exploration 1, p. 219.)

7. $y = 2x + 1$
   $y = 2x + 5$

8. $y + 8 = 0$
   $y = -8$

9. $x + y = 2$
   $5x + y = 9$

SOLVING A SYSTEM Solve the system. Explain your choice of method.

10. $y = 2x - 2$
    $y = 2x + 9$

11. $y = 3x + 1$
    $-x + 2y = -3$

12. $y = \frac{\pi}{3}x + \pi$
    $-\pi x + 3y = -6\pi$

13. $y = -\frac{1}{6}x + 5$
    $x + 6y = 30$

14. $\frac{1}{3}x + y = 1$
    $2x + 6y = 6$

15. $-2x + y = 1.3$
    $2(0.5x - y) = 4.6$

16. $2(x + y) = 9$
    $1 = -4(x + y)$

17. $y = 9x$
    $x + y = 1$

18. $0.2y = 4.6x + 1.2$
    $-2.3x = -0.1y + 0.6$

19. **MP YOU BE THE TEACHER** Your friend finds the number of solutions of the system. Is your friend correct? Explain your reasoning.

> $y = -2x + 4$
> $y = -2x + 6$
> The lines have the same slope, so there are infinitely many solutions.

20. **MP REASONING** In a pig race, your pig has a head start of 3 feet and runs at a rate of 2 feet per second. Your friend's pig also runs at a rate of 2 feet per second. A system of linear equations that represents this situation is $y = 2x + 3$ and $y = 2x$. Does your friend's pig catch up to your pig? Explain.

21. **(MP) REASONING** One equation in a system of linear equations has a slope of -3. The other equation has a slope of 4. How many solutions does the system have? Explain.

22. **(MP) LOGIC** How can you use the slopes and the y-intercepts of equations in a system of linear equations to determine whether the system has *one solution, infinitely many solutions,* or *no solution*?

23. **(MP) PROBLEM SOLVING** You and a friend both work two different jobs. The system of linear equations represents the total earnings (in dollars) for x hours worked at the first job and y hours worked at the second job. Your friend earns twice as much as you.

$$4x + 8y = 64 \qquad \text{You}$$
$$8x + 16y = 128 \qquad \text{Your Friend}$$

   a. One week, both of you work 4 hours at the first job. How many hours do you and your friend work at the second job?

   b. Both of you work the same number of hours at the second job. Compare the numbers of hours you and your friend work at the first job.

24. **(MP) MODELING REAL LIFE** You download a digital album for $10.00. Then you and your friend each download the same number of individual songs for $0.99 each. Write a system of linear equations that represents this situation. Will you and your friend spend the same amount of money? Explain.

25. **(MP) MODELING REAL LIFE** The table shows the research activities of two students at an observatory. How much does a student pay to use the telescope for one hour? the supercomputer for one hour?

	Telescope Use	Supercomputer Use	Total Cost
Student 1	5 hours	3 hours	$70.50
Student 2	6 hours	2 hours	$67.00

26. **(MP) PRECISION** Does the system shown *always, sometimes,* or *never* have a solution when $a = b$? $a \geq b$? $a < b$? Explain your reasoning.

$$y = ax + 1$$
$$y = bx + 4$$

Group	1	2	3
Number of Lift Tickets	36	24	18
Number of Ski Rentals	18	12	18
Total Cost (dollars)	684	456	432

27. **(MP) LOGIC** The table shows the numbers of lift tickets and ski rentals sold to different groups. Is it possible to determine how much each lift ticket costs using the information for Groups 1 and 2? Groups 1 and 3? Justify your answers.

28. **DIG DEEPER!** Find the values of a and b so the system shown has the solution $(2, 3)$. Does the system have any other solutions for these values of a and b? Explain.

$$12x - 2by = 12$$
$$3ax - by = 6$$

Mini-Assessment

Solve the system. Explain your choice of method.

1. $2x + 3y = 5$
$2x + 3y = 7$
no solution; Explanations will vary.

2. $x + 2y = 12$
$y = -\frac{1}{2}x + 6$
infinitely many solutions, all points on the line $y = -\frac{1}{2}x + 6$; Explanations will vary.

3. $-3x + 2y = 2$
$4x + 3y = 20$
(2, 4)

4. You and your friend buy fruit. You pay $4 for 5 apples and 6 bananas. Your friend pays $12 for 15 apples and 18 bananas. How much does each piece of fruit cost? There is not enough information to find the cost of each piece of fruit.

Section Resources

Surface Level	Deep Level
Resources by Chapter • Extra Practice • Reteach • Puzzle Time Student Journal • Self-Assessment • Practice Differentiating the Lesson Tutorial Videos Skills Review Handbook Skills Trainer	Resources by Chapter • Enrichment and Extension Graphic Organizers Dynamic Assessment System • Section Practice
Transfer Level	
Dynamic Assessment System • End-of-Chapter Quiz	Assessment Book • End-of-Chapter Quiz

 Concepts, Skills, & Problem Solving

21. one solution; The lines have different slopes.

22. When the slopes are different, there is one solution. When the slopes are the same, there is no solution if the y-intercepts are different and infinitely many solutions if the y-intercepts are the same.

23. a. 6 h

b. You both work the same number of hours.

24. $y = 0.99x + 10$
$y = 0.99x$;
no; The lines are parallel, so the amount you spend will always be $10 more.

25. $7.50; $11

26. never; sometimes; always; When $a = b$, the lines are parallel. When $a > b$ or $a < b$, the lines have different slopes.

27. no;
$36x + 18y = 684$
$24x + 12y = 456$
infinitely many solutions
yes;
$36x + 18y = 684$
$18x + 18y = 432$
Solution: (14, 10)

28. $a = 2$, $b = 2$; yes; The lines are the same.

Exercise 1
- Choosing a Solution Method for a System of Linear Equations
- Identifying Proportional Relationships

Exercise 2
- Choosing a Solution Method for a System of Linear Equations
- Finding Angle Measures

Exercise 3
- Choosing a Solution Method for a System of Linear Equations
- Perimeters and Areas of Similar Figures

ELL Support

Animal shelters are not common in every country. Students may be familiar with the word *shelter* as a place where people go during natural disasters. Ask them to share what they know. Discuss the concept of an animal shelter in the United States.

Using the Problem-Solving Plan

1. 30 cats, 35 dogs

2. $\angle 1 = 115°$, $\angle 2 = 65°$, $\angle 3 = 115°$, $\angle 4 = 65°$;
   $x = 2y - 15$
   $x + y = 180$
   Solution: $(115, 65)$
   Using vertical angles,
   $\angle 1 = \angle 3 = 115°$ and
   $\angle 2 = \angle 4 = 65°$.

3. 7200 ft^2; 1800 ft^2; Because the perimeter of Park A is 2 times the perimeter of Park B, the area of Park A is 4 times the area of Park B.
   $x + y = 9000$
   $x = 4y$
   Solution: $(7200, 1800)$

Performance Task

The *STEAM Video Performance Task* provides the opportunity for additional enrichment and greater depth of knowledge as students explore the mathematics of the chapter within a context tied to the chapter STEAM Video. The performance task and a detailed scoring rubric are provided at *BigIdeasMath.com*.

Laurie's Notes

Scaffolding Instruction

- The goal of this lesson is to help students become more comfortable with problem solving. These exercises combine solving systems of equations with prior skills from other chapters and courses. The solution for Exercise 1 is worked out below, to help you guide students through the problem-solving plan. Use the remaining class time to have students work on Exercises 2 and 3.
- **Emerging:** The goal for these students is to feel comfortable with the problem-solving plan. Allow students to work in pairs to write the beginning steps of the problem-solving plan for Exercise 2. Keep in mind that some students may only be ready to do the first step.
- **Proficient:** Students may be able to work independently or in pairs to complete Exercises 2 and 3.
- Visit each pair to review their plan for each problem. Ask students to describe their plans.

▶ Using the Problem-Solving Plan

Exercise 1

➡ **Understand the problem.** You know the total number of cats and dogs in an animal shelter, and the ratio of cats to dogs. You are asked to find the number of cats and the number of dogs in the shelter.

➡ **Make a plan.** Write a system of equations. Use the total number of cats and dogs to write an equation relating the number x of cats and the number y of dogs. Use the ratio of cats to dogs to write a second equation. Then solve the system.

➡ **Solve and check.** Use the plan to solve the problem. Then check your solution.

- Write a system of equations.
  Let x represent the number of cats and let y represent the number of dogs.
  Number of cats + Number of dogs = Total number of cats and dogs

  $$\frac{\text{Number of cats}}{\text{Number of dogs}} = \frac{6}{7}$$

  The system is: $\quad x + y = 65 \quad$ Equation 1
  $$\frac{x}{y} = \frac{6}{7} \quad \text{Equation 2}$$

- Solve the system. Rewrite Equation 2 as $x = \frac{6}{7}y$. Then substitute $\frac{6}{7}y$ for x in Equation 1 and solve to find the value of y.

$x + y = 65$	Equation 1
$\frac{6}{7}y + y = 65$	Substitute $\frac{6}{7}y$ for x.
$\frac{13}{7}y = 65$	Combine like terms.
$y = 35$	Multiply each side by $\frac{7}{13}$.

$x = \frac{6}{7}y$	Equation 2
$x = \frac{6}{7}(35)$	Substitute 35 for y.
$x = 30$	Multiply.

  So, there are 30 cats and 35 dogs in the shelter.

- **Check:** Substitute 30 for x and 35 for y in both equations.

  $x + y = 65 \qquad\qquad \frac{x}{y} = \frac{6}{7}$

  $30 + 35 = 65 \qquad\qquad \frac{30}{35} = \frac{6}{7}$

  $65 = 65 \checkmark \qquad\qquad \frac{6}{7} = \frac{6}{7} \checkmark$

Connecting Concepts

▶ *Using the Problem-Solving Plan*

1. An animal shelter has a total of 65 cats and dogs. The ratio of cats to dogs is 6 : 7. Find the number of cats and the number of dogs in the shelter.

Understand the problem.
You know the total number of cats and dogs in an animal shelter, and the ratio of cats to dogs. You are asked to find the number of cats and the number of dogs in the shelter.

Make a plan.
Write a system of equations. Use the total number of cats and dogs to write an equation relating the number x of cats and the number y of dogs. Use the ratio of cats to dogs to write a second equation. Then solve the system.

Solve and check.
Use the plan to solve the problem. Then check your solution.

2. The measure of $\angle 1$ is 15 degrees less than two times the measure of $\angle 2$. Find the measure of each of the four angles formed by the intersecting lines. Justify your answer.

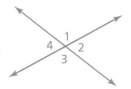

3. A landscaper plants grass seed over the entire area of two parks that are similar in shape. The ratio of the perimeter of Park A to the perimeter of Park B is 2 : 1. The parks have a combined area of 9000 square feet. How many square feet does the landscaper cover with grass seed at Park A? Park B? Justify your answer.

Performance Task

Mixing Alloys

At the beginning of this chapter, you watched a STEAM Video called "Gold Alloys." You are now ready to complete the performance task related to this video, available at *BigIdeasMath.com*. Be sure to use the problem-solving plan as you work through the performance task.

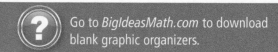

▶ Review Vocabulary

Write the definition and give an example of each vocabulary term.

system of linear equations, *p. 200*   solution of a system of linear equations, *p. 200*

▶ Graphic Organizers

You can use a **Four Square** to organize information about a concept. Each of the four squares can be a category, such as definition, vocabulary, example, non-example, words, algebra, table, numbers, visual, graph, or equation. Here is an example of a Four Square for *solving systems of linear equations by graphing*.

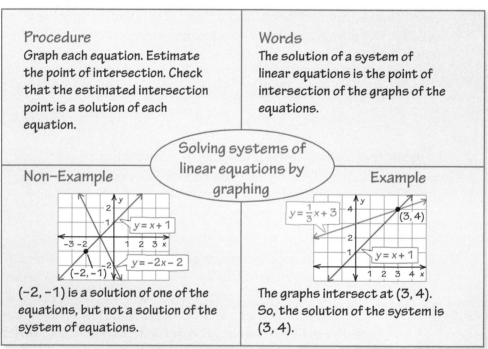

Procedure
Graph each equation. Estimate the point of intersection. Check that the estimated intersection point is a solution of each equation.

Words
The solution of a system of linear equations is the point of intersection of the graphs of the equations.

Solving systems of linear equations by graphing

Non-Example

$y = x + 1$
$y = -2x - 2$
$(-2, -1)$

$(-2, -1)$ is a solution of one of the equations, but not a solution of the system of equations.

Example

$y = \frac{1}{3}x + 3$
$(3, 4)$
$y = x + 1$

The graphs intersect at $(3, 4)$. So, the solution of the system is $(3, 4)$.

Choose and complete a graphic organizer to help you study the concept.

1. solving systems of linear equations by substitution

2. solving systems of linear equations by elimination

3. systems of linear equations with no solution

4. systems of linear equations with infinitely many solutions

Definition
A Japanese art form of growing miniature trees

Visual

Bonsai

Examples
Mini Maple
Tiny Piney

Fact
Bonsai trees can live longer than the full-size version.

Amazing! It doesn't look a day over 85.

"Here is my Four Square about bonsai. This bonsai tree is over 90 years old."

Review Vocabulary

- As a review of the chapter vocabulary, have students revisit the vocabulary section in their *Student Journals* to fill in any missing definitions and record examples of each term.

Graphic Organizers

Sample answers:

1.

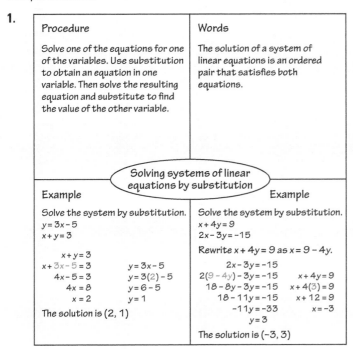

2–4. Answers at *BigIdeasMath.com*.

About this Organizer

A **Four Square** can be used to organize information about a concept. Students write the concept in the oval. Then students use each of the four squares surrounding the oval to represent a related category. Related categories may include: definition, vocabulary, example, non-example, words, algebra, table, numbers, visual, graph, or equation. Encourage students to use categories that will help them study the concept. Students can place their Four Squares on note cards to use as a quick study reference.

1. $(5, 7)$

2. $(6, -2)$

3. $(-4, -2)$

4. $(-1, 0.5)$

5. $(1.32, -2.74)$

6. $(4, -2)$

7. $23, 15$;
   $x + y = 38$
   $x - y = 8$
   Solution: $(23, 15)$

8. **a.** $y = x + 8$
      $y = 2x + 4$

   b. yes; 12 cm

9. *Sample answer:* $y = -3x + 2$
   $ y = 2x + 7$

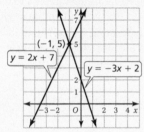

✓ *Chapter Self-Assessment*

The Success Criteria Self-Assessment chart can be found in the *Student Journal* or online at *BigIdeasMath.com*.

ELL Support

Allow students to work in pairs to complete the first section of the Chapter Self-Assessment. Provide graph paper. Once pairs have finished, check for understanding by having each pair hold up their graphs and solutions for Exercises 1–3. Check for understanding of Exercises 4–6 by having each pair display their solutions on a whiteboard for your review. Pairs should discuss and answer Exercises 7–9. Then have each pair compare their ideas with another pair and reach an agreement on the answers. Monitor discussions and provide support. Ask each group to share an answer to one of the exercises and ask other groups to critique the reasoning. Use similar techniques to check the remaining sections.

Common Errors

- **Exercises 1–3** Students may not show enough of the graph to see where the lines intersect. Encourage them to extend their lines until they intersect.
- **Exercises 4–6** Students may try to visually estimate the point of intersection of the graphs on their graphing calculator screens. Remind them to use the *intersect* feature to estimate the point of intersection.

▶ Chapter Self-Assessment

As you complete the exercises, use the scale below to rate your understanding of the success criteria in your journal.

1	**2**	**3**	**4**
I do not understand.	I can do it with help.	I can do it on my own.	I can teach someone else.

5.1 Solving Systems of Linear Equations by Graphing (pp. 199–204)

Learning Target: Understand how to solve systems of linear equations by graphing.

Solve the system by graphing.

1. $y = 2x - 3$
   $y = x + 2$

2. $y = -x + 4$
   $x + 3y = 0$

3. $x - y = -2$
   $2x - 3y = -2$

Use a graphing calculator to solve the system.

4. $y = -0.5x$
   $y = 0.75x + 1.25$

5. $y = 0.2x - 3$
   $10x + 3y = 5$

6. $2.6x + 1.3y = 7.8$
   $1.2x - 3.6y = 12$

7. The sum of two numbers is 38. Find each number when one number is 8 more than the other number. Use a system of linear equations to justify your answer.

8. You observe the heights of two plants for an experiment. Plant A has a height of 8 centimeters and grows 1 centimeter each week. Plant B has a height of 4 centimeters and grows 2 centimeters each week.

   a. Write a system of linear equations that represents this situation.

   b. Will the plants ever have the same height? If so, what is the height?

9. Write a system of linear equations containing the equation $y = -3x + 2$ and that has a solution of $(-1, 5)$. Use a graph to justify your answer.

5.2 Solving Systems of Linear Equations by Substitution (pp. 205–210)

Learning Target: Understand how to solve systems of linear equations by substitution.

Solve the system by substitution. Check your solution.

10. $y = -3x - 7$

$y = x + 9$

11. $\frac{1}{2}x + y = -4$

$y = 2x + 16$

12. $-x + 5y = 28$

$x + 3y = 20$

13. Zoo admission costs $6 for children and $9 for adults. On Monday, 2200 people visit the zoo and the zoo collects $14,850 in admissions.

  a. Write a system of linear equations that represents this situation.

  b. How many zoo visitors are children? adults?

Solve the system. Explain your choice of method.

14. $y = x - 2$

$y = -2x + 1$

15. $3y + 9 = 3x$

$y = -\frac{1}{3}x + 1$

16. $-x + 2y = -4$

$4y = x$

17. The measure of an acute angle in a right triangle is one-fourth the measure of the other acute angle. Write a system of linear equations that represents this situation and use it to find the measures of the acute angles of the triangle.

5.3 Solving Systems of Linear Equations by Elimination (pp. 211–218)

Learning Target: Understand how to solve systems of linear equations by elimination.

Solve the system by elimination. Check your solution.

18. $2x + 5y = 60$

$2x - 5y = -20$

19. $4x - 3y = 15$

$2x + y = -5$

20. A gift basket that contains jars of jam and packages of bread mix costs $45. There are 8 items in the basket. Jars of jam cost $6 each, and packages of bread mix cost $5 each. Write and solve a system of linear equations to find the number of each item in the gift basket.

21. When might it be easier to solve a system by elimination instead of graphing?

Common Errors

- **Exercises 10–12, 14–16, 18, and 19** Students may find one coordinate of the solution and stop. Remind them that the solution of a system of linear equations is a coordinate pair representing both an *x*-value and a *y*-value.
- **Exercises 18 and 19** Students may make careless errors. Remind students to line up like terms neatly in columns to avoid confusion about what terms to add or subtract. Also, tell them to take care with subtraction—it may help to change the sign of each term in the equation to be subtracted, so they can just add the terms.
- **Exercise 19** Students may make errors in multiplying through the whole equation. Tell them to clearly show what they are multiplying each equation by so they do not forget during the process. Students should check the sign and coefficient of each term after multiplying.

10. $(-4, 5)$

11. $(-8, 0)$

12. $(2, 6)$

13. **a.** $x + y = 2200$
$6x + 9y = 14{,}850$

 b. 1650 children; 550 adults

14. $(1, -1)$; Explanations will vary.

15. $(3, 0)$; Explanations will vary.

16. $(8, 2)$; Explanations will vary.

17. $x + y = 90$

 $x = \dfrac{1}{4}y;$

 $18°, 72°$

18. $(10, 8)$

19. $(0, -5)$

20. $x + y = 8$
$6x + 5y = 45;$
5 jars of jam, 3 packages of bread mix

21. *Sample answer:* when an equation is not easy to graph because the coefficients and constant are fractions or decimals

22. $x + y = 10$
    $0.05x + 0.1y = 0.7$;
    6 nickels, 4 dimes

23. $(-5, 0)$; Explanations will vary.

24. infinitely many solutions;
    Explanations will vary.

25. no solution; Explanations
    will vary.

26. no solution; Explanations
    will vary.

27. $(1, 0)$; Explanations will vary.

28. no solution; Explanations
    will vary.

29. **a.** $y = 10x + 50$
    $y = 10x + 25$

    b. no; The lines are parallel,
    so you will always have $25
    more in your account.

30. *Sample answer:* $y = 3x + 2$
    $ y = 3x - 5$

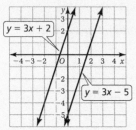

31. *Sample answer:* $y = 2x + 5$
    $ -4x + 2y = 10$

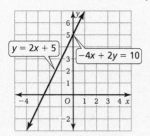

32. See Additional Answers.

33. no solution; Answers will vary.

34. Answers will vary.

Common Errors

- **Exercises 24–26 and 28** Students may see that the slope is the same for both equations and immediately say that the system of linear equations has no solution. Remind them that they need to compare the slopes *and* y-intercepts when determining the number of solutions.

Chapter Resources

Surface Level	Deep Level
Resources by Chapter • Extra Practice • Reteach • Puzzle Time Student Journal • Practice • Chapter Self-Assessment Differentiating the Lesson Tutorial Videos Skills Review Handbook Skills Trainer Game Library	Resources by Chapter • Enrichment and Extension Graphic Organizers Game Library
Transfer Level	
STEAM Video Dynamic Assessment System • Chapter Test	Assessment Book • Chapter Tests A and B • Alternative Assessment • STEAM Performance Task

22. You have a total of 10 coins consisting of nickels and dimes in your pocket. The value of the coins is $0.70. Write and solve a system of linear equations to find the numbers of nickels and dimes in your pocket.

5.4 Solving Special Systems of Linear Equations (pp. 219–224)

Learning Target: Solve systems with different numbers of solutions.

Solve the system. Explain your choice of method.

23. $x + 2y = -5$
$x - 2y = -5$

24. $3x - 2y = 1$
$9x - 6y = 3$

25. $8x - 2y = 16$
$-4x + y = 8$

26. $4y = x - 8$
$-\dfrac{1}{4}x + y = -1$

27. $-2x + y = -2$
$3x + y = 3$

28. $3x = \dfrac{1}{3}y + 2$
$9x - y = -6$

29. You have $50 in your savings account and plan to deposit $10 each week. Your friend has $25 in her savings account and plans to also deposit $10 each week.

    a. Write a system of linear equations that represents this situation.

    b. Will your friend's account ever have the same amount of money as your account? Explain.

Write a system of linear equations that fits the description. Use a graph to justify your answer.

30. The system has no solution.

31. The system has infinitely many solutions.

32. The system has one solution.

33. Solve the system by graphing, by substitution, and by elimination. Which method do you prefer? Explain your reasoning.

$$5x + y = 8$$
$$2y = -10x + 8$$

34. Your friend chooses to solve the system of equations by graphing. Would you choose the same method? Why or why not?

$$5x + 2y = 12$$
$$y = x - 8$$

Practice Test

1. Solve the system by graphing.

$$y = \frac{1}{2}x + 10$$

$$y = 4x - 4$$

2. Solve the system by substitution. Check your solution.

$$-3x + y = 2$$

$$-x + y - 4 = 0$$

3. Solve the system by elimination. Check your solution.

$$x + y = 12$$
$$3x = 2y + 6$$

4. Solve the system. Explain your choice of method.

$$-2x + y + 3 = 0$$
$$3x + 4y = -1$$

Without graphing or solving, determine whether the system of linear equations has *one solution*, *infinitely many solutions*, or *no solution*. Explain your reasoning.

5. $y = 4x + 8$

   $y = 5x + 1$

6. $2y = 16x - 2$

   $y = 8x - 1$

7. $y = -3x + 2$

   $6x + 2y = 10$

8. In the diagram, the measure of $\angle 1$ is three times the measure of $\angle 2$. Find the measure of each angle.

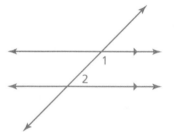

9. The price of 2 pears and 6 apples is $14. The price of 3 pears and 9 apples is $21. Can you determine the unit prices for pears and apples? Explain.

10. A bouquet of lilies and tulips has 12 flowers. Lilies cost $3 each, and tulips cost $2 each. The bouquet costs $32. Write and solve a system of linear equations to find the numbers of lilies and tulips in the bouquet.

GUEST CHECK

4 Specials
2 Glasses
    of milk

$28.00

GUEST CHECK

3 Specials
4 Glasses
   of milk

$26.25

11. How much does it cost for 2 specials and 2 glasses of milk?

Practice Test Item References

Practice Test Questions	Section to Review
1, 4, 8, 10, 11	5.1
2, 4, 8, 10, 11	5.2
3, 4, 8, 10, 11	5.3
5, 6, 7, 9	5.4

Test-Taking Strategies

Remind students to quickly look over the entire test before they start so that they can budget their time. This test involves solving systems of equations, and the answers take on several different forms. So, it is important that students use the **Stop** and **Think** strategy before they write their answers.

 ## Common Errors

- **Exercise 1** Students may not show enough of the graph to see where the lines intersect. Encourage them to extend their lines until they intersect.
- **Exercises 2–4** Students may find one coordinate of the solution and stop. Remind them that the solution of a system of linear equations is a coordinate pair representing both an x-value and a y-value.
- **Exercise 3** Students may make careless errors. Remind students to line up like terms neatly in columns to avoid confusion about what terms to add or subtract. Also, tell them to take care with subtraction—it may help to change the sign of each term in the equation to be subtracted, so they can just add the terms.
- **Exercise 3** Students may make errors in multiplying through the whole equation. Tell them to clearly show what they are multiplying each equation by so they do not forget during the process. Students should check the sign and coefficient of each term after multiplying.
- **Exercises 6 and 7** Students may see that the slope is the same for both equations and immediately say that the system of linear equations has no solution. Remind them that they need to compare the slopes *and* y-intercepts when determining the number of solutions.

1. $(4, 12)$
2. $(1, 5)$
3. $(6, 6)$
4. $(1, -1)$; Explanations will vary.
5. one solution; The lines have different slopes.
6. infinitely many solutions; The lines are the same.
7. no solution; The lines have the same slope and different y-intercepts.
8. $\angle 1 = 135°$, $\angle 2 = 45°$
9. no;
   $2x + 6y = 14$
   $3x + 9y = 21$
   infinitely many solutions
10. $x + y = 12$
    $3x + 2y = 32$;
    8 lilies, 4 tulips
11. $16.10

Cumulative Practice

1. D
2. 40
3. F

Item Analysis

1. **A.** The student finds one of the infinitely many solutions of the system of equations.

   B. The student finds one of the infinitely many solutions of the system of equations.

   C. If the student uses graphing to solve the system, the student makes an error rewriting the second equation in slope-intercept form. If the student uses substitution, the student forgets to distribute 6 to the second term in the expression $-\frac{2}{3}x - 1$ and gets $-1 \neq -6$. If the student uses elimination, the student forgets to keep the negative sign with the 1 on the right side when rewriting the first equation, writing $\frac{2}{3}x + y = 1$ instead of $\frac{2}{3}x + y = -1$.

   D. Correct answer

2. **Gridded Response:** Correct answer: 40

   Common error: The student thinks that the angles are congruent and gets $x = 140$.

3. **F.** Correct answer

   G. The student reflects the rectangle in the *x*-axis.

   H. The student translates the rectangle 4 units left instead of down.

   I. The student translates the rectangle 4 units up instead of down.

Cumulative Practice

1. What is the solution of the system of equations?

$$y = -\frac{2}{3}x - 1$$

$$4x + 6y = -6$$

A. $\left(-\frac{3}{2}, 0\right)$ **B.** $(0, -1)$

C. no solution

D. infinitely many solutions

2. What is the value of x?

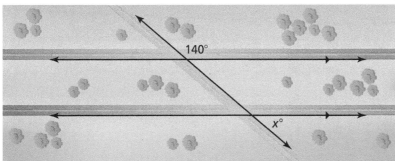

3. Which of the following shows Rectangle $E'F'G'H'$, the image of Rectangle $EFGH$ after it is translated 4 units down?

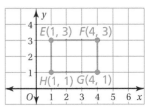

F.

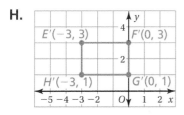

G.

H.

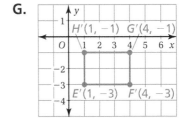

I.

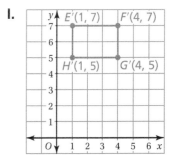

4. Which point is a solution of the system of equations?

$$x + 3y = 10$$
$$x = 2y - 5$$

A. $(1, 3)$

B. $(3, 1)$

C. $(55, -15)$

D. $(-35, -15)$

5. The graph of a system of two linear equations is shown. Which point is the solution of the system?

F. $(-1, 2)$

G. $(0, 4)$

H. $(2, -1)$

I. $(0, 0)$

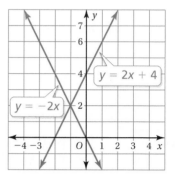

6. A scenic train ride has one price for adults and one price for children. One family of two adults and two children pays $62 for the train ride. Another family of one adult and four children pays $70. Which system of linear equations can you use to find the price x for an adult and the price y for a child?

A. $2x + 2y = 70$
  $x + 4y = 62$

B. $x + y = 62$
  $x + y = 70$

C. $2x + 2y = 62$
  $4x + y = 70$

D. $2x + 2y = 62$
  $x + 4y = 70$

7. Which of the following is true about the graph of the linear equation $y = -7x + 5$?

F. The slope is 5, and the y-intercept is -7.

G. The slope is -5, and the y-intercept is -7.

H. The slope is -7, and the y-intercept is -5.

I. The slope is -7, and the y-intercept is 5.

8. What is the measure (in degrees) of the exterior angle of the triangle?

Item Analysis (continued)

4. **A.** Correct answer

   B. The student checks the points by substituting for x and y in reverse order.

   C. The student finds a solution for the first equation but not the second equation.

   D. The student finds a solution for the second equation but not the first equation.

5. **F.** Correct answer

   G. The student finds a solution for $y = 2x + 4$ but not $y = -2x$.

   H. The student switches the x- and y-coordinates of the solution.

   I. The student finds a solution for $y = -2x$ but not $y = 2x + 4$.

6. **A.** The student uses the wrong cost for each family.

   B. The student defines x as the total amount spent on adults and y as total the amount spent on children for each family.

   C. The student defines x as the price for a child and y as the price for an adult.

   D. Correct answer

7. **F.** The student switches the slope and the y-intercept in interpreting the slope-intercept form.

   G. The student switches the slope and the y-intercept in interpreting the slope-intercept form, and misinterprets the slope as $-m$.

   H. The student misinterprets the y-intercept as $-b$.

   I. Correct answer

8. **Gridded Response:** Correct answer: 127

   Common error: The student finds the value of x instead of the measure of the exterior angle and gets 63.

4. A

5. F

6. D

7. I

8. 127

9. C

10. $7.50

11. H

12. D

13. G

14. B

Item Analysis (continued)

9. **A.** The student forgets to reverse the sign of -1 when subtracting it from 4.

   B. The student determines the slope incorrectly as the opposite of the change in x over the change in y.

   C. Correct answer

   D. The student determines the slope incorrectly as the change in x over the change in y.

10. **2 points** The student's work and explanations demonstrate a thorough understanding of how to solve a system of linear equations and interpret the solution. The solution is (7.5, 10). The x-value represents the cost of each T-shirt, $7.50. The student provides clear and complete work and explanations.

    1 point The student's work and explanations demonstrate a partial but limited understanding of how to solve a system of linear equations and interpret the solution. The student may set up or solve the system of linear equations incorrectly. If the solution is correct, the student incorrectly applies the solution to the problem.

    0 points The student provides no response, a completely incorrect or incomprehensible response, or a response that demonstrates insufficient understanding of how to solve a system of linear equations and interpret the solution.

11. **F.** The student incorrectly thinks that translating the red triangle 6 units left and 4 units down will map it onto the blue triangle.

    G. The student reflects the red triangle in the incorrect axis.

    H. Correct answer

    I. The student incorrectly thinks that rotating the red triangle 180° about the origin will map it onto the blue triangle.

12. **A.** The student misinterprets the graph as a vertical line instead of a horizontal line and switches the coordinates of a point that the line passes through.

    B. The student correctly identifies a point that the line passes through but misinterprets the graph as a vertical line instead of a horizontal line.

    C. The student switches the coordinates of a point that the line passes through.

    D. Correct answer

13. **F.** The student solves $\frac{1}{3} + n + 10 = 13$ instead of $\frac{1}{3}n + 10 = 13$.

    G. Correct answer

    H. The student incorrectly represents the sum of one-third of a number and ten as $\frac{1}{3}(n + 10)$.

    I. The student solves $\frac{1}{3}n = 10 + 13$ instead of $\frac{1}{3}n + 10 = 13$.

14. **A.** The student adds $7y$ to 16 instead of subtracting $7y$ from 16.

    B. Correct answer

    C. The student adds $7y$ to 16 instead of subtracting $7y$ from 16, and inverts the fraction when dividing by 4.

    D. The student does not divide $16 - 7y$ by 4.

9. The graph of which equation is parallel to the line that passes through the points $(-1, 5)$ and $(4, 7)$?

A. $y = \dfrac{2}{3}x + 6$

B. $y = -\dfrac{5}{2}x + 4$

C. $y = \dfrac{2}{5}x + 1$

D. $y = \dfrac{5}{2}x - 1$

10. You buy 3 T-shirts and 2 pairs of shorts for $42.50. Your friend buys 5 T-shirts and 3 pairs of shorts for $67.50. Use a system of linear equations to find the cost of each T-shirt. Show your work and explain your reasoning.

11. The red figure is congruent to the blue figure. Which of the following is a sequence of rigid motions between the figures?

F. Translate the red triangle 6 units left and then 4 units down.

G. Reflect the red triangle in the x-axis, and then translate 4 units down.

H. Reflect the red triangle in the y-axis, and then translate 4 units down.

I. Rotate the red triangle 180° clockwise about the origin.

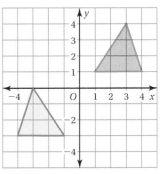

12. Which of the following is true about the graph of the linear equation $y = 2$?

A. The graph is a vertical line that passes through $(2, 0)$.

B. The graph is a vertical line that passes through $(0, 2)$.

C. The graph is a horizontal line that passes through $(2, 0)$.

D. The graph is a horizontal line that passes through $(0, 2)$.

13. The sum of one-third of a number and 10 is equal to 13. What is the number?

F. $\dfrac{8}{3}$ **G.** 9   **H.** 29   **I.** 69

14. Solve the equation $4x + 7y = 16$ for x.

A. $x = 4 + \dfrac{7}{4}y$

B. $x = 4 - \dfrac{7}{4}y$

C. $x = 4 + \dfrac{4}{7}y$

D. $x = 16 - 7y$

Data Analysis and Displays

6.1 Scatter Plots

6.2 Lines of Fit

6.3 Two-Way Tables

6.4 Choosing a Data Display

Chapter Learning Target:
Understand data displays.

Chapter Success Criteria:
- ☐ I can identify a data set.
- ☐ I can use appropriate data displays to represent a situation.
- ■ I can interpret a data set.
- ■ I can compare different data sets.

STEAM Video: "Fuel Economy"

Laurie's Notes

Chapter 6 Overview

This chapter is one of my favorites and students often feel the same way. They are interested in the variety of data sets and enjoy the opportunity to think about the different ways in which data sets can be displayed. Students will build upon their prior work with data displays and linear equations, so take time to review these skills throughout the chapter.

The chapter begins with students making and interpreting scatter plots to describe relationships between data, laying the foundation for the second lesson. Students will combine their understanding of scatter plots and their work with graphs of linear equations to write lines of fit and lines of best fit. Many real-life applications involve data that can be modeled by linear equations. Students will first learn to approximate a line of fit and then use graphing calculators to generate the line of best fit.

In the third lesson a new type of data display is introduced, a two-way table. Typically, students find reading a two-way table to be easy, but make sure they understand the difference between a *joint frequency* and a *marginal frequency*. These terms sound similar, so students often confuse them. Tell students to think of the marginal frequencies as appearing in the *margins* of a two-way table.

		Student	
		Studied	**Did Not Study**
Grade	**Passed**	21	2
	Failed	1	6

joint frequency

		Student		
		Studied	**Did Not Study**	**Total**
Grade	**Passed**	21	2	23
	Failed	1	6	7
	Total	22	8	30

marginal frequency

Students should be familiar with all of the data displays discussed in the last lesson. They will analyze a set of data to determine which display(s) are most appropriate for the situation. In choosing a type of data display, students must first consider the type of data they have and what would be an appropriate way to display it. For example, the numbers of students in your school who play basketball, football, soccer, or lacrosse could be displayed in a bar graph or a circle graph, but the data would lose its meaning in a dot plot. Students will also spend time identifying misleading data displays, which is a valuable real-life skill.

Chapter Opener	1 Day
Section 1	2 Days
Section 2	3 Days
Section 3	2 Days
Section 4	2 Days
Connecting Concepts	1 Day
Chapter Review	1 Day
Chapter Test	1 Day
Total Chapter 6	13 Days
Year-to-Date	86 Days

Chapter Learning Target
Understand data displays.

Chapter Success Criteria
- Identify a data set.
- Use appropriate data displays to represent a situation.
- Interpret a data set.
- Compare different data sets.

Chapter 6 Learning Targets and Success Criteria

Section	Learning Target	Success Criteria
6.1 Scatter Plots	Use scatter plots to describe patterns and relationships between two quantities.	• Make a scatter plot. • Identify outliers, gaps, and clusters in a scatter plot. • Use scatter plots to describe relationships between data.
6.2 Lines of Fit	Use lines of fit to model data.	• Write and interpret an equation of a line of fit. • Find an equation of a line of best fit. • Use a line of fit to make predictions.
6.3 Two-Way Tables	Use two-way tables to represent data.	• Read a two-way table. • Make a two-way table. • Use a two-way table to describe relationships between data.
6.4 Choosing a Data Display	Use appropriate data displays to represent situations.	• Choose appropriate data displays for situations. • Identify misleading data displays. • Analyze a variety of data displays.

Progressions

Through the Grades

Grade 7	Grade 8	High School
• Use samples to draw inferences about populations. • Compare two populations from random samples using measures of center and variability. • Approximate the probability of a chance event and predict the approximate relative frequency given the probability.	• Construct and interpret scatter plots. • Find and assess lines of fit for scatter plots. • Use equations of lines to solve problems and interpret the slope and the y-intercept. • Construct and interpret a two-way table summarizing data. Use relative frequencies to describe possible association between the two variables.	• Classify data as quantitative or qualitative, choose and create appropriate data displays, and analyze misleading graphs. • Make and use two-way tables to recognize associations in data by finding marginal, relative, and conditional relative frequencies. • Interpret scatter plots, determine how well lines of fit model data, and distinguish between correlation and causation.

Through the Chapter

Standard	6.1	6.2	6.3	6.4
8.SP.A.1 Construct and interpret scatter plots for bivariate measurement data to investigate patterns of association between two quantities. Describe patterns such as clustering, outliers, positive or negative association, linear association, and nonlinear association.	●	★		■
8.SP.A.2 Know that straight lines are widely used to model relationships between two quantitative variables. For scatter plots that suggest a linear association, informally fit a straight line, and informally assess the model fit by judging the closeness of the data points to the line.		★		
8.SP.A.3 Use the equation of a linear model to solve problems in the context of bivariate measurement data, interpreting the slope and intercept.		★		
8.SP.A.4 Understand that patterns of association can also be seen in bivariate categorical data by displaying frequencies and relative frequencies in a two-way table. Construct and interpret a two-way table summarizing data on two categorical variables collected from the same subjects. Use relative frequencies calculated for rows or columns to describe possible association between the two variables.			★	

Key

▲ = preparing   ★ = complete
● = learning   ■ = extending

Laurie's Notes

STEAM Video

1. 6466 in.^{2}

2. **a.** The fuel economy decreases.

   b. a car with a footprint of 50 square feet and a fuel economy of 40 miles per gallon; no; The fuel economy is greater than what you would expect for a car with a footprint of 50 square feet.

Performance Task

Sample answer: to determine whether a car is reasonably priced given its fuel economy

Mathematical Practices

Students have opportunities to develop aspects of the mathematical practices throughout the chapter. Here are some examples.

1. **Make Sense of Problems and Persevere in Solving Them**
   6.4 Math Practice note, *p. 258*

2. **Reason Abstractly and Quantitatively**
   6.2 Exercise 10, *p. 247*

3. **Construct Viable Arguments and Critique the Reasoning of Others**
   6.3 Math Practice note, *p. 249*

4. **Model with Mathematics**
   6.2 Exercise 14, *p. 248*

5. **Use Appropriate Tools Strategically**
   6.4 Math Practice note, *p. 255*

6. **Attend to Precision**
   6.1 Math Practice note, *p. 237*

7. **Look for and Make Use of Structure**
   6.4 Exercise 18, *p. 262*

8. **Look for and Express Regularity in Repeated Reasoning**
   6.2 Math Practice note, *p. 243*

STEAM Video

Before the Video

- To introduce the STEAM Video, read aloud the first paragraph of Fuel Economy and discuss the question with your students.
- "What are the benefits of using a car with high fuel economy?"

During the Video

- The video shows Robert and Tory discussing cars and fuel economy.
- Pause the video at 0:54 and ask, "Why do car makers have to pay attention to the fuel economy of their entire fleets and not just individual models?" Because of the CAFE (corporate average fuel economy) standards.
- "What are the CAFE standards?" a federal law that says car makers have to improve their fleet fuel economies every year or face penalties
- **FYI:** The CAFE standards were first enacted by Congress in 1975 with the purpose of reducing energy consumption by increasing the fuel economy of cars and light trucks.
- Watch the remainder of the video.

After the Video

- Have students work with a partner to answer Questions 1 and 2.
- As students discuss and answer the questions, listen for understanding of reading and interpreting a scatter plot.

Performance Task

- Use this information to spark students' interest and promote thinking about real-life problems.
- Ask, "Why might you want to know the relationship between the fuel economy and the purchase price of a vehicle?"
- After completing the chapter, students will have gained the knowledge needed to complete "Cost vs. Fuel Economy."

Fuel Economy

The *fuel economy* of a vehicle is a measure of the efficiency of the vehicle's engine. What are the benefits of using a car with high fuel economy?

Watch the STEAM Video "Fuel Economy." Then answer the following questions.

1. Tory says that the *footprint* of a vehicle is the area of the rectangle formed by the wheel base and the track width. What is the footprint of a car with a wheel base of 106 inches and a track width of 61 inches?

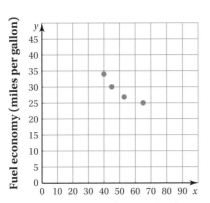

2. The graph shows the relationship between the fuel economy and the footprint for four vehicles.

   a. What happens to the fuel economy as the footprint increases?

   b. Plot the point (50, 40) on the graph. What does this point represent? Does the point fit in with the other points? Explain.

Performance Task

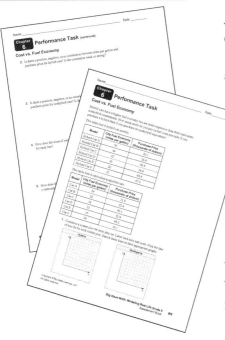

Cost vs. Fuel Economy

After completing this chapter, you will be able to use the concepts you learned to answer the questions in the *STEAM Video Performance Task*. You will be given fuel economies and purchase prices of hybrid and nonhybrid car models.

Model	City Fuel Economy (miles per gallon)	Purchase Price (thousands of dollars)
Car A	24	21.8
Car B	22	22.4
Car C	18	40.1

You will be asked to create graphs to compare car models. Why might you want to know the relationship between the fuel economy and the purchase price of a vehicle?

Getting Ready for Chapter

Chapter Exploration

1. **Work with a partner. The table shows the number of absences and the final grade for each student in a sample.**

   a. Write the ordered pairs from the table. Then plot them in a coordinate plane.

   b. Describe the relationship between absences and final grade.

   c. **MODELING** A student has been absent 6 days. Use the data to predict the student's final grade. Explain how you found your answer.

Absences	Final Grade
0	95
3	88
2	90
5	83
7	79
9	70
4	85
1	94
10	65
8	75

2. **Work with a partner. Match the data sets with the most appropriate scatter plot. Explain your reasoning.**

   a. month of birth and birth weight for infants at a day care

   b. quiz score and test score of each student in a class

   c. age and value of laptop computers

   i. 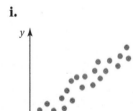 **ii.** 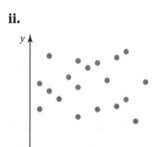 **iii.**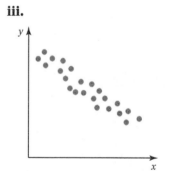

Vocabulary

The following vocabulary terms are defined in this chapter. Think about what each term might mean and record your thoughts.

scatter plot   two-way table
line of fit   joint frequency

Laurie's Notes

Check out the digital flash cards.
BigIdeasMath.com

Chapter Exploration

- **MP1 Make Sense of Problems and Persevere in Solving Them:** A scatter plot shows the relationship between two data sets. Students will find that there may be a positive linear relationship, a negative linear relationship, a nonlinear relationship, or no relationship.
- In Exercise 1, students may need help with scaling the axes. Students may want to use a broken vertical axis. You might let some students use a broken vertical axis and let others start at 0.
- If students use different scales for the vertical axis, have them display their scatter plots. Each plot will have a decreasing trend, but the steepness of the trend may look different.
- When students finish Exercise 1, ask volunteers to share their responses to parts (b) and (c).
- In Exercise 2, students should interpret the trend of each scatter plot in the context of the problem.
- Allow time for students to discuss the three descriptions and which scatter plots they match.
- **MP3 Construct Viable Arguments and Critique the Reasoning of Others:** Ask volunteers to explain how they matched the descriptions and scatter plots. If students disagree, they should give supporting arguments for their own answers and explain what they dislike about the other answers.

Vocabulary

- These terms represent some of the vocabulary that students will encounter in Chapter 6. Discuss the terms as a class.
- Where have students heard the term *joint frequency* outside of a math classroom? In what contexts? Students may not be able to write the actual definition, but they may write phrases associated with *joint frequency*.
- Allowing students to discuss these terms now will prepare them for understanding the terms as they are presented in the chapter.
- When students encounter a new definition, encourage them to write in their *Student Journals*. They will revisit these definitions during the Chapter Review.

ELL Support

Explain that the word *data* is not related to the word *date*, which sounds similar. A date is a day of the month or year. Data are numbers or information that has been collected and recorded. A table, plot, or graph that shows data is known as a *data display*. A display represents information visually.

Topics for Review

- Evaluating Expressions
- Making Data Displays
- Plotting Points
- Probability
- Writing a Linear Equation

Chapter Exploration

1. **a.** $(0, 95)$, $(3, 88)$, $(2, 90)$, $(5, 83)$, $(7, 79)$, $(9, 70)$, $(4, 85)$, $(1, 94)$, $(10, 65)$, $(8, 75)$

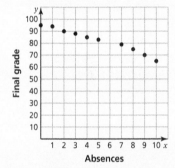

b. As the number of absences increases, the final grade decreases.

c. *Sample answer:* 80; The points $(5, 83)$ and $(7, 79)$ are on the graph. So, when $x = 6$, the y-value should be between 79 and 83.

2. **a.** ii; There is no relationship between month of birth and birth weights of infants. So, the points should show no pattern.

b. i; Students who do well on the quiz will most likely do well on the test. So, as the quiz score increases, the test score will increase.

c. iii; As the age of the laptop computer increases, the value will decrease.

STATE STANDARDS
8.SP.A.1

Learning Target

Use scatter plots to describe patterns and relationships between two quantities.

Success Criteria

- Make a scatter plot.
- Identify outliers, gaps, and clusters in a scatter plot.
- Use scatter plots to describe relationships between data.

Warm Up

Cumulative, vocabulary, and prerequisite skills practice opportunities are available in the *Resources by Chapter* or at *BigIdeasMath.com*.

ELL Support

Discuss the words *scatter* and *plot*. To demonstrate the word scatter, pantomime scattering seeds on the ground or tossing feed to chickens. Ask students what the word *plot* means. You may want to discuss its multiple meanings as you guide students to the idea that to plot information, you can make marks in a coordinate plane. Then have students guess what a scatter plot is and check their ideas as they work through the lesson.

Exploration 1

a. See Additional Answers.

b. yes; As weight increases, the circumference increases.

c. kickball: yes; *Sample answer:* An ordered pair representing the kickball would fit in with the other points on the graph; bowling ball: no; *Sample answer:* An ordered pair representing the bowling ball would not fit in with the other points on the graph.

T-237

Laurie's Notes

Preparing to Teach

- Students should be familiar with the concept of the slope of a line and know how to plot points in a coordinate plane. Now they will construct and interpret scatter plots.
- **MP1 Make Sense of Problems and Persevere in Solving Them:** A scatter plot shows the relationship between two data sets. Students will find that there may be a positive linear relationship, a negative linear relationship, a nonlinear relationship, or no relationship.

Motivate

- Discuss what students know about the construction, size, and weight of bowling balls.
- Ten-pin bowling balls range in weight from about 6 to 16 pounds and have a maximum circumference of 27 inches.
- "How are bowling balls like other sports balls?" *Sample answer:* A bowling ball is round and has a diameter close to that of a volleyball or soccer ball.
- "How are bowling balls different from other sports balls?" *Sample answers:* heavier than most, not filled with air, not intended to bounce

Exploration 1

- As an alternative to plotting by hand, students can use technology available at *BigIdeasMath.com* or graphing calculators to make the **scatter plot**.
- "How do you find the circumference of a sphere?" Use the formula $C = \pi d$, where d is the diameter of the sphere.
- "Which sports ball shown has the least circumference? the greatest circumference?" golf ball; basketball
- "Which sports ball is the lightest? the heaviest?" racquetball; basketball
- Students should plot the ordered pairs for the 9 sports balls. Students may want to make a table of the ordered pairs before plotting them.
- "Must the scale be the same for each axis?" no "What scale did you use for each axis?" Answers will vary.
- "Describe the scatter plot." *Sample answer:* There are two clusters of points.
- "What relationship between weight and circumference does the scatter plot suggest?" As weight increases, circumference tends to increase.
- "Does the scatter plot represent a positive or negative relationship?" positive
- "What do you think a scatter plot of data with a negative relationship looks like?" The points tend to fall from left to right. Tell students to think of lines with positive and negative slopes when describing the relationship.
- "What is an outlier?" A data value that is much greater or much less than the other values. "Would you say that the bowling ball is an outlier? Explain." Yes, the x-value (the weight of the bowling ball) is much greater than that of the other points.
- **MP7 Look for and Make Use of Structure:** "Were the relationships between the data sets obvious before making the scatter plot? Explain." Answers will vary.
- **Extension:** "How would switching the axis labels affect the relationship?" The relationship would still be positive and there would still be two clusters.

6.1 Scatter Plots

Learning Target: Use scatter plots to describe patterns and relationships between two quantities.

Success Criteria:
- I can make a scatter plot.
- I can identify outliers, gaps, and clusters in a scatter plot.
- I can use scatter plots to describe relationships between data.

EXPLORATION 1

Finding Relationships Between Data

Work with a partner. The weights and circumferences of several sports balls are shown.

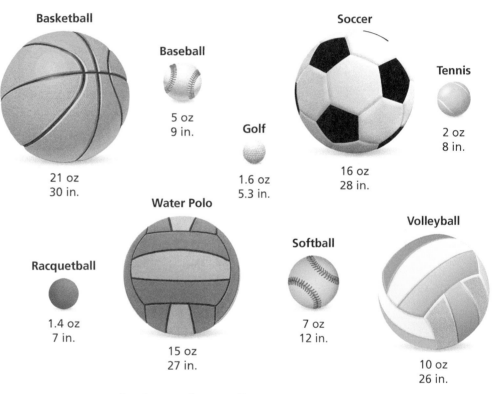

Basketball
21 oz
30 in.

Baseball
5 oz
9 in.

Golf
1.6 oz
5.3 in.

Soccer
16 oz
28 in.

Tennis
2 oz
8 in.

Racquetball
1.4 oz
7 in.

Water Polo
15 oz
27 in.

Softball
7 oz
12 in.

Volleyball
10 oz
26 in.

a. Represent the data in the coordinate plane. Explain your method.

b. Is there a relationship between the size and the weight of a sports ball? Explain your reasoning.

c. Is it reasonable to use the graph to predict the weights of the sports balls below? Explain your reasoning.

- **Kickball:** circumference = 26 in.

- **Bowling ball:** circumference = 27 in.

Math Practice

Label Axes
Can you graph the data with circumference on the x-axis and weight on the y-axis? Explain.

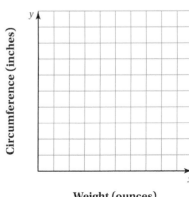

Circumference (inches)

Weight (ounces)

Key Vocabulary 🔊
scatter plot, *p. 238*

 **Key Idea**

Scatter Plot

A **scatter plot** is a graph that shows the relationship between two data sets. The two sets of data are graphed as ordered pairs in a coordinate plane.

EXAMPLE 1 **Making a Scatter Plot**

Age (years)	Data Used (gigabytes)
37	3.2
30	3.3
32	3.1
65	0.9
53	1.8
25	3.5
59	1.3
30	1.8
50	1.9
34	3.3

The table shows the ages of 10 adults and the numbers of gigabytes of cell phone data used by each adult in 1 month. Make a scatter plot of the data. Identify any outliers, gaps, or clusters.

Use ordered pairs (x, y) to represent the data, where x represents age (in years) and y represents data used (in gigabytes). Then plot the ordered pairs in a coordinate plane and analyze the scatter plot.

(37, 3.2)   (25, 3.5)

(30, 3.3)   (59, 1.3)

(32, 3.1)   (30, 1.8)

(65, 0.9)   (50, 1.9)

(53, 1.8)   (34, 3.3)

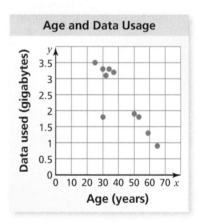

Age and Data Usage

There appears to be an outlier at (30, 1.8). There is a cluster of data from 25 years old to 37 years old and a gap in the data from 37 years old to 50 years old.

Try It

1. Make a scatter plot of the data. Identify any outliers, gaps, or clusters.

Study Time (min), *x*	30	20	80	90	45	10	30	75	120	80
Test Score, *y*	80	74	95	97	85	62	83	90	70	91

Laurie's Notes

Scaffolding Instruction

- In the exploration, students gained an intuitive understanding of how to construct and interpret scatter plots. They will continue to construct scatter plots and identify relationships between two data sets.
- **Emerging:** Students can plot ordered pairs, but they struggle with describing patterns and relationships between two quantities. They will benefit from guided instruction and practice.
- **Proficient:** Students are able to make and interpret a scatter plot for a set of data. They should proceed to the Self-Assessment exercises.

Key Idea

- Define scatter plot.
- Explain that a scatter plot displays the relationship, if any, between two variables, such as age and data used.
- Discuss the scatter plot made in the exploration. The two sets of data were the weights and circumferences of the balls.

EXAMPLE 1

- ? "Looking at the table, can you identify a relationship between age and data usage?" Answers will vary.
- Draw the scatter plot.
- ? "What relationship between age and data usage does the scatter plot suggest?" As age increases, data usage tends to decrease.
- ? "Are there any outliers in the data?" (30, 1.8)
- ? "Are there any gaps in the data? Explain." There is a gap between 37 years old and 50 years old because there are no data values between those ages.
- ? "Are there any clusters in the data? Explain." There is a cluster from 25 years old to 37 years old because those people are similar in age and use a similar amount of data.

Try It

- Students should work in pairs. Then have each pair check with another pair.
- **MP6 Attend to Precision:** A common difficulty for students is deciding how to scale the axes. Students should look at the range of numbers that need to be displayed and then decide whether it is necessary to start their axes at 0 or if another starting point (broken axes) makes sense.

ELL Support

After demonstrating Example 1, have students work in pairs to discuss and complete Try It Exercise 1. Provide graph paper and list the steps students need to take: (1) Plot the ordered pairs in a coordinate plane, (2) Identify any outliers, (3) Identify any gaps, and (4) Identify any clusters. Expect students to perform according to their language levels.

Beginner: Complete each step by graphing or writing answers.

Intermediate: Use phrases or simple sentences to discuss the process and identify any outliers, gaps, or clusters.

Advanced: Use detailed sentences to discuss the process and identify any outliers, gaps, or clusters.

Scaffold instruction to support all students in their learning. Learning is individualized and you may want to group students differently as they move in and out of these levels with each skill and concept. Student self-assessment and feedback help guide your instructional decisions about how and when to layer support for all students to become proficient learners.

Extra Example 1

The table shows the memory capacities (in gigabytes) and prices (in dollars) of 10 cell phones. Make a scatter plot of the data. Identify any outliers, gaps, or clusters.

Memory (GB)	Price (dollars)
8	20
16	40
32	150
8	60
32	200
16	50
32	210
16	60
8	40
16	130

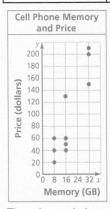

There is no obvious outlier. There is a cluster of data at 16 gigabytes and a gap in the data from 16 gigabytes to 32 gigabytes.

Try It

1. See Additional Answers.

Extra Example 2

Describe the relationship between the data in the scatter plot.

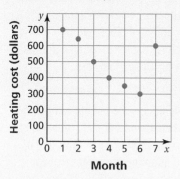

negative linear relationship

Try It

2. negative linear relationship

Formative Assessment Tip

Paired Verbal Fluency (PVF)

This technique is used between two partners where each person takes a turn speaking, uninterrupted, for a specified period of time. The roles reverse and the listener then speaks, uninterrupted, for the same amount of time. Verbalizing their understanding and being attentive listeners will activate student thinking and should help identify areas of difficulty or uncertainty. *Paired Verbal Fluency* can be used at the beginning, middle, or end of instruction. Used at the beginning of instruction, students share their prior knowledge about a particular topic, skill, or concept. Used at the end of instruction, students reflect on learning that occurred during the lesson or at the end of a connected group of lessons.

Self-Assessment
for Concepts & Skills

3. See Additional Answers.

4. (3.5, 3); (3.5, 3) is an outlier.

Discuss

- There are four general cases that describe the relationship between two data sets. Draw a quick example of each case.
- **Note:** Although the scatter plots shown are in the first quadrant only, scatter plots can be made in any quadrant(s).
- Discuss the scatter plots from the exploration and Example 1. The sports balls plot is an example of a positive relationship, and the age/data usage plot is an example of a negative relationship.
- The focus in this course is recognizing positive linear relationships, negative linear relationships, and nonlinear relationships.

EXAMPLE 2

- Have students review the scatter plot shown.
- To read information from the scatter plot, find a point. Move vertically to the x-axis to find the x-value of the point. Then return to the point, and move horizontally to the y-axis to find the y-value of the point.
- A scatter plot allows you to see trends in the data. You read a scatter plot from left to right.
- Ask students to complete these sentences. As the size of the television increases, the price_____. increases This is an example of a _____ relationship. positive
- **Connection:** By this point, some students may have made the connection between the slope of a line and the relationship shown in a scatter plot. A positive relationship is related to a positive slope.

Try It

- Have students display their answers on whiteboards. Discuss as a class.

✓ Self-Assessment for Concepts & Skills

- **Neighbor Check:** Have students work independently and then have their neighbors check their work. Have students discuss any discrepancies.
- ◉ **Paired Verbal Fluency:** Have students explain how to make a scatter plot, identify outliers, identify gaps, identify clusters, and describe the relationship between the data in a scatter plot.

ELL Support

Allow students to work in pairs for extra support. Ask pairs to display their scatter plots for your review. Have two pairs form a group to discuss their explanations for Exercise 4. Monitor discussions and provide support as needed. Review explanations as a class.

The Success Criteria Self-Assessment chart can be found in the *Student Journal* or online at *BigIdeasMath.com*.

A scatter plot can show relationships between two data sets.

Positive Linear Relationship	*Negative Linear Relationship*	*Nonlinear Relationship*	*No Relationship*
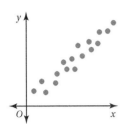	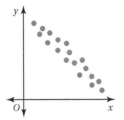	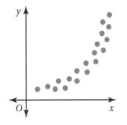	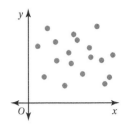
The points lie close to a line. As *x* increases, *y* increases.	The points lie close to a line. As *x* increases, *y* decreases.	The points lie in the shape of a curve.	The points show no pattern.

EXAMPLE 2 ## Identifying Relationships

Describe the relationship between the data in the scatter plot.

The points appear to lie close to a line with a positive slope. As *x* increases, *y* increases.

▶ So, the scatter plot shows a positive linear relationship.

The closer the points are to a line, the stronger the linear relationship. This scatter plot shows a strong linear relationship.

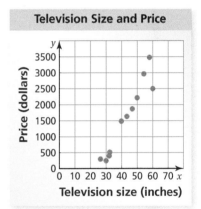

Try It

2. Describe the relationship between the data in Example 1.

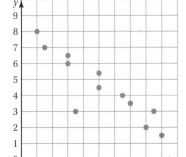

Self-Assessment *for Concepts & Skills*

Solve each exercise. Then rate your understanding of the success criteria in your journal.

3. **SCATTER PLOT** Make a scatter plot of the data. Identify any outliers, gaps, or clusters. Then describe the relationship between the data.

Phone Age (months), *x*	3	22	23	22	8	12	24	4	23
Start-up Time (sec), *y*	24	34	34	33	36	29	34	27	33

4. **WHICH ONE DOESN'T BELONG?** Using the scatter plot, which point does *not* belong with the other three? Explain your reasoning.

(1, 8) (3, 6.5) (3.5, 3) (8, 2)

EXAMPLE 3 **Modeling Real Life**

Fat (grams)	Calories
17	400
12	470
29	540
26	510
10	420
42	740
30	600
33	640
44	790
22	510
39	610
28	510

The table shows the amounts of fat and the numbers of calories in 12 restaurant sandwiches. How many grams of fat do you expect in a sandwich that contains 650 calories?

Use a scatter plot to determine whether a relationship exists between the data. If so, use the data to make a prediction.

Use ordered pairs (x, y), where x represents grams of fat and y represents the number of calories.

(17, 400)   (30, 600)

(12, 470)   (33, 640)

(29, 540)   (44, 790)

(26, 510)   (22, 510)

(10, 420)   (39, 610)

(42, 740)   (28, 510)

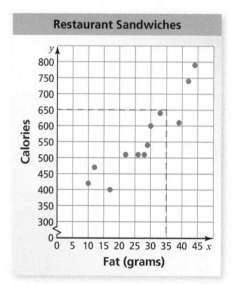

The points appear to lie close to a line with a positive slope. As x increases, y increases. So, the scatter plot shows a positive linear relationship.

▷ Looking at the graph, you can expect a sandwich that contains 650 calories to have about 35 grams of fat.

 Self-Assessment for Problem Solving

Solve each exercise. Then rate your understanding of the success criteria in your journal.

5. The table shows the high school and college grade point averages (GPAs) of 10 students. What college GPA do you expect for a high school student with a GPA of 2.7?

High School	2.6	2.8	3.2	4.0	3.8	3.7	3.5	3.5	3.4	1.4
College	2.4	2.5	3.0	3.6	3.5	3.6	3.6	3.4	3.2	0.5

6. The scatter plot shows the ages of 12 people and the numbers of pets each person owns. Identify any outliers, gaps, or clusters. Then describe the relationship between the data.

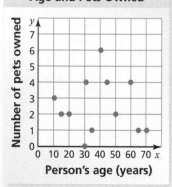

Laurie's Notes

EXAMPLE 3

- **MP1 Make Sense of Problems and Persevere in Solving Them:** This example helps students understand how to use a scatter plot to make a prediction. Discuss the labels on the axes and what an ordered pair represents: (grams of fat, number of calories). There are 12 different sandwiches represented.

- ? "Looking at the table, can you identify a relationship between the amounts of fat and the numbers of calories?" Answers will vary.

- Draw the scatter plot.

- ? "As the *x*-coordinate increases, is the *y*-coordinate increasing, decreasing, staying the same, *or* is there no pattern?" increasing

- ? "How many grams of fat do you expect in a sandwich that contains 650 calories?" Any answer from 35 to 40 grams of fat is acceptable.

✓ Self-Assessment for Problem Solving

- Students may benefit from trying the exercises independently and then working with peers to refine their work. It is important to provide time in class for problem solving, so that students become comfortable with the problem-solving plan.

- Have transparency grids available so that results can be shared quickly as a class. Discuss any discrepancies.

The Success Criteria Self-Assessment chart can be found in the *Student Journal* or online at *BigIdeasMath.com*.

Closure

- **Exit Ticket:** You empty a change purse and find 9 pennies, 5 nickels, 4 dimes, 7 quarters, and 1 half-dollar. Construct a scatter plot of (value of coin, number of coins). Interpret the scatter plot.

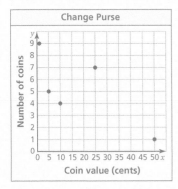

Answers will vary.

Extra Example 3

The table shows the amounts of fat and protein in 12 granola bars. How many grams of fat do you expect in a granola bar that contains 8 grams of protein?

Fat (grams)	Protein (grams)
3.5	2
5	2
6	4
4	2
12	10
9	6
3	1
7	5
6	3
1.5	1
4.5	2.5
9	5

about 10 grams of fat

Self-Assessment
for Problem Solving

5. *Sample answer:* 2.45

6. no outliers, gaps, or clusters; no relationship

Learning Target

Use scatter plots to describe patterns and relationships between two quantities.

Success Criteria

- Make a scatter plot.
- Identify outliers, gaps, and clusters in a scatter plot.
- Use scatter plots to describe relationships between data.

Review & Refresh

1. no solution

2. infinitely many solutions

3. $\left(\dfrac{4}{5}, -\dfrac{4}{5}\right)$

4. B

Concepts, Skills, & Problem Solving

5.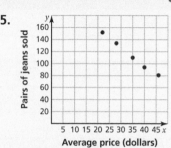

6. yes; As the average price of jeans increases, the number of pairs of jeans sold decreases.

7.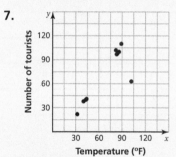

   outlier: (102, 63);
   gap: from 44°F to 82°F;
   cluster: from 82°F to 89°F

8.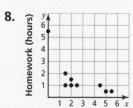

   outlier: (0, 5.5); gap:
   from 2.5 hours to 4.5 hours;
   no clusters

9. negative linear relationship;
   outlier: (15, 10);
   gap: from $x = 15$ to $x = 25$;
   no clusters

10. nonlinear relationship;
    no outliers, gaps, or clusters

11. no relationship; no outliers, gaps, or clusters

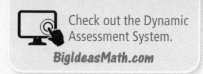

Check out the Dynamic Assessment System.
BigIdeasMath.com

Assignment Guide and Concept Check

Scaffold assignments to support all students in their learning progression. The suggested assignments are a starting point. Continue to assign additional exercises and revisit with spaced practice to move every student toward proficiency.

Level	Assignment 1	Assignment 2
Emerging	2, 4, 5, 6, 7, 9, 10, 11	8, 12, 13, 14, 15, 16
Proficient	2, 4, 5, 6, 7, 8, 9, 10, 11	12, 13, 14, 15, 16, 17
Advanced	2, 4, 5, 6, 7, 8, 9, 10, 11	13, 14, 15, 16, 17, 18

- Assignment 1 is for use after students complete the Self-Assessment for Concepts & Skills.
- Assignment 2 is for use after students complete the Self-Assessment for Problem Solving.
- The red exercises can be used as a concept check.

Review & Refresh Prior Skills

Exercises 1–3 Solving a System of Linear Equations
Exercise 4 Graphing a Proportional Relationship

Common Errors

- **Exercises 9–11** Students may mix up positive and negative relationships. Remind them about slope. The slope is positive when the line rises from left to right and negative when it falls from left to right. The same is true for relationships in a scatter plot. When the data rise from left to right, it is a positive relationship. When the data fall from left to right, it is a negative relationship.

6.1 Practice

Go to *BigIdeasMath.com* to get HELP with solving the exercises.

▶ Review & Refresh

Solve the system. Check your solution.

1. $y = -5x + 1$
   $y = -5x - 2$

2. $2x + 2y = 9$
   $x = 4.5 - y$

3. $y = -x$
   $6x + y = 4$

4. When graphing a proportional relationship represented by $y = mx$, which point is not on the graph?

   A. $(0, 0)$ **B.** $(0, m)$ **C.** $(1, m)$ **D.** $(2, 2m)$

▶▶ Concepts, Skills, & Problem Solving

USING A SCATTER PLOT The table shows the average prices (in dollars) of jeans sold at different stores and the numbers of pairs of jeans sold at each store in one month. (See Exploration 1, p. 237.)

5. Represent the data in a coordinate plane.

Average Price (dollars)	22	40	28	35	46
Number Sold	152	94	134	110	81

6. Is there a relationship between the average price and the number sold? Explain your reasoning.

MAKING A SCATTER PLOT Make a scatter plot of the data. Identify any outliers, gaps, or clusters.

7.

Temperature (°F), x	82	32	40	44	86	84	83	89	102	43
Number of Tourists, y	102	22	38	41	100	98	97	110	63	40

8.

Social Media (hours), x	0	1.5	2.5	5.5	2	1.5	1.5	2	4.5	5
Homework (hours), y	5.5	2	1	0.5	1	1	2	1.5	1	0.5

IDENTIFYING RELATIONSHIPS Describe the relationship between the data. Identify any outliers, gaps, or clusters.

9.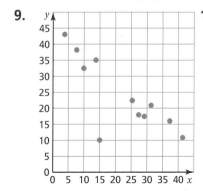

10.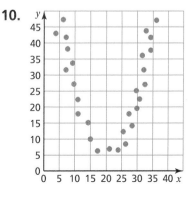

11.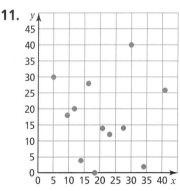

12. **CRITICAL THINKING** The table shows the average price per pound for honey at a store from 2014 to 2017. Describe the relationship between the data.

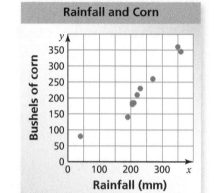

Year, x	2014	2015	2016	2017
Average Price per Pound, y	$4.65	$5.90	$6.50	$7.70

13. **MP MODELING REAL LIFE** The scatter plot shows the amount of rainfall and the amount of corn produced by a farm over the last 10 years. Describe the relationship between the amount of rainfall and the amount of corn produced.

Rainfall and Corn

14. **OPEN-ENDED** Describe a set of real-life data that has a negative linear relationship.

Earnings of a Food Server

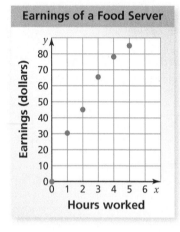

15. **MP MODELING REAL LIFE** The scatter plot shows the total earnings (wages and tips) of a food server during one day.

a. About how many hours must the server work to earn $70?

b. About how much does the server earn for 5 hours of work?

c. Describe the relationship shown by the data.

16. **MP PROBLEM SOLVING** The table shows the memory capacities (in gigabytes) and prices (in dollars) of tablet computers. (a) Make a scatter plot of the data. Then describe the relationship between the data. (b) Identify any outliers, gaps, or clusters. Explain why they might exist.

Memory (GB), x	128	16	64	32	64	16	64	32	16	128	16	128
Price (dollars), y	320	50	250	230	260	200	270	250	180	300	210	280

17. **MP PATTERNS** The scatter plot shows the numbers of drifting scooters sold by a company.

a. In what year were 1000 scooters sold?

b. About how many scooters were sold in 2015?

c. Describe the relationship shown by the data.

d. Assuming this trend continues, in what year are about 500 drifting scooters sold?

Drifting Scooter Sales

18. **DIG DEEPER!** Sales of sunglasses and beach towels at a store show a positive linear relationship in the summer. Does this mean that the sales of one item *cause* the sales of the other item to increase? Explain.

Common Errors

- **Exercises 15 and 17** When finding values from the graph, students may accidentally shift over or up too far and get an answer that is off by an increment. Encourage students to start at the given value and trace the graph to where the point is, and then trace down or left to the other axis for the answer.

Mini-Assessment

1. The table shows the average price (in dollars) of scooters sold at different stores and the number of scooters sold at each store in one month.

Average Price (dollars)	110	35	185	75	46	40	90	58	82
Number Sold	36	29	8	56	68	79	45	57	50

a. Make a scatter plot of the data.

b. Describe the relationship between the data. negative linear relationship

c. Identify any outliers, gaps, or clusters in the data. outlier at (35, 29), gap between $110 and $185, no obvious clusters in the data

Section Resources

Surface Level	Deep Level
Resources by Chapter • Extra Practice • Reteach • Puzzle Time Student Journal • Self-Assessment • Practice Differentiating the Lesson Tutorial Videos Skills Review Handbook Skills Trainer	Resources by Chapter • Enrichment and Extension Graphic Organizers Dynamic Assessment System • Section Practice

Concepts, Skills, & Problem Solving

12. positive linear relationship

13. positive linear relationship

14. *Sample answer:* bank account balance during a shopping spree

15. a. *Sample answer:* 3.5 h

    b. *Sample answer:* $85

    c. positive linear relationship

16. a.

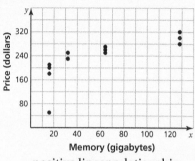

positive linear relationship

    b. outlier: (16, 50); gaps: from 32 GB to 64 GB and from 64 GB to 128 GB; clusters: at 16 GB, 32 GB, 64 GB, and 128 GB; *Sample answer:* The outlier exists because one tablet computer may be on clearance. The gaps and clusters exist because these memory capacities are the standard options for memory.

17. a. 2014

    b. *Sample answer:* 950 scooters

    c. negative linear relationship

    d. *Sample answer:* 2019

18. no; There could be other factors, such as summer weather.

Learning Target

Use lines of fit to model data.

Success Criteria

- Write and interpret an equation of a line of fit.
- Find an equation of a line of best fit.
- Use a line of fit to make predictions.

Warm Up

Cumulative, vocabulary, and prerequisite skills practice opportunities are available in the *Resources by Chapter* or at *BigIdeasMath.com*.

ELL Support

Discuss the word *fit*. Ask students what they understand it means and lead them to the idea that if something fits, it is the right shape or size. Have students use graph paper to plot the ordered pairs in the table. Then have students fit a line among the data points that best represents the data. Explain that this is a line of fit.

Laurie's Notes

STATE STANDARDS
8.SP.A.1, 8.SP.A.2, 8.SP.A.3

Preparing to Teach

- **MP1 Make Sense of Problems and Persevere in Solving Them:** Students should know how to make scatter plots and write equations in slope-intercept form. Now they will find a **line of fit** for data represented by a scatter plot and interpret what the equation means in the context of the problem.

Motivate

- Solicit information that students know about alligators. Then share some facts.
- The American alligator (*Alligator mississippiensis*) is the largest reptile in North America. The first reptiles appeared 300 million years ago. Ancestors of the American alligator appeared 200 million years ago.
- The name alligator comes from early Spanish explorers who called them "el lagarto" or "the lizard" when they first saw these giant reptiles.
- Louisiana and Florida have the most alligators.
- Alligators are about 10–12 inches in length when they are hatched from eggs. Growth rates vary from 2 inches per year to 12 inches per year, depending on the habitat, sex, size, and age of the alligator.
- Females can grow to about 9 feet in length and over 200 pounds. Males can grow to about 13 feet in length and over 500 pounds. The largest alligator ever recorded was caught in Alabama and measured 15 feet 9 inches.
- Alligators live about as long as humans, an average of 70 years.

Exploration 1

- Technology for this exploration is available at *BigIdeasMath.com*.
- "Look at the table of values. What do the ordered pairs represent?" (month, length of alligator)
- "Do the data represent the first 7 months of growth of a baby alligator? Explain." No, alligators are only about 10–12 inches long when they hatch.
- "Are there any observations about the data in the table?" Months are increasing by 1. Lengths are increasing from 0.5 inch to 1.5 inches each month.
- **MP8 Look for and Express Regularity in Repeated Reasoning:** Students will ask what drawing a line "that best describes the relationship between the data" means. You should explain that it is a line that passes as closely as possible to all the points. Use a piece of raw spaghetti to illustrate a line or use a straightedge to lightly draw the line.
- "What does the jagged symbol at the bottom of the *y*-axis mean?" broken axis
- "Do you think everyone in class drew the exact same line? Explain." No, they should be close, but they do not have to be exactly the same.
- "How did you write the equation for the line?" Listen for an approximation of the slope and the *y*-intercept. Write the equation in slope-intercept form.
- Does everyone have the same slope?" No, but they should be relatively close and match the observations made about the data when looking at the table.
- Have students interpret the slope and *y*-intercept in the context of the problem.
- "How does the equation help you answer part (c)?" You can substitute 12 for *x* and solve for *y*.
- "Without the equation, can you predict the length of the alligator next September?" Yes, you can extend the graph and approximate the ordered pair.

Exploration 1

a. *Sample answer:*

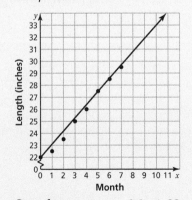

b. *Sample answer:* $y = 1.1x + 22$

c. *Sample answer:* 35.2 in.

6.2 Lines of Fit

Learning Target: Use lines of fit to model data.

Success Criteria:
- I can write and interpret an equation of a line of fit.
- I can find an equation of a line of best fit.
- I can use a line of fit to make predictions.

EXPLORATION 1

Representing Data by a Linear Equation

Work with a partner. You have been working on a science project for 8 months. Each month, you measured the length of a baby alligator.

The table shows your measurements.

September →   April →

Month, x	0	1	2	3	4	5	6	7
Length (in.), y	22.0	22.5	23.5	25.0	26.0	27.5	28.5	29.5

Math Practice

Find General Methods

How can you draw a line that "fits" the data? How should the line be positioned with respect to the points?

a. Use a scatter plot to draw a line that you think best describes the relationship between the data.

b. Write an equation for your line in part (a).

c. **MODELING** Use your equation in part (b) to predict the length of the baby alligator next September.

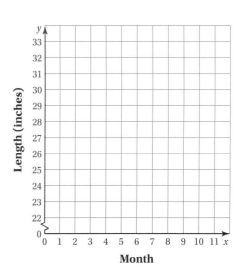

A **line of fit** is a line drawn on a scatter plot close to most of the data points. It can be used to estimate data on a graph.

EXAMPLE 1   Finding a Line of Fit

The table shows the number of absences in a school year and the final exam scores for several students. (a) Make a scatter plot of the data and draw a line of fit. (b) Write an equation of the line of fit. (c) Interpret the slope and the *y*-intercept of the line of fit.

Absences, x	Final Exam Score, y
0	97
3	88
2	93
5	83
7	73
9	70
5	88
1	94
9	65
8	73

a.   Plot the points in a coordinate plane. The scatter plot shows a negative linear relationship. Draw a line that is close to the data points. Try to have as many points above the line as below it.

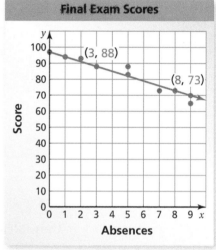

b.   The line passes through (3, 88) and (8, 73).

$$\text{slope} = \frac{\text{rise}}{\text{run}} = \frac{-15}{5} = -3$$

You can use the slope -3 and the point (3, 88) to determine that the *y*-intercept is 97.

So, an equation of the line of fit is $y = -3x + 97$.

> A line of fit does not need to pass through any of the data points.

c.   The slope is -3 and the *y*-intercept is 97. So, a student with 0 absences is expected to earn a 97 on the exam, and the score decreases by about 3 points per absence.

Try It

1.   The table shows the numbers of people who attend a festival over an eight-year period. (a) Make a scatter plot of the data and draw a line of fit. (b) Write an equation of the line of fit. (c) Interpret the slope and the *y*-intercept of the line of fit.

Year, x	1	2	3	4	5	6	7	8
Attendance, y	420	500	650	900	1100	1500	1750	2400

Laurie's Notes

Scaffolding Instruction

- In the exploration, students gained an intuitive understanding of writing an equation for a line of fit and using it to make a prediction. Students will now draw the line of fit for a scatter plot and analyze the equation of the line.
- **Emerging:** Students can draw a line of fit, but they may struggle with writing an equation or using it to make predictions. They will benefit from guided instruction for the examples.
- **Proficient:** Students can draw the line of fit, write an equation of the line, and analyze it. Work through Example 2 with students and explain how to use a graphing calculator to find an equation of the line of best fit. Then have students complete the Self-Assessment exercises.
- **Note:** If your standards do not require finding lines of *best* fit, you may skip Examples 2 and 3.

Discuss

- **MP5 Use Appropriate Tools Strategically:** Define and discuss a line of fit. It is helpful to model this with a piece of raw spaghetti. Draw a scatter plot on a transparency. Model how the spaghetti can approximate the trend of the data.
- Move the spaghetti so that it does *not* represent the data. Then move the spaghetti so that it does. Tell students to use their eyesight when judging where to draw the line.
- ❓ "What problems might this create?" *Sample answer:* Placing the line is a judgement call so different people may have different lines.

EXAMPLE 1

- ❓ "How does the final exam score change as the number of absences increase?" The scores decrease.
- When drawing a line of fit, try to put as many points above the line as below it. Students may draw different lines of fit and still get reasonable answers.
- In this example, the line passes through two actual data points, (3, 88) and (8, 73). As stated in the push-pin note, a line of fit does not need to pass through any of the data points. Tell students that if a line of fit does not pass through any of the data points, then they can use the grid lines to approximate two points on the line of fit.
- **MP4 Model with Mathematics:** The purpose of writing the equation of the line of fit is to make predictions. The equation becomes a model for the data, describing its behavior.
- Remind students of the difference between *correlation* and *causation*. Missing class does not *cause* a student to earn a lower grade. Similarly, attending class does not *cause* a student to earn a higher grade.

Try It

- This is a nice summary problem. Students should quickly observe the positive relationship just from the table of values.

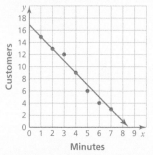

Laurie's Notes

Discuss

- Tell students that you can use a graphing calculator to determine the **line of best fit**. This is called *linear regression*.
- Explain that in addition to calculating the line of best fit, the calculator also gives a value called the *correlation coefficient*. This is a measure of how well the line fits the data.
- Say, "The correlation coefficient is a number between -1 and 1." Draw and label the graphic shown. Describe positive, negative, and no correlation.

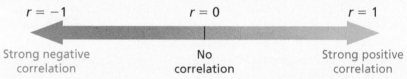

$r = -1$	$r = 0$	$r = 1$
Strong negative correlation	No correlation	Strong positive correlation

- **Common Misconception:** Students may think that a strong negative correlation is *bad*. Stress that the "negative" merely refers to the downward trend of the data, or slope.

EXAMPLE 2

- Ask a student to read the problem.
- Go through the procedure for making the scatter plot and performing the linear regression on a graphing calculator.
- On many calculators, the correlation coefficient is a feature that can be turned on and off. Instruct students how to turn this feature on so that it is displayed when they perform the regression. An r^2-value may also be displayed, which students may learn about in a future course. Tell students to round the values when writing the equation.
- **?** "What is the line of best fit?" $y = 0.3x - 23$
- **?** "What is the correlation coefficient and what does it mean?" $r \approx 0.977$; It implies a strong positive correlation between goals scored and games won.

Try It

- Have students work in pairs. Then have each pair share with another pair.

✓ Self-Assessment for Concepts & Skills

- Have students work in pairs.
- ◉ **Writing Prompt:** How can you write and interpret an equation of a line of fit? How can you use a line of fit to make a prediction?

ELL Support

Have students work in pairs, as suggested in Laurie's Notes. Verify that students understand the information provided in the table for Exercise 3. Have pairs draw their scatter plots and write their answers on whiteboards to hold up for your review.

The Success Criteria Self-Assessment chart can be found in the *Student Journal* or online at *BigIdeasMath.com*.

Extra Example 2

Use a graphing calculator to find an equation of the line of best fit for the data in Extra Example 1. Identify and interpret the correlation coefficient. $y = -2.1x + 17$; $r \approx -0.991$; The relationship between minutes and customers in line is a strong negative correlation and the equation closely models the data.

Try It

2. $y = -3.3x + 99$; about -0.972; strong negative correlation

Self-Assessment
for Concepts & Skills

3. a. *Sample answer:*

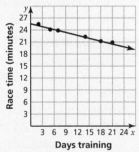

b. *Sample answer:*
$y = -0.24x + 25.52$

c. *Sample answer:* A person who trains 0 days is expected to have a race time of 25.52 minutes, and the race time decreases by 0.24 minute per day spent training.

4. $y = -0.233x + 25.57$; about -0.991; strong negative correlation

Graphing calculators use *linear regression* to find a **line of best fit**. Calculators often give a value *r* called the *correlation coefficient*. Values of *r* range from -1 to 1, with values close to -1 indicating a strong negative correlation, values close to 1 indicating a strong positive correlation, and values close to 0 indicating no correlation.

EXAMPLE 2 — **Identifying Relationships**

Goals, x	Games Won, y
219	39
249	50
215	36
183	28
282	55
241	41
263	50
256	48

The table shows the numbers of goals scored and games won by 8 hockey teams. Use a graphing calculator to find an equation of the line of best fit. Identify and interpret the correlation coefficient.

Step 1: Enter the data from the table into your calculator.

Step 2: Use the *linear regression* feature.

An equation of the line of best fit is $y = 0.3x - 23$. The correlation coefficient is about 0.977. This means that the relationship between goals scored and games won is a strong positive correlation and the equation closely models the data.

Try It

2. Find an equation of the line of best fit for the data in Example 1. Identify and interpret the correlation coefficient.

Self-Assessment for Concepts & Skills

Solve each exercise. Then rate your understanding of the success criteria in your journal.

Days Training, x	Race Time (minutes), y
2	25.45
14	22.30
7	23.85
5	24.10
21	20.90
18	21.20

3. **FINDING A LINE OF FIT** The table shows the numbers of days spent training and the race times for several people in a race.
   a. Make a scatter plot of the data and draw a line of fit.
   b. Write an equation of the line of fit.
   c. Interpret the slope and the *y*-intercept of the line of fit.

4. **IDENTIFYING RELATIONSHIPS** Find an equation of the line of best fit for the data at the left. Identify and interpret the correlation coefficient.

EXAMPLE 3 **Modeling Real Life**

The table shows the number of bats in a cave each year from 2010 to 2017, where $x = 0$ represents the year 2010. Assuming this trend continues, in what year will there be 65,000 bats in the cave?

Year, x	Bats (thousands), y
0	327
1	306
2	299
3	270
4	254
5	232
6	215
7	197

Understand the problem. You are given the number of bats in a cave each year from 2010 to 2017. You are asked to predict in which year there will be 65,000 bats in the cave.

Make a plan. Use a graphing calculator to find an equation of the line of best fit. Then solve the equation for x when $y = 65$.

Solve and check. Enter the data from the table into your calculator and use the *linear regression* feature.

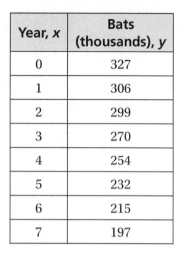

```
LinReg
y=ax+b
a=-18.83333333
b=328.4166667
r²=.9938069824
r=-.9968986821
```

Check Reasonableness
Use a graphing calculator to make a scatter plot and graph the line of best fit. ✓

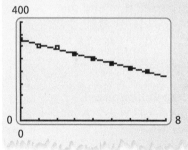

An equation of the line of best fit is $y = -18.8x + 328$. Solve the equation for x when $y = 65$.

$y = -18.8x + 328$	Write the equation.
$65 = -18.8x + 328$	Substitute 65 for y.
$-263 = -18.8x$	Subtract 328 from each side.
$14 \approx x$	Divide each side by -18.8.

▷ There should be 65,000 bats in the cave in 2024.

 Self-Assessment for Problem Solving

Solve each exercise. Then rate your understanding of the success criteria in your journal.

Height (ft), x	Completions, y
4	27
4.2	22
4.4	18
4.5	16
4.6	11
4.7	8

5. The ordered pairs show amounts y (in inches) of rainfall equivalent to x inches of snow. About how many inches of rainfall are equivalent to 6 inches of snow? Justify your answer.

(16, 1.5) (12, 1.3) (18, 1.8) (15, 1.5) (20, 2.1) (23, 2.4)

6. The table shows the heights (in feet) of a high jump bar and the number of people who successfully complete each jump. Identify and interpret the correlation coefficient.

Laurie's Notes

EXAMPLE 3

- In this example, the data have not been collected from an experiment. The data have been collected through research and recorded in the table.
- Ask a student to read the problem and another to explain what the problem is asking. Make sure students understand that they are making a prediction about the future by analyzing known data.
- Students could complete a Four Square as you work through the problem-solving plan.
- **?** "What observations can you make about the data in the table?" Students may recognize that the number of bats is decreasing by about 15–20 (in thousands) per year.
- **MP4 Model with Mathematics:** Have students interpret the slope and y-intercept in the context of the problem. A slope of -18.8 means that the number of bats in the cave is decreasing by about 18,800 bats each year. A y-intercept of 328 means that in 2010, there were about 328,000 bats in the cave. Explain that the number of the bats in 2010 from the table differs from the number in the equation because the equation is an approximation of the line.
- **?** "How can you use the equation to predict the year that there will be 65,000 bats?" Substitute 65 for y and solve for x.

✓ Self-Assessment for Problem Solving

- Encourage students to use a Four Square to complete these exercises. Until students become comfortable with the problem-solving plan, they may only be ready to complete the first square.

The Success Criteria Self-Assessment chart can be found in the *Student Journal* or online at *BigIdeasMath.com*.

Formative Assessment Tip

Open-Ended Question
This technique allows you to determine the breadth and depth of students' understanding of a concept. *Open-Ended Questions* require students to think, persevere, and justify the answer. When there are many possible answers, *Open-Ended Questions* offer accessibility and deeper thinking.

Closure

- **Open-Ended Question:** Give an example of a situation in which there is correlation between the variables. *Sample answer:* the number of teachers in a school and the number of students in the school

---

Extra Example 3

The table shows the number of people living in a city each year from 2010 to 2017, where $x = 0$ represents the year 2010. Assuming this trend continues, in what year will there be 80,000 people living in the city?

Year, x	People (thousands), y
0	25
1	31
2	32
3	35
4	39
5	45
6	51
7	66

2021

Self-Assessment
for Problem Solving

5. about 0.56 in. An equation of the line of best fit is $y = 0.11x - 0.1$. When $x = 6$, $y = 0.11(6) - 0.1 = 0.56$.

6. about -0.988; strong negative correlation

Learning Target

Use lines of fit to model data.

Success Criteria

- Write and interpret an equation of a line of fit.
- Find an equation of a line of best fit.
- Use a line of fit to make predictions.

Review & Refresh

1. negative linear relationship; outlier: (6, 10); no gaps or clusters

2. no relationship; no outliers, gaps, or clusters

3. positive linear relationship; no outliers or gaps; cluster: from $x = 11$ to $x = 15$

4. 0.29, 29%   5. 0.28, 28%

6. 0.66, 66%

Concepts, Skills, & Problem Solving

7. *Sample answer:*

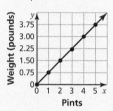

8. *Sample answer:*

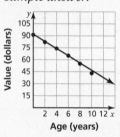

9. a. *Sample answer:*

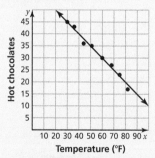

   b. *Sample answer:*
   $y = -0.5x + 60$

   c. *Sample answer:* You could expect that 60 hot chocolates are sold when the temperature is 0°F, and the sales decrease by 1 hot chocolate for every 2°F increase in temperature.

10. -0.98; It is closer to -1 than 0.91 is to 1.

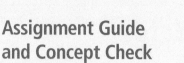

Assignment Guide and Concept Check

Scaffold assignments to support all students in their learning progression. The suggested assignments are a starting point. Continue to assign additional exercises and revisit with spaced practice to move every student toward proficiency.

Level	Assignment 1	Assignment 2
Emerging	3, 5, 7, 8, 9, 10, 11	12, 14, 15
Proficient	3, 5, 7, 8, 9, 10, 11	12, 13, 14, 15,
Advanced	3, 5, 7, 8, 9, 10, 11	12, 13, 14, 15

- Assignment 1 is for use after students complete the Self-Assessment for Concepts & Skills.
- Assignment 2 is for use after students complete the Self-Assessment for Problem Solving.
- The red exercises can be used as a concept check.

Review & Refresh Prior Skills

Exercises 1–3   Identifying Relationships
Exercise 4   Writing Fractions as Decimals and Percents

Common Errors

- **Exercises 7–9** Students may use inconsistent increments or forget to label the graph. Remind them to use consistent increments to represent the data and to label the axes so that information can be read from the graph.
- **Exercises 7–9** Students may draw a line of fit that does not accurately reflect the data trend. Remind them that the line does not have to go through any of the data points. Also remind students that the line should go through the middle of the data so that about half of the data points are above the line and half are below. One strategy is to draw an oval around the data and then draw a line through the middle of the oval. For example:

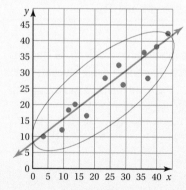

? Go to *BigIdeasMath.com* to get HELP with solving the exercises.

Review & Refresh

Describe the relationship between the data. Identify any outliers, gaps, or clusters.

1.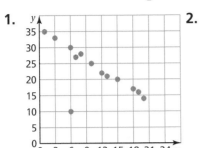

2.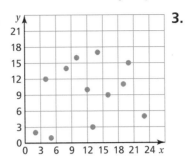

3.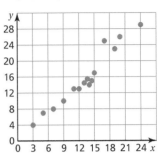

Write the fraction as a decimal and a percent.

4. $\dfrac{29}{100}$

5. $\dfrac{7}{25}$

6. $\dfrac{33}{50}$

Concepts, Skills, & Problem Solving

REPRESENTING DATA BY A LINEAR EQUATION Use a scatter plot to draw a line that you think best describes the relationship between the data. *(See Exploration 1, p. 243.)*

7.

Blueberries (pints), x	0	1	2	3	4	5
Weight (pounds), y	0	0.8	1.50	2.20	3.0	3.75

8.

Age (years), x	0	2	4	6	8	10
Value (dollars), y	91	82	74	65	55	43

9. **FINDING A LINE OF FIT** The table shows the daily high temperatures (°F) and the numbers of hot chocolates sold at a coffee shop for eight randomly selected days.

Temperature (°F), x	30	36	44	51	60	68	75	82
Hot Chocolates, y	45	43	36	35	30	27	23	17

   a. Make a scatter plot of the data and draw a line of fit.

   b. Write an equation of the line of fit.

   c. Interpret the slope and the y-intercept of the line of fit.

10. **MP NUMBER SENSE** Which correlation coefficient indicates a stronger relationship: -0.98 or 0.91? Explain.

11. **IDENTIFYING RELATIONSHIPS** The table shows the admission costs (in dollars) and the average number of daily visitors at an amusement park each year for the past 8 years. Find an equation of the line of best fit. Identify and interpret the correlation coefficient.

Cost (dollars), x	20	21	22	24	25	27	28	30
Daily Attendance, y	940	935	940	925	920	905	910	890

12. **MP REASONING** The table shows the weights (in pounds) and the prescribed dosages (in milligrams) of medicine for six patients.

Weight (lb), x	Dosage (mg), y
94	72
119	90
135	103
150	115
185	140
202	156

   a. Find an equation of the line of best fit. Identify and interpret the correlation coefficient.

   b. Interpret the slope of the line of best fit.

   c. A patient who weighs 140 pounds is prescribed 135 milligrams of medicine. How does this affect the line of best fit?

Population (millions), x	Electoral Votes, y
4.4	8
0.7	3
20.6	29
6.6	11
8.9	14
8.4	13
27.9	38
39.3	55

13. **MP MODELING REAL LIFE** The table shows the populations (in millions) and the numbers of electoral votes assigned for eight states in the 2016 presidential election.

   a. Find an equation of the line of best fit. Identify and interpret the correlation coefficient.

   b. Interpret the slope of the line of best fit.

   c. Interpret the y-intercept of the line of best fit.

   d. **RESEARCH** Research the Electoral College to explain the meaning of your answer in part (c).

14. **MP MODELING REAL LIFE** The table shows the numbers (in millions) of active accounts for two social media websites over the past five years. Assuming this trend continues, how many active accounts will Website B have when Website A has 280 million active accounts? Justify your answer.

Website A, x	Website B, y
312	188
306	215
300	235
299	236
293	253

Seconds, x	Height (feet), y
0	3
0.5	39
1	67
1.5	87
2	99

15. **DIG DEEPER!** The table shows the heights y (in feet) of a baseball x seconds after it was hit.

   a. Predict the height after 5 seconds.

   b. The actual height after 5 seconds is about 3 feet. Why might this be different from your prediction?

Mini-Assessment

1. The table shows the distance you travel over a six-hour period.

Hours, x	Distance (miles), y
1	50
2	102
3	153
4	204
5	254
6	305

a. Make a scatter plot of the data and draw a line of fit.

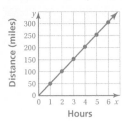

b. Write an equation of the line of fit. *Sample answer:* $y = 51x$

c. Interpret the slope and the y-intercept of the line of fit. *Sample answer:* The slope is 51 and the y-intercept is 0. So, you travel 0 miles at 0 hours and you travel about 51 miles each hour.

d. Find an equation of the line of best fit. Identify and interpret the correlation coefficient. $y = 50.9x - 0.2$; $r \approx 1.000$; The relationship between hours and distances traveled is a very strong positive correlation and the equation closely models the data.

Section Resources

Surface Level	Deep Level
Resources by Chapter • Extra Practice • Reteach • Puzzle Time Student Journal • Self-Assessment • Practice Differentiating the Lesson Tutorial Videos Skills Review Handbook Skills Trainer	Resources by Chapter • Enrichment and Extension Graphic Organizers Dynamic Assessment System • Section Practice
Transfer Level	
Dynamic Assessment System • Mid-Chapter Quiz	Assessment Book • Mid-Chapter Quiz

11. $y = -4.9x + 1042$; about -0.969; strong negative correlation

12. a. $y = 0.8x - 1$; about 0.999; strong positive correlation

b. The dosage increases by 0.8 milligram for every 1 pound increase in weight.

c. The line of best fit changes from $y = 0.8x - 1$ to $y = 0.7x + 6$. The correlation coefficient decreases from about 0.999 to about 0.934. So, the new equation of the line of best fit does not model the data as closely as the original equation because the point $(140, 135)$ appears to be an outlier.

13. a. $y = 1.3x + 2$; about 0.9995; strong positive correlation

b. The number of electoral votes increases by 1.3 for every increase of 1 million people in the state.

c. A state with a population of 0 has 2 electoral votes.

d. *Sample answer:* The number of electoral votes a state has is based on the number of members that state has in Congress. Each state has 2 Senators, plus a number of members of the House of Representatives based on its population. So, the y-intercept is 2 because a hypothetical state with no population would still have 2 Senators.

14. about 302 million; An equation of the line of best fit is $y = -3.4x + 1254$. When $x = 280$, $y = -3.4(280) + 1254 = 302$.

15. a. 251 ft

b. The height of the baseball is not linear.

Learning Target

Use two-way tables to represent data.

Success Criteria

- Read a two-way table.
- Make a two-way table.
- Use a two-way table to describe relationships between data.

Warm Up

Cumulative, vocabulary, and prerequisite skills practice opportunities are available in the *Resources by Chapter* or at *BigIdeasMath.com.*

Exploration 1

a. Bottom row: 20, 18, 14, 5, 8
   Right column: 12, 16, 14, 11, 12

b. no; The cell where the black-and-gold row meets the XL column has a 0.

c. Bottom row: 25, 30, 35, 30, 25
   Right column: 29, 29, 29, 29, 29
   Bottom right cell: 145

d. *Sample answer:* Use the tables to determine how many shirts in each category sold. Then, order less of the shirt categories that didn't sell well and more of the shirt categories that did sell well.

T-249

Laurie's Notes

STATE STANDARDS
8.SP.A.4

Preparing to Teach

- Students should know how to display data using different types of displays, such as histograms, box-and-whisker plots, and scatter plots. Now they will add another data display to their toolkits, the two-way table.
- **MP2 Reason Abstractly and Quantitatively:** In this section, students are translating information into an organized table to make sense of the problem and to make observations and reason about the information. The goal is not to simply construct a table or read information from the table, but to reason about relationships that exist between categories in the table.

Motivate

- **Story Time:** Tell students about a few of the sessions and workshops you attended at a three-day math conference. When you returned, you submitted your expenses.

	Day 1	Day 2	Day 3	Totals
Meals				A
Lodging				
Taxi				
Totals		B		C

- The school district does not want to share your expenses publicly so they are blacked out.
- ❓ "What do the numbers in A, B, and C represent?" A is the total amount spent on meals for 3 days; B is the total expenses for day 2; C is the total expenses for all 3 days.
- ❓ "How do you find C?" Find the sum of the last column or the sum of the last row.
- If students do not know the vocabulary—column and row—be sure to clarify.

Exploration 1

- Students should find that reading a **two-way table** is relatively easy. The term *two-way table* is new to students, yet they do not need a formal definition to make sense of the problem and what it is asking. In fact, some students will jump in and start adding the entries in the rows and columns without reading the introduction.
- When students have finished, discuss their responses to part (d).
- ❓ "What size(s) of shirts sold well?" XL and L "What size(s) of shirts did not sell well?" S and M
- ❓ "What color(s) of shirts sold well?" black/white "What color(s) of shirts did not sell well?" blue/gold
- ❓ "Is there a way to quantify or rank the popular sizes and colors?" Yes, you can compute the percent of each size or color that was sold.
- ❓ "Do you think merchants keep track of inventory in this manner?" Answers will vary. Successful merchants do track inventory to see what is selling.

6.3 Two-Way Tables

Learning Target: Use two-way tables to represent data.

Success Criteria:
- I can read a two-way table.
- I can make a two-way table.
- I can use a two-way table to describe relationships between data.

EXPLORATION 1

Analyzing Data

Work with a partner. You are the manager of a sports shop. The table shows the numbers of soccer T-shirts that your shop has left in stock at the end of a soccer season.

		T-Shirt Size					
		S	M	L	XL	XXL	Total
Color	Blue/White	5	4	1	0	2	
	Blue/Gold	3	6	5	2	0	
	Red/White	4	2	4	1	3	
	Black/White	3	4	1	2	1	
	Black/Gold	5	2	3	0	2	
	Total						65

a. Complete the table.

b. Are there any black-and-gold XL T-shirts in stock? Justify your answer.

c. The numbers of T-shirts you ordered at the beginning of the soccer season are shown below. Complete the table.

		T-Shirt Size					
		S	M	L	XL	XXL	Total
Color	Blue/White	5	6	7	6	5	
	Blue/Gold	5	6	7	6	5	
	Red/White	5	6	7	6	5	
	Black/White	5	6	7	6	5	
	Black/Gold	5	6	7	6	5	
	Total						

Math Practice

Listen and Ask Questions

Listen to another pair explain their answer in part (d). Ask any questions you have about their reasoning.

d. **MP REASONING** How would you alter the numbers of T-shirts you order for the next soccer season?

6.3 Lesson

Key Vocabulary 🔊
two-way table, *p. 250*
joint frequency, *p. 250*
marginal frequency,
  p. 250

A **two-way table** displays two categories of data collected from the same source.

You randomly survey students about their grades on a test and whether they studied for the test. The two-way table shows the results. Each entry in the table is called a **joint frequency**.

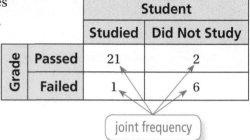

		Student	
		Studied	**Did Not Study**
Grade	**Passed**	21	2
	Failed	1	6

joint frequency

EXAMPLE 1   Reading a Two-Way Table

How many students in the survey above studied for the test and passed?

The entry in the "Studied" column and "Passed" row is 21.

▷   So, 21 of the students in the survey studied for the test and passed.

Try It

1. How many students in the survey above studied for the test and failed?

The sums of the rows and columns in a two-way table are called **marginal frequencies**.

EXAMPLE 2   Finding Marginal Frequencies

Find and interpret the marginal frequencies for the survey above.

Create a new column and a new row for the sums. Then add the entries.

		Student		
		Studied	**Did Not Study**	**Total**
Grade	**Passed**	21	2	23 ◀ 23 students passed.
	Failed	1	6	7 ◀ 7 students failed.
	Total	22	8	30 ◀ 30 students were surveyed.

22 students studied.

8 students did not study.

Try It

	Football Game	
	Attend	**Not Attend**
Dance **Attend**	35	5
Not Attend	16	20

2. You randomly survey students in a cafeteria about their plans for a football game and a school dance. The two-way table shows the results. Find and interpret the marginal frequencies for the survey.

Laurie's Notes

Scaffolding Instruction

- In the exploration, students read two-way tables. Now they will construct two-way tables and identify relationships between the categories of a two-way table.
- **Emerging:** Students may be able to read a two-way table, but they need practice describing relationships between the data. They will benefit from guided instruction for the examples.
- **Proficient:** Students read and interpret data in a two-way table with ease. They should work through Examples 2 and 3 before completing the Self-Assessment exercises.

Discuss

- Define two-way table. Emphasize that information is known about two categories from the same source. The focus in this lesson is drawing conclusions from the data in a two-way table.
- Refer to the exploration in explaining "information about two categories from the same source," such as soccer shirts-size and color.
- Define joint frequency. Each entry in the two-way table is a frequency for two categories, hence the name joint frequency.

EXAMPLE 1

? "What category do the rows represent?" test grade: passed or failed
? "What category do the columns represent?" preparation of the student: studied or did not study

Try It

- Have students display their answers on whiteboards. Discuss any discrepancies.

EXAMPLE 2

- Define marginal frequencies. Tell students that the sums of the rows and columns appear in the *margins* of the two-way table.
- Expand the two-way table. Label the new row and new column "Total."
- Add the rows and columns. Identify the sums using the labels shown.
- Ask students general questions about the row and column totals.
- Make sure students understand that 30 students were surveyed, not 60. Because each student is tallied twice, once for each category, you do not add 22 + 8 + 23 + 7 to find the number surveyed. The sum of the rows and the sum of the columns should be equal.
- ? "What can you conclude about the data?" *Sample answer:* Of the 30 students, all but one of those who studied for the test passed.

Try It

- ? **Extension:** Ask students percent questions such as, "What percent of the students in the survey are *not* planning to attend either event?" about 26%

ELL Support

Have students work in pairs to discuss and complete Try It Exercises 1 and 2. Have students ask each other questions that can be answered from the tables. For Exercise 2, have students find and interpret the marginal frequencies. Expect students to perform according to their language levels.

Beginner: Write the answer(s).

Intermediate: Use simple sentences to state the answer(s).

Advanced: Use detailed sentences to state the answer(s).

Try It

2. 51 students will attend the game; 25 students will not attend the game;
   40 students will attend the dance; 36 students will not attend the dance;
   76 students were surveyed.

Extra Example 3

You randomly survey students in sixth, seventh, and eighth grade about whether they are going to try to join student council. The results are shown in the tally sheets. Make a two-way table that includes the marginal frequencies.

Join

Grade	Tally
6	☐☐ ☐☐ ☐
7	☐☐ ☐☐ ☐☐☐
8	☐☐ ☐☐

Not Join

Grade	Tally
6	☐☐ ☐☐
7	☐☐ ☐☐ ☐☐☐☐
8	☐☐ ☐☐ ☐☐

		Grade			
		6	**7**	**8**	**Total**
Join Student Council	**Yes**	11	13	7	31
	No	10	14	15	39
	Total	21	27	22	70

Try It

3. See Additional Answers.

Self-Assessment
for Concepts & Skills

4. 8 students; 14 students

5. See Additional Answers.

EXAMPLE 3

- Guide students through the construction of the table and ask them to explain what several of the values represent.
- The amount of data in the two-way table may be overwhelming to some students. Make sure to talk through the problem, giving students time to stop and think about what each entry represents.
- **Teaching Tip:** Use two colors in the table, one for the joint frequencies and one for the marginal frequencies. This makes it easier to read.
- "What do the marginal frequencies tell you?" *Sample answers:* The total number of students who ride the bus and the total number of students who do not ride the bus is the same (50). There were 15 fewer 14- to 15-year-olds surveyed than 12- to 13-year-olds.
- "What is an advantage of the two-way table over the tally marks on the sheets of paper?" Answers will vary. Students might say the table is more organized, easier to read, and more condensed.

Try It

- Students should work independently on this exercise.
- **Popsicle Sticks:** Select students to share their tables.

Teaching Strategy

Students are often asked to share or discuss ideas with a partner. Model the following strategies and encourage students to use them in their discussions.

Revoicing: Rephrase what you have heard to clarify your understanding. "So, you are saying _____. Do I have that right?"

Repeating: Ask the speaker to explain his or her idea in another way. "Can you please rephrase that?"

Questioning: Ask the class, "Do you agree or disagree and why?"

Adding On: Ask the class, "Would someone like to add on to that statement?"

These strategies help students learn to communicate with one another effectively.

✓ Self-Assessment *for Concepts & Skills*

- **Teaching Strategy:** Students should work independently and then justify their conclusions to the class
- Have students use *Fist of Five* to indicate their understanding of:
  - reading a two-way table,
  - making a two-way table, and
  - using a two-way table to describe relationships between data.

The Success Criteria Self-Assessment chart can be found in the *Student Journal* or online at *BigIdeasMath.com*.

EXAMPLE 3 **Making a Two-Way Table**

Rides Bus

Age	Tally
12-13	~~卌~~ ~~卌~~ ~~卌~~ ~~卌~~ IIII
14-15	~~卌~~ ~~卌~~ II
16-17	~~卌~~ ~~卌~~ IIII

Does Not Ride Bus

Age	Tally
12-13	~~卌~~ ~~卌~~ ~~卌~~ I
14-15	~~卌~~ ~~卌~~ III
16-17	~~卌~~ ~~卌~~ ~~卌~~ ~~卌~~ I

You randomly survey students between the ages of 12 and 17 about whether they ride the bus to school. The results are shown in the tally sheets. Make a two-way table that includes the marginal frequencies.

The two categories for the table are the ages and whether or not students ride the bus. Use the tally sheets to calculate each joint frequency. Then add to find each marginal frequency.

		Age			
		12–13	**14–15**	**16–17**	**Total**
Student	**Rides Bus**	24	12	14	50
	Does Not Ride Bus	16	13	21	50
	Total	40	25	35	100

Try It

3. You randomly survey students about whether they buy a school lunch or pack a lunch. The results are shown. Make a two-way table that includes the marginal frequencies.

Grade 6 Students	Grade 7 Students	Grade 8 Students
11 pack lunch, 9 buy school lunch	23 pack lunch, 27 buy school lunch	16 pack lunch, 14 buy school lunch

Self-Assessment *for Concepts & Skills*

Solve each exercise. Then rate your understanding of the success criteria in your journal.

Zoo

Gender	Tally
Male	~~卌~~ ~~卌~~ ~~卌~~ III
Female	~~卌~~ ~~卌~~ ~~卌~~ ~~卌~~ I

Museum

Gender	Tally
Male	~~卌~~ ~~卌~~ II
Female	~~卌~~ ~~卌~~ IIII

4. **READING A TWO-WAY TABLE** The results of a music survey are shown in the two-way table. How many students dislike both country and jazz? How many students like country but dislike jazz?

		Jazz	
		Likes	**Dislikes**
Country	**Likes**	26	14
	Dislikes	17	8

5. **MAKING A TWO-WAY TABLE** You randomly survey students about their preference for a class field trip. The results are shown in the tally sheets. Make a two-way table that includes the marginal frequencies.

EXAMPLE 4 **Modeling Real Life**

For each age group in Example 3, what percent of the students ride the bus? do not ride the bus? Determine whether there is a relationship between age and riding the bus to school.

Divide each joint frequency by the total number of students in the corresponding age group. Organize the results in a two-way table.

		Age		
		12–13	**14–15**	**16–17**
Student	**Rides Bus**	$\frac{24}{40} = 60\%$	$\frac{12}{25} = 48\%$	$\frac{14}{35} = 40\%$
	Does Not Ride Bus	$\frac{16}{40} = 40\%$	$\frac{13}{25} = 52\%$	$\frac{21}{35} = 60\%$

Check
The percents in each column of the table should sum to 100%.

$60\% + 40\% = 100\%$
$48\% + 52\% = 100\%$
$40\% + 60\% = 100\%$ ✓

Each age group increase corresponds with a decrease in the percent of students who ride the bus and an increase in the percent of students who do not ride the bus.

 So, the table shows that as age increases, students are less likely to ride the bus to school.

 Self-Assessment for *Problem Solving*

Solve each exercise. Then rate your understanding of the success criteria in your journal.

		Voter's Age		
		18–34	**35–64**	**65+**
Candidate	**A**	36	25	6
	B	12	32	24

6. The results of a voting survey are shown in the two-way table. For each age group, what percent of voters prefer Candidate A? Candidate B? Determine whether there is a relationship between age and candidate preference.

7. You randomly survey 40 students about whether they play an instrument. You find that 8 males play an instrument and 13 females do not play an instrument. A total of 17 students in the survey play an instrument. Make a two-way table that includes the marginal frequencies.

8. Collect data from each student in your math class about whether they like math and whether they like science. Is there a relationship between liking math and liking science? Justify your answer.

Laurie's Notes

EXAMPLE 4

- Have a student read the problem. Ask another student to explain what the problem is asking. Make sure students understand that the problem is asking about percents within each *age group*—the data represented in the columns.
- ❓ "How many 12- to 13-year-olds ride the bus?" 24 "How many 12- to 13-year-olds are in the survey?" 40
- ❓ "What percent of the 12- to 13-year-olds ride the bus?" $\frac{24}{40} = 60\%$
- Guide students through the construction of the two-way table. Ask them to explain what each entry represents.
- **MP2 Reason Abstractly and Quantitatively:** Ask students to make an observation about the percents. As age increases, students are less likely to ride the bus to school. Ask students why this might be the case, encouraging them to reason about data.
- ❓ "In the table, the sums of the columns are each 100%. Why don't the rows add up to 100%?" The base used to compute the percents refers to each of the age groups, not whether the student rides the bus.
- ❓ "Can percents in the table be found using the row totals?" yes "What would be the first entry in the table and what would it represent?" $\frac{24}{50} = 48\%$; 48% of the students who ride the bus are 12–13 years old.

✓ Self-Assessment for Problem Solving

- Allow time in class for students to practice using the problem-solving plan. Remember, some students may only be able to complete the first step.
- Students should read each problem independently and then make a plan for each problem. Then have students share and discuss their plans with a partner before solving the problems independently.
- For Exercise 8, draw a large two-way table on the board for students to record their preferences with tally marks.

		Science	
		Likes	Does Not Like
Math	**Likes**		
	Does Not Like		

The Success Criteria Self-Assessment chart can be found in the *Student Journal* or online at *BigIdeasMath.com*.

Closure

- **Discuss:** In Example 1, is it likely that if you study for a test you will pass? Explain. Yes, the table shows that the majority of students who studied for the test passed and the majority of students who did not study for the test failed. (See the Teaching Strategy on page T-251.)

Extra Example 4

For each grade in Extra Example 3, what percent of the students are going to try to join student council? not going to try to join student council? Determine whether there is a relationship between grade and trying to join student council.

		Grade		
		6	7	8
Join Student Council	**Yes**	52%	48%	32%
	No	48%	52%	68%

Yes, the table shows that as grade level increases, students are less likely to try to join student council.

Self-Assessment for Problem Solving

6.

		Voter's Age		
		18–34	35–64	65+
Candidate	**A**	75%	43.9%	20%
	B	25%	56.1%	80%

Yes, the table shows that as age increases, preference for Candidate B increases.

7. See Additional Answers.

8. Check students' work.

Learning Target

Use two-way tables to represent data.

Success Criteria

- Read a two-way table.
- Make a two-way table.
- Use a two-way table to describe relationships between data.

▼ Review & Refresh

1. $y = 12.6x + 75.8$

2. $y = 3.9x - 1$

3.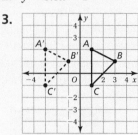

4.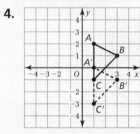

5.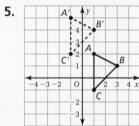

►► Concepts, Skills, & Problem Solving

6. 4 shirts

7. 0 shirts

8. 1 shirt

9. 51 female students

10. 30 male students

11. 71 students are juniors;
    75 students are seniors;
    93 students will attend the
    school play; 53 students will not
    attend the school play;
    146 students were surveyed.

12. 172 people have a limited
    data plan; 310 people have an
    unlimited data plan; 253 people
    use Company A; 229 people use
    Company B; 482 people were
    surveyed.

13. See Additional Answers.

Assignment Guide and Concept Check

Scaffold assignments to support all students in their learning progression. The suggested assignments are a starting point. Continue to assign additional exercises and revisit with spaced practice to move every student toward proficiency.

Level	Assignment 1	Assignment 2
Emerging	2, 4, 5, 6, 7, 8, 9, 10, 11, 12, 13	14, 15, 17, 18
Proficient	2, 4, 5, 6, 7, 8, 9, 10, 11, 12, 13	14, 15, 16, 17, 18
Advanced	2, 4, 5, 6, 7, 8, 9, 10, 11, 12, 13	14, 15, 16, 17, 18

- Assignment 1 is for use after students complete the Self-Assessment for Concepts & Skills.
- Assignment 2 is for use after students complete the Self-Assessment for Problem Solving.
- The red exercises can be used as a concept check.

Review & Refresh Prior Skills

Exercises 1 and 2   Finding a Line of Best Fit
Exercises 3–5   Translating a Figure

⬞ Common Errors

- **Exercises 11–13** Students may incorrectly identify joint frequencies as marginal frequencies. Remind them of these definitions.

? Go to *BigIdeasMath.com* to get HELP with solving the exercises.

Review & Refresh

Find an equation of the line of best fit for the data.

1.

x	0	1	2	3	4
y	75	91	101	109	129

2.

x	7	8	10	13	15
y	25	29	41	48	57

The vertices of a triangle are $A(1, 2)$, $B(3, 1)$, and $C(1, -1)$. Draw the figure and its image after the translation.

3. 4 units left

4. 2 units down

5. $(x - 2, y + 3)$

Concepts, Skills, & Problem Solving

ANALYZING DATA In Exploration 1, determine how many of the indicated T-shirt are in stock at the end of the soccer season. (See Exploration 1, p. 249.)

6. black-and-white M

7. blue-and-gold XXL

8. blue-and-white L

READING A TWO-WAY TABLE You randomly survey students about participating in a yearly fundraiser. The two-way table shows the results.

9. How many female students participate in the fundraiser?

10. How many male students do *not* participate in the fundraiser?

		Fundraiser	
		No	Yes
Gender	Female	22	51
	Male	30	29

FINDING MARGINAL FREQUENCIES Find and interpret the marginal frequencies.

11.

		School Play	
		Attend	Not Attend
Class	Junior	41	30
	Senior	52	23

12.

		Cell Phone Company	
		A	B
Data Plan	Limited	78	94
	Unlimited	175	135

Treatment
Improved: 34
Did not improve: 10

No Treatment
Improved: 12
Did not improve: 29

13. **MAKING A TWO-WAY TABLE** A researcher randomly surveys people with a medical condition about whether they received a treatment and whether their condition improved. The results are shown. Make a two-way table that includes the marginal frequencies.

14. **MP** **MODELING REAL LIFE** You randomly survey students in your school about the color of their eyes. The results are shown in the tables.

Eye Color of Males Surveyed		
Green	Blue	Brown
5	16	27

Eye Color of Females Surveyed		
Green	Blue	Brown
3	19	18

a. Make a two-way table.

b. Find and interpret the marginal frequencies for the survey.

c. For each eye color, what percent of the students in the survey are male? female? Organize the results in a two-way table.

15. **MP** **REASONING** Use the information from Exercise 14. For each gender, what percent of the students in the survey have green eyes? blue eyes? brown eyes? Organize the results in a two-way table.

16. **CRITICAL THINKING** What percent of students in the survey in Exercise 14 are either female or have green eyes? What percent of students in the survey are males who do not have green eyes? Find and explain the sum of these two percents.

17. **MP** **MODELING REAL LIFE** You randomly survey people in your neighborhood about whether they have at least $1000 in savings. The results are shown in the tally sheets. For each age group, what percent of the people have at least $1000 in savings? do not have at least $1000 in savings? Determine whether there is a relationship between age and having at least $1000 in savings.

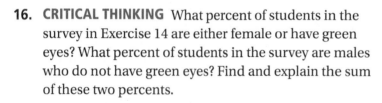

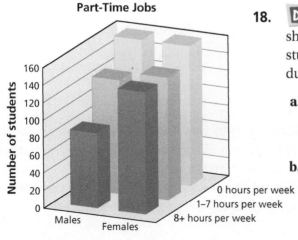

Part-Time Jobs

18. **DIG DEEPER!** The three-dimensional bar graph shows information about the numbers of hours students at a high school work at part-time jobs during the school year.

a. Make a two-way table that represents the data. Use estimation to find the entries in your table.

b. A newspaper article claims that more males than females drop out of high school to work full-time. Do the data support this claim? Explain your reasoning.

Common Errors

- **Exercise 14** In part (c), students may find the percents based on all students surveyed, not just the students from each eye color group. Remind students to read the problem carefully to determine what is being asked.

Mini-Assessment

1. You randomly survey students about whether they are involved in school sports.
   Grade 5: 12 involved, 26 not involved
   Grade 8: 23 involved, 19 not involved

   a. Make a two-way table that includes the marginal frequencies.

		Grade		
		5	8	Total
School Sports	Involved	12	23	35
	Not Involved	26	19	45
	Total	38	42	80

   b. For each grade level, what percent of the students are involved in school sports? not involved in school sports? Organize the results in a two-way table.

		Grade	
		5	8
School Sports	Involved	32%	55%
	Not Involved	68%	45%

   c. Does the table in part (b) show a relationship between grade level and involvement in school sports? Explain. yes; Students in Grade 8 are more likely to be involved in school sports than students in Grade 5.

Section Resources

Surface Level	Deep Level
Resources by Chapter • Extra Practice • Reteach • Puzzle Time Student Journal • Self-Assessment • Practice Differentiating the Lesson Tutorial Videos Skills Review Handbook Skills Trainer	Resources by Chapter • Enrichment and Extension Graphic Organizers Dynamic Assessment System • Section Practice

Concepts, Skills, & Problem Solving

14. a–b. See Additional Answers.

c.

		Eye Color		
		Green	Blue	Brown
Gender	Male	62.5%	45.7%	60%
	Female	37.5%	54.3%	40%

15.

		Eye Color		
		Green	Blue	Brown
Gender	Male	10.4%	33.3%	56.3%
	Female	7.5%	47.5%	45%

16. about 51.1%; about 48.9%; 100%; These two percents account for everyone in the survey.

17.

		Age		
		20–29	30–39	40–49
Saved at Least $1000	Yes	28%	45%	62.5%
	No	72%	55%	37.5%

Yes, the table shows that as age increases, people are more likely to have at least $1000 in savings.

18. a. *Sample answer:*

		Gender		
		Males	Females	Total
Hours	0 hours per week	150	150	300
	1–7 hours per week	115	120	235
	8+ hours per week	75	115	190
	Total	340	385	725

b. no; The data do not support or oppose the claim because the data are not about students dropping out or working full-time jobs.

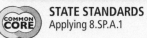
Learning Target

Use appropriate data displays to represent situations.

Success Criteria

- Choose appropriate data displays for situations.
- Identify misleading data displays.
- Analyze a variety of data displays.

Warm Up

Cumulative, vocabulary, and prerequisite skills practice opportunities are available in the *Resources by Chapter* or at *BigIdeasMath.com*.

ELL Support

Before beginning the lesson, review the types of data displays that students have studied in this chapter, scatter plots and two-way tables. Discuss the rationale for the use of each.

Exploration 1

a. *Sample answer:*

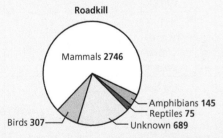

Roadkill

Mammals **2746**

Amphibians **145**
Reptiles **75**
Birds **307**
Unknown **689**

The circle graph shows the kinds of animals as parts of a whole.

b. See Additional Answers.

c. See Additional Answers.

d. *Sample answer:* Reduce the speed limit on some roads.

T-255

Laurie's Notes

Preparing to Teach

- If your standards do not require choosing appropriate data displays for situations, you may skip this lesson and proceed to the next. However, knowing how to identify misleading data displays is useful in real life.
- **MP3 Construct Viable Arguments and Critique the Reasoning of Others:** In this section, students will make decisions about how to display data. They will need to explain their reasoning for selecting a particular display. If two students select different data displays, it is important that they discuss the reasoning behind their choices.

Motivate

- The theme for the exploration is roadkill. While students may giggle at the thought, automobile accidents involving large animals can be serious.
- You may want to share your experiences with automobile accidents involving animals. Allow time for students to share personal stories too.
- Use the Internet to research and share vehicular data with students, such as the number of miles of roads in the U.S., the number of registered vehicles, the number of accidents, and the number of animal-related accidents.

Discuss

- Discuss the data displays with which students are familiar: pictograph, bar graph, line graph, circle graph, stem-and-leaf plot, histogram, dot plot, box-and-whisker plot, and scatter plot. Have students describe the features of each display.
- Discuss the different numerical tools students have for describing data: mean, median, mode, range, mean absolute deviation, quartile, and interquartile range.

Exploration 1

- Students need to decide which display makes sense for the type of data that they have. There may be more than one appropriate answer.
- **MP3 Construct Viable Arguments and Critique the Reasoning of Others:** Discuss students' choices and their explanations.
- Possible data displays:
  - Part (a): a circle graph (what part of the whole set is each animal) or a bar graph (compare the different categories, although there is a large difference in bar heights: 75 to 2746)
  - Part (b): a scatter plot and line of best fit (pair data, show trend over time, and make predictions for the future) or a line graph
  - Part (c): a stem-and-leaf plot (spread of data), along with calculating the mean (about 16.7) and median (17.1)
  - Part (d): As a class, discuss students' ideas for minimizing the number of animals killed by vehicles.

6.4 Choosing a Data Display

Learning Target: Use appropriate data displays to represent situations.

Success Criteria:
• I can choose appropriate data displays for situations.
• I can identify misleading data displays.
• I can analyze a variety of data displays.

EXPLORATION 1

Displaying Data

Work with a partner. Analyze and display each data set in a way that best describes the data. Explain your choice of display.

a. **NEW ENGLAND ROADKILL** A group of schools in New England participated in a two-month study. They reported 3962 dead animals.

Birds: 307   Mammals: 2746
Amphibians: 145   Reptiles: 75
Unknown: 689

b. **BLACK BEAR ROADKILL** The data below show the numbers of black bears killed on a state's roads each year for 20 years.

Year 1:	30	Year 8:	47	Year 15:	99
Year 2:	37	Year 9:	49	Year 16:	129
Year 3:	46	Year 10:	61	Year 17:	111
Year 4:	33	Year 11:	74	Year 18:	127
Year 5:	43	Year 12:	88	Year 19:	141
Year 6:	35	Year 13:	82	Year 20:	135
Year 7:	43	Year 14:	109		

Math Practice

Choose Tools
For each set of data, is there more than one way that you can accurately display the data?

c. **RACCOON ROADKILL** A one-week study along a four-mile section of road found the following weights (in pounds) of raccoons that had been killed by vehicles.

13.4	14.8	17.0	12.9
21.3	21.5	16.8	14.8
15.2	18.7	18.6	17.2
18.5	9.4	19.4	15.7
14.5	9.5	25.4	21.5
17.3	19.1	11.0	12.4
20.4	13.6	17.5	18.5
21.5	14.0	13.9	19.0

d. What can be done to minimize the number of animals killed by vehicles?

Key Idea

Data Display	What does it do?	
Pictograph	shows data using pictures	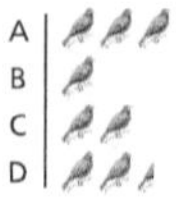
Bar Graph	shows data in specific categories	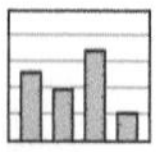
Circle Graph	shows data as parts of a whole	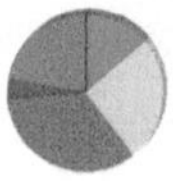
Line Graph	shows how data change over time	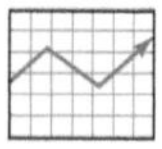
Histogram	shows frequencies of data values in intervals of the same size	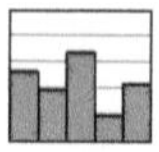
Stem-and-Leaf Plot	orders numerical data and shows how they are distributed	
Box-and-Whisker Plot	shows the variability of a data set by using quartiles	
Dot Plot	shows the number of times each value occurs in a data set	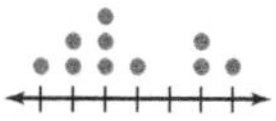
Scatter Plot	shows the relationship between two data sets by using ordered pairs in a coordinate plane	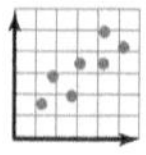

EXAMPLE 1 Choosing an Appropriate Data Display

Choose an appropriate data display for the situation. Explain your reasoning.

a. the number of students in a marching band each year

> A line graph shows change over time. So, a line graph is an appropriate data display.

b. a comparison of people's shoe sizes and their heights

> You want to compare two different data sets. So, a scatter plot is an appropriate data display.

Try It **Choose an appropriate data display for the situation. Explain your reasoning.**

1. the population of the United States divided into age groups

2. the number of students in your school who play basketball, football, soccer, or lacrosse

Laurie's Notes

Scaffolding Instruction

- In the exploration, students reviewed choosing a data display to best describe a set of data. They will continue choosing and constructing appropriate data displays for situations. Students will also practice identifying misleading data displays.
- **Emerging:** Students may need to continue reviewing the different types of data displays and how to make them. They will benefit from guided instruction for the Key Idea and examples.
- **Proficient:** Students can choose an appropriate data display and analyze a variety of data displays. They should review the Key Idea and Example 3 before completing the Self-Assessment exercises.

Key Idea

- Write the Key Idea. This is a terrific summary of data displays that students have learned to make.
- Emphasize that *choosing an appropriate display* is more art than science, but it is clearly possible to use any of the graphs in misleading ways.
- **MP3 Construct Viable Arguments and Critique the Reasoning of Others:** Students should be able to state their reasons for selecting a particular data display *and* why they did not select a different data display. If another student selected a different data display, students should compare their reasoning.
- Have students look for examples of each of these displays around your room, at home, in a newspaper, or on the Internet.

EXAMPLE 1

- Read each problem. Students should not have difficulty determining the appropriate data display for each problem.

Try It

- **Think-Pair-Share:** Students should read each exercise independently and then work in pairs to complete the exercises. Then have each pair compare their answers with another pair and discuss any discrepancies.

Scaffold instruction to support all students in their learning. Learning is individualized and you may want to group students differently as they move in and out of these levels with each skill and concept. Student self-assessment and feedback help guide your instructional decisions about how and when to layer support for all students to become proficient learners.

Extra Example 1
Choose an appropriate data display for the situation. Explain your reasoning.

a. the number of students in a survey who most fear spiders, stink bugs, or mosquitoes *Sample answers:* circle graph: shows data as parts of a whole; bar graph: shows data in specific categories; pictograph: shows data using pictures.

b. a student's test scores throughout a school year *Sample answer:* line graph: shows how data change over time

Try It

1. *Sample answer:* histogram; shows frequencies of data values in intervals of the same size

2. *Sample answer:* bar graph; shows data in specific categories

Laurie's Notes

Extra Example 2

Tell whether each data display is appropriate for representing the data in Example 2. Explain your reasoning.

a. pictograph no; It would not be convenient to show the number of hits for each month using pictures because the numbers have a small greatest common factor (5).

b. scatter plot yes; A scatter plot would show the number of hits for each month, with the months labeled on the *x*-axis.

c. box-and-whisker plot no; A box-and-whisker plot would not show how the number of hits changes over time.

Try It

3. no; A dot plot would not show how the number of hits changed over time.

4. yes; A circle graph would show the fraction or percent of the total number of hits for each month.

5. no; A stem-and-leaf plot would not show how the number of hits changed over time.

EXAMPLE 2

- Write the data on the board and ask a volunteer to read the problem.
- ? "Looking at the data, how would you describe the change in website hits over the five-month period?" increasing
- Remind students that they are looking for a data display that will show how the data changes during the 5 months.
- ? "How does the bar graph represent the change in the number of website hits?" by using different bar heights
- ? "Why are there only 3 bars in the histogram?" data have been grouped
- ? "What key information is lost in the histogram? Explain." time; You can no longer see the months.
- ? "How are the line graph and bar graph alike?" They have the same shape. Connecting the midpoints of the tops of the bars creates a graph that looks like the line graph.

Try It

- These exercises provide a review of three additional data displays.
- **Turn and Talk:** Have students discuss their answers. Remind them of *Talk Moves* that they can use in their discussions. Then review the answers as a class.

ELL Support

After demonstrating Example 2, have students work in groups to discuss and complete Try It Exercises 3–5. Remind students to consider the reasons for choosing each type of data display. Expect students to perform according to their language levels.

Beginner: State *yes*, *no*, or use a simple phrase.

Intermediate: Use simple sentences to contribute to discussion.

Advanced: Use complex sentences and help guide discussion.

EXAMPLE 2 **Identifying an Appropriate Data Display**

You record the number of hits for your school's new website for 5 months. Tell whether each data display is appropriate for representing how the number of hits changed during the 5 months. Explain your reasoning.

Month	Hits
August	250
September	320
October	485
November	650
December	925

a.

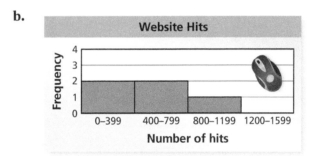

▷ The bar graph shows the number of hits for each month. So, it is an appropriate data display.

Math Practice

Maintain Oversight

What can you look for in the data displays to determine whether they show data changing over time?

b.

Website Hits

▷ The histogram does not show the number of hits for each month or how the number of hits changes over time. So, it is *not* an appropriate data display.

c.

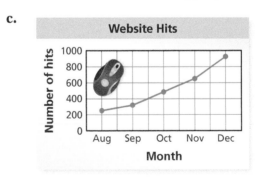

▷ The line graph shows how the number of hits changes over time. So, it is an appropriate data display.

Try It Tell whether the data display is appropriate for representing the data in Example 2. Explain your reasoning.

3. dot plot   **4.** circle graph   **5.** stem-and-leaf plot

EXAMPLE 3 **Identifying a Misleading Data Display**

Which line graph is misleading? Explain.

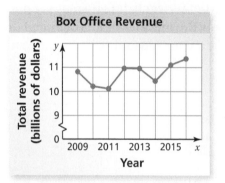

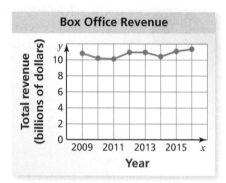

The vertical axis of the line graph on the left has a break ($\downarrow$) and begins at 9. This graph makes it appear that the total revenue fluctuated drastically from 2009 to 2016. The graph on the right has an unbroken axis. It is more honest and shows that the total revenue changed much less from 2009 to 2016.

 So, the graph on the left is misleading.

Try It

6. Which bar graph is misleading? Explain.

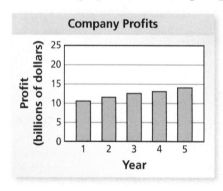

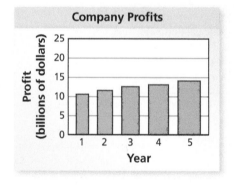

Self-Assessment for Concepts & Skills

Solve each exercise. Then rate your understanding of the success criteria in your journal.

CHOOSING A DATA DISPLAY **Choose an appropriate data display for the situation. Explain your reasoning.**

7. the percent of band students playing each instrument

8. a comparison of the amount of time spent using a tablet computer and the remaining battery life

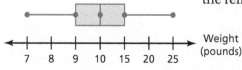

Weight (pounds)

9. **IDENTIFYING A MISLEADING DISPLAY** Is the box-and-whisker plot misleading? Explain.

Laurie's Notes

Discuss

- **Teaching Tip:** I have a collection of misleading data displays. When you find a data display in a newspaper or magazine that is misleading, cut it out and save it for later use. Ask colleagues in your school to do the same.
- **MP6 Attend to Precision:** Often what makes a graph misleading is the scale selected for one, or both, of the axes. By spreading out the scale, or condensing it, the graph becomes misleading.
- Ask students if they remember looking at any data displays that were misleading.
- As I always tell my students, the person who makes the data display influences how you will view it. They control the extent to which you can see, or not see, features of the data.
- ❔ "Who might want to use a misleading data display?" *Sample answers:* advertisers, politicians

EXAMPLE 3

- ❔ "The same data are displayed in each line graph. How do the graphs differ?" The vertical scale is different.
- ❔ "Which graph is misleading and why?" the first graph; The differences in total revenue appear greater than they actually are.
- **Extension:** Tell students to pretend that both graphs appear in a newspaper with an article. Ask them what they would use for a headline for each article. What story does the author want readers to see when they look at each graph?

Try It

- Use *Popsicle Sticks* to solicit responses. Utilize *Talk Moves* to include more students.

✔ Self-Assessment for Concepts & Skills

- **Neighbor Check:** Have students work independently and then have their neighbors check their work. Have students discuss any discrepancies.
- ◉ **Open-Ended Question:** Why is it important to identify misleading data displays? Who might use misleading data displays and why?

ELL Support

Allow students to work in pairs for extra support and to practice language. Have two pairs discuss their answers and come to an agreement. Monitor discussions and provide support as needed.

The Success Criteria Self-Assessment chart can be found in the *Student Journal* or online at *BigIdeasMath.com*.

Extra Example 3

Which line graph is misleading? Explain.

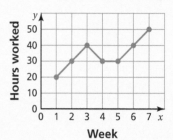

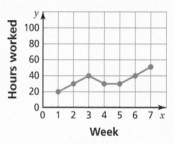

the second graph; The *y*-scale makes the change from week to week appear smaller.

Try It

6. the graph on the right; The bars become wider as the years progress, making the increase in profit appear greater.

Self-Assessment
for Concepts & Skills

7. *Sample answer:* circle graph; shows data as parts of a whole

8. *Sample answer:* scatter plot; shows the relationship between two data sets

9. yes; *Sample answer:* The increments on the number line are not equal, which makes it seem like the distribution is symmetric.

Extra Example 4

A pet store employee creates the circle graph shown.

Favorite Pets

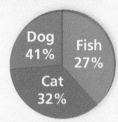

Dog 41%
Fish 27%
Cat 32%

a. A shopper concludes that more people chose cats as their favorite pet than dogs. Determine whether this conclusion is accurate.
not accurate

b. If you survey 120 people, how many would you expect to choose each pet?
dog: about 49 people
fish: about 32 people
cat: about 38 people

Self-Assessment
for Problem Solving

10. no; The increments on the vertical axis are not equal, which makes it seem like the number of 7-year-old to 9-year-old dogs is triple the number of 1-year-old to 3-year-old dogs. The number of 7-year-old to 9-year-old dogs is actually double the number of 1-year-old to 3-year-old dogs.

11. a. Employee salary appears to increase rapidly; The scale for the y-axis is missing.

    b. See Additional Answers.

Learning Target
Use appropriate data displays to represent situations.

Success Criteria
- Choose appropriate data displays for situations.
- Identify misleading data displays.
- Analyze a variety of data displays.

EXAMPLE 4

- Have students "read" the pictograph and ask them to summarize what information it describes. Many students will conclude that the amount of cans and the amount of boxes is about the same due to the horizontal distance each set of icons takes up.
- ❓ "Approximately how many cans of food and boxes of food have been donated?" 11 cans × 20 = 220 cans; 6 boxes × 20 = 120 boxes
- Almost twice as many cans of food have been donated as boxes, so this is misleading. The box icon is too large. It should be the same width as the can.

✓ Self-Assessment for Problem Solving

- Students may benefit from trying the exercises independently and then working with peers to refine their work. It is important to provide time in class for problem solving, so that students become comfortable with the problem-solving plan.
- **Think-Pair-Share:** Students should read each exercise independently and then work in pairs to complete the exercises. Then have each pair compare their answers with another pair and discuss any discrepancies.

The Success Criteria Self-Assessment chart can be found in the *Student Journal* or online at *BigIdeasMath.com*.

Formative Assessment Tip

I Used to Think... But Now I Know

This technique asks students to consider how their thinking about a concept or skill has changed from the beginning of instruction to the end of instruction. This can be done orally or in writing. It is important for students to be able to self-assess and reflect on their own learning. Use this technique at the end of the formal lesson.

If time permits, have students discuss with one another or the whole class how their understanding developed and/or changed.

Closure

- **I Used to Think... But Now I Know:** Have students reflect on how their thinking about data displays has changed.
- Students should write their responses as an *Entry Ticket*. Discuss their ideas at the start of the next class. For students who forget their *Entry Tickets*, have extra tickets available with the prompt written on them. Those students can complete their *Entry Tickets* at the back of the room before going to their seats.

EXAMPLE 4 Modeling Real Life

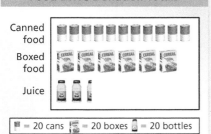

Food Drive Donation Totals

Canned food

Boxed food

Juice

🥫 = 20 cans 📦 = 20 boxes 🧃 = 20 bottles

The organizer of a food drive creates the pictograph shown. **(a) A volunteer concludes that the numbers of cans of food and boxes of food donated were about the same. Determine whether this conclusion is accurate. (b) Estimate the number of each item that has been donated.**

a. Each icon represents the same number of items. Because the box icon is larger than the can icon, it looks like the number of boxes is about the same as the number of cans. The number of boxes is actually about half of the number of cans.

 ▷ So, the conclusion is not accurate.

b. Each icon represents 20 items. Multiply each number of icons by 20.

$$11 \times 20 = 220 \text{ cans}$$

$$6 \times 20 = 120 \text{ boxes}$$

$$2\frac{1}{2} \times 20 = 50 \text{ bottles}$$

 ▷ So, about 220 cans, 120 boxes, and 50 bottles have been donated.

Self-Assessment for Problem Solving

Solve each exercise. Then rate your understanding of the success criteria in your journal.

10. An employee at an animal shelter creates the histogram shown. A visitor concludes that the number of 7-year-old to 9-year-old dogs is triple the number of 1-year-old to 3-year-old dogs. Determine whether this conclusion is accurate. Explain.

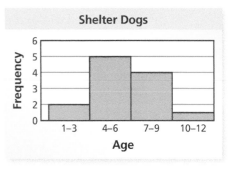

Employee Salary

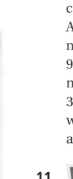

11. **DIG DEEPER!** A business manager creates the line graph shown. (a) How do the data *appear* to change over time? Explain why this conclusion may not be accurate. (b) Why might the business manager want to use this line graph?

Go to *BigIdeasMath.com* to get HELP with solving the exercises.

▶ Review & Refresh

You randomly survey students about whether they recycle. The two-way table shows the results.

		Recycle	
		Yes	No
Gender	Female	28	9
	Male	24	14

1. How many male students recycle? How many female students do *not* recycle?

2. Find and interpret the marginal frequencies.

Find the slope and the *y*-intercept of the graph of the linear equation.

3. $y = 4x + 10$ 4. $y = -3.5x - 2$ 5. $y - 8 = -x$

▶▶ Concepts, Skills, & Problem Solving

6. **DISPLAYING DATA** Analyze and display the data in a way that best describes the data. Explain your choice of display. (See Exploration 1, p. 255.)

Notebooks Sold in One Week		
192 red	170 green	203 black
183 pink	230 blue	165 yellow
210 purple	250 orange	179 white

CHOOSING A DATA DISPLAY **Choose an appropriate data display for the situation. Explain your reasoning.**

7. a student's test scores and how the scores are spread out

8. the prices of different televisions and the numbers of televisions sold

9. the outcome of rolling a number cube

10. the distance a person drives each month

11. **IDENTIFYING AN APPROPRIATE DISPLAY**
    A survey asked 800 students to choose their favorite school subject. The results are shown in the table. Tell whether each data display is appropriate for representing the portion of students who prefer math. Explain your reasoning.

Favorite School Subject	
Subject	Number of Students
Science	224
Math	176
Literature	240
Social studies	160

a. Favorite School Subject

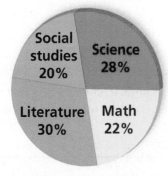

b.

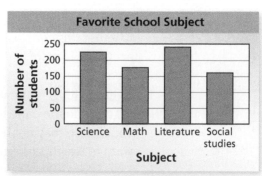

Assignment Guide and Concept Check

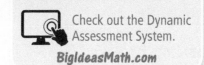

Scaffold assignments to support all students in their learning progression. The suggested assignments are a starting point. Continue to assign additional exercises and revisit with spaced practice to move every student toward proficiency.

Level	Assignment 1	Assignment 2
Emerging	1, 2, 5, 6, 7, 8, 9, 10, 11, 14	12, 15, 17, 18, 19, 20
Proficient	1, 2, 5, 6, 7, 8, 9, 10, 11, 13, 15	12, 14, 16, 17, 18, 19, 20
Advanced	1, 2, 5, 6, 7, 8, 9, 10, 12, 13, 15	14, 16, 17, 18, 19, 20

- Assignment 1 is for use after students complete the Self-Assessment for Concepts & Skills.
- Assignment 2 is for use after students complete the Self-Assessment for Problem Solving.
- The red exercises can be used as a concept check.

Review & Refresh Prior Skills

Exercise 1 Reading a Two-Way Table
Exercise 2 Finding Marginal Frequencies
Exercises 3–5 Identifying Slopes and y-Intercepts

Common Errors

- **Exercises 7–10** Students may confuse or forget the names of some of the data displays. For example, they may say that a dot plot should be used when they mean a scatter plot. Have them refer to the Key Idea for the names and descriptions of data displays.
- **Exercise 11** Students may guess whether a given data display is appropriate. Encourage them to carefully read the problem and then carefully think about whether the display is appropriate.

▶ *Review & Refresh*

1. 24 male students; 9 female students

2. 37 females were surveyed; 38 males were surveyed; 52 students recycle; 23 students do not recycle; 75 students were surveyed.

3. slope: 4; y-intercept: 10

4. slope: -3.5; y-intercept: -2

5. slope: -1; y-intercept: 8

▶ *Concepts, Skills, & Problem Solving*

6. *Sample answer:*

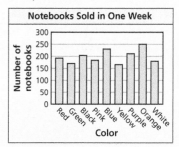

Notebooks Sold in One Week

A bar graph shows the data in different color categories.

7. *Sample answer:* stem-and-leaf plot; shows how data is distributed

8. *Sample answer:* scatter plot; shows the relationship between two sets of data

9. *Sample answer:* dot plot; shows the number of times each outcome occurs

10. *Sample answer:* line graph; shows how data change over time

11. **a.** yes; The circle graph shows the data as parts of the whole.

    b. no; The bar graph shows the number of students, not the portion of students.

Concepts, Skills, & Problem Solving

12. **a.** yes; The pictograph shows the number of hours worked each month using pictures.

    b. yes; The bar graph shows the number of hours worked each month.

13. when the data are in terms of intervals of one category, as opposed to multiple categories; *Sample answer:* You can use a histogram to display the frequencies of voters in the last election by age group.

14. the graph on the left; The pictures of the bikes are the largest on Monday and the smallest on Wednesday, which makes it seem like the distance is the same each day.

15. the graph on the right; The interval for the third bar is greater than the interval for the other two bars, which makes it seem like there is an increasing trend.

Common Errors

- **Exercise 12** Students may guess whether a given data display is appropriate. Encourage them to carefully read the problem and then carefully think about whether the display is appropriate.

- **Exercises 14 and 15** Students may not be able to recognize which data display is misleading. As a class, make a list of things to look for when analyzing a data display. For instance, students should check the increments or intervals for the axes if possible.

12. **IDENTIFYING AN APPROPRIATE DISPLAY** The table shows how many hours you worked as a lifeguard from May to August. Tell whether each data display is appropriate for representing how the number of hours worked changed during the 4 months. Explain your reasoning.

Lifeguard Schedule	
Month	**Hours Worked**
May	40
June	80
July	160
August	120

a.

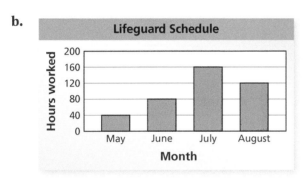

Key: = 20 hours

b.

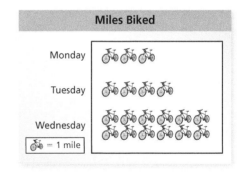

13. **WRITING** When should you use a histogram instead of a bar graph to display data? Use an example to support your answer.

IDENTIFYING MISLEADING DISPLAYS **Which data display is misleading? Explain.**

14.

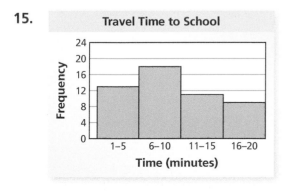

15.

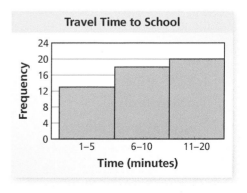

16. **MP REASONING** What type of data display is appropriate for showing the mode of a data set?

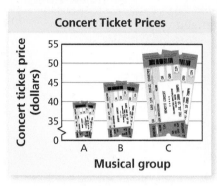

Concert Ticket Prices

17. **CRITICAL THINKING** The director of a music festival creates the data display shown. A customer concludes that the ticket price for Group C is more than double the ticket price for Group A. Determine whether this conclusion is accurate. Explain.

18. **MP PATTERNS** A scientist gathers data about a decaying chemical compound and creates the scatter plot shown.

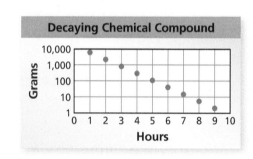

a. The scientist concludes that there is a negative linear relationship between the data. Determine whether this conclusion is accurate. Explain.

b. Estimate the amount of the compound remaining after 1 hour, 3 hours, 5 hours, and 7 hours.

19. **MP REASONING** A survey asks 100 students to choose their favorite sports. The results are shown in the circle graph.

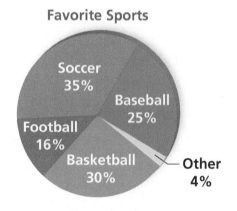

Favorite Sports

a. Explain why the graph is misleading.

b. What type of data display is more appropriate for the data? Explain.

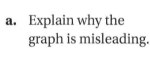

20. **MP STRUCTURE** With the help of computers, mathematicians have computed and analyzed trillions of digits of the irrational number π. One of the things they analyze is the frequency of each of the numbers 0 through 9. The table shows the frequency of each number in the first 100,000 digits of π.

a. Display the data in a bar graph.

b. Display the data in a circle graph.

c. Which data display is more appropriate? Explain.

d. Describe the distribution.

Number	0	1	2	3	4	5	6	7	8	9
Frequency	9999	10,137	9908	10,025	9971	10,026	10,029	10,025	9978	9902

Common Errors

- **Exercise 16** Students may say that an appropriate data display for showing the mode is a stem-and-leaf plot, because the stem with the most leaves would be the mode. However, the stem with the most leaves may have data that is not part of the mode. Remind students that a dot plot isolates each data value and shows the frequency of each individual number, so it would be a more appropriate display.

Mini-Assessment

Choose an appropriate display for the situation. Explain your reasoning.

1. the outcomes of flipping a coin 20 times *Sample answer:* pictograph, bar graph, or dot plot; shows the number of times you get heads or tails

2. comparison of students' test scores and how long students studied *Sample answer:* scatter plot; compares two data sets

3. the number of students participating in after-school sports each year *Sample answer:* line graph; shows changes over time

Section Resources

Surface Level	Deep Level
Resources by Chapter • Extra Practice • Reteach • Puzzle Time Student Journal • Self-Assessment • Practice Differentiating the Lesson Tutorial Videos Skills Review Handbook Skills Trainer	Resources by Chapter • Enrichment and Extension Graphic Organizers Dynamic Assessment System • Section Practice

Transfer Level	
Dynamic Assessment System • End-of-Chapter Quiz	Assessment Book • End-of-Chapter Quiz

Concepts, Skills, & Problem Solving

16. *Sample answer:* dot plot

17. no; The tickets vary in width and the vertical axis has a break, which makes it seem like the ticket price for Group C is more than double the ticket price for Group A. The ticket price for Group A is actually about $40, and the ticket price for Group C is actually about $53.

18. a. no; The vertical axis has a scale that increases by powers of 10, which makes it seem like the points lie close to a line when they actually do not.

    b. *Sample answer:* 8000 g, 900 g, 100 g, 20 g

19. a. The percents do not sum to 100%.

    b. *Sample answer:* bar graph; It would show the frequency of each sport.

20. a.

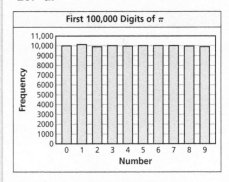

    b. First 100,000 Digits of π

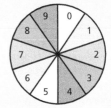

    c. *Sample answer:* the bar graph; It shows that some digits occur slightly more than others, which is hard to tell from the circle graph.

    d. Each digit occurs about 10% of the time, leading to a relatively *flat*, or *uniform* distribution.

Skills Needed

Exercise 1
- Finding an Experimental Probability
- Finding Marginal Frequencies

Exercise 2
- Finding a Line of Best Fit
- Translating a Figure

Exercise 3
- Making a Two-Way Table
- Writing and Interpreting Ratios

ELL Support

In Exercise 1, support students' understanding of the problem by discussing the types of movies listed in the two-way table. In Exercise 3, point out that a field trip is an educational school outing, not a trip to a field.

Using the Problem-Solving Plan

1. $\frac{40}{91}$, or about 44%

2. The slope does not change. The y-intercept increases by 7, from 2.35 to 9.35.

3. See Additional Answers.

Performance Task

The *STEAM Video Performance Task* provides the opportunity for additional enrichment and greater depth of knowledge as students explore the mathematics of the chapter within a context tied to the chapter STEAM Video. The performance task and a detailed scoring rubric are provided at *BigIdeasMath.com*.

Scaffolding Instruction

- The goal of this lesson is to help students become more comfortable with problem solving. These exercises combine data analysis and displays with prior skills from other chapters and courses. The solution for Exercise 1 is worked out below, to help you guide students through the problem-solving plan. Use the remaining class time to have students work on the other exercises.
- **Emerging:** The goal for these students is to feel comfortable with the problem-solving plan. Allow students to work in pairs to write the beginning steps of the problem-solving plan for Exercise 2. Keep in mind that some students may only be ready to do the first step.
- **Proficient:** Students may be able to work independently or in pairs to complete Exercises 2 and 3.
- Visit each pair to review their plan for each problem. Ask students to describe their plans.

▶ *Using the Problem-Solving Plan*

Exercise 1

⇨ **Understand the problem.** You know the results of a survey about movie preference. You are asked to estimate the probability that a randomly selected middle school student prefers action movies.

⇨ **Make a plan.** Find the marginal frequencies for the data. Then use the marginal frequencies to find the probability that a randomly selected middle school student prefers action movies.

⇨ **Solve and check.** Use the plan to solve the problem. Then check your solution.

- Find the marginal frequencies for the data.

		Grade			
		6	**7**	**8**	**Total**
Genre	**Action**	12	18	10	40
	Comedy	8	6	3	17
	Animation	9	11	14	34
	Total	29	35	27	91

- Find the probability that a randomly selected middle school student prefers action movies.

    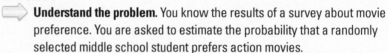

    $P(\text{action movies}) = \frac{40}{91} \approx 44\%$

    So, the probability of randomly selecting a middle school student that prefers action movies is $\frac{40}{91}$, or about 44%.

- **Check:** Verify that 44% of 91 total students is about 40 students.

    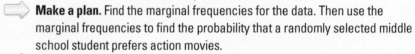

    $a = p\% \cdot w$
    $a = 0.44 \cdot 91$
    $a = 40.04$, or about 40 students. ✓

6 Connecting Concepts

▶ Using the Problem-Solving Plan

1. You randomly survey middle school students about whether they prefer action, comedy, or animation movies. The two-way table shows the results. Estimate the probability that a randomly selected middle school student prefers action movies.

		Grade		
		6	7	8
Genre	**Action**	12	18	10
	Comedy	8	6	3
	Animation	9	11	14

Understand the problem. ▶ You know the results of a survey about movie preference. You are asked to estimate the probability that a randomly selected middle school student prefers action movies.

Make a plan. ▶ Find the marginal frequencies for the data. Then use the marginal frequencies to find the probability that a randomly selected middle school student prefers action movies.

Solve and check. ▶ Use the plan to solve the problem. Then check your solution.

2. An equation of the line of best fit for a data set is $y = -0.68x + 2.35$. Describe what happens to the slope and the y-intercept of the line when each y-value in the data set increases by 7.

3. On a school field trip, there must be 1 adult chaperone for every 16 students. There are 8 adults who are willing to be a chaperone for the trip, but only the number of chaperones that are necessary will attend. In a class of 124 students, 80 attend the trip. Make a two-way table that represents the data.

Performance Task

Cost vs. Fuel Economy

At the beginning of this chapter, you watched a STEAM Video called "Fuel Economy." You are now ready to complete the performance task related to this video, available at *BigIdeasMath.com*. Be sure to use the problem-solving plan as you work through the performance task.

▶ Review Vocabulary

Write the definition and give an example of each vocabulary term.

scatter plot, *p. 238*   line of best fit, *p. 245*   joint frequency, *p. 250*

line of fit, *p. 244*   two-way table, *p. 250*   marginal frequency, *p. 250*

▶ Graphic Organizers

You can use an **Information Frame** to help organize and remember a concept. Here is an example of an Information Frame for *scatter plots*.

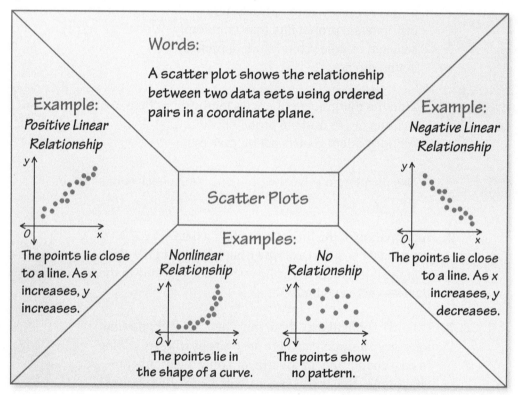

Choose and complete a graphic organizer to help you study the concept.

1. lines of fit

2. two-way tables

3. data displays

"Dear Teacher, I am emailing my Information Frame showing the characteristics of circles."

Review Vocabulary

- As a review of the chapter vocabulary, have students revisit the vocabulary section in their *Student Journals* to fill in any missing definitions and record examples of each term.

Graphic Organizers

Sample answers:

1.

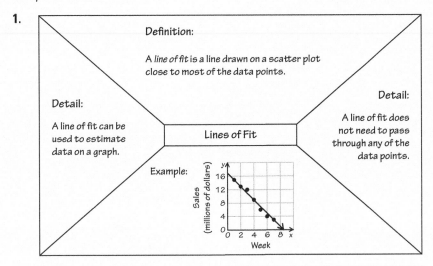

2.

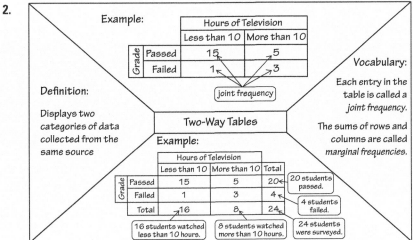

3.

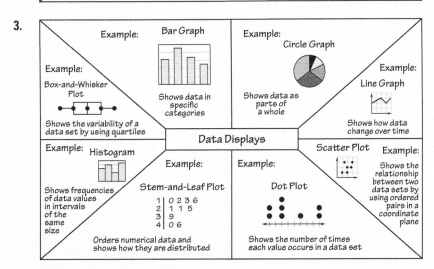

List of Organizers

Available at *BigIdeasMath.com*
Definition and Example Chart
Example and Non-Example Chart
Four Square
Information Frame
Summary Triangle

About this Organizer

An **Information Frame** can be used to help students organize and remember concepts. Students write the concept in the middle rectangle. Then students write related categories in the spaces around the rectangle. Related categories may include: words, numbers, algebra, example, definition, non-example, visual, procedure, details, or vocabulary. Students can place their Information Frames on note cards to use as a quick study reference.

1.

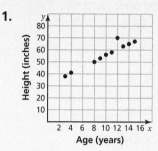

outlier: (12, 70); gap: from 4 years old to 8 years old; no clusters

2. negative linear relationship; outlier: (21, 40); no gaps or clusters

3. no relationship; no outliers or gaps; cluster: around (12, 16)

4. positive linear relationship; no outliers; gap: from $x = 12$ to $x = 18$; no clusters

5. negative linear relationship

6. a. *Sample answer:* time spent running on a treadmill and number of calories burned

   b. *Sample answer:* grade on a test and shoe size

7. *Sample answer:* 5.6 h

✓ Chapter Self-Assessment

The Success Criteria Self-Assessment chart can be found in the *Student Journal* or online at *BigIdeasMath.com*.

ELL Support

Allow students to work in pairs to complete the first section of the Chapter Self-Assessment. Provide graph paper for Exercises 1 and 7. Check for understanding by having pairs hold up their graphs for your review. For exercises that do not require graphing, have pairs display their answers on whiteboards for your review. This would include outliers, gaps, and clusters for Exercises 2–4 and the answer to Exercise 7. Have each pair discuss and answer Exercises 5 and 6, then compare their ideas with another pair and reach an agreement on the answers. Monitor discussions and provide support. Use similar techniques to check the remaining sections of the Chapter Self-Assessment.

Common Errors

- **Exercises 2–4** Students may mix up positive and negative relationships. Remind them about slope. The slope is positive when the line rises from left to right and negative when it falls from left to right. The same is true for relationships in a scatter plot. When the data rise from left to right, it is a positive relationship. When the data fall from left to right, it is a negative relationship.

▷ Chapter Self-Assessment

As you complete the exercises, use the scale below to rate your understanding of the success criteria in your journal.

1	**2**	**3**	**4**
I do not understand.	I can do it with help.	I can do it on my own.	I can teach someone else.

6.1 Scatter Plots (pp. 237–242)

Learning Target: Use scatter plots to describe patterns and relationships between two quantities.

1. Make a scatter plot of the data. Identify any outliers, gaps, or clusters.

Age (years), *x*	15	3	14	12	8	11	9	4	13	10
Height (inches), *y*	67	38	65	70	50	58	53	41	63	56

Describe the relationship between the data. Identify any outliers, gaps, or clusters.

2.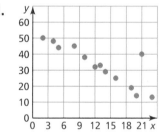

3.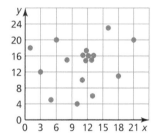

4.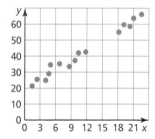

5. Your school is ordering custom T-shirts. The scatter plot shows the numbers of T-shirts ordered and the cost per shirt. Describe the relationship between the numbers of T-shirts ordered and the cost per T-shirt.

6. Describe a set of real-life data that has each relationship.

   a. positive linear relationship

   b. no relationship

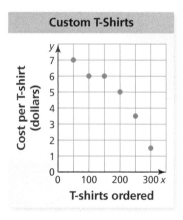

7. The table shows the numbers of hours a waitress works and the amounts she earns in tips. How many hours do you expect the waitress to work when she earns $42 in tips?

Hours Worked, *x*	2	5.5	1	7	2.5	8	3	5
Tips (dollars), *y*	15	40	7	50	18	55	20	36

6.2 Lines of Fit (pp. 243–248)

Learning Target: Use lines of fit to model data.

8. The table shows the numbers of students at a middle school over a 10-year period.

   a. Make a scatter plot of the data and draw a line of fit.

   b. Write an equation of the line of fit.

   c. Interpret the slope and the y-intercept of the line of fit.

   d. Predict the number of students in year 11.

Year, x	Number of Students, y
1	492
2	507
3	520
4	535
5	550
6	562
7	577
8	591
9	604
10	618

9. Find an equation of the line of best fit for the data in Exercise 8. Identify and interpret the correlation coefficient.

10. The table shows the revenue (in millions of dollars) for a company over an eight-year period. Assuming this trend continues, how much revenue will there be in year 9?

Year, x	1	2	3	4	5	6	7	8
Revenue (millions of dollars), y	20	35	46	56	68	82	92	108

6.3 Two-Way Tables (pp. 249–254)

Learning Target: Use two-way tables to represent data.

You randomly survey students about participating in the science fair. The two-way table shows the results.

11. How many male students participate in the science fair?

12. How many female students *do not* participate in the science fair?

		Science Fair	
		No	Yes
Gender	Female	15	22
Gender	Male	12	32

13. You randomly survey students in your school about whether they liked a recent school play. The two-way table shows the results. Find and interpret the marginal frequencies.

		Student	
		Liked	Did Not Like
Gender	Male	48	12
Gender	Female	56	14

Common Errors

- **Exercise 8** Students may use inconsistent increments or forget to label the graph. Remind them to use consistent increments to represent the data and to label the axes so that information can be read from the graph.
- **Exercise 8** Students may draw a line of fit that does not accurately reflect the data trend. Remind them that the line does not have to go through any of the data points. Also remind students that the line should go through the middle of the data so that about half of the data points are above the line and half are below. One strategy is to draw an oval around the data and then draw a line through the middle of the oval.
  For example:

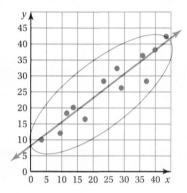

- **Exercise 13** Students may incorrectly identify joint frequencies as marginal frequencies. Remind them of these definitions.

8. **a.** *Sample answer:*

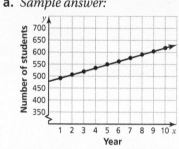

b. *Sample answer:*
$y = 14x + 478$

c. *Sample answer:* The number of students in the year prior to the 10-year period was 478, and the number of students increases by 14 students per year.

d. *Sample answer:* 632 students

9. $y = 14.0x + 478.7$; about 0.9999; strong positive correlation

10. about 118.8 million

11. 32 male students

12. 15 female students

13. 60 males were surveyed;
70 females were surveyed;
104 students liked the play;
26 students did not like the play;
130 students were surveyed.

14. See Additional Answers.

15.

		Food Court	
		Likes	**Dislikes**
Age Group	**Teenagers**	96%	4%
	Adults	21%	79%
	Senior Citizens	18%	82%

16. Yes, the table shows that teenagers tend to like the food court, but adults and senior citizens tend to dislike the food court.

17. *Sample answer:* line graph; shows how data change over time

18. *Sample answer:* circle graph; shows data as parts of a whole

19. a. no; The histogram does not show the number of bandings for each year or how the number of bandings changes over time.

b. yes; The line graph shows how the number of bandings changes over time.

20. *Sample answer:*

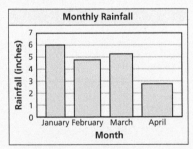

Monthly Rainfall

The widths of the bars are different, which makes it look like some months have more rainfall.

21. *Sample answer:* You want to display the daily low temperature in your city during a specific month; The dot plot will show the number of times each temperature occurs in the data set.

Common Errors

- **Exercise 14** Students may incorrectly identify joint frequencies as marginal frequencies. Remind them of these definitions.
- **Exercise 15** Students may find the percents based on all people surveyed, not just the people from each age group. Encourage students to read the problem carefully to determine what is being asked.
- **Exercises 17 and 18** Students may confuse or forget the names of some of the data displays. For example, they may say that a dot plot should be used when they mean a scatter plot. Have them refer to the Key Idea on page 256 for the names and descriptions of data displays.
- **Exercise 19** Students may guess whether a given data display is appropriate. Encourage them to carefully read the problem and then carefully think about whether the display is appropriate.

Chapter Resources

Surface Level	Deep Level
Resources by Chapter • Extra Practice • Reteach • Puzzle Time Student Journal • Practice • Chapter Self-Assessment Differentiating the Lesson Tutorial Videos Skills Review Handbook Skills Trainer Game Library	Resources by Chapter • Enrichment and Extension Graphic Organizers Game Library
Transfer Level	
STEAM Video Dynamic Assessment System • Chapter Test	Assessment Book • Chapter Tests A and B • Alternative Assessment • STEAM Performance Task

You randomly survey people at a mall about whether they like the new food court. The results are shown.

14. Make a two-way table that includes the marginal frequencies.

15. For each group, what percent of the people surveyed like the food court? dislike the food court? Organize your results in a two-way table.

16. Does your table in Exercise 15 show a relationship between age and whether people like the food court?

> **Teenagers**
> 96 likes, 4 dislikes
>
> **Adults**
> 21 likes, 79 dislikes
>
> **Senior Citizens**
> 18 likes, 82 dislikes

6.4 Choosing a Data Display *(pp. 255–262)*

Learning Target: Use appropriate data displays to represent situations.

Choose an appropriate data display for the situation. Explain your reasoning.

17. the numbers of pairs of shoes sold by a store each week

18. the percent of votes that each candidate received in an election

19. *Bird banding* is attaching a tag to a bird's wing or leg to track the movement of the bird. This provides information about the bird's migration patterns and feeding behaviors. The table shows the numbers of robins banded in Pennsylvania over 5 years. Tell whether each data display is appropriate for representing how the number of bandings changed during the 5 years. Explain your reasoning.

Year	Number of Bandings
2012	168
2013	142
2014	355
2015	330
2016	345

a.

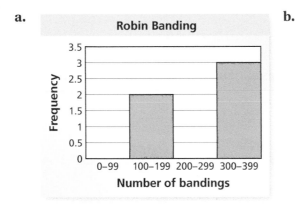

b.

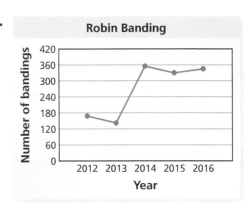

20. Give an example of a bar graph that is misleading. Explain your reasoning.

21. Give an example of a situation where a dot plot is an appropriate data display. Explain your reasoning.

1. The graph shows the population (in millions) of the United States from 1960 to 2010.

   a. In what year was the population of the United States about 180 million?

   b. What was the approximate population of the United States in 1990?

   c. Describe the relationship shown by the data.

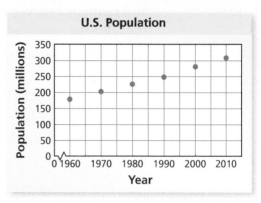

U.S. Population

2. The table shows the weight of a baby over several months.

   a. Make a scatter plot of the data and draw a line of fit.

   b. Write an equation of the line of fit.

   c. Interpret the slope and the y-intercept of the line of fit.

   d. Predict how much the baby will weigh at 7 months.

Age (months)	Weight (pounds)
1	8
2	9.25
3	11.75
4	13
5	14.5
6	16

		Nonfiction	
		Likes	Dislikes
Fiction	Likes	26	20
	Dislikes	22	2

3. You randomly survey students at your school about what type of books they like to read. The two-way table shows your results. Find and interpret the marginal frequencies.

Choose an appropriate data display for the situation. Explain your reasoning.

4. magazine sales grouped by price range

5. the distance a person hikes each week

6. The table shows the numbers y of AP exams (in thousands) taken from 2012 to 2016, where $x = 12$ represents the year 2012. Find an equation of the line of best fit. Identify and interpret the correlation coefficient.

Year, x	12	13	14	15	16
Number of AP Exams, y	3698	3938	4176	4479	4705

7. You randomly survey shoppers at a supermarket about whether they use reusable bags. Of 60 male shoppers, 15 use reusable bags. Of 110 female shoppers, 60 use reusable bags. Organize your results in a two-way table. Include the marginal frequencies. Estimate the probability that a randomly selected male shopper uses reusable bags.

Practice Test Item References

Practice Test Questions	Section to Review
1	6.1
2, 6	6.2
3, 7	6.3
4, 5	6.4

Test-Taking Strategies

Remind students to quickly look over the entire test before they start so that they can budget their time. Have them use the **Stop** and **Think** strategy before they write their answers.

Common Errors

- **Exercise 1** When finding values from the graph, students may accidentally shift over or up too far and get an answer that is off by an increment. Encourage students to start at the given value and trace the graph to where the point is, and then trace down or left to the other axis for the answer.
- **Exercise 3** Students may incorrectly identify joint frequencies as marginal frequencies. Remind them of these definitions.
- **Exercises 4 and 5** Students may confuse or forget the names of some of the data displays. For example, they may say that a dot plot should be used when they mean a scatter plot. Have them refer to the Key Idea on page 256 for the names and descriptions of data displays.

1. a. 1960

  b. 250 million

  c. positive linear relationship

2. a. *Sample answer:*

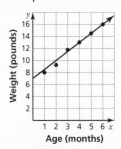

  b. *Sample answer:* $y = 1.5x + 7$

  c. *Sample answer:* The baby gains 1.5 pounds per month and was born with a weight of 7 pounds.

  d. *Sample answer:* 17.5 pounds

3. 48 students like nonfiction;
22 students dislike nonfiction;
46 students like fiction;
24 students dislike fiction;
70 students were surveyed.

4. *Sample answer:* histogram; shows frequencies of data values in intervals of the same size

5. *Sample answer:* line graph; shows how data change over time

6. $y = 255.5x + 622.2$; about 0.999; strong positive correlation

7.

		Use reusable bags?		
		Yes	No	Total
Gender	Male	15	45	60
	Female	60	50	110
	Total	75	95	170

$\frac{1}{4}$, or 25%

Test-Taking Strategies

Available at *BigIdeasMath.com*

After Answering Easy Questions, Relax
Answer Easy Questions First
Estimate the Answer
Read All Choices before Answering
Read Question before Answering
Solve Directly or Eliminate Choices
Solve Problem before Looking at Choices
Use Intelligent Guessing
Work Backwards

About this Strategy

When taking a multiple-choice test, be sure to read each question carefully and thoroughly. It is also very important to read each answer choice carefully. Do not pick the first answer that you think is correct! If two answer choices are the same, eliminate them both. Unless the question states otherwise, there can only be one answer.

Cumulative Practice

1. B

2. F

3. 12

Item Analysis

1. A. The student interchanges the *x*- and *y*-coordinates.

B. Correct answer

C. The student interchanges the *x*- and *y*-coordinates, and omits a negative.

D. The student omits a negative.

2. F. Correct answer

G. The student confuses alternate interior angles with corresponding angles.

H. The student picks an angle on the same side of the transversal as $\angle 6$, but not the corresponding angle.

I. The student confuses supplementary angles with corresponding angles.

3. Gridded Response: Correct answer: 12

Common error: The student adds the entries in the "No" column and gets an answer of 29.

1. What is the solution of the system of linear equations?

$$y = 2x - 1$$
$$y = 3x + 5$$

A. $(-13, -6)$

B. $(-6, -13)$

C. $(-13, 6)$

D. $(-6, 13)$

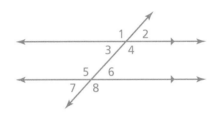

Test-Taking Strategy
Read All Choices Before Answering

Which type of graph would best show the percent of cats who said tuna is their favorite food?
Ⓐ Ⓑ Ⓒ Ⓓ

Did someone say "tuna"?

"Reading all choices before answering can sometimes point out the obvious answer!"

2. The diagram shows parallel lines cut by a transversal. Which angle is the corresponding angle for $\angle 6$?

F. $\angle 2$ G. $\angle 3$

H. $\angle 4$ I. $\angle 8$

3. You randomly survey students in your school. You ask whether they have jobs. You display your results in the two-way table. How many male students do *not* have a job?

		Job	
		Yes	No
Gender	**Male**	27	12
	Female	31	17

4. Which scatter plot shows a negative relationship between x and y?

A.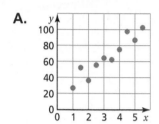

B.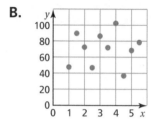

C.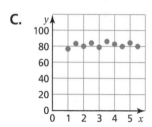

D.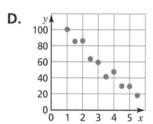

5. A system of two linear equations has no solution. What can you conclude about the graphs of the two equations?

F. The lines have the same slope and the same y-intercept.

G. The lines have the same slope and different y-intercepts.

H. The lines have different slopes and the same y-intercept.

I. The lines have different slopes and different y-intercepts.

6. What is the solution of the equation?

$$0.22(x + 6) = 0.2x + 1.8$$

A. $x = 2.4$

B. $x = 15.6$

C. $x = 24$

D. $x = 156$

7. A person who is $5\frac{1}{2}$ feet tall casts a $3\frac{1}{2}$-foot-long shadow. A nearby flagpole casts a 28-foot-long shadow. What is the height (in feet) of the flagpole?

Item Analysis (continued)

4. **A.** The student confuses positive and negative relationships.

   B. The student confuses no relationship with a negative relationship.

   C. The student confuses constant and negative relationships.

   D. Correct answer

5. **F.** The student thinks the lines must coincide.

   G. Correct answer

   H. The student reverses the idea that the slopes are the same and the y-intercepts are different.

   I. The student incorrectly reasons that both the slopes and y-intercepts must be different.

6. **A.** The student makes an error placing a decimal point.

   B. The student adds 1.32 to 1.8 instead of subtracting 1.32 from 1.8, and makes an error placing a decimal point.

   C. Correct answer

   D. The student adds 1.32 to 1.8 instead of subtracting 1.32 from 1.8.

7. **Gridded Response:** Correct answer: 44

   Common error: The student incorrectly reasons that because the person is 2 feet taller than the length of his or her shadow, then the building must be 2 feet taller than the length of its shadow, getting an answer of 30.

4. D

5. G

6. C

7. 44

8. G

9. A

10. *Part A*

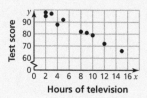

Part B negative linear relationship

Part C Enter the data in the calculator and find the correlation coefficient.

Item Analysis (continued)

8. F. The student does not realize that the underlying idea here is to show change over time, something a circle graph is not capable of showing.

  G. Correct answer

  H. The student does not realize that the underlying idea here is to show change over time, something a histogram is not capable of showing.

  I. The student does not realize that the underlying idea here is to show change over time, something a stem-and-leaf plot is not capable of showing.

9. A. Correct answer

  B. The student reflects the trapezoid in the *y*-axis instead of rotating it 90° clockwise about the origin.

  C. The student rotates the figure 180° about the origin instead of 90° clockwise about the origin.

  D. The student rotates the figure 90° counterclockwise about the origin instead of clockwise.

10. **4 points** The student's work and explanations demonstrate a thorough understanding of using a scatter plot to determine the relationship between two data sets. In Part A, the student correctly plots all the points. In Part B, the student states that there is negative linear relationship between the hours of television watched and the test scores. In Part C, the student describes entering the data in the calculator and finding the correlation coefficient. The student provides accurate work with clear and complete explanations.

3 points The student's work and explanations demonstrate an essential but less than thorough understanding of using a scatter plot to determine the relationship between two data sets. For example, the relationship between the data sets is stated correctly, but one or more points may be plotted incorrectly, or the correlation coefficient is not correctly interpreted.

2 points The student's work and explanations demonstrate a partial but limited understanding of using a scatter plot to determine the relationship between two data sets. There are errors in plotting the points and interpreting the scatter plot or the correlation coefficient.

1 point The student's work and explanations demonstrate a very limited understanding of using a scatter plot to determine the relationship between two data sets. Points are plotted incorrectly or not at all, and the interpretations are incorrect.

0 points The student provides no response, a completely incorrect or incomprehensible response, or a response that demonstrates insufficient understanding of using a scatter plot to determine the relationship between two data sets.

8. A store records total sales (in dollars) each month for three years. Which type of graph can best show how sales increase over this time period?

F. circle graph

G. line graph

H. histogram

I. stem-and-leaf plot

9. Trapezoid *KLMN* is graphed in the coordinate plane shown.

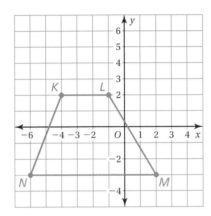

Rotate Trapezoid *KLMN* 90° clockwise about the origin. What are the coordinates of point *M'*, the image of point *M* after the rotation?

A. $(-3, -2)$

B. $(-2, -3)$

C. $(-2, 3)$

D. $(3, 2)$

10. The table shows the numbers of hours students spent watching television from Monday through Friday for one week and their scores on a test that Friday.

Think Solve Explain

Hours of Television, x	5	2	10	15	3	4	8	2	12	9
Test Score, y	92	98	79	66	97	88	82	95	72	81

Part A Make a scatter plot of the data.

Part B Describe the relationship between the hours of television watched and the test scores.

Part C Explain how to justify your answer in Part B using the *linear regression* feature of a graphing calculator.

7 Functions

Chapter Learning Target:
Understand functions.

Chapter Success Criteria:
- I can identify functions.
- I can represent functions in a variety of ways.
- I can evaluate functions.
- I can solve problems using function rules.

STEAM Video: "Apparent Temperature"

Laurie's Notes

Chapter 7 Overview

In this chapter, students will gain a conceptual understanding of functions. A function is a relationship between two sets, inputs and outputs, where each input is paired with exactly one output. The pairing may be a mathematical rule such as "double the input and add 1." The pairing may also be something contextual such as a person's name and eye color.

After learning to identify relations that are functions, students will focus on representing functions in a variety of ways.

Words: The output is one more than twice the input.

Equation: $y = 2x + 1$

Input-Output Table	

Input, x	Output, y
-1	-1
0	1
1	3
2	5

Mapping Diagram

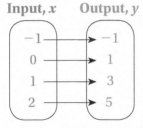

Graph

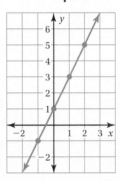

In the third lesson, students will use functions to model linear relationships. Students will build upon their understanding from Chapter 4, where they wrote linear equations in slope-intercept form. The work is familiar to students, but the function language is new.

The next lesson focuses on the differences between linear and nonlinear functions. Students will look for a constant rate of change when identifying the data as linear or nonlinear. If students graph the data to look for a constant rate of change, accurately scaling the axes and plotting the ordered pairs is crucial. Encourage students to verify their conjectures by examining the change in y for each x-value.

Linear Function

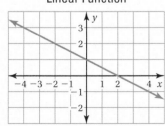

Nonlinear Function

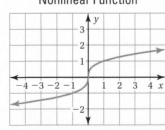

The chapter concludes with analyzing and sketching graphs without numbers. Students will reason about the relationship between two quantities by analyzing a graph. They will look for increasing, decreasing, and constant patterns. The increasing and decreasing patterns may be linear or nonlinear. Given a verbal description, students will sketch a graph to represent the situation.

Suggested Pacing

Chapter Opener	1 Day
Section 1	2 Days
Section 2	2 Days
Section 3	2 Days
Section 4	2 Days
Section 5	2 Days
Connecting Concepts	1 Day
Chapter Review	1 Day
Chapter Test	1 Day
Total Chapter 7	14 Days
Year-to-Date	100 Days

Chapter Learning Target
Understand functions.

Chapter Success Criteria
- Identify functions.
- Represent functions in a variety of ways.
- Evaluate functions.
- Solve problems using function rules.

Chapter 7 Learning Targets and Success Criteria

Section	Learning Target	Success Criteria
7.1 Relations and Functions	Understand the concept of a function.	• Represent a relation as a set of ordered pairs. • Determine whether a relation is a function. • Use functions to solve real-life problems.
7.2 Representations of Functions	Represent functions in a variety of ways.	• Write a function rule that describes a relationship. • Evaluate functions for given inputs. • Represent functions using tables and graphs.
7.3 Linear Functions	Use functions to model linear relationships.	• Write linear functions to model relationships. • Interpret linear functions in real-life situations.
7.4 Comparing Linear and Nonlinear Functions	Understand differences between linear and nonlinear functions.	• Recognize linear functions represented as tables, equations, and graphs. • Compare linear and nonlinear functions.
7.5 Analyzing and Sketching Graphs	Use graphs of functions to describe relationships between quantities.	• Describe relationships between quantities in graphs. • Sketch graphs given verbal descriptions of relationships.

Progressions

Through the Grades		
Grade 7	**Grade 8**	**High School**
• Identify the constant of proportionality in tables, graphs, equations, diagrams, and verbal descriptions. • Represent proportional relationships with equations.	• Understand the definition of a function. • Compare and write functions represented in different ways (words, tables, and graphs). • Understand that $y = mx + b$ is a linear function and recognize nonlinear functions. • Interpret the rate of change and the initial value of a function. • Describe qualitatively the functional relationship between two quantities by analyzing a graph. Sketch a graph that exhibits the qualitative features of a function that has been described verbally.	• Use function notation to evaluate, interpret, and graph functions. • Compare square root functions and compare cube root functions using average rates of change. • Graph and use linear and quadratic functions in different forms. • Graph square root, cube root, and piecewise functions, including step and absolute value functions. • Use intercept form to find zeros of functions. • Identify even and odd functions.

Through the Chapter					
Standard	**7.1**	**7.2**	**7.3**	**7.4**	**7.5**
8.F.A.1 Understand that a function is a rule that assigns to each input exactly one output. The graph of a function is the set of ordered pairs consisting of an input and the corresponding output.	●	★			
8.F.A.2 Compare properties of two functions each represented in a different way (algebraically, graphically, numerically in tables, or by verbal descriptions).			★		
8.F.A.3 Interpret the equation $y = mx + b$ as defining a linear function, whose graph is a straight line; give examples of functions that are not linear.			●	★	
8.F.B.4 Construct a function to model a linear relationship between two quantities. Determine the rate of change and initial value of the function from a description of a relationship or from two (x, y) values, including reading these from a table or from a graph. Interpret the rate of change and initial value of a linear function in terms of the situation it models, and in terms of its graph or a table of values.		●	★		
8.F.B.5 Describe qualitatively the functional relationship between two quantities by analyzing a graph (e.g., where the function is increasing or decreasing, linear or nonlinear). Sketch a graph that exhibits the qualitative features of a function that has been described verbally.					★

Key

▲ = preparing   ★ = complete
● = learning   ■ = extending

Laurie's Notes

1. 80.9°F

2. yellow

Performance Task

Sample answer: to determine whether it is safe to remain outside for an extended period of time

Mathematical Practices

Students have opportunities to develop aspects of the mathematical practices throughout the chapter. Here are some examples.

1. **Make Sense of Problems and Persevere in Solving Them**
   7.2 Exercise 36, *p. 288*

2. **Reason Abstractly and Quantitatively**
   7.2 Exercise 39, *p. 288*

3. **Construct Viable Arguments and Critique the Reasoning of Others**
   7.1 Exercise 15, *p. 280*

4. **Model with Mathematics**
   7.3 Exercise 14, *p. 294*

5. **Use Appropriate Tools Strategically**
   7.4 Exploration 1, *p. 295*

6. **Attend to Precision**
   7.4 Math Practice note, *p. 295*

7. **Look for and Make Use of Structure**
   7.4 Exercise 19, *p. 300*

8. **Look for and Express Regularity in Repeated Reasoning**
   7.1 Exercise 21, *p. 280*

STEAM Video

Before the Video

- To introduce the STEAM Video, read aloud the first paragraph of Apparent Temperature and discuss the question with your students.
- ❓ "What weather factors might contribute to the apparent temperature?"

During the Video

- The video shows Robert and Tory discussing apparent temperature.
- ❓ Pause the video at 1:06 and ask, "What factors affect how you perceive temperature?" solar radiation (sunlight), humidity, wind
- Watch the remainder of the video.

After the Video

- ❓ "Why did the military create a formula for the apparent temperature?" To prepare for and relieve the effects of heat.
- Have students work with a partner to answer Questions 1 and 2.
- As students discuss and answer the questions, listen for understanding of evaluating an expression.

Performance Task

- Use this information to spark students' interest and promote thinking about real-life problems.
- ❓ Ask, "Why is it useful to know the heat index?"
- After completing the chapter, students will have gained the knowledge needed to complete "Heat Index."

Apparent Temperature

Sometimes it feels hotter or colder outside than the actual temperature. How hot or cold it feels is called the *apparent temperature.* What weather factors might contribute to the apparent temperature?

Watch the STEAM Video "Apparent Temperature."
Then answer the following questions.

1. Robert says that the Wet-Bulb Globe Temperature (WBGT) index is used as a measure of apparent temperature.

$$WBGT = 0.7T_W + 0.2T_G + 0.1T_D$$

WBGT Categories

Category	WBGT, °F	Flag Color
1	< 82	White
2	82–84.9	Green
3	85–87.9	Yellow
4	88–89.9	Red
5	≥ 90	Black

In the formula, T_W is the natural wet-bulb temperature, T_G is the black-globe temperature, and T_D is the dry-bulb temperature. Find *WBGT* when $T_W = 75°F$, $T_G = 100°F$, and $T_D = 84°F$.

2. Different categories of Wet-Bulb Globe Temperatures are shown in the chart. Each category can be represented by a different-colored flag. Which flag color is displayed when $WGBT = 87.5°F$?

Heat Index

After completing this chapter, you will be able to use the concepts you learned to answer the questions in the *STEAM Video Performance Task.* You will be given information about temperature and the *heat index.*

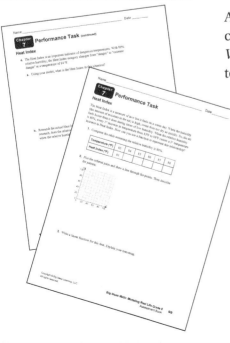

Temperature (°F)	83	84	85	86	87	88
Heat Index (°F)	91					

You will be asked to create a graph of the temperatures and heat indices. Why is it useful to know the heat index?

Getting Ready for Chapter

Chapter Exploration

Work with a partner. Copy and complete the diagram.

1. Area A

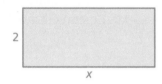

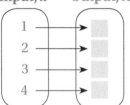

2. Perimeter P

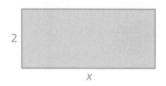

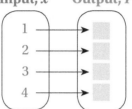

3. Circumference C

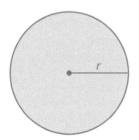

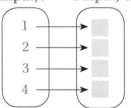

4. Volume V

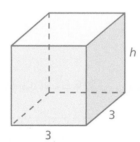

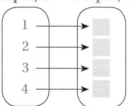

Vocabulary

The following vocabulary terms are defined in this chapter. Think about what each term might mean and record your thoughts.

input   mapping diagram   nonlinear function

output   linear function

Laurie's Notes

Check out the digital flash cards.
BigIdeasMath.com

Chapter Exploration

- **MP2 Reason Abstractly and Quantitatively:** In this exploration, students will use familiar formulas to complete mapping diagrams. Mathematically proficient students are able to make sense of quantities and their relationships in problem situations.

- ❓ "What is meant by the area and perimeter of a rectangle? How do you compute each?" Area is the amount of surface covered. Perimeter is the distance around the rectangle.

- For each part, students will use a familiar formula. When they are given a particular dimension, they will solve for a certain measurement, such as area or perimeter.

- Students do not need to label the output with units as none are given for the input.

- **Big Idea:** A mapping diagram is one way of showing the result of evaluating an expression or formula for a set of numbers. The results are recorded in two ovals with an arrow connecting each input with its output(s). For the diagrams shown, students will know the formulas to use. A mapping diagram is similar to making a table of value.

- For each problem, have students state the formula used. $A = 2x$; $P = 2x + 4$; $C = 2\pi r$; $V = 9h$

- ❓ "Can the inputs of the diagrams be extended to other numbers, say 5, 6, and 7? Explain." Yes, the variable dimension in each figure could be 5, 6, or 7.

- ❓ "Can the outputs of the diagrams be extended to other numbers, say 0, −1, and −2? Explain." No, for each figure, the variable dimension only makes sense for positive numbers.

Vocabulary

- These terms represent some of the vocabulary that students will encounter in Chapter 7. Discuss the terms as a class.

- Where have students heard the term *input* outside of a math classroom? In what contexts? Students may not be able to write the actual definition, but they may write phrases associated with *input*.

- Allowing students to discuss these terms now will prepare them for understanding the terms as they are presented in the chapter.

- When students encounter a new definition, encourage them to write in their *Student Journals*. They will revisit these definitions during the Chapter Review.

ELL Support

Students may think of the word *function* as meaning "in working order" or "serve a purpose." Explain that in math, *function* has a special meaning. A function is a relation (a set of ordered pairs) that pairs each input with *exactly one* output. A *function rule* is an equation that describes the relationship between inputs and outputs.

Topics for Review

- Evaluating Algebraic Expressions
- Finding Area, Perimeter, and Circumference
- Graphing and Writing Linear Equations in Slope-Intercept Form
- Identifying Patterns
- Operations with Decimals and Fractions
- Plotting Points in a Coordinate Plane
- Slope of a Line

Chapter Exploration

1. 2; 4; 6; 8
2. 6; 8; 10; 12
3. 2π; 4π; 6π; 8π
4. 9; 18; 27; 36

STATE STANDARDS
8.F.A.1

Learning Target

Understand the concept of a function.

Success Criteria

- Represent a relation as a set of ordered pairs.
- Determine whether a relation is a function.
- Use functions to solve real-life problems.

Warm Up

Cumulative, vocabulary, and prerequisite skills practice opportunities are available in the *Resources by Chapter* or at *BigIdeasMath.com*.

ELL Support

Discuss the word *relation*. Explain that a relation describes a connection between concepts, objects, or people. The word is most commonly used to explain that a person is in your family. You may want to demonstrate using the word to describe family relationships. Explain that the inputs and outputs of a function have a special relation. Discuss the meanings of the compound words *input* and *output* by analyzing their prefixes and the root word *put*.

Exploration 1

a. The output is the square of the input; output: 64; *Sample answer:* input: 9; yes; The input 8 only has one possible output, but the output 81 has two possible inputs.

b. The output is a possible color of the input (fruit); *Sample answer:* input: lime; output: green; yes; The missing input could be any fruit that is green.

Exploration 2

a–c. See Additional Answers.

Laurie's Notes

Preparing to Teach

- **MP2 Reason Abstractly and Quantitatively:** In these explorations, students will complete mapping diagrams and describe relationships between quantities. Mathematically proficient students are able to make sense of quantities and their relationships in problem situations.

Motivate

❓ "What is a vending machine and what does it do?" Give students time to explain how vending machines operate. Have them discuss the idea of inserting money (**input**) and getting the desired item (**output**).
- Share some history of vending machines.
  - A Greek mathematician invented a machine in 215 B.C. to vend holy water in Egyptian temples.
  - During the early 1880s, the first commercial coin-operated vending machines were introduced in London, England, and dispensed postcards.
  - Vending machines soon offered other things, including stamps. In Philadelphia, a completely coin-operated restaurant called Horn & Hardart was opened in 1902 and served customers until 1962.

Exploration 1

- Tell students that these diagrams are similar to a vending machine because they have an input and an output.
- **MP7 Look for and Make Use of Structure:** Mathematically proficient students will study the first diagram to discover a relationship between the inputs and the outputs. They will recognize that a **mapping diagram** is similar to a table of values.
❓ If students are struggling, ask, "What can you do to the input to get the output?" As students offer conjectures, ask them if their conjectures work for each pair of values.
- In part (b), students should recognize that the missing output (color) must make sense for both an apple and the missing input (fruit).
- Ask students to share their answers and reasoning for part (b).

Exploration 2

- Part (a) is very literal. Students state how many outputs there are for each input. In Play A, each input has exactly one output. In Play B, the inputs each have multiple outputs.
- In part (b), describing the ticket prices helps students realize how a mapping diagram can be used to show a relationship between two real-life quantities.
- Play B is more complicated than Play A. Students need to analyze the mapping diagram carefully.
- Ask volunteers to share their descriptions of the ticket prices for each play.
- In part (c), encourage students to use *Paired Verbal Fluency* to discuss their ideas. Circulate and listen to discussions, making note of any ideas that should be shared with the class.

7.1 Relations and Functions

Learning Target: Understand the concept of a function.

Success Criteria:
• I can represent a relation as a set of ordered pairs.
• I can determine whether a relation is a function.
• I can use functions to solve real-life problems.

EXPLORATION 1

Interpreting Diagrams

Work with a partner. Describe the relationship between the *inputs* and *outputs* in each diagram. Then complete each diagram. Is there more than one possible answer? Explain your reasoning.

a.

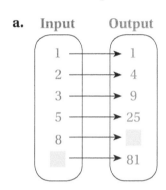

b.

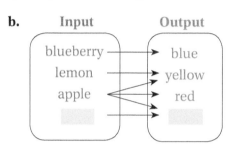

EXPLORATION 2

Describing Relationships Between Quantities

Work with a partner. The diagrams show the numbers of tickets bought by customers for two different plays and the total costs (in dollars).

Play A

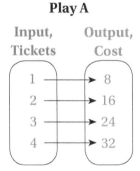

Play B

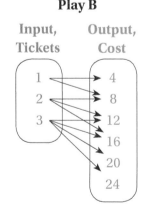

Math Practice

Analyze Relationships

Is it possible for one person to pay $16 for 2 tickets to Play B and another person to pay $8 for 2 tickets to Play B? Explain.

a. For each diagram, how many outputs does each input have?

b. Describe the prices of tickets for each play.

c. A person buys 4 tickets for each play. Can you determine the total cost of all 8 tickets? Explain.

7.1 Lesson

Ordered pairs can be used to show **inputs** and **outputs**.

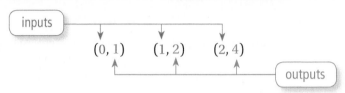

🔑 Key Ideas

Relations and Mapping Diagrams

A **relation** pairs inputs with outputs. A relation can be represented by ordered pairs or a **mapping diagram**.

Ordered Pairs	*Mapping Diagram*
$(0, 1)$	
$(1, 2)$	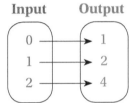
$(2, 4)$	

EXAMPLE 1 **Listing Ordered Pairs of Relations**

List the ordered pairs shown in each mapping diagram.

a.

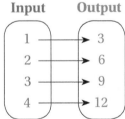

b.

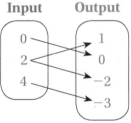

▷ The ordered pairs are $(1, 3)$, $(2, 6)$, $(3, 9)$, and $(4, 12)$.

▷ The ordered pairs are $(0, 0)$, $(2, 1)$, $(2, -2)$, and $(4, -3)$.

Try It List the ordered pairs shown in the mapping diagram.

1.

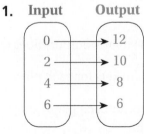

2.

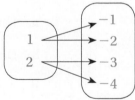

Laurie's Notes

Scaffolding Instruction

- Students have explored mapping diagrams. Now they will use ordered pairs and mapping diagrams to display **functions**.
- **Emerging:** Students may struggle with describing relationships between inputs and outputs in a mapping diagram. They will benefit from guided instruction for the Key Ideas and examples.
- **Proficient:** Students can describe relationships between inputs and outputs in a mapping diagram. They recognize that the inputs and outputs represent a set of ordered pairs. These students should work through Example 2 and then proceed to the Self-Assessment exercises.

Discuss

- Write the ordered pairs. Point out the **inputs** and the **outputs**. Explain that inputs and outputs can be used to write ordered pairs (input, output).

Key Ideas

- Use the following set of ordered pairs to explain the vocabulary.
    (Santa Fe, New Mexico)
    (Boise, Idaho)
    (Frankfort, Kentucky)
    (Columbus, Ohio)
- Stress that an ordered pair has an *order* associated with it, and the order matters! In the above example, the ordered pairs are (state capital, state).
- Spend time discussing the idea of a relation. A **relation** pairs each input with its output(s). A **mapping diagram** is a relation. A set of ordered pairs is also a relation.

EXAMPLE 1

- **MP5 Use Appropriate Tools Strategically:** A mapping diagram is a helpful model to show the set of all the inputs and the set of all the outputs, while also showing the relationship between each input and its output(s).
- Note the use of color to differentiate between the input and output.
- **Common Question:** Why are the inputs (or outputs) not listed more than once when they are used more than once, as in part (b)? The inputs (or outputs) are a set of data. It is not customary to list elements in a data set more than once in a mapping diagram. The arrows in a mapping diagram show when an input (or output) is used more than once.

Try It

- Students should write their answers on whiteboards. Then list the ordered pairs on the board and discuss any discrepancies.

Scaffold instruction to support all students in their learning. Learning is individualized and you may want to group students differently as they move in and out of these levels with each skill and concept. Student self-assessment and feedback help guide your instructional decisions about how and when to layer support for all students to become proficient learners.

Extra Example 1

List the ordered pairs shown in each mapping diagram.

a.   Input   Output

(2, 1), (4, 2), (6, 3), (8, 4)

b.   Input   Output

(1, 4), (2, 0), (2, −5), (3, −6)

ELL Support

After demonstrating Example 1, have students work in pairs to discuss and complete Try It Exercises 1 and 2. Have one student ask another, "What are the ordered pairs?" Have students alternate the roles of asking and answering questions.

Beginner: Write the ordered pairs.

Intermediate: State the ordered pairs.

Advanced: Use complete sentences to state the ordered pairs.

Try It

1. $(0, 12), (2, 10), (4, 8), (6, 6)$
2. $(1, -1), (1, -2), (2, -3),$
   $(2, -4)$

Determine whether each relation is a function.

a.
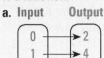

not a function

b.

function

Try It

3. not a function

4. function

ELL Support

Allow students to work in pairs on the Self-Assessment for Concepts & Skills exercises for extra support and to practice language. Have two pairs form a group to discuss and reach a consensus for their descriptions for Exercises 5 and 8. Review their explanations as a class. Have each pair display their answers for Exercises 6 and 7 on a whiteboard for your review. Then ask if the relation is a function. Have students use a thumbs up for *yes* and a thumbs down for *no*.

Self-Assessment
for Concepts & Skills

5. A relation pairs inputs with outputs. A function is a relation that pairs each input with exactly one output.

6. $(10, 1), (15, 1), (20, 13), (25, 7)$; function

7. $(0, -5), (0, -4), (1, -4), (2, -3), (3, -2)$; not a function

8. See Additional Answers.

Laurie's Notes

Discuss

- Write the definition of a **function**.
- Spend time discussing the idea of a function. Each input has exactly one output. For example, each state capital is in one state. Each country is in one continent.
- Show examples of functions represented as ordered pairs and as mapping diagrams.
- Refer back to the mapping diagrams in the explorations and Example 1. Ask students to identify which mapping diagrams represent functions.
  Exploration 1(a), Exploration 2 Play A, and Example 1(a)

EXAMPLE 2

- Make sure students can identify the ordered pairs for each mapping diagram.
- Part (a) shows that a relation is a function when output values are repeated, as long as no input values are repeated.

Try It

- **MP2 Reason Abstractly and Quantitatively:** Students should be able to describe the pattern of inputs and outputs in Exercise 4.

Formative Assessment Tip

Example and Non-Example Chart
This technique allows students to demonstrate their understanding of a concept by comparing examples and non-examples. Students write examples of the concept in the left column and non-examples in the right column. Students should be able to explain their choices and reasoning. Allow time for students to receive feedback from you and their peers.

✓ Self-Assessment for Concepts & Skills

- **Neighbor Check:** Have students work independently and then have their neighbors check their work. Have students discuss any discrepancies.
- ◉ **Example and Non-Example:** Have students create an *Example and Non-Example Chart* for functions. Students should include at least one mapping diagram and at least one set of ordered pairs on each side. Then have students compare and discuss their charts with their neighbors. Select several volunteers to present their charts to the class. *Sample answer:*

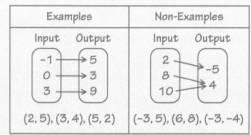

The Success Criteria Self-Assessment chart can be found in the *Student Journal* or online at *BigIdeasMath.com*.

A relation that pairs each input with *exactly one* output is a **function**.

EXAMPLE 2 **Determining Whether Relations Are Functions**

Determine whether each relation is a function.

a.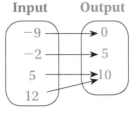

b.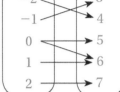

▷ Each input has exactly one output. So, the relation is a function.

▷ The input 0 has two outputs, 5 and 6. So, the relation is *not* a function.

Try It Determine whether the relation is a function.

3.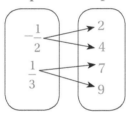

4.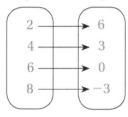

 Self-Assessment for Concepts & Skills

Solve each exercise. Then rate your understanding of the success criteria in your journal.

5. **MP PRECISION** Describe how relations and functions are different.

IDENTIFYING FUNCTIONS **List the ordered pairs shown in the mapping diagram. Then determine whether the relation is a function.**

6. Input   Output

Input	Output
10	
15	1
20	7
25	13

7. Input   Output

Input	Output
0	−5
1	−4
2	−3
3	−2

Input	Output
−8	−4
0	−2
8	0
16	2

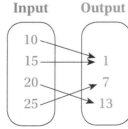

8. **OPEN-ENDED** Copy and complete the mapping diagram at the left to represent a relation that is a function. Then describe how you can modify the mapping diagram so that the relation is *not* a function.

EXAMPLE 3 **Modeling Real Life**

Input, Zone	Output, Price
0	➤$2.00
1	➤$3.50
2	➤$5.00
3	➤$6.50

The mapping diagram represents the prices of one-way subway tickets to different zones of a city.

a. **Is the price of a subway ticket a function of the zone number?**

Each input has exactly one output.

▷ So, the price of a subway ticket is a function of the zone number.

b. **Describe the relationship between the price and the zone number.**

Identify the relationship between the inputs and the outputs.

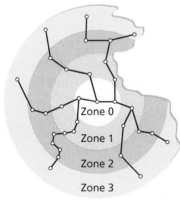

	Input, Zone	Output, Price	
+1	0	➤$2.00	+$1.50
+1	1	➤$3.50	+$1.50
+1	2	➤$5.00	+$1.50
	3	➤$6.50	

As each input increases by 1, the output increases by $1.50.

▷ So, the price of a one-way subway ticket increases by $1.50 for each additional zone traveled.

Self-Assessment for *Problem Solving*

Solve each exercise. Then rate your understanding of the success criteria in your journal.

9. The mapping diagram represents the costs of reserving a hotel room for different numbers of nights.

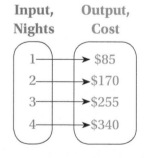

Input, Nights	Output, Cost
1	➤ $85
2	➤$170
3	➤$255
4	➤$340

a. Is the cost a function of the number of nights reserved?

b. Describe the relationship between the cost and the number of nights reserved.

10. **DIG DEEPER!** The graph represents the number of contestants in each round of a talent competition.

a. Is the number of contestants a function of the round number?

b. Predict the number of contestants in the talent competition during Round 7. Explain your reasoning.

Talent Competition Contestants

(graph: Number of contestants vs. Round; y-axis 0 to 128 by 16; points at approximately (1, 128), (2, 64), (3, 32), (4, 16))

Laurie's Notes

EXAMPLE 3

- Ask a volunteer to read the problem and another to interpret the problem.
- **?** Draw the mapping diagram and ask, "Is this relation a function? Explain." Yes, each input has exactly one output.
- In part (a), make sure students understand the "function of" language used in the question and the solution. The output (the price of a subway ticket) is a function of the input (the zone number).
- Students may not be able to write an algebraic rule describing how to generate the output given an input, but they should be able to describe the pattern in words.
- The curved arrows are a convenient way to record what is changing as you move from one input to the next and from one output to the next.
- **Common Error:** Students often describe only what is happening to the output. In fact, the input is also changing. Encourage students to describe the change in output in terms of what is happening to the input. In this example, the description indicates that as the input increases by 1, the output increases by $1.50.

 Self-Assessment for Problem Solving

- Students may benefit from trying the exercises independently and then working with peers to refine their work. It is important to provide time in class for problem solving, so that students become comfortable with the problem-solving plan.
- **Neighbor Check:** Have students work independently and then have their neighbors check their work. Have students discuss any discrepancies.

The Success Criteria Self-Assessment chart can be found in the *Student Journal* or online at *BigIdeasMath.com*.

Closure

- Describe the pattern in the mapping diagram. Complete the mapping diagram. Is the relation a function?

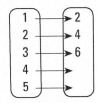

As each input increases by 1, the output increases by 2; 8 and 10; yes

Extra Example 3

The mapping diagram represents the costs of different numbers of grapefruits purchased.

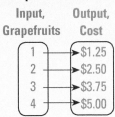

a. Is the cost a function of the number of grapefruits purchased? yes

b. Describe the relationship between the cost and the number of grapefruits purchased. The cost increases by $1.25 for each additional grapefruit purchased.

Self-Assessment
for Problem Solving

9. a. yes

    b. The cost increases by $85 for each additional night reserved.

10. a. yes

    b. 2; The number of contestants in a given round is half of the number of contestants in the previous round. So, there will be 8 contestants in Round 5, 4 contestants in Round 6, and 2 contestants in Round 7.

Learning Target

Understand the concept of a function.

Success Criteria

- Represent a relation as a set of ordered pairs.
- Determine whether a relation is a function.
- Use functions to solve real-life problems.

Check out the Dynamic
Assessment System.
BigIdeasMath.com

▶ *Review & Refresh*

1. *Sample answer:* histogram;
   shows frequencies of data
   values in intervals of the same
   size

2. *Sample answer:* scatter plot;
   shows the relationship between
   two data sets

3.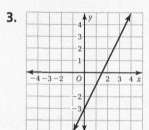

4.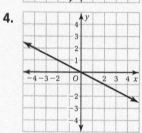

5. See Additional Answers.

6. A

▶▶ *Concepts, Skills, & Problem Solving*

7. As the input increases by 1,
   the output decreases by 4;
   output: −17; input: 6; The input
   5 only has one possible output,
   and the output −21 only has
   one possible input.

8. The output is the first letter
   of the input (sport); *Sample
   answer:* softball; yes; The
   missing input could be any
   sport that starts with the
   letter "s".

9. (0, 4), (3, 5), (6, 6), (9, 7)

10. (1, 8), (3, 8), (3, 4), (5, 6), (7, 2)

11. (6, −5), (7, −5), (8, −10),
    (9, −10)

12. not a function

13. function

14. function

Assignment Guide and Concept Check

Scaffold assignments to support all students in their learning progression. The suggested assignments are a starting point. Continue to assign additional exercises and revisit with spaced practice to move every student toward proficiency.

Level	Assignment 1	Assignment 2
Emerging	2, 5, 6, 7, 8, 9, 11, 13, 15	10, 12, 14, 16, 17, 18, 20
Proficient	2, 5, 6, 7, 8, 9, 10, 12, 13, 14, 15	16, 17, 18, 19, 20, 21
Advanced	2, 5, 6, 7, 8, 9, 10, 12, 13, 14, 15	16, 17, 18, 19, 20, 21

- Assignment 1 is for use after students complete the Self-Assessment for Concepts & Skills.
- Assignment 2 is for use after students complete the Self-Assessment for Problem Solving.
- The red exercises can be used as a concept check.

Review & Refresh Prior Skills

Exercises 1 and 2 Choosing a Data Display
Exercises 3–5 Graphing a Linear Equation
Exercise 6 Identifying Congruent Figures

Common Errors

- **Exercises 7 and 8** Students may describe the pattern of the outputs only. Remind them that the inputs are changing as well, and it is important to describe the change in inputs that results in the specified change in outputs.
- **Exercises 9–11** Students may mix up the ordered pairs and write the output first and then the input. Encourage students to use the arrow as a guide. The arrow points from the first number in the ordered pair (the input) to the second number in the ordered pair (the output).

7.1 Practice

Go to *BigIdeasMath.com* to get
HELP with solving the exercises.

▶ Review & Refresh

Choose an appropriate data display for the situation. Explain your reasoning.

1. the number of runners in each age group at a marathon

2. the high temperature and the attendance at a water park each day

Graph the linear equation.

3. $y = 2x - 3$

4. $y = -0.5x$

5. $y = -3x + 4$

6. Which word best describes two figures that have the same size and the same shape?

   A. congruent   **B.** adjacent   **C.** parallel   **D.** similar

▶▶ Concepts, Skills, & Problem Solving

INTERPRETING DIAGRAMS **Describe the relationship between the *inputs* and *outputs* in the diagram. Then complete the diagram. Is there more than one possible answer? Explain your reasoning.** (See Exploration 1, p. 275.)

7.
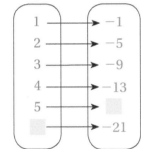

8.
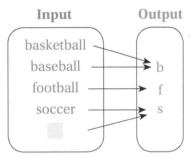

LISTING ORDERED PAIRS **List the ordered pairs shown in the mapping diagram.**

9.
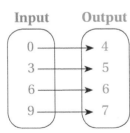

10.
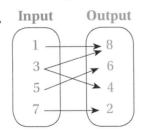

11.
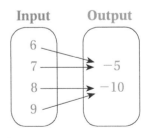

IDENTIFYING FUNCTIONS **Determine whether the relation is a function.**

12.
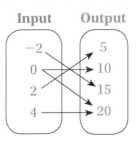

13.
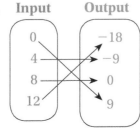

14.
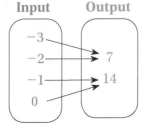

15. **MP YOU BE THE TEACHER** Your friend determines whether the relation shown in the mapping diagram is a function. Is your friend correct? Explain your reasoning.

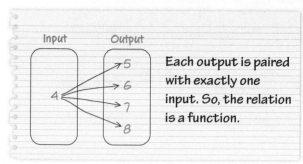

Each output is paired with exactly one input. So, the relation is a function.

MP REASONING Draw a mapping diagram that represents the relation. Then determine whether the relation is a function. Explain.

16.
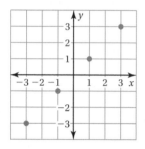

17.
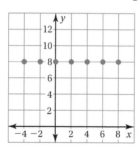

18.
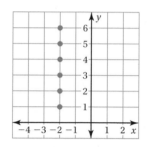

19. **MP MODELING REAL LIFE** The normal pressure at sea level is 1 atmosphere of pressure (1 ATM). As you dive below sea level, the pressure changes. The mapping diagram represents the pressures at different depths.

a. Complete the mapping diagram.

b. Is pressure a function of depth?

c. Describe the relationship between pressure and depth.

d. List the ordered pairs. Then plot the ordered pairs in a coordinate plane. What do you notice about the points?

e. **RESEARCH** What are common depths for beginner scuba divers? What are common depths for experienced scuba divers?

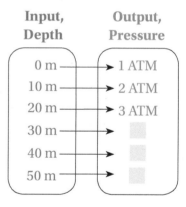

20. **DIG DEEPER!** The table shows the cost of purchasing 1, 2, 3, or 4 T-shirts from a souvenir shop.

a. Is the cost a function of the number of T-shirts purchased?

b. Describe the relationship between the cost and the number of T-shirts purchased. How does the *cost per T-shirt* change as you purchase more T-shirts?

T-Shirts	Cost
1	$10
2	$18
3	$24
4	$28

21. **MP REPEATED REASONING** The table shows the outputs for several inputs. Use two methods to predict the output for an input of 200.

Input, x	0	1	2	3	4
Output, y	25	30	35	40	45

Common Errors

- **Exercises 19 and 20** Students may describe the pattern of the outputs only. Remind them that the inputs are changing as well, and it is important to describe the change in inputs that results in the specified change in outputs.

Mini-Assessment

1. List the ordered pairs shown in the mapping diagram. Then determine whether the relation is a function.

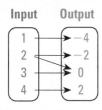

(1, −4), (2, −2), (2, 0), (3, 0), (4, 2); not a function

2. Describe the relationship between the inputs and outputs in the diagram. Then determine whether the relation is a function.

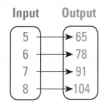

As each input increases by 1, the output increases by 13; function

Section Resources

Surface Level	Deep Level
Resources by Chapter • Extra Practice • Reteach • Puzzle Time Student Journal • Self-Assessment • Practice Differentiating the Lesson Tutorial Videos Skills Review Handbook Skills Trainer	Resources by Chapter • Enrichment and Extension Graphic Organizers Dynamic Assessment System • Section Practice

Concepts, Skills, & Problem Solving

15. no; In order for a relation to be a function, each input must be paired with exactly one output. So, the relation is not a function.

16.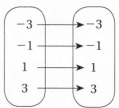

function; Each input has exactly one output.

17. See Additional Answers.

18. See Additional Answers.

19. **a.** 4 ATM; 5 ATM; 6 ATM

b. yes

c. The pressure increases by 1 ATM for each 10-meter increase in the depth.

d. (0, 1), (10, 2), (20, 3), (30, 4), (40, 5), (50, 6);

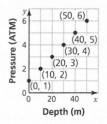

Sample answer: The points lie on a line.

e. *Sample answer:* A beginner scuba diver should not go below 30 meters; The safe limit for an experienced scuba diver should be around 60 meters.

20. **a.** yes

b. For each additional T-shirt purchased, the cost increases by $2 less than the previous increase; For each additional T-shirt purchased, the cost per T-shirt decreases by $1.

21. 1025

Learning Target

Represent functions in a variety of ways.

Success Criteria

- Write a function rule that describes a relationship.
- Evaluate functions for given inputs.
- Represent functions using tables and graphs.

Warm Up

Cumulative, vocabulary, and prerequisite skills practice opportunities are available in the *Resources by Chapter* or at *BigIdeasMath.com*.

Teaching Strategy

If you prepare bags of materials for students, label them with the chapter and section number for reuse in following years. Store the prepared bags in a larger bag. Label and file the larger bag with other chapter materials. Make a note in your teaching edition of where the materials are stored.

ELL Support

Read aloud the learning target and then discuss the word *represent*. Emphasize that there are a variety (more than one) of ways to represent a function. Discuss the relationship of the words *vary* and *variety*. Explain that vary means "to change." Warn students not to confuse it with the word *very*.

Exploration 1

a–b. See Additional Answers.

Exploration 2

a. false

b. true; $y = 16.4x$

T-281

Laurie's Notes

Preparing to Teach

- **MP3 Construct Viable Arguments and Critique the Reasoning of Others:** In these explorations, students will write equations that represent functions presented in various ways and construct arguments about the data.

Motivate

- The daily admission at a theme park is $73 for ages 10 and up.
- **?** "What would it cost for a family of 4, ages 10 and up, to visit for one day?" $4 \times \$73 = \$292$
- **?** "What would an equation be that calculates the cost for *n* people (all older than 10 years) to visit the theme park?" cost = $73*n*

Exploration 1

- **Teaching Strategy:** Provide square tiles to students. Templates are available at *BigIdeasMath.com*. As students construct each figure with the tiles, they sometimes see the pattern that was not obvious to them from the figure.
- Make sure students understand that the inputs for each table are the figure numbers, not the number of tiles in each figure.
- After students complete the table, ask, "What is the area of the *x*th figure?" $(2x - 1)$ square units; x^2 square units
- **?** "Are these relationships functions? Explain." Yes, in both relationships, each input is paired with exactly one output.
- **FYI:** The outputs in part (b) are known as *square numbers*. A square number of tiles can be arranged into a square: 16 tiles can form a 4×4 square. Some numbers of tiles cannot be arranged into a square: 6 tiles can form a 1×6 rectangle or a 2×3 rectangle, but not a square.
- **Extension:** To help students understand why the numbers 1, 4, 9, 16 … are called *square numbers*, have them rearrange the tiles in each figure of part (b) to form a square.

Exploration 2

- **MP1 Make Sense of Problems and Persevere in Solving Them:** The first step to understand each problem is to graph the data. Each set of data is in Quadrant I. Students should scale the axes with convenient values.
- The two graphs are different. The first has scattered points with no apparent pattern. The second appears to have a pattern. A graph that contains separate points represents *discrete* data. Both of these graphs represent discrete data. Discrete data points are often connected with a line or curve, with the understanding that only certain points make sense for the context.
- In part (b), students may recognize that every 100 cubic inches adds another 1640 cubic centimeters, but not know how to write an equation for the pattern.
- **?** Ask, "If only 1 cubic inch was added, how many cubic centimeters would be added?" $\frac{1}{100} \cdot 1640 \text{ cm}^3 = 16.4 \text{ cm}^3$. This may be enough to help students recognize the equation: $y = 16.4x$.
- Discuss student answers. Focus on how they determined whether the statement was true. Discuss the equation written for part (b).

7.2 Representations of Functions

Learning Target: Represent functions in a variety of ways.

Success Criteria:
- I can write a function rule that describes a relationship.
- I can evaluate functions for given inputs.
- I can represent functions using tables and graphs.

EXPLORATION 1

Using a Table to Describe Relationships

1 square unit

Work with a partner. Make a table that shows the relationship between the figure number x and the area A of each figure. Then use an equation to find which figure has an area of 81 square units when the pattern continues.

a.

Figure 1   Figure 2   Figure 3   Figure 4

b.

Figure 1   Figure 2   Figure 3   Figure 4

EXPLORATION 2

Using a Graph

Work with a partner. Use a graph to test the truth of each statement. If the statement is true, write an equation that shows how to obtain one measurement from the other.

Math Practice

Construct Arguments

How does the graph help you determine whether the statement is true?

a. "You can find the horsepower of a race-car engine if you know its volume in cubic inches."

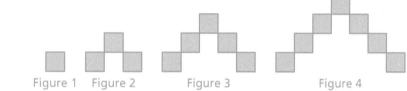

Volume (cubic inches), x	200	350	350	500
Horsepower, y	375	650	250	600

b. "You can find the volume of a race-car engine in cubic centimeters if you know its volume in cubic inches."

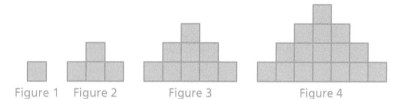

Volume (cubic inches), x	100	200	300
Volume (cubic centimeters), y	1640	3280	4920

Key Vocabulary 🔊
function rule, *p. 282*

Remember

An independent variable represents a quantity that can change freely. A dependent variable depends on the independent variable.

🔑 Key Idea

Functions as Equations

A **function rule** is an equation that describes the relationship between inputs (independent variable) and outputs (dependent variable).

EXAMPLE 1 **Writing Function Rules**

a. Write a function rule for "The output is five less than the input."

Words	The output is five less than the input.
Equation	y = $x - 5$

▸ A function rule is $y = x - 5$.

b. Write a function rule for "The output is the square of the input."

Words	The output is the square of the input.
Equation	y = x^2

▸ A function rule is $y = x^2$.

Try It

1. Write a function rule for "The output is one-fourth of the input."

EXAMPLE 2 **Evaluating a Function**

What is the value of $y = 2x + 5$ when $x = 3$?

$y = 2x + 5$	Write the equation.
$= 2(3) + 5$	Substitute 3 for *x*.
$= 11$	Simplify.

Try It **Find the value of *y* when *x* = 5.**

2. $y = 4x - 1$ **3.** $y = 10x$ **4.** $y = 7 - 3x$

Laurie's Notes

Scaffolding Instruction

- Students explored different ways to represent a function. Now they will represent functions by writing equations in two variables, using input-output tables, and using graphs.
- **Emerging:** Students may be able to represent functions using tables and/or graphs, but they struggle with writing equations. They will benefit from guided instruction for the Key Ideas and examples.
- **Proficient:** Students can write equations to represent functions. They should complete the Try It exercises and then proceed to the Self-Assessment exercises.

Key Idea

- The term **function rule** is used to introduce the idea of writing an equation to represent the relationship between the input (independent variable) and output (dependent variable), the two variables in the equation.
- It is common to write equations using the variables x and y, where x is the input and y is the output.
- **Discuss:** In the Motivate, the equation was written as cost $=$ $\$73n$. The equation could have been written as $c = 73n$. Notice the use of two variables. While any variable names could have been chosen, n and c were chosen to represent *n*umber of people and *c*ost of admission.
- Remind students to always identify the variables used. For instance, $c =$ cost and $n =$ number of people.
- Make a point of reading the Remember note.

EXAMPLE 1

- In part (a), read and write the function rule as: The output, y, is five less than the input, x.
- In part (b), read and write the function rule as: The output, y, is the square of the input, x.
- Note the use of color to help students connect the words and symbols.

Try It

- Have students write their answers on whiteboards. Discuss any discrepancies as a class.

EXAMPLE 2

- "For the equation $y = 2x + 5$, describe in words what operations are performed on the input x." The value of x is multiplied by 2 and then 5 is added.
- "What is the rule in words for this function?" Double the input and add 5.
- Have students make a mapping diagram to represent the function.

Try It

- **Connection:** Students already know how to evaluate algebraic expressions. Previously, students would have been asked to evaluate $4x - 1$ when $x = 5$. Now the same problem is written as an equation with the answer called the output.

Extra Example 1

a. Write a function rule for "The output is eight more than the input." $y = x + 8$

b. Write a function rule for "The output is four times the input." $y = 4x$

Try It

1. $y = \frac{1}{4}x$

Extra Example 2

What is the value of $y = -2x + 7$ when $x = 2$? $y = 3$

Try It

2. 19

3. 50

4. -8

Extra Example 3

Graph the function $y = -x + 3$.

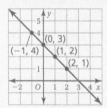

After demonstrating Example 3, have students work in pairs to discuss and complete Try It Exercises 5–7. Provide graph paper and list the steps they need to take: (1) Make a table, (2) Plot the ordered pairs, and (3) Draw a line through the points. Expect students to perform according to their language levels.

Beginner: Complete the steps by writing and graphing.

Intermediate: Use simple sentences to identify information and describe how to graph the function.

Advanced: Use detailed sentences to identify information and complete the process.

Try It

5.

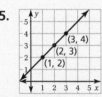

6.

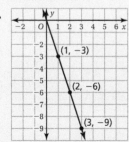

7. See Additional Answers.

Key Idea

- Write the Key Idea.
- The ordered pairs from the table are plotted. The input is x and is found along the horizontal axis. The output is y and is found along the vertical axis. The graph shows the relationship between inputs and outputs.
- In Exploration 2, students graphed discrete data. If the context of the problem allows any points on the graph, then the graph represents *continuous* data, as in this case.
- Discuss with students why connecting the points with a line is the graph of all of the solutions of the equation $y = x + 2$. For instance, if $x = 1.5$, $y = 3.5$. Find this point on the graph.
- **?** "Is the ordered pair (3, 1) a solution of $y = x + 2$?" no "Is (3, 1) on the graph?" no
- Students should recall that the graph of an equation represents all the solutions of the equation. The same is true for functions. The graph of a function represents all the solutions of the function.

EXAMPLE 3

- The table is a good reminder of how equations are evaluated and how solutions can be recorded as ordered pairs. Remind students that when creating the table, they can choose any of the valid inputs for the function.
- **?** "Is the set of ordered pairs in the table a function? Explain." Yes, each input is paired with exactly one output.
- Students may ask about calling the equation $y = -2x + 1$ a function rather than a linear equation in slope-intercept form. Tell them that it is actually both! It is a *linear function*.
- Knowing the equation is a function assures you that each input has exactly one output. Linear functions are just one type of function that students will study.
- Remind students that if they know the function is linear, they only need to plot two points. If students do not know the shape of the graph from looking at the function rule, they will need to plot more points.
- Students may ask about using the slope and y-intercept to graph a linear function. This will be discussed in the next section, but you could choose to discuss it now.
- Students should also note that not all functions can be written as equations. Graphs that do not have a predictable pattern may represent functions, but they cannot be written as equations.

Try It

- **Neighbor Check:** Have students work independently and then have their neighbors check their work. Have students discuss any discrepancies.

 **Key Idea**

Functions as Tables and Graphs

A function can be represented by an input-output table and by a graph. The table and graph below represent the function $y = x + 2$.

Input, x	Output, y	Ordered Pair, (x, y)
1	3	(1, 3)
2	4	(2, 4)
3	5	(3, 5)

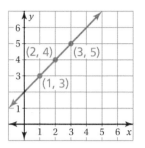

By drawing a line through the points, you graph *all* of the solutions of the function $y = x + 2$.

EXAMPLE 3 **Graphing a Function**

Graph the function $y = -2x + 1$.

Make an input-output table using inputs of -1, 0, 1, and 2.

Input, x	−2x + 1	Output, y	Ordered Pair, (x, y)
−1	−2(−1) + 1	3	(−1, 3)
0	−2(0) + 1	1	(0, 1)
1	−2(1) + 1	−1	(1, −1)
2	−2(2) + 1	−3	(2, −3)

Plot the ordered pairs and draw a line through the points.

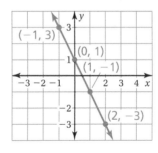

Try It **Graph the function.**

5. $y = x + 1$ **6.** $y = -3x$ **7.** $y = 3x + 2$

 **Summary**

Representations of Functions

Words The output is 2 more than the input.

Equation $y = x + 2$

Input-Output Table		**Mapping Diagram**	**Graph**

Input, x	Output, y
−1	1
0	2
1	3
2	4

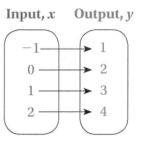

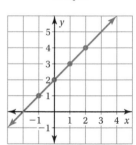

Self-Assessment for Concepts & Skills

Solve each exercise. Then rate your understanding of the success criteria in your journal.

WRITING FUNCTION RULES **Write a function rule for the statement.**

8. The output is three times the input.

9. The output is eight more than one-seventh of the input.

EVALUATING A FUNCTION **Find the value of y when $x = -5$.**

10. $y = 6x$

11. $y = 11 - x$

12. $y = \frac{1}{5}x + 1$

GRAPHING A FUNCTION **Graph the function.**

13. $y = -2x$

14. $y = x - 3$

15. $y = 9 - 3x$

16. **DIFFERENT WORDS, SAME QUESTION** Which is different? Find "both" answers.

What output is 4 more than twice the input 3?

What output is twice the sum of the input 3 and 4?

What output is the sum of 2 times the input 3 and 4?

What output is 4 increased by twice the input 3?

Laurie's Notes

Summary

- Discuss the Summary with students. They have represented functions using words, equations, input-output tables, mapping diagrams, and graphs.
- **Connection:** In future mathematics courses, students will study connections between the various forms of functions.
- **FYI:** It is not always possible to represent a function in a particular form. For instance, some functions can be represented in a table and a graph, but not as an equation. Also, the points on a graph do not have to be connected with a line or a curve to represent a function.

✔ Self-Assessment for Concepts & Skills

- **Think-Pair-Share:** Students should read each exercise independently and then work in pairs to complete the exercises. Then have each pair compare their answers with another pair and discuss any discrepancies.
- ⊙ Ask students to use *Fist of Five* to indicate their understanding of each success criterion.

ELL Support

Have students work in pairs, as suggested in Laurie's Notes. Have each pair display their answers and graphs for Exercises 8–15 on a whiteboard for your review. Review explanations for Exercise 16 as a class.

The Success Criteria Self-Assessment chart can be found in the *Student Journal* or online at *BigIdeasMath.com*.

Self-Assessment
for Concepts & Skills

8. $y = 3x$

9. $y = \dfrac{1}{7}x + 8$

10. -30

11. 16

12. 0

13.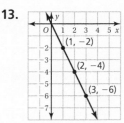

14.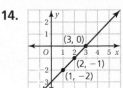

15.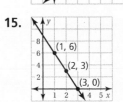

16. What output is twice the sum of the input 3 and 4?;
$2(3 + 4) = 14$; $2(3) + 4 = 10$

Laurie's Notes

Extra Example 4

The distance (in miles) traveled by a car is 35 times the number of gallons of gasoline used by the car. Write and graph a function that describes the relationship. $m = 35g$

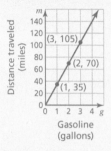

Self-Assessment
for Problem Solving

17. 575 health-care workers

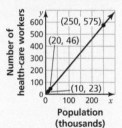

18. $y = \dfrac{11}{9}x$

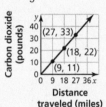

Learning Target

Represent functions in a variety of ways.

Success Criteria

- Write a function rule that describes a relationship.
- Evaluate functions for given inputs.
- Represent functions using tables and graphs.

EXAMPLE 4

- Ask a student to read the problem and another student to explain it.
- Students could complete a Four Square as you work through the problem-solving plan.
- **MP1 Make Sense of Problems and Persevere in Solving Them & MP4 Model with Mathematics:** Writing a verbal model helps students to make sense of the problem and to write an equation that represents the function.
- **?** "What do the variables represent?" p = pounds of carbon dioxide, g = gallons of gasoline used
- **?** "What is the independent variable?" g "What is the dependent variable?" p
- **Common Misconception:** Students sometimes believe that the axes have to be scaled in the same units.
- **?** "Is it possible for $g = 1.5$?" yes "What is the output for $g = 1.5$?" 30
- **?** "Is the ordered pair (1.5, 30) on the graph?" yes
- **Connection:** Students should remember unit rate from the previous course and slope from Chapter 4.
  - **?** "How can you describe the relationship using a unit rate?" 20 lb : 1 gal
  - **?** "What is the slope of the linear equation?" 20
- **?** **Extension:** "Is it possible to estimate g when $p = 50$? Explain." Yes, g appears to be 2.5 on the graph when p is 50.

✔ Self-Assessment *for Problem Solving*

- Encourage students to use a Four Square to complete these exercises. Until students become comfortable with the problem-solving plan, they may only be ready to complete the first square.
- **Neighbor Check:** Have students work independently to complete their Four Squares and then have their neighbors check their work. Have students discuss any discrepancies.

The Success Criteria Self-Assessment chart can be found in the *Student Journal* or online at *BigIdeasMath.com*.

Closure

- **Exit Ticket:** An output is 1 less than twice the input. Represent the function in four different ways.
  Sample answer:
  Words: An output is 1 less than twice the input.
  Equation: $y = 2x - 1$

  Mapping Diagram: **Graph:**

  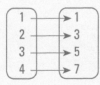   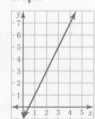

EXAMPLE 4   **Modeling Real Life**

A car produces 20 pounds of carbon dioxide for every gallon of gasoline burned. Write and graph a function that describes the relationship.

Use a verbal model to write a function rule.

| Verbal Model | Carbon dioxide (pounds) | = | Pounds per gallon | · | Gasoline used (gallons) |

Variable   Let p represent the number of pounds of carbon dioxide, and let g represent the number of gallons of gasoline used.

Equation p = 20 · g

Math Practice

Analyze Relationships
Which variable is the independent variable? the dependent variable? Explain.

Make an input-output table that represents the function $p = 20g$.

Input, g	20g	Output, p	Ordered Pair, (g, p)
1	20(1)	20	(1, 20)
2	20(2)	40	(2, 40)
3	20(3)	60	(3, 60)

Plot the ordered pairs and draw a line through the points.

Because you cannot burn a negative number of gallons of gasoline, use only positive values of g.

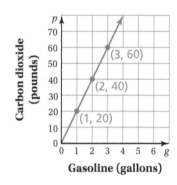

Self-Assessment for Problem Solving

Solve each exercise. Then rate your understanding of the success criteria in your journal.

17. The World Health Organization (WHO) suggests having 23 health-care workers for every 10,000 people. How many health-care workers are needed to meet the WHO suggestion for a population of 250,000 people? Justify your answer using a graph.

18. **DIG DEEPER!**   A truck produces 22 pounds of carbon dioxide for every gallon of diesel fuel burned. The fuel economy of the truck is 18 miles per gallon. Write and graph a function that describes the relationship between carbon dioxide produced and distance traveled.

7.2 Practice

 Go to *BigIdeasMath.com* to get HELP with solving the exercises.

▶ Review & Refresh

Determine whether the relation is a function.

1.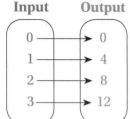

2.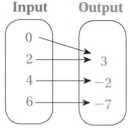

3.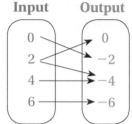

Find the slope of the line.

4.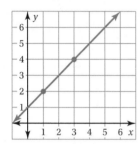

5.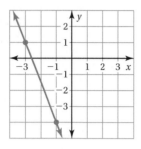

6.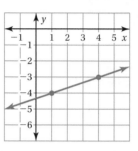

▶▶ Concepts, Skills, & Problem Solving

USING A GRAPH Use a graph to test the truth of the statement. If the statement is true, write an equation that shows how to obtain one measurement from the other measurement. (See Exploration 2, p. 281.)

7. "You can find the weight of a cell phone in ounces if you know its screen size in inches."

Screen Size (inches), x	4	4.7	5	5.5
Weight (ounces), y	4	4.8	4.8	6.4

8. "You can find the age of a child in years if you know the age of the child in months."

Age (months), x	9	12	15	24
Age (years), y	0.75	1	1.25	2

WRITING FUNCTION RULES Write a function rule for the statement.

9. The output is half of the input.

10. The output is eleven more than the input.

11. The output is three less than the input.

12. The output is the cube of the input.

13. The output is six times the input.

14. The output is one more than twice the input.

Assignment Guide and Concept Check

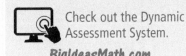

Scaffold assignments to support all students in their learning progression. The suggested assignments are a starting point. Continue to assign additional exercises and revisit with spaced practice to move every student toward proficiency.

Level	Assignment 1	Assignment 2
Emerging	1, 2, 5, 6, 8, 9, 11, 13, 15, 17, 19, 21, 23, 25	12, 14, 18, 20, 22, 24, 27, 28, 29, 30, 31, 32, 33, 40
Proficient	1, 2, 5, 6, 8, 11, 12, 14, 18, 20, 22, 24, 26	19, 23, 27, 28, 29, 30, 31, 32, 34, 35, 36, 37, 38, 39, 40
Advanced	1, 2, 5, 6, 8, 11, 12, 14, 19, 20, 22, 23, 26	27, 28, 29, 30, 31, 34, 35, 36, 37, 38, 39, 40, 41

- Assignment 1 is for use after students complete the Self-Assessment for Concepts & Skills.
- Assignment 2 is for use after students complete the Self-Assessment for Problem Solving.
- The red exercises can be used as a concept check.

Review & Refresh Prior Skills

Exercises 1–3 Identifying Functions
Exercises 4–6 Finding Slope

Common Errors

- **Exercises 9–14** Students may mix up the *x* and *y* variables when writing the equation. Remind them that *x* represents the input and *y* represents the output. Students may also need to be reminded how to write expressions from word phrases.

 Review & Refresh

1. function

2. function

3. not a function

4. 1

5. $-\dfrac{5}{2}$

6. $\dfrac{1}{3}$

 Concepts, Skills, & Problem Solving

7. false

8. true; $y = \dfrac{1}{12}x$

9. $y = \dfrac{1}{2}x$

10. $y = x + 11$

11. $y = x - 3$

12. $y = x^3$

13. $y = 6x$

14. $y = 2x + 1$

Concepts, Skills, & Problem Solving

15. 8

16. -35

17. -17

18. 3.5

19. 54

20. 3

21–24. See Additional Answers.

25.

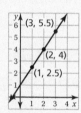

26.

27. B

28. C

29. A

30. no; The order of the x- and y-coordinates is reversed in each coordinate pair.

31. a. $p = 30d$

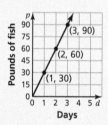

b. 900 lb

32. Wednesday;

$y = 55 - 1.5x$

$49 = 55 - 1.5x$

$4 = x$

So, you will add water 4 days after Saturday, which is Wednesday.

33. -3

34. -4

35. 36

Common Errors

- **Exercises 15–20** Students may forget the order of operations for some of the exercises and try to add or subtract before multiplying or dividing after substituting the value of *x*. Remind them of the order of operations and how to evaluate an expression.

- **Exercises 21–26** Students may mix up their axes or label one or both axes inconsistently. Remind them that the input (*x*) values are horizontal and the output (*y*) values are vertical. Encourage students to label each axis in specific increments that easily show the points plotted and will give a line through the points.

- **Exercises 27–29** Students may just guess which equation goes with each graph without testing any values. Encourage them to find a point or two on the graph and substitute the values into the equations to find which one matches.

EVALUATING A FUNCTION Find the value of y for the given value of x.

15. $y = x + 5$; $x = 3$

16. $y = 7x$; $x = -5$

17. $y = 1 - 2x$; $x = 9$

18. $y = 3x + 2$; $x = 0.5$

19. $y = 2x^3$; $x = 3$

20. $y = \dfrac{x}{2} + 9$; $x = -12$

GRAPHING A FUNCTION Graph the function.

21. $y = x + 4$

22. $y = 2x$

23. $y = -5x + 3$

24. $y = \dfrac{x}{4}$

25. $y = \dfrac{3}{2}x + 1$

26. $y = 1 + 0.5x$

MATCHING Match the graph with the function it represents.

27.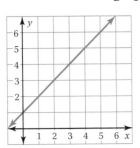

28.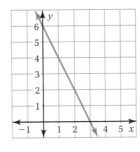

29.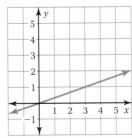

A. $y = \dfrac{x}{3}$

B. $y = x + 1$

C. $y = -2x + 6$

30. (MP) **YOU BE THE TEACHER** Your friend graphs the function represented by the input-output table. Is your friend correct? Explain your reasoning.

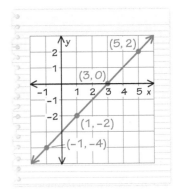

Input, x	-4	-2	0	2
Output, y	-1	1	3	5

31. **MODELING REAL LIFE** A dolphin eats 30 pounds of fish per day.

    a. Write and graph a function that relates the number p of pounds of fish that a dolphin eats in d days.

    b. How many total pounds of fish does a dolphin eat in 30 days?

32. (MP) **MODELING REAL LIFE** You fill a fish tank with 55 gallons of water on Saturday. The water evaporates at a rate of 1.5 gallons per day. You plan to add water when the tank reaches 49 gallons. When will you add water? Justify your answer.

USING AN EQUATION Find the value of x for the given value of y.

33. $y = 5x - 7$; $y = -22$

34. $y = 9 - 7x$; $y = 37$

35. $y = \dfrac{x}{4} - 7$; $y = 2$

36. **(MP) PROBLEM SOLVING** You decide to make and sell bracelets. The cost of your materials is $84.00. You charge $3.50 for each bracelet.

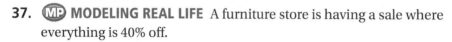

   a. Write a function that represents the profit P for selling b bracelets.

   b. Which variable is independent? dependent? Explain.

   c. You will *break even* when the cost of your materials equals your income. How many bracelets must you sell to break even?

37. **(MP) MODELING REAL LIFE** A furniture store is having a sale where everything is 40% off.

   a. Write and graph a function that represents the amount of discount on an item at regular price.

   b. You buy a bookshelf that has a regular price of $85. What is the sale price of the bookshelf?

38. **(MP) REASONING** You want to take a two-hour airboat tour. Which is a better deal, Snake Tours or Gator Tours? Use functions to justify your answer.

39. **(MP) REASONING** The graph of a function is a line that passes through the points $(3, 2)$, $(5, 8)$, and $(8, y)$. What is the value of y?

40. **CRITICAL THINKING** Make a table where the independent variable is the side length of a square and the dependent variable is the *perimeter*. Make a second table where the independent variable is the side length of a square and the dependent variable is the *area*. Graph both functions in the same coordinate plane. Compare the functions.

41. **PUZZLE** The blocks that form the diagonals of each square are shaded. Each block has an area of one square unit. Find the "green area" of Square 20. Find the "green area" of Square 21. Explain your reasoning.

Square 1

Square 2

Square 3

Square 4

Square 5

Mini-Assessment

1. Write a function rule for "The output is one-third of the input." $y = \frac{1}{3}x$

2. Write a function rule for "The output is four less than three times the input."
   $y = 3x - 4$

Find the value of y for the given value of x.

3. $y = 6x$; $x = -4$ $y = -24$

4. $y = \frac{x}{5} - 8$; $x = 50$ $y = 2$

5. Graph the function $y = 3x - 4$.

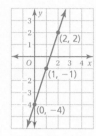

6. **You are selling magazines to raise money for your school. Each subscription you sell earns $8 for your school.**

   a. Write a function that represents the total amount d that you can raise for your school after selling s subscriptions. $d = 8s$

   b. How much money will you raise if you sell 20 subscriptions? $160

Section Resources

Surface Level	Deep Level
Resources by Chapter • Extra Practice • Reteach • Puzzle Time Student Journal • Self-Assessment • Practice Differentiating the Lesson Tutorial Videos Skills Review Handbook Skills Trainer	Resources by Chapter • Enrichment and Extension Graphic Organizers Dynamic Assessment System • Section Practice

Concepts, Skills,
& Problem Solving

36. a. $P = 3.5b - 84$

    b. independent variable: b; dependent variable: P; The profit depends on the number of bracelets sold.

    c. 24 bracelets

37. a. $y = 0.4x$

    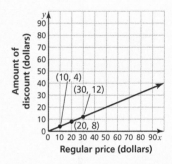

    b. $51

38. Snake Tours;
    Snake Tours: $y = 25x$
    $ = 25(2)$
    $ = \$50$
    Gator Tours: $y = 35 + 10x$
    $ = 35 + 10(2)$
    $ = \$55$

39. 17

40. See Additional Answers.

41. 44 square units; 45 square units; *Sample answer:* The "green area" of an even numbered square is equal to four more than twice the square number. The "green area" of an odd numbered square is equal to three more than twice the square number.

Learning Target

Use functions to model linear relationships.

Success Criteria

- Write linear functions to model relationships.
- Interpret linear functions in real-life situations.

Warm Up

Cumulative, vocabulary, and prerequisite skills practice opportunities are available in the *Resources by Chapter* or at *BigIdeasMath.com*.

ELL Support

Students should understand that in this context, a table is a type of chart, not a type of furniture. Clarify this if necessary.

Exploration 1

a. x is the width of the rectangle; y is the perimeter; $y = 2x + 8$; yes; *Sample answer:* The function is in slope-intercept form.

b. x is the radius of the circle; y is the area; $y = \pi x^2$; no; *Sample answer:* The function cannot be written in slope-intercept form.

c. x is the length of one of the bases of the trapezoid; y is the area; $y = x + 4$; yes; *Sample answer:* The function is in slope-intercept form.

d. x is the width of the prism; y is the surface area; $y = 12x + 16$; yes; *Sample answer:* The function is in slope-intercept form.

T-289

Laurie's Notes

Preparing to Teach

- **MP8 Look for and Express Regularity in Repeated Reasoning:** The goal is for students to recognize that a linear pattern occurs when there is a constant rate of change in a table of values or in a graph. In Chapter 4, students wrote linear equations in slope-intercept form. What is new is the language—the linear equation is referred to as a function. Students will recognize a pattern (constant rate of change) in the data and write the function.

Motivate

- Play a quick matching game with students. Have 4–5 graphs on the board with slopes and y-intercepts that are different enough so that students can distinguish between them. Write the equations in a list. Have students work with partners to match the correct equation with each graph.
- Make sure that students are still focusing on key information from the graph. Is it increasing or decreasing from left to right? Is the slope steeper than 1 or close to 0? Is the y-intercept positive or negative?

Exploration 1

- The challenge in these problems is that the equation relates to a geometric formula. The figure shown for each problem should provide a hint as to what the variables x and y represent in the problem.
- For part (a), students should know that two formulas involving a rectangle are perimeter ($P = 2\ell + 2w$) and area ($A = \ell w$). They can substitute 4 for the length and the value of x for the width in each formula. The value of the perimeter will match the y-values in the table.
- For part (b), students should know that two formulas involving π and a circle are circumference ($C = 2\pi r$) and area ($A = \pi r^2$). Substitute the value of x for the radius in each formula. The value of the area will match the y-values in the table.
- ❓ "Could y represent the perimeter for part (c)? Explain." No, you only know 3 of the 4 side lengths, and the sum of the three sides you know is greater than y.
- For part (c), students know that the formula for the area of a trapezoid is $A = \frac{1}{2}h(b_1 + b_2)$. Substitute 4 for b_2, 2 for h, and the value of x for b_1. The value of the area will match the y-values in the table.
- For part (d), students should know that two formulas involving a rectangular prism are surface area ($S = 2\ell w + 2wh + 2\ell h$) and volume ($V = \ell wh$). Substitute 4 for the length, 2 for the height, and the value of x for the width in each formula. The value of the surface area will match the y-values in the table.
- Note that in parts (a), (c), and (d), there is a numeric pattern in the table. Have students describe the numeric pattern. Encourage them to use language such as "as x increases by 1, y increases by 2."
- ❓ **Extension:** "In part (c), how does the diagram of the trapezoid change as the value of x increases?" When $x = 4$, the trapezoid becomes a rectangle. When $x > 4$, the upper base becomes the longer of the two bases.

7.3 Linear Functions

Learning Target: Use functions to model linear relationships.

Success Criteria:
- I can write linear functions to model relationships.
- I can interpret linear functions in real-life situations.

EXPLORATION 1

Writing and Graphing Functions

Work with a partner. Each table shows a familiar pattern from geometry.

- Determine what the variables x and y represent. Then write a function rule that relates y to x.

- Is the function a *linear function*? Explain your reasoning.

Math Practice

Interpret Results
How can you determine whether a function is a linear function using a graph? an equation?

a.

x	1	2	3	4
y	10	12	14	16

b.

x	1	2	3	4
y	π	4π	9π	16π

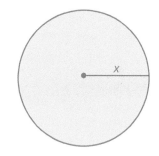

c.

x	1	2	3	4
y	5	6	7	8

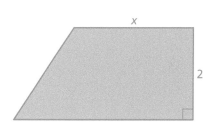

d.

x	1	2	3	4
y	28	40	52	64

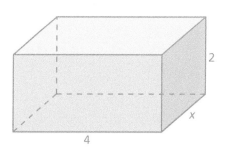

Key Vocabulary 🔊
linear function, p. 290

A **linear function** is a function whose graph is a nonvertical line. A linear function can be written in the form $y = mx + b$, where m is the slope and b is the y-intercept.

EXAMPLE 1 **Writing a Linear Function Using a Graph**

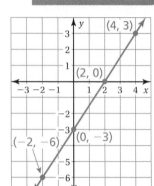

Use the graph to write a linear function that relates y to x.

Find the slope of the line using the points $(2, 0)$ and $(4, 3)$.

$$m = \frac{\text{change in } y}{\text{change in } x} = \frac{3 - 0}{4 - 2} = \frac{3}{2}$$

Because the line crosses the y-axis at $(0, -3)$, the y-intercept is -3.

▶ So, the linear function is $y = \dfrac{3}{2}x - 3$.

Try It

1. Use the graph to write a linear function that relates y to x.

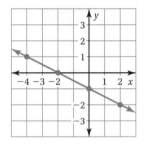

EXAMPLE 2 **Writing a Linear Function Using a Table**

Use the table to write a linear function that relates y to x.

x	−3	−2	−1	0
y	9	7	5	3

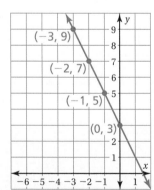

Plot the points in the table. Draw a line through the points.

Find the slope of the line using the points $(-2, 7)$ and $(-3, 9)$.

$$m = \frac{\text{change in } y}{\text{change in } x} = \frac{9 - 7}{-3 - (-2)} = \frac{2}{-1} = -2$$

Because the line crosses the y-axis at $(0, 3)$, the y-intercept is 3.

▶ So, the linear function is $y = -2x + 3$.

Try It

2. Use the table to write a linear function that relates y to x.

x	−2	−1	0	1
y	2	2	2	2

🔊 Multi-Language Glossary at *BigIdeasMath.com*

Laurie's Notes

Scaffolding Instruction

- In the exploration, students gained additional practice in writing function rules and identifying linear functions. Now they will continue writing linear functions by recognizing patterns in graphs and tables.
- **Emerging:** Students may be able to describe the pattern in a graph or table of values, but they struggle with writing the function rule. They will benefit from guided instruction for the examples.
- **Proficient:** Students can write linear functions using both graphs and tables. They should work through Example 3 before proceeding to the Self-Assessment exercises.

Discuss

- Review the definition of a function: a relation that pairs each input with exactly one output. Also review the definitions for slope and y-intercept.
- Write the definition for a **linear function**.
- **Extension:** From the definition, students might guess that there are other types of functions besides linear functions. Draw a parabola or sine wave to make this connection.

EXAMPLE 1

- Students worked on similar problems in Chapter 4. The difference here is the function terminology.
- **Teaching Tip:** To find the slope, draw a right triangle with the hypotenuse between two of the points. Label the legs of the triangle to represent the rise and run. Then compute the slope.
- "Does it matter which two points you select to find the slope? Explain." No, the ratio of rise to run will be the same because the slope triangles are similar. It is unlikely students will say this; however, it is the case.
- **MP8 Look for and Express Regularity in Repeated Reasoning:** Demonstrate that it does not matter which two points are selected to compute the slope. The slope between $(0, -3)$ and $(2, 0)$ is $\frac{3}{2}$. The slope between $(0, -3)$ and $(4, 3)$ is $\frac{6}{4} = \frac{3}{2}$.

Try It

- Students should work with a partner.

EXAMPLE 2

- "Can you tell anything about the function without plotting the points? Explain." Yes, as x increases by 1 (run), y decreases by 2 (rise). So, the function is linear and the graph has a slope of -2.
- Plot the ordered pairs and repeat the steps from Example 1.

Try It

- Students may need to graph this function. Once graphed, they will recognize this as a horizontal line whose equation is $y = 2$.

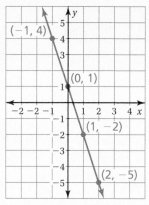

The table shows the number y of calories you burn in x hours of jogging.

Hours Jogging, x	Calories Burned, y
2	800
4	1600
6	2400
8	3200

a. Write and graph a linear function that relates y to x. $y = 400x$

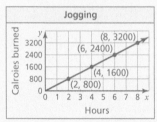

b. Interpret the slope and the y-intercept. The slope indicates that you burn 400 calories per hour jogging. The y-intercept indicates that at the moment you begin to jog, you have not burned any calories yet.

Try It

3. **a.** See Additional Answers.

   b. The slope indicates that the height decreases 1000 feet per minute. The y-intercept indicates that the descent begins at a cruising altitude of 65,000 feet.

ELL Support

Allow students to work in pairs on the Self-Assessment for Concepts & Skills exercises. Verify that students understand the information in the table. Have each pair display their answers on a whiteboard for your review.

Self-Assessment
for Concepts & Skills

4. $y = -4x - 2$

5. See Additional Answers.

Laurie's Notes

EXAMPLE 3

- Read the problem and write the table of values.
- Ask questions to check for understanding.
  - "Does the table of values represent a function? Explain." Yes, each input is associated with exactly one output.
  - "What is the independent variable (input)?" x (the time in minutes since the UAV started to descend)
  - "What is the dependent variable (output)? Explain." y (the height in thousands of feet of the UAV); The height depends on how many minutes x have passed.
  - "Is the function linear? How do you know?" Yes, the table shows that as x increases by 10, y decreases by 5.
  - "Is the slope positive or negative? How do you know?" negative; Because as x increases, y decreases.
- Compute the slope using two ordered pairs.
- Because (0, 65) is in the data set, you know the y-intercept. You could use the slope and y-intercept to graph the function rather than simply plotting points from the table.
- "Why is the graph confined to Quadrant I?" In the context of the problem, x (time) cannot be negative, and y (height) cannot be negative.
- Note that when a real-life problem makes sense only for nonnegative values of x like this, the initial value is the y-intercept.
- Students should understand that once a function has been written, you can evaluate the function for values of x that are not in the table of values.
- "Does the function make sense for fractional values of x and y?" yes "Describe all the possible values of y for the function." all real numbers between 0 and 65

Try It

- **MP2 Reason Abstractly and Quantitatively:** Students should reason that by doubling the rate of descent, the amount of time it takes the UAV to reach the ground is cut in half.

✓ Self-Assessment for Concepts & Skills

- **Neighbor Check:** Have students work independently and then have their neighbors check their work. Have students discuss any discrepancies.
- ⊙ **Agree-Disagree Statement:** See page T-292 for a description of *Agree-Disagree Statement*. Ask students if they agree or disagree with each statement below. Students should explain why or why not.
  - Vertical lines are graphs of linear functions. disagree; Vertical lines are linear, but they only have one input and it is paired with infinite outputs.
  - Horizontal lines are graphs of linear functions. agree; Horizontal lines are linear and each input is paired with exactly one output.

The Success Criteria Self-Assessment chart can be found in the *Student Journal* or online at *BigIdeasMath.com*.

EXAMPLE 3 **Interpreting a Linear Function**

An unmanned aerial vehicle (UAV) is used for surveillance. The table shows the height y (in thousands of feet) of the UAV x minutes after it begins to descend from cruising altitude.

Minutes, x	Height (thousands of feet), y
0	65
10	60
20	55

a. Write and graph a linear function that relates y to x.

The table shows a constant rate of change, so you can write a linear function that relates the dependent variable y to the independent variable x.

The point $(0, 65)$ indicates that the y-intercept is 65. Use the points $(0, 65)$ and $(10, 60)$ to find the slope.

$$m = \frac{\text{change in } y}{\text{change in } x} = \frac{60 - 65}{10 - 0} = \frac{-5}{10} = -0.5$$

So, the linear function is $y = -0.5x + 65$. Plot the points in the table and draw a line through the points.

UAV Flight

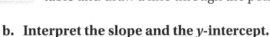

$y = -0.5x + 65$

b. Interpret the slope and the y-intercept.

The slope indicates that the height decreases 500 feet per minute. The y-intercept indicates that the descent begins at a cruising altitude of 65,000 feet.

Try It

3. **WHAT IF?** The rate of descent doubles. Repeat parts (a) and (b).

Self-Assessment for Concepts & Skills

Solve each exercise. Then rate your understanding of the success criteria in your journal.

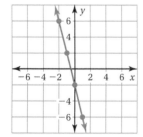

4. **WRITING A LINEAR FUNCTION** Use the graph to write a linear function that relates y to x.

5. **INTERPRETING A LINEAR FUNCTION** The table shows the revenue R (in millions of dollars) of a company when it spends A (in millions of dollars) on advertising.

Advertising, A	0	2	4	6	8
Revenue, R	2	6	10	14	18

a. Write and graph a linear function that relates R to A.

b. Interpret the slope and the y-intercept.

EXAMPLE 4 **Modeling Real Life**

The cost y (in dollars) of buying x cubic yards of mulch from Company A, including a one-time shipping fee, is represented by the linear function $y = 29x + 30$. The table shows the cost, including a one-time shipping fee, of buying mulch from Company B. Which company charges more per cubic yard of mulch? How much more?

Mulch (cubic yards), x	Cost (dollars), y
1	48.50
2	82.00
3	115.50

Understand the problem.

You are given functions that represent the costs of buying mulch from two different companies. You are asked to determine which company charges more per cubic yard of mulch and how much more it charges.

Make a plan.

The table shows a constant rate of change, so the relationship is linear. The cost per cubic yard of mulch for each company is represented by the slope of the graph of each function. Find and compare the slopes.

Solve and check.

Company A

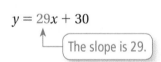

$y = 29x + 30$

The slope is 29.

Company A charges $29.00 per cubic yard.

Company B

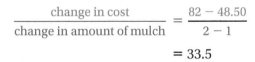

$$\frac{\text{change in cost}}{\text{change in amount of mulch}} = \frac{82 - 48.50}{2 - 1}$$

$$= 33.5$$

Company B charges $33.50 per cubic yard.

Check Reasonableness

For Company B, use the points (2, 82) and (3, 115.50) to find the slope.

$$\text{slope} = \frac{115.50 - 82.00}{3 - 2}$$

$$= 33.5 \checkmark$$

So, Company B charges $33.50 - 29.00 = \$4.50$ more per cubic yard of mulch.

 Self-Assessment for Problem Solving

Solve each exercise. Then rate your understanding of the success criteria in your journal.

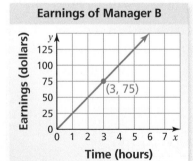

Earnings of Manager B

(3, 75)

Time (hours)

6. Manager A earns $15 per hour and receives a $50 bonus. The graph shows the earnings of Manager B. (a) Which manager has a greater hourly wage? (b) After how many hours does Manager B earn more money than Manager A?

7. Each month, you start with 2 gigabytes of data and use 0.08 gigabyte per day. The table shows the amount y (in gigabytes) of data that your friend has left x days after the start of each month. Who runs out of data first? Justify your answer.

Day, x	Data (gigabytes), y
0	3
7	2.3
14	1.6

Laurie's Notes

EXAMPLE 4

- Notice that the cost of buying mulch from Company A is given as an equation and includes a fixed charge, which represents a one-time shipping fee.
- ❔ "What part of the equation tells you the unit price of the mulch from Company A?" $29x$ "What is the unit price?" $29 per cubic yard of mulch
- Explain that the unit price also represents the slope.
- The cost of buying mulch from Company B is given in a table of values.
- ❔ "How can you determine the unit price of the mulch from Company B?" Find the slope of the line that represents the table of values.
- Have students calculate the slope.
- ❔ "Can you write a linear function to represent the total cost of buying mulch from Company B?" yes "Do you need an equation to answer the questions? Explain." No, the questions only ask about the prices per cubic yard of mulch (the unit prices), not the total cost.

✅ Self-Assessment for Problem Solving

- The goal for all students is to feel comfortable with the problem-solving plan. It is important for students to problem-solve in class, where they may receive support from you and their peers. Keep in mind that some students may only be ready for the first step.
- Students should work with a partner to make a plan for each problem and then solve the problems independently.

The Success Criteria Self-Assessment chart can be found in the *Student Journal* or online at *BigIdeasMath.com*.

Closure

- **Exit Ticket:** Plot the points given in the table and write a linear equation for the function.

x	−2	0	2	4	6
y	2	3	4	5	6

$y = \dfrac{1}{2}x + 3$

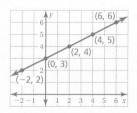

Extra Example 4

Your earnings y (in dollars) for working x hours, including a one-time bonus, are represented by the function $y = 6x + 12$. The table shows the earnings of your friend. Who earns more per hour? How much more?

Time (hours)	1	2	3	4
Earnings ($)	9	18	27	36

your friend; $3 more per hour

Self-Assessment
for Problem Solving

6. **a.** Manager B

   b. 5 h

7. you;
   you: $y = 2 - 0.08x$
   $0 = 2 - 0.08x$
   $25 = x$
   your friend: $y = 3 - 0.1x$
   $0 = 3 - 0.1x$
   $30 = x$

Learning Target

Use functions to model linear relationships.

Success Criteria

- Write linear functions to model relationships.
- Interpret linear functions in real-life situations.

Review & Refresh

1. $y = x - 10$

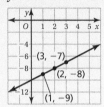

2. $y = \dfrac{1}{3}x$

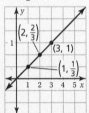

3. $(-1, 4)$ 4. $(3, -7)$

5. $(-5, -2)$

Concepts, Skills, & Problem Solving

6. x is the length of the base of the triangle; y is the area; $y = 2x$; yes; *Sample answer:* The function is in slope-intercept form.

7. x is diameter of the circle; y is the circumference; $y = \pi x$; yes; *Sample answer:* The function is in slope-intercept form.

8. $y = \dfrac{4}{3}x + 2$ 9. $y = 3$

10. $y = -\dfrac{1}{4}x$ 11. $y = \dfrac{2}{3}x + 5$

12. **a.** $y = 0.5x + 11$

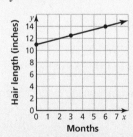

b. The slope indicates the hair length increases by 0.5 inch per month. The y-intercept indicates that the initial hair length is 11 inches.

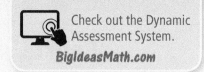
Assignment Guide and Concept Check

Scaffold assignments to support all students in their learning progression. The suggested assignments are a starting point. Continue to assign additional exercises and revisit with spaced practice to move every student toward proficiency.

Level	Assignment 1	Assignment 2
Emerging	1, 2, 5, 6, 7, 8, 10, 12, 13	9, 11, 14, 15, 17
Proficient	1, 2, 5, 6, 7, 8, 9, 10, 12, 13	11, 14, 15, 16, 17
Advanced	1, 2, 5, 6, 7, 8, 9, 10, 12, 13	14, 15, 16, 17, 18

- Assignment 1 is for use after students complete the Self-Assessment for Concepts & Skills.
- Assignment 2 is for use after students complete the Self-Assessment for Problem Solving.
- The red exercises can be used as a concept check.

Review & Refresh Prior Skills

Exercises 1 and 2 Writing Function Rules
Exercises 3–5 Choosing a Solution Method for a System of Linear Equations

Common Errors

- **Exercise 8** Students may find the wrong slope because they misread the scale on an axis. Encourage them to label the points and to use the points they know to write the slope.
- **Exercise 9** Students may not remember how to write an equation for a horizontal line. They may write $x = 3$ instead of $y = 3$. Encourage students to think about the slope-intercept form of a linear equation.
- **Exercises 10 and 11** Students may write the reciprocal of the slope when writing the equation from the table. Encourage students to substitute a point into the equation and check to make sure that the equation is true for that point.

Go to *BigIdeasMath.com* to get HELP with solving the exercises.

▶ Review & Refresh

Write a function rule for the statement. Then graph the function.

1. The output is ten less than the input.

2. The output is one-third of the input.

Solve the system.

3. $y = x + 5$
   $y = -3x + 1$

4. $x + y = -4$
   $6x + 2y = 4$

5. $-4x + 3y = 14$
   $y = 2x + 8$

▶▶ Concepts, Skills, & Problem Solving

WRITING AND GRAPHING FUNCTIONS The table shows a familiar pattern from geometry. (a) Determine what the variables x and y represent. Then write a function rule that relates y to x. (b) Is the function a *linear function*? Explain your reasoning. (See Exploration 1, p. 289.)

6.

x	1	2	3	4	5
y	2	4	6	8	10

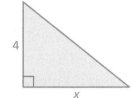

7.

x	1	2	3	4	5
y	π	2π	3π	4π	5π

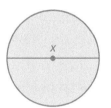

WRITING LINEAR FUNCTIONS Use the graph or table to write a linear function that relates y to x.

8.

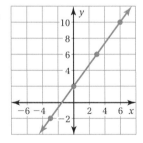

9.

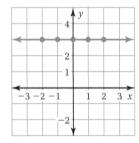

10.

x	−8	−4	0	4
y	2	1	0	−1

11.

x	−3	0	3	6
y	3	5	7	9

12. **INTERPRETING A LINEAR FUNCTION** The table shows the length y (in inches) of a person's hair after x months.

   a. Write and graph a linear function that relates y to x.

   b. Interpret the slope and the y-intercept.

Months, x	Hair Length, y
0	11.0
3	12.5
6	14.0

13. **INTERPRETING A LINEAR FUNCTION** The table shows the percent y (in decimal form) of battery power remaining x hours after you turn on a laptop computer.

Hours, x	0	2	4
Power Remaining, y	1.0	0.6	0.2

   a. Write and graph a linear function that relates y to x.

   b. Interpret the slope, the x-intercept, and the y-intercept.

   c. After how many hours is the battery power at 75%?

14. **MP MODELING REAL LIFE** The number y of calories burned after x minutes of kayaking is represented by the linear function $y = 4.5x$. The graph shows the number of calories burned by hiking.

   a. Which activity burns more calories per minute?

   b. You perform each activity for 45 minutes. How many total calories do you burn? Justify your answer.

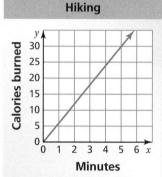

Hiking

Calories burned vs. Minutes

15. **DIG DEEPER!** You and a friend race each other. You give your friend a 50-foot head start. The distance y (in feet) your friend runs after x seconds is represented by the linear function $y = 14x + 50$. A 10-second race ends in a tie. Write an equation for the distance y (in feet) you run after x seconds. When do you win the race? Explain your reasoning.

16. **MP REASONING** You and your friend are saving money to buy bicycles that cost \$175 each. You have \$45 to start and save an additional \$5 each week. The graph shows the amount y (in dollars) that your friend has after x weeks. Who can buy a bicycle first? Justify your answer.

Friend's Savings

Savings (dollars) vs. Weeks — (0, 15), (3, 39)

17. **CRITICAL THINKING** Is every linear equation a linear function? Explain your reasoning.

18. **MP PROBLEM SOLVING** The heat index is calculated using the relative humidity and the temperature. For every 1 degree increase in the temperature from 94°F to 97°F at 75% relative humidity, the heat index rises 4°F. On a summer day, the relative humidity is 75%, the temperature is 94°F, and the heat index is 124°F. Estimate the heat index when the relative humidity is 75% and the temperature is 100°F. Use a function to justify your answer.

Mini-Assessment

Use the graph or table to write a linear function that relates y to x.

1.

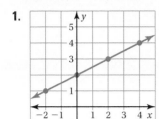

$y = \dfrac{1}{2}x + 2$

2.

x	-2	-1	0	1
y	9	4	-1	-6

$y = -5x - 1$

3. The growth y (in feet) of a maple tree in x years is represented by the linear function $y = 1.5x$. The table shows the yearly growth for a pine tree. Which tree grows faster? How much faster?

Time (year), x	1	2	3	4
Growth (feet), y	0.75	1.5	2.25	3

maple; 0.75 foot per year

Section Resources

Surface Level	Deep Level
Resources by Chapter • Extra Practice • Reteach • Puzzle Time Student Journal • Self-Assessment • Practice Differentiating the Lesson Tutorial Videos Skills Review Handbook Skills Trainer	Resources by Chapter • Enrichment and Extension Graphic Organizers Dynamic Assessment System • Section Practice
Transfer Level	
Dynamic Assessment System • Mid-Chapter Quiz	Assessment Book • Mid-Chapter Quiz

 Concepts, Skills, & Problem Solving

13. a. $y = -0.2x + 1$

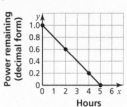

b. The slope indicates that the power decreases by 20% per hour. The x-intercept indicates that the battery lasts 5 hours. The y-intercept indicates that the battery power is at 100% when you turn on the laptop.

c. 1.25 h

14. a. hiking

b. 472.5 calories;
kayaking: $y = 4.5x = 4.5(45)$
$= 202.5$ calories

hiking: $y = 6x = 6(45)$
$= 270$ calories
$202.5 + 270 = 472.5$ calories

15. $y = 19x$; for any distance greater than 190 feet; You catch up to your friend after you run 190 feet, so you will be ahead of your friend for any distance greater than 190 feet.

16. your friend;
you: $y = 5x + 45$
$175 = 5x + 45$
$26 = x$
your friend: $y = 8x + 15$
$175 = 8x + 15$
$20 = x$

17. no; Any linear equation of the form $x = a$ is not a linear function because its graph is a vertical line.

18. 148°F;
$y = 4x - 252 = 4(100) - 252$
$= 148$°F

Learning Target

Understand differences between linear and nonlinear functions.

Success Criteria

- Recognize linear functions represented as tables, equations, and graphs.
- Compare linear and nonlinear functions.

Warm Up

Cumulative, vocabulary, and prerequisite skills practice opportunities are available in the *Resources by Chapter* or at *BigIdeasMath.com.*

ELL Support

Discuss the words *linear* and *nonlinear*. Ask students what the word *linear* means. Clarify any misunderstandings. Write the word *non/linear* on the board with a slash as shown. Ask students what the prefix *non-* means and what it does to the word *linear*. Guide them to understand that *non-* means "no" or "not," and when used as a prefix the word has the opposite meaning.

Laurie's Notes

STATE STANDARDS
COMMON CORE
8.F.A.3

Preparing to Teach

- **MP4 Model with Mathematics & MP8 Look for and Express Regularity in Repeated Reasoning:** The goal is for students to recognize when a pattern in real life is linear or nonlinear. Using falling objects, students will look for numeric patterns. The presence or absence of a *constant rate of change* will help students determine whether the data represent a linear or nonlinear function.

Motivate

- "How many of you would like to try skydiving? Why?"
- Share with students that the first successful parachute jump made from a moving airplane was made by Captain Albert Berry in St. Louis, in 1912.
- The first parachute jump from a balloon was completed by André-Jacques Garnerin in 1797 over Monceau Park in Paris.
- Tell students that today they will explore whether the function that describes the height of a skydiver is linear or nonlinear.
- Students will study many types of nonlinear functions, such as quadratic functions, radical functions, and rational functions, in future mathematics courses.

Exploration 1

- Discuss the two falling objects—one with a parachute and one that is free-falling.
- "Is there a difference in the rate at which two objects fall when one is attached to a parachute and the other is left to free-fall? Explain." Listen for discussion of rate. It is unlikely students will bring up acceleration.
- You could make a small parachute using a handkerchief, tape, floss, and a small figurine to model a parachute-controlled fall. Then model a free-fall.
- Students may graph the skydiver equation using the slope and *y*-intercept, but they need to make a table of values for the bowling ball equation.
- "Do the scales for the *x*- and *y*-axis need to be the same? Explain." No, one scale represents the height, which includes larger numbers and the other scale represents time, which includes smaller numbers.
- After students have plotted the points, ask about the two graphs. First note that the two graphs begin at the same height (*y*-intercept), 300 feet.
  - "How far has the skydiver fallen after 4 seconds?" 60 feet "How far has the bowling ball fallen after 4 seconds?" 256 feet
  - "What is the difference in the way the graphs look?" The graph of the skydiver appears to be a line and the graph of the bowling ball is not.
  - "Describe the fall of the skydiver." falling at a constant rate of 15 feet per second
  - "Describe the fall of the bowling ball. Why is it not a straight line?" Listen for students to describe that the bowling ball is picking up speed as it falls.
- "How are the two equations different?" Students should recognize that there is an exponent in the bowling ball equation but not the skydiver equation.

Exploration 1

a.

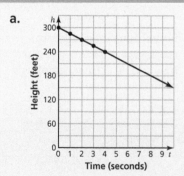

Sample answer: Plot points and connect them with a line; linear

b. See Additional Answers.

7.4 Comparing Linear and Nonlinear Functions

Learning Target: Understand differences between linear and nonlinear functions.

Success Criteria:
• I can recognize linear functions represented as tables, equations, and graphs.
• I can compare linear and nonlinear functions.

EXPLORATION 1

Comparing Functions

Work with a partner. Each equation represents the height *h* (in feet) of a falling object after *t* seconds.

• **MP** **CHOOSE TOOLS** Graph each equation. Explain your method.

• Decide whether each graph represents a *linear* or *nonlinear* function.

• Compare the falling objects.

a. Skydiver

$$h = 300 - 15t$$

b. Bowling ball

$$h = 300 - 16t^2$$

Math Practice

Label Axes
Did you use the same scale on the axes? How does the scale affect how you compare the falling objects?

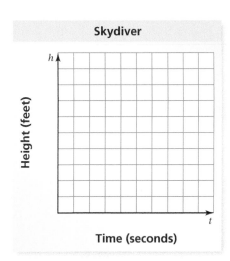

Skydiver

Height (feet) / Time (seconds)

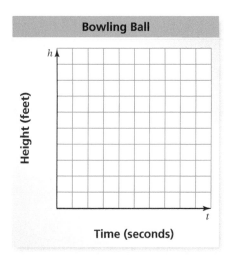

Bowling Ball

Height (feet) / Time (seconds)

Key Vocabulary 🔊
nonlinear function,
p. 296

The graph of a linear function shows a constant rate of change. A **nonlinear function** does not have a constant rate of change. So, its graph is *not* a line.

EXAMPLE 1 **Identifying Functions from Tables**

Does each table represent a *linear* or *nonlinear* function? Explain.

a.

+3 +3 +3

x	3	6	9	12
y	40	32	24	16

−8 −8 −8

▷ As *x* increases by 3, *y* decreases by 8. The rate of change is constant. So, the function is linear.

b.

+2 +2 +2

x	1	3	5	7
y	2	11	33	88

+9 +22 +55

▷ As *x* increases by 2, *y* increases by different amounts. The rate of change is *not* constant. So, the function is nonlinear.

Try It Does the table represent a *linear* or *nonlinear* function? Explain.

1.

x	2	4	6	8
y	−8	−4	0	4

2.

x	0	3	7	12
y	25	20	15	10

EXAMPLE 2 **Identifying Functions from Equations**

Does each equation represent a *linear* or *nonlinear* function? Explain.

a. $y = 4(x - 1)$

▷ You can rewrite $y = 4(x - 1)$ in slope-intercept form as $y = 4x - 4$. The function has a constant rate of change. So, the function is linear.

b. $y = \dfrac{4}{x}$

▷ You cannot rewrite $y = \dfrac{4}{x}$ in slope-intercept form. The function does not have a constant rate of change. So, the function is nonlinear.

Try It Does the equation represent a *linear* or *nonlinear* function? Explain.

3. $y = x + 5$

4. $y = \dfrac{4x}{3}$

5. $y = 1 - x^2$

🔊 Multi-Language Glossary at *BigIdeasMath.com*

Laurie's Notes

Scaffolding Instruction

- Students explored the graphs of functions that were linear and nonlinear. Now they will compare linear and nonlinear functions.
- **Emerging:** Students can graph functions using tables, but they need more practice understanding differences between linear and nonlinear functions. They will benefit from guided instruction for the examples.
- **Proficient:** Students easily recognize the differences between linear and nonlinear functions in tables or graphs. Have them work through Example 2 before proceeding to the Self-Assessment exercises.

Discuss

- Discuss linear functions, nonlinear functions, and their rates of change. Refer back to the graphs in the exploration.

EXAMPLE 1

- Write the first table of values. Draw attention to the change in x (increasing by 3 each time) and the change in y (decreasing by 8 each time). Because the rate of change is constant, the function is linear.
- Write the second table of values. Draw attention to the change in x (increasing by 2 each time) and the change in y (increasing by different amounts each time). This is a nonlinear function.

Try It

- Students should work independently.
- **Popsicle Sticks:** Select students to share their explanations.

EXAMPLE 2

- Remind students that all linear functions can be written in slope-intercept form.
- **MP7 Look for and Make Use of Structure:** Students often see $y = \dfrac{4}{x}$ and $y = \dfrac{x}{4}$ as *the same kind of function*. So, many students think this will be a linear function. Remind students of how fractions are multiplied, and use the examples $\dfrac{4}{x}$ and $\dfrac{x}{4}$.

$$\frac{4}{x} = \frac{4}{1} \cdot \frac{1}{x} = 4 \cdot \frac{1}{x} \qquad \frac{x}{4} = \frac{x}{1} \cdot \frac{1}{4} = x \cdot \frac{1}{4} = \frac{1}{4} \cdot x$$

So, $y = \dfrac{x}{4}$ is linear with a slope of $\dfrac{1}{4}$. The equation $y = \dfrac{4}{x}$ cannot be written as a linear equation.
- **Note:** The equation $y = \dfrac{4}{x}$ shows inverse variation.

? "If an equation can be written in slope-intercept form, why must it be a linear function?" An equation that can be written in slope-intercept form must be a line and have constant rate of change.

Try It

- In Exercise 5, students should see the exponent of 2 and quickly decide that the function is nonlinear.

Extra Example 1

Does each table represent a *linear* or *nonlinear* function? Explain.

a.

x	3	4	5	6
y	1	2	3	4

linear; As x increases by 1, y increases by 1.

b.

x	2	5	8	11
y	4	7	12	19

nonlinear; As x increases by 3, y increases by different amounts.

Try It

1. linear; As x increases by 2, y increases by 4.

2. nonlinear; As y decreases by 5, x increases by different amounts.

Extra Example 2

Does each equation represent a *linear* or *nonlinear* function? Explain.

a. $y = 6x - 3$ linear; The equation is in slope-intercept form.

b. $y = 4x^2$ nonlinear; You cannot rewrite the equation in slope-intercept form.

ELL Support

Have students work in groups to discuss and complete Try It Exercises 1–5. Provide guiding questions: Is the rate of change constant or not? What does that mean? Expect students to perform according to their language levels.

Beginner: Contribute to discussion using simple phrases.
Intermediate: Contribute to discussion using simple sentences.
Advanced: Use detailed sentences and help guide discussion.

Try It

3. linear; The equation is in slope-intercept form.

4. linear; You can rewrite the equation in slope-intercept form.

5. See Additional Answers.

Does each graph represent a *linear* or *nonlinear* function? Explain.

a.

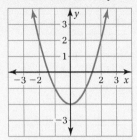

nonlinear; The graph is not a line.

b.

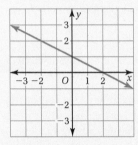

linear; The graph is a line.

Try It

6. nonlinear; The graph is not a line.

7. linear; The graph is a line.

Self-Assessment
for Concepts & Skills

8. linear; As *x* decreases by 4, *y* increases by 2.

9. nonlinear; The graph is not a line.

10. $5xy = 2$; You cannot rewrite the equation in slope-intercept form.

Laurie's Notes

EXAMPLE 3

- Part (b) may seem obvious, but the horizontal line seems like a special case to students. They may not be sure it is a linear function.
- **?** "What is the slope of the line in part (b)?" 0 "What is the constant rate of change?" As *x* increases by 1, *y* stays the same.

Try It

- Discuss Exercise 6 as a class. There are two parts of this function. The rate of change is not constant because it changes from positive to negative.

Formative Assessment Tip

Point of Most Significance

This technique is the opposite of *Muddiest Point*. Students are asked to identify the most significant idea, learning, or concept they gained in the lesson. Students reflect on the lesson and identify the key example, problem, or point that contributed to their attainment of the learning target. It is important to know whether the lesson was effective or whether the lesson should be modified. Share with students what you learn from their reflections. Students will take reflections more seriously if they see that you value and use them.

✔ Self-Assessment for Concepts & Skills

- ◉ Stop and ask students, "What was the *Point of Most Significance* in this lesson?"
- Students should work independently and then *Turn and Talk* with a neighbor to discuss their results.

ELL Support

Allow students to work in pairs for extra support and to practice language. Have two pairs discuss their answers and come to an agreement. Monitor discussions and provide support as needed. Review answers as a class.

The Success Criteria Self-Assessment chart can be found in the *Student Journal* or online at *BigIdeasMath.com*.

EXAMPLE 3 **Identifying Functions from Graphs**

Does each graph represent a *linear* or *nonlinear* function? Explain.

a.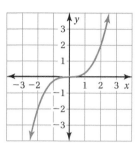

b.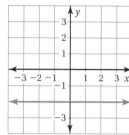

▷ The graph is *not* a line. So, the function is nonlinear.

▷ The graph is a line. So, the function is linear.

Try It **Does the graph represent a *linear* or *nonlinear* function? Explain.**

6.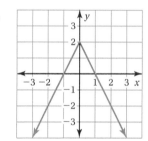

7.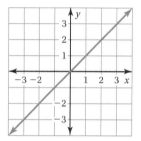

Self-Assessment for Concepts & Skills

Solve each exercise. Then rate your understanding of the success criteria in your journal.

IDENTIFYING FUNCTIONS Does the table or graph represent a *linear* or *nonlinear* function? Explain.

8.

x	3	−1	−5	−9
y	0	2	4	6

9.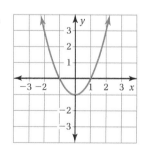

10. **WHICH ONE DOESN'T BELONG?** Which equation does *not* belong with the other three? Explain your reasoning.

$$15y = 6x \qquad y = \frac{2}{5}x \qquad 10y = 4x \qquad 5xy = 2$$

EXAMPLE 4 **Modeling Real Life**

Year, t	Account A Balance	Account B Balance
0	$100	$100
1	$110	$110
2	$120	$121
3	$130	$133.10
4	$140	$146.41
5	$150	$161.05

Two accounts earn different types of interest. The table shows the balances of each account for five years. Graph the data and compare the balances of the accounts over time.

Plot the points in the table for each account.

The points for Account A lie on a line. Draw a line through the points.

The points for Account B do not lie on a line. Draw a *curve* through the points.

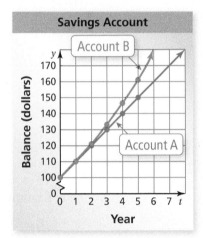

The graphs show that both balances are positive and increasing. The graphs also show that the balance of Account B grows faster.

The balance of Account A has a constant rate of change of $10. The balance of Account B increases by different amounts each year. So, Account A shows linear growth and Account B shows nonlinear growth.

Self-Assessment for Problem Solving

Solve each exercise. Then rate your understanding of the success criteria in your journal.

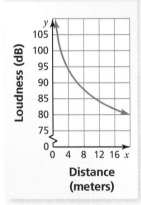
Loudness of Sound

Distance (meters)

11. The loudness of sound is measured in *decibels* (dB). The graph shows the loudness y of a sound (in decibels) x meters from the source of the sound. Is the relationship between loudness and distance *linear* or *nonlinear*? Approximate the loudness of the sound 12 meters from the source.

12. DIG DEEPER! A *video blogger* is someone who records a video diary. A new website currently hosts 90 video bloggers and projects a gain of 10 video bloggers per month. The table below shows the actual numbers of video bloggers. How does the projection differ from the actual change?

Month	0	1	2	3	4	5
Video Bloggers	90	97	110	128	153	190

Laurie's Notes

EXAMPLE 4

- **Financial Literacy:** Ask a volunteer to read the problem. In addition to looking at linear and nonlinear functions, you also want to integrate financial literacy skills when appropriate. Ask students to recall the simple interest formula $I = Prt$, which they studied in the previous course.
- Point out that both functions have the same initial value. Explain to students that they should interpret the initial value as the starting balance, or the principal, in the context of the problem.
- ❓ "Each time the year increases by 1, what happens to the balance of Account A?" It increases by $10.
- ❓ "Each time the year increases by 1, what happens to the balance of Account B?" It increases by a greater amount each year.
- **Extension:** Show students how to calculate the values in the table. Account A's balance is found using $P + I = P + Prt$, where $P = 100$, $r = 0.1$, and $t =$ year. Account A earns simple interest. Account B's balance can also be found $P + I = P + Prt$, but $P =$ the previous year's balance and $t = 1$. Account B earns compound interest, which students will study in future mathematics courses.

✅ Self-Assessment for Problem Solving

- Allow time in class for students to practice using the problem-solving plan. Remember, some students may only be able to complete the first step.
- Have students read the problems independently and make a plan for each. As students are writing their plans, circulate and make notes about students who have good plans. When all students are finished, ask those students to share their ideas with the class. After hearing other ideas, some students may want to change their plans before solving.

The Success Criteria Self-Assessment chart can be found in the *Student Journal* or online at *BigIdeasMath.com*.

Closure

- ⊙ **Exit Ticket:** Describe how to determine if a function is linear or nonlinear from (a) a table, (b) an equation, and (c) a graph.
  - a. If the rate of change is constant, then the function is linear. Otherwise, the function is nonlinear.
  - b. If the equation can be written in slope-intercept form, then the function is linear. Otherwise, the function is nonlinear.
  - c. If the graph is a line, then the function is linear. Otherwise, the function is nonlinear.

Extra Example 4

Two accounts earn different types of interest. The table shows the balances of each account for five years. Graph the data and compare the balances of the accounts over time.

Year, t	Account A Balance	Account B Balance
0	$50	$50
1	$55	$55
2	$60	$60.50
3	$65	$66.55
4	$70	$73.21
5	$75	$80.53

Account A shows linear growth and Account B shows nonlinear growth.

Self-Assessment
for Problem Solving

11. nonlinear; *Sample answer:* 85 dB

12. *Sample answer:* The actual change for Months 1 and 2 is close to the projection, but the actual change for Months 3 through 5 is greater than the projection.

Learning Target

Understand differences between linear and nonlinear functions.

Success Criteria

- Recognize linear functions represented as tables, equations, and graphs.
- Compare linear and nonlinear functions.

Review & Refresh

1. $y = x - 2$

2. $y = -\dfrac{2}{3}x + 5$

3.
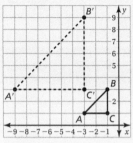
enlargement

4.
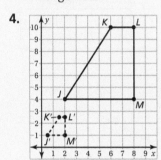
reduction

Concepts, Skills, & Problem Solving

5. See Additional Answers.

6. See Additional Answers.

7. linear; As x increases by 1, y increases by 4.

8. nonlinear; As x decreases by 1, y decreases by different amounts.

9. linear; You can rewrite the equation in slope-intercept form.

10. linear; You can rewrite the equation in slope-intercept form.

11. nonlinear; You cannot rewrite the equation in slope-intercept form.

12. linear; The graph is a line.

13. nonlinear; The graph is not a line.

Assignment Guide and Concept Check

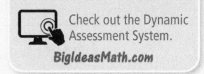
Scaffold assignments to support all students in their learning progression. The suggested assignments are a starting point. Continue to assign additional exercises and revisit with spaced practice to move every student toward proficiency.

Level	Assignment 1	Assignment 2
Emerging	1, 2, 4, 5, 6, 7, 8, 9, 10, 11, 12, 13	14, 15, 16, 17
Proficient	1, 2, 4, 5, 6, 7, 8, 9, 10, 11, 12, 13	14, 15, 16, 17, 18, 19
Advanced	1, 2, 4, 5, 6, 7, 8, 9, 10, 11, 12, 13	14, 15, 16, 17, 18, 19

- Assignment 1 is for use after students complete the Self-Assessment for Concepts & Skills.
- Assignment 2 is for use after students complete the Self-Assessment for Problem Solving.
- The red exercises can be used as a concept check.

Review & Refresh Prior Skills

Exercises 1 and 2 Writing Linear Functions
Exercises 3 and 4 Dilating a Figure

Common Errors

- **Exercises 7 and 8** Students may say that the function is linear because the x-values are increasing or decreasing by the same amount each time. Encourage students to examine the y-values to see if the graph represents a line.
- **Exercises 9–11** Students may not rewrite the equation in slope-intercept form and will guess whether the equation is linear. Remind them to attempt to write the equation in slope-intercept form.

7.4 Practice

? Go to *BigIdeasMath.com* to get HELP with solving the exercises.

▶ Review & Refresh

Write a linear function that relates y to x.

1.
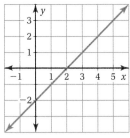

2.

x	0	1.5	3	4.5
y	5	4	3	2

The vertices of a figure are given. Draw the figure and its image after a dilation with the given scale factor. Identify the type of dilation.

3. $A(-3, 1)$, $B(-1, 3)$, $C(-1, 1)$; $k = 3$

4. $J(2, 4)$, $K(6, 10)$, $L(8, 10)$, $M(8, 4)$; $k = \dfrac{1}{4}$

▶▶ Concepts, Skills, & Problem Solving

COMPARING FUNCTIONS Graph each equation. Decide whether each graph represents a *linear* or *nonlinear* function. (See Exploration 1, p. 295.)

5. $h = 5 + 6t$ Equation 1

$h = 5 + 6t^2$ Equation 2

6. $y = -\dfrac{x}{3}$ Equation 1

$y = -\dfrac{3}{x}$ Equation 2

IDENTIFYING FUNCTIONS FROM TABLES Does the table represent a *linear* or *nonlinear* function? Explain.

7.

x	0	1	2	3
y	4	8	12	16

8.

x	6	5	4	3
y	21	15	10	6

IDENTIFYING FUNCTIONS FROM EQUATIONS Does the equation represent a *linear* or *nonlinear* function? Explain.

9. $2x + 3y = 7$

10. $y + x = 4x + 5$

11. $y = \dfrac{8}{x^2}$

IDENTIFYING FUNCTIONS FROM GRAPHS Does the graph represent a *linear* or *nonlinear* function? Explain.

12.
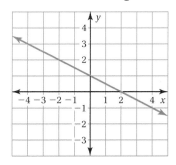

13.
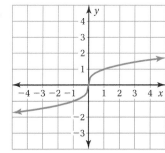

Section 7.4   Comparing Linear and Nonlinear Functions   **299**

14. **IDENTIFYING A FUNCTION** The graph shows the volume V (in cubic feet) of a cube with an edge length of x feet. Does the graph represent a *linear* or *nonlinear* function? Explain.

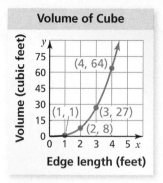

Volume of Cube

15. **MODELING REAL LIFE** The frequency y (in terahertz) of a light wave is a function of its wavelength x (in nanometers). Is the function relating the wavelength of light to its frequency *linear* or *nonlinear*?

Color	Red	Yellow	Green	Blue	Violet
Wavelength, x	660	595	530	465	400
Frequency, y	454	504	566	645	749

16. **DIG DEEPER!** The table shows the cost y (in dollars) of x pounds of sunflower seeds.

Pounds, x	Cost, y
2	2.80
3	?
4	5.60

   a. What is the missing y-value that makes the table represent a linear function?

   b. Write a linear function that represents the cost y of x pounds of seeds. Interpret the slope.

   c. Does the function have a maximum value? Explain your reasoning.

17. **MODELING REAL LIFE** A birch tree is 9 feet tall and grows at a rate of 2 feet per year. The table shows the height h (in feet) of a willow tree after x years.

Years, x	Height, h
0	5
1	11
4	17
9	23

   a. Does the table represent a *linear* or *nonlinear* function? Explain.

   b. Which tree is taller after 10 years? Explain.

18. **CRITICAL THINKING** In their first year, Show A has 7 million viewers and Show B has 5 million viewers. Each year, Show A has 90% of the viewers it had in the previous year. Show B loses 200,000 viewers each year.

   a. Determine whether the function relating the year to the number of viewers is *linear* or *nonlinear* for each show.

   b. Which show has more viewers in its sixth year?

19. **PATTERNS** The ordered pairs represent a function.

$$(0, -1), (1, 0), (2, 3), (3, 8), \text{ and } (4, 15)$$

   a. Graph the ordered pairs and describe the pattern. Is the function *linear* or *nonlinear*?

   b. Write an equation that represents the function.

Common Errors

- **Exercise 15** Students may try to graph the ordered pairs to determine if the function is linear and make an incorrect assumption depending upon how they scale their axes. Encourage students to examine the change in y for each change in x.

Mini-Assessment

Does the table, equation, or graph represent a *linear* or *nonlinear* function? Explain.

1.

x	-2	0	2	4
y	8	0	8	64

nonlinear; As x increases by 2, y increases by different amounts.

2.

x	-1	0	1	2
y	15	22	29	36

linear; As x increases by 1, y increases by 7.

3. $5x + 4y = 12$ linear; You can rewrite the equation in slope-intercept form.

4.

linear; The graph is a line.

Section Resources

Surface Level	Deep Level

Resources by Chapter
  • Extra Practice
  • Reteach
  • Puzzle Time
Student Journal
  • Self-Assessment
  • Practice
Differentiating the Lesson
Tutorial Videos
Skills Review Handbook
Skills Trainer
	Resources by Chapter
	  • Enrichment and Extension
	Graphic Organizers
	Dynamic Assessment System
	  • Section Practice

Concepts, Skills, & Problem Solving

14. nonlinear; The graph is not a line.

15. nonlinear

16. a. 4.20

   b. $y = 1.4x$; The slope indicates that the cost per pound of sunflower seeds is $1.40.

   c. no; You can always increase the cost by increasing the amount of sunflower seeds purchased.

17. a. nonlinear; As h increases by 6, x increases by different amounts.

   b. the birch tree; After 10 years, the birch tree will be 29 feet tall. The willow tree grew 6 feet in the last 5 years, so it will likely grow less than 6 feet in the next year and will not reach 29 feet.

18. a. Show A: nonlinear; Show B: linear

   b. Show A

19. a.

As x increases by 1, y increases by 2 more than the previous increase; nonlinear

   b. $y = x^2 - 1$

Learning Target

Use graphs of functions to describe relationships between quantities.

Success Criteria

- Describe relationships between quantities in graphs.
- Sketch graphs given verbal descriptions of relationships.

Warm Up

Cumulative, vocabulary, and prerequisite skills practice opportunities are available in the *Resources by Chapter* or at *BigIdeasMath.com*.

ELL Support

Explain that the word *sketch* means "to make a rough drawing." So, when you sketch a graph, you make a rough drawing of the graph.

Exploration 1

a. C; *Sample answer:* The graph increases when your speed increases, is horizontal when your speed is constant, and decreases when you slow down.

b. A; *Sample answer:* The graph increases when your speed increases, and then gets steeper when you go faster down a hill. When you come to a quick stop, the speed decreases to zero.

c. D; *Sample answer:* The graph increases when your speed increases, decreases when you come to a stop, and is zero when you are in the store. When you continue to ride, increasing your speed, the graph increases.

d. See Additional Answers.

Exploration 2

See Additional Answers.

Laurie's Notes

STATE STANDARDS
8.F.B.5

Preparing to Teach

- Students are familiar with graphs of linear and nonlinear functions. Now they will extend this understanding to analyze graphs without numbers.
- **MP2 Reason Abstractly and Quantitatively & MP3 Construct Viable Arguments and Critique the Reasoning of Others:** In the explorations, students will interpret and communicate their thinking about quantitative relationships represented as graphs without numbers. Expect students to critique the reasoning of their classmates as they use the slopes and y-intercepts to interpret the graphs.

Motivate

- Ask 3 students to volunteer to be *walkers*. Each will stand 5 feet from the front wall and do the following when you say, "Go."
  - Walker A: Walk slowly to the back wall at a constant rate
  - Walker B: Walk quickly to the back wall at a constant rate.
  - Walker C: Stay where you are. Do not walk.
- Have the rest of the class sketch a graph representing the distance of each walker from the front wall over time. Ask what information they can show in the graphs without including a scale.

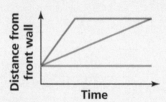

- Ask students to share their graphs.

Exploration 1

- Students will quickly comment that there are no numbers on the graphs.
- Give students sufficient time to discuss the graphs with their partners and then to do the matching.
- **MP6 Attend to Precision:** Students should use precise language to explain their reasoning. Listen for how the pattern of increasing, decreasing, and constant speeds represents the situation.
- Graph B is the only graph with a y-intercept not equal to 0. Do students point out this feature when they describe their graphs?
- **Extension:** Have students make graphs with numbers. Then swap graphs with classmates and describe reasonable scenarios for the graphs.

Exploration 2

- Give students a few minutes to discuss the graph with their partners.
- **Popsicle Sticks:** Select students to share their paragraphs.
- Features to listen for: The height increases for a time, then it decreases for a time. Then the height repeats this pattern 2 more times before it increases again. None of the rates of increase or decrease are constant.
- Have students share the different situations they come up with and why the graph can represent their situations.

7.5 Analyzing and Sketching Graphs

Learning Target: Use graphs of functions to describe relationships between quantities.

Success Criteria:
• I can describe relationships between quantities in graphs.
• I can sketch graphs given verbal descriptions of relationships.

EXPLORATION 1

Matching Situations to Graphs

Work with a partner. Each graph shows your speed during a bike ride. Match each situation with its graph. Explain your reasoning.

A.
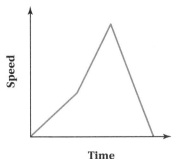

B.
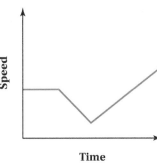

C.
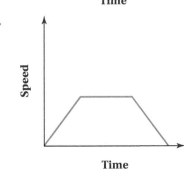

D.
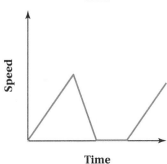

Math Practice

Analyze Relationships

A graph relating distance and time shows a positive linear relationship. Describe a graph relating speed and time in this situation.

a. You increase your speed, then ride at a constant speed along a bike path. You then slow down until you reach your friend's house.

b. You increase your speed, then go down a hill. You then quickly come to a stop at an intersection.

c. You increase your speed, then stop at a store for a couple of minutes. You then continue to ride, increasing your speed.

d. You ride at a constant speed, then go up a hill. Once on top of the hill, you increase your speed.

EXPLORATION 2

Interpreting a Graph

Work with a partner. Write a short paragraph that describes how the height changes over time in the graph shown. What situation can this graph represent?

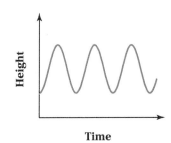

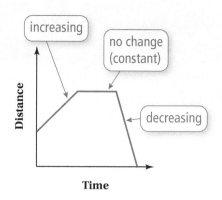

Graphs can show the relationship between quantities without using specific numbers on the axes.

EXAMPLE 1 Analyzing Graphs

The graphs show the temperatures throughout the day in two cities.

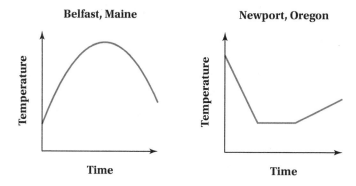

a. **Describe the change in temperature in each city.**

   Belfast: The temperature increases at the beginning of the day. The rate of increase slows until the temperature begins to decrease. Then the temperature decreases at a faster and faster rate for the rest of the day.

   Newport: The temperature decreases at a constant rate at the beginning of the day. Then the temperature stays the same for a while before increasing at a constant rate for the rest of the day.

b. **Write an explanation for the decrease in temperature and the increase in temperature in Newport, Oregon.**

   A storm moves through the city in the morning, causing the temperature to drop. When the storm ends, the temperature increases at a constant rate.

Math Practice

Make Sense of Quantities

Are there other possible explanations for the changes in temperature in Example 1(b)? Explain.

Try It

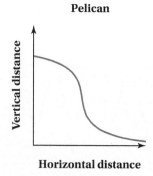

Pelican

1. The graph shows the location of a pelican relative to your location.

   a. Describe the path of the pelican.

   b. Write an explanation for the decrease in the vertical distance of the pelican.

Laurie's Notes

Scaffolding Instruction

- Students explored graphs showing the relationship between quantities without using specific numbers. Now students will use their knowledge of slope to analyze and sketch graphs without using specific numbers.
- **Emerging:** Students struggle to interpret graphs without specific numbers. They will benefit from guided instruction for the examples.
- **Proficient:** Students have an intuitive understanding of relationships between quantities in graphs. They should work through Example 2 and then proceed to the Self-Assessment exercises.

Discuss

- Draw the time-distance graph and discuss the three sections.
- ? "What does the increasing slope mean?" The distance is increasing.
- ? "What does the constant slope mean?" The distance is not changing.
- ? "What does the decreasing slope mean?" The distance is decreasing.

EXAMPLE 1

- Draw the time-temperature graphs for the two cities.
- Both cities are at 44°N latitude, but are on opposite sides of the country.
- ? **MP6 Attend to Precision:** "How does the temperature change during the day in Belfast, Maine?" The temperature increases, but at a slowing rate, until it starts to decrease. It decreases more and more rapidly.
- ? **MP6 Attend to Precision:** "How does the temperature change during the day in Newport, Oregon?" The temperature decreases at a constant rate, then it stays constant for a time, and then it increases at a constant rate.
- Ask students to discuss the graphs with a neighbor, making at least three comparisons. After a few minutes, students should be ready to share their thinking about the graphs.
- If students do not mention linear versus nonlinear features, bring it up.

Try It

- First, give students time alone to write their thoughts. Then have them share their thinking with their neighbors before discussing as a whole class.

ELL Support

After demonstrating Example 1, have students work in groups to discuss and complete Try It Exercise 1. Discuss the meaning of the word *pelican*, if students are not familiar with it. Make sure students understand what is shown on the graph before they begin. Expect students to perform according to their language levels.

Beginner: Use simple phrases or one-word answers.

Intermediate: Use simple sentences to contribute to discussion.

Advanced: Use complex sentences and help guide discussion.

Extra Example 1

The graphs show the temperatures throughout the day in two cities.

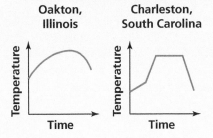

Oakton, Illinois   Charleston, South Carolina

a. Describe the change in temperature in each city.

Oakton: The temperature increases at the beginning of the day. The rate of increase slows until the temperature begins to decrease. Then the temperature decreases at a faster and faster rate for the rest of the day.

Charleston: The temperature increases at a constant rate, then increases at a faster, constant rate. It stays the same for a while before decreasing at a constant rate for the rest of the day.

b. Write an explanation for the increase in temperature and the decrease in temperature in Charleston, South Carolina.

The temperature increases in the morning as the sun comes up. As the sun goes down, the temperature decreases at a constant rate.

Try It

1. **a.** The pelican descends slowly at first, and then more and more quickly before slowing down again and gradually approaching ground level.

   b. *Sample answer:* While flying, the pelican dives to land on a pier.

Extra Example 2

Extra Example 2

A soapbox derby car picks up speed at a constant rate as it travels downhill. It continues to pick up speed until the racer applies the brakes after crossing the finish line. Once the brakes are applied, the car decreases speed at a constant rate until it stops completely. Sketch a graph that represents this situation.

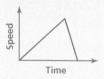

Try It

2.

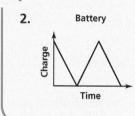

Battery

ELL Support

Have students work in pairs to complete the Self-Assessment for Concepts & Skills exercises. Then have two pairs form a group to discuss their answers. Monitor discussions and provide support as needed. Have each group present their description, explanation, and graph.

Self-Assessment
for Concepts & Skills

3. **a.** The growth rate remains constant, then decreases at a constant rate, and then increases at a constant rate.

   b. *Sample answer:* There is a period of time with a lack of rain. Then there is a period of time with a lot of rain.

4. See Additional Answers.

Laurie's Notes

EXAMPLE 2

- Write the problem statement, or display it on the overhead projector or document camera.
- Explain that in this problem a situation is described in words and students are asked to sketch a graph that represents the situation.

? "What does the first sentence tell you about the graph?" The train starts from a stop, so the graph begins at the origin. The train gains speed at a constant rate, which can be graphed as a line segment with a positive slope.

? "What does the second sentence tell you about the graph?" The train travels at its maximum speed for a while, which can be graphed as a horizontal segment. Then it slows down at a constant rate until it comes to a stop. This can be graphed as a line segment with a negative slope and an endpoint on the x-axis.

? "How would the graph change if the train sped up more and more rapidly until reaching its maximum speed? The first part of the graph would be nonlinear and would become steeper and steeper.

Try It

- **Think-Pair-Share:** Students should read the exercise independently and then work in pairs to complete the exercise. Then have each pair compare their answers with another pair and discuss any discrepancies.

Formative Assessment Tip

Every Graph Tells a Story

This open-ended technique reveals how students make sense of a graph. Give students a graph of a data set with labeled axes and a missing title. Then ask students to provide a story (or scenario) that makes sense for the data. As they create their situations, students should also consider statements and conclusions that can be made using the graph.

✓ **Self-Assessment** *for Concepts & Skills*

- **Neighbor Check:** Have students work independently and then have their neighbors check their work. Have students discuss any discrepancies.
- ◉ **Every Graph Tells a Story:** Display the graph. Ask students to describe a situation that could be represented by the graph.

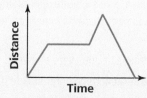

The Success Criteria Self-Assessment chart can be found in the *Student Journal* or online at *BigIdeasMath.com*.

You can sketch graphs showing relationships between quantities that are described verbally.

EXAMPLE 2 **Sketching Graphs**

A stopped subway train gains speed at a constant rate until it reaches its maximum speed. It travels at this speed for a while, and then slows down at a constant rate until coming to a stop at the next station. Sketch a graph that represents this situation.

Draw the axes. Label the vertical axis "Speed" and the horizontal axis "Time." Then sketch the graph.

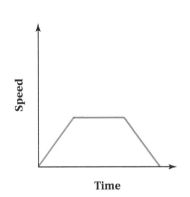

Words	**Graph**
A stopped subway train gains speed at a constant rate . . .	increasing line segment starting at the origin
until it reaches its maximum speed. It travels at this speed for a while, . . .	horizontal line segment
and then slows down at a constant rate until coming to a stop at the next station.	decreasing line segment ending at the horizontal axis

Try It

2. A fully-charged battery loses its charge at a constant rate until it has no charge left. You plug it in, and it fully recharges at a constant rate. Then it loses its charge at a constant rate until it has no charge left. Sketch a graph that represents this situation.

Self-Assessment for Concepts & Skills

Solve each exercise. Then rate your understanding of the success criteria in your journal.

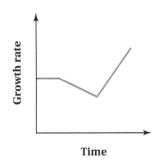

3. **ANALYZING GRAPHS** The graph shows the growth rate of a plant over time.

   a. Describe the change in growth rate.

   b. Write an explanation for the decrease in growth rate and the increase in growth rate.

4. **SKETCHING GRAPHS** As you snowboard down a hill, you gain speed at a constant rate. You come to a steep section of the hill and gain speed at a greater constant rate. You then slow down at a constant rate until you come to a stop. Sketch a graph that represents this situation.

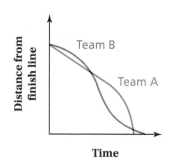

EXAMPLE 3 Modeling Real Life

The graph shows the distances traveled by two runners in a race from start to finish. Describe the speed of each runner throughout the race. Then determine who finishes first.

Runner A

The red line increases at a constant rate at the beginning of the race, stays horizontal for a short time in the middle, and then increases at a constant rate at the end of the race.

So, Runner A starts running at a constant speed, stops to rest, and then continues to run at a constant speed.

Runner B

The blue line increases at a constant rate for most of the race, and then increases at a faster and faster rate at the end of the race.

So, Runner B starts running at a constant speed and continues to run that speed for most of the race. Near the end of the race, Runner B accelerates through the finish line.

▷ The graph shows that Runner B travels the same distance as Runner A, but in a shorter amount of time. So, Runner B wins the race.

Self-Assessment for Problem Solving

Solve each exercise. Then rate your understanding of the success criteria in your journal.

5. Two rowing teams are in a race. The graph shows their distances from the finish line over time. Describe the speed of each team throughout the race. Then determine which team finishes first.

6. **DIG DEEPER!** The graphs show the movements of two airplanes over time. Describe the movement of each airplane.

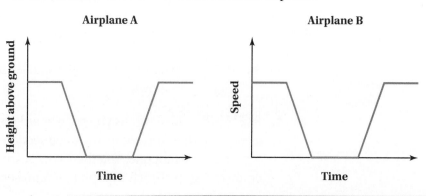

Laurie's Notes

EXAMPLE 3

- Ask a volunteer to read the problem aloud.
- Divide students into two groups. Assign one group the graph for Runner A and the other group the graph for Runner B. Have students discuss the speed of their assigned runner throughout the race. Then have students share and discuss their ideas with the class.
- ❓ "What is the connection between Runner A's speed and the slope of each line segment on the graph of Runner A?" The slope of each line segment represents the change in distance over the change in time, which is the speed of the runner. The steeper the line, the faster the runner is running.
- ❓ "Who finishes first?" Runner B "How do you know?" Because the graph of Runner B reaches the greatest distance for both graphs at a shorter amount of time than the graph of Runner A.

✅ Self-Assessment for Problem Solving

- Students may benefit from trying the exercises independently and then working with peers to refine their work. It is important to provide time in class for problem solving, so that students become comfortable with the problem-solving plan.
- Students should work independently and then discuss each problem as a class.
- ◉ **Thumbs Up:** Ask students to indicate their understanding of each success criterion.

The Success Criteria Self-Assessment chart can be found in the *Student Journal* or online at *BigIdeasMath.com*.

Closure

- Draw a graph without numbers that represents the temperature in your town or city over the last 24 hours (or for the daytime hours yesterday). Answers will vary.

Extra Example 3

The graph shows the numbers of laps traveled by two racecars in a race from start to finish. Describe the speed of each car throughout the race. Then determine which car finishes first.

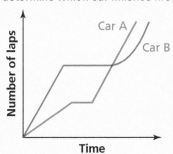

Car A starts driving at a constant speed, stops to refuel, and then continues to drive at a constant speed. Car B starts driving at a constant speed, stops to refuel, and then drives at an increasing speed for the rest of the race; Car A

Self-Assessment
for Problem Solving

5. Team A rows at a constant speed for most of the race. Near the end of the race, Team A accelerates to the finish line. Team B rows slowly at first, and then more and more quickly before slowing down again and gradually approaching the finish line; Team A

6. See Additional Answers.

Learning Target

Use graphs of functions to describe relationships between quantities.

Success Criteria

- Describe relationships between quantities in graphs.
- Sketch graphs given verbal descriptions of relationships.

Review & Refresh

1. linear; As *x* increases by 4, *y* decreases by 2.

2. nonlinear; You cannot rewrite the equation in slope-intercept form.

3.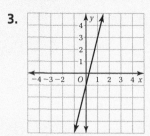

4–5. See Additional Answers.

Concepts, Skills, & Problem Solving

6. C   7. D   8. A   9. B

10. The volume of the balloon increases at a constant rate, then stays constant, then increases at a constant rate, then stays constant, and then increases at a constant rate.

11. Sales decrease at a constant rate and then increase at a constant rate.

12. Horsepower increases at an increasing rate and then increases at a decreasing rate.

13. Grams decrease at a decreasing rate.

14. The hair length increases at a constant rate, then decreases instantly, then increases at a constant rate, then decreases instantly, and then increases at a constant rate.

15. The loan balance remains constant, then decreases instantly, then remains constant, then decreases instantly, and then remains constant.

16. *Sample answer:* You blow air into a balloon, pause to take a breath, and then repeat this process.

Assignment Guide and Concept Check

Scaffold assignments to support all students in their learning progression. The suggested assignments are a starting point. Continue to assign additional exercises and revisit with spaced practice to move every student toward proficiency.

Level	Assignment 1	Assignment 2
Emerging	1, 2, 5, 6, 7, 8, 9, 11, 13, 15, 18	10, 12, 14, 16, 17, 19, 20, 21, 22
Proficient	1, 2, 5, 6, 7, 8, 9, 10, 12, 14, 16, 18, 20	17, 19, 21, 22, 23
Advanced	1, 2, 5, 6, 7, 8, 9, 10, 12, 14, 16, 18, 20	19, 21, 22, 23, 24

- Assignment 1 is for use after students complete the Self-Assessment for Concepts & Skills.
- Assignment 2 is for use after students complete the Self-Assessment for Problem Solving.
- The red exercises can be used as a concept check.

Review & Refresh Prior Skills

Exercise 1   Identifying Functions from Tables

Exercise 2   Identifying Functions from Equations

Exercises 3–5   Graphing an Equation

Common Errors

- **Exercise 14** Students may get confused because the graph has breaks in it. Remind them that because of growth, your hair length gradually increases until you get a haircut. Then the length is suddenly shorter.
- **Exercise 15** Students may get confused because the graph has breaks in it. Remind them that the horizontal lines represent the balance owed. A break occurs when a payment is made.

Go to **BigIdeasMath.com** to get HELP with solving the exercises.

▶ Review & Refresh

Does the table or equation represent a *linear* or *nonlinear* function? Explain.

1.

x	−5	−1	3	7
y	14	12	10	8

2. $y = x^2 + 8$

Graph the linear equation.

3. $-4x + y = -1$

4. $2x - 3y = 12$

5. $5x + 10y = 30$

▶▶ Concepts, Skills, & Problem Solving

MATCHING DESCRIPTIONS WITH GRAPHS The graph shows your speed during a run. **Match the verbal description with the part of the graph it describes.** (See Exploration 1, p. 301.)

6. You run at a constant speed.

7. You slow down at a constant rate.

8. You increase your speed at a constant rate.

9. You increase your speed at a faster and faster rate.

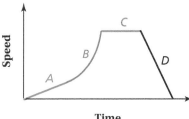

ANALYZING GRAPHS **Describe the relationship between the two quantities.**

10. Balloon

11. Sales

12. Engine Power

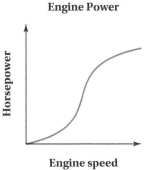

13. Decay

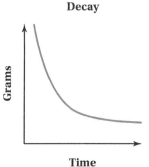

14. Hair

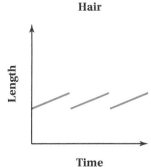

15. Loan

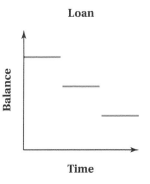

16. **ANALYZING GRAPHS** Write an explanation for the relationship shown in the graph in Exercise 10.

17. **MP MODELING REAL LIFE** The graph shows the natural gas usage for a house.

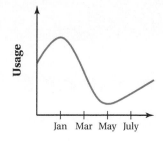

    a. Describe the change in usage from January to March.

    b. Describe the change in usage from March to May.

SKETCHING GRAPHS **Sketch a graph that represents the situation.**

18. The value of a television decreases at a constant rate, and then remains constant.

19. The distance from the ground changes as your friend swings on a swing.

20. The value of a rare coin increases at a faster and faster rate.

21. You are typing at a constant rate. You pause to think about your next paragraph, and then you resume typing at the same constant rate.

22. **CRITICAL THINKING** The graph shows the speed of an object over time.

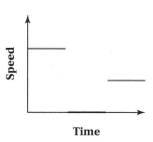

    a. Sketch a graph that shows the distance traveled by the object over time.

    b. Describe a possible situation represented by the graphs.

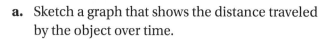

23. **MP MODELING REAL LIFE** The graph shows the average scores of two bowlers from the start of a season to the end of the season.

    a. Describe each bowler's performance.

    b. Who had a greater average score most of the season? Who had a greater average score at the end of the season?

    c. Write an explanation for the change in each bowler's average score throughout the bowling season.

24. **DIG DEEPER!** You can use a *supply and demand model* to understand how the price of a product changes in a market. The *supply curve* of a particular product represents the quantity suppliers will produce at various prices. The *demand curve* for the product represents the quantity consumers are willing to buy at various prices.

    a. Describe and interpret each curve.

    b. Which part of the graph represents a surplus? a shortage? Explain your reasoning.

    c. The curves intersect at the *equilibrium point*, which is where the quantity produced equals the quantity demanded. Suppose that demand for a product suddenly increases, causing the entire demand curve to shift to the right. What happens to the equilibrium point?

Mini-Assessment

1. Describe the change in the bacteria population over time.

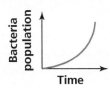

As time increases, the bacteria population increases at an increasing rate.

2. After takeoff, the altitude of an airplane increases at a constant rate, then remains constant for a time, and then decreases at a constant rate until the airplane lands. Sketch a graph that represents this situation.

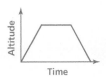

Section Resources

Surface Level	Deep Level
Resources by Chapter • Extra Practice • Reteach • Puzzle Time Student Journal • Self-Assessment • Practice Differentiating the Lesson Tutorial Videos Skills Review Handbook Skills Trainer	Resources by Chapter • Enrichment and Extension Graphic Organizers Dynamic Assessment System • Section Practice

Transfer Level	
Dynamic Assessment System • End-of-Chapter Quiz	Assessment Book • End-of-Chapter Quiz

Concepts, Skills, & Problem Solving

17. a. The usage decreases at an increasing rate.

  b. The usage decreases at a decreasing rate.

18.

Television

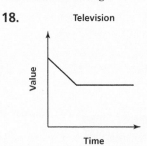

19.

Swinging

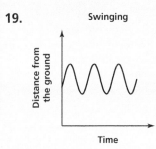

20.

Coin

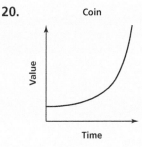

21–22. See Additional Answers.

23. a. Bowler A's average score increased at an increasing rate. Bowler B's average score increased at a decreasing rate.

  b. Bowler B; Bowler A

  c. *Sample answer:* Bowler A starts to practice more often. Bowler B starts to practice less often.

24. See Additional Answers.

Exercise 1

- Finding a Line of Best Fit
- Identifying Functions
- Interpreting a Linear Function
- Writing Linear Functions

Exercise 2

- Choosing a Solution Method for a System of Linear Equations
- Listing Ordered Pairs
- Using a Graph

ELL Support

Review standard measurements used in the United States, such as inches and pounds. Point out that they are different from measurements in the metric system, which include centimeters and kilograms.

Using the Problem-Solving Plan

1. not a function; *Sample answer:* 8.2 lb

2. $(-1, -4)$;
   Function 1: $y = -4x - 8$
   Function 2: $y = 3x - 1$
   Solution of the system: $(-1, -4)$

Performance Task

The *STEAM Video Performance Task* provides the opportunity for additional enrichment and greater depth of knowledge as students explore the mathematics of the chapter within a context tied to the chapter STEAM Video. The performance task and a detailed scoring rubric are provided at *BigIdeasMath.com*.

Laurie's Notes

Scaffolding Instruction

- The goal of this lesson is to help students become more comfortable with problem solving. These exercises combine work with functions with prior skills from other chapters. The solution for Exercise 1 is worked out below, to help you guide students through the problem-solving plan. Use the remaining class time to have students work on the other exercise.
- **Emerging:** The goal for these students is to feel comfortable with the problem-solving plan. Allow students to work in pairs to write the beginning steps of the problem-solving plan for Exercise 2. Keep in mind that some students may only be ready to do the first step.
- **Proficient:** Students may be able to work independently or in pairs to complete Exercise 2.
- Visit each pair to review their plan. Ask students to describe their plans.

▶ Using the Problem-Solving Plan

Exercise 1

⇨ **Understand the problem.** You know the lengths and weights of several infants. You are asked to determine whether weight is a function of length and to estimate the weight of a 20-inch-long infant.

⇨ **Make a plan.** Determine whether any of the lengths are paired with more than one weight. Then use a graphing calculator to find an equation that represents the data. Evaluate the equation when $x = 20$ to estimate the weight of a 20-inch-long infant.

⇨ **Solve and check.** Use the plan to solve the problem. Then check your solution.

- Determine whether weight is a function of length.
  The input 19.2 has two outputs, 6.9 and 7.0, so weight is not a function of length.

- Use a graphing calculator to find an equation that represents the data.

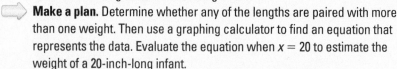

Use the *linear regression* feature.

An equation of the line of best fit is $y = 1.48x - 21.4$.

- Evaluate $y = 1.48x - 21.4$ when $x = 20$.

$y = 1.48x - 21.4$	Write the equation.
$y = 1.48(20) - 21.4$	Substitute 20 for x.
$y = 8.2$	Simplify.

  So, an infant that is 20 inches long weighs about 8.2 pounds.

- **Check:** Find an equation that represents the data, including $(20, 8.2)$.

  ```
  LinReg
   y=ax+b
   a=1.5
   b=-21.8125
   r²=.9530112508
   r=.9762229514
  ```

  $y = 1.5x - 21.8$ graphs a line close to $y = 1.48x - 21.4$. ✓

7 Connecting Concepts

▶ Using the Problem-Solving Plan

1. The table shows the lengths x (in inches) and weights y (in pounds) of several infants born at a hospital. Determine whether weight is a function of length. Then estimate the weight of an infant that is 20 inches long.

Length, x	Weight, y
19.2	6.9
19.3	7.3
18.9	6.5
19.4	7.2
19.7	7.6
19.2	7.0
19.5	7.6

Understand the problem. You know the lengths and weights of several infants. You are asked to determine whether weight is a function of length and to estimate the weight of a 20-inch-long infant.

Make a plan. Determine whether any of the lengths are paired with more than one weight. Then use a graphing calculator to find an equation that represents the data. Evaluate the equation when $x = 20$ to estimate the weight of a 20-inch-long infant.

Solve and check. Use the plan to solve the problem. Then check your solution.

2. Each mapping diagram represents a linear function. At what point do the graphs of the functions intersect? Justify your answer.

Function 1

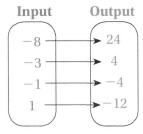

Function 2

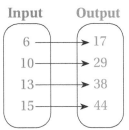

Performance Task

Heat Index

At the beginning of this chapter, you watched a STEAM Video called "Apparent Temperature." You are now ready to complete the performance task related to this video, available at *BigIdeasMath.com*. Be sure to use the problem-solving plan as you work through the performance task.

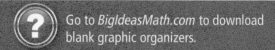

Go to *BigIdeasMath.com* to download blank graphic organizers.

▷ Review Vocabulary

Write the definition and give an example of each vocabulary term.

input, *p. 276*   mapping diagram, *p. 276*   linear function, *p. 290*
output, *p. 276*   function, *p. 277*   nonlinear function, *p. 296*
relation, *p. 276*   function rule, *p. 282*

▷ Graphic Organizers

You can use an **Example and Non-Example Chart** to list examples and non-examples of a concept. Here is an Example and Non-Example Chart for *functions*.

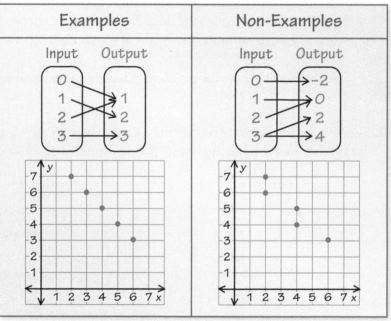

Functions

Choose and complete a graphic organizer to help you study the concept.

1. linear functions

2. nonlinear functions

3. linear functions with positive slope

4. linear functions with negative slope

"I finished my Example and Non-Example Chart about animals living in the Grand Canyon."

Review Vocabulary

- As a review of the chapter vocabulary, have students revisit the vocabulary section in their *Student Journals* to fill in any missing definitions and record examples of each term.

Graphic Organizers

Sample answers:

1. Linear Functions

Examples	Non-Examples
$y = 3x + 2$	$y = x^2 - 2$

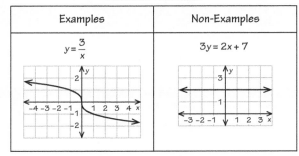

2. Nonlinear Functions

Examples	Non-Examples
$y = \dfrac{3}{x}$	$3y = 2x + 7$

3. Linear Functions with Positive Slope

Examples	Non-Examples
$y = x - 1$	$y = -x + 1$
$y = 3x$	$y = -\dfrac{1}{2}x - 3$
$x - 3y = 0$	$3x + 2y = 10$

4. Answer at *BigIdeasMath.com*.

List of Organizers

Available at *BigIdeasMath.com*
Definition and Example Chart
Example and Non-Example Chart
Four Square
Information Frame
Summary Triangle

About this Organizer

An **Example and Non-Example Chart** can be used to list examples and non-examples of a concept. Students write examples of the concept in the left column and non-examples in the right column. This organizer can be used to assess students' understanding of two concepts that have subtle, but important differences. Blank Example and Non-Example Charts can be included on tests or quizzes for this purpose.

1. $(1, -4), (3, 6), (5, 0), (7, 6),$ $(7, 8)$; not a function

2. $(0, 0), (1, 10), (2, 5), (3, 15)$; function

3. $(-1, 0), (-1, 1), (0, 1), (1, 2),$ $(3, 3)$; not a function

4. x-coordinate; y-coordinate

5. **Input**   **Output**

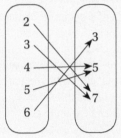

function; Each input has exactly one output.

6. **a.** yes

   b. The length of the rubber band increases by 2 centimeters for each 0.7-Newton increase in the force applied to the rubber band.

✓ *Chapter Self-Assessment*

The Success Criteria Self-Assessment chart can be found in the *Student Journal* or online at *BigIdeasMath.com*.

ELL Support

Allow students to work in pairs to complete the first section of the Chapter Self-Assessment. For answers to Exercises 1–3 and other *yes* or *no* questions, have students use a thumbs up for *yes* or a thumbs down for *no*. For Exercises 4 and 5, have each pair display their answers on a whiteboard for your review. Review students' explanations as a class. Have pairs discuss and answer Exercise 6. Then have each pair compare their ideas with another pair and come to an agreement on their answers. Monitor discussions and provide support. Use similar techniques to check the remaining sections of the Chapter Self-Assessment.

Common Errors

- **Exercises 1–3** Students may mix up the ordered pairs and write the output first and then the input. Encourage students to use the arrow as a guide. The arrow points from the first number in the ordered pair (the input) to the second number in the ordered pair (the output).
- **Exercise 6** Students may describe the pattern of the outputs only. Remind them that the inputs are changing as well, and it is important to describe the change in inputs that results in the specified change in outputs.

Chapter Self-Assessment

As you complete the exercises, use the scale below to rate your understanding of the success criteria in your journal.

1	**2**	**3**	**4**
I do not understand.	I can do it with help.	I can do it on my own.	I can teach someone else.

7.1 Relations and Functions (pp. 275–280)

Learning Target: Understand the concept of a function.

List the ordered pairs shown in the mapping diagram. Then determine whether the relation is a function.

1.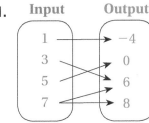

2.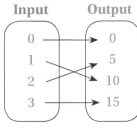

3.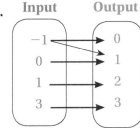

4. For ordered pairs that represent relations, which coordinate represents the input? the output?

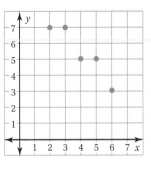

5. Draw a mapping diagram that represents the relation shown in the graph. Then determine whether the relation is a function. Explain.

6. The mapping diagram represents the lengths (in centimeters) of a rubber band when different amounts of force (in Newtons) are applied.

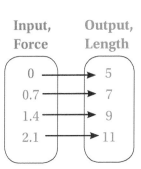

   a. Is the length of a rubber band a function of the force applied to the rubber band?

   b. Describe the relationship between the length of a rubber band and the force applied to the rubber band.

7.2 Representations of Functions *(pp. 281–288)*

Learning Target: Represent functions in a variety of ways.

Write a function rule for the statement.

7. The output is two less than the input.

8. The output is two more than one-fourth of the input.

Find the value of *y* for the given value of *x*.

9. $y = 2x - 3$; $x = -4$ **10.** $y = 2 - 9x$; $x = \dfrac{2}{3}$ **11.** $y = \dfrac{x}{3} + 5$; $x = 6$

Graph the function.

12. $y = x + 3$ **13.** $y = -5x$ **14.** $y = 3 - 3x$

15. An online music store sells songs for $0.90 each.

    a. Write a function that you can use to find the cost *C* of buying *s* songs.

    b. What is the cost of buying 5 songs?

7.3 Linear Functions *(pp. 289–294)*

Learning Target: Use functions to model linear relationships.

Use the graph or table to write a linear function that relates *y* to *x*.

16.

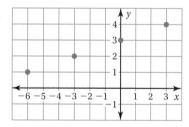

17.

x	−2	0	2	4
y	−7	−7	−7	−7

18. The table shows the age *x* (in weeks) of a puppy and its weight *y* (in pounds).

Age, x	6	8	10	12
Weight, y	12	15	18	21

    a. Write and graph a linear function that relates *y* to *x*.

    b. Interpret the slope and the *y*-intercept.

    c. After how many weeks will the puppy weigh 33 pounds?

Common Errors

- **Exercises 7 and 8** Students may mix up the x and y variables when writing the equation. Remind them that x represents the input and y represents the output. Students may also need to be reminded how to write expressions from word phrases.
- **Exercises 12–14** Students may mix up their axes or label one or both axes inconsistently. Remind them that the input (x) values are horizontal and the output (y) values are vertical. Encourage students to label each axis in specific increments that easily show the points plotted and will give a line through the points.
- **Exercise 16** Students may try to write the linear function without first finding the slope and y-intercept, or they may use the reciprocal of the slope in the function. Encourage them to check their work by making sure that all of the given points are solutions.
- **Exercise 17** Students may not remember how to write an equation for a horizontal line. They may write $x = -7$ instead of $y = -7$. Encourage students to think about the slope-intercept form of a linear equation.

7. $y = x - 2$

8. $y = \dfrac{1}{4}x + 2$

9. -11

10. -4

11. 7

12.

13.

14.

15. **a.** $C = 0.9s$

   b. \$4.50

16. $y = \dfrac{1}{3}x + 3$

17. $y = -7$

18. **a.** $y = 1.5x + 3$

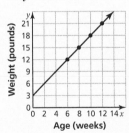

   b. The slope indicates that the weight of the puppy increases 1.5 pounds per week. The y-intercept indicates that the puppy weighs 3 pounds at birth.

   c. 20 weeks

19. linear; As x increases by 3, y increases by 9.

20. nonlinear; As x increases by 2, y changes by different amounts.

21. nonlinear; The graph is not a line.

22. linear; The equation is in slope-intercept form.

23. The population increases at a constant rate, then remains the same, and then decreases at a constant rate.

24.

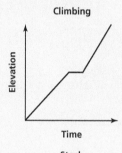

25.

26. **a.** The sales of Company A increase at a constant rate, then decrease at a constant rate, and then increase at a constant rate. The sales of Company B increase then decrease, then increase and decrease again, but none of the rates of increase or decrease are constant.

   b. Company A

   c. *Sample answer:* Company A offers a promotion, and then the promotion ends. A little while later, Company A offers another promotion. Company B offers seasonal promotions.

Common Errors

- **Exercises 19 and 20** Students may say that the function is linear because the x-values are increasing or decreasing by the same amount each time. Encourage students to examine the y-values to see if the graph represents a line.

Chapter Resources

Surface Level	Deep Level
Resources by Chapter • Extra Practice • Reteach • Puzzle Time Student Journal • Practice • Chapter Self-Assessment Differentiating the Lesson Tutorial Videos Skills Review Handbook Skills Trainer Game Library	Resources by Chapter • Enrichment and Extension Graphic Organizers Game Library
Transfer Level	
STEAM Video Dynamic Assessment System • Chapter Test	Assessment Book • Chapter Tests A and B • Alternative Assessment • STEAM Performance Task

7.4 Comparing Linear and Nonlinear Functions (pp. 295–300)

Learning Target: Understand differences between linear and nonlinear functions.

Does the table represent a *linear* or *nonlinear* function? Explain.

19.

x	3	6	9	12
y	1	10	19	28

20.

x	1	3	5	7
y	3	1	1	3

21. Does the graph represent a *linear* or *nonlinear* function? Explain.

22. Does the equation $y = 2.3x$ represent a *linear* or *nonlinear* function? Explain.

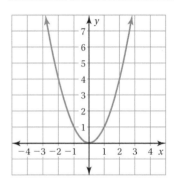

7.5 Analyzing and Sketching Graphs (pp. 301–306)

Learning Target: Use graphs of functions to describe relationships between quantities.

23. Describe the relationship between the two quantities in the graph.

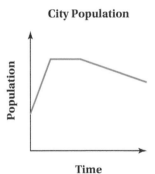

City Population

Sketch a graph that represents the situation.

24. You climb a climbing wall. You climb halfway up the wall at a constant rate, then stop and take a break. You then climb to the top of the wall at a greater constant rate.

25. The price of a stock increases at a constant rate for several months before the stock market crashes. The price then quickly decreases at a constant rate.

26. The graph shows the sales of two companies during a particular year.

   a. Describe the sales of each company.

   b. Which company has greater total sales for the year?

   c. Give a possible explanation for the change in each company's sales throughout the year.

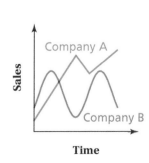

1. List the ordered pairs shown in the mapping diagram. Then determine whether the relation is a function.

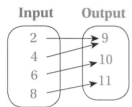

2. Draw a mapping diagram that represents the relation. Then determine whether the relation is a function. Explain.

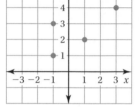

3. Write a function rule for "The output is twice the input."

4. Graph the function $y = 1 - 3x$.

5. Use the graph to write a linear function that relates y to x.

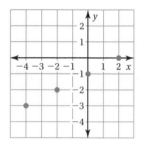

6. Does the table represent a *linear* or *nonlinear* function? Explain.

x	0	2	4	6
y	8	0	−8	−16

7. The table shows the number of meters y a water-skier travels in x minutes.

Minutes, x	1	2	3	4	5
Meters, y	600	1200	1800	2400	3000

   a. Write a function that relates y to x.

   b. Graph the linear function.

   c. At this rate, how many kilometers will the water-skier travel in 12 minutes?

   d. Another water-skier travels at the same rate but starts a minute after the first water-skier. Will this water-skier catch up to the first water-skier? Explain.

8. The graph shows the prices of two stocks during one day.

   a. Describe the changes in the price of each stock.

   b. Which stock has a greater price at the end of the day?

   c. Give a possible explanation for the change in the price of Stock B throughout the day.

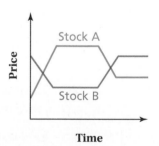

9. You are competing in a footrace. You begin the race by increasing your speed at a constant rate. You then run at a constant speed until you get a cramp and have to stop. You wait until your cramp goes away before you start increasing your speed again at a constant rate. Sketch a graph that represents the situation.

Practice Test Item References

Practice Test Questions	Section to Review
1, 2	7.1
3, 4	7.2
5, 7	7.3
6	7.4
8, 9	7.5

Test-Taking Strategies

Remind students to quickly look over the entire test before they start so that they can budget their time. Have them use the **Stop** and **Think** strategy before they write their answers.

Common Errors

- **Exercise 1** Students may mix up the ordered pairs and write the output first and then the input. Encourage students to use the arrow as a guide. The arrow points from the first number in the ordered pair (the input) to the second number in the ordered pair (the output).
- **Exercise 3** Students may mix up the x and y variables when writing the equation. Remind them that x represents the input and y represents the output. Students may also need to be reminded how to write expressions from word phrases.
- **Exercise 4** Students may mix up their axes or label one or both axes inconsistently. Remind them that the input (x) values are horizontal and the output (y) values are vertical. Encourage students to label each axis in specific increments that easily show the points plotted and will give a line through the points.
- **Exercise 5** Students may try to write the linear function without first finding the slope and y-intercept, or they may use the reciprocal of the slope in the function. Encourage them to check their work by making sure that all of the given points are solutions.
- **Exercise 6** Students may try to graph the ordered pairs to determine if the function is linear and make an incorrect assumption depending upon how they scale their axes. Encourage students to examine the change in y for each change in x.

1. $(2, 9), (4, 9), (6, 10), (8, 11)$; function

2. Input   Output

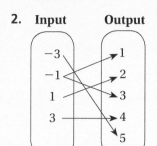

not a function; The input -1 has two outputs, 1 and 3.

3. $y = 2x$

4.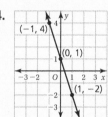

5. $y = \frac{1}{2}x - 1$

6. linear; As x increases by 2, y decreases by 8.

7. **a.** $y = 600x$

   b.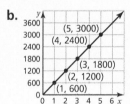

   c. 7.2 km

   d. no; Because both water-skiers travel at the same rate, the second water-skier will always be 600 meters behind the first water-skier.

8. See Additional Answers.

9.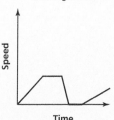

Running a Race

T-312

Test-Taking Strategies

Available at *BigIdeasMath.com*

After Answering Easy Questions, Relax

Answer Easy Questions First

Estimate the Answer

Read All Choices before Answering

Read Question before Answering

Solve Directly or Eliminate Choices

Solve Problem before Looking at Choices

Use Intelligent Guessing

Work Backwards

About this Strategy

One way to answer the question is to work backwards. Try placing the responses into the question, one at a time, to see if you can find the correct solution.

Cumulative Practice

1. B

2. I

3. 7

4. A

Item Analysis

1. **A.** The student incorrectly thinks $-4 - 1 = -3$.

   B. Correct answer

   C. The student incorrectly thinks $5 - (-3) = 2$ and $-4 - 1 = -3$.

   D. The student incorrectly thinks $5 - (-3) = 2$.

2. **F.** The student subtracts 9 from the left side instead of adding. The student then divides the left side by 3 instead of multiplying.

   G. The student divides the left side by 3 instead of multiplying.

   H. The student subtracts 9 from the left side instead of adding.

   I. Correct answer

3. Gridded Response: Correct answer: 7

   Common error: The student does not divide the differences between the outputs by 3 and gets an answer of 21.

4. **A.** Correct answer

   B. The student switches the x- and y-coordinates of the solution.

   C. The student finds a solution for $3x + 2y = 5$ but not $x = y + 5$.

   D. The student finds a solution for $x = y + 5$ but not $3x + 2y = 5$.

1. What is the slope of the line?

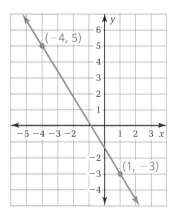

A. $-\dfrac{8}{3}$

B. $-\dfrac{8}{5}$

C. $-\dfrac{2}{3}$

D. $-\dfrac{2}{5}$

2. Which value of a makes the equation $24 = \dfrac{a}{3} - 9$ true?

F. 5

G. 11

H. 45

I. 99

3. A mapping diagram is shown.

What number belongs in the box so that the equation describes the function represented by the mapping diagram?

$$y = \boxed{}\, x + 5$$

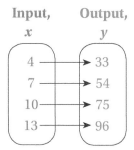

Input, x	Output, y
4	33
7	54
10	75
13	96

4. What is the solution of the system of linear equations?

$$3x + 2y = 5$$
$$x = y + 5$$

A. $(3, -2)$

B. $(-2, 3)$

C. $(-1, 4)$

D. $(1, -4)$

5. The director of a research lab wants to present data to donors. The data show how the lab uses a large amount of donated money for research and only a small amount of money for other expenses. Which type of display best represents these data?

    F. box-and-whisker plot   **G.** circle graph

    H. line graph   **I.** scatter plot

6. Which graph shows a nonlinear function?

A. 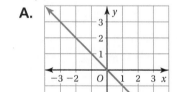   **B.**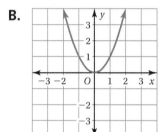

C. 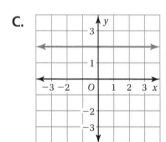   **D.**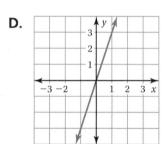

7. Which equation of a line passes through the point $(-2, 3)$ and has a slope of $\frac{3}{4}$?

    F. $y - 3 = \frac{3}{4}(x + 2)$

    G. $y + 3 = \frac{3}{4}(x - 2)$

    H. $y + 2 = \frac{3}{4}(x - 3)$

    I. $y = \frac{3}{4}(x + 2)$

Item Analysis (continued)

5. **F.** The student does not realize that a box-and-whisker plot is inappropriate because it does not allow a reader to compare parts of a whole.

   G. Correct answer

   H. The student does not realize that a line graph is inappropriate because it does not allow a reader to compare parts of a whole.

   I. The student does not realize that a scatter plot is inappropriate because it does not allow a reader to compare parts of a whole.

6. **A.** The student incorrectly thinks that a line with a negative slope is nonlinear.

   B. Correct answer

   C. The student incorrectly thinks that a horizontal line is nonlinear.

   D. The student incorrectly thinks that a steep line with a positive slope is nonlinear.

7. **F.** Correct answer

   G. The student incorrectly thinks that point-slope form of a linear equation is $y + y_1 = m(x + x_1)$ instead of $y - y_1 = m(x - x_1)$.

   H. The student switches the x_1- and y_1-coordinates in the equation.

   I. The student forgets to include the y_1-coordinate in the equation.

5. G

6. B

7. F

8. *Part A* yes; The sales change by the same amount each year.

   Part B no; The sales do not change by the same amount each year.

9. C

10. 4

Item Analysis (continued)

8. **2 points** The student's work and explanations demonstrate a thorough understanding of how to determine whether data show a linear function or a nonlinear function. The first table shows a linear function. The second table shows a nonlinear function. The student provides clear and complete work and explanations.

   1 point The student's work and explanations demonstrate a partial but limited understanding of how to determine whether data show a linear function or a nonlinear function. The student provides some correct work and/or explanation.

   0 points The student provides no response, a completely incorrect or incomprehensible response, or a response that demonstrates insufficient understanding of how to determine whether data show a linear function or a nonlinear function.

9. **A.** The student incorrectly associates 0 with a solution.

   B. The student selects this choice because $y = -x + 4$ equals 0 when $x = 4$.

   C. Correct answer

   D. The student has no idea how to interpret the table or does not see that the functions are equal at $x = 8$.

10. **Gridded Response:** Correct answer: 4

    Common error: The student gives the x-coordinate of the image of B instead of the y-coordinate and gets an answer of 2.

8. The tables show the sales (in millions of dollars) for two companies over a five-year period.

Year	1	2	3	4	5
Sales	2	4	6	8	10

Year	1	2	3	4	5
Sales	1	1	2	3	5

Part A Does the first table show a linear function? Explain your reasoning.

Part B Does the second table show a linear function? Explain your reasoning.

9. The equations $y = -x + 4$ and $y = \frac{1}{2}x - 8$ form a system of linear equations.

The table shows the values of y for given values of x.

x	0	2	4	6	8	10
$y = -x + 4$	4	2	0	-2	-4	-6
$y = \frac{1}{2}x - 8$	-8	-7	-6	-5	-4	-3

What can you conclude from the table?

A. The system has one solution, when $x = 0$.

B. The system has one solution, when $x = 4$.

C. The system has one solution, when $x = 8$.

D. The system has no solution.

10. The vertices of a triangle are $A(-1, 3)$, $B(1, 2)$, and $C(-1, -1)$. Dilate the triangle using a scale factor of 2. What is the y-coordinate of the image of B?

8 Exponents and Scientific Notation

Chapter Learning Target:
Understand exponents and scientific notation.

Chapter Success Criteria:
- I can write products using exponents.
- I can describe the value of powers.
- I can evaluate expressions.
- I can compare quantities using scientific notation.

STEAM Video: "Carbon Atoms"

Laurie's Notes

Chapter 8 Overview

In this chapter, students will build upon their knowledge of powers and exponents from prior courses. The first lesson reviews their previous work with powers but now negative bases are also included. Students need to pay careful attention to how they write and evaluate powers with negative bases. For instance, $(-3)^2 = (-3)(-3) = 9$ but $-3^2 = -(3)(3) = -9$.

In the next three lessons, students will extend their understanding of the pattern in the number of zeros when powers of 10 are multiplied, and apply these rules to other bases. They will learn to use properties of exponents to simplify expressions. Students will also discover the meanings of zero and negative exponents.

Be aware that students often confuse the Product of Powers Property and the Power of a Power Property with one another.

Product of Powers Property: $5^2 \cdot 5^3 = 5^{2+3} = 5^5$

Power of a Power Property: $(5^2)^3 = 5^{2 \cdot 3} = 5^6$

Another common error is changing the base when using the Product of Powers Property or the Quotient of Powers Property. For example, students may say $4^2 \cdot 4^3 = 16^5$ instead of 4^5 or $\dfrac{3^7}{3^5} = 1^2$ instead of 3^2. You can clarify these misconceptions by expanding the powers.

$$4^2 \cdot 4^3 = 4 \cdot 4 \cdot 4 \cdot 4 \cdot 4 = 4^5$$

$$\frac{3^7}{3^5} = \frac{3 \cdot 3 \cdot 3 \cdot 3 \cdot 3 \cdot 3 \cdot 3}{3 \cdot 3 \cdot 3 \cdot 3 \cdot 3} = \frac{\overset{1}{\cancel{3}} \cdot \overset{1}{\cancel{3}} \cdot \overset{1}{\cancel{3}} \cdot \overset{1}{\cancel{3}} \cdot \overset{1}{\cancel{3}} \cdot 3 \cdot 3}{\underset{1}{\cancel{3}} \cdot \underset{1}{\cancel{3}} \cdot \underset{1}{\cancel{3}} \cdot \underset{1}{\cancel{3}} \cdot \underset{1}{\cancel{3}}} = 3 \cdot 3 = 3^2$$

Students may think that a power with a zero exponent is equal to zero. This misconception can be clarified using powers of 10. Students should know that $10^m \cdot 10^n = 10^{m+n}$ for whole numbers m and n. Build upon that understanding to show that because $10^m \cdot 10^0 = 10^{m+0} = 10^m$, then 10^0 must equal 1.

The fifth lesson prepares students for working with numbers written in scientific notation. Experiences of using properties of exponents to work with estimates of very large and very small numbers help students make sense of operations with numbers in scientific notation.

The chapter concludes with two lessons on scientific notation. Students will first learn to convert between scientific notation and standard form. Then they will use properties of exponents to perform operations with numbers written in scientific notation.

Suggested Pacing

Chapter Opener	1 Day
Section 1	2 Days
Section 2	2 Days
Section 3	2 Days
Section 4	2 Days
Section 5	2 Days
Section 6	2 Days
Section 7	2 Days
Connecting Concepts	1 Day
Chapter Review	1 Day
Chapter Test	1 Day
Total Chapter 8	18 Days
Year-to-Date	118 Days

Chapter Learning Target
Understand exponents and scientific notation.

Chapter Success Criteria
- Write products using exponents.
- Describe the value of powers.
- Evaluate expressions.
- Compare quantities using scientific notation.

Chapter 8 Learning Targets and Success Criteria

Section	Learning Target	Success Criteria
8.1 Exponents	Use exponents to write and evaluate expressions.	• Write products using exponents. • Evaluate expressions involving powers. • Use exponents to solve real-life problems.
8.2 Product of Powers Property	Generate equivalent expressions involving products of powers.	• Find products of powers that have the same base. • Find powers of powers. • Find powers of products.
8.3 Quotient of Powers Property	Generate equivalent expressions involving quotients of powers.	• Find quotients of powers that have the same base. • Simplify expressions using the Quotient of Powers Property. • Solve real-life problems involving quotients of powers.
8.4 Zero and Negative Exponents	Understand the concepts of zero and negative exponents.	• Explain the meanings of zero and negative exponents. • Evaluate numerical expressions involving zero and negative exponents. • Simplify algebraic expressions involving zero and negative exponents.
8.5 Estimating Quantities	Round numbers and write the results as the product of a single digit and a power of 10.	• Round very large and very small numbers. • Write a multiple of 10 as a power. • Compare very large or very small quantities.
8.6 Scientific Notation	Understand the concept of scientific notation.	• Convert between scientific notation and standard form. • Choose appropriate units to represent quantities. • Use scientific notation to solve real-life problems.
8.7 Operations in Scientific Notation	Perform operations with numbers written in scientific notation.	• Explain how to add and subtract numbers in scientific notation. • Explain how to multiply and divide numbers in scientific notation. • Use operations in scientific notation to solve real-life problems.

Progressions

Through the Grades		
Grade 7	**Grade 8**	**High School**
• Solve problems involving the four operations with rational numbers. • Understand that rewriting expressions in different forms can show how the quantities are related.	• Use the properties of integer exponents to generate equivalent expressions. • Use numbers expressed as the product of a single digit and a power of 10 to estimate very large or very small quantities. • Perform operations with numbers expressed in scientific notation and other forms. Interpret scientific notation that has been generated by technology.	• Evaluate and simplify expressions with exponents, including rational exponents. Find *nth* roots. • Use properties of exponents to interpret and transform expressions for exponential functions. • Identify, evaluate, and graph exponential functions.

Through the Chapter							
Standard	**8.1**	**8.2**	**8.3**	**8.4**	**8.5**	**8.6**	**8.7**
8.EE.A.1 Know and apply the properties of integer exponents to generate equivalent numerical expressions.	▲	●	●	★			
8.EE.A.3 Use numbers expressed in the form of a single digit times an integer power of 10 to estimate very large or very small quantities, and to express how many times as much one is than the other.					●	★	
8.EE.A.4 Perform operations with numbers expressed in scientific notation, including problems where both decimal and scientific notation are used. Use scientific notation and choose units of appropriate size for measurements of very large or very small quantities (e.g., use millimeters per year for seafloor spreading). Interpret scientific notation that has been generated by technology.						●	★

Key

▲ = preparing   ★ = complete

● = learning   ■ = extending

Laurie's Notes

STEAM Video

1. 23.4 lb; 11.25 lb

2. 15×10^{22} or 1.5×10^{23} carbon atoms

Performance Task

Sample answer: the burning of fossil fuels

Mathematical Practices

Students have opportunities to develop aspects of the mathematical practices throughout the chapter. Here are some examples.

1. **Make Sense of Problems and Persevere in Solving Them**
   8.2 Math Practice note, *p. 325*

2. **Reason Abstractly and Quantitatively**
   8.4 Exercise 23, *p. 342*

3. **Construct Viable Arguments and Critique the Reasoning of Others**
   8.1 Exercise 24, *p. 323*

4. **Model with Mathematics**
   8.3 Exercise 24, *p. 336*

5. **Use Appropriate Tools Strategically**
   8.6 Exercise 8, *p. 353*

6. **Attend to Precision**
   8.4 Exercise 39, *p. 342*

7. **Look for and Make Use of Structure**
   8.5 Math Practice note, *p. 343*

8. **Look for and Express Regularity in Repeated Reasoning**
   8.3 Math Practice note, *p. 331*

STEAM Video

Before the Video

- To introduce the STEAM Video, read aloud the first paragraph of Carbon Atoms and discuss the question with your students.
- "In what other real-life situations are exponents used?"

During the Video

- The video shows two people discussing elements, particularly carbon.
- Pause the video at 0:41 and ask, "What are the four main elements of life?" carbon, nitrogen, hydrogen, and oxygen
- Watch the remainder of the video.

After the Video

- "What did Steven use to help him interpret 50,000 billion billion pencil dots?" scientific notation
- Have students work with a partner to answer Questions 1 and 2.
- As students discuss and answer the questions, listen for understanding of finding percents of numbers and multiplying a very large number by a single digit.

Performance Task

- Use this information to spark students' interest and promote thinking about real-life problems.
- Ask, "What might cause the amount of carbon dioxide in the atmosphere to increase over time?"
- After completing the chapter, students will have gained the knowledge needed to complete "Elements in the Universe."

Carbon Atoms

Carbon is one of the four main elements of life. The number of carbon atoms in a compound can be represented using exponents. In what other real-life situations are exponents used?

Watch the STEAM Video "Carbon Atoms." Then answer the following questions.

1. The table shows the percents carbon by weight for humans and plants. How many pounds of carbon are in a 130-pound person? a 25-pound plant?

	Percent Carbon by Weight
Human	18%
Plant	45%

2. Steven says 5×10^{22}, or 50,000,000,000,000,000,000,000, carbon atoms are in 1 gram of carbon. How many carbon atoms are in 3 grams of carbon?

Elements in the Universe

After completing this chapter, you will be able to use the concepts you learned to answer the questions in the *STEAM Video Performance Task*. You will be given information about the *atomic masses* of the four most common elements in the universe: oxygen, hydrogen, helium, and carbon.

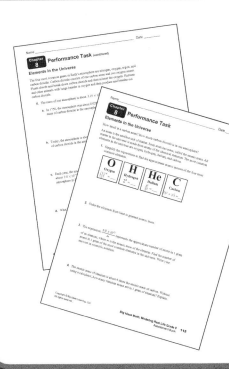

O	H	He	C
Oxygen	**Hydrogen**	**Helium**	**Carbon**
$\left(\dfrac{1}{2}\right)^{-4} =$ ___	$2^{0} =$ ___	$\dfrac{2^{5}}{2^{3}} =$ ___	$(3^{2} + 3^{1}) =$ ___

You will be asked to solve problems about the amounts of carbon dioxide in Earth's atmosphere for several years. What might cause the amount of carbon dioxide in the atmosphere to increase over time?

Getting Ready for Chapter 8

Chapter Exploration

1. Work with a partner. Write each distance as a whole number. Which numbers do you know how to write in words? For instance, in words, 10^2 is equal to *one hundred*.

a. 10^{27} meters: diameter of the observable universe

b. 10^{21} meters: diameter of the Milky Way galaxy

c. 10^{16} meters: diameter of the solar system

d. 10^7 meters: diameter of Earth

e. 10^4 meters: diameter of Halley's Comet

f. 10^3 meters: diameter of a meteor crater

2. Work with a partner. Write the numbers of wives, sacks, cats, and kits as powers.

> *As I was going to St. Ives*
> *I met a man with seven wives*
> *Each wife had seven sacks*
> *Each sack had seven cats*
> *Each cat had seven kits*
> *Kits, cats, sacks, wives*
> *How many were going to St. Ives?*

Nursery Rhyme, 1730

Vocabulary

The following vocabulary terms are defined in this chapter. Think about what each term might mean and record your thoughts.

power

base of a power

exponent of a power

scientific notation

Laurie's Notes

Check out the digital flash cards.
BigIdeasMath.com

Chapter Exploration

- Students should know how to raise a number to an exponent.
- In Exercise 1, students will write powers of 10 as whole numbers. The distances represent magnitudes, powers of 10, not exact distances.
- **FYI:** There is a classic video made by two designers in the late 1970s called *Powers of Ten*, which is readily available on the Internet.
- ❓ "Which numbers do you know the names for in parts (a)–(f)?" part (d): ten million; part (e): ten thousand; part (f): one thousand
- Share vocabulary that might be of interest:

million $= 10^6$	billion $= 10^9$	trillion $= 10^{12}$
quadrillion $= 10^{15}$	quintillion $= 10^{18}$	hexillion $= 10^{21}$
heptillion $= 10^{24}$	octillion $= 10^{27}$	nonillion $= 10^{30}$
decillion $= 10^{33}$	unodecillion $= 10^{36}$	duodecillion $= 10^{39}$

- Some of the above prefixes are the same ones used in naming polygons, so they should look familiar.
- In Exercise 2, students are given a classic rhyme. The answer to the question in the rhyme is one because the man and his wives were coming *from* St. Ives.
- For this problem, suggest to students that they draw a picture or diagram to help them solve the problem.
- **Summary:** wives $= 7^1$, sacks $= 7^2$, cats $= 7^3$, kits $= 7^4$

Vocabulary

- These terms represent some of the vocabulary that students will encounter in Chapter 8. Discuss the terms as a class.
- Where have students heard the term *power* outside of a math classroom? In what contexts? Students may not be able to write the actual definition, but they may write phrases associated with a *power*.
- Allowing students to discuss these terms now will prepare them for understanding the terms as they are presented in the chapter.
- When students encounter a new definition, encourage them to write in their *Student Journals*. They will revisit these definitions during the Chapter Review.

ELL Support

Students may know the word *power* from everyday language. Explain that in the context of math, *power* has a very specific meaning. In everyday language, *power* means "strength" or "force." In math, a power is a product of repeated factors.

Topics for Review

- Commutative and Associative Properties
- Converting Measures
- Distributive Property
- Factors
- Multiplicative Inverse Property
- Multiplying and Dividing Decimals
- Order of Operations
- Place Value
- Reciprocals
- Simplifying Expressions

Chapter Exploration

1. a.
1,000,000,000,000,000,000,000,000,000 m

b.
1,000,000,000,000,000,000,000 m

c. 10,000,000,000,000,000 m

d. 10,000,000 m; ten million

e. 10,000 m; ten thousand

f. 1000 m; one thousand

2. wives: 7^1; sacks: 7^2; cats: 7^3; kits: 7^4

Learning Target

Use exponents to write and evaluate expressions.

Success Criteria

- Write products using exponents.
- Evaluate expressions involving powers.
- Use exponents to solve real-life problems.

Warm Up

Cumulative, vocabulary, and prerequisite skills practice opportunities are available in the *Resources by Chapter* or at *BigIdeasMath.com*.

ELL Support

Students may know the word *product* from everyday language. A product is something that is made to be sold. In the context of math, a product is the result of multiplication. When you multiply two or more numbers, the answer is called the product.

Exploration 1

a. See Additional Answers.

b. -3 is used as a factor n times; Write -3 as a factor n times and multiply.

Exploration 2

$3 \cdot 3 \cdot 3 \cdot 3 = 3^4 = \$81$; The large cube is made up of $3 \cdot 3 \cdot 3$ small cubes. Because each small cube is worth \$3, the total value of the large cube is $3 \cdot 3 \cdot 3 \cdot 3 = 3^4 = \$81$.

T-319

Laurie's Notes

STATE STANDARDS
Preparing for 8.EE.A.1
COMMON CORE

Preparing to Teach

- Students should know how to raise a number to an exponent. The work in this section should be review for students, except **powers** with negative bases are now included.
- **MP8 Look for and Express Regularity in Repeated Reasoning:** In Exploration 1, students will raise a negative number to whole-number exponents and observe patterns that emerge.

Motivate

- "How big is a cubic millimeter?" *Sample answer:* about the size of a grain of salt
- Use a metric ruler and your fingers to show the length of a millimeter. A cubic millimeter is 1 mm $\times$ 1 mm $\times$ 1 mm.
- "How big is a cubic meter?" *Sample answer:* about the size of a baby's play pen
- Use 3 meter sticks to demonstrate 1 m $\times$ 1 m $\times$ 1 m.
- "How many cubic millimeters are in a cubic meter?" Students may or may not have an answer.
- Give students time to think. Someone might ask how many millimeters there are in a meter. The prefix *milli-* means $\frac{1}{1000}$.
- The volume of a cubic meter in terms of cubic millimeters is
- $1000 \times 1000 \times 1000 = 1{,}000{,}000{,}000 = 1$ billion cubic millimeters.
- "Can 1 billion be expressed using exponents?" 1000^3 or 10^9

Exploration 1

- **MP6 Attend to Precision:** Review the vocabulary associated with **exponents**.
- Have students work with their partners to complete the table. Students should recognize that a calculator is not necessary. They only need to multiply their previous product by -3.
- When students have finished, discuss the problem.
- "What do you notice about the values in the third column?" The values alternate signs—negative, positive, negative …
- Students might also mention: all values are odd and divisible by 3; last digits repeat in a cluster of 4: 3, 9, 7, 1, 3, 9, 7, 1,…; there are 2 one-digit numbers, 2 two-digit numbers, 2 three-digit numbers, and predict 2 four-digit numbers
- In part (b), students will likely describe the exponent n in $(-3)^n$ as how many times -3 is multiplied by itself. Encourage students to say that the exponent tells the number of times the **base** is used as a factor.
- "How can you find the value of $(-3)^n$?" Write -3 as a factor n times and multiply.

Exploration 2

- Although not all of the cubes are visible, students generally know that the cube contains 3^3 or 27 smaller cubes. At \$3 per small cube, the total value of the large cube is $3 \times 3^3 = 3^4$, or \$81.

8.1 Exponents

Learning Target: Use exponents to write and evaluate expressions.

Success Criteria:
- I can write products using exponents.
- I can evaluate expressions involving powers.
- I can use exponents to solve real-life problems.

The expression 3^5 is called a *power*. The *base* is 3. The *exponent* is 5.

$$\text{base} \longrightarrow 3^5 \longleftarrow \text{exponent}$$

EXPLORATION 1

Using Exponent Notation

Work with a partner.

a. Copy and complete the table.

Power	Repeated Multiplication Form	Value
$(-3)^1$	-3	-3
$(-3)^2$	$(-3) \cdot (-3)$	9
$(-3)^3$		
$(-3)^4$		
$(-3)^5$		
$(-3)^6$		
$(-3)^7$		

Math Practice

Build Arguments

When is the value of $(-3)^n$ positive? negative?

b. Describe what is meant by the expression $(-3)^n$. How can you find the value of $(-3)^n$?

EXPLORATION 2

Using Exponent Notation

Work with a partner. On a game show, each small cube is worth $3. The small cubes are arranged to form a large cube. Show how you can use a power to find the total value of the large cube. Then write an explanation to convince a friend that your answer is correct.

Key Vocabulary 🔊
power, *p. 320*
base, *p. 320*
exponent, *p. 320*

A **power** is a product of repeated factors. The **base** of a power is the repeated factor. The **exponent** of a power indicates the number of times the base is used as a factor.

base → → exponent

$$\left(\frac{1}{2}\right)^5 = \frac{1}{2} \cdot \frac{1}{2} \cdot \frac{1}{2} \cdot \frac{1}{2} \cdot \frac{1}{2}$$

power $\frac{1}{2}$ is used as a factor 5 times.

EXAMPLE 1 **Writing Expressions Using Exponents**

Write each product using exponents.

a. $(-7) \cdot (-7) \cdot (-7)$

Because -7 is used as a factor 3 times, its exponent is 3.

▷ So, $(-7) \cdot (-7) \cdot (-7) = (-7)^3$.

Math Practice

Communicate Precisely
Explain why you need to use parentheses to write powers when the base is negative.

b. $\pi \cdot \pi \cdot r \cdot r \cdot r$

Because π is used as a factor 2 times, its exponent is 2. Because r is used as a factor 3 times, its exponent is 3.

▷ So, $\pi \cdot \pi \cdot r \cdot r \cdot r = \pi^2 r^3$.

Try It Write the product using exponents.

1. $\frac{1}{4} \cdot \frac{1}{4} \cdot \frac{1}{4} \cdot \frac{1}{4} \cdot \frac{1}{4}$

2. $0.3 \cdot 0.3 \cdot 0.3 \cdot 0.3 \cdot x \cdot x$

EXAMPLE 2 **Evaluating Expressions**

Evaluate each expression.

a. $(-2)^4$

$(-2)^4 = (-2) \cdot (-2) \cdot (-2) \cdot (-2)$ Write as repeated multiplication.

The base is -2.

$= 16$ Simplify.

b. -2^4

$-2^4 = -(2 \cdot 2 \cdot 2 \cdot 2)$ Write as repeated multiplication.

The base is 2.

$= -16$ Simplify.

Try It Evaluate the expression.

3. 12^2

4. $(-2)^6$

5. -5^4

6. $\left(-\frac{1}{6}\right)^3$

🔊 Multi-Language Glossary at *BigIdeasMath.com*

Laurie's Notes

Scaffolding Instruction

- Students have explored writing numbers with exponents. Now they will write expressions involving exponents and evaluate powers.
- **Emerging:** Students may recognize patterns in values of powers, but they may have difficulty reversing the process. They will benefit from additional practice provided in the examples and Try It exercises.
- **Proficient:** Students have no trouble evaluating expressions involving powers or writing products using exponents. They should work through Example 3 before completing the Self-Assessment exercises.

Discuss

- Write the definitions for power, base, and exponent. Note the use of *factor* instead of *multiplying the base by itself*.
- Write the example shown. When this power is evaluated, the answer is $\frac{1}{32}$. You say, "$\frac{1}{2}$ to the fifth power is $\frac{1}{32}$."
- Exponents are used to rewrite an expression involving repeated factors.

EXAMPLE 1

- ❓ "Is it necessary to write the multiplication dot between the factors in part (a)? Explain." No, parentheses indicate multiplication.
- **Common Error:** Parentheses *must* be used when you write a power with a negative base. This is a common error that students will make. For example: $(-2)^2 = (-2)(-2) = 4$, but $-2^2 = -(2)(2) = -4$. With the parentheses, the number being squared is -2, and the product is 4. Without the parentheses, the number being squared is 2, and then you multiply the product by -1. The underlying property is the order of operations. Exponents are performed before multiplication.
- Variables and constants are expressed using exponents in a similar fashion, as shown in part (b).

Try It

- **MP6 Attend to Precision:** In Exercise 1, $\frac{1}{4}$ needs to be written with parentheses so that both the numerator and the denominator are raised to an exponent. Without parentheses, it could be read as $\frac{1^5}{4}$.

EXAMPLE 2

- ❓ "What is the base in each problem?" -2; 2 "What will be used as the factor in each problem?" -2; 2
- **MP6 Attend to Precision:** This example addresses the need to write the base within parentheses when the base is negative.

Try It

- **Whiteboards:** Have students write their work and answers on whiteboards. Be sure to check the signs of their answers.

Extra Example 1

Write each product using exponents.

a. $4 \cdot 4 \cdot 4 \cdot 4$ 4^4

b. $(-2) \cdot (-2) \cdot x \cdot x \cdot x$ $(-2)^2 x^3$

Try It

1. $\left(\frac{1}{4}\right)^5$

2. $0.3^4 x^2$

Extra Example 2

Evaluate each expression.

a. $(-3)^3$ -27

b. -3^3 -27

ELL Support

After demonstrating Examples 1 and 2, have students work in pairs to discuss and complete Try It Exercises 1–6. Have one student ask another, "What is the answer?" Have students alternate roles asking and answering questions.

Beginner: Write the answer.

Intermediate: State the answer.

Advanced: Use a complete sentence to state the answer.

Try It

3. 144

4. 64

5. -625

6. $-\dfrac{1}{216}$

Extra Example 3

Evaluate each expression.

a. $2 - 4 \cdot 5^2$ -98

b. $5 + 6^2 \div 4$ 14

c. $-2 \cdot (32 - 6^2)$ 8

Try It

7. -7

8. 1

9. -6

ELL Support

Allow students to work in pairs to complete the Self-Assessment for Concepts & Skills exercises. Have pairs display their answers for Exercises 10–16 on whiteboards for your review. Have two pairs form a group to discuss and come to an agreement for the explanation in Exercise 17. Review explanations as a class.

Self-Assessment
for Concepts & Skills

10. $(-0.9)^3$

11. $\left(\dfrac{1}{8}\right)^2 y^3$

12. 121

13. -216

14. 0.0081

15. 6

16. -3

17. -8^2; The other three expressions equal 64.

EXAMPLE 3

- You may wish to review the order of operations or wait to see how students evaluate the expressions.
- **Common Error:** Students may evaluate the problem left to right, performing the addition first. They need to be reminded of the order of operations.
- ? "What should you do first in part (a)?" evaluate the power
- Continue to evaluate the expression as shown.
- In part (b), there are two powers to evaluate. After that is done, division is performed before subtraction.
- In part (c), there is only one power. Note that the negative is not included in the base and the operation in the parentheses must be performed before multiplying by -3.

Try It

- Encourage students to write out the steps in their solutions. Discourage them from performing multiple steps in their heads. It may be helpful for students to provide a reason for each step.
- If there are errors, discuss them as a class so that students understand their mistakes. Negative signs often cause issues.

Formative Assessment Tip

Response Cards

This technique is used as a quick check to see whether students' knowledge of a skill, technique, or procedure is correct. Students are given cards at the beginning of class that are held up in front of them in response to a question. The cards are prepared in advance with particular responses, such as: A, B, C, and D; or 1, 2, and 3; or True and False. The cards can also be left blank for students to write their responses on. If you plan to use the cards multiple times, consider laminating them. *Response Cards* give all students the opportunity to participate in the lesson, because you are soliciting information from everyone and not just those who raise their hands. Because the cards are held facing the teacher, it is a private way to gather quick information about students' understanding.

✔ Self-Assessment for Concepts & Skills

- **Neighbor Check:** Have students work independently and then have their neighbors check their work. Have students discuss any discrepancies.
- ◉ **Response Cards:** Distribute *Response Cards* with *True* and *False* to students. Ask if each statement is true or false. Solicit explanations.

    a. $-3^2 = (-3)^2$ false

    b. $\left(\dfrac{2}{3}\right)^3 = \dfrac{8}{27}$ true

    c. $4^2 - 8(2) + 3^3 = 27$ true

    d. $-1^4 = 1$ false

The Success Criteria Self-Assessment chart can be found in the *Student Journal* or online at *BigIdeasMath.com*.

EXAMPLE 3 **Using Order of Operations**

Evaluate each expression.

a. $3 + 2 \cdot 3^4 = 3 + 2 \cdot 81$ Evaluate the power.

$= 3 + 162$ Multiply.

$= 165$ Add.

b. $3^3 - 8^2 \div 2 = 27 - 64 \div 2$ Evaluate the powers.

$= 27 - 32$ Divide.

$= -5$ Subtract.

c. $-3 \cdot (-10^2 + 70) = -3 \cdot (-100 + 70)$ Evaluate the power.

$= -3 \cdot (-30)$ Perform operation in parentheses.

$= 90$ Multiply.

Math Practice

Look for Structure
Can you use the Distributive Property to evaluate the expression in part (c)? Explain.

Try It Evaluate the expression.

7. $9 - 2^5 \cdot 0.5$ **8.** $\left| -3^3 \div 27 \right|$ **9.** $(7 \cdot 4 - 4^3) \div 6$

Self-Assessment for Concepts & Skills

Solve each exercise. Then rate your understanding of the success criteria in your journal.

WRITING EXPRESSIONS USING EXPONENTS **Write the product using exponents.**

10. $(-0.9) \cdot (-0.9) \cdot (-0.9)$ **11.** $\frac{1}{8} \cdot \frac{1}{8} \cdot y \cdot y \cdot y$

EVALUATING EXPRESSIONS **Evaluate the expression.**

12. 11^2 **13.** -6^3 **14.** $(-0.3)^4$

USING ORDER OF OPERATIONS **Evaluate the expression.**

15. $\left| -24 \div 2^2 \right|$ **16.** $(3^3 - 6 \cdot 8) \div 7$

17. **WHICH ONE DOESN'T BELONG?** Which expression does *not* belong with the other three? Explain your reasoning.

$(-2)^6$ -8^2

8^2 2^6

EXAMPLE 4 **Modeling Real Life**

The annual profit P (in thousands of dollars) earned by a technology company x years after opening is represented by the equation $P = 0.1x^3 + 3$. How much more profit is earned in year 5 than in year 4?

Use the equation to find the profits earned in year 4 and year 5. Then subtract the profit in year 4 from the profit in year 5 to determine how much more profit is earned in year 5.

Year 4		**Year 5**
$P = 0.1x^3 + 3$	Write the equation.	$P = 0.1x^3 + 3$
$= 0.1(4)^3 + 3$	Substitute.	$= 0.1(5)^3 + 3$
$= 0.1(64) + 3$	Evaluate the power.	$= 0.1(125) + 3$
$= 9.4$	Simplify.	$= 15.5$

▷ So, the company earns $15.5 - 9.4 = 6.1$, or $6100 more profit in year 5 than in year 4.

Self-Assessment for Problem Solving

Solve each exercise. Then rate your understanding of the success criteria in your journal.

18. **DIG DEEPER!** Consider the diameters of three planets.

   Planet A: 10^9 m   **Planet B:** 10^7 m   **Planet C:** 10^8 m

   a. Write each diameter as a whole number.

   b. A dwarf planet is discovered with a radius that is $\dfrac{1}{100}$ the radius of Planet C. Write the diameter of the dwarf planet as a power.

19. A fish jumps out of the water at a speed of 12 feet per second. The height y (in feet) of the fish above the surface of the water is represented by the equation $y = -16x^2 + 12x$, where x is the time (in seconds) since the jump began. The fish reaches its highest point above the surface of the water after 0.375 second. How far above the surface is the fish at this time?

Laurie's Notes

EXAMPLE 4

- Ask a volunteer to read the problem.
- **?** **Whiteboards:** Ask the following questions and have students display their answers.
  - "What do you need to find first?" profits earned in year 4 and in year 5
  - "How can you find the profit earned in year 4? in year 5?" Substitute 4 for x in the equation and then solve for P; Substitute 5 for x in the equation and then solve for P.
  - "Will the results answer the question? Explain." No, you need to subtract the two profits.

✓ Self-Assessment for Problem Solving

- The goal for all students is to feel comfortable with the problem-solving plan. It is important for students to problem-solve in class, where they may receive support from you and their peers. By now, students should be more comfortable with the problem-solving plan and be able to move past the first step.
- Students should read each problem independently and make a plan for solving each problem. Then have students share and discuss their plans with a partner before solving the problems independently.

The Success Criteria Self-Assessment chart can be found in the *Student Journal* or online at *BigIdeasMath.com*.

Closure

- **Exit Ticket:** Evaluate the expression.

  a. $-3^2 + 4(2) - 4^3$ -65

  b. $\left(-\dfrac{2}{3}\right)^3 + |5^2 - 2 \cdot 15|$ $\dfrac{127}{27} \approx 4.7$

Extra Example 4
The annual profit P (in thousands of dollars) earned by a bakery x years after opening is represented by the equation $P = 0.2x^3 + 7$. How much more profit is earned in year 4 than in year 3? $7400

Self-Assessment
for Problem Solving

18. **a.** Planet A: 1,000,000,000 m;
        Planet B: 10,000,000 m;
        Planet C: 100,000,000 m

    b. 10^6 m

19. 2.25 ft

Learning Target

Use exponents to write and evaluate expressions.

Success Criteria

- Write products using exponents.
- Evaluate expressions involving powers.
- Use exponents to solve real-life problems.

1.
Trading Card

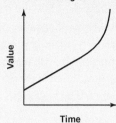

2.
River

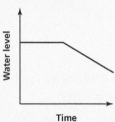

3. $A'(-4, 0), B'(-1, 0), C'(-1, -2)$

4. $E'(-1, -2), F'(-1, -3),$
$G'(-4, -3), H'(-4, -2)$

Concepts, Skills, & Problem Solving

5. $4 \cdot 4 \cdot 4 \cdot 4;\ 256$

6. $(-8) \cdot (-8);\ 64$

7. $(-2) \cdot (-2) \cdot (-2);\ -8$

8. 3^4

9. $(-6)^2$

10. $\left(-\dfrac{1}{2}\right)^3$

11. $\left(\dfrac{1}{3}\right)^3$

12. $\pi^3 x^4$

13. $(-4)^3 y^2$

14. $6.4^4 b^3$

15. $(-t)^5$

16. -7^5

17. $-\left(\dfrac{1}{4}\right)^4$

18. 25

19. -1331

20. 1

21. $\dfrac{1}{64}$

22. $\dfrac{1}{144}$

23. $-\dfrac{1}{729}$

24. no; The negative sign is not part of the base.

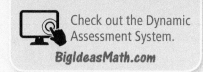

Assignment Guide and Concept Check

Scaffold assignments to support all students in their learning progression. The suggested assignments are a starting point. Continue to assign additional exercises and revisit with spaced practice to move every student toward proficiency.

Level	Assignment 1	Assignment 2
Emerging	1, 4, 5, 7, 9, 11, 13, 15, 17, 19, 21, 23, 29, 31	10, 12, 16, 20, 22, 24, 25, 28, 30, 32, 34, 36, 39
Proficient	1, 4, 5, 7, 8, 10, 12, 15, 17, 19, 20, 22, 23, 30, 32	24, 26, 28, 34, 35, 37, 38, 39
Advanced	1, 4, 5, 7, 8, 10, 12, 15, 17, 19, 20, 22, 23, 30, 32	24, 27, 28, 34, 37, 38, 39, 40

- Assignment 1 is for use after students complete the Self-Assessment for Concepts & Skills.
- Assignment 2 is for use after students complete the Self-Assessment for Problem Solving.
- The red exercises can be used as a concept check.

Review & Refresh Prior Skills

Exercises 1 and 2 Sketching Graphs
Exercises 3 and 4 Rotating a Figure

Common Errors

- **Exercises 8–17** Students may count the wrong number of factors. Remind them to check their work.
- **Exercises 19, 20, 22, and 23** Students may have the wrong sign in their answers. Remind them that when the negative sign is inside the parentheses, it is part of the base. When the negative sign is outside the parentheses, it is not part of the base.

8.1 Practice

Go to *BigIdeasMath.com* to get HELP with solving the exercises.

▶ Review & Refresh

Sketch a graph that represents the situation.

1. A trading card becomes more valuable over time. The value increases at a constant rate, and then at a faster and faster rate.

2. The water level of a river remains constant, and then decreases at a constant rate.

The vertices of a figure are given. Rotate the figure as described. Find the coordinates of the image.

3. $A(0, -4)$, $B(0, -1)$, $C(2, -1)$
   90° clockwise about the origin

4. $E(1, 2)$, $F(1, 3)$, $G(4, 3)$, $H(4, 2)$
   180° about the origin

▶▶ Concepts, Skills, & Problem Solving

USING EXPONENT NOTATION Write the power in repeated multiplication form. Then find the value of the power. (See Exploration 1, p. 319.)

5. 4^4

6. $(-8)^2$

7. $(-2)^3$

WRITING EXPRESSIONS USING EXPONENTS Write the product using exponents.

8. $3 \cdot 3 \cdot 3 \cdot 3$

9. $(-6) \cdot (-6)$

10. $\left(-\dfrac{1}{2}\right) \cdot \left(-\dfrac{1}{2}\right) \cdot \left(-\dfrac{1}{2}\right)$

11. $\dfrac{1}{3} \cdot \dfrac{1}{3} \cdot \dfrac{1}{3}$

12. $\pi \cdot \pi \cdot \pi \cdot x \cdot x \cdot x \cdot x$

13. $(-4) \cdot (-4) \cdot (-4) \cdot y \cdot y$

14. $6.4 \cdot 6.4 \cdot 6.4 \cdot 6.4 \cdot b \cdot b \cdot b$

15. $(-t) \cdot (-t) \cdot (-t) \cdot (-t) \cdot (-t)$

16. $-(7 \cdot 7 \cdot 7 \cdot 7 \cdot 7)$

17. $-\left(\dfrac{1}{4} \cdot \dfrac{1}{4} \cdot \dfrac{1}{4} \cdot \dfrac{1}{4}\right)$

EVALUATING EXPRESSIONS Evaluate the expression.

18. 5^2

19. -11^3

20. $(-1)^6$

21. $\left(\dfrac{1}{2}\right)^6$

22. $\left(-\dfrac{1}{12}\right)^2$

23. $-\left(\dfrac{1}{9}\right)^3$

24. **MP YOU BE THE TEACHER** Your friend evaluates the power -6^2. Is your friend correct? Explain your reasoning.

$$-6^2 = (-6) \cdot (-6) = 36$$

MP STRUCTURE Write the prime factorization of the number using exponents.

25. 675

26. 280

27. 363

28. **MP PATTERNS** The largest doll is 12 inches tall. The height of each of the other dolls is $\frac{7}{10}$ the height of the next larger doll. Write an expression involving a power that represents the height of the smallest doll. What is the height of the smallest doll?

USING ORDER OF OPERATIONS Evaluate the expression.

29. $5 + 3 \cdot 2^3$

30. $2 + 7 \cdot (-3)^2$

31. $(13^2 - 12^2) \div 5$

32. $\frac{1}{2}(4^3 - 6 \cdot 3^2)$

33. $\left| \frac{1}{2}(7 + 5^3) \right|$

34. $\left| \left(-\frac{1}{2} \right)^3 \div \left(\frac{1}{4} \right)^2 \right|$

35. $(9^2 - 15 \cdot 2) \div 17$

36. $-6 \cdot (-5^2 + 20)$

37. $(-4 + 12 - 6^2) \div 7$

38. **MP STRUCTURE** Copy and complete the table. Compare the values of $2^h - 1$ with the values of 2^{h-1}. When are the values the same?

h	1	2	3	4	5
$2^h - 1$					
2^{h-1}					

39. **MP MODELING REAL LIFE** Scientists use carbon-14 dating to determine the age of a sample of organic material.

   a. The amount C (in grams) of carbon-14 remaining after t years of a sample of organic material is represented by the equation $C = 100(0.99988)^t$. Find the amount of carbon-14 remaining after 4 years.

   b. What percent of the carbon-14 remains after 4 years?

40. **DIG DEEPER!** The frequency (in vibrations per second) of a note on a piano is represented by the equation $F = 440(1.0595)^n$, where n is the number of notes above A440. Each black or white key represents one note. Use the frequencies of A and A440 to make a conjecture about frequencies of notes on a piano. Explain your reasoning.

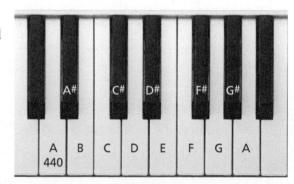

 Common Errors

- **Exercises 29–37** Students may not remember the definition for absolute value or the correct order of operations. Review these topics with students.

Mini-Assessment

Write the product using exponents.

1. $2 \cdot 2 \cdot 2 \cdot 2 \cdot 2 \cdot 2 \cdot 2$ 2^7

2. $a \cdot a \cdot b \cdot b \cdot b \cdot b$ $a^2 b^4$

Evaluate the expression.

3. 7^2 49

4. -3^4 -81

5. $(-3)^4$ 81

6. $\frac{3}{4}\left(2^5 - 6 \div \left(\frac{1}{2}\right)^2\right)$ 6

Section Resources

Surface Level	Deep Level
Resources by Chapter • Extra Practice • Reteach • Puzzle Time Student Journal • Self-Assessment • Practice Differentiating the Lesson Tutorial Videos Skills Review Handbook Skills Trainer	Resources by Chapter • Enrichment and Extension Graphic Organizers Dynamic Assessment System • Section Practice

 Concepts, Skills, & Problem Solving

25. $3^3 \cdot 5^2$

26. $2^3 \cdot 5 \cdot 7$

27. $3 \cdot 11^2$

28. $12 \cdot \left(\frac{7}{10}\right)^3$; 4.116 in.

29. 29

30. 65

31. 5

32. 5

33. 66

34. 2

35. 3

36. 30

37. -4

38.

h	1	2	3
$2^h - 1$	1	3	7
2^{h-1}	1	2	4

h	4	5
$2^h - 1$	15	31
2^{h-1}	8	16

Sample answer: $2^h - 1 > 2^{h-1}$ when $h > 1$; $h = 1$

39. **a.** about 99.95 g

    b. 99.95%

40. The frequency of A is about double the frequency of A440. So, the frequencies of notes on a piano double every 12 notes.

Learning Target

Generate equivalent expressions involving products of powers.

Success Criteria

- Find products of powers that have the same base.
- Find powers of powers.
- Find powers of products.

Warm Up

Cumulative, vocabulary, and prerequisite skills practice opportunities are available in the *Resources by Chapter* or at *BigIdeasMath.com*.

ELL Support

Students may be familiar with the word *property* from everyday life as it refers to possessions that a person owns. Explain that in math, the word *property* refers to a rule. Write the words *equal* and *equivalent* and ask students what is similar about the words. Underline *equ-* in each word and explain that the words are synonyms. Equivalent expressions are expressions that represent equal values.

Exploration 1

a. See Additional Answers.

b. $(7^3)^2 = 7^3 \cdot 7^3 = 7^{3+3} = 7^6$;
$(6^2)^2 = 6^2 \cdot 6^2 = 6^{2+2} = 6^4$;
$(3^2)^3 = 3^2 \cdot 3^2 \cdot 3^2 = 3^{2+2+2} = 3^6$;
$(2^2)^4 = 2^2 \cdot 2^2 \cdot 2^2 \cdot 2^2$
$= 2^{2+2+2+2} = 2^8$;

$\left(\left(\frac{1}{2}\right)^2\right)^5 = \left(\frac{1}{2}\right)^2 \cdot \left(\frac{1}{2}\right)^2 \cdot \left(\frac{1}{2}\right)^2 \cdot \left(\frac{1}{2}\right)^2 \cdot \left(\frac{1}{2}\right)^2$

$= \left(\frac{1}{2}\right)^{2+2+2+2+2}$

$= \left(\frac{1}{2}\right)^{10}$;

$(a^m)^n = a^{mn}$

Exploration 2

See Additional Answers.

T-325

Laurie's Notes

Preparing to Teach

- **MP8 Look for and Express Regularity in Repeated Reasoning:** In the explorations, students will find products of powers, powers of powers, and powers of products, and observe patterns that emerge.

Motivate

- **Story Time:** Tell students that you were offered a salary of $2000 a month or a special salary schedule for one month. On day 1 you will receive 1 cent, on day 2 you will receive 2 cents, on day 3 you will receive 4 cents, and so on, with your salary doubling every work day for the month. There are 23 work days this month. Which salary should you take?
- Give time for students to start the tabulation for the second option. Let them use a calculator for speed. The table below shows the daily pay (in cents).

1	$2 = 2^1$	$4 = 2^2$	$8 = 2^3$
$16 = 2^4$	$32 = 2^5$	$64 = 2^6$	$128 = 2^7$
$256 = 2^8$	$512 = 2^9$	$1024 = 2^{10}$	$2048 = 2^{11}$
$4096 = 2^{12}$	$8192 = 2^{13}$	$16{,}384 = 2^{14}$	$32{,}768 = 2^{15}$
$65{,}536 = 2^{16}$	$131{,}072 = 2^{17}$	$262{,}144 = 2^{18}$	$524{,}288 = 2^{19}$
$1{,}048{,}576 = 2^{20}$	$2{,}097{,}152 = 2^{21}$	$4{,}194{,}304 = 2^{22}$	

- In this penny doubling problem, each day you are paid a power of 2. Your salary is actually the *sum* of all these amounts (8,388,607 cents = $83,886.07).

Exploration 1

- Tell students that the general rule should explain how to simplify the expression using any numbers. Have pairs complete the table. It may help students if you point out that in the middle column, *Repeated Multiplication Form* means the expanded form of each power in the product.

? "Why is the first column labeled 'Product'?" Two powers are being multiplied.

? "What do you notice about the number of factors in the middle column and the exponent used to write the power?" They are the same number.

- **MP5 Use Appropriate Tools Strategically:** Have students use calculators to evaluate the products and the powers to confirm their answers.
- Write the general rule for part (a): $a^m \cdot a^n = a^{m+n}$. Stress that the bases must be the same, which is why a is the base for both powers. This rule does not apply to products of unlike bases, such as $3^3 \cdot 4^2$.
- Students often confuse the Product of Powers Property with the Powers of Powers Property. Make sure students can explain how $4^3 \cdot 4^2$ is different from $(4^3)^2$. Expanding the expressions helps to demonstrate this.

Exploration 2

- In an expression such as $(2 \cdot 3)^3$, students are often unsure how to simplify. Using repeated multiplication, $(2 \cdot 3)^3 = (2 \cdot 3)(2 \cdot 3)(2 \cdot 3)$. The Commutative and Associative Properties allow you to rewrite the expression as $2 \cdot 2 \cdot 2 \cdot 3 \cdot 3 \cdot 3$, which is equivalent to $2^3 \cdot 3^3$. So, the general rule is $(ab)^m = a^m b^m$.

8.2 Product of Powers Property

Learning Target: Generate equivalent expressions involving products of powers.

Success Criteria:
- I can find products of powers that have the same base.
- I can find powers of powers.
- I can find powers of products.

EXPLORATION 1

Finding Products of Powers

Work with a partner.

a. Copy and complete the table. Use your results to write a *general rule* for finding $a^m \cdot a^n$, a product of two powers with the same base.

Product	Repeated Multiplication Form	Power
$2^2 \cdot 2^4$		
$(-3)^2 \cdot (-3)^4$		
$7^3 \cdot 7^2$		
$5.1^1 \cdot 5.1^6$		
$(-4)^2 \cdot (-4)^2$		
$10^3 \cdot 10^5$		
$\left(\frac{1}{2}\right)^5 \cdot \left(\frac{1}{2}\right)^5$		

Math Practice

Consider Similar Problems

How are the expressions in part (b) similar to the expressions in part (a)?

b. Show how to use your rule in part (a) to write each expression below as a single power. Then write a *general rule* for finding $(a^m)^n$, a power of a power.

$$(7^3)^2 \qquad (6^2)^2 \qquad (3^2)^3 \qquad (2^2)^4 \qquad \left(\left(\frac{1}{2}\right)^2\right)^5$$

EXPLORATION 2

Finding Powers of Products

Work with a partner. Copy and complete the table. Use your results to write a *general rule* for finding $(ab)^m$, a power of a product.

Power	Repeated Multiplication Form	Product of Powers
$(2 \cdot 3)^3$		
$(2 \cdot 5)^2$		
$(5 \cdot 4)^3$		
$(-2 \cdot 4)^2$		
$(-3 \cdot 2)^4$		

🔑 Key Ideas

Common Error

When multiplying powers, do not multiply the bases.

$4^2 \cdot 4^3 = 4^5$, not 16^5.

Product of Powers Property

Words To multiply powers with the same base, add their exponents.

Numbers $4^2 \cdot 4^3 = 4^{2+3} = 4^5$

Algebra $a^m \cdot a^n = a^{m+n}$

Power of a Power Property

Words To find a power of a power, multiply the exponents.

Numbers $(4^6)^3 = 4^{6 \cdot 3} = 4^{18}$

Algebra $(a^m)^n = a^{mn}$

Power of a Product Property

Words To find a power of a product, find the power of each factor and multiply.

Numbers $(3 \cdot 2)^5 = 3^5 \cdot 2^5$

Algebra $(ab)^m = a^m b^m$

EXAMPLE 1 **Multiplying Powers with the Same Base**

a. $2^4 \cdot 2^5 = 2^{4+5}$ Product of Powers Property

$\quad\quad\quad = 2^9$ Simplify.

When a number is written without an exponent, its exponent is 1.

b. $-5 \cdot (-5)^6 = (-5)^1 \cdot (-5)^6$ Rewrite -5 as $(-5)^1$.

$\quad\quad\quad\quad = (-5)^{1+6}$ Product of Powers Property

$\quad\quad\quad\quad = (-5)^7$ Simplify.

c. $x^3 \cdot x^7 = x^{3+7}$ Product of Powers Property

$\quad\quad\quad = x^{10}$ Simplify.

Try It Simplify the expression. Write your answer as a power.

1. $6^2 \cdot 6^4$ **2.** $\left(-\dfrac{1}{2}\right)^3 \cdot \left(-\dfrac{1}{2}\right)^6$ **3.** $z \cdot z^{12}$

Laurie's Notes

Scaffolding Instruction

- Students explored properties of powers. Now they will use the Product of Powers Property, the Power of a Power Property, and the Power of a Product Property to simplify expressions.
- **Emerging:** Students may have difficulty distinguishing between the three properties. They will benefit from guided instruction for the Key Ideas and examples.
- **Proficient:** Students can explain the three properties and their general rules. They should proceed to the Self-Assessment exercises.

Key Ideas

- **Teaching Strategy:** Write the Key Ideas. Explain the Words, Numbers, and Algebra.
- Explain that this and the following section mirror each other. However, this section contains more properties. Essentially, the properties in this section are the "multiplication properties" of exponents and in the next section students will study the "division property" of exponents.

EXAMPLE 1

- Write and simplify the expression in part (a). The base is 2 for each power, so add the exponents.
- **?** "In part (b), what is the base for each power?" -5 "To what exponent is each base raised?" 1 and 6
- **Common Error:** When the exponent is 1, it is not written. When it is not written, students sometimes forget to add 1 in their answers.
- The Product of Powers Property applies to variables as well as numbers, as shown in part (c).

Try It

- Have students write out the steps in their solutions and use their property cards to help justify each step.
- **Popsicle Sticks:** Select students to write their solutions on the board and explain them to the class.

ELL Support

After demonstrating Example 1, have students work in pairs to discuss and complete Try It Exercises 1–3. Have one student ask another, "What is the base for each power? To what exponent is each base raised? What is your answer?" Have students alternate roles asking and answering questions.

Beginner: Write the answers.

Intermediate: State the answers.

Advanced: Use complete sentences to state the answers.

Scaffold instruction to support all students in their learning. Learning is individualized and you may want to group students differently as they move in and out of these levels with each skill and concept. Student self-assessment and feedback help guide your instructional decisions about how and when to layer support for all students to become proficient learners.

Teaching Strategy

Ask students to use an index card for each property: Product of Powers Property, Power of a Power Property, and Power of a Product Property. On each card, have students write the name of the property and then write the property in words, with numbers, and with variables (the general rule). They may want to include other information as well. Students can use these cards to help them identify the different properties being used as they proceed through the lesson. Matching a problem to a property will aid in their ability to differentiate between properties. Students should continue making cards as they encounter new properties.

Extra Example 1

Simplify each expression. Write your answer as a power.

a. $6^2 \cdot 6^7$ 6^9

b. $-2 \cdot (-2)^3$ $(-2)^4$

c. $x^2 \cdot x^5$ x^7

Try It

1. 6^6

2. $\left(-\dfrac{1}{2}\right)^9$

3. z^{13}

Laurie's Notes

Extra Example 2

Simplify each expression. Write your answer as a power.

a. $(5^2)^3$ 5^6

b. $(y^4)^6$ y^{24}

Try It

4. 4^{15}

5. y^8

6. $(-4)^6$

Extra Example 3

Simplify each expression.

a. $(4x)^2$ $16x^2$

b. $(wz)^3$ w^3z^3

Try It

7. $625y^4$

8. a^5b^5

9. $0.25m^2n^2$

Self-Assessment
for Concepts & Skills

10. 4^{11}

11. g^{18}

12. $\left(-\dfrac{1}{3}\right)^{12}$

13. $4096t^4$

14. y^6z^6

15. $\dfrac{1}{64}g^3h^3$

16. no; The bases are not the same.

17. *Sample answer:* $x^6 \cdot x^6$

EXAMPLE 2

❓ "In part (a), what does the exponent of 3 tell you to do in the expression $(3^4)^3$?" Use 3^4 as a factor three times.

• Use the Power of a Power Property and multiply the exponents.

• The Power of a Power Property applies to variables as well as numbers, as shown in part (b).

Try It

• **Whiteboards:** Have students write out the steps in their solutions and use their property cards to help justify each step. Discuss any discrepancies as a class.

EXAMPLE 3

• Be careful and deliberate with language when simplifying these expressions.

❓ "In part (a), what does the exponent of 3 tell you to do in the expression $(2x)^3$?" Use $2x$ as a factor three times.

• **MP7 Look for and Make Use of Structure:** To verify the solution of part (a), you could write the factor $2x$ three times. Properties of Multiplication (Associative and Commutative) allow you to reorder the terms. You can identify six factors: 2, 2, 2, x, x, and x. Use exponents to write the factors. Finally, 2^3 is rewritten as 8 and the final answer is $8x^3$.

• Follow the same procedure to verify the solution in part (b), by writing $3xy$ as a factor twice. It is very common for students to write $x \cdot x = 2x$. Do not assume that students will see this error.

Try It

• Have students write out the steps in their solutions and use their property cards to help justify each step.

• Select students to share with the class.

✔ Self-Assessment *for Concepts & Skills*

• **Neighbor Check:** Have students work independently and then have their neighbors check their work. Have students discuss any discrepancies.

◉ **One-Minute Card:** Explain the differences between finding products of powers, powers of powers, and powers of products. Collect the cards and review them with students at the beginning of the next class.

ELL Support

Allow students to work in pairs for additional support and to practice language. Have pairs display their answers for Exercises 10–15 on whiteboards for your review. Have two pairs form a group to discuss and come to an agreement for the answers to Exercises 16 and 17. Then have each group present their explanation and expression to the class.

The Success Criteria Self-Assessment chart can be found in the *Student Journal* or online at *BigIdeasMath.com*.

EXAMPLE 2 **Finding a Power of a Power**

a. $(3^4)^3 = 3^{4 \cdot 3}$ Power of a Power Property

      $= 3^{12}$ Simplify.

b. $(w^5)^4 = w^{5 \cdot 4}$ Power of a Power Property

      $= w^{20}$ Simplify.

Try It Simplify the expression. Write your answer as a power.

4. $(4^3)^5$ **5.** $(y^2)^4$ **6.** $\left((-4)^3\right)^2$

EXAMPLE 3 **Finding a Power of a Product**

a. $(2x)^3 = 2^3 \cdot x^3$ Power of a Product Property

      $= 8x^3$ Simplify.

b. $(3xy)^2 = 3^2 \cdot x^2 \cdot y^2$ Power of a Product Property

      $= 9x^2y^2$ Simplify.

Try It Simplify the expression.

7. $(5y)^4$ **8.** $(ab)^5$ **9.** $(0.5mn)^2$

Self-Assessment for Concepts & Skills

Solve each exercise. Then rate your understanding of the success criteria in your journal.

FINDING POWERS Simplify the expression. Write your answer as a power.

10. $4^7 \cdot 4^4$ **11.** $(g^6)^3$ **12.** $\left(-\dfrac{1}{3}\right)^5 \cdot \left(-\dfrac{1}{3}\right)^7$

FINDING A POWER OF A PRODUCT Simplify the expression.

13. $(8t)^4$ **14.** $(yz)^6$ **15.** $\left(\dfrac{1}{4}gh\right)^3$

16. **CRITICAL THINKING** Can you use the Product of Powers Property to simplify $5^2 \cdot 6^4$? Explain.

17. **OPEN-ENDED** Write an expression that simplifies to x^{12} using the Product of Powers Property.

EXAMPLE 4 **Modeling Real Life**

Details	⌄
Local Disk (C:)	
Local Disk	
Free Space: 16 GB	
Total Space: 64 GB	

One gigabyte (GB) of computer storage space is 2^{30} bytes. The storage details of a computer are shown. How many bytes of total storage space does the computer have?

The computer has 64 gigabytes of total storage space. Notice that you can write 64 as a power, 2^6.

Use a verbal model to solve the problem.

$$\begin{array}{ccc} \text{Total number} \\ \text{of bytes} \end{array} = \begin{array}{c} \text{Number of} \\ \text{bytes in a} \\ \text{gigabyte} \end{array} \cdot \begin{array}{c} \text{Number of} \\ \text{gigabytes} \end{array}$$

$$= 2^{30} \cdot 2^6 \qquad \text{Substitute.}$$

$$= 2^{30+6} \qquad \text{Product of Powers Property}$$

$$= 2^{36} \qquad \text{Simplify.}$$

▸ So, the computer has 2^{36} bytes of total storage space.

 Self-Assessment for Problem Solving

Solve each exercise. Then rate your understanding of the success criteria in your journal.

18. A newborn blue whale weighs 3^7 kilograms. An adult blue whale weighs 81 times the weight of the newborn. How many kilograms does the adult blue whale weigh?

19. One megabyte of cell phone storage space is 2^{20} bytes. An app uses 4^4 megabytes of storage space. How many bytes of storage space does the app use?

20. **DIG DEEPER!** The diagram shows the area of a small circular rug. The radius of a large circular rug is 3 times the radius of the small rug. Write an expression for the area of the large rug in terms of x. Justify your answer.

$A = \frac{1}{4}\pi x^2$

Laurie's Notes

EXAMPLE 4

- Ask a volunteer to read the problem aloud.
- ? "What information do you know?" Each gigabyte is 2^{30} bytes and the total storage space is 64 gigabytes. Explain that computers often use numbers that are powers with a base of 2.
- ? "How can you find the total storage space in bytes?" Multiply 2^{30} by 64.
- Writing a verbal model is helpful in this problem because the terms *gigabytes* and *bytes* may not be familiar to all students. Point out that the first sentence is a conversion fact: 1 GB = 2^{30} bytes. Students may naturally write $2^{30} \times 64$ to solve the problem.
- Rewriting 64 as a power with a base of 2, $64 = 2^6$, allows you to use the Product of Powers Property to simplify the expression.

Extra Example 4
In Example 4, the total storage space of a computer is 32 gigabytes. How many bytes of total storage space does the computer have? 2^{35} bytes

✓ Self-Assessment for Problem Solving

- Students may benefit from trying the exercises independently and then working with peers to refine their work. It is important to provide time in class for problem solving, so that students become comfortable with the problem-solving plan.
- Students should read each problem and write a verbal model independently. Then have students check their verbal models with their neighbors and discuss any discrepancies. Remind students that there may be more than one correct verbal model, but they should be similar. Have students solve the problems independently and then check their answers with their neighbors.
- For Exercise 20, there are several ways to approach the problem.

  - Students might rewrite the area of the small rug as $A = \pi\left(\frac{1}{2}x\right)^2$, so
  $r = \frac{1}{2}x$. Then the area of the large rug is $A = \pi\left(3 \cdot \frac{1}{2}x\right)^2 = \frac{9}{4}\pi x^2$.

  Students may recognize that because $r = \frac{1}{2}x$, x must represent the diameter of the small rug.
  - Alternatively, students may recognize that the rugs are similar figures and use ratio relationships to find the area of the large rug.

The Success Criteria Self-Assessment chart can be found in the *Student Journal* or online at *BigIdeasMath.com*.

Self-Assessment
for Problem Solving

18. 3^{11} kg

19. 2^{28} bytes

20. $\frac{9}{4}\pi x^2$; *Sample answer:*

The area of the small rug is
$A = \frac{1}{4}\pi x^2 = \pi\left(\frac{1}{2}x\right)^2$, so
$r = \frac{1}{2}x$.

Then, the area of the large rug
is $A = \pi\left(3 \cdot \frac{1}{2}x\right)^2 = \frac{9}{4}\pi x^2$.

Closure

- Refer back to the penny doubling problem in the Motivate. On what days was your daily pay more than $1000 (100,000 cents)? days 18–23

Learning Target

Generate equivalent expressions involving products of powers.

Success Criteria

- Find products of powers that have the same base.
- Find powers of powers.
- Find powers of products.

Review & Refresh

1. 11^5

2. $(-6)^3 z^2$

3. -28

4. -4

5. 1

6. B

Concepts, Skills, & Problem Solving

7. $5 \cdot 5 \cdot 5 \cdot 5 \cdot 5 \cdot 5 \cdot 5 \cdot 5 \cdot 5;\ 5^9$

8. $6 \cdot 6 \cdot 6 \cdot 6 \cdot 6 \cdot 6 \cdot 6 \cdot 6;\ 6^8$

9. $(-8) \cdot (-8) \cdot (-8) \cdot (-8) \cdot (-8) \cdot (-8) \cdot (-8);\ (-8)^7$

10. 3^4

11. 8^{14}

12. 5^{12}

13. $(-3)^8$

14. $(-4)^{12}$

15. h^7

16. b^{36}

17. $\left(\dfrac{2}{3}\right)^8$

18. 3.8^{12}

19. n^{15}

20. $\left(-\dfrac{3}{4}\right)^{10}$

21. $\left(-\dfrac{5}{7}\right)^{17}$

22. no; The bases should not be multiplied.

23. no; The exponents should be multiplied, not added.

24. $216g^3$

25. $-243v^5$

26. $\dfrac{1}{25}k^2$

27. $2.0736m^4$

28. $r^{12}t^{12}$

29. $-\dfrac{27}{64}p^3$

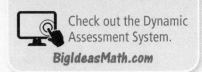

Assignment Guide and Concept Check

Scaffold assignments to support all students in their learning progression. The suggested assignments are a starting point. Continue to assign additional exercises and revisit with spaced practice to move every student toward proficiency.

Level	Assignment 1	Assignment 2
Emerging	2, 5, 6, 7, 8, 11, 13, 15, 17, 19, 22, 24, 26	9, 14, 16, 18, 20, 21, 23, 25, 27, 28, 31, 33, 37
Proficient	2, 5, 6, 7, 8, 12, 14, 15, 18, 20, 22, 24, 26, 28	9, 16, 21, 23, 29, 30, 31, 32, 33, 35, 37
Advanced	2, 5, 6, 8, 9, 12, 14, 16, 18, 20, 22, 26, 28, 29	21, 23, 30, 31, 32, 33, 34, 35, 36, 37

- Assignment 1 is for use after students complete the Self-Assessment for Concepts & Skills.
- Assignment 2 is for use after students complete the Self-Assessment for Problem Solving.
- The red exercises can be used as a concept check.

Review & Refresh Prior Skills

Exercises 1 and 2 Writing Expressions Using Exponents
Exercises 3–5 Evaluating a Function
Exercise 6 Finding an Interior Angle Measure

Common Errors

- **Exercises 10, 11, 14, 15, 17, and 21** Students may multiply the bases. Remind them that the base stays the same and only the exponent changes when using the Product of Powers Property.
- **Exercises 10–21** Students may confuse the Product of Powers Property and the Power of a Power Property. Explain why it makes sense to add exponents when using the Product of Powers Property and multiply exponents when using the Power of a Power Property.
- **Exercises 24–29** Students may forget to find the power of both factors and write, for example, $(6g)^3 = 6g^3$ instead of $(6g)^3 = 6^3 g^3 = 216g^3$. Remind them of the Power of a Product Property.

? Go to *BigIdeasMath.com* to get HELP with solving the exercises.

▶ Review & Refresh

Write the product using exponents.

1. $11 \cdot 11 \cdot 11 \cdot 11 \cdot 11$

2. $(-6) \cdot (-6) \cdot (-6) \cdot z \cdot z$

Find the value of y for the given value of x.

3. $y = -4x; \; x = 7$

4. $y = 5x + 6; \; x = -2$

5. $y = 10 - 3x; \; x = 3$

6. What is the measure of each interior angle of the regular polygon?

   A. $45°$

   B. $135°$

   C. $1080°$

   D. $1440°$

▶▶ Concepts, Skills, & Problem Solving

FINDING PRODUCTS OF POWERS Write the expression in repeated multiplication form. Then write the expression as a power. (See Exploration 1, p. 325.)

7. $5^6 \cdot 5^3$

8. $(6^4)^2$

9. $(-8)^3 \cdot (-8)^4$

FINDING POWERS Simplify the expression. Write your answer as a power.

10. $3^2 \cdot 3^2$

11. $8^{10} \cdot 8^4$

12. $(5^4)^3$

13. $((-3)^2)^4$

14. $(-4)^5 \cdot (-4)^7$

15. $h^6 \cdot h$

16. $(b^{12})^3$

17. $\left(\dfrac{2}{3}\right)^2 \cdot \left(\dfrac{2}{3}\right)^6$

18. $(3.8^3)^4$

19. $(n^3)^5$

20. $\left(\left(-\dfrac{3}{4}\right)^5\right)^2$

21. $\left(-\dfrac{5}{7}\right)^8 \cdot \left(-\dfrac{5}{7}\right)^9$

MP YOU BE THE TEACHER Your friend simplifies the expression. Is your friend correct? Explain your reasoning.

22.
$$5^2 \cdot 5^9 = (5 \cdot 5)^{2+9}$$
$$= 25^{11}$$

23.
$$(r^6)^4 = r^{6+4}$$
$$= r^{10}$$

FINDING A POWER OF A PRODUCT Simplify the expression.

24. $(6g)^3$

25. $(-3v)^5$

26. $\left(\dfrac{1}{5}k\right)^2$

27. $(1.2m)^4$

28. $(rt)^{12}$

29. $\left(-\dfrac{3}{4}p\right)^3$

w in.

w in.

30. **MP PRECISION** Is $3^2 + 3^3$ equal to 3^5? Explain.

31. **MP PROBLEM SOLVING** A display case for the artifact shown is in the shape of a cube. Each side of the display case is three times longer than the width w of the artifact.

    a. Write a power that represents the volume of the case.

    b. Simplify your expression in part (a).

32. **MP LOGIC** Show that $(3 \cdot 8 \cdot x)^7 = 6^7 \cdot 4^7 \cdot x^7$.

33. **MP MODELING REAL LIFE** The lowest altitude of an altocumulus cloud is about 3^8 feet. The highest altitude of an altocumulus cloud is about 3 times the lowest altitude. What is the highest altitude of an altocumulus cloud? Write your answer as a power.

34. **GEOMETRY** A square pyramid has a height h and a base with side length s. The side lengths of the base increase by 50%. Write a formula for the volume of the new pyramid in terms of s and h.

35. **MP MODELING REAL LIFE** The United States Postal Service delivers about $2^4 \cdot 3 \cdot 5^3$ pieces of mail each second. There are $2^8 \cdot 3^4 \cdot 5^2$ seconds in 6 days. How many pieces of mail does the United States Postal Service deliver in 6 days? Write your answer as an expression involving three powers.

36. **MP REASONING** The row numbers y and column numbers x of a chessboard are shown. Each position on the chessboard has a stack of pennies. (Only the first row is shown.) The number of pennies in each stack is $2^x \cdot 2^y$.

    a. Which locations have 32 pennies in their stacks?

    b. How much money (in dollars) is in the location with the tallest stack?

    c. A penny is about 0.06 inch thick. About how tall is the tallest stack?

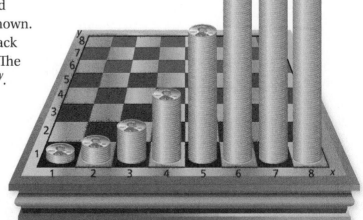

37. **CRITICAL THINKING** Find the value of x in the equation without evaluating the power.

    a. $2^5 \cdot 2^x = 256$

    b. $\left(\dfrac{1}{3}\right)^2 \cdot \left(\dfrac{1}{3}\right)^x = \dfrac{1}{729}$

Mini-Assessment

Simplify the expression. Write your answer as a power.

1. $b^2 \cdot b^6$ b^8

2. $(-2)^3 \cdot (-2)^2$ $(-2)^5$

3. $(c^8)^3$ c^{24}

Simplify the expression.

4. $(-5w)^4$ $625w^4$

5. $(st)^{11}$ $s^{11}t^{11}$

 Concepts, Skills,
& Problem Solving

30. no; $3^2 + 3^3 = 9 + 27 = 36$ and $3^5 = 243$

31. **a.** $(3w)^3$

    b. $27w^3$

32. $(3 \cdot 8 \cdot x)^7 = (3 \cdot 2 \cdot 4 \cdot x)^7$
    $= (6 \cdot 4 \cdot x)^7$
    $= 6^7 \cdot 4^7 \cdot x^7$

33. 3^9 ft

34. $V = \dfrac{3}{4}s^2h$

35. $2^{12} \cdot 3^5 \cdot 5^5$ pieces of mail

36. **a.** $(1, 4), (2, 3), (3, 2), (4, 1)$

    b. $655.36

    c. 3932.16 in.

37. **a.** 3

    b. 4

Section Resources

Surface Level	Deep Level
Resources by Chapter • Extra Practice • Reteach • Puzzle Time Student Journal • Self-Assessment • Practice Differentiating the Lesson Tutorial Videos Skills Review Handbook Skills Trainer	Resources by Chapter • Enrichment and Extension Graphic Organizers Dynamic Assessment System • Section Practice

Learning Target

Generate equivalent expressions involving quotients of powers.

Success Criteria

- Find quotients of powers that have the same base.
- Simplify expressions using the Quotient of Powers Property.
- Solve real-life problems involving quotients of powers.

Warm Up

Cumulative, vocabulary, and prerequisite skills practice opportunities are available in the *Resources by Chapter* or at *BigIdeasMath.com*.

ELL Support

Review the multiplication term *product*. Explain that division uses its own terms, and the answer to a division problem is the quotient. Compare *quotient* to *product*. Write an equation to represent each. Circle the product and quotient.

Exploration 1

a–b. See Additional Answers.

Laurie's Notes

STATE STANDARDS
8.EE.A.1

Preparing to Teach

- Students should know how to simplify fractions by dividing out common factors. Now they will extend this concept to powers.
- **MP8 Look for and Express Regularity in Repeated Reasoning:** In the exploration, students will find quotients of powers and observe the pattern that emerges.
- Remember to use correct vocabulary in this lesson. The numbers are not *canceling*. The factors that are common in the numerator and the denominator are being divided out, similar to simplifying fractions. The fraction $\frac{2}{4} = \frac{1}{2}$ because there is a common factor of 2 in both the numerator and denominator that divides out. This same concept of dividing out common factors is why the Quotient of Powers Property works.

Motivate

- Tell students that you spent last evening working on a very long problem and you want them to give it a try. Write the problem on the board.

$$\frac{1}{2} \cdot \frac{2}{3} \cdot \frac{3}{4} \cdot \frac{4}{5} \cdot \frac{5}{6} \cdot \frac{6}{7} \cdot \frac{7}{8} \cdot \frac{8}{9} \cdot \frac{9}{10}$$

- It is likely that at least one of your students will recognize the answer immediately after you finish writing the problem. Act surprised and ask for his or her strategy … because you spent a long time on the problem.
- You want all students to recognize that the common factors in the numerator divide out with common factors in the denominator, leaving only $\frac{1}{10}$ as the final answer.

Exploration 1

- Have students work with their partners to complete the table. It may help students if you point out that in the middle column, *Repeated Multiplication Form* means the expanded form of each power in the quotient.
- Notice that integers and decimals are used as bases.
- **?** "Why is the first column labeled 'Quotient'?" Two powers are being divided.
- **?** "What do you notice about the number of factors in the numerator and denominator of the middle column, and the exponent used to write the power?" When you subtract the number of factors in the denominator from the number of factors in the numerator, it equals the exponent in the power.
- **?** "How can you write a general rule?" $\frac{a^m}{a^n} = a^{m-n}$ Stress that the bases must be the same to use this property.

8.3 Quotient of Powers Property

Learning Target: Generate equivalent expressions involving quotients of powers.

Success Criteria:
- I can find quotients of powers that have the same base.
- I can simplify expressions using the Quotient of Powers Property.
- I can solve real-life problems involving quotients of powers.

EXPLORATION 1

Finding Quotients of Powers

Work with a partner.

a. Copy and complete the table. Use your results to write a *general rule* for finding $\dfrac{a^m}{a^n}$, a quotient of two powers with the same base.

Math Practice

Find General Methods

How does writing the expanded form of each expression help you find a general rule?

Quotient	Repeated Multiplication Form	Power
$\dfrac{2^4}{2^2}$	$\dfrac{2 \cdot 2 \cdot 2 \cdot 2}{2 \cdot 2}$	
$\dfrac{(-4)^5}{(-4)^2}$		
$\dfrac{7^7}{7^3}$		
$\dfrac{8.5^9}{8.5^6}$		
$\dfrac{10^8}{10^5}$		
$\dfrac{3^{12}}{3^4}$		
$\dfrac{(-5)^7}{(-5)^5}$		
$\dfrac{11^4}{11^1}$		
$\dfrac{x^6}{x^2}$		

b. Use your rule in part (a) to simplify the quotients in the first column of the table above. Does your rule give the results in the third column?

 **Key Idea**

Quotient of Powers Property

Words To divide powers with the same base, subtract their exponents.

Numbers $\dfrac{4^5}{4^2} = 4^{5-2} = 4^3$ **Algebra** $\dfrac{a^m}{a^n} = a^{m-n}$, where $a \neq 0$

EXAMPLE 1 **Dividing Powers with the Same Base**

a. $\dfrac{2^6}{2^4} = 2^{6-4}$ Quotient of Powers Property

$= 2^2$ Simplify.

 **Common Error**

When dividing powers, do not divide the bases.
$\dfrac{2^6}{2^4} = 2^2$, not 1^2.

b. $\dfrac{(-7)^9}{(-7)^3} = (-7)^{9-3}$ Quotient of Powers Property

$= (-7)^6$ Simplify.

c. $\dfrac{h^7}{h^6} = h^{7-6}$ Quotient of Powers Property

$= h^1 = h$ Simplify.

Try It Simplify the expression. Write your answer as a power.

1. $\dfrac{9^7}{9^4}$ **2.** $\dfrac{4.2^6}{4.2^5}$ **3.** $\dfrac{(-8)^8}{(-8)^4}$ **4.** $\dfrac{x^8}{x^3}$

EXAMPLE 2 **Simplifying an Expression**

Simplify $\dfrac{3^4 \cdot 3^2}{3^3}$. Write your answer as a power.

The numerator is a product of powers. Add the exponents in the numerator.

$\dfrac{3^4 \cdot 3^2}{3^3} = \dfrac{3^{4+2}}{3^3}$ Product of Powers Property

$= \dfrac{3^6}{3^3}$ Simplify.

$= 3^{6-3}$ Quotient of Powers Property

$= 3^3$ Simplify.

Try It Simplify the expression. Write your answer as a power.

5. $\dfrac{6^7 \cdot 6^3}{6^5}$ **6.** $\dfrac{2^{15}}{2^3 \cdot 2^5}$ **7.** $\dfrac{m^8 \cdot m^6}{m^5}$

Laurie's Notes

Scaffolding Instruction

- Students explored finding quotients of powers. Now they will use the Quotient of Powers Property to simplify expressions.
- **Emerging:** Students should be able to simplify quotients of powers that have the same base number by first rewriting them in repeated multiplication form. They struggle with quotients involving variable terms or applying the general rule. These students will benefit from guided instruction for the Key Idea and examples.
- **Proficient:** Students recognize the relationship between factors in quotients involving numbers or variables, and they can apply the general rule. They should proceed to the Self-Assessment exercises.

Key Idea

- Write the Key Idea. Discuss the Words, Numbers, and Algebra.
- Students should make another index card to add to the properties from the previous section.

EXAMPLE 1

- **MP6 Attend to Precision:** Write and simplify the expression in part (a). The base is 2 for each power. Ask the following questions to help develop correct vocabulary.
  - "How many factors of 2 are in the numerator?" 6
  - "How many factors of 2 are in the denominator?" 4
  - "How many factors of 2 are common in *both* the numerator and denominator?" 4
  - "How many factors of 2 remain after you divide out the common factors?" 2
- Repeat similar questions for parts (b) and (c).
- Point out the Common Error note. Remind students that the base remains the same. It does not divide out.

Try It

- Have students complete the exercises on whiteboards. Use *Popsicle Sticks* to select students to explain their answers.

EXAMPLE 2

- This example combines two properties. Ask the following questions.
  - "How many factors of 3 are in the numerator?" $4 + 2 = 6$
  - "How many factors of 3 are in the denominator?" 3
  - "How many factors of 3 are common in *both* the numerator and denominator?" 3
  - **MP7 Look for and Make Use of Structure:** "How many factors of 3 remain after you divide out the common factors?" 3

Try It

- Students should work with a partner.

Scaffold instruction to support all students in their learning. Learning is individualized and you may want to group students differently as they move in and out of these levels with each skill and concept. Student self-assessment and feedback help guide your instructional decisions about how and when to layer support for all students to become proficient learners.

Extra Example 1
Simplify each expression. Write your answer as a power.

a. $\dfrac{4^5}{4^2}$ 4^3

b. $\dfrac{(-2)^{10}}{(-2)^3}$ $(-2)^7$

c. $\dfrac{p^9}{p^8}$ p

Try It

1. 9^3	2. 4.2
3. $(-8)^4$	4. x^5
5. 6^5	6. 2^7
7. m^9	

Extra Example 2
Simplify $\dfrac{5^6 \cdot 5^2}{5^4}$. Write your answer as a power. 5^4

ELL Support

After demonstrating Examples 1 and 2, have students work in groups to discuss and complete Try It Exercises 1–7. Provide guiding questions such as, "Which property can you apply? How do you simplify? What is the answer?" Expect students to perform according to their language levels.

Beginner: Write out the steps.

Intermediate: Use simple sentences to explain and contribute to discussion.

Advanced: Use detailed sentences and help guide discussion.

Laurie's Notes

Extra Example 3

Simplify each expression. Write your answer as a power.

a. $\dfrac{(-6)^9}{(-6)^5} \cdot \dfrac{(-6)^3}{(-6)^2}$ $(-6)^5$

b. $\dfrac{z^6}{z^2} \cdot \dfrac{z^8}{z^5}$ z^7

Try It

8. $(-5)^6$

9. d^5

10. p^{10}

ELL Support

Allow students to work in pairs to complete the Self-Assessment for Concepts & Skills exercises. Have each pair display their answers for Exercises 11–16 on a whiteboard for your review. Have two pairs form a group to discuss and come to an agreement for their explanation in Exercise 17. Then have each group present their explanation to the class.

Self-Assessment
for Concepts & Skills

11. $(-3)^7$

12. 8^3

13. x

14. 5^6

15. $(-2)^5$

16. b^{13}

17. $\dfrac{(-4)^8}{(-3)^4}$; The other quotients have powers with the same base.

EXAMPLE 3

- This example also combines two properties.
- Work through the problems as shown.
- Discuss the approach with students. Each quotient was simplified first and then the product of the two expressions was found.
- ❓ "Will the answer be the same if the product of the two expressions is found and then the quotient is simplified? Explain." Yes, it is similar to multiplying two fractions and then simplifying the answer.
- Simplify one of the expressions using the alternate approach in the push-pin note.

$$\frac{a^{10}}{a^6} \cdot \frac{a^7}{a^4} = \frac{a^{10} \cdot a^7}{a^6 \cdot a^4} = \frac{a^{10+7}}{a^{6+4}} = \frac{a^{17}}{a^{10}} = a^{17-10} = a^7$$

Try It

- There is more than one way to simplify these expressions. Remind students to think about the number of factors as they work through the problems.
- In Exercises 9 and 10, students may forget that $d = d^1$ and $p = p^1$.
- Ask volunteers to write their solutions on the board.

Formative Assessment Tip

Misconception Check

This technique gives students the opportunity to think about their own understanding of a concept or process. Write a worked-out problem on the board that demonstrates a common misconception, a mistake that students often make about a concept or process. Ask students if they agree or disagree with the solution and to explain why. Allow time for students to think about the problem independently and write an explanation. Then ask volunteers to share their explanations with the class. Listening to the thinking of others may solidify or modify their own beliefs.

✅ Self-Assessment *for Concepts & Skills*

- **Neighbor Check:** Have students work independently and then have their neighbors check their work. Have students discuss any discrepancies.
- ◉ **Misconception Check:** Write the following problem on the board. Then ask, "Do you agree or disagree with this solution? Explain."

$$\frac{(-3d)^4 \cdot (2x)^8}{(2x)^6 \cdot (-3d)^2} = \frac{(-3d)^4 \cdot (2x)^8}{(-3d)^2 \cdot (2x)^6}$$

$$= \frac{d^4 x^8}{d^2 x^6}$$

$$= d^2 x^2$$

disagree; The constant terms, -3 and 2, cannot be divided out in the second step because they are each raised to an exponent outside of the parentheses.

The Success Criteria Self-Assessment chart can be found in the *Student Journal* or online at *BigIdeasMath.com*.

EXAMPLE 3 **Simplifying Expressions**

a. $\dfrac{(-4)^9}{(-4)^5} \cdot \dfrac{(-4)^8}{(-4)^2} = (-4)^{9-5} \cdot (-4)^{8-2}$ Quotient of Powers Property

$= (-4)^4 \cdot (-4)^6$ Simplify.

$= (-4)^{4+6}$ Product of Powers Property

$= (-4)^{10}$ Simplify.

Math Practice

Look for Structure
Show how you can simplify the expression in part (b) by first multiplying the numerators and then multiplying the denominators.

b. $\dfrac{a^{10}}{a^6} \cdot \dfrac{a^7}{a^4} = a^{10-6} \cdot a^{7-4}$ Quotient of Powers Property

$= a^4 \cdot a^3$ Simplify.

$= a^{4+3}$ Product of Powers Property

$= a^7$ Simplify.

Try It **Simplify the expression. Write your answer as a power.**

8. $\dfrac{(-5)^7 \cdot (-5)^6}{(-5)^5 \cdot (-5)^2}$ 9. $\dfrac{d^5}{d} \cdot \dfrac{d^9}{d^8}$ 10. $\dfrac{p^3 \cdot p^6}{p^2} \cdot \dfrac{p^4}{p}$

Self-Assessment for Concepts & Skills

Solve each exercise. Then rate your understanding of the success criteria in your journal.

SIMPLIFYING EXPRESSIONS **Simplify the expression. Write your answer as a power.**

11. $\dfrac{(-3)^9}{(-3)^2}$ 12. $\dfrac{8^6 \cdot 8^2}{8^5}$ 13. $\dfrac{x^{11}}{x^4 \cdot x^6}$

14. $\dfrac{5^6}{5} \cdot \dfrac{5^3}{5^2}$ 15. $\dfrac{(-2)^9 \cdot (-2)^4}{(-2)^4 \cdot (-2)^4}$ 16. $\dfrac{b^{10} \cdot b^3}{b^2} \cdot \dfrac{b^5}{b^3}$

17. **WHICH ONE DOESN'T BELONG?** Which quotient does *not* belong with the other three? Explain your reasoning.

$$\dfrac{(-10)^7}{(-10)^2} \qquad \dfrac{6^3}{6^2}$$

$$\dfrac{(-4)^8}{(-3)^4} \qquad \dfrac{5^6}{5^3}$$

EXAMPLE 4 **Modeling Real Life**

Land area:
about 5.9^6 mi^2

The projected population of Tennessee in 2030 is about $5 \cdot 5.9^8$. Predict the average number of people per square mile in Tennessee in 2030.

You can find the average number of people per square mile in 2030 by dividing the projected population of Tennessee in 2030 by the land area.

$$\text{People per square mile} = \frac{\text{Population in 2030}}{\text{Land area}}$$

$$= \frac{5 \cdot 5.9^8}{5.9^6} \qquad \text{Substitute.}$$

$$= 5 \cdot \frac{5.9^8}{5.9^6} \qquad \text{Rewrite.}$$

$$= 5 \cdot 5.9^2 \qquad \text{Quotient of Powers Property}$$

$$= 174.05 \qquad \text{Evaluate.}$$

▶ So, you can predict that there will be about 174 people per square mile in Tennessee in 2030.

 Self-Assessment for *Problem Solving*

Solve each exercise. Then rate your understanding of the success criteria in your journal.

18. You want to purchase a cat tracker. Tracker A detects your cat within a radius of $4 \cdot 10^2$ feet of your home. Tracker B detects your cat within a radius of 10^4 feet of your home. Which tracker has a greater radius? How many times greater?

19. **DIG DEEPER!** An earthquake of magnitude 3.0 is 10^2 times stronger than an earthquake of magnitude 1.0. An earthquake of magnitude 8.0 is 10^7 times stronger than an earthquake of magnitude 1.0. How many times stronger is an earthquake of magnitude 8.0 than an earthquake of magnitude 3.0?

20. The edge length of a cube-shaped crate is the square of the edge length of a cube-shaped box. Write an expression for the number of boxes that can fit in the crate. Justify your answer.

Laurie's Notes

EXAMPLE 4

- Ask a volunteer to read the problem aloud.
- This problem is about population density, the number of people per square unit. In this case, it is the projected number of people in Tennessee per square mile in 2030.
- "What do you need to know to solve this problem?" projected population in 2030 and land area
- When working through this problem, notice that the factor 5 in the numerator does not have the same base as the two powers.
- **MP7 Look for and Make Use of Structure:** "Why can you move 5 out of the numerator and write it as a whole number times the quotient of $(5.9)^8$ and $(5.9)^6$?" definition of multiplying fractions
- Simplify the quotient and multiply by 5.
- Use local landmarks to help students visualize the size of a square mile.

✓ Self-Assessment for Problem Solving

- Allow time in class for students to practice using the problem-solving plan. By now, most students should be able to get past the first step.
- **Neighbor Check:** Have students work independently and then have their neighbors check their work. Have students discuss any discrepancies.

The Success Criteria Self-Assessment chart can be found in the *Student Journal* or online at *BigIdeasMath.com*.

Closure

- **Exit Ticket:** Explain how the Quotient of Powers Property is related to simplifying fractions. You divide out the common factors.

Self-Assessment
for Problem Solving

18. Tracker B; 25 times greater

19. 10^5 times stronger

20. s^3;
    Volume of box $= s^3$
    Volume of crate $= (s^2)^3 = s^6$
    $\dfrac{s^6}{s^3} = s^3$

Learning Target

Generate equivalent expressions involving quotients of powers.

Success Criteria

- Find quotients of powers that have the same base.
- Simplify expressions using the Quotient of Powers Property.
- Solve real-life problems involving quotients of powers.

Review & Refresh

1. 4^5

2. a^{25}

3. $x^7 y^7$

4. *Sample answer:* Dilate the red figure using a scale factor of 2 and then translate the image 3 units right and 1 unit up.

5. *Sample answer:* Dilate the red figure using a scale factor of $\frac{1}{2}$ and then reflect the image in the *x*-axis.

 ## Concepts, Skills, & Problem Solving

6. $\dfrac{7 \cdot 7 \cdot 7 \cdot 7 \cdot 7 \cdot 7 \cdot 7 \cdot 7 \cdot 7}{7 \cdot 7 \cdot 7 \cdot 7 \cdot 7 \cdot 7}$; 7^3

7–8. See Additional Answers.

9. 6^6

10. 8^2

11. $(-3)^3$

12. 4.5^2

13. 64

14. $(-17)^3$

15. $(-6.4)^2$

16. π^4

17. no; The exponents should be subtracted, not divided.

18. 7^6

19. 6^7

20. $(-6.1)^2$

21. π^8

22. c^5

23. z^6

Assignment Guide and Concept Check

Scaffold assignments to support all students in their learning progression. The suggested assignments are a starting point. Continue to assign additional exercises and revisit with spaced practice to move every student toward proficiency.

Level	Assignment 1	Assignment 2
Emerging	1, 2, 3, 5, 7, 9, 11, 15, 17, 18, 21, 26	12, 14, 16, 23, 24, 25, 27, 29, 32
Proficient	1, 2, 3, 5, 7, 10, 12, 14, 16, 17, 18, 20, 21, 22, 25, 27	24, 29, 30, 31, 32, 33
Advanced	1, 2, 3, 5, 7, 12, 14, 16, 17, 18, 20, 21, 22, 25, 30	24, 31, 32, 33, 34

- Assignment 1 is for use after students complete the Self-Assessment for Concepts & Skills.
- Assignment 2 is for use after students complete the Self-Assessment for Problem Solving.
- The red exercises can be used as a concept check.

Review & Refresh Prior Skills

Exercises 1 and 2   Finding Powers
Exercise 3   Finding a Power of a Product
Exercises 4 and 5   Describing a Similarity Transformation

Common Errors

- **Exercises 9–16 and 18–23** Students may divide the exponents when they should be subtracting them. Remind students that the Quotient of Powers Property states that the exponents are subtracted.
- **Exercises 9–16 and 18–23** Students may multiply and/or divide the bases when simplifying the expression. Remind them that the base does not change when they use the Quotient of Powers or Product of Powers Property.

8.3 Practice

Go to *BigIdeasMath.com* to get HELP with solving the exercises.

Review & Refresh

Simplify the expression. Write your answer as a power.

1. $4^2 \cdot 4^3$

2. $\left(a^5\right)^5$

3. $(xy)^7$

The red figure is similar to the blue figure. Describe a similarity transformation between the figures.

4.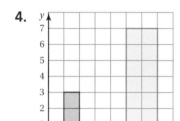

5.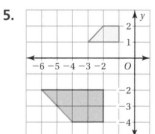

Concepts, Skills, & Problem Solving

FINDING QUOTIENTS OF POWERS **Write the quotient as repeated multiplication. Then write the quotient as a power.** (See Exploration 1, p. 331.)

6. $\dfrac{7^9}{7^6}$

7. $\dfrac{(-4.5)^6}{(-4.5)^2}$

8. $\dfrac{m^{10}}{m^5}$

DIVIDING POWERS WITH THE SAME BASE **Simplify the expression. Write your answer as a power.**

9. $\dfrac{6^{10}}{6^4}$

10. $\dfrac{8^9}{8^7}$

11. $\dfrac{(-3)^4}{(-3)^1}$

12. $\dfrac{4.5^5}{4.5^3}$

13. $\dfrac{64^4}{64^3}$

14. $\dfrac{(-17)^5}{(-17)^2}$

15. $\dfrac{(-6.4)^8}{(-6.4)^6}$

16. $\dfrac{\pi^{11}}{\pi^7}$

17. **MP YOU BE THE TEACHER** Your friend simplifies the quotient. Is your friend correct? Explain your reasoning.

$$\frac{6^{15}}{6^5} = 6^{15/5}$$
$$= 6^3$$

SIMPLIFYING AN EXPRESSION **Simplify the expression. Write your answer as a power.**

18. $\dfrac{7^5 \cdot 7^3}{7^2}$

19. $\dfrac{6^{13}}{6^4 \cdot 6^2}$

20. $\dfrac{(-6.1)^{11}}{(-6.1)^7 \cdot (-6.1)^2}$

21. $\dfrac{\pi^{30}}{\pi^{18} \cdot \pi^4}$

22. $\dfrac{c^{22}}{c^8 \cdot c^9}$

23. $\dfrac{z^8 \cdot z^6}{z^8}$

24. **MP MODELING REAL LIFE** The sound intensity of a normal conversation is 10^6 times greater than the quietest noise a person can hear. The sound intensity of a jet at takeoff is 10^{14} times greater than the quietest noise a person can hear. How many times more intense is the sound of a jet at takeoff than the sound of a normal conversation?

SIMPLIFYING AN EXPRESSION Simplify the expression. Write your answer as a power.

25. $\dfrac{(-4)^8 \cdot (-4)^3}{(-4)^4 \cdot (-4)^2}$

26. $\dfrac{6^2}{6} \cdot \dfrac{6^{12}}{6^8}$

27. $\dfrac{3^2 \cdot 3^6}{3^2} \cdot \dfrac{3^5}{3}$

28. $\dfrac{z^7 \cdot z^6}{z \cdot z^2}$

29. $\dfrac{x^5}{x^4} \cdot \dfrac{x^{13}}{x^8}$

30. $\dfrac{y^8 \cdot y^2}{y^7} \cdot \dfrac{y^4}{y} \cdot \dfrac{y^7}{y^2}$

Device	Storage (GB)	Price
A	2^5	$30
B	2^6	$50
C	2^7	$70
D	2^8	$90
E	2^9	$110

31. **MP REASONING** The storage capacities and prices of five devices are shown in the table.

   a. How many times more storage does Device D have than Device B?

   b. Do storage and price have a linear relationship? Explain.

32. **DIG DEEPER!** Consider the equation $\dfrac{9^m}{9^n} = 9^{2n}$.

   a. Find two numbers m and n that satisfy the equation.

   b. Describe the number of solutions that satisfy the equation. Explain your reasoning.

Milky Way galaxy: $10 \cdot 10^{10}$ stars

33. **MP MODELING REAL LIFE** A scientist estimates that there are about 10^{24} stars in the universe and that each galaxy has, on average, approximately the same number of stars as the Milky Way galaxy. About how many galaxies are in the universe?

34. **MP NUMBER SENSE** Find the value of x that makes $\dfrac{8^{3x}}{8^{2x+1}} = 8^9$ true. Explain how you found your answer.

Mini-Assessment

Simplify the expression. Write your answer as a power.

1. $\dfrac{(-4)^3}{(-4)^1}$ $(-4)^2$

2. $\dfrac{9.7^7}{9.7^3}$ 9.7^4

3. $\dfrac{5^4 \cdot 5^2}{5^3}$ 5^3

4. $\dfrac{m^{10}}{m^5 \cdot m^2}$ m^3

5. $\dfrac{y^{17}}{y^{10}} \cdot \dfrac{y^6}{y^3}$ y^{10}

Concepts, Skills, & Problem Solving

24. 10^8 times more intense

25. $(-4)^5$

26. 6^5

27. 3^{10}

28. z^{10}

29. x^6

30. y^{11}

31. **a.** 4 times more storage

    b. no; As the price increases by $20, the storage capacity doubles.

32. **a.** *Sample answer:* $m = 9$, $n = 3$

    b. infinitely many solutions; Any two numbers that satisfy the equation $m - n = 2n$ are solutions.

33. 10^{13} galaxies

34. 10; The difference in the exponents needs to be 9. To find x, solve the equation $3x - (2 + 1) = 9$.

Section Resources

Surface Level	Deep Level

Resources by Chapter
  • Extra Practice
  • Reteach
  • Puzzle Time
Student Journal
  • Self-Assessment
  • Practice
Differentiating the Lesson
Tutorial Videos
Skills Review Handbook
Skills Trainer
	Resources by Chapter
	  • Enrichment and Extension
	Graphic Organizers
	Dynamic Assessment System
	  • Section Practice

Learning Target

Understand the concepts of zero and negative exponents.

Success Criteria

- Explain the meanings of zero and negative exponents.
- Evaluate numerical expressions involving zero and negative exponents.
- Simplify algebraic expressions involving zero and negative exponents.

Warm Up

Cumulative, vocabulary, and prerequisite skills practice opportunities are available in the *Resources by Chapter* or at *BigIdeasMath.com*.

ELL Support

Remind students that negative numbers are numbers less than 0. Numbers greater than 0 are positive numbers. The words *negative* and *positive* are considered opposites. In everyday language, the word *negative* is associated with bad experiences, while *positive* is associated with good experiences. The words *no* and *not*, and the prefix *non-* indicate negative meanings.

Exploration 1

a. See Additional Answers.

b. Each expression equals 1; You can equate the powers in the last column of the table in part (a) to 1. So, based on these results, you can conclude that $a^0 = 1$, where $a \neq 0$.

Exploration 2

a–b. See Additional Answers.

c. $a^{-n} = \dfrac{1}{a^n}$

Laurie's Notes

Preparing to Teach

- **MP8 Look for and Express Regularity in Repeated Reasoning:** In the explorations, students will use previously learned properties to define zero and negative exponents.

Motivate

- Writing a number in expanded form should be familiar to students.
- "How do you write 234 in expanded form?" $200 + 30 + 4$
- "How do you write the expanded form using powers of 10?"
  $2 \times 10^2 + 3 \times 10 + 4 \times 1$
- "Do you think it is possible to write 234.56 in expanded form using powers of 10?" Answers will vary.
- Explain that in today's explorations, students will explore zero and negative exponents, which can be used to write a decimal in expanded notation.

Exploration 1

- Have students work with their partners to complete the table. To fill in the middle column, students should use the Quotient of Powers Property to rewrite the quotients in the first column. For example, $\dfrac{5^3}{5^3} = 5^{3-3}$. To fill in the last column, students should write the expression with a single exponent, 5^0.
- As students work through the exploration, they should discover that all of the powers in the last column of the table have an exponent of zero.
- In part (b), students should notice that each quotient in the first column of the table is equivalent to 1. They should summarize their findings by writing $a^0 = 1$.
- Discuss the fact that some of the language used in earlier sections does not apply here. For instance, when referring to 5^0, you do not say, "5 used as a factor 0 times." You just say, "5 to the 0 power."

Exploration 2

- Introduce this exploration by having students evaluate 2^3, 2^2, 2^1, and 2^0. I like to present this vertically, so the pattern is more evident.
- "What is the pattern represented by these powers?" As the exponent decreases by 1, the power is divided by 2.
- "What do you think the values of 2^{-1} and 2^{-2} will be?" Answers will vary.
- This exploration uses the Product of Powers Property to help students come up with the definition for a negative exponent.
- Have students work with their partners to complete the table. To fill in the middle column, students should use the Product of Powers Property to rewrite the products in the first column. For example, $5^{-3} \cdot 5^3 = 5^{-3+3}$.
- The Multiplicative Inverse Property states that the product of a number and its reciprocal is 1. Make sure students see the connection between negative exponents and reciprocals.
- Ask several students to explain their definitions in part (c).
- "Was your prediction for the values of 2^{-1} and 2^{-2} correct?" Answers will vary.

8.4 Zero and Negative Exponents

Learning Target: Understand the concepts of zero and negative exponents.

Success Criteria:
- I can explain the meanings of zero and negative exponents.
- I can evaluate numerical expressions involving zero and negative exponents.
- I can simplify algebraic expressions involving zero and negative exponents.

EXPLORATION 1

Understanding Zero Exponents

Work with a partner.

a. Copy and complete the table.

Quotient	Quotient of Powers Property	Power
$\dfrac{5^3}{5^3}$		
$\dfrac{6^2}{6^2}$		
$\dfrac{(-3)^4}{(-3)^4}$		
$\dfrac{(-4)^5}{(-4)^5}$		

Math Practice

Find Entry Points

How can you use what you know about division to evaluate the expressions in the table?

b. Evaluate each expression in the first column of the table in part (a). How can you use these results to define a^0, where $a \neq 0$?

EXPLORATION 2

Understanding Negative Exponents

Work with a partner.

a. Copy and complete the table.

Product	Product of Powers Property	Power	Value
$5^{-3} \cdot 5^3$			
$6^2 \cdot 6^{-2}$			
$(-3)^4 \cdot (-3)^{-4}$			
$(-4)^{-5} \cdot (-4)^5$			

b. How can you use the Multiplicative Inverse Property to rewrite the powers containing negative exponents in the first column of the table?

c. Use your results in parts (a) and (b) to define a^{-n}, where $a \neq 0$ and n is an integer.

8.4 Lesson

 **Key Ideas**

Zero Exponents

Words For any nonzero number a, $a^0 = 1$. The power 0^0 is *undefined*.

Numbers $4^0 = 1$ **Algebra** $a^0 = 1$, where $a \neq 0$

Negative Exponents

Words For any integer n and any nonzero number a, a^{-n} is the reciprocal of a^n.

Numbers $4^{-2} = \dfrac{1}{4^2}$ **Algebra** $a^{-n} = \dfrac{1}{a^n}$, where $a \neq 0$

EXAMPLE 1 **Evaluating Expressions**

a. $3^{-4} = \dfrac{1}{3^4}$ Definition of a negative exponent

   $= \dfrac{1}{81}$ Evaluate the power.

b. $(-8.5)^{-4} \cdot (-8.5)^4 = (-8.5)^{-4+4}$ Product of Powers Property

   $= (-8.5)^0$ Simplify.

   $= 1$ Definition of a zero exponent

c. $\dfrac{2^6}{2^8} = 2^{6-8}$ Quotient of Powers Property

   $= 2^{-2}$ Simplify.

   $= \dfrac{1}{2^2}$ Definition of a negative exponent

   $= \dfrac{1}{4}$ Evaluate the power.

Try It **Evaluate the expression.**

1. 4^{-2} **2.** $(-2)^{-5}$ **3.** $6^{-8} \cdot 6^8$

4. $\dfrac{(-3)^5}{(-3)^6}$ **5.** $\dfrac{1}{5^7} \cdot \dfrac{1}{5^{-4}}$ **6.** $\dfrac{4^5 \cdot 4^{-3}}{4^2}$

Laurie's Notes

Scaffolding Instruction

- Students have explored zero and negative exponents. Now they will use the definitions of zero and negative exponents to evaluate and simplify expressions.
- **Emerging:** Students may struggle with negative exponents. They will benefit from guided instruction for the Key Ideas, examples, and Try It exercises.
- **Proficient:** Students recognize the pattern formed by decreasing exponents and can evaluate expressions using zero and negative exponents. They should proceed to the Self-Assessment exercises.

Key Ideas

- The definition of zero exponents is easily understood by most students. Writing a negative exponent as a unit fraction with a positive exponent in the denominator takes time for some students to understand. They need to see multiple examples of simplifying fractions using the Quotient of Powers Property and of dividing out common factors, where the exponent in the denominator is greater than the exponent in the numerator.

- Example: $\dfrac{5^2}{5^3} = 5^{2-3} = 5^{-1}$ $\qquad \dfrac{5^2}{5^3} = \dfrac{\overset{1}{\cancel{5}} \cdot \overset{1}{\cancel{5}}}{\underset{1}{\cancel{5}} \cdot \underset{1}{\cancel{5}} \cdot 5} = \dfrac{1}{5}$

  The Quotient of Powers Property is used on the left. Dividing out common factors is used on the right. Because both starting expressions are the same, the results must be equivalent. So, $5^{-1} = \dfrac{1}{5^1}$.

- Note that 0^0 is undefined.
- Students should make index cards to add these definitions to their property cards.

EXAMPLE 1

- Part (a) is a direct application of the definition of a negative exponent.
- In part (b), the bases are the same, so the exponents are added.
- In part (c), the Quotient of Powers Property is used first, resulting in a negative exponent. Use the definition of a negative exponent and simplify.

Try It

- Students should show their work and justify each step.
- Exercise 5 can be done by thinking about simple fractions and how they are multiplied. The product of these two fractions is $\dfrac{1}{5^7 \cdot 5^{-4}} = \dfrac{1}{5^3}$.
- **MP2 Reason Abstractly and Quantitatively & MP7 Look for and Make Use of Structure:** Several of these expressions can be evaluated in more than one way. Ask students to share their methods.

Extra Example 1
Evaluate each expression.

a. 4^{-3} $\quad \dfrac{1}{64}$

b. $(-3.7)^{-2} \cdot (-3.7)^2$ $\quad 1$

c. $\dfrac{3^6}{3^9}$ $\quad \dfrac{1}{27}$

ELL Support

After demonstrating Example 1, have students work in groups to discuss and complete Try It Exercises 1–6. Provide guiding questions such as, "Can you use any properties? How can you rewrite a power with a negative exponent? with a zero exponent? How do you simplify?" Expect students to perform according to their language levels.

Beginner: Write out the steps.

Intermediate: Use simple sentences to explain and contribute to discussion.

Advanced: Use detailed sentences and help guide discussion.

Try It

1. $\dfrac{1}{16}$ 2. $-\dfrac{1}{32}$

3. 1 4. $-\dfrac{1}{3}$

5. $\dfrac{1}{125}$ 6. 1

Laurie's Notes

Extra Example 2

Simplify. Write each expression using only positive exponents.

a. $-2x^0$ $\;-2$

b. $\dfrac{4b^{-4}}{b^7}$ $\;\dfrac{4}{b^{11}}$

c. $\dfrac{m^{-5} \cdot m^{-8}}{2}$ $\;\dfrac{1}{2m^{13}}$

Try It

7. $\dfrac{8}{x^2}$

8. $\dfrac{1}{b^{10}}$

9. $\dfrac{1}{15z^3}$

Self-Assessment
for Concepts & Skills

10. $\dfrac{1}{49}$

11. $\dfrac{1}{64}$

12. $\dfrac{1}{81}$

13. $\dfrac{10}{t^5}$

14. $\dfrac{1}{w^6}$

15. $\dfrac{1}{4}$

16. Write $(-3) \cdot (-3) \cdot (-3)$ as a power with an integer base.; $(-3)^3$; 3^{-3}

EXAMPLE 2

- **MP6 Attend to Precision:** It is assumed that the variables are nonzero in expressions such as those given in this example, so that the rules for zero and negative exponents can be used. Discuss this with students.
- **Common Error:** In part (a), some students see the zero exponent and immediately think the answer is 1. Remind students that only the variable is being raised to the 0 exponent; -5 is not.
- **Common Error:** In part (b), the constant 9 is not being raised to an exponent, only the variables are. Students need to distinguish this. In the step where the expression has been simplified to $9y^{-8}$, ask, "What is being raised to the -8 power? In other words, what is the base for the exponent?" y
- **MP1 Make Sense of Problems and Persevere in Solving Them:** Work through the steps slowly. It takes time for students to make sense of all that is going on in each problem. Because there is often more than one approach to simplifying the expression, it can confuse students. Instead of seeing it as a way to show that the properties are all connected, students see it as a way of trying to confuse them. Students will better recognize these connections if they write the properties or reasons that justify each step of their work.

Try It

- Have students share their work at the board, *and* explain aloud what they did. Students need to hear the words and see the work. It also helps students become better communicators when they have the opportunity to practice their skills.

✓ Self-Assessment *for Concepts & Skills*

- **Neighbor Check:** Have students work independently and then have their neighbors check their work. Have students discuss any discrepancies.
- Select several students to share their work with the class.
- ◉ **Quick Write:** Explain the difference between negative exponents and positive exponents.

ELL Support

Allow students to work in pairs for extra support and to practice language. Have each pair display their answers for Exercises 10–15 on a whiteboard for your review. Have two pairs form a group to discuss and come to an agreement for their answers in Exercise 16. Review the answers as a class.

The Success Criteria Self-Assessment chart can be found in the *Student Journal* or online at *BigIdeasMath.com*.

EXAMPLE 2 **Simplifying Expressions**

a. $-5x^0 = -5(1)$ Definition of a zero exponent

$= -5$ Multiply.

b. $\dfrac{9y^{-3}}{y^5} = 9y^{-3-5}$ Quotient of Powers Property

$= 9y^{-8}$ Simplify.

$= \dfrac{9}{y^8}$ Definition of a negative exponent

c. $\dfrac{n^4 \cdot n^{-7}}{6} = \dfrac{n^{4+(-7)}}{6}$ Product of Powers Property

$= \dfrac{n^{-3}}{6}$ Simplify.

$= \dfrac{1}{6n^3}$ Definition of a negative exponent

Try It Simplify. Write the expression using only positive exponents.

7. $8x^{-2}$ **8.** $b^0 \cdot b^{-10}$ **9.** $\dfrac{z^6}{15z^9}$

Self-Assessment for Concepts & Skills

Solve each exercise. Then rate your understanding of the success criteria in your journal.

EVALUATING EXPRESSIONS Evaluate the expression.

10. 7^{-2} **11.** $4^{-3} \cdot 4^0$ **12.** $\dfrac{(-9)^5}{(-9)^7}$

SIMPLIFYING EXPRESSIONS Simplify. Write the expression using only positive exponents.

13. $10t^{-5}$ **14.** $w^3 \cdot w^{-9}$ **15.** $\dfrac{r^8 \cdot r^{-8}}{4}$

16. **DIFFERENT WORDS, SAME QUESTION** Which is different? Find "both" answers.

Write $\dfrac{1}{3 \cdot 3 \cdot 3}$ using a negative exponent.

Write 3 to the negative third.

Write $\dfrac{1}{3}$ cubed as a power with an integer base.

Write $(-3) \cdot (-3) \cdot (-3)$ as a power with an integer base.

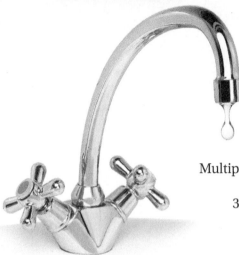

EXAMPLE 3 **Modeling Real Life**

One drop of water leaks from a faucet every second. How many liters of water leak from the faucet in 1 hour?

Because you know how much water leaks per second, convert 1 hour to seconds.

$$1 \cancel{h} \times \frac{60 \cancel{\text{min}}}{1 \cancel{h}} \times \frac{60 \text{ sec}}{1 \cancel{\text{min}}} = 3600 \text{ sec}$$

Multiply the rate that water leaks by 3600 seconds.

$$3600 \cancel{\text{sec}} \cdot \frac{50^{-2} \text{ L}}{1 \cancel{\text{sec}}} = 3600 \cdot \frac{1}{50^2} \text{ L} \qquad \text{Definition of a negative exponent}$$

$$= 3600 \cdot \frac{1}{2500} \text{ L} \qquad \text{Evaluate the power.}$$

$$= \frac{3600}{2500} \text{ L} \qquad \text{Multiply.}$$

$$= 1\frac{11}{25}, \text{ or } 1.44 \text{ L} \qquad \text{Simplify.}$$

So, 1.44 liters of water leak from the faucet in 1 hour.

Drop of water: 50^{-2} liter

Self-Assessment for Problem Solving

Solve each exercise. Then rate your understanding of the success criteria in your journal.

17. The mass of a grain of sand is about 10^{-3} gram. About how many grains of sand are in a 10-kilogram bag of sand?

18. A one-celled, aquatic organism called a *dinoflagellate* is 1000 micrometers long. A microscope magnifies the dinoflagellate 100 times. What is the magnified length of the dinoflagellate in meters? (1 micrometer is 10^{-6} meter.)

19. **DIG DEEPER!** A garden is 12 yards long. Assuming the snail moves at a constant speed, how many minutes does it take the snail to travel the length of the garden? Justify your answer.

Speed: 5^{-2} foot per second

Laurie's Notes

EXAMPLE 3

- Ask a student to read the problem aloud.
- Model solving this problem using a *KNWS Chart*. A sample chart is shown.

K	N	W	S
• the rate of leaking (in drops per second) • the amount of liters in a drop	• the picture	• To find how many liters of water leak from the faucet in 1 hour.	• Convert 1 hour to seconds. Then multiply the rate that water leaks by the number of seconds in 1 hour.

? As you fill in a *KNWS Chart*, ask students probing questions.
- "What do you know?" the rate of leaking (in drops per second) and the amount of liters in a drop
- "What are you asked to find?" the amount of water (in liters) that the faucet leaks in 1 hour
- "Is there anything else you need to know to solve this problem?" the number of seconds in an hour
- Work through the dimensional analysis steps as shown.

✓ Self-Assessment *for Problem Solving*

- The goal for all students is to feel comfortable with the problem-solving plan. It is important for students to problem-solve in class, where they may receive support from you and their peers. By now, most students should be able to get past the first step.
- Have students work with a partner and use a *KNWS Chart* to help solve each problem.

The Success Criteria Self-Assessment chart can be found in the *Student Journal* or online at *BigIdeasMath.com*.

Closure

- **Exit Ticket:** Simplify.

  a. $4x^{-3}$ $\dfrac{4}{x^3}$

  b. $\dfrac{6^3}{6^5}$ $\dfrac{1}{36}$

  c. $\dfrac{4n^0}{n^2}$ $\dfrac{4}{n^2}$

Extra Example 3

A faucet leaks water at a rate of 4^{-6} liter per second. How many liters of water leak from the faucet in 1 hour? *about 0.88 L*

Self-Assessment
for Problem Solving

17. 10^7 grains of sand

18. 10^{-1} m

19. 15 min; *Sample answer:*
    12 yd = 36 ft

    $5^{-2} = \dfrac{1}{5^2} = \dfrac{1}{25}$ ft/sec

    $\dfrac{36 \text{ ft}}{\frac{1}{25} \text{ ft/sec}} = 900 \text{ sec} = 15 \text{ min}$

Learning Target

Understand the concepts of zero and negative exponents.

Success Criteria

- Explain the meanings of zero and negative exponents.
- Evaluate numerical expressions involving zero and negative exponents.
- Simplify algebraic expressions involving zero and negative exponents.

Review & Refresh

1. 10^4

2. y^2

3. $(-3)^9$

4. yes; The triangles have two pairs of congruent angles.

5. no; The triangles do not have the same angle measures.

6. D

 Concepts, Skills, & Problem Solving

7. $7^{-4\,+\,4}$; 7^0; 1

8. $(-2)^{5\,+\,(-5)}$; $(-2)^0$; 1

9. 1

10. 125

11. 1

12. 1

13. $\dfrac{1}{36}$

14. 1

15. $\dfrac{1}{16}$

16. $-\dfrac{1}{3}$

17. $\dfrac{1}{4}$

18. $\dfrac{1}{243}$

19. $\dfrac{1}{125}$

20. 1

21. no; The negative sign goes with the exponent, not the base.

22. 2^0; 10^0

Assignment Guide and Concept Check

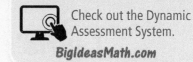 Check out the Dynamic Assessment System.

BigIdeasMath.com

Scaffold assignments to support all students in their learning progression. The suggested assignments are a starting point. Continue to assign additional exercises and revisit with spaced practice to move every student toward proficiency.

Level	Assignment 1	Assignment 2
Emerging	3, 4, 5, 6, 7, 8, 9, 11, 13, 15, 17, 19, 21, 24, 27	10, 12, 14, 16, 18, 20, 23, 25, 28, 33, 35, 37, 38
Proficient	3, 4, 5, 6, 7, 8, 10, 12, 16, 18, 19, 20, 21, 24, 26	22, 23, 29, 30, 31, 32, 34, 36, 37, 38, 39
Advanced	3, 4, 5, 6, 7, 8, 10, 12, 16, 18, 19, 20, 21, 26, 29	22, 23, 30, 31, 32, 34, 36, 37, 38, 39, 40

- Assignment 1 is for use after students complete the Self-Assessment for Concepts & Skills.
- Assignment 2 is for use after students complete the Self-Assessment for Problem Solving.
- The red exercises can be used as a concept check.

Review & Refresh Prior Skills

Exercises 1 and 2 Dividing Powers with the Same Base
Exercise 3 Simplifying an Expression
Exercises 4 and 5 Identifying Similar Triangles
Exercise 6 Choosing a Data Display

Common Errors

- **Exercises 9–12, 14, and 20** Students may think that a power with a zero exponent is equal to zero. Remind them of the definition of a zero exponent.
- **Exercises 11–13 and 15–20** Students may think that a negative exponent makes the power negative. Remind them of the definition of a negative exponent.
- **Exercises 9–20** Students may forget to complete the solution; they may simplify the expression, but leave the expression with exponents. Point out that they need to evaluate any powers to complete the solution.

8.4 Practice

? Go to **BigIdeasMath.com** to get HELP with solving the exercises.

▷ **Review & Refresh**

Simplify the expression. Write your answer as a power.

1. $\dfrac{10^8}{10^4}$

2. $\dfrac{y^9}{y^7}$

3. $\dfrac{(-3)^8 \cdot (-3)^3}{(-3)^2}$

Tell whether the triangles are similar. Explain.

4.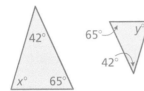

5.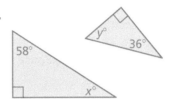

6. Which data display best orders numerical data and shows how they are distributed?

A. bar graph

B. line graph

C. scatter plot

D. stem-and-leaf plot

▷▷ **Concepts, Skills, & Problem Solving**

UNDERSTANDING NEGATIVE EXPONENTS Copy and complete the table. (See Exploration 2, p. 337.)

	Product	Product of Powers Property	Power	Value
7.	$7^{-4} \cdot 7^4$			
8.	$(-2)^5 \cdot (-2)^{-5}$			

EVALUATING EXPRESSIONS Evaluate the expression.

9. $\dfrac{8^7}{8^7}$

10. $5^0 \cdot 5^3$

11. $(-2)^{-8} \cdot (-2)^8$

12. $9^4 \cdot 9^{-4}$

13. 6^{-2}

14. 158^0

15. $\dfrac{4^3}{4^5}$

16. $\dfrac{-3}{(-3)^2}$

17. $2^2 \cdot 2^{-4}$

18. $3^{-3} \cdot 3^{-2}$

19. $\dfrac{1}{5^{-3}} \cdot \dfrac{1}{5^6}$

20. $\dfrac{(1.5)^2}{(1.5)^{-2} \cdot (1.5)^4}$

21. 🔴 **YOU BE THE TEACHER** Your friend evaluates 4^{-3}. Is your friend correct? Explain your reasoning.

> $4^{-3} = (-4)(-4)(-4)$
> $= -64$

22. **CRITICAL THINKING** How can you write the number 1 as a power with base 2? a power with base 10?

23. **MP** **NUMBER SENSE** Without evaluating, order 5^0, 5^4, and 5^{-5} from least to greatest. Explain your reasoning.

SIMPLIFYING EXPRESSIONS **Simplify. Write the expression using only positive exponents.**

24. $6y^{-4}$

25. $8^{-2} \cdot a^7$

26. $\dfrac{9c^3}{c^{-4}}$

27. $\dfrac{5b^{-2}}{b^{-3}}$

28. $\dfrac{8x^3}{2x^9}$

29. $3d^{-4} \cdot 4d^4$

30. $m^{-2} \cdot n^3$

31. $\dfrac{3^{-2} \cdot k^0 \cdot w^0}{w^{-6}}$

32. **OPEN-ENDED** Write two different powers with negative exponents that have the same value. Justify your answer.

MP **REASONING** **In Exercises 33–36, use the table.**

33. How many millimeters are in a decimeter?

34. How many micrometers are in a centimeter?

35. How many nanometers are in a millimeter?

36. How many micrometers are in a meter?

Unit of Length	Length (meter)
Decimeter	10^{-1}
Centimeter	10^{-2}
Millimeter	10^{-3}
Micrometer	10^{-6}
Nanometer	10^{-9}

37. **MP** **MODELING REAL LIFE** A bacterium is 100 micrometers long. A virus is 1000 times smaller than the bacterium.

    a. Using the table above, find the length of the virus in meters.

    b. Is the answer to part (a) *less than, greater than,* or *equal to* 1 micrometer?

38. **DIG DEEPER!** Every 2 seconds, someone in the United States needs blood. A sample blood donation is shown.

    a. One cubic millimeter of blood contains about 10^4 white blood cells. How many white blood cells are in the donation? ($1 \text{ mm}^3 = 10^{-3} \text{ mL}$)

    b. One cubic millimeter of blood contains about 5×10^6 red blood cells. How many red blood cells are in the donation?

    c. Compare your answers for parts (a) and (b).

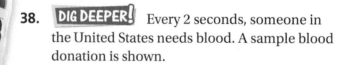

39. **MP** **PRECISION** Describe how to rewrite a power with a positive exponent as a fraction with a power in the denominator. Use the definition of negative exponents to justify your reasoning.

40. **MP** **REASONING** The definition of a negative exponent states that $a^{-n} = \dfrac{1}{a^n}$. Explain why this rule does not apply when $a = 0$.

 # Common Errors

- **Exercises 24 and 26–29** In an expression such as $6y^{-4}$, students may think that both the constant and the variable have the exponent -4. Make sure students understand that in such an expression, the base for the exponent is y and not $6y$.

Mini-Assessment

Evaluate the expression.

1. 5^{-3} $\dfrac{1}{125}$

2. 9^0 1

3. $\dfrac{1}{2^{-2}} \cdot \dfrac{1}{2^5}$ $\dfrac{1}{8}$

Simplify. Write the expression using only positive exponents.

4. $4b^{-5}$ $\dfrac{4}{b^5}$

5. $\dfrac{2^{-4} \cdot m^0 \cdot n^{-3}}{n^{-4}}$ $\dfrac{n}{16}$

Section Resources

Surface Level	Deep Level

Resources by Chapter
  • Extra Practice
  • Reteach
  • Puzzle Time
Student Journal
  • Self-Assessment
  • Practice
Differentiating the Lesson
Tutorial Videos
Skills Review Handbook
Skills Trainer
	Resources by Chapter
	  • Enrichment and Extension
	Graphic Organizers
	Dynamic Assessment System
	  • Section Practice

Transfer Level	

Dynamic Assessment System
  • Mid-Chapter Quiz
	Assessment Book
	  • Mid-Chapter Quiz

 # Concepts, Skills, & Problem Solving

23. $5^{-5}, 5^0, 5^4$; Each base is 5, so order the exponents.

24. $\dfrac{6}{y^4}$

25. $\dfrac{a^7}{64}$

26. $9c^7$

27. $5b$

28. $\dfrac{4}{x^6}$

29. 12

30. $\dfrac{n^3}{m^2}$

31. $\dfrac{w^6}{9}$

32. *Sample answer:* $2^{-4}; 4^{-2};$
    $2^{-4} = \dfrac{1}{2^4} = \dfrac{1}{16}, 4^{-2} = \dfrac{1}{4^2} = \dfrac{1}{16}$

33. 100 mm

34. 10,000 micrometers

35. 1,000,000 nanometers

36. 1,000,000 micrometers

37. **a.** 10^{-7} m

    b. less than

38. **a.** 5,000,000,000 white blood cells

    b. 2,500,000,000,000 red blood cells

    c. There are 500 times as many red blood cells as white blood cells in the donation.

39. Write the power as 1 divided by a power with the same base and a negative exponent;
    $a^n = a^{-(-n)} = \dfrac{1}{a^{-n}}$

40. When $a = 0$ and n is positive, $0^n = 0$. Because you cannot divide by 0, the expression $\dfrac{1}{0}$ is undefined.

Learning Target

Round numbers and write the results as the product of a single digit and a power of 10.

Success Criteria

- Round very large and very small numbers.
- Write a multiple of 10 as a power.
- Compare very large or very small quantities.

Warm Up

Cumulative, vocabulary, and prerequisite skills practice opportunities are available in the *Resources by Chapter* or at *BigIdeasMath.com*.

ELL Support

Ask students if they know what the word *estimating* means. If they need support, explain that it means, "roughly calculating a value." Students may be familiar with the word *round*, as it describes the shape of a circle. If needed, draw a circle on the board to demonstrate. Explain that *round* can also be used to describe a process of changing a number to one that is less exact but easier to use. Quickly demonstrate the process of rounding a number.

Exploration 1

a. 6×10^{-2} m   **b.** 6×10^3 m

c. 2×10^{-1} m   **d.** 1×10^1 m

Sample answer: Start with the picture that is the most zoomed out and match it with the largest distance. Then, each successive zoom in can be matched with the next largest distance.

Exploration 2

See Additional Answers.

Laurie's Notes

Preparing to Teach

- In a previous course, students studied patterns in the number of zeros of the product when multiplying a number by powers of 10. They will use this knowledge and their understanding of powers to approximate and write very large and very small numbers as the product of a single digit and a power of 10. This section prepares students for working with numbers written in scientific notation in the next two sections.
- **MP2 Reason Abstractly and Quantitatively:** Students will reason about very large and very small numbers. Mathematically proficient students recognize the efficiency of using approximations (products of single digits and powers of 10) to comprehend and compare very large or very small numbers.

Motivate

- ❓ "Have you had your millionth heartbeat?" Answers will vary.
- Assume that your heart beats once per second, and it has since you were born. Convert 1 million seconds to days.

$$10^6 \text{ sec} \cdot \frac{1 \text{ min}}{60 \text{ sec}} \cdot \frac{1 \text{ h}}{60 \text{ min}} \cdot \frac{1 \text{ day}}{24 \text{ h}} \approx 11.57 \text{ days}$$

- Clearly, all of your students have had their millionth heartbeat, but have they had their billionth? Because there are 1000 million in 1 billion,

$$11.57 \text{ days} \times 1000 = 11{,}570 \text{ days and}$$

$$11{,}570 \text{ days} \cdot \frac{1 \text{ year}}{365 \text{ days}} \approx 31.7 \text{ years.}$$

Exploration 1

- Most students will enjoy trying to figure out what is in each picture.
- Make a transparency of the photos or display them under a document camera to facilitate discussion.
- ❓ "What clues did you use to match the photos with the distances?" Answers will vary.

Exploration 2

- ❓ "How can you match each number with its closest approximation?" Guide students towards comparing the number of zeros with the exponents.
- ❓ "How are the single digits in List 2 related to the numbers in List 1?" *Sample answer:* If you round the numbers in List 1 so that they each contain only one nonzero digit, these nonzero digits represent the single digits in List 2. For example, 180,000,000,000,000 rounds to 200,000,000,000,000 so the single digit is 2.
- Allow time for students to work on matching the two lists with their partners.
- Ask students to explain their methods.
- ❓ "Did you have any trouble determining the powers of 10 that represent the very small numbers? Explain." Answers will vary.

8.5 Estimating Quantities

Learning Target: Round numbers and write the results as the product of a single digit and a power of 10.

Success Criteria:
- I can round very large and very small numbers.
- I can write a multiple of 10 as a power.
- I can compare very large or very small quantities.

EXPLORATION 1

Using Powers of 10

Work with a partner. Match each picture with the most appropriate distance. Explain your reasoning.

$$6 \times 10^3 \, \text{m} \qquad 1 \times 10^1 \, \text{m} \qquad 2 \times 10^{-1} \, \text{m} \qquad 6 \times 10^{-2} \, \text{m}$$

a.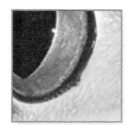

b.

c.

d.

EXPLORATION 2

Approximating Numbers

Work with a partner. Match each number in List 1 with its closest approximation in List 2. Explain your method.

Math Practice

Look for Patterns

How can you use the number of zeros to determine the value of the exponent for each number in List 1?

	List 1		*List 2*
a.	180,000,000,000,000	A.	3×10^{11}
b.	0.0000000011	B.	1×10^{-5}
c.	302,000,000,000	C.	2×10^{14}
d.	0.00000028	D.	3×10^{13}
e.	0.0000097	E.	3×10^{-7}
f.	330,000,000,000,000	F.	1×10^{-9}
g.	26,000,000,000,000	G.	2×10^{-5}
h.	0.000023	H.	3×10^{14}

8.5 Lesson

> **Round the number so that it contains exactly one nonzero digit.**

One way to approximate a very large or a very small number is to round the number and write the result as the product of a single digit and a power of 10.

EXAMPLE 1 **Approximating a Large Number**

Earth contains about 332,500,000 cubic miles of water. The blue sphere represents all of the water on Earth, relative to the size of the planet.

Round the volume of water on Earth. Write the result as the product of a single digit and a power of 10.

$$332{,}500{,}000 \approx 300{,}000{,}000 \qquad \text{Round to the nearest 100,000,000.}$$
$$= 3 \times 100{,}000{,}000 \qquad \text{Factor out 3.}$$
$$= 3 \times 10^8 \qquad \text{Write 100,000,000 as a power of 10.}$$

▷ Earth contains about 3×10^8 cubic miles of water.

Try It **Round the number. Write the result as the product of a single digit and a power of 10.**

1. 8,031,426,100

2. 98,247,836,218

EXAMPLE 2 **Approximating a Small Number**

A blood vessel has a diameter of 0.0000924 meter. Round the diameter of the blood vessel. Write the result as the product of a single digit and a power of 10.

$$0.0000924 \approx 0.00009 \qquad \text{Round to the nearest 0.00001.}$$
$$= 9 \times 0.00001 \qquad \text{Factor out 9.}$$
$$= 9 \times 10^{-5} \qquad \text{Write 0.00001 as a power of 10.}$$

▷ The diameter of the blood vessel is about 9×10^{-5} meter.

Try It **Round the number. Write the result as the product of a single digit and a power of 10.**

3. 0.000384509

4. 0.00000726

Laurie's Notes

Scaffolding Instruction

- Students explored very large and very small numbers written as the product of a single digit and a power of 10. Now they will approximate very large and very small numbers using powers of 10.
- **Emerging:** Students may struggle with approximating very large and very small numbers using powers of 10. They will benefit from guided instruction for the examples.
- **Proficient:** Students can use powers of 10 to approximate very large and very small numbers. They should proceed to the Self-Assessment exercises.

Discuss

- Students may struggle with *why* they would want to write numbers as the product of a single digit and a power of 10. Explain that it is helpful to approximate numbers in this way when comparing quantities and performing operations.
- Discuss the push-pin note.

EXAMPLE 1

- Ask a volunteer to read the problem and text below the picture.
- ❓ "To what place value should you round 332,500,000?" hundred millions "Why?" So there is exactly one nonzero digit.
- ❓ "How can you rewrite 300,000,000 as a product in which one of the factors is a single digit?" $3 \times 100,000,000$ Students may suggest different products. Encourage students to read the problem again to see the other factor must be a power of 10.
- ❓ "How can you write 100,000,000 as a power of 10?" 10^8
- Remind students to include appropriate units in their answers.

Try It

- Have students solve these problems on whiteboards. Check answers as a class.

EXAMPLE 2

- Ask a volunteer to read the problem.
- ❓ "To what place value should you round 0.0000924?" hundred thousandths "Why?" So there is exactly one nonzero digit.
- ❓ "How can you rewrite 0.00009 as a product in which one of the factors is a power of 10?" 9×0.00001
- Show students why $0.00001 = 10^{-5}$.

$$0.00001 = \frac{1}{100,000}$$
$$= \frac{1}{10^5}$$
$$= 10^{-5}$$

Try It

- Have students solve these problems on whiteboards. Check answers as a class.

Extra Example 1
Aside from the Sun, Proxima Centauri is the closest star to Earth. It is about 40,208,000,000,000 kilometers from Earth. Round the distance between Earth and Proxima Centauri. Write the result as the product of a single digit and a power of 10.
40,000,000,000,000 km; 4×10^{13} km

Try It

1. 8×10^9
2. 1×10^{11}
3. 4×10^{-4}
4. 7×10^{-6}

Extra Example 2
An atom has an ionic radius of 0.000000000196 meter. Round the ionic radius of the atom. Write the result as the product of a single digit and a power of 10.
0.0000000002 m; 2×10^{-10} m

ELL Support

After demonstrating Examples 1 and 2, have students work in pairs to discuss and complete Try It Exercises 1–4. Provide guiding questions such as, "To what place value should you round? What number should you factor out? What is the exponent?" Expect students to perform according to their language levels.

Beginner: Write out the steps.

Intermediate: Use phrases and simple sentences.

Advanced: Use detailed sentences.

Extra Example 3

The distance from Uranus to Jupiter is about 2,095,220,000 kilometers. The distance from Jupiter to Neptune is about 2 times this distance. What is the approximate distance from Jupiter to Neptune?

A. 4×10^9 kilometers

B. 6×10^9 kilometers

C. 4×10^{10} kilometers

D. 6×10^{10} kilometers

A

Try It

5. $4 \times 10^8 \, \text{mi}$

ELL Support

Have students work in groups to complete the Self-Assessment for Concepts & Skills exercises. Arrange the groups so that there is at least one Intermediate or Advanced student in each group that can read Exercise 10. Have each group display their answers on a whiteboard for your review.

Self-Assessment
for Concepts & Skills

6. 9×10^{11}

7. 6×10^{10}

8. 3×10^{-6}

9. 1×10^{-5}

10. $5 \times 10^{10} \, \text{m}^3$

EXAMPLE 3

- Ask a volunteer to read the problem aloud.
- ❓ "What do you know from the problem?" The distance from Saturn to Neptune and that the distance from Mercury to Neptune is 1.5 times that distance.
- Point out that these are *average* distances because the distances between planets vary depending upon their orbits.
- ❓ "What do you need to find?" the approximate distance from Mercury to Neptune
- ❓ "How can you find the distance from Mercury to Neptune?" Multiply the distance from Saturn to Neptune by 1.5.
- Work through the solution as shown.
- **Note:** Some students may suggest multiplying by 1.5 before estimating 1,911,674,960 as the product of a single digit and a power of 10. While this is a valid method, it is not as efficient as the method shown.
- Point out the Common Error note.

Try It

- **Neighbor Check:** Have students work independently and then have their neighbors check their work. Have students discuss any discrepancies.

Formative Assessment Tip

Chalkboard Splash

This technique allows students to solve a problem, while others critique their reasoning. Several students respond to a prompt at the same time on the board. *Chalkboard Splash* is a good way to show multiple representations of the same problem. To be informative, students must show all steps. Once complete, allow the rest of the class to ask questions. The students at the board will need to be able to defend and explain their reasoning. *Chalkboard Splash* allows you to check students' conceptual knowledge and ability to construct a viable argument.

✅ Self-Assessment for Concepts & Skills

- **Chalkboard Splash:** After completing the exercises independently, choose four or five students to put their work on the board for Exercise 6. Look for different approaches and encourage other students to ask questions. Repeat for the remaining exercises.
- ◉ **Thumbs Up:** Ask students to indicate their understanding of the first two success criteria.

The Success Criteria Self-Assessment chart can be found in the *Student Journal* or online at *BigIdeasMath.com*.

EXAMPLE 3 **Approximating a Quantity**

The distance from Saturn to Neptune is about 1,911,674,960 miles. The distance from Mercury to Neptune is about 1.5 times this distance. What is the approximate distance from Mercury to Neptune?

A. 2×10^9 miles

B. 3×10^9 miles

C. 2×10^{10} miles

D. 3×10^{10} miles

Round the distance from Saturn to Neptune. Write the result as the product of a single digit and a power of 10.

$$1,911,674,960 \approx 2,000,000,000 \qquad \text{Round to the nearest 1,000,000,000.}$$
$$= 2 \times 1,000,000,000 \qquad \text{Factor out 2.}$$
$$= 2 \times 10^9 \qquad \text{Write 1,000,000,000 as a power of 10.}$$

Math Practice

Justify Conclusions
Explain to a classmate why you do not use the Distributive Property to multiply 1.5 and (2×10^9).

The distance from Mercury to Neptune is about 1.5 times the distance from Saturn to Neptune. So, the distance from Mercury to Neptune is about $1.5(2 \times 10^9)$, or 3×10^9, miles.

 The correct answer is **B.**

Try It

5. The distance from Mercury to Mars is about 105,651,744 miles. The distance from Saturn to Jupiter is about 4 times this distance. What is the approximate distance from Saturn to Jupiter?

 Self-Assessment for *Concepts & Skills*

Solve each exercise. Then rate your understanding of the success criteria in your journal.

APPROXIMATING A NUMBER **Round the number. Write the result as the product of a single digit and a power of 10.**

6. 899,032,878,300

7. 62,322,118,987

8. 0.00000278101

9. 0.000013094

10. **APPROXIMATING A QUANTITY** Lake A has a volume of 21,150,427,000 cubic meters. Lake B has a volume that is 2.5 times the volume of Lake A. What is the approximate volume of Lake B?

EXAMPLE 4 **Modeling Real Life**

The population of the Philippines is about 104,260,000 and the population of India is about 1,282,000,000. Approximately how many times greater is the population of India than the population of the Philippines?

Understand the problem.

You are given the populations of the Philippines and India. You are asked to approximate the number of times greater the population of India is than the population of the Philippines.

Make a plan.

Round each number. Write each result as the product of a single digit and a power of 10. Then divide the population of India by the population of the Philippines.

Solve and check.

Philippines	*India*
$104,260,000 \approx 100,000,000$	$1,282,000,000 \approx 1,000,000,000$
$= 1 \times 100,000,000$	$= 1 \times 1,000,000,000$
$= 1 \times 10^8$	$= 1 \times 10^9$

Divide the population of India by the population of the Philippines.

$$\frac{1 \times 10^9}{1 \times 10^8} = \frac{10^9}{10^8} \qquad \text{Multiplication Property of One}$$

$$= 10^{9-8} \qquad \text{Quotient of Powers Property}$$

$$= 10^1 \qquad \text{Simplify.}$$

Check Use a calculator to divide the numbers.

$$\frac{1,282,000,000}{104,260,000} \approx 12.3 \approx 10 \checkmark$$

So, the population of India is about 10 times greater than the population of the Philippines.

Self-Assessment for *Problem Solving*

Solve each exercise. Then rate your understanding of the success criteria in your journal.

11. On average, a small dog's heart beats about 530,000,000 times during its lifetime, and a large dog's heart beats about 1.4 times this amount. What is the approximate number of heartbeats in the lifetime of a large dog?

12. **DIG DEEPER!** A physicist observes a gamma ray with a wavelength of 0.00000000135 millimeter and an X-ray with a wavelength of 0.00000012 millimeter. (a) About how many times shorter is the wavelength of the gamma ray than the wavelength of the X-ray? (b) The diagram shows wavelengths of visible light. Which ray has a wavelength closer to the wavelength of dark blue light?

Visible Light

4×10^{-4} 7×10^{-4}

Wavelength (millimeters)

Laurie's Notes

EXAMPLE 4

- ◉ This example addresses the last success criterion.
- • Ask a volunteer to read the problem.
- • Give students time to analyze the problem.
- ❓ "What do you need to do to solve this problem?" Divide the population of India by the population of the Philippines.
- ❓ "How can you make the division easier?" Round each population and then write the numbers as the product of a single digit and a power of 10.
- • Work through the solution as shown.
- • Point out the Check note and remind students to always check their answers.
- ❓ "What is another way you can check the reasonableness of your answer?" Multiply the population of the Philippines by 10 to see if it is reasonably close to the population of India.

✔ Self-Assessment for Problem Solving

- • The goal for all students is to feel comfortable with the problem-solving plan. It is important for students to problem-solve in class, where they may receive support from you and their peers.
- • **Neighbor Check:** Have students work independently and then have their neighbors check their work. Have students discuss any discrepancies.
- ◉ **Thumbs Up:** Ask students to indicate their understanding of the last success criterion.

The Success Criteria Self-Assessment chart can be found in the *Student Journal* or online at *BigIdeasMath.com*.

Closure

- • What examples have you read or heard about that involve very large or very small numbers? Answers will vary.

Extra Example 4

The population of Bolivia is about 11,138,000 and the population of China is about 1,407,007,000. Approximately how many times greater is the population of China than the population of Bolivia? about 100 times greater

Self-Assessment
for Problem Solving

11. 7×10^8 heartbeats

12. **a.** 100 times shorter

  b. X-ray

Learning Target

Round numbers and write the results as the product of a single digit and a power of 10.

Success Criteria

- • Round very large and very small numbers.
- • Write a multiple of 10 as a power.
- • Compare very large or very small quantities.

▶ Review & Refresh

1. $\dfrac{3}{x^5}$

2. $\dfrac{1}{d^4}$

3. $\dfrac{1}{2a^5}$

4. $y - 2 = -\dfrac{1}{3}(x + 1)$

5. $y - 4 = \dfrac{3}{4}(x - 3)$

6. $y + 4 = -2(x - 1)$

 ## Concepts, Skills, & Problem Solving

7. B

8. D

9. C

10. A

11. 4×10^{11}

12. 2×10^5

13. 3×10^{10}

14. 4×10^{10}

15. 1×10^{12}

16. 6×10^8

17. 5×10^8 dollars

18. 1×10^{-6}

19. 4×10^{-5}

20. 2×10^{-5}

21. 6×10^{-4}

22. 3×10^{-9}

23. 1×10^{-9}

24. yes; The rounding and the product are correct.

Assignment Guide and Concept Check

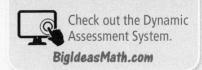

Scaffold assignments to support all students in their learning progression. The suggested assignments are a starting point. Continue to assign additional exercises and revisit with spaced practice to move every student toward proficiency.

Level	Assignment 1	Assignment 2
Emerging	1, 2, 3, 4, 7, 8, 9, 10, 11, 13, 19, 21, 25	15, 17, 22, 24, 26, 28, 29, 30, 31
Proficient	1, 2, 3, 4, 7, 8, 9, 10, 12, 14, 18, 20, 25	17, 23, 24, 26, 27, 28, 29, 30, 31, 32
Advanced	1, 2, 3, 4, 7, 8, 9, 10, 14, 17, 20, 22, 25	26, 27, 28, 29, 30, 31, 32, 33, 34

- Assignment 1 is for use after students complete the Self-Assessment for Concepts & Skills.
- Assignment 2 is for use after students complete the Self-Assessment for Problem Solving.
- The red exercises can be used as a concept check.

Review & Refresh Prior Skills

Exercises 1–3   Simplifying Expressions

Exercises 4–6   Writing an Equation in Point-Slope Form

✏ Common Errors

- **Exercises 7–23**   Students may round incorrectly. Remind them to round the number so that it contains exactly one nonzero digit. You may also want to remind students of rounding rules.

Go to *BigIdeasMath.com* to get HELP with solving the exercises.

Review & Refresh

Simplify. Write the expression using only positive exponents.

1. $3x^{-5}$

2. $d^0 \cdot d^{-4}$

3. $\dfrac{a^6}{2a^{11}}$

Write an equation in point-slope form of the line that passes through the given point and has the given slope.

4. $(-1, 2)$; $m = -\dfrac{1}{3}$

5. $(3, 4)$; $m = \dfrac{3}{4}$

6. $(1, -4)$; $m = -2$

Concepts, Skills, & Problem Solving

APPROXIMATING NUMBERS Match the number with its closest approximation.
(See Exploration 2, p. 343.)

7. 0.000618

8. 7,257,993,201

9. 0.0006781004

10. 782,309,441

A. 8×10^8

B. 6×10^{-4}

C. 7×10^{-4}

D. 7×10^9

APPROXIMATING A LARGE NUMBER Round the number. Write the result as a product of a single digit and a power of 10.

11. 414,148,636,008

12. 231,210

13. 28,007,806,203

14. 38,108,996,999

15. 1,003,111,391,008

16. 627,638,538

17. **APPROXIMATING A LARGE NUMBER** A company earns $518,204,500. Round the number. Write the result as a product of a single digit and a power of 10.

APPROXIMATING A SMALL NUMBER Round the number. Write the result as a product of a single digit and a power of 10.

18. 0.00000124

19. 0.00003946

20. 0.00001726

21. 0.00063718

22. 0.00000000305

23. 0.000000000994

24. **MP YOU BE THE TEACHER** Your friend rounds 0.000468 to the nearest ten thousandth and writes the result as a product of a single digit and a power of 10. Is your friend correct? Explain your reasoning.

$$0.000468 \approx 0.0005$$
$$= 5 \times 0.0001$$
$$= 5 \times 10^{-4}$$

25. **APPROXIMATING A QUANTITY** A series of mystery books contains 2,029,242 words. A series of science fiction books contains about 3.5 times the number of words as the mystery book series. What is the approximate number of words in the science fiction book series?

26. **APPROXIMATING A QUANTITY** A volcanic eruption ejects about 43,600,000,000 cubic feet of volcanic rock. A smaller volcanic eruption ejects about 75% of this amount. What is the approximate amount of volcanic rock that the smaller volcanic eruption ejects?

27. **MP STRUCTURE** Find a number that is approximately 1.5 times 61,040,000,100. Write the result as the product of a single digit and a power of 10.

Mitochondrion

28. **APPROXIMATING A QUANTITY** A mitochondrion has a diameter of about 0.00000031 meter. The diameter of a chloroplast is about 3 times that of the mitochondrion. What is the approximate diameter of the chloroplast?

29. **MP MODELING REAL LIFE** A photo taken with a smartphone has 1,227,104 pixels. A photo taken with a camera has 11,943,936 pixels. Approximately how many times more pixels are in the photo taken with the camera?

30. **MP MODELING REAL LIFE** A star has a core temperature of about 115,000,000°F. The temperature of a lightning strike is about 10,300°F. Approximately how many times hotter is the core temperature of the star than the temperature of the lightning strike?

31. **MP REASONING** The table shows the diameters of five types of animal hairs.

Animal	Buffalo	Rat	Camel	Cow	Donkey
Diameter (meter)	0.00011	0.00004	0.00008	0.00016	0.00005

a. Order the hair types from greatest to least diameter.

b. What unit should be used to represent these data? Explain your reasoning.

32. **MP PROBLEM SOLVING** The distance between New York City and Princeton is about 68,500 meters. The distance between New York City and San Antonio is about 40 times this distance. What is the approximate distance between New York City and San Antonio? Write the result as the product of a single digit and a power of 10.

33. **MP REASONING** Is 5×10^6 a better approximation of 5,447,040 or 5,305,004? Explain.

34. **MP NUMBER SENSE** A proton weighs 0.00000000000167 nanogram. About how much do 8 protons weigh? Write the result as the product of a single digit and a power of 10. Is your answer an overestimate or an underestimate?

Common Errors

- **Exercises 25, 26, and 28** Students may multiply both factors of the product of a single digit and a power of 10 by the number of times greater or the percent. Remind them to only multiply one of the factors. For example, in Exercise 25, students may say $3.5(2 \times 10^6) = (3.5 \times 2) \times (3.5 \times 10^6)$ instead of 7×10^6.

Mini-Assessment

Round the number. Write the result as a product of a single digit and a power of 10.

1. 0.00000876 0.000009; 9×10^{-6}

2. 52,976,000,000 50,000,000,000; 5×10^{10}

3. Company A sells $4,406,000 worth of merchandise in one year. Company B sells 2 times this amount. What is the approximate amount of merchandise sold by Company B? about 9×10^6 dollars

4. The population of Cornville, Maine is about 1314. The population of Maine is about 1,328,361. Approximately how many times greater is the population of Maine than the population of Cornville? about 1000 times greater

Concepts, Skills, & Problem Solving

25. 7×10^6 words

26. $3 \times 10^{10} \, \text{ft}^3$

27. 9×10^{10}

28. $9 \times 10^{-7} \, \text{m}$

29. 10 times more pixels

30. 10,000 times hotter

31. **a.** cow, buffalo, camel, donkey, rat

    b. *Sample answer:* millimeters; A millimeter is a common unit used to represent small quantities.

32. $3 \times 10^6 \, \text{m}$

33. 5,305,004; 5,305,004 is closer to 5×10^6.

34. 2×10^{-11} nanogram; overestimate

Section Resources

Surface Level	Deep Level
Resources by Chapter • Extra Practice • Reteach • Puzzle Time Student Journal • Self-Assessment • Practice Differentiating the Lesson Tutorial Videos Skills Review Handbook Skills Trainer	Resources by Chapter • Enrichment and Extension Graphic Organizers Dynamic Assessment System • Section Practice

Laurie's Notes

Preparing to Teach

• **MP5 Use Appropriate Tools Strategically:** Students will use graphing
calculators to explore powers of 10 and scientific notation. Students will then
explain the meanings of the resulting calculator displays.

Motivate

• Share some information about the Florida Keys.
• The Florida Keys are made up of approximately 1700 islands, or keys, that
stretch about 126 miles from the mainland to the last key, Key West. Most
of the islands are uninhabited, but the populated keys are connected by a
highway that crosses 42 bridges.
❓ "Do you know how big a square foot is?" Answers will vary.
• The Florida Keys are approximately 3.83×10^9 square feet.
❓ "Is the area of the Keys more than or less than a billion square feet?" more
than Students will probably need to write 3.83×10^9 square feet in standard
form to answer.

Warm Up

Cumulative, vocabulary, and
prerequisite skills practice
opportunities are available in
the *Resources by Chapter* or at
BigIdeasMath.com.

ELL Support

Ask students if they are familiar
with a word that sounds like the
first syllable of *notation*. Discuss the
possible meanings of *note*. Point out
that *noting* something by writing it
down can also be called "making
a notation." Explain that scientific
notation is a way of writing numbers
that are too large or too small to
easily be written in standard form.
Point out numbers that are written
in scientific notation in the
Key Idea on page 350.

Exploration 1

• Students will need graphing calculators for this exploration. If they do not
have graphing calculators, parts (a) and (c) can be completed using scientific
calculators. Technology is also available at *BigIdeasMath.com*.
❓ "What does standard form mean in the context of this exploration?" The
number is written using digits, such as 123.
❓ "What does expanded form mean?" The number is written showing the value
of each digit, such as $1 \times 100 + 2 \times 10 + 3 \times 1$.
• This exploration gives students time to explore how scientific notation is displayed
on their calculators. Different calculators may display scientific notation differently.
Students may also want to try using calculators on their cell phones.
• "When the display on a calculator reads 4.5E8, what does this mean?"
Multiply 4.5 by 10^8, or $4.5 \times 100,000,000$.
❓ "How do you write 4.5E8?" 450,000,000
• Discuss the results in part (b). If different calculators were used, determine if
the calculator displays changed at the same value of x.
• Part (c) is similar to part (a), except with very small numbers.
• Review place values less than 1.
• **Summary:** Check to see that everyone was successful in getting both large
and small numbers to display. Check for understanding of the notation.

❓ "What does E4 and E–6 mean on the calculator?" 10^4 and $10^{-6} = \dfrac{1}{10^6}$

❓ "How many digits will your calculator display?" Answers will vary
depending on the calculator.
❓ "When the display on a calculator reads 6.2E–6, what does this mean?"
Multiply 6.2 by 10^{-6}, or 6.2×0.000001.
• Write on the board: 6.2E–6 = 0.0000062.
• Part (d) is similar to part (b), except with very small numbers.

Exploration 1

a. See Additional Answers.

b. *Sample answer:* yes; $y = 10^6$
gives a result of 1E6, which is
1×10^6, or 1,000,000.

c. *Answer should include, but is not
limited to:* The student realizes
that the number to the right of E
is the exponent of a power of 10,
and that the number to the left
of E is multiplied by the power
of 10.

d. *Sample answer:* yes; $y = \left(\dfrac{1}{10}\right)^6$
gives a result of 1E-6, which is
1×10^{-6}, or 0.000001.

8.6 Scientific Notation

Learning Target: Understand the concept of scientific notation.

Success Criteria:
- I can convert between scientific notation and standard form.
- I can choose appropriate units to represent quantities.
- I can use scientific notation to solve real-life problems.

EXPLORATION 1

Using a Graphing Calculator

Work with a partner. Use a graphing calculator.

a. Experiment with multiplying very large numbers until your calculator displays an answer that is *not* in standard form. What do you think the answer means?

b. Enter the function $y = 10^x$ into your graphing calculator. Use the *table* feature to evaluate the function for positive integer values of x until the calculator displays a y-value that is not in standard form. Do the results support your answer in part (a)? Explain.

```
Plot1 Plot2 Plot3
\Y1■10^X
\Y2=
\Y3=
\Y4=
\Y5=
\Y6=
\Y7=
```

```
 X    │ Y1
 1    │ 10
 2    │ 100
 3    │ 1000
 4    │ 10000
 5    │ 100000
 6    │ 1E6
 7    │ 1E7
X=6
```

c. Repeat part (a) with very small numbers.

d. Enter the function $y = \left(\dfrac{1}{10}\right)^x$ into your graphing calculator. Use the *table* feature to evaluate the function for positive integer values of x until the calculator displays a y-value that is not in standard form. Do the results support your answer in part (c)? Explain.

Math Practice

Make Sense of Quantities

How can writing $\dfrac{1}{10}$ as a power of 10 help you understand the calculator display?

```
Plot1 Plot2 Plot3
\Y1■(1/10)^X
\Y2=
\Y3=
\Y4=
\Y5=
\Y6=
\Y7=
```

```
 X    │ Y1
 1    │ .1
 2    │ .01
 3    │ .001
 4    │ 1E-4
 5    │ 1E-5
 6    │ 1E-6
 7    │ 1E-7
X=6
```

Key Vocabulary
scientific notation,
p. 350

A number is written in **scientific notation** when it is represented as the product of a factor and a power of 10. The factor must be greater than or equal to 1 and less than 10.

The factor is greater than or equal to 1 and less than 10. → 8.3×10^{-7} ← The power of 10 has an integer exponent.

 Key Idea

Writing Numbers in Scientific Notation

Move the decimal point so it is located to the right of the leading nonzero digit. The number of places you moved the decimal point indicates the exponent of the power of 10, as shown below.

Number Greater Than or Equal to 10

Use a positive exponent when you move the decimal point to the left.

$$8600 = 8.6 \times 10^3$$
3

Number Between 0 and 1

Use a negative exponent when you move the decimal point to the right.

$$0.0024 = 2.4 \times 10^{-3}$$
3

> If the number is greater than or equal to 10, then the exponent is positive. If the number is between 0 and 1, then the exponent is negative.

EXAMPLE 1 **Writing Numbers in Scientific Notation**

a. Write 173,000,000 in scientific notation.

Move the decimal point 8 places to the left. → $173{,}000{,}000 = 1.73 \times 10^8$ ← The number is greater than 10. So, the exponent is positive.
8

b. Write 0.0000032 in scientific notation.

Move the decimal point 6 places to the right. → $0.0000032 = 3.2 \times 10^{-6}$ ← The number is between 0 and 1. So, the exponent is negative.
6

Try It **Write the number in scientific notation.**

1. 50,000   **2.** 25,000,000   **3.** 683

4. 0.005   **5.** 0.00000033   **6.** 0.000506

Laurie's Notes

Scaffolding Instruction

- Students explored very large and very small numbers written in scientific notation using graphing calculators. Now they will convert between scientific notation and standard form.
- **Emerging:** Students may struggle with converting numbers from standard form to scientific notation and vice versa. They will benefit from guided instruction for the Key Ideas and the examples.
- **Proficient:** Students convert between scientific notation and standard form with ease. They should proceed to the Self-Assessment exercises.

Discuss

- Write the definition for scientific notation. There are two parts to the definition; the factor is a number n, with $1 \leq n < 10$, and it is multiplied by a power of 10 with an integer exponent.
- Emphasize that the factor is greater than or equal to 1 and less than 10, which means that the factor can be a decimal.

Key Idea

- Write the Key Idea.
  - If the number is greater than or equal to 10, the exponent is positive and the decimal point moves to the left.
  - If the number is between 0 and 1, the exponent is negative and the decimal point moves to the right.
- From their work in the previous section, students should find it reasonable that the exponent of the power of 10 is connected to place value.
- From previous courses, students should recall that when they "move the decimal point," they are multiplying or dividing by a power of 10.

EXAMPLE 1

- **Teaching Tip:** Have students underline the first nonzero digit and the digit to its right. In scientific notation, the decimal point is placed between these two digits.
- **?** "How do you read the number in part (a)?" one hundred seventy-three million
- **FYI:** Drawing the movement of the decimal point under the numbers helps students keep track of their counting.
- **? MP3 Construct Viable Arguments and Critique the Reasoning of Others:** "How do you know if the exponent of the power of 10 will be positive or negative?" If the standard form of the number is greater than or equal to 10, the exponent is positive. If the standard form of the number is between 0 and 1, the exponent is negative.
- Note that reading the number in part (b) takes time, and you have to count place values. The number is thirty-two ten millionths.

Try It

- Students should work independently.
- **Teaching Strategy:** Select a few students to share their work.

Extra Example 1

a. Write **2,450,000** in scientific notation.
2.45×10^6

b. Write **0.0000045** in scientific notation.
4.5×10^{-6}

Try It

1. 5×10^4
2. 2.5×10^7
3. 6.83×10^2
4. 5×10^{-3}
5. 3.3×10^{-7}
6. 5.06×10^{-4}

Laurie's Notes

Key Idea

- Write the Key Idea.
- ❓ "What is absolute value?" the distance between a number and 0 on a number line
- If the exponent is positive, the number will be larger, so the decimal point moves to the right. Conversely, if the exponent is negative, the number will be smaller, so the decimal point moves to the left.
- Have students fill in the blanks.
  - "A power of 10 with a positive exponent is _____ 1." greater than or equal to
  - "A power of 10 with a negative exponent is _____ 1." less than

EXAMPLE 2

- In part (a), 3.22 is the factor and -4 is the exponent. The number in standard form will be less than 3.22, so the decimal point moves to the left 4 places.
- In part (b), 7.9 is the factor and 5 is the exponent. The number in standard form will be greater than 7.9, so the decimal point moves to the right 5 places.

Try It

- **Think-Pair-Share:** Students should read each exercise independently and then work in pairs to complete the exercises. Then have each pair compare their answers with another pair and discuss any discrepancies.

✅ Self-Assessment for Concepts & Skills

- Students should work independently.
- **Teaching Strategy:** Select a few students to share their work.
- ◉ "Is 12×10^4 written in scientific notation? Explain." No, the factor is greater than 10.

ELL Support

Allow students to work in pairs for extra support and to practice language. Have each pair write their answers for Exercises 10–15 on a whiteboard for your review. Have two pairs form a group to discuss and come to an agreement on the answer for Exercise 16. Have each group present their explanation to the class.

The Success Criteria Self-Assessment chart can be found in the *Student Journal* or online at *BigIdeasMath.com*.

Extra Example 2

a. Write 2.75×10^{-3} in standard form.
0.00275

b. Write 6.38×10^7 in standard form.
63,800,000

Try It

7. 60,000,000

8. 0.000099

9. 12,850

Self-Assessment
for Concepts & Skills

10. 6.75×10^8

11. 8.4×10^{-8}

12. 1.2001×10^{-5}

13. 0.0000008

14. 38,760,000

15. 0.0000111

16. 10×9.2^{-13}; All of the other numbers are written in scientific notation.

 **Key Idea**

Writing Numbers in Standard Form

The absolute value of the exponent indicates how many places to move the decimal point.

- If the exponent is negative, move the decimal point to the left.
- If the exponent is positive, move the decimal point to the right.

EXAMPLE 2 **Writing Numbers in Standard Form**

a. **Write 3.22×10^{-4} in standard form.**

$$3.22 \times 10^{-4} = 0.000322 \quad \text{Move the decimal point } |-4| = 4 \text{ places to the left.}$$
$$\quad\quad\quad\quad\quad\quad\quad\quad 4$$

b. **Write 7.9×10^5 in standard form.**

$$7.9 \times 10^5 = 790,000 \quad \text{Move the decimal point } |5| = 5 \text{ places to the right.}$$
$$\quad\quad\quad\quad\quad 5$$

Try It Write the number in standard form.

7. 6×10^7 **8.** 9.9×10^{-5} **9.** 1.285×10^4

 Self-Assessment for Concepts & Skills

Solve each exercise. Then rate your understanding of the success criteria in your journal.

WRITING NUMBERS IN SCIENTIFIC NOTATION Write the number in scientific notation.

10. 675,000,000   **11.** 0.000000084   **12.** 0.000012001

WRITING NUMBERS IN STANDARD FORM Write the number in standard form.

13. 8×10^{-7} **14.** 3.876×10^7 **15.** 1.11×10^{-5}

16. **WHICH ONE DOESN'T BELONG?** Which number does *not* belong with the other three? Explain.

$$2.8 \times 10^{15} \quad\quad 4.3 \times 10^{-30} \quad\quad 1.05 \times 10^{28} \quad\quad 10 \times 9.2^{-13}$$

EXAMPLE 3 **Modeling Real Life**

A female flea consumes about 1.4×10^{-5} liter of blood each day.

A dog has 100 female fleas. What is the total amount of blood consumed by the fleas each day? Express your answer using more-appropriate units.

Write 1.4×10^{-5} in standard form. Then multiply the number by 100 to determine the amount of blood that 100 female fleas consume each day.

$$1.4 \times 10^{-5} = 0.000014$$
$$\phantom{1.4 \times 10^{-5} = 0.0000}5$$

Move the decimal point $\left| -5 \right| = 5$ places to the left.

So, 100 female fleas consume about $100(0.000014) = 0.0014$ liter of blood per day. You can use milliliters to express this quantity using more-appropriate units.

$$0.0014 \, \text{L} = 0.0014 \, \cancel{L} \times \frac{1000 \, \text{mL}}{1 \, \cancel{L}} = 1.4 \, \text{mL}$$

▷ The fleas consume about 0.0014 liter, or 1.4 milliliters, of blood each day.

Self-Assessment for Problem Solving

Solve each exercise. Then rate your understanding of the success criteria in your journal.

17. A series of movies is about 3.285×10^4 seconds long. How long does it take to watch the series twice? Express your answer using more-appropriate units.

18. The total power of a space shuttle during launch is the sum of the power from its solid rocket boosters and the power from its main engines. The power from the solid rocket boosters is 9,750,000,000 watts. What is the power from the main engines?

Total Power = 1.174×10^{10} watts

19. The area of a trampoline is about 1.8×10^4 square inches. Write this number in standard form. Then represent the area of the trampoline using more-appropriate units.

20. **DIG DEEPER!** The *epidermis, dermis,* and *hypodermis* are layers of your skin. The dermis is about 3.5 millimeters thick. The epidermis is about 1.25×10^{-3} meter thick. The hypodermis is about 0.15 centimeter thick. What is the difference in thickness of the thickest layer and the thinnest layer? Justify your answer.

Laurie's Notes

EXAMPLE 3

- Ask a student to read the problem.
- Before students get too concerned about fleas, remind them that 1.4×10^{-5} liter is a small amount!
- Work through the solution as shown. Students could complete a Four Square as you work through the problem-solving plan.
- Students should be comfortable multiplying by powers of 10.
- ❓ "Can you multiply 10^{-5} by 100 first, and then multiply by 1.4? Explain." Yes, multiplication is commutative.
- ❓ "Can you change 100 to 10^2 first, and then multiply by 1.4? Explain." Yes, then you can use the Product of Powers Property: $1.4 \times 10^{-5} \times 10^2 = 1.4 \times 10^{-3} = 0.0014$.
- ❓ "Which units would be more appropriate?" milliliters
- **Popsicle Sticks:** Select a student to explain how to convert 0.0014 liter to milliliters.

✓ Self-Assessment for Problem Solving

- Encourage students to use a Four Square to complete these exercises. By now, most students should be able to get past the first square.
- **MP4 Model with Mathematics:** Encourage students to check their work by making sure their answers make sense in the context of the problem.
- **Neighbor Check:** Have students work independently and then have their neighbors check their work. Have students discuss any discrepancies.

The Success Criteria Self-Assessment chart can be found in the *Student Journal* or online at *BigIdeasMath.com*.

Closure

- **Writing Prompt:** Explain how to write 0.00076 in scientific notation. Explain how to write 6.45×10^8 in standard form.

Extra Example 3

In Example 3, a dog has 50 female fleas. What is the total amount of blood consumed by the fleas each day? Express your answer using more-appropriate units.

0.7 milliliter of blood each day

Self-Assessment
for Problem Solving

17. *Sample answer:* 18.25 h

18. 1,990,000,000 watts

19. 18,000 in.^{2}; *Sample answer:* 125 ft^2

20. 2.25 mm;
dermis: 3.5 mm
epidermis:
1.25×10^{-3} m = 0.00125 m
               = 1.25 mm
hypodermis: 0.15 cm = 1.5 mm
$3.5 - 1.25 = 2.25$ mm

Learning Target

Understand the concept of scientific notation.

Success Criteria

- Convert between scientific notation and standard form.
- Choose appropriate units to represent quantities.
- Use scientific notation to solve real-life problems.

Review & Refresh

1. 1×10^{-6}
2. 4×10^9
3. 2×10^{-7}
4. 9×10^8
5. 4^5
6. $3^3 y^3$
7. $(-2)^3$

Concepts, Skills, & Problem Solving

8. 0.0000000001
9. 10,240,000,000,000
10. 2.1×10^{-3}
11. 5.43×10^6
12. 3.21×10^8
13. 6.25×10^{-6}
14. 4×10^{-5}
15. 1.07×10^7
16. 4.56×10^{10}
17. 9.256×10^{-12}
18. 8.4×10^5
19. 70,000,000
20. 0.008
21. 500
22. 0.00027
23. 0.000044
24. 2100
25. 1,660,000,000
26. 0.0000000385
27. 9,725,000
28. 2.83×10^4 ft
29. 0.00025 ft; 0.003 in.

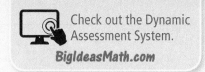

Check out the Dynamic Assessment System.
BigIdeasMath.com

Assignment Guide and Concept Check

Scaffold assignments to support all students in their learning progression. The suggested assignments are a starting point. Continue to assign additional exercises and revisit with spaced practice to move every student toward proficiency.

Level	Assignment 1	Assignment 2
Emerging	3, 4, 6, 8, 11, 13, 15, 17, 19, 21, 23, 25, 27	9, 14, 16, 24, 26, 28, 29, 30, 31, 32, 33, 34, 39
Proficient	3, 4, 6, 9, 10, 12, 14, 16, 18, 20, 22, 24, 27	28, 29, 30, 31, 32, 33, 34, 35, 36, 37, 38, 39, 40
Advanced	3, 4, 6, 9, 10, 16, 22, 25	30, 31, 32, 33, 34, 35, 36, 37, 38, 39, 40

- Assignment 1 is for use after students complete the Self-Assessment for Concepts & Skills.
- Assignment 2 is for use after students complete the Self-Assessment for Problem Solving.
- The red exercises can be used as a concept check.

Review & Refresh Prior Skills

Exercises 1 and 3 Approximating a Small Number
Exercises 2 and 4 Approximating a Large Number
Exercises 5–7 Writing Expressions Using Exponents

Common Errors

- **Exercises 10–18** Students may write an exponent with the opposite sign of what is correct. Remind them that large numbers have positive exponents in scientific notation and that small numbers have negative exponents in scientific notation.
- **Exercises 19–27** Students may move the decimal point in the wrong direction. Remind them that when the exponent is negative they move the decimal point to the left, and when it is positive they move the decimal point to the right.

8.6 Practice

Go to *BigIdeasMath.com* to get HELP with solving the exercises.

▷ Review & Refresh

Round the number. Write the result as the product of a single digit and a power of 10.

1. 0.00000129

2. 4,241,933,200

3. 0.0000001801

4. 879,679,466

Write the product using exponents.

5. $4 \cdot 4 \cdot 4 \cdot 4 \cdot 4$

6. $3 \cdot 3 \cdot 3 \cdot y \cdot y \cdot y$

7. $(-2) \cdot (-2) \cdot (-2)$

▷ Concepts, Skills, & Problem Solving

MP USING TOOLS Use a graphing calculator to evaluate the function when $x = 10$. Write the number in standard form. (See Exploration 1, p. 349.)

8. $y = \left(\dfrac{1}{10}\right)^x$

9. $y = 20^x$

WRITING NUMBERS IN SCIENTIFIC NOTATION Write the number in scientific notation.

10. 0.0021

11. 5,430,000

12. 321,000,000

13. 0.00000625

14. 0.00004

15. 10,700,000

16. 45,600,000,000

17. 0.000000000009256

18. 840,000

WRITING NUMBERS IN STANDARD FORM Write the number in standard form.

19. 7×10^7

20. 8×10^{-3}

21. 5×10^2

22. 2.7×10^{-4}

23. 4.4×10^{-5}

24. 2.1×10^3

25. 1.66×10^9

26. 3.85×10^{-8}

27. 9.725×10^6

28. **MP MODELING REAL LIFE** The U.S. Brig *Niagara*, a warship from the Battle of Lake Erie in 1813, uses about 28,300 feet of rope to operate its sails and spars. Write this number in scientific notation.

29. **MP MODELING REAL LIFE** The radius of a fishing line is 2.5×10^{-4} feet. Write this number in standard form. Then write your answer using inches.

Blood: 2.7×10^8 platelets per milliliter

30. **MP** **MODELING REAL LIFE** Platelets are cell-like particles in the blood that help form blood clots.

   a. How many platelets are in 3 milliliters of blood? Write your answer in standard form.

   b. An adult human body contains about 5 liters of blood. How many platelets are in an adult human body?

CHOOSING APPROPRIATE UNITS Match each value with the most appropriate unit of measurement.

31. height of a skyscraper: 2.6×10^2

32. distance between two asteroids: 2.5×10^5

33. depth of a bathtub: 1.6×10^1

34. length of memory chip: 7.8×10^0

   A. inches

   B. millimeters

   C. miles

   D. meters

35. **MP** **NUMBER SENSE** Describe how the value of a number written in scientific notation changes when you increase the exponent by 1.

36. **MP** **PROBLEM SOLVING** The area of the Florida Keys National Marine Sanctuary is about 9600 square kilometers. The area of the Florida Reef Tract is about 16.2% of the area of the sanctuary. What is the area of the Florida Reef Tract? Write your answer in scientific notation.

37. **MP** **REASONING** A gigameter is 1.0×10^6 kilometers. How many square kilometers are in 5 square gigameters?

38. **MP** **PROBLEM SOLVING** There are about 1.4×10^9 cubic kilometers of water on Earth. About 2.5% of the water is freshwater. How much freshwater is on Earth?

39. **CRITICAL THINKING** The table shows the speed of light through each of five media. Determine in which media light travels the fastest and the slowest.

Medium	Speed
Air	6.7×10^8 mi/h
Glass	6.6×10^8 ft/sec
Ice	2.3×10^5 km/sec
Vacuum	3.0×10^8 m/sec
Water	2.3×10^{10} cm/sec

Equivalent to 1 Atomic Mass Unit
8.3×10^{-24} carat
1.66×10^{-21} milligram

40. **MP** **STRUCTURE** The mass of an atom or molecule is measured in atomic mass units. Which is greater, a *carat* or a *milligram*? Explain.

Mini-Assessment

Write the number in scientific notation.

1. 0.00035 $\quad 3.5 \times 10^{-4}$

2. 0.0000000000567 $\quad 5.67 \times 10^{-11}$

3. 25,500,000 $\quad 2.55 \times 10^7$

Write the number in standard form.

4. $1.66 \times 10^3 \quad 1660$

5. $5 \times 10^{-4} \quad 0.0005$

6. $4.576 \times 10^8 \quad 457,600,000$

 Concepts, Skills, & Problem Solving

30. **a.** 810,000,000 platelets

    b. 1,350,000,000,000 platelets

31. D

32. C

33. A

34. B

35. The value of the number is 10 times greater.

36. 1.5552×10^3

37. $5 \times 10^{12} \text{ km}^2$

38. $35,000,000 \text{ km}^3$

39. fastest: vacuum; slowest: glass

40. carat; 1 carat $\approx 1.2 \times 10^{23}$ atomic mass units, 1 milligram $\approx 6.02 \times 10^{20}$ atomic mass units, and $1.2 \times 10^{23} > 6.02 \times 10^{20}$.

Section Resources

Surface Level	Deep Level
Resources by Chapter • Extra Practice • Reteach • Puzzle Time Student Journal • Self-Assessment • Practice Differentiating the Lesson Tutorial Videos Skills Review Handbook Skills Trainer	Resources by Chapter • Enrichment and Extension Graphic Organizers Dynamic Assessment System • Section Practice

Learning Target

Perform operations with numbers written in scientific notation.

Success Criteria

- Explain how to add and subtract numbers in scientific notation.
- Explain how to multiply and divide numbers in scientific notation.
- Use operations in scientific notation to solve real-life problems.

Warm Up

Cumulative, vocabulary, and prerequisite skills practice opportunities are available in the *Resources by Chapter* or at *BigIdeasMath.com.*

ELL Support

Students might know the word *operation* from a medical context. Explain that a doctor may perform an operation on a person. In the context of math, you may perform an operation on numbers or variables. Addition, subtraction, multiplication, and division are common operations.

Exploration 1

a. See Additional Answers.

b. Use the Distributive Property to group the factors a and b. Then add or subtract a and b.

Exploration 2

a–b. See Additional Answers.

Laurie's Notes

STATE STANDARDS
8.EE.A.4

Preparing to Teach

- In the previous section, students wrote numbers in scientific notation. Now they will perform operations with numbers in scientific notation.
- **MP3 Construct Viable Arguments and Critique the Reasoning of Others:** Mathematically proficient students are able to give explanations for how a computation is performed. They reference definitions and properties in establishing the validity of their arguments.

Motivate

- Write the following problem on the board and ask students to evaluate it.

  $$40 \times 10 + 8 \times 10 + 0.5 \times 10 + 0.07 \times 10$$

- ❓ "How did you evaluate this expression?" It is likely that students found the sum of the four products.
- ❓ "Is there another method that could be used?" Students might mention factoring out the 10.
- **MP7 Look for and Make Use of Structure:** Underline the 10s and ask students how the Distributive Property could be used to evaluate the expression. Then write: $10(40 + 8 + 0.5 + 0.07)$.
- Tell students to use mental math to find the product: $10(48.57) = 485.7$.

Exploration 1

- After working through the Motivate, students should have a strategy for working through this exploration. What students might not recognize is that 10^4 is a common factor of the expressions in the first row, just like 10 was a common factor in the Motivate.
- ❓ "What is 10^4 in standard form?" 10,000
- Make sure students understand that "the difference of Expression 1 and Expression 2" means to subtract Expression 2 from Expression 1.
- In part (b), listen for students explaining the rules for adding numbers in scientific notation and subtracting numbers in scientific notation. Make notes about the order in which you want to call on students, so you can control the sequence of responses.

Exploration 2

- ❓ "How can you write the product in the first row?" $(3 \times 10^4) \times (1 \times 10^4)$
- ❓ "What properties can you use to simplify the product?" Commutative Property of Multiplication, Associative Property of Multiplication, and Product of Powers Property
- Make sure students understand that "the quotient of Expression 1 and Expression 2" means to divide Expression 1 by Expression 2.
- ❓ "What properties can you use to simplify the quotient?" Quotient of Powers Property
- In part (b), listen for students explaining the rules for multiplying numbers in scientific notation and dividing numbers in scientific notation. Make notes about the order in which you want to call on students, so you can control the sequence of responses.

8.7 Operations in Scientific Notation

Learning Target: Perform operations with numbers written in scientific notation.

Success Criteria:
- I can explain how to add and subtract numbers in scientific notation.
- I can explain how to multiply and divide numbers in scientific notation.
- I can use operations in scientific notation to solve real-life problems.

EXPLORATION 1

Adding and Subtracting in Scientific Notation

Work with a partner.

a. Complete the table by finding the sum and the difference of Expression 1 and Expression 2. Write your answers in scientific notation. Explain your method.

Expression 1	Expression 2	Sum	Difference
3×10^4	1×10^4		
4×10^{-3}	2×10^{-3}		
4.1×10^{-7}	1.5×10^{-7}		
8.3×10^6	1.5×10^6		

Math Practice

Look for Structure

How might you find the sum or difference of two expressions in scientific notation that contain different powers of 10?

b. Use your results in part (a) to explain how to find $(a \times 10^n) + (b \times 10^n)$ and $(a \times 10^n) - (b \times 10^n)$.

EXPLORATION 2

Multiplying and Dividing in Scientific Notation

Work with a partner.

a. Complete the table by finding the product and the quotient of Expression 1 and Expression 2. Write your answers in scientific notation. Explain your method.

Expression 1	Expression 2	Product	Quotient
3×10^4	1×10^4		
4×10^3	2×10^2		
7.7×10^{-2}	1.1×10^{-3}		
4.5×10^5	3×10^{-1}		

b. Use your results in part (a) to explain how to find $(a \times 10^n) \times (b \times 10^m)$ and $(a \times 10^n) \div (b \times 10^m)$. Describe any properties that you use.

8.7 Lesson

To add or subtract numbers written in scientific notation with the same power of 10, add or subtract the factors. When the numbers have different powers of 10, first rewrite the numbers so they have the same power of 10.

EXAMPLE 1 Adding and Subtracting in Scientific Notation

Find the sum or difference.

a. $(4.6 \times 10^3) + (8.72 \times 10^3)$

$$= (4.6 + 8.72) \times 10^3 \qquad \text{Distributive Property}$$

$$= 13.32 \times 10^3 \qquad \text{Add.}$$

$$= (1.332 \times 10^1) \times 10^3 \qquad \text{Write 13.32 in scientific notation.}$$

$$= 1.332 \times 10^4 \qquad \text{Product of Powers Property}$$

b. $(3.5 \times 10^{-2}) - (6.6 \times 10^{-3})$

Rewrite 6.6×10^{-3} so that it has the same power of 10 as 3.5×10^{-2}.

$$6.6 \times 10^{-3} = 6.6 \times 10^{-1} \times 10^{-2} \qquad \text{Rewrite } 10^{-3} \text{ as } 10^{-1} \times 10^{-2}.$$

$$= 0.66 \times 10^{-2} \qquad \text{Rewrite } 6.6 \times 10^{-1} \text{ as } 0.66.$$

Subtract the factors.

$$(3.5 \times 10^{-2}) - (0.66 \times 10^{-2})$$

$$= (3.5 - 0.66) \times 10^{-2} \qquad \text{Distributive Property}$$

$$= 2.84 \times 10^{-2} \qquad \text{Subtract.}$$

> **Math Practice**
>
> **Look for Structure**
> Solve Example 1(b) by rewriting 3.5×10^{-2} as 35×10^{-3}.

Try It **Find the sum or difference.**

1. $(8.2 \times 10^2) + (3.41 \times 10^{-1})$ **2.** $(7.8 \times 10^{-5}) - (4.5 \times 10^{-5})$

To multiply or divide numbers written in scientific notation, multiply or divide the factors and powers of 10 separately.

EXAMPLE 2 Multiplying in Scientific Notation

Find $(3 \times 10^{-5}) \times (5 \times 10^{-2})$.

$$(3 \times 10^{-5}) \times (5 \times 10^{-2})$$

$$= 3 \times 5 \times 10^{-5} \times 10^{-2} \qquad \text{Commutative Property of Multiplication}$$

$$= (3 \times 5) \times (10^{-5} \times 10^{-2}) \qquad \text{Associative Property of Multiplication}$$

$$= 15 \times 10^{-7} \qquad \text{Simplify.}$$

$$= (1.5 \times 10^1) \times 10^{-7} \qquad \text{Write 15 in scientific notation.}$$

$$= 1.5 \times 10^{-6} \qquad \text{Product of Powers Property}$$

> **Check**
> Use standard form to check your answer.
>
> (3×10^{-5})
> $\times (5 \times 10^{-2})$
> $= 0.00003 \times 0.05$
> $= 0.0000015$
> $= 1.5 \times 10^{-6}$ ✓

Laurie's Notes

Scaffolding Instruction

- Students explored how to use properties to perform operations with numbers written in scientific notation. They will continue to practice these skills in the lesson.
- **Emerging:** Students may struggle with recognizing common factors in sums or differences and applying properties to perform operations with numbers written in scientific notation. They will benefit from guided instruction for the examples and Try It exercises.
- **Proficient:** Students can perform operations with numbers written in scientific notation. They should proceed to the Self-Assessment exercises.

Discuss

- Read and discuss the paragraph at the top of the page.
- Students may want to make an index card for adding numbers written in scientific notation and another for subtracting. They should include explanations of each process and add examples as they work through the lesson. They can also make index cards for multiplication and division.

EXAMPLE 1

- **Note:** In part (a), students do not always recognize the Distributive Property when it is used to factor out a common factor, such as 10^3.
- ? "Why not leave the answer as 13.32×10^3?" It is not in scientific notation.
- In part (b), rewriting 6.6×10^{-3} can be confusing to students. Tell them this step is similar to rewriting 24×6 as $12 \times 2 \times 6$.
- Show students that this expression can also be simplified by rewriting 3.5×10^{-2} as 35×10^{-3}.
- ? "Why can't the numbers just be subtracted?" The factors are multiplied by different powers of 10.
- **Alternative Method:** In part (b), write the numbers in standard form, subtract, and then write the answer in scientific notation.
- Ask students which method they prefer and why.

Try It

- **Neighbor Check:** Have students work independently and then have their neighbors check their work. Have students discuss any discrepancies.

EXAMPLE 2

- Even though you cannot add or subtract numbers in scientific notation with different powers of 10 (without rewriting the numbers), you can multiply them.
- ? "How would you multiply the numbers?" Most students will immediately suggest multiplying the factors and then multiplying the powers of 10.
- **MP3 Construct Viable Arguments and Critique the Reasoning of Others:** Make sure that students realize that the Commutative and Associative Properties allow this to happen. The Product of Powers Property is used to multiply the powers of 10.

Scaffold instruction to support all students in their learning. Learning is individualized and you may want to group students differently as they move in and out of these levels with each skill and concept. Student self-assessment and feedback help guide your instructional decisions about how and when to layer support for all students to become proficient learners.

Extra Example 1

Find the sum or difference.

a. $(2.1 \times 10^{-4}) + (9.74 \times 10^{-4})$
1.184×10^{-3}

b. $(4.7 \times 10^5) - (7.2 \times 10^3)$ $\quad 4.628 \times 10^5$

Try It

1. 8.20341×10^2
2. 3.3×10^{-5}

Extra Example 2

Find $(2 \times 10^{-4}) \times (6 \times 10^{-3})$. $\quad 1.2 \times 10^{-6}$

Try It

3. 4.8×10^{-4}

4. 2.1×10^{8}

5. 1.2×10^{-2}

6. 2.7×10^{12}

Extra Example 3

Find $\dfrac{5.3 \times 10^{8}}{4 \times 10^{-3}}$. $\quad 1.325 \times 10^{11}$

Try It

7. 2×10^{12}

8. 2×10^{-6}

9. 3×10^{-1}

10. 4×10^{-6}

Self-Assessment
for Concepts & Skills

11. Use the Distributive Property to group the factors together. Then add or subtract the factors. The number may need to be rewritten so that it is still in scientific notation.

12. no; You can use properties to multiply or divide without rewriting the numbers.

13. 1.066×10^{5}

14. 2.64×10^{-5}

15. 9.12×10^{-2}

16. 4×10^{9}

Laurie's Notes

Try It

- **Neighbor Check:** Have students work independently and then have their neighbors check their work. Have students discuss any discrepancies.
- Ask volunteers to present their work to the class.

EXAMPLE 3

- Before working through the example, work through a simple, but related problem such as: $\dfrac{2}{3} \cdot \dfrac{9}{10} = \dfrac{\cancel{2}^{1}}{\cancel{3}_{1}} \cdot \dfrac{\cancel{9}^{3}}{\cancel{10}_{5}} = \dfrac{3}{5}$. Point out how the common factors divide out.
- Write the example and relate it to the problem above.
- **?** "Why not leave the answer as 0.25×10^{-15}?" It is not in scientific notation.

Try It

- **Common Error:** Students may use the Quotient of Powers Property incorrectly when simplifying the fractions with powers of 10.

Formative Assessment Tip

Write Your Own

This technique allows students to practice writing and evaluating their own problems. You provide a description of the type of problem students are to create. Descriptions may be broad or specific. Students write and solve their own problems to check that the conditions are met and the problems are solved correctly.

✓ Self-Assessment for Concepts & Skills

- **Neighbor Check:** Have students work independently and then have their neighbors check their work. Have students discuss any discrepancies.
- ⊙ **Write Your Own:** Write a problem for each of the four operations (addition, subtraction, multiplication, and division) with numbers written in scientific notation. Students should solve their own problems. They will present their problems and solutions to the class in the Closure.
- ⊙ Have students use *Thumbs Up* to indicate their understanding of the first two success criteria.

ELL Support

Allow students to work in pairs for extra support and to practice language. After completing Exercises 11 and 12, have two pairs present their answers to one another. Then each pair should refine their answers based on the input from the other pair. Have each pair display their answers for Exercises 13–16 on a whiteboard for your review.

The Success Criteria Self-Assessment chart can be found in the *Student Journal* or online at *BigIdeasMath.com*.

Try It **Find the product.**

3. $6 \times (8 \times 10^{-5})$

4. $(7 \times 10^2) \times (3 \times 10^5)$

5. $(2 \times 10^4) \times (6 \times 10^{-7})$

6. $(3 \times 10^8) \times (9 \times 10^3)$

EXAMPLE 3 **Dividing in Scientific Notation**

Find $\dfrac{1.5 \times 10^{-8}}{6 \times 10^7}$.

$$\frac{1.5 \times 10^{-8}}{6 \times 10^7} = \frac{1.5}{6} \times \frac{10^{-8}}{10^7} \qquad \text{Rewrite as a product of fractions.}$$

$$= 0.25 \times \frac{10^{-8}}{10^7} \qquad \text{Divide 1.5 by 6.}$$

$$= 0.25 \times 10^{-15} \qquad \text{Quotient of Powers Property}$$

$$= (2.5 \times 10^{-1}) \times 10^{-15} \qquad \text{Write 0.25 in scientific notation.}$$

$$= 2.5 \times 10^{-16} \qquad \text{Product of Powers Property}$$

Try It **Find the quotient.**

7. $(9.2 \times 10^{12}) \div 4.6$

8. $(1.5 \times 10^{-3}) \div (7.5 \times 10^2)$

9. $(3.75 \times 10^{-8}) \div (1.25 \times 10^{-7})$

10. $(9.2 \times 10^6) \div (2.3 \times 10^{12})$

 Self-Assessment for *Concepts & Skills*

Solve each exercise. Then rate your understanding of the success criteria in your journal.

11. **WRITING** Describe how to add or subtract two numbers written in scientific notation with the same power of 10.

12. **MP NUMBER SENSE** Two numbers written in scientific notation have different powers of 10. Do you have to rewrite the numbers so they have the same power of 10 before multiplying or dividing? Explain.

OPERATIONS IN SCIENTIFIC NOTATION **Evaluate the expression. Write your answer in scientific notation.**

13. $(7.26 \times 10^4) + (3.4 \times 10^4)$

14. $(2.8 \times 10^{-5}) - (1.6 \times 10^{-6})$

15. $(2.4 \times 10^4) \times (3.8 \times 10^{-6})$

16. $(5.2 \times 10^{-3}) \div (1.3 \times 10^{-12})$

EXAMPLE 4 **Modeling Real Life**

Diameter ≈ 1,400,000,000 m

An aluminum ion has a diameter of about 5×10^{-11} meter. How many times greater is the diameter of the Sun than the diameter of the ion?

Write the diameter of the Sun in scientific notation.

$$1{,}400{,}000{,}000 = 1.4 \times 10^9$$
$$9$$

Divide the diameter of the Sun by the diameter of the aluminum ion.

$\dfrac{1.4 \times 10^9}{5 \times 10^{-11}} = \dfrac{1.4}{5} \times \dfrac{10^9}{10^{-11}}$	Rewrite as a product of fractions.
$= 0.28 \times \dfrac{10^9}{10^{-11}}$	Divide 1.4 by 5.
$= 0.28 \times 10^{20}$	Quotient of Powers Property
$= (2.8 \times 10^{-1}) \times 10^{20}$	Write 0.28 in scientific notation.
$= 2.8 \times 10^{19}$	Product of Powers Property

> The diameter of the Sun is about 2.8×10^{19} times greater than the diameter of the aluminum ion.

Check
Use a calculator to check your answer.

```
(1.4E9)/(5E-11)
        2.8E19
```
✓

 Self-Assessment for Problem Solving

Solve each exercise. Then rate your understanding of the success criteria in your journal.

17. It takes the Sun about 2.3×10^8 years to orbit the center of the Milky Way. It takes Pluto about 2.5×10^2 years to orbit the Sun. How many times does Pluto orbit the Sun while the Sun completes one orbit around the Milky Way?

18. A person typically breathes about 8.64×10^3 liters of air per day. The life expectancy of a person in the United States at birth is about 29,200 days. Estimate the total amount of air a person born in the United States breathes over a lifetime.

19. **DIG DEEPER!** In one week, about 4100 movie theaters each sold an average of 2200 tickets for Movie A. About 3.6×10^7 total tickets were sold at the theaters during the week. An article claims that about 25% of all tickets sold during the week were for Movie A. Is this claim accurate? Justify your answer.

Laurie's Notes

EXAMPLE 4

- Ask a volunteer to read the problem.
- ❓ "What information do you know from the problem?" the diameter of an aluminum ion and the diameter of the Sun (from the picture)
- ❓ "What do you need to find?" How many times greater the diameter of the Sun is than the diameter of the ion.
- ❓ "How can you solve this problem?" Divide the diameter of the Sun by the diameter of the ion.
- Work through the solution as shown.
- Use a calculator to check the answer, as shown in the Check note.
- Another way to check the answer is to multiply the answer by the diameter of the aluminum ion. The product should be the diameter of the Sun.

✔ Self-Assessment for Problem Solving

- Allow time in class for students to practice using the problem-solving plan. By now, students should be more comfortable with the problem-solving plan and be able to move past the first step.
- Make sure students make a plan for each problem before performing the computations. Discuss different plans as a class.
- ⊙ Have students use *Thumbs Up* to indicate their understanding of the last success criterion.

The Success Criteria Self-Assessment chart can be found in the *Student Journal* or online at *BigIdeasMath.com*.

Closure

- Have students present their problems from the *Write Your Own* in the Self-Assessment for Concepts & Skills. Each student should present a problem. To save time, ask several students to write their problems on the board at the same time and then have each student explain his or her solution. If you have a document camera, students could display their work under the document camera instead of on the board.

Self-Assessment
for Problem Solving

17. 9.2×10^5 times

18. about 2.52×10^8 L

19. yes;
$$\frac{(4.1 \times 10^3) \times (2.2 \times 10^3)}{3.6 \times 10^7}$$
$$\approx 2.5 \times 10^{-1}$$
$$= 0.25 \text{ or } 25\%$$

Learning Target

Perform operations with numbers written in scientific notation.

Success Criteria

- Explain how to add and subtract numbers in scientific notation.
- Explain how to multiply and divide numbers in scientific notation.
- Use operations in scientific notation to solve real-life problems.

Review & Refresh

1. 3.8×10^{-3}

2. 7.4×10^{7}

3. 4.75×10^{-5}

4. $\frac{3}{4}; \frac{9}{16}$

5. $\frac{3}{2}; \frac{9}{4}$

Concepts, Skills, & Problem Solving

6. sum: 5×10^{3};
   difference: 1×10^{3};
   product: 6×10^{6};
   quotient: 1.5×10^{0}

7. sum: 7.5×10^{-4};
   difference: 4.5×10^{-4};
   product: 9×10^{-8};
   quotient: 4×10^{0}

8. 5.8×10^{5}

9. 1.83×10^{-9}

10. 5.2×10^{8}

11. 1.264×10^{-5}

12. 7.555×10^{7}

13. 2.51×10^{-3}

14. 1.037×10^{7}

15. 1.85×10^{-1}

16. yes; The sum is correct.

17. 3.5×10^{8}

18. 2.9×10^{-3}

19. 3×10^{-6}

20. 1.5×10^{0}

21. 5×10^{-1}

22. 2.88×10^{-7}

23. 9.1×10^{3}

24. 1.12×10^{-2}

Assignment Guide and Concept Check

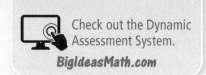
Check out the Dynamic Assessment System.
BigIdeasMath.com

Scaffold assignments to support all students in their learning progression. The suggested assignments are a starting point. Continue to assign additional exercises and revisit with spaced practice to move every student toward proficiency.

Level	Assignment 1	Assignment 2
Emerging	2, 3, 4, 5, 6, 7, 9, 11, 13, 16, 17, 19, 21	12, 14, 22, 24, 25, 26, 27, 28, 29, 30, 31, 34
Proficient	2, 3, 4, 5, 6, 7, 10, 12, 14, 16, 20, 22, 24	25, 26, 27, 28, 29, 30, 31, 33, 34
Advanced	2, 3, 4, 5, 6, 7, 10, 14, 16, 22, 24	25, 26, 27, 28, 30, 32, 33, 34, 35

- Assignment 1 is for use after students complete the Self-Assessment for Concepts & Skills.
- Assignment 2 is for use after students complete the Self-Assessment for Problem Solving.
- The red exercises can be used as a concept check.

Review & Refresh Prior Skills

Exercises 1–3   Writing Numbers in Scientific Notation
Exercises 4 and 5   Perimeters and Areas of Similar Figures

Common Errors

- **Exercises 12–15** Students may incorrectly rewrite a number when adding or subtracting numbers with different powers of 10. Remind them to show the intermediate step of rewriting the power of 10. For example, $7.8 \times 10^{7} = 7.8 \times 10^{1} \times 10^{6} = 78 \times 10^{6}$.
- **Exercises 17–24** Students may multiply or divide the factors and leave the factor less than 1 or leave the factor greater than or equal to 10. Remind them that the factor in scientific notation must be at least 1 and less than 10.
- **Exercises 18, 19, 21, and 24** Students may use the Quotient of Powers Property incorrectly when simplifying fractions containing powers of 10. Remind students that the Quotient of Powers Property states that the exponents are subtracted.

8.7 Practice

Go to *BigIdeasMath.com* to get HELP with solving the exercises.

▶ *Review & Refresh*

Write the number in scientific notation.

1. 0.0038   **2.** 74,000,000   **3.** 0.0000475

Find the values of the ratios (red to blue) of the perimeters and areas of the similar figures.

4.

5.

▶▶ *Concepts, Skills, & Problem Solving*

OPERATIONS IN SCIENTIFIC NOTATION **Find the sum, difference, product, and quotient of Expression 1 and Expression 2. Write your answers in scientific notation.**
(See Explorations 1 and 2, p. 355.)

6. 3×10^3 Expression 1
     2×10^3 Expression 2

7. 6×10^{-4} Expression 1
     1.5×10^{-4} Expression 2

ADDING AND SUBTRACTING IN SCIENTIFIC NOTATION **Find the sum or difference. Write your answer in scientific notation.**

8. $(2 \times 10^5) + (3.8 \times 10^5)$

9. $(6.33 \times 10^{-9}) - (4.5 \times 10^{-9})$

10. $(9.2 \times 10^8) - (4 \times 10^8)$

11. $(7.2 \times 10^{-6}) + (5.44 \times 10^{-6})$

12. $(7.8 \times 10^7) - (2.45 \times 10^6)$

13. $(5 \times 10^{-5}) + (2.46 \times 10^{-3})$

14. $(9.7 \times 10^6) + (6.7 \times 10^5)$

15. $(2.4 \times 10^{-1}) - (5.5 \times 10^{-2})$

16. **MP YOU BE THE TEACHER**
Your friend adds 2.5×10^9 and 5.3×10^8. Is your friend correct? Explain your reasoning.

$(2.5 \times 10^9) + (5.3 \times 10^8) = (2.5 \times 10^9) + (0.53 \times 10^9)$
$= (2.5 + 0.53) \times 10^9$
$= 3.03 \times 10^9$

MULTIPLYING AND DIVIDING IN SCIENTIFIC NOTATION **Find the product or quotient. Write your answer in scientific notation.**

17. $5 \times (7 \times 10^7)$

18. $(5.8 \times 10^{-6}) \div (2 \times 10^{-3})$

19. $(1.2 \times 10^{-5}) \div 4$

20. $(5 \times 10^{-7}) \times (3 \times 10^6)$

21. $(3.6 \times 10^7) \div (7.2 \times 10^7)$

22. $(7.2 \times 10^{-1}) \times (4 \times 10^{-7})$

23. $(6.5 \times 10^8) \times (1.4 \times 10^{-5})$

24. $(2.8 \times 10^4) \div (2.5 \times 10^6)$

MATCHING You use technology to find four sums. Match the sum with its standard form.

25. 4.3E8

26. 4.3E−8

27. 4.3E10

28. 4.3E−10

A. 0.00000000043

B. 0.000000043

C. 430,000,000

D. 43,000,000,000

29. **MP MODELING REAL LIFE** How many times greater is the thickness of a dime than the thickness of a dollar bill?

Thickness = 0.135 cm

Thickness = 1.0922×10^{-2} cm

30. **MULTIPLE CHOICE** On a social media website, Celebrity A has about 8.6×10^7 followers and Celebrity B has about 4.1×10^6 followers. Determine which of the following is the best estimate for the number of followers for Celebrity A compared to the number of followers for Celebrity B.

    A. more than 2 times greater   **B.** less than 2 times greater

    C. more than 20 times greater   **D.** less than 20 times greater

MP REASONING Evaluate the expression. Write your answer in scientific notation.

31. $5,200,000 \times (8.3 \times 10^2) - (3.1 \times 10^8)$

32. $(9 \times 10^{-3}) + (2.4 \times 10^{-5}) \div 0.0012$

33. **GEOMETRY** Find the perimeter of the rectangle at the right.

Area = 5.612×10^{14} cm²

9.2×10^7 cm   *Not drawn to scale*

34. **DIG DEEPER!** A human heart pumps about 7×10^{-2} liter of blood per heartbeat. The average human heart beats about 72 times per minute. How many liters of blood does a heart pump in 1 year? 70 years?

35. **MP MODELING REAL LIFE** Use the Internet or another reference to find the populations and areas (in square miles) of India, China, Argentina, the United States, and Egypt. Round each population to the nearest million and each area to the nearest thousand square miles.

    a. Write each population and area in scientific notation.

    b. Use your answers to part (a) to find and order the population densities (people per square mile) of each country from least to greatest.

Common Errors

- **Exercise 35** Students may not understand what *population density* means in part (b). Explain that population density is the average number of people for some amount of land area. To find the population density, you divide the population by the land area.

Mini-Assessment

Evaluate the expression. Write your answer in scientific notation.

1. $(3.4 \times 10^6) + (8.1 \times 10^6)$ 1.15×10^7

2. $(4.3 \times 10^{-3}) + (7.8 \times 10^{-4})$ 5.08×10^{-3}

3. $(5.6 \times 10^{-8}) - (1.9 \times 10^{-8})$ 3.7×10^{-8}

4. $(1.7 \times 10^2) \times (4.3 \times 10^4)$ 7.31×10^6

5. $(6.2 \times 10^5) \div (2 \times 10^{-4})$ 3.1×10^9

6. The mass of Earth is about 6.58×10^{21} tons. The mass of Mars is about 7.07×10^{20} tons. How much greater is the mass of Earth than the mass of Mars?   about 5.873×10^{21} tons

Concepts, Skills, & Problem Solving

25. C

26. B

27. D

28. A

29. about 12 times greater

30. C

31. 4.006×10^9

32. 2.9×10^{-2}

33. 1.962×10^8 cm

34. about 2.65×10^6 L; about 1.85×10^8 L

35. *Answer should include, but is not limited to:* Make sure calculations using scientific notation are done correctly.

Section Resources

Surface Level	Deep Level
Resources by Chapter • Extra Practice • Reteach • Puzzle Time Student Journal • Self-Assessment • Practice Differentiating the Lesson Tutorial Videos Skills Review Handbook Skills Trainer	Resources by Chapter • Enrichment and Extension Graphic Organizers Dynamic Assessment System • Section Practice
Transfer Level	
Dynamic Assessment System • End-of-Chapter Quiz	Assessment Book • End-of-Chapter Quiz

Exercise 1

- Adding in Scientific Notation
- Finding a Line of Best Fit
- Multiplying in Scientific Notation

Exercise 2

- Choosing Appropriate Units
- Multiplying in Scientific Notation
- Perimeters of Similar Figures

Exercise 3

- Adding in Scientific Notation
- Making a Two-Way Table

ELL Support

Review the basic structure of an atom. An atom consists of a nucleus that is surrounded by electrons. The nucleus contains protons and neutrons. Protons have a positive charge and electrons have a negative charge. Neutrons do not have a charge.

Using the Problem-Solving Plan

1. 1.1×10^{-22} g

2. *Sample answer:* about 35.1 in.

3. See Additional Answers.

Performance Task

The *STEAM Video Performance Task* provides the opportunity for additional enrichment and greater depth of knowledge as students explore the mathematics of the chapter within a context tied to the chapter STEAM Video. The performance task and a detailed scoring rubric are provided at *BigIdeasMath.com*.

Laurie's Notes

Scaffolding Instruction

- The goal of this lesson is to help students become more comfortable with problem solving. These exercises combine operations with exponents and scientific notation with prior skills from other chapters. The solution for Exercise 1 is worked out below, to help you guide students through the problem-solving plan. Use the remaining class time to have students work on the other exercises.
- **Emerging:** The goal for these students is to feel comfortable with the problem-solving plan. Allow students to work in pairs to write the beginning steps of the problem-solving plan for Exercise 2. Keep in mind that some students may only be ready to do the first step.
- **Proficient:** Students may be able to work independently or in pairs to complete Exercises 2 and 3.
- Visit each pair to review their plan for each problem. Ask students to describe their plans.

▶ *Using the Problem-Solving Plan*

Exercise 1

⇨ **Understand the problem.** You know the numbers of protons and the masses of several atoms. You are asked to use the line of best fit to estimate the mass of an atom that has 29 protons.

⇨ **Make a plan.** Use a graphing calculator to find an equation of the line of best fit. Then evaluate the equation when $x = 29$.

⇨ **Solve and check.** Use the plan to solve the problem. Then check your solution.

- Use a graphing calculator to find an equation of the line of best fit. Use the *linear regression* feature. An equation of the line of best fit is $y = (3.97 \times 10^{-24})x - (5.47 \times 10^{-24})$.

```
LinReg
 y=ax+b
 a=3.967708E-24
 b=-5.4652E-24
 r²=.9952423234
 r=.9976183255
```

- Evaluate $y = (3.97 \times 10^{-24})x - (5.47 \times 10^{-24})$ when $x = 29$.

$y = (3.97 \times 10^{-24})x - (5.47 \times 10^{-24})$	Write the equation.
$y = (3.97 \times 10^{-24})(29) - (5.47 \times 10^{-24})$	Substitute 29 for x.
$y = (115.13 \times 10^{-24}) - (5.47 \times 10^{-24})$	Multiply 3.97 by 29.
$y = (115.13 - 5.47) \times 10^{-24}$	Distributive Property
$y = 109.66 \times 10^{-24}$	Subtract.
$y = 1.0966 \times 10^2 \times 10^{-24}$	Write 109.66 in scientific notation.
$y = 1.0966 \times 10^{-22}$	Product of Powers Property

So, an atom made of 29 protons has a mass of about 1.1×10^{-22} grams.

- **Check:** Find an equation that represents the data, including $(29, 1.1 \times 10^{-22})$. Use the *linear regression* feature. After rounding the slope and y-intercept, the equation is $y = (3.97 \times 10^{-24})x - (5.45 \times 10^{-24})$, which is close to $y = (3.97 \times 10^{-24})x - (5.47 \times 10^{-24})$. ✓

8 Connecting Concepts

▷ *Using the Problem-Solving Plan*

1. Atoms are made of protons, neutrons, and electrons. The table shows the numbers of protons and the masses of several atoms. Use a line of best fit to estimate the mass (in grams) of an atom that has 29 protons.

Protons, x	Mass (gram), y
1	1.67×10^{-24}
5	1.79×10^{-23}
53	2.11×10^{-22}
20	6.65×10^{-23}
14	4.66×10^{-23}
3	1.15×10^{-23}
40	1.51×10^{-22}
16	5.32×10^{-23}

Understand the problem. You know the numbers of protons and the masses of several atoms. You are asked to use the line of best fit to estimate the mass of an atom that has 29 protons.

Make a plan. Use a graphing calculator to find an equation of the line of best fit. Then evaluate the equation when $x = 29$.

Solve and check. Use the plan to solve the problem. Then check your solution.

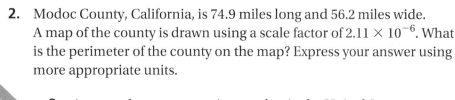

2. Modoc County, California, is 74.9 miles long and 56.2 miles wide. A map of the county is drawn using a scale factor of 2.11×10^{-6}. What is the perimeter of the county on the map? Express your answer using more appropriate units.

3. A research company estimates that in the United States, about 8.37×10^7 adult males and 6.59×10^7 adult females watch NFL football, while 3.13×10^7 adult males and 5.41×10^7 adult females do *not* watch NFL football. Organize the results in a two-way table. Include the marginal frequencies.

Modoc County

Performance Task

Elements in the Universe

At the beginning of this chapter, you watched a STEAM Video called "Carbon Atoms." You are now ready to complete the performance task related to this video, available at *BigIdeasMath.com*. Be sure to use the problem-solving plan as you work through the performance task.

Chapter Review

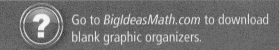 Go to *BigIdeasMath.com* to download blank graphic organizers.

▶ Review Vocabulary

Write the definition and give an example of each vocabulary term.

power, *p. 320*   exponent, *p. 320*
base, *p. 320*   scientific notation, *p. 350*

▶ Graphic Organizers

You can use a **Definition and Example Chart** to organize information about a concept. Here is an example of a Definition and Example Chart for the vocabulary term *power*.

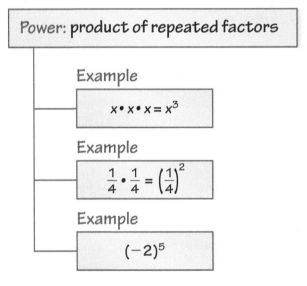

Power: product of repeated factors

Example
$$x \cdot x \cdot x = x^3$$

Example
$$\frac{1}{4} \cdot \frac{1}{4} = \left(\frac{1}{4}\right)^2$$

Example
$$(-2)^5$$

Choose and complete a graphic organizer to help you study the concept.

1. Product of Powers Property

2. Power of a Power Property

3. Power of a Product Property

4. Quotient of Powers Property

5. negative exponents

6. scientific notation

7. adding and subtracting numbers in scientific notation

8. multiplying and dividing numbers in scientific notation

Ancient monumental structures built by the Mayans

EXAMPLE
El Castillo Chichen Itza, Mexico

EXAMPLE
Temple of the Masks in Tikal, Guatemala

You seem confused on the concept of a selfie.

"Here is my **Definition and Example Chart.** I'm going to take a selfie from the top of the pyramid. Do you want to hold the camera?"

Review Vocabulary

- As a review of the chapter vocabulary, have students revisit the vocabulary section in their *Student Journals* to fill in any missing definitions and record examples of each term.

Graphic Organizers

Sample answers:

1.

Product of Powers Property: To multiply powers with the same base, add their exponents.

Example
$$3^4 \cdot 3^5 = 3^{4+5} = 3^9$$

Example
$$a \cdot a^2 = a^{1+2} = a^3$$

Example
$$(-7)^3 \cdot (-7)^8 = (-7)^{3+8} = (-7)^{11}$$

2.

Power of a Power Property: To find a power of a power, multiply the exponents.

Example
$$(3^4)^2 = 3^{4 \cdot 2} = 3^8$$

Example
$$(b^5)^3 = b^{5 \cdot 3} = b^{15}$$

Example
$$((-2^7))^4 = (-2)^{7 \cdot 4} = (-2)^{28}$$

3.

Power of a Product Property: To find a power of a product, find the power of each factor and multiply.

Example
$$(3y)^5 = 3^5 y^5 = 243 y^5$$

Example
$$(mn)^2 = m^2 \cdot n^2 = m^2 n^2$$

Example
$$(2ab)^3 = 2^3 \cdot a^3 \cdot b^3 = 8a^3 b^3$$

4–8. Answer at *BigIdeasMath.com*.

List of Organizers
Available at *BigIdeasMath.com*
Definition and Example Chart
Example and Non-Example Chart
Four Square
Information Frame
Summary Triangle

About this Organizer

A **Definition and Example Chart** can be used to organize information about a concept. Students fill in the top rectangle with a term and its definition or description. Students fill in the rectangles that follow with examples to illustrate the term. Each sample answer shows three examples, but students can show more or fewer examples. Definition and Example Charts are useful for concepts that can be illustrated with more than one type of example.

1. $(-9)^5$

2. $2^3 n^2$

3. 1331

4. $-\dfrac{1}{16}$

5. 100

6. $\$650$

7. p^7

8. n^{22}

9. $\left(-\dfrac{2}{5}\right)^5$

10. $16k^4$

11. *Sample answer:* $(x^3)^8$

12. 2^{12} bytes

13. Write 27 as 3^3. Then, using the Product of Powers Property, $3^3 \cdot 3^2 = 3^{3\,+\,2} = 3^5$.

✓ *Chapter Self-Assessment*

The Success Criteria Self-Assessment chart can be found in the *Student Journal* or online at *BigIdeasMath.com.*

ELL Support

Allow students to work in pairs to complete the first section of the Chapter Self-Assessment. Have pairs display their answers on whiteboards for your review. Use similar techniques to check remaining sections of the Chapter Self-Assessment. For discussion questions, have two pairs compare ideas and come to an agreement. Review explanations as a class. Monitor discussions and provide support.

Common Errors

- **Exercises 1 and 2** Students may count the wrong number of factors. Remind them to check their work.
- **Exercises 3–5** Students may treat the exponent as a factor. For example, some may think that 11^3 means 11×3. Remind them of the definition of an exponent.
- **Exercises 4 and 5** Students may have the wrong sign in their answers. Remind them that when the negative sign is inside the parentheses, it is part of the base. When the negative sign is outside the parentheses, it is not part of the base.
- **Exercise 5** Students may not use the correct order of operations when they evaluate the expression. Review the order of operations with students.
- **Exercises 7–9** Students may confuse the Product of Powers Property and the Power of a Power Property. Explain why it makes sense to add exponents when using the Product of Powers Property and multiply exponents when using the Power of a Power Property.
- **Exercise 9** Students may multiply the bases. Remind them that the base stays the same and only the exponent changes when using the Product of Powers Property.
- **Exercise 10** Students may forget to find the power of both factors and write, $(-2k)^4 = -2k^4$ instead of $(-2k)^4 = (-2)^4\, k^4 = 16k^4$. Remind them of the Power of a Product Property.

Chapter Self-Assessment

As you complete the exercises, use the scale below to rate your understanding of the success criteria in your journal.

1	2	3	4
I do not understand.	I can do it with help.	I can do it on my own.	I can teach someone else.

8.1 Exponents *(pp. 319–324)*

Learning Target: Use exponents to write and evaluate expressions.

Write the product using exponents.

1. $(-9) \cdot (-9) \cdot (-9) \cdot (-9) \cdot (-9)$

2. $2 \cdot 2 \cdot 2 \cdot n \cdot n$

Evaluate the expression.

3. 11^3

4. $-\left(\dfrac{1}{2}\right)^4$

5. $\left| \dfrac{1}{2}(16 - 6^3) \right|$

6. The profit P (in dollars) earned by a local merchant selling x items is represented by the equation $P = 0.2x^3 - 10$. How much more profit does he earn selling 15 items than 5 items?

8.2 Product of Powers Property *(pp. 325–330)*

Learning Target: Generate equivalent expressions involving products of powers.

Simplify the expression. Write your answer as a power.

7. $p^5 \cdot p^2$

8. $(n^{11})^2$

9. $\left(-\dfrac{2}{5}\right)^3 \cdot \left(-\dfrac{2}{5}\right)^2$

10. Simplify $(-2k)^4$.

11. Write an expression that simplifies to x^{24} using the Power of a Power Property.

12. You send an email with a file size of 4 kilobytes. One kilobyte is 2^{10} bytes. What is the file size of your email in bytes?

13. Explain how to use properties of exponents to simplify the expression $27 \cdot 3^2$.

8.3 Quotient of Powers Property (pp. 331–336)

Learning Target: Generate equivalent expressions involving quotients of powers.

Simplify the expression. Write your answer as a power.

14. $\dfrac{8^8}{8^3}$

15. $\dfrac{5^2 \cdot 5^9}{5}$

16. $\dfrac{w^8}{w^7} \cdot \dfrac{w^5}{w^2}$

17. $\dfrac{m^8}{m^6} \cdot \dfrac{m^{10} \cdot m^2}{m^9}$

18. Write an expression that simplifies to x^3 using the Quotient of Powers Property.

19. At the end of a fiscal year, a company has made 1.62×7^7 dollars in profit. The company employs 7^3 people. How much will each person receive if the company divides the profit equally among its employees?

8.4 Zero and Negative Exponents (pp. 337–342)

Learning Target: Understand the concepts of zero and negative exponents.

Evaluate the expression.

20. 2^{-4}

21. 95^0

22. $\dfrac{8^2}{8^4}$

23. $(-12)^{-7} \cdot (-12)^7$

24. $\dfrac{1}{7^9} \cdot \dfrac{1}{7^{-6}}$

25. $\dfrac{9^4 \cdot 9^{-2}}{9^2}$

Simplify. Write the expression using only positive exponents.

26. $x^{-2} \cdot x^0$

27. $y^{-8}y^3$

28. $\dfrac{3^{-1} \cdot z^5}{z^{-2}}$

29. Write an expression that simplifies to x^{-4}.

30. Water flows from a showerhead at a rate of 24^{-1} gallon per second. How many gallons do you use when taking a 15-minute shower? a 20-minute shower?

31. Explain two different methods for simplifying $w^{-2} \cdot w^5$.

Common Errors

- **Exercises 14–17** Students may divide the exponents when they should be subtracting them. Remind students that the Quotient of Powers Property states that the exponents are subtracted.
- **Exercises 14–17** Students may multiply and/or divide the bases when simplifying the expression. Remind them that the base does not change when they use the Quotient of Powers or Product of Powers Property.
- **Exercises 20–25** Students may forget to complete the solution; they may simplify the expression, but leave the expression with exponents. Point out that they need to evaluate any powers to complete the solution.
- **Exercises 20 and 22–25** Students may think that a negative exponent makes the power negative. Remind them of the definition of a negative exponent.
- **Exercises 21, 23, and 25** Students may think that a power with a zero exponent is equal to zero. Remind them of the definition of a zero exponent.

14. 8^5

15. 5^{10}

16. w^4

17. m^5

18. *Sample answer:* $\dfrac{x^{13}}{x^{10}}$

19. $3889.62

20. $\dfrac{1}{16}$

21. 1

22. $\dfrac{1}{64}$

23. 1

24. $\dfrac{1}{343}$

25. 1

26. $\dfrac{1}{x^2}$

27. $\dfrac{1}{y^5}$

28. $\dfrac{z^7}{3}$

29. *Sample answer:* $\dfrac{x^4}{x^8}$

30. 37.5 gal; 50 gal

31. 1) Using the Product of Powers Property,
$w^{-2} \cdot w^5 = w^{-2+5} = w^3$.

2) Using the definition of a negative exponent, $w^{-2} = \dfrac{1}{w^2}$.

So, $w^{-2} \cdot w^5 = \dfrac{1}{w^2} \cdot w^5 = \dfrac{w^5}{w^2}$.

Then, using the Quotient of Powers Property,
$\dfrac{w^5}{w^2} = w^{5-2} = w^3$.

32. 3×10^7

33. 6×10^{-7}

34. 9×10^8 m

35. 100 times greater

36. 3.6×10^{-4}

37. 8×10^5

38. 7.92×10^7

39. 20,000,000

40. 0.0048

41. 625,000

42. *Sample answer:* 0.0752 mg

43. 6.32×10^9

44. 4.1×10^{-4}

45. 3.773×10^4

46. 2×10^{-4}

47. 1.5 times greater

Common Errors

- **Exercises 32 and 33** Students may round incorrectly. Remind them to round the number so that it contains exactly one nonzero digit. You may also want to remind students of rounding rules.
- **Exercises 36–38** Students may write an exponent with the opposite sign of what is correct. Remind them that large numbers have positive exponents in scientific notation and that small numbers have negative exponents in scientific notation.
- **Exercises 39–41** Students may move the decimal point in the wrong direction. Remind them that when the exponent is negative they move the decimal point to the left, and when it is positive they move the decimal point to the right.
- **Exercises 43–46** Students may multiply or divide the factors and leave the factor less than 1 or leave the factor greater than or equal to 10. Remind them that the factor in scientific notation must be at least 1 and less than 10.

Chapter Resources

Surface Level	Deep Level
Resources by Chapter • Extra Practice • Reteach • Puzzle Time Student Journal • Practice • Chapter Self-Assessment Differentiating the Lesson Tutorial Videos Skills Review Handbook Skills Trainer Game Library	Resources by Chapter • Enrichment and Extension Graphic Organizers Game Library
Transfer Level	
STEAM Video Dynamic Assessment System • Chapter Test	Assessment Book • Chapter Tests A and B • Alternative Assessment • STEAM Performance Task

8.5 Estimating Quantities (pp. 343–348)

Learning Target: Round numbers and write the results as the product of a single digit and a power of 10.

Round the number. Write the result as a product of a single digit and a power of 10.

32. 29,197,543

33. 0.000000647

34. The speed of light is 299,792,458 meters per second. About how far can a light beam travel in 3 seconds? Write your answer as a product of a single digit and a power of 10.

35. The population of Albany, New York is about 98,989 and the population of Moscow, Russia is about 12,235,448. Approximately how many times greater is the population of Moscow than the population of Albany?

8.6 Scientific Notation (pp. 349–354)

Learning Target: Understand the concept of scientific notation.

Write the number in scientific notation.

36. 0.00036

37. 800,000

38. 79,200,000

Write the number in standard form.

39. 2×10^7

40. 4.8×10^{-3}

41. 6.25×10^5

42. The mass of a single dust particle is 7.52×10^{-10} kilogram. What is the mass of a dust ball made of 100 dust particles? Express your answer using more-appropriate units.

8.7 Operations in Scientific Notation (pp. 355–360)

Learning Target: Perform operations with numbers written in scientific notation.

Evaluate the expression. Write your answer in scientific notation.

43. $(4.2 \times 10^8) + (5.9 \times 10^9)$

44. $(5.9 \times 10^{-4}) - (1.8 \times 10^{-4})$

45. $(7.7 \times 10^8) \times (4.9 \times 10^{-5})$

46. $(3.6 \times 10^5) \div (1.8 \times 10^9)$

Diameter $\approx 8 \times 10^{-6}$ m

47. A white blood cell has a diameter of about 0.000012 meter. How many times greater is the diameter of a white blood cell than the diameter of a red blood cell?

8 Practice Test

Write the product using exponents.

1. $(-15) \cdot (-15) \cdot (-15)$

2. $4 \cdot 4 \cdot x \cdot x \cdot x$

Evaluate the expression.

3. $10 + 3^3 \div 9$

4. $\dfrac{-2 \cdot (-2)^{-4}}{(-2)^{-2}}$

Simplify the expression. Write your answer as a power.

5. $9^{10} \cdot 9$

6. $(6^6)^5$

7. $\dfrac{(-3.5)^{13} \cdot (-3.5)^2}{(-3.5)^9}$

8. Simplify $(2y)^7$.

Round the number. Write the result as a product of a single digit and a power of 10.

9. $4{,}610{,}428{,}970$

10. 0.00000572

Write the number in standard form.

11. 3×10^7

12. 9.05×10^{-3}

Evaluate the expression. Write your answer in scientific notation.

13. $(7.8 \times 10^7) + (9.9 \times 10^7)$

14. $(6.4 \times 10^5) - (5.4 \times 10^4)$

15. $(3.1 \times 10^6) \times (2.7 \times 10^{-2})$

16. $(9.6 \times 10^7) \div (1.2 \times 10^{-4})$

17. Is $(xy^2)^3$ the same as $(xy^3)^2$? Explain.

18. One scoop of rice weighs about 3^9 milligrams.

    a. Write a linear function that relates the weight of rice to the number of scoops. What is the weight of 5 scoops of rice?

    b. A grain of rice weighs about 3^3 milligrams. About how many grains of rice are in 1 scoop?

19. There are about 10,000 taste buds on a human tongue. Write this number in scientific notation.

20. From 1978 to 2008, the amount of lead allowed in the air in the United States was 1.5×10^{-6} gram per cubic meter. In 2008, the amount allowed was reduced by 90%. What is the new amount of lead allowed in the air?

Practice Test Item References

Practice Test Questions	Section to Review
1, 2, 3	8.1
5, 6, 8, 17	8.2
7, 18	8.3
4	8.4
9, 10	8.5
11, 12, 19, 20	8.6
13, 14, 15, 16	8.7

Test-Taking Strategies

Remind students to quickly look over the entire test before they start so that they can budget their time. Have them use the **Stop** and **Think** strategy before they write their answers.

Common Errors

- **Exercises 1 and 2** Students may count the wrong number of factors. Remind them to check their work.
- **Exercise 3** Students may not use the correct order of operations when they evaluate the expression. Review the order of operations with students.
- **Exercises 4 and 7** Students may have the wrong sign in their answers. Remind them that when the negative sign is inside the parentheses, it is part of the base. When the negative sign is outside the parentheses, it is not part of the base.
- **Exercises 4 and 7** Students may divide the exponents when they should be subtracting them. Remind students that the Quotient of Powers Property states that the exponents are subtracted.
- **Exercises 4–8** Students may confuse the Product of Powers Property and the Power of a Power Property. Explain why it makes sense to add exponents when using the Product of Powers Property and multiply exponents when using the Power of a Power Property.
- **Exercises 11 and 12** Students may move the decimal point in the wrong direction. Remind them that when the exponent is negative they move the decimal point to the left, and when it is positive they move the decimal point to the right.
- **Exercises 13–16** Students may multiply or divide the factors and leave the factor less than 1 or leave the factor greater than or equal to 10. Remind them that the factor in scientific notation must be at least 1 and less than 10.

1. $(-15)^3$

2. $4^2 x^3$

3. 13

4. $-\dfrac{1}{2}$

5. 9^{11}

6. 6^{30}

7. $(-3.5)^6$

8. $128 y^7$

9. 5×10^9

10. 6×10^{-6}

11. 30,000,000

12. 0.00905

13. 1.77×10^8

14. 5.86×10^5

15. 8.37×10^4

16. 8×10^{11}

17. no;
$(xy^2)^3 = x^3(y^2)^3 = x^3 y^{2 \cdot 3} = x^3 y^6$
$(xy^3)^2 = x^2(y^3)^2 = x^2 y^{3 \cdot 2} = x^2 y^6$

18. **a.** $y = 3^9 x$; 98,415 mg

   b. 3^6 grains

19. 1×10^4 taste buds

20. 1.5×10^{-7} gram per cubic meter

Test-Taking Strategies

Available at *BigIdeasMath.com*
After Answering Easy Questions, Relax
Answer Easy Questions First
Estimate the Answer
Read All Choices before Answering
Read Question before Answering
Solve Directly or Eliminate Choices
Solve Problem before Looking at Choices
Use Intelligent Guessing
Work Backwards

About this Strategy

When taking a multiple-choice test, be sure to read each question carefully and thoroughly. Sometimes you may not know the answer. So… guess intelligently! Look at the choices and choose the ones that are reasonable answers.

Cumulative Practice

1. B
2. I
3. D
4. 46

Item Analysis

1. **A.** The student miscounts when moving the decimal point.

    B. Correct answer

    C. The student miscounts when moving the decimal point.

    D. The student thinks there should be 7 zeros.

2. **F.** The student is finding the sum of the angle measures of a quadrilateral.

    G. The student is finding the sum of the measures of two acute angles of a right triangle.

    H. The student finds the measure of the wrong angle.

    I. Correct answer

3. **A.** The student multiplies the exponents instead of adding them.

    B. The student multiplies the bases instead of keeping the same base.

    C. The student multiplies all of the numbers in the expression.

    D. Correct answer

4. **Gridded Response:** Correct answer: 46

    Common error: The student finds the number of male students who took the survey instead of female students and gets an answer of 41.

Cumulative Practice

1. Mercury's distance from the Sun is approximately 5.79×10^7 kilometers. What is this distance in standard form?

   A. 5,790,000 km   B. 57,900,000 km

   C. 579,000,000 km   D. 5,790,000,000 km

2. Your friend solves the problem. What should your friend change to correctly answer the question?

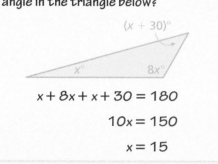

How many degrees are in the largest angle in the triangle below?

$(x + 30)°$

$x°$ $8x°$

$$x + 8x + x + 30 = 180$$
$$10x = 150$$
$$x = 15$$

Test-Taking Strategy
Use Intelligent Guessing

Cats were first tamed $3 \cdot 2^{10}$ years ago in Egypt. How long ago was that?

Ⓐ 3000   Ⓑ 3072   Ⓒ 5000   Ⓓ 40

Who says I am tame? Growl. Hiss.

"It can't be 40 or 5000 because they aren't divisible by 3. So, you can intelligently guess between 3000 and 3072."

   F. The left side of the equation should equal 360° instead of 180°.

   G. The sum of the acute angles should equal 90°.

   H. Evaluate the smallest angle when $x = 15$.

   I. Evaluate the largest angle when $x = 15$.

3. Which expression is equivalent to the expression $2^4 2^3$?

   A. 2^{12} B. 4^7

   C. 48   D. 128

4. You randomly survey students in your school about whether they have a pet. You display your results in the two-way table. How many female students took the survey?

		Pet	
		Yes	No
Gender	Male	33	8
	Female	35	11

5. A bank account pays interest so that the amount in the account doubles every 10 years. The account started with $5,000 in 1940. Which expression represents the amount (in dollars) in the account n decades later?

F. $2^n \cdot 5000$

G. $5000(n + 1)$

H. 5000^n

I. $2^n + 5000$

6. The formula for the volume V of a pyramid is $V = \frac{1}{3}Bh$.

Which equation represents a formula for the height h of the pyramid?

A. $h = \frac{1}{3}VB$

B. $h = \frac{3V}{B}$

C. $h = \frac{V}{3B}$

D. $h = V - \frac{1}{3}B$

7. The gross domestic product (GDP) is a way to measure how much a country produces economically in a year. The table below shows the approximate population and GDP for the United States.

United States, 2016	
Population	324,000,000
GDP	$18,600,000,000,000

Part A Write the population and the GDP using scientific notation.

Part B Find the GDP per person for the United States using your answers from *Part A*. Write your answer in scientific notation. Show your work and explain your reasoning.

8. What is the equation of the line shown in the graph?

F. $y = -\frac{1}{3}x + 3$

G. $y = \frac{1}{3}x + 1$

H. $y = -3x + 3$

I. $y = 3x - \frac{1}{3}$

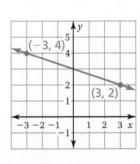

Item Analysis (continued)

5. F. Correct answer

   G. The student multiplies 5000 by one more than the number of decades.

   H. The student uses 5000 as the base.

   I. The student adds 2^n and 5000 instead of multiplying.

6. A. The student does not use inverse operations.

   B. Correct answer

   C. The student divides V by 3 instead of multiplying V by 3.

   D. The student subtracts $\frac{1}{3}B$ from V instead of dividing V by $\frac{1}{3}B$.

7. 2 points The student's work and explanations demonstrate a thorough understanding of writing and dividing numbers in scientific notation. In Part A, the student correctly writes the population as 3.24×10^8 and the GDP as 1.86×10^{13} dollars. In Part B, the student correctly finds the quotient $\frac{1.86 \times 10^{13}}{3.24 \times 10^8} \approx 5.74 \times 10^4$ dollars. The student provides clear and complete work and explanations.

   1 point The student's work and explanations demonstrate a partial but limited understanding of writing and dividing numbers in scientific notation. The student provides some correct work and/or explanation. The population and the GDP are written is scientific notation correctly, but the student does not find the correct quotient.

   0 points The student provides no response, a completely incorrect or incomprehensible response, or a response that demonstrates insufficient understanding of writing and dividing numbers in scientific notation.

8. F. Correct answer

   G. The student miscalculates slope as positive and then chooses the equation that has (3, 2) as a solution.

   H. The student determines the slope incorrectly as the change in x over the change in y.

   I. The student switches the slope and the y-intercept in the equation.

5. F

6. B

7. *Part A* population: 3.24×10^8; GDP: 1.86×10^{13} dollars

   Part B about 5.74×10^4 dollars

8. F

9. B

10. 0.16 or $\frac{4}{25}$

11. G

12. C

Item Analysis (continued)

9. **A.** The student incorrectly thinks that a graph composed of line segments and a ray represents a linear function.

   B. Correct answer

   C. The student incorrectly thinks that a graph with a continuous curve represents a linear function.

   D. The student incorrectly thinks that a graph with a continuous curve represents a linear function.

10. **Gridded Response:** Correct answer: 0.16 or $\frac{4}{25}$

    Common error: The student writes the answer as a negative number.

11. **F.** The student mistakes the roles of the slope and y-intercept, thinking that same y-intercept means what same slope means.

    G. Correct answer

    H. The student chooses a conclusion for lines that have the same y-intercept and the same slope, overlooking that these lines have different slopes.

    I. The student thinks that because the two lines have the same y-intercept, they must have the same slope.

12. **A.** The student pairs each input with the output in the corresponding position.

    B. The student does not include $(2, -2)$.

    C. Correct answer

    D. The student reverses the order of inputs and outputs.

9. Which graph represents a linear function?

A.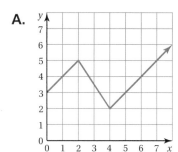

B.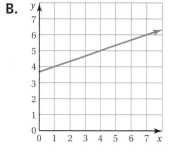

C.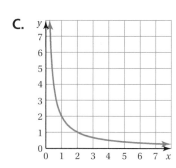

D.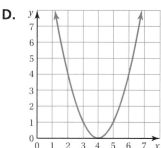

10. Find $(-2.5)^{-2}$.

11. Two lines have the same y-intercept. The slope of one line is 1, and the slope of the other line is -1. What can you conclude?

  F. The lines are parallel.

  G. The lines meet at exactly one point.

  H. The lines meet at more than one point.

  I. The situation described is impossible.

12. Which list of ordered pairs represents the mapping diagram?

  A. $(1, 2), (2, 0), (3, -2)$

  B. $(1, 0), (2, 2), (3, -2)$

  C. $(1, 0), (2, 2), (2, -2), (3, -2)$

  D. $(0, 1), (2, 2), (-2, 2), (-2, 3)$

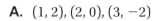

9 Real Numbers and the Pythagorean Theorem

Chapter Learning Target:
Understand square roots.

Chapter Success Criteria:
- I can describe a square root.
- I can find the square root(s) of a number.
- I can approximate the value of the square root of a number.
- I can explain the Pythagorean Theorem.

STEAM Video: "Metronome Design"

Laurie's Notes

Chapter 9 Overview

Irrational numbers are formally introduced in this chapter, completing student's study of real numbers. The Pythagorean Theorem is also introduced, a famous theorem that connects the fields of algebra and geometry, and is the basis of trigonometry.

In the first lesson, students find square roots of numbers and evaluate expressions involving square roots. They also use square roots to solve equations. Squaring a number and taking a square root are inverse operations, a key understanding in this lesson. For example, $\sqrt{4^2} = \sqrt{16} = 4$ and $(\sqrt{4})^2 = 2^2 = 4$. It is important for students to understand that every positive number has a positive and a negative square root; however, the context of the problem may exclude one of them from the solution. For instance, if you are solving for a variable that represents a distance, you can only take the positive square root because distance cannot be negative.

The second lesson introduces the Pythagorean Theorem, a relationship that is used to solve a variety of real-life applications. Take time for students to understand the visual "proof" in the exploration. You want them to understand that $a^2 + b^2 = c^2$ is more than three variables. The variables represent three side lengths of a *right* triangle.

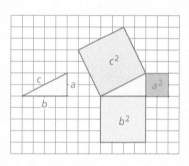

There is a natural progression from square roots to cube roots in the third lesson. The work involves evaluating expressions and solving cubic equations. Students should be able to explain why the cube root of a negative number is a real number, which is not true for the square root of a negative number. For example, $\sqrt[3]{-8} = -2$ and $\sqrt{-8}$ has no real root. It is very common at this point for students to ask if there are other types of numbers. Do not go into great detail about imaginary numbers, but do not mislead students by saying you cannot take the square root of a negative number.

In the next two lessons, students work with rational and irrational numbers, including learning to write repeating decimals as fractions or mixed numbers. Make calculators available and let students explore patterns within rational numbers. The irrational numbers (non-repeating, non-terminating) are then introduced. Remind students that they used π in the previous course when computing areas and circumferences of circles, and π is an irrational number.

The chapter concludes with a lesson on using the converse of the Pythagorean Theorem, a theorem used to determine whether a triangle is a right triangle or not. Make sure students understand that not all theorems have converses that are true. An informal "proof" is provided in Exploration 2.

Suggested Pacing

Chapter Opener	1 Day
Section 1	2 Days
Section 2	2 Days
Section 3	2 Days
Section 4	2 Days
Section 5	2 Days
Section 6	2 Days
Connecting Concepts	1 Day
Chapter Review	1 Day
Chapter Test	1 Day
Total Chapter 9	16 Days
Year-to-Date	134 Days

Chapter Learning Target
Understand square roots.

Chapter Success Criteria
- Describe a square root.
- Find the square root(s) of a number.
- Approximate the value of the square root of a number.
- Explain the Pythagorean Theorem.

Chapter 9 Learning Targets and Success Criteria

Section	Learning Target	Success Criteria
9.1 Finding Square Roots	Understand the concept of a square root of a number.	• Find square roots of numbers. • Evaluate expressions involving square roots. • Use square roots to solve equations.
9.2 The Pythagorean Theorem	Understand the Pythagorean Theorem.	• Explain the Pythagorean Theorem. • Use the Pythagorean Theorem to find unknown side lengths of triangles. • Use the Pythagorean Theorem to find distances between points in a coordinate plane.
9.3 Finding Cube Roots	Understand the concept of a cube root of a number.	• Find cube roots of numbers. • Evaluate expressions involving cube roots. • Use cube roots to solve equations.
9.4 Rational Numbers	Convert between different forms of rational numbers.	• Explain the meaning of rational numbers. • Write fractions and mixed numbers as decimals. • Write repeating decimals as fractions or mixed numbers.
9.5 Irrational Numbers	Understand the concept of irrational numbers.	• Classify real numbers as rational or irrational. • Approximate irrational numbers. • Solve real-life problems involving irrational numbers.
9.6 The Converse of the Pythagorean Theorem	Understand the converse of the Pythagorean Theorem.	• Explain the converse of the Pythagorean Theorem. • Identify right triangles given three side lengths. • Identify right triangles in a coordinate plane.

Progressions

Through the Grades		
Grade 7	**Grade 8**	**High School**
• Add, subtract, multiply, and divide rational numbers. • Understand that every quotient of integers (nonzero divisor) is a rational number. • Convert a rational number to a decimal using long division.	• Understand that numbers that are not rational are irrational. • Compare irrational numbers using rational approximations. • Evaluate square roots and cube roots, including those resulting from solving equations. • Explain a proof of the Pythagorean Theorem and its converse. • Use the Pythagorean Theorem to find missing measures of right triangles and distances between points in a coordinate plane.	• Evaluate and simplify expressions with exponents, including rational exponents; find nth roots. • Simplify expressions and perform operations, using the properties of radicals. • Solve radical equations and identify extraneous solutions. • Solve quadratic equations by using square roots. • Find side lengths and solve real-life problems involving special right triangles. • Find segment lengths using the Distance Formula.

Through the Chapter						
Standard	**9.1**	**9.2**	**9.3**	**9.4**	**9.5**	**9.6**
8.NS.A.1 Know that numbers that are not rational are called irrational. Understand informally that every number has a decimal expansion; for rational numbers show that the decimal expansion repeats eventually, and convert a decimal expansion which repeats eventually into a rational number.				●	★	
8.NS.A.2 Use rational approximations of irrational numbers to compare the size of irrational numbers, locate them approximately on a number line diagram, and estimate the value of expressions.					★	
8.EE.A.2 Use square root and cube root symbols to represent solutions to equations of the form $x^2 = p$ and $x^3 = p$, where p is a positive rational number. Evaluate square roots of small perfect squares and cube roots of small perfect cubes. Know that $\sqrt{2}$ is irrational.	●	●	★			
8.G.B.6 Explain a proof of the Pythagorean Theorem and its converse.		●				★
8.G.B.7 Apply the Pythagorean Theorem to determine unknown side lengths in right triangles in real-world and mathematical problems in two and three dimensions.		★				
8.G.B.8 Apply the Pythagorean Theorem to find the distance between two points in a coordinate system.		★				

Key

▲ = preparing   ★ = complete
● = learning   ■ = extending

Laurie's Notes

1. 6; 7; 8

2. 2 sec; Using the pattern in the table in Exercise 1, $\sqrt{100} = 10$. So, $T = 0.2\sqrt{100} = 0.2(10) = 2$ sec.

Performance Task

Sample answer: The values you substitute into a formula must be consistent with how the variables in the formula are defined. Failing to make sure the units are the same as the formula can result in values that are incorrect.

Mathematical Practices

Students have opportunities to develop aspects of the mathematical practices throughout the chapter. Here are some examples.

1. **Make Sense of Problems and Persevere in Solving Them**
   9.3 Math Practice note, *p. 389*

2. **Reason Abstractly and Quantitatively**
   9.1 Exercise 40, *p. 379*

3. **Construct Viable Arguments and Critique the Reasoning of Others**
   9.2 Exercise 13, *p. 386*

4. **Model with Mathematics**
   9.4 Exercise 28, *p. 400*

5. **Use Appropriate Tools Strategically**
   9.5 Exercise 34, *p. 407*

6. **Attend to Precision**
   9.5 Math Practice note, *p. 401*

7. **Look for and Make Use of Structure**
   9.4 Exercise 38, *p. 400*

8. **Look for and Express Regularity in Repeated Reasoning**
   9.1 Exercise 50, *p. 380*

STEAM Video

Before the Video

- To introduce the STEAM Video, read aloud the first paragraph of Metronome Design and discuss the question with your students.
- "Why do musicians use metronomes?"

During the Video

- The video shows Alex and Tony discussing how metronomes and clocks work.
- Pause the video at 1:36 and ask, "What is each swing (back and forth) of a pendulum called?" the period
- "Why are pendulums used to run clocks and metronomes?" Because they keep precisely predictable time.
- Watch the remainder of the video.

After the Video

- Ask, "How are the marks on a metronome spaced?" The marks are not evenly spaced because they are spaced according to the square root function.
- Have students work with a partner to answer Questions 1 and 2.
- As students discuss and answer the questions, listen for a basic understanding of square roots.

Performance Task

- Use this information to spark students' interest and promote thinking about real-life problems.
- Ask, "Why is it important to pay attention to units when substituting values into a formula?"
- After completing the chapter, students will have gained the knowledge needed to complete "Identify and Correct the Error!"

Metronome Design

A *metronome* is a device that ticks at a constant rate. A metronome includes a pendulum, which swings back and forth in a precise time called a *period*. Why do musicians use metronomes?

Watch the STEAM Video "Metronome Design." Then answer the following questions. The equation $T = 0.2\sqrt{L}$ relates the period T (in seconds) and the length L (in centimeters) of a pendulum, where $\sqrt{L}$ is the *square root* of L.

1. The table shows the square roots of several values of L. Use the pattern to find the values of $\sqrt{36}$, $\sqrt{49}$, and $\sqrt{64}$.

L	1	4	9	16	25
$\sqrt{L}$	1	2	3	4	5

2. What is the period of a pendulum that is 100 centimeters long? Justify your answer.

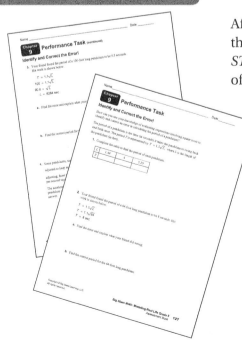

Identify and Correct the Error!

After completing this chapter, you will be able to use the concepts you learned to answer the questions in the *STEAM Video Performance Task*. You will be given the lengths of several pendulums.

Length (feet)	1.44	4	5.29
Period (seconds)			

You will be asked to identify and correct errors in calculations of periods. Why is it important to pay attention to units when substituting values into a formula?

Getting Ready for Chapter

Chapter Exploration

When you multiply a number by itself, you square the number.

> Symbol for squaring is the exponent 2.
>
> $4^2 = 4 \cdot 4$
>
> $= 16$ 4 squared is 16.

To "undo" this, take the *square root* of the number.

> Symbol for square root is a *radical sign*, $\sqrt{\ }$.
>
> $\sqrt{16} = \sqrt{4^2} = 4$ The square root of 16 is 4.

1. Work with a partner. Find the radius of each circle.

a.
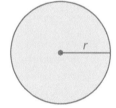
Area $= 36\pi$ in.^{2}

b.
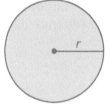
Area $= \pi$ yd^2

c.
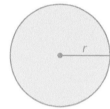
Area $= 0.25\pi$ ft^2

d.
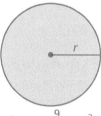
Area $= \frac{9}{16}\pi$ m^2

e.
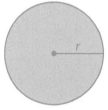
Area $= 0.49\pi$ cm^2

f.
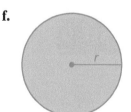
Area $= 1.44\pi$ in.^{2}

2. **WRITING GUIDELINES** Work with a partner. Explain how you can find the radius and diameter of a circular object when you are given its area. Justify your answer using an example that is different from those in Exercise 1.

Vocabulary

The following vocabulary terms are defined in this chapter. Think about what the terms might mean and record your thoughts.

square root   cube root   irrational number

perfect square   perfect cube

Laurie's Notes

Check out the digital flash cards.
BigIdeasMath.com

Chapter Exploration

- **MP6 Attend to Precision:** In this exploration, students will need to multiply fractions and decimals and recall perfect squares.
- ❓ "How do you find the area of a circle?" $A = \pi r^2$
- ❓ "If you know the area of a circle, can you solve for the radius?" yes
- Do not give away too much at this point. Let students think through the problems in Exercise 1. Part (a) involves an obvious perfect square.
- **Common Error:** In parts (c), (e), and (f), students may forget how decimals are multiplied. For instance, in part (c), students will often answer 0.05 instead of 0.5.
- Discuss students' answers and reasoning in Exercise 2. They should explain that to find the radius, you must find a number whose square times π is the area. Then you can multiply the radius by 2 to find the diameter.
- **Popsicle Sticks:** Select several students to share their examples.

Vocabulary

- These terms represent some of the vocabulary that students will encounter in Chapter 9. Discuss the terms as a class.
- Where have students heard the term *perfect square* outside of a math classroom? In what contexts? Students may not be able to write the actual definition, but they may write phrases associated with a *perfect square*.
- Allowing students to discuss these terms now will prepare them for understanding the terms as they are presented in the chapter.
- When students encounter a new definition, encourage them to write in their *Student Journals*. They will revisit these definitions during the Chapter Review.

ELL Support

Students may know the word *perfect* as meaning "absolutely ideal, without faults." Explain that when *perfect* is used to describe a square or a cube in math, it refers to integers. A perfect square or a perfect cube is a number whose square root or cube root is an integer.

Topics for Review

- Comparing and Ordering Decimals and Fractions
- Converting Fractions or Mixed Numbers to Decimals
- Converting Terminating Decimals to Fractions or Mixed Numbers
- Evaluating Algebraic Expressions
- Exponents
- Number Line
- Order of Operations
- Solving Equations
- Triangles

Chapter Exploration

1. **a.** 6 in.
   b. 1 yd
   c. 0.5 ft
   d. $\frac{3}{4}$ m
   e. 0.7 cm
   f. 1.2 in.

2. To find the radius, find a number whose square times π is the area. The diameter is twice this number; *Sample answer:* $A = 64\pi$ in.^{2}, so $r = 8$ in. because $8^2 \cdot \pi = 64\pi$, and $d = 2(8) = 16$ in.

STATE STANDARDS
8.EE.A.2

Learning Target

Understand the concept of a square root of a number.

Success Criteria

- Find square roots of numbers.
- Evaluate expressions involving square roots.
- Use square roots to solve equations.

Warm Up

Cumulative, vocabulary, and prerequisite skills practice opportunities are available in the *Resources by Chapter* or at *BigIdeasMath.com*.

ELL Support

Students may know the word *root* as referring to a part of a plant or a word's origin. They may also know a square as a geometric figure. Explain that a square root is neither. Write $2^2 = 2 \cdot 2 = 4$ on the board. Circle 2^2 and say "two squared." Underline a 2 in the product and say "two is the square root of four." Explain that the square of a number is the product of a number and itself. The square root of a number refers to the number that is multiplied by itself.

Exploration 1

9 yd; 18 cm; 19 mi; 15 mi; 1.7 in.; $\frac{2}{3}$ ft; Find a number whose square is the area.

Exploration 2

See Additional Answers.

T-373

Laurie's Notes

Preparing to Teach

- Students have found squares of numbers and areas of squares. They will build upon this understanding to explore square roots.
- **MP6 Attend to Precision:** In these explorations, students will need to multiply fractions and decimals and recall perfect squares.

Motivate

- Distribute 1-centimeter grid paper to students. Grid paper is available online at *BigIdeasMath.com*.
- Have students draw a square with side lengths of 1 centimeter.
- "What is the area of the square?" 1 square centimeter
- Repeat for squares with side lengths of 2 centimeters, 3 centimeters, 4 centimeters, and 5 centimeters. 4 square centimeters; 9 square centimeters; 16 square centimeters; 25 square centimeters
- "What are two different methods that can be used to find the areas of the squares?" Multiply the length by the width (s^2) or count the grid squares.
- In Exploration 1, students are given the area of a square and they are asked to find the side length.

Exploration 1

- Cut out a square with side lengths of 6 centimeters from 1-centimeter grid paper. Hold it up for students to see.
- "What is the area of the square?" 36 square centimeters
- "If you know the area of a square, how can you find the dimensions without measuring the side lengths?" Answers will vary.
- **Common Error:** Students may say to divide by 4 (perimeter) or divide by 2. Using the 6-centimeter-by-6-centimeter square, remind students that the side lengths are the same and they are multiplied together to get 36 square centimeters. So, the side lengths must be 6 centimeters because $6 \cdot 6 = 36$.
- Students should now be ready to begin the exploration.
- When students have finished, discuss the answers and the strategies they used.

Exploration 2

- "What number can you multiply by itself to get 81?" −9 and 9 Students will likely only answer 9. Remind them that $(-9) \cdot (-9) = 81$.
- "Why wasn't −9 an answer for the square with an area of 81 square yards in Exploration 1?" Lead students to understand that the answers in Exploration 1 represent distances, which are always positive.
- After students have completed the exploration, discuss their strategies and reasoning as a class. Use *Popsicle Sticks* to solicit explanations.

9.1 Finding Square Roots

Learning Target: Understand the concept of a square root of a number.

Success Criteria:
- I can find square roots of numbers.
- I can evaluate expressions involving square roots.
- I can use square roots to solve equations.

EXPLORATION 1

Finding Side Lengths

Work with a partner. Find the side length s of each square. Explain your method.

Area = 81 yd^2
s

Area = 324 cm^2
s

Area = 361 mi^2
s

Area = 225 mi^2
s

Area = 2.89 in.^{2}
s

Area = $\frac{4}{9}$ ft^2
s

EXPLORATION 2

Finding Solutions of Equations

Work with a partner. Use mental math to solve each equation. How many solutions are there for each equation? Explain your reasoning.

Math Practice

Use Operations

How do the sign rules for multiplying integers help you find the solution(s) of each equation?

$x^2 = 0$

$x^2 = 1$

$x^2 = 4$

$x^2 = 9$

$x^2 = 16$

$x^2 = 25$

9.1 Lesson

Key Vocabulary 🔊
square root, p. 374
perfect square, p. 374
radical sign, p. 374
radicand, p. 374

A **square root** of a number p is a number whose square is equal to p. So, a square root of a number p is a solution of the equation $x^2 = p$. Every positive number has a positive *and* a negative square root. A **perfect square** is a number with integers as its square roots.

EXAMPLE 1 Finding Square Roots of a Perfect Square

Find the two square roots of 49.

Math Practice

Use Definitions
Explain why 0 only has one square root.

$7^2 = 49$ and $(-7)^2 = 49$

▷ So, the square roots of 49 are 7 and -7.

Try It Find the two square roots of the number.

1. 36   **2.** 100   **3.** 121

The symbol $\sqrt{}$ is called a **radical sign**. It is used to represent a square root. The number under the radical sign is called the **radicand**.

- $\sqrt{p}$ represents the *positive* square root of p.
- $-\sqrt{p}$ represents the *negative* square root of p.
- $\pm\sqrt{p}$ represents *both* square roots of p.

EXAMPLE 2 Finding Square Roots

Find the square root(s).

a. $\sqrt{25}$

$\sqrt{25}$ represents the *positive* square root.

▷ Because $5^2 = 25$, $\sqrt{25} = 5$.

b. $-\sqrt{49}$

$-\sqrt{49}$ represents the *negative* square root.

▷ Because $7^2 = 49$, $-\sqrt{49} = -7$.

c. $\pm\sqrt{16}$

$\pm\sqrt{16}$ represents both the *positive* and the *negative* square roots.

▷ Because $4^2 = 16$, $\pm\sqrt{16} = -4$ and 4.

Try It Find the square root(s).

4. $\sqrt{4}$ **5.** $-\sqrt{81}$ **6.** $\pm\sqrt{64}$

Laurie's Notes

Scaffolding Instruction

- Students explored square roots. Now they will find square roots, evaluate expressions, and solve equations involving square roots.
- **Emerging:** Students may struggle with finding square roots of fractions and decimals, along with determining the sign(s) of the square root(s). They will benefit from guided instruction for the definitions and examples.
- **Proficient:** Students grasp the concept of finding square roots of numbers. They should proceed to Examples 4 and 5 before completing the Self-Assessment exercises.

Discuss

- Write and discuss the definitions for **square root** of a number and **perfect square**. In the exploration, students used mental math to find their answers. They should now realize that they were actually finding square roots.
- Students are often confused when you say "every positive number has a positive *and* a negative square root." Use $(-3) \cdot (-3) = 9$ and $3 \cdot 3 = 9$ to explain.
- ❓ "What number has only one square root? Explain." 0; 0 is neither positive nor negative, so $\sqrt{0} = 0$.

EXAMPLE 1

- Note that the direction line is written in words without the square root symbol. The notation is introduced after this example.
- ❓ "What is the product of two positive numbers? two negative numbers?" Both are positive.
- Remind students that when squaring a negative number, they must use parentheses. For example, $(-7)^2 = (-7) \cdot (-7) = 49$, but $-7^2 = -1 \cdot 7 \cdot 7 = -49$.
- Point out that the square root of a negative number is *not* rational. Explain that if a product of two numbers is negative, one number must be negative and the other must be positive, so they cannot be the same number.

Discuss

- **MP6 Attend to Precision:** It is important for students to use correct language and be familiar with the symbols $\sqrt{}$, $-\sqrt{}$, and $\pm\sqrt{}$.
- The square root symbol is called a **radical sign** and the number under the radical sign is the **radicand**.
- Explain to students that the symbol $\pm$ is often read as "plus or minus."

EXAMPLE 2

- Remind students to pay close attention to the signs that precede the radical sign.
- ❓ "Why doesn't the answer in part (a) include -5?" Because $\sqrt{25}$ represents the positive square root of 25.
- In part (c), note that the answers of -4 and 4 can also be written as ± 4.

Try It

- Have students write their answers on whiteboards. Make sure they use appropriate sign(s) for each answer.

Scaffold instruction to support all students in their learning. Learning is individualized and you may want to group students differently as they move in and out of these levels with each skill and concept. Student self-assessment and feedback help guide your instructional decisions about how and when to layer support for all students to become proficient learners.

Extra Example 1
Find the two square roots 16. 4 and -4

Try It

1. 6 and -6
2. 10 and -10
3. 11 and -11

Extra Example 2
Find the square root(s).
a. $-\sqrt{36}$ -6
b. $\sqrt{9}$ 3
c. $\pm\sqrt{100}$ -10 and 10

Try It

4. 2
5. -9
6. -8 and 8

Extra Example 3
Find the square root(s).

a. $\pm\sqrt{\dfrac{9}{64}}$ $-\dfrac{3}{8}$ and $\dfrac{3}{8}$

b. $\sqrt{1.21}$ 1.1

Try It

7. $-\dfrac{1}{10}$

8. $-\dfrac{2}{5}$ and $\dfrac{2}{5}$

9. 3.5

Extra Example 4
Evaluate each expression.

a. $2\sqrt{144} - 30$ -6

b. $\sqrt{\dfrac{36}{4}} + \dfrac{1}{6}$ $3\dfrac{1}{6}$

c. $49 - \left(\sqrt{49}\right)^2$ 0

Try It

10. -3

11. 4.4

12. 11

EXAMPLE 3

? "How do you multiply fractions?" Write the product of the numerators over the product of the denominators.

? "What fraction is multiplied by itself to get $\dfrac{9}{16}$?" $\dfrac{3}{4}$

Try It

- **Think-Pair-Share:** Students should read each exercise independently and then work in pairs to complete the exercises. Then have each pair compare their answers with another pair and discuss any discrepancies.

EXAMPLE 4

- **Teaching Tip:** In these examples, remind students that square roots are numbers, so you can evaluate numerical expressions that include square roots. Students see a *symbol*, think *variable*, and suddenly they forget things like the order of operations. In part (a), some students think of this as $5x + 7$ and will not know what to do.
- Write the expression in part (a).
- **?** "Which operations are involved in this problem?" evaluating a square root, multiplication, and addition
- Work through parts (a) and (b) as shown. Make sure students understand the reason for each step.
- Write the expression in part (c). Discuss that squaring and taking the square root are inverse operations, as stated before the example.
- **?** "What is $\sqrt{81}$?" 9 "What is 9^2?" 81
- Say, "So, taking the square root of 81 and then squaring the answer results in 81." Finish evaluating the expression as shown.
- **?** "Can you name inverse operations?" addition and subtraction, multiplication and division, squaring and taking the square root

Try It

- Ask volunteers to share their work at the board for each of the problems.
- Exercise 11 looks more difficult because of the fraction. You may want to point out that $\dfrac{28}{7} = 4$.

ELL Support

After demonstrating Examples 3 and 4, have students work in pairs to discuss and complete Try It Exercises 7–12. Students may want to work together to solve the problems or one student can ask another, "What is the square root?" or "What is the answer?" Have students alternate the roles of asking and answering questions.

Beginner: Write the steps used to solve the problem.

Intermediate: State the answer and use simple sentences to explain the process used.

Advanced: Use detailed sentences to explain the process used.

EXAMPLE 3   Finding Square Roots

Find the square root(s).

a. $\sqrt{\dfrac{9}{16}}$

> Because $\left(\dfrac{3}{4}\right)^2 = \dfrac{9}{16}$, $\sqrt{\dfrac{9}{16}} = \dfrac{3}{4}$.

b. $\pm\sqrt{2.25}$

> Because $1.5^2 = 2.25$, $\pm\sqrt{2.25} = -1.5$ and 1.5.

Try It   **Find the square root(s).**

7. $-\sqrt{\dfrac{1}{100}}$ **8.** $\pm\sqrt{\dfrac{4}{25}}$ **9.** $\sqrt{12.25}$

Squaring a number and finding a square root "undo" each other. So, they are inverse operations. For example,

$$\sqrt{4^2} = \sqrt{16} = 4 \text{ and } \left(\sqrt{4}\right)^2 = 2^2 = 4.$$

You can use this relationship to evaluate expressions.

EXAMPLE 4   Evaluating Expressions Involving Square Roots

Evaluate each expression.

a. $5\sqrt{36} + 7 = 5(6) + 7$ Evaluate the square root.

          $= 30 + 7$ Multiply.

          $= 37$ Add.

b. $\dfrac{1}{4} + \sqrt{\dfrac{18}{2}} = \dfrac{1}{4} + \sqrt{9}$ Simplify.

          $= \dfrac{1}{4} + 3$ Evaluate the square root.

          $= 3\dfrac{1}{4}$ Add.

c. $\left(\sqrt{81}\right)^2 - 5 = 81 - 5$ Evaluate the power using inverse operations.

          $= 76$ Subtract.

Try It   **Evaluate the expression.**

10. $12 - 3\sqrt{25}$ **11.** $\sqrt{\dfrac{28}{7}} + 2.4$ **12.** $15 - \left(\sqrt{4}\right)^2$

Because squaring a number and taking the square root are inverse operations, you can solve an equation of the form $x^2 = p$ by taking the square root of each side.

EXAMPLE 5 **Solving Equations Using Square Roots**

Solve each equation.

When solving an equation by taking square roots, take both the positive and the negative square roots.

a. $x^2 = 81$

$x^2 = 81$ Write the equation.

$x = \pm\sqrt{81}$ Take the square root of each side.

$x = \pm 9$ Simplify.

> The solutions are $x = -9$ and $x = 9$.

b. $3a^2 = 48$

$3a^2 = 48$ Write the equation.

$a^2 = 16$ Divide each side by 3.

$a = \pm\sqrt{16}$ Take the square root of each side.

$a = \pm 4$ Simplify.

> The solutions are $a = -4$ and $a = 4$.

Try It **Solve the equation.**

13. $k^2 = 169$ **14.** $7n^2 = 175$ **15.** $190 = 4b^2 - 6$

Self-Assessment for Concepts & Skills

Solve each exercise. Then rate your understanding of the success criteria in your journal.

FINDING SQUARE ROOTS **Find the square root(s).**

16. $\sqrt{256}$ **17.** $-\sqrt{\dfrac{1}{9}}$ **18.** $\pm\sqrt{1.44}$

EVALUATING EXPRESSIONS **Evaluate the expression.**

19. $\sqrt{\dfrac{81}{9}} - 7$ **20.** $-1 - \sqrt{121}$ **21.** $5 + \left(\sqrt{6}\right)^2$

SOLVING EQUATIONS **Solve the equation.**

22. $2r^2 = 162$ **23.** $d^2 + 5 = 41$ **24.** $-42 = 7b^2 - 385$

Laurie's Notes

EXAMPLE 5

- Write the equation in part (a).
- ? "What is the inverse operation of squaring a number?" taking the square root
- ? "Why do you need to take both the positive and negative square roots of 81?" Because both values will work in the equation.
- Students may want to write $\pm x = \pm 9$ as the solution. Explain that writing $\pm x = \pm 9$ is the same as writing $x = \pm 9$ *and* $-x = \pm 9$, which represent the following equations.

$$x = -9 \qquad x = 9 \qquad -x = -9 \qquad -x = 9$$
$$\qquad\qquad\qquad\qquad\qquad x = 9 \qquad\qquad x = -9$$

So, there are only two solutions, $x = -9$ and $x = 9$, which can be represented by $x = \pm 9$.

- **Check:** Substitute $x = -9$ and $x = 9$ into the original equation.

$$x^2 = 81 \qquad\qquad x^2 = 81$$
$$(-9)^2 \overset{?}{=} 81 \qquad (9)^2 \overset{?}{=} 81$$
$$81 = 81\checkmark \qquad\quad 81 = 81\checkmark$$

- Solve part (b) as shown.
- Remind students to check the solutions in the original equation.

Try It

- **Think-Pair-Share:** Students should read each exercise independently and then work in pairs to complete the exercises. Then have each pair compare their answers with another pair and discuss any discrepancies.

✔ Self-Assessment for Concepts & Skills

- **Neighbor Check:** Have students work independently and then have their neighbors check their work. Have students discuss any discrepancies
- ◉ **Agree-Disagree Statement:** Ask students if they agree or disagree with each statement below. Students should explain why or why not.
  - If $x^2 = 100$, then $x = 10$. disagree; $x = 10$ and $x = -10$
  - If $m^2 = 225$, then $m = -15$ and $m = 15$. agree; $(-15)^2 = 225$ and $15^2 = 225$

ELL Support

Allow students to work in pairs. Have each pair display their answers on a whiteboard for your review. As a class, review exercises that are particularly difficult.

The Success Criteria Self-Assessment chart can be found in the *Student Journal* or online at *BigIdeasMath.com*.

Extra Example 5
Solve each equation.

a. $y^2 = 121$ $y = -11$ and $y = 11$

b. $2b^2 = 98$ $b = -7$ and $b = 7$

Try It

13. $k = -13$ and $k = 13$
14. $n = -5$ and $n = 5$
15. $b = -7$ and $b = 7$

Self-Assessment
for Concepts & Skills

16. 16
17. $-\dfrac{1}{3}$
18. -1.2 and 1.2
19. -4
20. -12
21. 11
22. $r = -9$ and $r = 9$
23. $d = -6$ and $d = 6$
24. $b = -7$ and $b = 7$

Laurie's Notes

EXAMPLE 6

- Ask a volunteer to read the problem.
- ❓ "What do you know?" the area of the crop circle
- ❓ "What do you want to find?" the radius of the crop circle
- ❓ "How do you find the area of a circle?" $A = \pi r^2$
- The numbers involved may be overwhelming to students. Reassure them that this is an equation with one variable and that they know how to solve equations!
- Write the formula for the area of a circle. Then substitute 45,216 for A and 3.14 for π.
- Use a calculator or long division to divide 45,216 by 3.14.
- When you get to the step $14,400 = r^2$, remind students that whatever you do to one side of an equation, you must do to the other side. So, to get r by itself, you need to undo the squaring. So, take the square root of each side.
- Point out the push-pin note. Discuss with students why a negative square root does not make sense in this context. You cannot have a negative radius, so you can "ignore" the negative square root.
- Discuss the Check note with students.

✔ Self-Assessment for Problem Solving

- Students may benefit from trying the exercises independently and then working with peers to refine their work. It is important to provide time in class for problem solving, so that students become comfortable with the problem-solving plan.
- **Think-Pair-Share:** Students should read each exercise independently and then work in pairs to complete the exercises. Then have each pair compare their answers with another pair and discuss any discrepancies.

The Success Criteria Self-Assessment chart can be found in the *Student Journal* or online at *BigIdeasMath.com*.

Self-Assessment
for Problem Solving

25. 64 ft

26. **a.** 70 m/sec

   b. The speed decreases; As the value of d decreases, the value of $\sqrt{9.8d}$ also decreases.

Learning Target

Understand the concept of a square root of a number.

Success Criteria

- Find square roots of numbers.
- Evaluate expressions involving square roots.
- Use square roots to solve equations.

Formative Assessment Tip

Parking Lot

Give each student two sticky notes. Ask them to write something they learned on one note and something they still have a question about on the other. Write "Parking Lot" at the top of a large sheet of paper and draw a line down the middle of the paper. On one side write "Something I Learned" and on the other side write "Something I Have a Question About." Hang the paper near the door so students can place their sticky notes as they leave. Replace the paper for each class and review the notes to help direct your instruction for the next day.

Closure

◉ Use *Parking Lot* to assess students' understanding of the lesson. Discuss students' responses the next day.

EXAMPLE 6 **Modeling Real Life**

The area of a crop circle is 45,216 square feet. What is the radius of the crop circle?

Understand the problem.

You are given the area of a crop circle. You are asked to find the radius of the crop circle.

Make a plan.

Use the formula for the area of a circle. Substitute 45,216 for the area and 3.14 for π. Then solve for the radius.

Solve and check.

$$A = \pi r^2$$ Write the formula for the area of a circle.

$$45{,}216 \approx 3.14r^2$$ Substitute 45,216 for A and 3.14 for π.

$$14{,}400 = r^2$$ Divide each side by 3.14.

$$\sqrt{14{,}400} = r$$ Take the positive square root of each side.

$$120 = r$$ Simplify.

The radius of a circle cannot be negative, so you do not need to take the negative square root.

▶ The radius of the crop circle is about 120 feet.

Check Find the area of a circle with a radius of 120 feet.

$$A = \pi r^2 = \pi(120)^2 = 14{,}400\pi \approx 45{,}216 \text{ ft}^2 \checkmark$$

Self-Assessment for Problem Solving

Solve each exercise. Then rate your understanding of the success criteria in your journal.

25. Your distance d (in miles) from the horizon can be approximated by $d = 1.22\sqrt{h}$, where h is your eye level (in feet above ground level). What is your eye level when you are 9.76 miles from the horizon?

26. **DIG DEEPER!** The speed s (in meters per second) of a tsunami can be modeled by the function $s = \sqrt{9.8d}$, where d is the water depth (in meters).

    a. What is the speed of the tsunami when the water depth is 500 meters?

    b. What happens to the speed of the tsunami as the depth decreases? Explain.

Go to *BigIdeasMath.com* to get HELP with solving the exercises.

▶ Review & Refresh

Evaluate the expression. Write your answer in scientific notation.

1. $(4.3 \times 10^3) + (2.4 \times 10^3)$

2. $(1.5 \times 10^{-2}) - (3.5 \times 10^{-3})$

3. $9 \times (7 \times 10^{-2})$

4. $(6.6 \times 10^{-5}) \div (1.1 \times 10^4)$

Make a scatter plot of the data. Identify any outliers, gaps, or clusters.

5.

Length (meters), x	1	8	3.5	2	2.5	3	2.5	2.5	3	9
Weight (pounds), y	4	33	17	8	9	9	8	8.5	11	36

6.

Volume (gallons), x	0.25	1	1	0.5	0.125	1	0.5	1
Cost (dollars), y	0.99	3.95	3.99	5.50	0.50	4.05	2.00	4.00

▶▶ Concepts, Skills, & Problem Solving

FINDING SIDE LENGTHS **Find the side length s of the square.** (See Exploration 1, p. 373.)

7. Area = 441 cm²

8. Area = 1.69 km²

9. Area = $\frac{36}{49}$ yd²

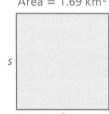

FINDING SQUARE ROOTS OF A PERFECT SQUARE **Find the two square roots of the number.**

10. 9

11. 64

12. 4

13. 144

FINDING SQUARE ROOTS **Find the square root(s).**

14. $\sqrt{625}$

15. $\pm\sqrt{196}$

16. $-\sqrt{1600}$

17. $\pm\sqrt{2500}$

18. $\sqrt{\dfrac{1}{16}}$

19. $\sqrt{\dfrac{49}{576}}$

20. $\pm\sqrt{\dfrac{1}{961}}$

21. $-\sqrt{\dfrac{9}{100}}$

22. $\pm\sqrt{4.84}$

23. $\sqrt{7.29}$

24. $-\sqrt{361}$

25. $-\sqrt{2.25}$

Assignment Guide and Concept Check

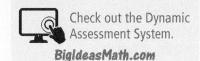
Check out the Dynamic Assessment System.
BigIdeasMath.com

Scaffold assignments to support all students in their learning progression. The suggested assignments are a starting point. Continue to assign additional exercises and revisit with spaced practice to move every student toward proficiency.

Level	Assignment 1	Assignment 2
Emerging	2, 4, 6, 7, 10, 12, 15, 17, 19, 21, 23, 25, 32, 41, 43	11, 13, 18, 22, 26, 27, 29, 35, 40, 42, 45, 47
Proficient	2, 4, 6, 8, 11, 13, 14, 16, 21, 22, 23, 32, 43, 45	19, 25, 26, 27, 28, 30, 33, 38, 40, 44, 47, 48, 49, 56, 57
Advanced	2, 4, 6, 9, 11, 13, 16, 19, 20, 22, 23, 33, 43, 46	26, 28, 36, 38, 47, 48, 49, 50, 51, 52, 53, 54, 55, 56, 59

- Assignment 1 is for use after students complete the Self-Assessment for Concepts & Skills.
- Assignment 2 is for use after students complete the Self-Assessment for Problem Solving.
- The red exercises can be used as a concept check.

Review & Refresh Prior Skills

Exercises 1 and 2 Adding and Subtracting in Scientific Notation
Exercises 3 and 4 Multiplying and Dividing in Scientific Notation
Exercises 5 and 6 Making a Scatter Plot

 Common Errors

- **Exercises 10–13** Students may only find the positive square root of the number given. Remind them that a square root can be positive or negative, and the problem is asking for both.
- **Exercises 14–25** Students may divide the number by two instead of finding a number that, when multiplied by itself, gives the radicand. Remind them that taking the square root of a number is the inverse of squaring a number.

Review & Refresh

1. 6.7×10^3 **2.** 1.15×10^{-2}

3. 6.3×10^{-1} **4.** 6×10^{-9}

5.
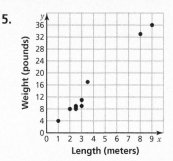

outliers: (8, 33) and (9, 36); gap: from 3.5 meters to 8 meters; cluster: from 2 meters to 3 meters

6.
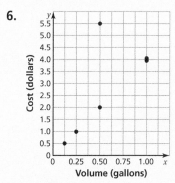

outlier: (0.5, 5.50); gap: from 0.5 gallon to 1 gallon; cluster: at 1 gallon

Concepts, Skills, & Problem Solving

7. 21 cm   **8.** 1.3 km

9. $\frac{6}{7}$ yd   **10.** 3 and -3

11. 8 and -8 **12.** 2 and -2

13. 12 and -12 **14.** 25

15. -14 and 14   **16.** -40

17. -50 and 50   **18.** $\frac{1}{4}$

19. $\frac{7}{24}$

20. $-\frac{1}{31}$ and $\frac{1}{31}$ **21.** $-\frac{3}{10}$

22. -2.2 and 2.2   **23.** 2.7

24. -19 **25.** -1.5

Concepts, Skills, & Problem Solving

26. no; Both the positive and negative square roots should have been given.

27. 1.5 in.

28. The radius of the button cannot be negative.

29. >

30. =

31. <

32. 14

33. −116

34. 7

35. 9

36. 8

37. 25

38. −2

39. 40

40. The value decreases.

41. $x = -10$ and $x = 10$

42. $d = -8$ and $d = 8$

43. $z = -6$ and $z = 6$

44. $m = -6$ and $m = 6$

45. $r = -14$ and $r = 14$

46. $h = -3$ and $h = 3$

47. yes; The solution is correct.

48. 2.25 ft

Common Errors

- **Exercises 32–39** Students may not follow the order of operations when evaluating the expression. Remind them of the order of operations. Because taking a square root is the inverse of squaring, it is evaluated before multiplication and division.

26. **(MP) YOU BE THE TEACHER** Your friend finds $\pm\sqrt{\frac{1}{4}}$. Is your friend correct? Explain your reasoning.

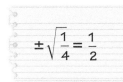

$$\pm\sqrt{\frac{1}{4}} = \frac{1}{2}$$

27. **(MP) MODELING REAL LIFE** The area of a square patch of fabric is 2.25 square inches. What is the side length of the patch?

28. **CRITICAL THINKING** There are two square roots of 25. Why is there only one answer for the radius of the button?

$A = 25\pi$ mm²

(MP) NUMBER SENSE Copy and complete the statement with <, >, or =.

29. $\sqrt{81}$ ⬜ 8

30. 0.5 ⬜ $\sqrt{0.25}$

31. $\frac{3}{2}$ ⬜ $\sqrt{\frac{25}{4}}$

EVALUATING EXPRESSIONS Evaluate the expression.

32. $\left(\sqrt{9}\right)^2 + 5$

33. $28 - \left(\sqrt{144}\right)^2$

34. $3\sqrt{16} - 5$

35. $10 - 4\sqrt{\frac{1}{16}}$

36. $\sqrt{6.76} + 5.4$

37. $8\sqrt{8.41} + 1.8$

38. $2\left(\sqrt{\frac{80}{5}} - 5\right)$

39. $4\left(\sqrt{\frac{147}{3}} + 3\right)$

40. **(MP) NUMBER SENSE** Without calculating, describe how the value of $\sqrt{\frac{1}{a}}$ changes as a increases. Assume $a > 0$.

SOLVING EQUATIONS Solve the equation.

41. $x^2 = 100$

42. $42 = d^2 - 22$

43. $4z^2 = 144$

44. $\sqrt{\frac{36}{9}} = \frac{1}{3}m^2 - 10$

45. $0.25r^2 = 49$

46. $3h^2 = h^2 + 18$

47. **(MP) YOU BE THE TEACHER** Your friend solves the equation $9x^2 = 36$. Is your friend correct? Explain your reasoning.

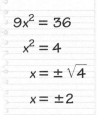

$9x^2 = 36$
$x^2 = 4$
$x = \pm\sqrt{4}$
$x = \pm 2$

48. **(MP) PROBLEM SOLVING** The *period* of a pendulum is the time the pendulum takes to complete one back-and-forth swing. The period T (in seconds) can be modeled by the function $T = 1.1\sqrt{L}$, where L is the length (in feet) of the pendulum. Estimate the length of a pendulum with a period of 1.65 seconds.

49. **MP** **MODELING REAL LIFE** The area of a sail is $40\frac{1}{2}$ square feet. The base and the height of the sail are equal. What is the height of the sail?

50. **MP** **REPEATED RASONING** Find several products of perfect squares. What do you notice? Is this true for all products of perfect squares? Explain.

51. **MP** **PROBLEM SOLVING** The kinetic energy K (in joules) of a falling apple is represented by $K = \frac{v^2}{2}$, where v is the speed of the apple (in meters per second). How fast is the apple traveling when the kinetic energy is 32 joules?

Area = 4π cm^2

52. **MP** **PRECISION** The areas of the two watch faces have a ratio of $16 : 25$.

    a. What is the ratio of the radius of the smaller watch face to the radius of the larger watch face?

    b. What is the radius of the larger watch face?

53. **MP** **PROBLEM SOLVING** The cost C (in dollars) of making a square window with a side length of n inches is represented by $C = \frac{n^2}{5} + 175$. A window costs \$355. What is the side length (in feet) of the window? Justify your answer.

54. **DIG DEEPER!** Albert Einstein's most famous equation is $E = mc^2$, where E is the energy of an object (in joules), m is the mass of the object (in kilograms), and c is the speed of light (in meters per second). A hydrogen atom has 15.066×10^{-11} joule of energy and a mass of 1.674×10^{-27} kilogram. What is the speed of light? Write your answer in scientific notation.

55. **MP** **GEOMETRY** The area of the triangle is represented by the formula $A = \sqrt{s(s - 21)(s - 17)(s - 10)}$, where s is equal to half the perimeter. What is the height of the triangle?

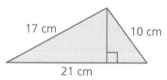

17 cm   10 cm

21 cm

56. **WRITING** Can you find the square root of a negative number? Explain.

MP **REASONING** Without solving, determine the number of solutions of the equation.

57. $x^2 = 1$

58. $b^2 = -\sqrt{\dfrac{1}{9}}$

59. $z = \sqrt{-144}$

Mini-Assessment

1. Find the two square roots of 169. 13 and -13

Find the square root(s).

2. $\sqrt{225}$ 15

3. $\pm\sqrt{4.41}$ -2.1 and 2.1

4. $-\sqrt{\dfrac{16}{25}}$ $-\dfrac{4}{5}$

5. Solve the equation $x^2 - 4 = 32$. $x = -6$ and $x = 6$

49. 9 ft

50. The product of two perfect squares is always a perfect square; yes; *Sample answer:* For the perfect squares a^2 and b^2, $a^2 b^2 = a \cdot a \cdot b \cdot b = (a \cdot b) \cdot (a \cdot b) = (a \cdot b)^2$.

51. 8 m/sec

52. a. 4 : 5

  b. 2.5 cm

53. 2.5 ft; $355 = \dfrac{n^2}{5} + 175$, so

  $n = 30$ in. and $\dfrac{30}{12} = 2.5$ ft.

54. 3×10^8 m/sec

55. 8 cm

56. no; The square of a positive or negative number is never negative.

57. 2

58. 0

59. 0

Section Resources

Surface Level	Deep Level
Resources by Chapter • Extra Practice • Reteach • Puzzle Time Student Journal • Self-Assessment • Practice Differentiating the Lesson Tutorial Videos Skills Review Handbook Skills Trainer	Resources by Chapter • Enrichment and Extension Graphic Organizers Dynamic Assessment System • Section Practice

Learning Target

Understand the Pythagorean Theorem.

Success Criteria

- Explain the Pythagorean Theorem.
- Use the Pythagorean Theorem to find unknown side lengths of triangles.
- Use the Pythagorean Theorem to find distances between points in a coordinate plane.

Warm Up

Cumulative, vocabulary, and prerequisite skills practice opportunities are available in the *Resources by Chapter* or at *BigIdeasMath.com*.

ELL Support

Students may know the word *theory* from science. Have them share what they understand about a theory. If necessary, explain that a theory is an idea that tries to explain events after having carefully viewed them. It comes from a Latin and Greek root meaning "view." *Theorem* comes from the same root, and literally means "that which is viewed." In science and math, a theorem is a rule, or theory, that can be proved.

Exploration 1

a. See Additional Answers.

b. *Answer should include, but is not limited to:* The two values should be close to each other.

Laurie's Notes

Preparing to Teach

- **MP2 Reason Abstractly and Quantitatively:** In the exploration, students will analyze the relationship between the two models they create. This represents an "informal proof" of the Pythagorean Theorem.

Motivate

- Share information about Pythagoras, who was born in Greece around 570 B.C.
  - He is known as the *Father of Numbers*.
  - He traveled extensively in Egypt, learning math, astronomy, and music.
  - Pythagoras urged the citizens of Cretona to follow his religious, political, and philosophical goals.
  - His followers were known as Pythagoreans. They observed a rule of silence called *echemythia*. One had to remain silent for *five years* before he could contribute to the group. Breaking this silence was punishable by death!

Exploration 1

- **Suggestions:** Use 1-centimeter grid paper for ease of manipulating the cut pieces. Grid paper is available online at *BigIdeasMath.com*. Suggest that students draw the original triangle in the upper left of the grid paper, and then make a working copy of the triangle towards the middle of the paper. This gives enough room for the squares to be drawn on each side of the triangle.
- Vertices of the triangle need to be on lattice points. You do not want every student in the room to use the same triangle. Suggest other lengths for the shorter sides (3 and 4, 3 and 6, 2 and 4, 2 and 3, and so on).
- **Model:** Drawing the square on the longest side of the triangle is the challenging step. Model one technique for accomplishing the task using a right triangle with shorter side lengths of 2 units and 5 units.
  - Notice that the longest side has a slope of "right 5 units, up 2 units."
  - Place your pencil on the upper right endpoint and rotate the paper 90° clockwise. Move your pencil right 5 units and up 2 units. Mark a point.
  - Repeat rotating and moving "right 5 units, up 2 units" until you get back to the longest side of the triangle.
  - Use a straightedge to connect the four points (two that you marked and two on the endpoints of the longest side) to form the square.
- Before students cut, check that they have 3 squares of the correct size.
- Give students time to discover how to arrange the figures on the grid paper. Here is one example. You may want to show students one arrangement and then have them find the other.
- **Big Idea:** The two large squares have equal area. Referring to areas, if $c^2 + (4 \text{ triangles}) = a^2 + b^2 + (4 \text{ triangles})$, then $c^2 = a^2 + b^2$ by subtracting the 4 triangles from each side of the equation.
- The work in this exploration constitutes an "informal proof" of the **Pythagorean Theorem**. There are many proofs of this **theorem**, and this version is generally understood by middle school students.

9.2 The Pythagorean Theorem

Learning Target: Understand the Pythagorean Theorem.

Success Criteria:
- I can explain the Pythagorean Theorem.
- I can use the Pythagorean Theorem to find unknown side lengths of triangles.
- I can use the Pythagorean Theorem to find distances between points in a coordinate plane.

Pythagoras was a Greek mathematician and philosopher who proved one of the most famous rules in mathematics. In mathematics, a rule is called a **theorem**. So, the rule that Pythagoras proved is called the *Pythagorean Theorem*.

Pythagoras
(c. 570–c. 490 B.C.)

EXPLORATION 1

Discovering the Pythagorean Theorem

Work with a partner.

- **On grid paper, draw a right triangle with one horizontal side and one vertical side.**

- **Label the lengths of the two shorter sides a and b. Label the length of the longest side c.**

- **Draw three squares that each share a side with your triangle. Label the areas of the squares a^2, b^2, and c^2.**

- **Cut out each square. Then make eight copies of the right triangle and cut them out.**

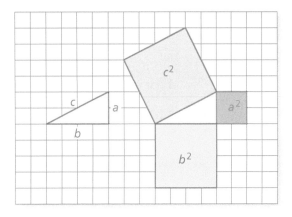

Math Practice

Construct Arguments

Is the relationship among a^2, b^2, and c^2 true for all right triangles? Explain.

a. Arrange the figures to show how a^2 and b^2 relate to c^2. Use an equation to represent this relationship.

b. Estimate the side length c of your triangle. Then use the relationship in part (a) to find c. Compare the values.

Key Ideas

Sides of a Right Triangle

The sides of a right triangle have special names.

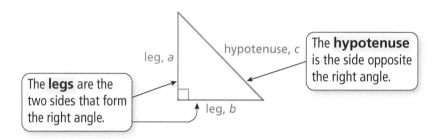

The **legs** are the two sides that form the right angle.

hypotenuse, *c*

The **hypotenuse** is the side opposite the right angle.

leg, *a*

leg, *b*

> In a right triangle, the legs are the shorter sides and the hypotenuse is always the longest side.

The Pythagorean Theorem

Words In any right triangle, the sum of the squares of the lengths of the legs is equal to the square of the length of the hypotenuse.

Algebra $a^2 + b^2 = c^2$

EXAMPLE 1 ## Finding the Length of a Hypotenuse

Find the length of the hypotenuse of the triangle.

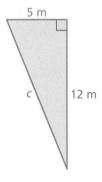

5 m

c   12 m

$a^2 + b^2 = c^2$	Write the Pythagorean Theorem.
$5^2 + 12^2 = c^2$	Substitute 5 for *a* and 12 for *b*.
$25 + 144 = c^2$	Evaluate the powers.
$169 = c^2$	Add.
$13 = c$	Take the positive square root of each side.

▷ The length of the hypotenuse is 13 meters.

Try It **Find the length of the hypotenuse of the triangle.**

1.
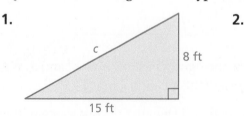
c
8 ft
15 ft

2.
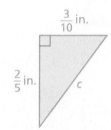
$\frac{3}{10}$ in.
$\frac{2}{5}$ in.
c

Laurie's Notes

Scaffolding Instruction

- Students have investigated a visual "proof" of the Pythagorean Theorem. They will now use the Pythagorean Theorem to find missing side lengths of right triangles.
- **Emerging:** Students may confuse the legs and the hypotenuse of a right triangle. They will need guided instruction for the Key Ideas and examples.
- **Proficient:** Students understand the difference between the legs and the hypotenuse of a right triangle. They can use substitution to find missing side lengths. These students should proceed to Examples 3 and 4 before completing the Self-Assessment exercises.

Key Ideas

- Draw a right triangle and label the legs and the hypotenuse. The hypotenuse is always opposite the right angle and is the longest side of a right triangle.
- Try not to have all right triangles in the same orientation.
- Write the Pythagorean Theorem.
- **Common Error:** Students often forget that the Pythagorean Theorem is a relationship that is *only* true for right triangles.

EXAMPLE 1

- Draw and label the triangle. Review the symbol used to show that an angle is a right angle.
- ❓ "What information is known for this triangle?" The legs are 5 meters and 12 meters.
- Substitute and solve as shown. Explain that you disregard the negative square root because length is always positive.
- Note that the values for *a* and *b* could be interchanged.

Try It

- Give time for students to work through the problems. Knowing perfect squares is helpful.
- **MP2 Reason Abstractly and Quantitatively:** In Exercise 2, if students recognize that the decimal equivalents of the given fractions are 0.3 and 0.4, finding the hypotenuse may be quick for them.

Extra Example 1
Find the length of the hypotenuse of the triangle.

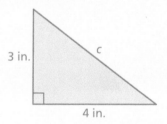

3 in.
c
4 in.

5 in.

Try It

1. 17 ft
2. $\frac{1}{2}$ in.

Laurie's Notes

Extra Example 2

Find the missing length of the triangle.

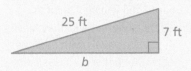

24 ft

Try It

3. 30 yd

4. 4 m

Extra Example 3

Find the slant height of the square pyramid.

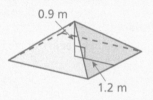

1.5 m

Try It

5. 15 yd

6. 11 ft

EXAMPLE 2

❓ **"What information is known for this triangle?"** One leg is 2.1 centimeters and the hypotenuse is 2.9 centimeters.

• Substitute and solve as shown.

• **Common Error:** Students need to be careful with decimal multiplication. It is very common for students to multiply the decimal by 2 instead of multiplying the decimal by itself.

• **FYI:** The triangle is similar to a 20-21-29 right triangle.

Try It

• **Think-Pair-Share:** Students should read each exercise independently and then work in pairs to complete the exercises. Then have each pair compare their answers with another pair and discuss any discrepancies.

EXAMPLE 3

• Students need to analyze the diagram before solving. It may look complicated, but this problem is very similar to Example 1, in which students found the hypotenuse of a right triangle.

❓ **"What information is known?"** The legs of a right triangle are 6.4 inches and 4.8 inches.

❓ **"How do you find the slant height?"** Substitute the values for a and b into the Pythagorean Theorem and solve for c.

• Remind students that the values for a and b could be interchanged.

Try It

• Remind students to analyze the diagram before solving.

• **Neighbor Check:** Have students work independently and then have their neighbors check their work. Have students discuss any discrepancies.

ELL Support

After demonstrating Examples 2 and 3, have students work in pairs to discuss and complete Try It Exercises 3–6. Have one student ask another, "What values do you substitute for a, b, and/or c? What is the equation? What is the length of the unknown side?" Have students alternate the roles of asking and answering questions.

Beginner: Write the steps used to solve the problem.

Intermediate: Use phrases or simple sentences to answer and explain.

Advanced: Use detailed sentences to answer and explain.

EXAMPLE 2 **Finding the Length of a Leg**

Find the missing length of the triangle.

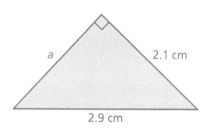

$$a^2 + b^2 = c^2$$ Write the Pythagorean Theorem.

$$a^2 + 2.1^2 = 2.9^2$$ Substitute 2.1 for *b* and 2.9 for *c*.

$$a^2 + 4.41 = 8.41$$ Evaluate the powers.

$$a^2 = 4$$ Subtract 4.41 from each side.

$$a = 2$$ Take the positive square root of each side.

▶ The missing length is 2 centimeters.

Try It **Find the missing length of the triangle.**

3.
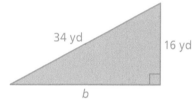

4.
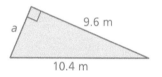

You can use right triangles and the Pythagorean Theorem to find lengths of three-dimensional figures.

EXAMPLE 3 **Finding a Length of a Three-Dimensional Figure**

Find the slant height of the square pyramid.

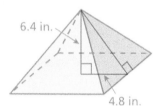

$$a^2 + b^2 = c^2$$ Write the Pythagorean Theorem.

$$6.4^2 + 4.8^2 = c^2$$ Substitute 6.4 for *a* and 4.8 for *b*.

$$40.96 + 23.04 = c^2$$ Evaluate the powers.

$$64 = c^2$$ Add.

$$8 = c$$ Take the positive square root of each side.

▶ The slant height is 8 inches.

Try It **Find *x*.**

5.
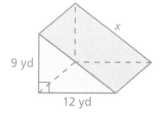

6.
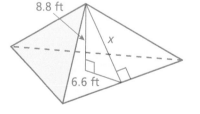

You can use right triangles and the Pythagorean Theorem to find distances between points in a coordinate plane.

EXAMPLE 4 **Finding a Distance in a Coordinate Plane**

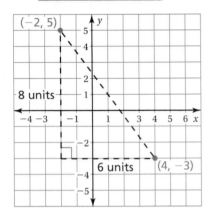

Find the distance between $(-2, 5)$ and $(4, -3)$.

Plot the points in a coordinate plane. Then draw a right triangle with a hypotenuse that represents the distance between the points.

Use the Pythagorean Theorem to find the length of the hypotenuse.

$a^2 + b^2 = c^2$	Write the Pythagorean Theorem.
$8^2 + 6^2 = c^2$	Substitute 8 for a and 6 for b.
$64 + 36 = c^2$	Evaluate the powers.
$100 = c^2$	Add.
$10 = c$	Take the positive square root of each side.

▶ The distance between $(-2, 5)$ and $(4, -3)$ is 10 units.

Try It **Find the distance between the points.**

7. $(3, 6)$ and $(7, 9)$ **8.** $(-3, -4)$ and $(2, 8)$

Self-Assessment *for Concepts & Skills*

Solve each exercise. Then rate your understanding of the success criteria in your journal.

FINDING A MISSING LENGTH **Find x.**

9.
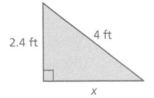

10.
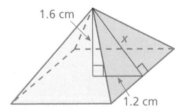

11. FINDING A DISTANCE Find the distance between $(-5, 2)$ and $(7, -7)$.

12. DIFFERENT WORDS, SAME QUESTION Which is different? Find "both" answers.

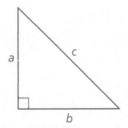

Which side is the hypotenuse?	Which side is the longest?
Which side is a leg?	Which side is opposite the right angle?

Laurie's Notes

EXAMPLE 4

- Have students plot the points in a coordinate plane and then draw a right triangle with a hypotenuse that represents the distance between the points.
- ❓ "Is there enough information to use the Pythagorean Theorem? Explain." Yes, the lengths of both legs of the right triangle can be found and then used to find the length of the hypotenuse (the distance between the points).
- ❓ "How can you find the length of each leg?" Students will likely count the grid squares.
- ❓ "Can you count the grid squares for the hypotenuse? Explain." No, the hypotenuse is neither vertical nor horizontal, so the increments do not represent 1 unit.
- Work through the remainder of the solution.
- Note that the values for a and b could be interchanged.
- Have students check the value of c in the Pythagorean Theorem.
- Remind students that in the context of distance, they should only consider positive values.
- **FYI:** This example previews the *distance formula*, which students will study in high school. Deriving the distance formula is not required in this course; however, in Practice Exercise 36, students will unknowingly derive the formula.

Try It

- **Neighbor Check:** Have students work independently and then have their neighbors check their work. Have students discuss any discrepancies.

Formative Assessment Tip

Fact-First Questioning

This is a higher-order questioning technique that goes beyond asking straight recall questions. Instead, this strategy allows you to assess students' growing understanding of a concept or skill.

First, state a fact. Then ask students why, or how, or to explain. Student thinking is activated and you gain insight into the depth of students' conceptual understanding. Example: Make the statement, "If you are given two side lengths of a right triangle, you can find the third side length." Then ask, "Why is this true?"

✔ Self-Assessment for Concepts & Skills

- Students should work independently and then discuss their answers with a partner.
- ◉ **Fact-First Questioning:** Make the statement, "The Pythagorean Theorem can be used to find the distances between points in a coordinate plane." Then ask, "Why this is true?"

The Success Criteria Self-Assessment chart can be found in the *Student Journal* or online at *BigIdeasMath.com*.

Extra Example 4
Find the distance between $(-3, -5)$ and $(2, 7)$. 13 units

Try It

7. 5 units

8. 13 units

ELL Support

Allow students to work in pairs for the Self-Assessment for Concepts & Skills exercises. Have each pair display their answers for Exercises 9–11 on a whiteboard for your review. Have two pairs form a group to discuss and come to an agreement on their answers for Exercise 12. Then have each group present their explanation to the class.

Self-Assessment
for Concepts & Skills

9. 3.2 ft

10. 2 cm

11. 15 units

12. Which side is a leg?; a or b; c

Extra Example 5

You and your cousin are planning to go to an amusement park. You live 36 miles south of the amusement park and 15 miles west of your cousin. How far away from the amusement park does your cousin live? 39 mi

EXAMPLE 5

- Ask a student to read the problem.
- ❓ "Given the compass directions stated, what is a reasonable way to represent this information?" in a coordinate plane
- **MP4 Model with Mathematics:** Explain that east is the positive x-direction and north is the positive y-direction. Draw the situation in a coordinate plane.
- ❓ "Is there enough information to use the Pythagorean Theorem? Explain."
  Yes, the lengths of both legs of the right triangle can be found and then used to find the length of the hypotenuse (the distance between you and the other team's base).

Self-Assessment
for Problem Solving

13. 8.4 mi^2; $2.4^2 + x^2 = 7.4^2$, so $x = 7$ mi. Then, $A = \frac{1}{2}(2.4)(7) = 8.4 \text{ mi}^2$.

14. 9 P.M.; 225 miles is equivalent to 15 units on the coordinate plane. The cargo ship is 9 units north of the shipyard, so it will be 15 units away when it is 12 units east of the shipyard because $9^2 + 12^2 = 15^2$. It is traveling 1 unit per hour, so it will take 12 hours to travel 12 units. 12 hours after 9 A.M. is 9 P.M.

✔ Self-Assessment for Problem Solving

- The goal for all students is to feel comfortable with the problem-solving plan. It is important for students to problem-solve in class, where they may receive support from you and their peers.
- **Think-Pair-Share:** Students should read each exercise independently and then work in pairs to complete the exercises. Then have each pair compare their answers with another pair and discuss any discrepancies.

The Success Criteria Self-Assessment chart can be found in the *Student Journal* or online at *BigIdeasMath.com*.

Closure

- **Exit Ticket:** You draw a right triangle with shorter side lengths of 4 and 6 on grid paper. What is the area of the square drawn on the longest side of the triangle? 52 square units

Learning Target

Understand the Pythagorean Theorem.

Success Criteria

- Explain the Pythagorean Theorem.
- Use the Pythagorean Theorem to find unknown side lengths of triangles.
- Use the Pythagorean Theorem to find distances between points in a coordinate plane.

EXAMPLE 5 **Modeling Real Life**

You play capture the flag. You are 50 yards north and 20 yards east of your team's base. The other team's base is 80 yards north and 60 yards east of your base. How far are you from the other team's base?

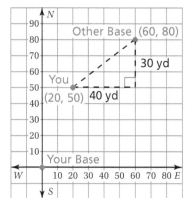

Step 1: Draw the situation in a coordinate plane. Let the origin represent your team's base. From the descriptions, you are at (20, 50) and the other team's base is at (60, 80).

Step 2: Draw a right triangle with a hypotenuse that represents the distance between you and the other team's base. The lengths of the legs are 30 yards and 40 yards.

Step 3: Use the Pythagorean Theorem to find the length of the hypotenuse.

$$a^2 + b^2 = c^2 \qquad \text{Write the Pythagorean Theorem.}$$
$$30^2 + 40^2 = c^2 \qquad \text{Substitute 30 for } a \text{ and 40 for } b.$$
$$900 + 1600 = c^2 \qquad \text{Evaluate the powers.}$$
$$2500 = c^2 \qquad \text{Add.}$$
$$50 = c \qquad \text{Take the positive square root of each side.}$$

So, you are 50 yards from the other team's base.

Self-Assessment for Problem Solving

Solve each exercise. Then rate your understanding of the success criteria in your journal.

13. A zookeeper knows that an escaped red panda is hiding somewhere in the triangular region shown. What is the area (in square miles) that the zookeeper needs to search? Explain.

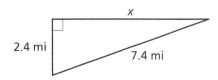

14. **DIG DEEPER!** Objects detected by radar are plotted in a coordinate plane where each unit represents 15 miles. The point (0, 0) represents the location of a shipyard. A cargo ship is traveling at a constant speed and in a constant direction parallel to the coastline. At 9 A.M., the radar shows the cargo ship at (0, 9). At 10 A.M., the radar shows the cargo ship at (1, 9). At what time will the cargo ship be 225 miles from the shipyard? Explain.

? Go to *BigIdeasMath.com* to get HELP with solving the exercises.

▶ Review & Refresh

Solve the equation.

1. $7z^2 = 252$

2. $0.75q^2 = 108$

3. $\sqrt{\dfrac{1000}{10}} = n^2 - 54$

4. What is the solution of the system of linear equations $y = 4x + 1$ and $2x + y = 13$?

    A. $(1, 5)$ **B.** $(5, 3)$ **C.** $(2, 9)$ **D.** $(9, 2)$

▶▶ Concepts, Skills, & Problem Solving

USING GRID PAPER **Find c.** (See Exploration 1, p. 381.)

5.
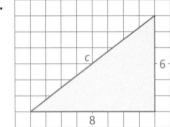

6.
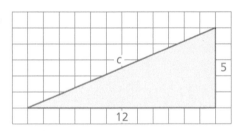

FINDING A MISSING LENGTH **Find the missing length of the triangle.**

7.
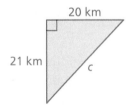

8.
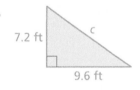

9.

10.
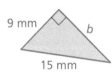

11.
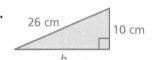

12.

13. **MP YOU BE THE TEACHER** Your friend finds the missing length of the triangle. Is your friend correct? Explain your reasoning.

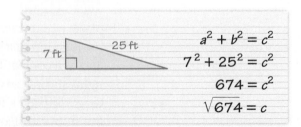

Assignment Guide and Concept Check

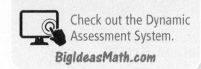

Check out the Dynamic Assessment System.
BigIdeasMath.com

Scaffold assignments to support all students in their learning progression. The suggested assignments are a starting point. Continue to assign additional exercises and revisit with spaced practice to move every student toward proficiency.

Level	Assignment 1	Assignment 2
Emerging	1, 4, 5, 7, 9, 11, 13, 14, 15, 18, 19	8, 10, 12, 16, 17, 21, 23, 24, 26, 28, 36
Proficient	2, 4, 6, 8, 10, 12, 13, 15, 16, 18, 20, 22, 24	17, 25, 26, 27, 28, 30, 31, 32, 34, 35, 36
Advanced	3, 4, 6, 8, 10, 12, 13, 15, 16, 19, 22, 24	17, 25, 26, 29, 30, 31, 32, 33, 34, 35, 36

- Assignment 1 is for use after students complete the Self-Assessment for Concepts & Skills.
- Assignment 2 is for use after students complete the Self-Assessment for Problem Solving.
- The red exercises can be used as a concept check.

Review & Refresh Prior Skills

Exercises 1–3 Solving Equations Using Square Roots
Exercise 4 Choosing a Solution Method for a System of Linear Equations

 Common Errors

- **Exercises 7–12** Students may substitute the given lengths in the wrong part of the formula. For example, in Exercise 7, they may write $20^2 + c^2 = 21^2$ instead of $20^2 + 21^2 = c^2$. Remind students that the side opposite the right angle is the hypotenuse c.
- **Exercises 7–12** Students may multiply each side length by two instead of squaring the side length. Remind them of the definition of exponents.

▶ Review & Refresh

1. $z = -6$ and $z = 6$
2. $q = -12$ and $q = 12$
3. $n = -8$ and $n = 8$
4. C

▶ Concepts, Skills, & Problem Solving

5. 10
6. 13
7. 29 km
8. 12 ft
9. 9 in.
10. 12 mm
11. 24 cm
12. 6 yd
13. no; The length of the hypotenuse should be substituted for c, not b.

Concepts, Skills, & Problem Solving

14. 26 ft

15. 50 in.

16. 1.2 m

17. 6 cm

18. 15 units

19. 5 units

20. 41 units

21. 29 units

22. 37 units

23. 30.5 units

24. 16 cm

25. 37 mm

26. 57 ft

27. yes; The distance from the player's mouth to the referee's ear is 25 feet.

Common Errors

- **Exercises 24 and 25** Students may think that there is not enough information to find the value of *x*. Tell them that is possible to find *x*; however, they may have to make an extra calculation before writing an equation for *x*.

FINDING LENGTHS OF THREE-DIMENSIONAL FIGURES Find *x*.

14.

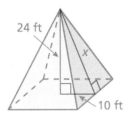

24 ft

x

10 ft

15.

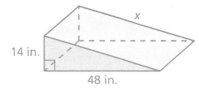

x

14 in.

48 in.

16.

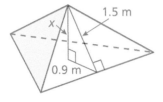

1.5 m

x

0.9 m

17.

6.5 cm

x

2.5 cm

FINDING DISTANCES IN THE COORDINATE PLANE Find the distance between the points.

18. $(0, 0), (9, 12)$

19. $(1, 2), (-3, 5)$

20. $(-18, 9), (22, 0)$

21. $(-7, -2), (13, -23)$

22. $(15, -17), (-20, -5)$

23. $(-13, -3.5), (17, 2)$

FINDING A MISSING LENGTH Find *x*.

24.

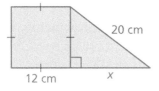

20 cm

12 cm   *x*

25.

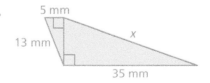

5 mm

13 mm   *x*

35 mm

26. **MP MODELING REAL LIFE** The figure shows the location of a golf ball after a tee shot. How many feet from the hole is the ball?

27. **MP MODELING REAL LIFE** A tennis player asks the referee a question. The sound of the player's voice travels 30 feet. Can the referee hear the question? Explain.

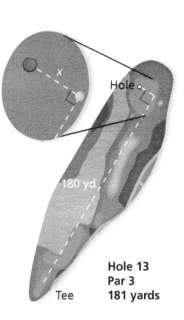

x

Hole

180 yd

Hole 13
Par 3
181 yards

Tee

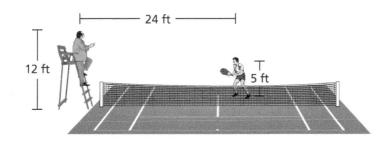

24 ft

12 ft

5 ft

28. **MP PROBLEM SOLVING** You are cutting a rectangular piece of fabric in half along a diagonal. The fabric measures 28 inches wide and $1\frac{1}{4}$ yards long. What is the length (in inches) of the diagonal?

29. **PROJECT** Measure the length, width, and height of a rectangular room. Use the Pythagorean Theorem to find the distance from B to C and the distance from A to B.

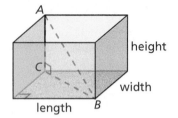

30. **MP STRUCTURE** The legs of a right triangle have lengths of 28 meters and 21 meters. The hypotenuse has a length of $5x$ meters. What is the value of x?

31. **MP PRECISION** You and a friend stand back-to-back. You run 20 feet forward, then 15 feet to your right. At the same time, your friend runs 16 feet forward, then 12 feet to her right. She stops and hits you with a snowball.

    a. Draw the situation in a coordinate plane.

    b. How far does your friend throw the snowball?

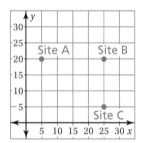

32. **MP MODELING REAL LIFE** The coordinate plane shows dig sites for archaeological research. Each unit on the grid represents 1 square foot. What is the distance from Site A to Site C?

33. **MP PRECISION** A box has a length of 30 inches, a width of 40 inches, and a height of 120 inches. Can a cylindrical rod with a length of 342.9 centimeters fit in the box? Explain your reasoning.

34. **MP MODELING REAL LIFE** A *green roof* is like a traditional roof but covered with plants. Plants used for a green roof cost $0.75 per square foot. The roof at the right is 40 feet long. How much does it cost to cover both sides of the roof? Justify your answer.

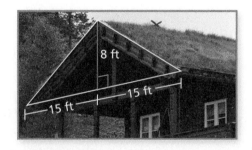

35. **CRITICAL THINKING** A triangle has coordinates $A(2, 1)$, $B(2, 4)$, and $C(5, 1)$. Write an expression for the length of $\overline{BC}$. Use a calculator to find the length of $\overline{BC}$ to the nearest hundredth.

36. **DIG DEEPER!** Write an equation for the distance d between the points (x_1, y_1) and (x_2, y_2). Explain how you found the equation.

For Your Information

- **Exercise 31** There is more than one correct drawing for this exercise. Encourage students to start at the origin and move along an axis to begin.

Mini-Assessment

Find the missing length of the triangle.

1.

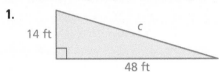

14 ft

c

48 ft

50 ft

2.

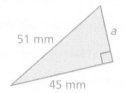

51 mm

a

45 mm

24 mm

3.

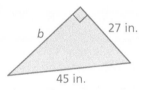

b

27 in.

45 in.

36 in.

Find the distance between the points.

4. $(0, 4)$, $(3, 0)$ 5 units

5. $(-3, -1)$, $(5, 5)$ 10 units

Concepts, Skills, & Problem Solving

28. 53 in.

29. Check students' work.

30. 7

31. **a.** *Sample answer:*

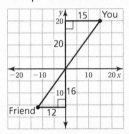

b. 45 ft

32. 25 ft

33. no; The rod is 135 inches long, and the diagonal from a top corner to the opposite bottom corner is 130 inches long.

34. $1020; $15^2 + 8^2 = c^2$, so $c = 17$ ft. Then, the area of the entire roof is $2(40 \cdot 17) = 1360$ ft^2, and $1360 \cdot \$0.75 = \$1020$.

35. $\sqrt{18}$; 4.24 units

36. $d = \sqrt{(x_2 - x_1)^2 + (y_2 - y_1)^2}$; Draw a right triangle with d as the hypotenuse. The length of the horizontal leg is equal to $x_2 - x_1$ and the length of the vertical leg is equal to $y_2 - y_1$. Using the Pythagorean Theorem, $(x_2 - x_1)^2 + (y_2 - y_1)^2 = d^2$, so $d = \sqrt{(x_2 - x_1)^2 + (y_2 - y_1)^2}$.

Section Resources

Surface Level	Deep Level
Resources by Chapter • Extra Practice • Reteach • Puzzle Time Student Journal • Self-Assessment • Practice Differentiating the Lesson Tutorial Videos Skills Review Handbook Skills Trainer	Resources by Chapter • Enrichment and Extension Graphic Organizers Dynamic Assessment System • Section Practice

Learning Target

Understand the concept of a cube root of a number.

Success Criteria

- Find cube roots of numbers.
- Evaluate expressions involving cube roots.
- Use cube roots to solve equations.

Warm Up

Cumulative, vocabulary, and prerequisite skills practice opportunities are available in the *Resources by Chapter* or at *BigIdeasMath.com*.

ELL Support

Review the terms *square* and *square root* from Section 9.1. Write $2^3 = 2 \cdot 2 \cdot 2 = 8$ on the board. Circle 2^3 and say, "two cubed." Underline a 2 in the product and say "two is the cube root of eight." Explain that the cube of a number is the number multiplied by itself two times. A cube root of a number refers to the number that is multiplied by itself two times.

Exploration 1

2 cm; 3 ft; 5 m; 7 in.; 0.1 cm; $\frac{1}{2}$ yd; Find a number whose cube is the volume.

Exploration 2

$x^3 = -27$: $x = -3$; one solution
$x^3 = -8$: $x = -2$; one solution
$x^3 = -1$: $x = -1$; one solution
$x^3 = 1$: $x = 1$; one solution
$x^3 = 8$: $x = 2$; one solution
$x^3 = 27$: $x = 3$; one solution
Each equation has one solution because there is only one number whose cube is the number on the right side of the equation.

Laurie's Notes

Preparing to Teach

- **MP2 Reason Abstractly and Quantitatively:** Students have found square roots of numbers. When finding a cube root, they must think about multiplying a number by itself twice.

Motivate

- Use 8 cubes to build a 2-by-2-by-2 cube. Inch-cubes or larger are best for visibility in the class. Display the large cube by holding it up on a rigid surface so that all students are able to see it.
- "Describe this shape." It is a cube.
- "Can you describe any of the numerical attributes of the cube?" *Sample answer:* The dimensions are $2 \times 2 \times 2$ and the volume is 8.
- "If the edge length of each small cube is 1 inch, what are the units for the volume of the large cube?" cubic inches
- Summarize by saying, "So, $8 = 2 \cdot 2 \cdot 2 = 2^3$. Cubing the edge length gives the volume."
- Hold another cube that is not made of smaller cubes, such as a cube of sticky notes.
- **MP8 Look for and Express Regularity in Repeated Reasoning:** "If you knew the volume of this cube, do you think you could find the dimensions—without measuring?" Give students time to think about this question and then introduce the explorations.

Exploration 1

- **MP1 Make Sense of Problems and Persevere in Solving Them:** Before you jump in with answers, remind students to think about the Motivate problem and the relationship between edge length and volume.
- Students may think that a calculator is necessary to solve these problems, but they may not find the **cube root** key (if the calculator has one). If a calculator helps them explore the problem, let them use it.
- **MP6 Attend to Precision:** Remind students that answers need correct labels (units).
- When students finish, ask volunteers to describe their reasoning behind their solutions. They should describe thinking about what number can be multiplied by itself twice to get the volume.
- Students will often say that they need a number that, when multiplied by itself 3 times, will be the volume. Clarify that the number (edge length) is used as a factor 3 times, but it is multiplied by itself only 2 times.

Exploration 2

- "When solving an equation of the form $x^2 = p$, such as $x^2 = 4$, there are two solutions ($x = \pm 2$). Are there two solutions for the equation $x^3 = -27$? Explain." No, when there are three factors of the same number, the product must have the same sign as the number.
- After students solve the problems, discuss their solutions and reasoning. Clarify any discrepancies.

9.3 Finding Cube Roots

Learning Target: Understand the concept of a cube root of a number.

Success Criteria:
- I can find cube roots of numbers.
- I can evaluate expressions involving cube roots.
- I can use cube roots to solve equations.

EXPLORATION 1

Finding Edge Lengths

Work with a partner. Find the edge length s of each cube. Explain your method.

Math Practice

Consider Similar Problems

How is finding the edge length of a cube with a given volume similar to finding the side length of a square with a given area?

Volume = 8 cm³
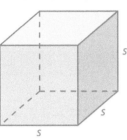

Volume = 27 ft³
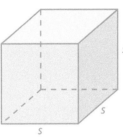

Volume = 125 m³
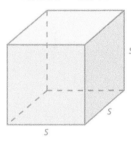

Volume = 343 in.³
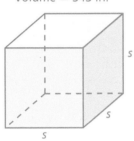

Volume = 0.001 cm³
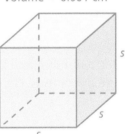

Volume = $\frac{1}{8}$ yd³
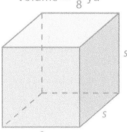

EXPLORATION 2

Finding Solutions of Equations

Work with a partner. Use mental math to solve each equation. How many solutions are there for each equation? Explain your reasoning.

$$x^3 = -27$$

$$x^3 = -8$$

$$x^3 = -1$$

$$x^3 = 1$$

$$x^3 = 8$$

$$x^3 = 27$$

9.3 Lesson

Key Vocabulary 🔊
cube root, p. 390
perfect cube, p. 390

A **cube root** of a number p is a number whose cube is equal to p. So, a cube root of a number p is a solution of the equation $x^3 = p$. The symbol $\sqrt[3]{}$ is used to represent a cube root. A **perfect cube** is a number that can be written as the cube of an integer.

EXAMPLE 1   Finding Cube Roots

Find each cube root.

a. $\sqrt[3]{8}$

▷ Because $2^3 = 8$, $\sqrt[3]{8} = 2$.

b. $\sqrt[3]{-27}$

▷ Because $(-3)^3 = -27$, $\sqrt[3]{-27} = -3$.

c. $\sqrt[3]{\dfrac{1}{64}}$

▷ Because $\left(\dfrac{1}{4}\right)^3 = \dfrac{1}{64}$, $\sqrt[3]{\dfrac{1}{64}} = \dfrac{1}{4}$.

Try It Find the cube root.

1. $\sqrt[3]{1}$ 2. $\sqrt[3]{-343}$ 3. $\sqrt[3]{-\dfrac{27}{1000}}$

Cubing a number and finding a cube root "undo" each other. So, they are inverse operations. For example,

$$\sqrt[3]{8^3} = \sqrt[3]{512} = 8 \text{ and } \left(\sqrt[3]{8}\right)^3 = 2^3 = 8.$$

You can use this relationship to evaluate expressions.

EXAMPLE 2   Evaluating Expressions Involving Cube Roots

Evaluate each expression.

a. $2\sqrt[3]{-216} = 2(-6)$ Evaluate the cube root.

$\phantom{2\sqrt[3]{-216}} = -12$ Multiply.

b. $\left(\sqrt[3]{125}\right)^3 + 21 = 125 + 21$ Evaluate the power using inverse operations.

$\phantom{\left(\sqrt[3]{125}\right)^3 + 21} = 146$ Add.

Try It Evaluate the expression.

4. $18 - 4\sqrt[3]{8}$ 5. $\left(\sqrt[3]{-64}\right)^3 + 43$ 6. $5\sqrt[3]{512} - 19$

Laurie's Notes

Scaffolding Instruction

- Students explored cubed roots. Now they will find cube roots, evaluate expressions, and solve equations using cube roots.
- **Emerging:** Students may be able to find cube roots, but they need help evaluating expressions and solving equations. They will benefit from guided instruction for the definitions and examples.
- **Proficient:** Students can find cube roots and solve equations using cube roots. They should proceed to the Self-Assessment exercises.

Discuss

- Define the vocabulary: **cube root** and **perfect cube**.
- **FYI:** Every real number has three cube roots, one real and two imaginary. Students only need to be concerned with the real cube root in this lesson.
- Compare square roots and cube roots. A number has two possible square roots but only one cube root. This idea is explored in Practice Exercise 35.

EXAMPLE 1

- "Write part (a) and ask, "What number times itself twice equals 8?" 2
- "Write part (b) and ask, "What number times itself twice equals −27?" −3
- "Write part (c) and ask, "What number times itself twice equals $\frac{1}{64}$?" $\frac{1}{4}$

Try It

- **Neighbor Check:** Have students work independently and then have their neighbors check their work. Have students discuss any discrepancies.
- Students are sometimes intimidated by the notation. Assure them that a calculator is not needed. Each radicand is either a perfect cube or related to perfect cubes.

EXAMPLE 2

- The cube root of a perfect cube is an integer and can be evaluated as part of an expression.
- Write part (a) and ask, "What is the cube root of −216?" −6
- Replace $\sqrt[3]{-216}$ with −6 and continue to evaluate the expression.
- Emphasize that cubing a number and finding a cube root are inverse operations, as stated before the example.
- Work through part (b), which helps students make the connection between cubing and taking the cube root.
- **MP2 Reason Abstractly and Quantitatively & MP3 Construct Viable Arguments and Critique the Reasoning of Others:** "In general, do you think $\left(\sqrt[3]{n}\right)^3 = n$? Explain." Listen for an understanding of how taking the cube root of a number and then cubing the result gives the original number, because taking a cube root and cubing a number are inverse operations.

Try It

- Students should work independently.
- Ask volunteers to share their work at the board.

Scaffold instruction to support all students in their learning. Learning is individualized and you may want to group students differently as they move in and out of these levels with each skill and concept. Student self-assessment and feedback help guide your instructional decisions about how and when to layer support for all students to become proficient learners.

Extra Example 1
Find each cube root.

a. $\sqrt[3]{512}$ 8

b. $\sqrt[3]{-729}$ −9

c. $\sqrt[3]{-\dfrac{125}{343}}$ $-\dfrac{5}{7}$

Try It

1. 1		**2.** −7	
3. $-\dfrac{3}{10}$		**4.** 10	
5. −21		**6.** 21	

Extra Example 2
Evaluate each expression.

a. $3\sqrt[3]{125} - 8$ 7

b. $\left(\sqrt[3]{27}\right)^3 - 4$ 23

ELL Support

After demonstrating Examples 1 and 2, have students work in pairs to discuss and complete Try It Exercises 1–6. Students may want to work together to solve the problems or one student can ask another, "Is the answer positive or negative? What is the cube root?" or "What is the answer?" Have students alternate the roles of asking and answering questions.

Beginner: Write the steps used to solve the problem.

Intermediate: State the answer and use simple sentences to explain the steps.

Advanced: Use detailed sentences to explain the process used.

Laurie's Notes

Extra Example 3

Solve each equation.

a. $y^3 = -64$ $y = -4$

b. $\frac{1}{3}k^3 = 9$ $k = 3$

EXAMPLE 3

- Discuss the text before the example. It might be helpful to show students a simple example.

$$n^3 = 8$$
$$\sqrt[3]{n^3} = \sqrt[3]{8}$$
$$n = 2$$

- Work through each part as shown. Encourage students to check their solutions by substituting the solution into the original equation.
- In part (b), point out that when solving an equation involving a variable term with an exponent (other than 1), students should isolate the variable with the exponent before taking the root of both sides.

Try It

7. $z = -10$

8. $b = 7$

9. $m = -5$

Try It

- **Think-Pair-Share:** Students should read each exercise independently and then work in pairs to complete the exercises. Then have each pair compare their answers with another pair and discuss any discrepancies.

ELL Support

Proceed as described in Laurie's Notes for the Self-Assessment for Concepts & Skills exercises, but allow students to work in pairs. Then have each pair check the work of a neighbor pair and discuss any discrepancies.

Formative Assessment Tip

Pass the Problem

This technique provides students the opportunity to work with others to solve a problem that requires more than a few steps. One way to use *Pass the Problem* is to begin by placing students in groups. Pose a problem that one student from each group begins to work on. After the completion of the first step, the problem is passed to the student seated to the right. The recipient completes the next step, or makes corrections to the problem. If changes are made, they must explain why there was an error. This continues until all steps are complete. *Pass the Problem* gives all students the opportunity to participate in the lesson and receive feedback on their work. When students have finished the problem, they will confer with one another to discuss the problem and offer additional feedback. One thing you hope to hear is positive feedback on the clarity of thinking that was recorded, allowing students to make sense of the work.

Self-Assessment
for Concepts & Skills

10. 4

11. -6

12. $-\dfrac{7}{10}$

13. 34

14. 30

15. -23

16. $d = 8$

17. $w = -4$

18. $m = 3$

✔ Self-Assessment *for Concepts & Skills*

- **Neighbor Check:** Have students complete Exercises 10–17 independently and then have their neighbors check their work. Have students discuss any discrepancies.
- For Exercise 18, have students work in groups of four to *Pass the Problem*. Each student in the group should complete one step of the solution on a separate piece of paper. Then have students pass their papers to the right. The recipient checks the first step, discusses any errors with the group, and then completes the second step. Students continue to pass papers to the right until the problem is completed, including a check of the solution.

The Success Criteria Self-Assessment chart can be found in the *Student Journal* or online at *BigIdeasMath.com*.

Because cubing a number and taking the cube root are inverse operations, you can solve equations of the form $x^3 = p$ by taking the cube root of each side.

EXAMPLE 3 **Solving Equations Using Cube Roots**

Solve each equation.

a. $x^3 = 216$

$$x^3 = 216 \qquad \text{Write the equation.}$$
$$\sqrt[3]{x^3} = \sqrt[3]{216} \qquad \text{Take the cube root of each side.}$$
$$x = 6 \qquad \text{Simplify.}$$

 The solution is $x = 6$.

Check
$$x^3 = 216$$
$$6^3 \stackrel{?}{=} 216$$
$$216 = 216 \checkmark$$

b. $-\dfrac{1}{4}n^3 = 2$

Check
$$-\dfrac{1}{4}n^3 = 2$$
$$-\dfrac{1}{4}(-2)^3 \stackrel{?}{=} 2$$
$$-\dfrac{1}{4}(-8) \stackrel{?}{=} 2$$
$$2 = 2 \checkmark$$

$$-\dfrac{1}{4}n^3 = 2 \qquad \text{Write the equation.}$$
$$n^3 = -8 \qquad \text{Multiply each side by } -4.$$
$$\sqrt[3]{n^3} = \sqrt[3]{-8} \qquad \text{Take the cube root of each side.}$$
$$n = -2 \qquad \text{Simplify.}$$

The solution is $n = -2$.

Try It Solve the equation.

7. $z^3 = -1000$ **8.** $3b^3 = 1029$ **9.** $33 = -\dfrac{1}{5}m^3 + 8$

 Self-Assessment *for Concepts & Skills*

Solve each exercise. Then rate your understanding of the success criteria in your journal.

FINDING CUBE ROOTS **Find the cube root.**

10. $\sqrt[3]{64}$ **11.** $\sqrt[3]{-216}$ **12.** $\sqrt[3]{-\dfrac{343}{1000}}$

EVALUATING EXPRESSIONS **Evaluate the expression.**

13. $\left(\sqrt[3]{-27}\right)^3 + 61$ **14.** $15 + 3\sqrt[3]{125}$ **15.** $2\sqrt[3]{-729} - 5$

SOLVING EQUATIONS **Solve the equation.**

16. $d^3 = 512$ **17.** $w^3 - 12 = -76$ **18.** $-\dfrac{1}{3}m^3 + 13 = 4$

EXAMPLE 4 **Modeling Real Life**

The baseball display case is made of plastic. How many square inches of plastic are used to make the case?

Volume = 125 in.³

The case is in the shape of a cube. Use the formula for the volume of a cube to find the edge length *s*.

$$V = s^3$$ Write the formula for volume.

$$125 = s^3$$ Substitute 125 for *V*.

$$\sqrt[3]{125} = \sqrt[3]{s^3}$$ Take the cube root of each side.

$$5 = s$$ Simplify.

The edge length is 5 inches. Use a formula to find the surface area of the cube.

$$S = 6s^2$$ Write the formula for surface area.

$$= 6(5)^2$$ Substitute 5 for *s*.

$$= 150$$ Simplify.

▶ So, 150 square inches of plastic are used to make the case.

Self-Assessment for Problem Solving

Solve each exercise. Then rate your understanding of the success criteria in your journal.

19. You have 275 square inches of wrapping paper. Do you have enough wrapping paper to wrap the gift box shown? Explain.

Volume = 343 in.³

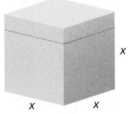

20. A cube-shaped end table has a volume of 216,000 cubic centimeters. Does the end table fit in the corner shown? Justify your answer.

21. **DIG DEEPER!** The relationship between the volumes and the lengths of two cereal boxes is represented by

$$\frac{\text{Volume of Box A}}{\text{Volume of Box B}} = \left(\frac{\text{Length of Box A}}{\text{Length of Box B}}\right)^3.$$

Box A has a volume of 192 cubic inches and a length of 8 inches. Box B has a volume of 375 cubic inches. What is the length of Box B? Justify your answer.

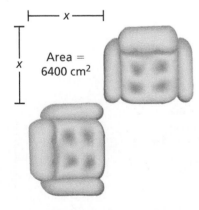

Area = 6400 cm²

Laurie's Notes

EXAMPLE 4

- Ask a student to read the problem.
- **Discuss:**
  - "What do you know?" The case is a cube with a volume of 125 cubic inches.
  - "What are you asked to find?" How many square inches of plastic are used to make the case (the surface area).
  - "What other information do you need to solve the problem?" the edge length
- **Teaching Tip:** Some tissue boxes are close to the shape of a cube. Use a tissue box or an actual cube as a prop.
- "How do you find the volume of a cube?" Cube the edge length, $V = s^3$.
- "If you know the volume of the cube, can you find the edge length? Explain." Yes, find the cube root of the volume. Students should be thinking, "What number multiplied by itself twice equals 125?"
- "How do you find the surface area of a cube?" Find the area of one face and multiply by 6, $S = 6s^2$.
- Continue to work through the problem as shown.

✔ Self-Assessment for Problem Solving

- Allow time in class for students to practice using the problem-solving plan. By now, most students should be able to get past the first step.
- **Neighbor Check:** Have students complete the exercises independently and then have their neighbors check their work. Have students discuss any discrepancies.
- Exercise 21 previews the concept of similar solids, which students will study in Section 10.4.

The Success Criteria Self-Assessment chart can be found in the *Student Journal* or online at *BigIdeasMath.com*.

Closure

- Explain the difference between $\sqrt{64}$ and $\sqrt[3]{64}$. $\sqrt{64}$ is a number that when multiplied by itself is equal to 64, and $\sqrt[3]{64}$ is a number that when multiplied by itself twice is equal to 64.

Extra Example 4
A cube-shaped plant stand is made of concrete and has a volume of 8 cubic feet. What is the surface area of the stand? 24 ft^2

Self-Assessment
for Problem Solving

19. no; The surface area of the gift box is 294 square inches.

20. yes; The edge length of the end table is $\sqrt[3]{216,000} = 60$ cm, and $x = \sqrt{6400} = 80$ cm.

21. 10 in.; $\dfrac{192}{375} = \left(\dfrac{8}{x}\right)^3$, so $x = 10$ in.

Learning Target

Understand the concept of a cube root of a number.

Success Criteria

- Find cube roots of numbers.
- Evaluate expressions involving cube roots.
- Use cube roots to solve equations.

Review & Refresh

1. 40 m
2. 16 ft
3. C

Concepts, Skills, & Problem Solving

4. 6 in.
5. $\frac{1}{3}$ ft
6. 0.4 m
7. 9
8. −5
9. −10
10. 12
11. −$\frac{1}{8}$
12. $\frac{7}{4}$
13. −9
14. $3\frac{5}{8}$
15. 21
16. $\frac{7}{12}$
17. 38
18. 74
19. 55
20. −276
21. 135

Assignment Guide and Concept Check

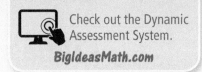

Scaffold assignments to support all students in their learning progression. The suggested assignments are a starting point. Continue to assign additional exercises and revisit with spaced practice to move every student toward proficiency.

Level	Assignment 1	Assignment 2
Emerging	2, 3, 4, 7, 9, 11, 13, 14, 17, 19, 22, 23, 24	8, 10, 12, 16, 18, 20, 25, 26, 28, 29, 30, 31, 32, 33
Proficient	2, 3, 5, 8, 10, 12, 14, 16, 18, 19, 21, 22, 25, 26	27, 28, 29, 30, 31, 32, 33, 34, 35, 38
Advanced	2, 3, 7, 8, 10, 12, 14, 16, 18, 19, 21, 23, 25, 27	29, 30, 31, 32, 33, 34, 35, 36, 37, 40

- Assignment 1 is for use after students complete the Self-Assessment for Concepts & Skills.
- Assignment 2 is for use after students complete the Self-Assessment for Problem Solving.
- The red exercises can be used as a concept check.

Review & Refresh Prior Skills

Exercises 1 and 2 Finding a Missing Length in a Right Triangle
Exercise 3 Writing Linear Functions

Common Errors

- **Exercises 8, 9, and 11** Students may disregard the negative in the radicand. Remind them to pay attention to the sign of the radicand and to check the sign of their answers.
- **Exercises 13–21** Students may not follow the order of operations when evaluating the expression. Remind them of the order of operations. Because taking a cube root is the inverse of cubing, it is evaluated before multiplication and division.

Go to *BigIdeasMath.com* to get HELP with solving the exercises.

▶ Review & Refresh

Find the missing length of the triangle.

1.

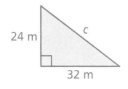

24 m   *c*   32 m

2.

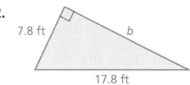

7.8 ft   *b*   17.8 ft

3. Which linear function is shown by the table?

A. $y = \dfrac{1}{3}x + 1$ **B.** $y = 4x$

C. $y = 3x + 1$ **D.** $y = \dfrac{1}{4}x$

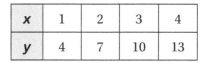

x	1	2	3	4
y	4	7	10	13

▶▶ Concepts, Skills, & Problem Solving

FINDING EDGE LENGTHS **Find the edge length *s* of the cube.** (See Exploration 1, p. 389.)

4. Volume = 216 in.³

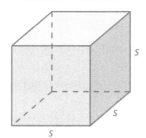

s *s* *s*

5. Volume = $\dfrac{1}{27}$ ft³

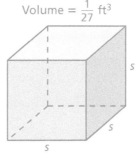

s *s*

6. Volume = 0.064 m³

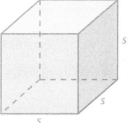

s *s*

FINDING CUBE ROOTS **Find the cube root.**

7. $\sqrt[3]{729}$

8. $\sqrt[3]{-125}$

9. $\sqrt[3]{-1000}$

10. $\sqrt[3]{1728}$

11. $\sqrt[3]{-\dfrac{1}{512}}$

12. $\sqrt[3]{\dfrac{343}{64}}$

EVALUATING EXPRESSIONS **Evaluate the expression.**

13. $18 - \left(\sqrt[3]{27}\right)^3$

14. $\left(\sqrt[3]{-\dfrac{1}{8}}\right)^3 + 3\dfrac{3}{4}$

15. $5\sqrt[3]{729} - 24$

16. $\dfrac{1}{4} - 2\sqrt[3]{-\dfrac{1}{216}}$

17. $54 + \sqrt[3]{-4096}$

18. $4\sqrt[3]{8000} - 6$

EVALUATING EXPRESSIONS **Evaluate the expression for the given value of the variable.**

19. $\sqrt[3]{\dfrac{n}{4}} + \dfrac{n}{10}, n = 500$

20. $\sqrt[3]{6w} - w, w = 288$

21. $2d + \sqrt[3]{-45d}, d = 75$

SOLVING EQUATIONS Solve the equation.

22. $x^3 = 8$

23. $t^3 = -343$

24. $-75 = y^3 + 50$

25. $-\dfrac{1}{2}z^3 = -108$

26. $2h^3 - 11 = 43$

27. $-600 = \dfrac{2}{5}k^3 + 750$

28. **MP** **MODELING REAL LIFE** The volume of a cube-shaped compost bin is 27 cubic feet. What is the edge length of the compost bin?

29. **MP** **MODELING REAL LIFE** The volume of a cube of ice for an ice sculpture is 64,000 cubic inches.

   a. What is the edge length of the cube of ice?

   b. What is the surface area of the cube of ice?

30. **MP** **NUMBER SENSE** There are three numbers that are their own cube roots. What are the numbers?

MP **REASONING** Copy and complete the statement with <, >, or =.

31. $-\dfrac{1}{4}$ ▢ $\sqrt[3]{-\dfrac{8}{125}}$

32. $\sqrt[3]{0.001}$ ▢ 0.01

33. $\sqrt[3]{64}$ ▢ $\sqrt{64}$

Area of square base = 64 in.²

34. **DIG DEEPER!** You bake a dessert in the baking pan shown. You cut the dessert into cube-shaped pieces of equal size. Each piece has a volume of 8 cubic inches. How many pieces do you get from one pan? Justify your answer.

35. **MP** **LOGIC** Determine whether each statement is true for square roots. Then determine whether each statement is true for cube roots. Explain your reasoning.

   a. You cannot find the square root of a negative number.

   b. Every positive number has a positive square root and a negative square root.

36. **GEOMETRY** The pyramid has a volume of 972 cubic inches. What are the dimensions of the pyramid?

37. **MP** **REASONING** The ratio $125 : x$ is equivalent to the ratio $x^2 : 125$. What is the value of x?

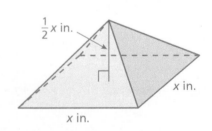

$\frac{1}{2}x$ in.

x in.

x in.

CRITICAL THINKING Solve the equation.

38. $(3x + 4)^3 = 2197$

39. $(8x^3 - 9)^3 = 5832$

40. $\left((5x - 16)^3 - 4\right)^3 = 216{,}000$

Mini-Assessment

1. Find $\sqrt[3]{-512}$. -8

Evaluate the expression.

2. $3 + 4\sqrt[3]{27}$ 15

3. $\left(\sqrt[3]{-8}\right)^3 + 15$ 7

4. Evaluate $\left(\sqrt[3]{5b}\right) - \dfrac{3b}{5}$ when $b = 25$. -10

5. Solve $2x^3 - 5 = -21$. $x = -2$

Section Resources

Surface Level	Deep Level
Resources by Chapter • Extra Practice • Reteach • Puzzle Time Student Journal • Self-Assessment • Practice Differentiating the Lesson Tutorial Videos Skills Review Handbook Skills Trainer	Resources by Chapter • Enrichment and Extension Graphic Organizers Dynamic Assessment System • Section Practice

Transfer Level	
Dynamic Assessment System • Mid-Chapter Quiz	Assessment Book • Mid-Chapter Quiz

Concepts, Skills, & Problem Solving

22. $x = 2$

23. $t = -7$

24. $y = -5$

25. $z = 6$

26. $h = 3$

27. $k = -15$

28. 3 ft

29. **a.** 40 in.

   b. 9600 in.^{2}

30. $-1, 0, 1$

31. $>$

32. $>$

33. $<$

34. 16 pieces; The edge length of each piece is $\sqrt[3]{8} = 2$ in. So, the base area of each piece is $2^2 = 4$ in.^{2}, and $\dfrac{64}{4} = 16$ pieces.

35. **a.** true; The square of a positive or negative number is never negative; not true; *Sample answer:* $\sqrt[3]{-8} = -2$

   b. true; The square of a number equals the square of its opposite; not true; *Sample answer:* 64 only has a positive cube root.

36. The side length of the square base is 18 inches and the height of the pyramid is 9 inches.

37. 25

38. $x = 3$

39. $x = \dfrac{3}{2}$

40. $x = 4$

Learning Target

Convert between different forms of rational numbers.

Success Criteria

- Explain the meaning of rational numbers.
- Write fractions and mixed numbers as decimals.
- Write repeating decimals as fractions or mixed numbers.

Warm Up

Cumulative, vocabulary, and prerequisite skills practice opportunities are available in the *Resources by Chapter* or at *BigIdeasMath.com*.

ELL Support

Students may know the word *rational* as meaning "reasonable" or "sensible." Explain that when *rational* is used in math to describe a number, it has a very specific meaning. A rational number is a number that can be written as $\frac{a}{b}$, where a and b are integers and b does not equal 0.

Exploration 1

a. $10x = 6.666\ldots$; $10x = 1.111\ldots$; $10x = 2.444\ldots$

b. See Additional Answers.

c. $\frac{4}{33}$; $\frac{5}{11}$; $\frac{3}{11}$; $\frac{931}{990}$; The procedure involves writing and solving an equation that does not have a repeating decimal; The procedure involves multiplying each side of the original equation by 100 instead of 10.

d. Let x equal the repeating decimal d. Subtract the equation $x = d$ from the equation $10^n x = 10^n d$, where n is the number of repeating digits. Then solve for x.

Laurie's Notes

STATE STANDARDS
8.NS.A.1

Preparing to Teach

- Students have written fractions and mixed numbers as decimals. They have also written terminating decimals as fractions or mixed numbers. Now they will extend their understanding to writing repeating decimals as fractions or mixed numbers.
- **MP7 Look for and Make Use of Structure:** Mathematically proficient students discern a pattern or structure. Recognizing the equivalence of equations written in different forms and using the equations to write and solve a third equation requires that students be able to manipulate equations.

Motivate

- Ask students to use a calculator to help write the fractions $\frac{1}{11}, \frac{2}{11}, \frac{3}{11}, \ldots, \frac{10}{11}$ as decimals. To save time, have students work in groups on different fractions instead of trying to write decimal equivalents for all of them.
- Record the results on the board.
- ❓ "What patterns do you observe?" *Sample answers:* All of the decimals have two repeating digits, and the sum of those two digits is equal to 9. Also, the first of the two repeating digits is one less than the numerator of the fraction.
- Explain that today students will learn how to do the reverse of this process, writing a repeating decimal as a fraction.

Exploration 1

- Allow time for students to complete part (a).
- ❓ "What was the result of multiplying each number in the first column by 10?" Answers will vary. Students should recognize that the decimal points moved one place to the right, but the decimals are still repeating.
- For part (b), work through the first row as a class. Help students understand that when you subtract the first equation from the second, the repeating decimal subtracts out and you are left with a simple equation to solve.

$$10x = 3.333\ldots$$
$$\underline{-(x = 0.333\ldots)}$$
$$9x = 3$$
$$x = \frac{1}{3}$$

- After completing part (b), have students check their answers with a calculator.
- In part (c), work through $x = 0.\overline{12}$ as a class. Begin by multiplying the equation by 10 to get $10x = 1.212121\ldots$.
- ❓ Ask, "When you subtract $x = 1.212121\ldots$ from $10x = 1.212121\ldots$, does the repeating decimal subtract out? Explain." No, you need to multiply $10x = 1.212121\ldots$ by 10 again, or multiply $x = 0.121212\ldots$ by 100.
- Complete the solution and then allow time for students to finish part (c) with their partners. Have students share their work with the class.
- **Three-Minute Pause:** Have students discuss and write their explanations for part (d). See the Formative Assessment Tip on page T-396 for a description of *Three-Minute Pause*.

9.4 Rational Numbers

Learning Target: Convert between different forms of rational numbers.

Success Criteria:
- I can explain the meaning of rational numbers.
- I can write fractions and mixed numbers as decimals.
- I can write repeating decimals as fractions or mixed numbers.

EXPLORATION 1

Writing Repeating Decimals as Fractions

Work with a partner.

a. Complete the table.

x	$10x$
$x = 0.333\ldots$	$10x = 3.333\ldots$
$x = 0.666\ldots$	
$x = 0.111\ldots$	
$x = 0.2444\ldots$	

Math Practice

Look for Structure
Why was it helpful to multiply each side of the equation $x = d$ by 10 in part (a)?

b. For each row of the table, use the two equations and what you know about solving systems of equations to write a third equation that does not involve a repeating decimal. Then solve the equation. What does your solution represent?

c. Write each repeating decimal below as a fraction. How is your procedure similar to parts (a) and (b)? How is it different?

$$x = 0.\overline{12} \qquad x = 0.\overline{45}$$

$$x = 0.\overline{27} \qquad x = 0.9\overline{40}$$

d. Explain how to write a repeating decimal with n repeating digits as a fraction.

Recall that a *rational number* is a number that can be written as $\frac{a}{b}$, where a and b are integers and $b \neq 0$. Every rational number can be written as a decimal that will either *terminate* or *repeat*.

You can think of a terminating decimal as a decimal that has repeating zeros at the end.

Terminating Decimals	Repeating Decimals
$0.25, 4.736, -1.03$	$5.222\ldots, -4.\overline{38}, 12.\overline{015}$

A rational number that can be written as $\frac{a}{b}$, where a is an integer and b is a power of 10, has a decimal form that terminates.

EXAMPLE 1 **Writing Fractions and Mixed Numbers as Decimals**

a. Write $1\frac{4}{25}$ as a decimal.

Notice that $1\frac{4}{25} = \frac{29}{25}$. Because $\frac{29}{25}$ can be written as $\frac{a}{b}$, where a is an integer and b is a power of 10, the decimal form of the number terminates.

$$\frac{29}{25} = \frac{29 \times 4}{25 \times 4} = \frac{116}{100} = 1.16$$

▷ So, $1\frac{4}{25} = 1.16$.

b. Write $\frac{5}{33}$ as a decimal.

Because $\frac{5}{33}$ cannot be written as $\frac{a}{b}$, where a is an integer and b is a power of 10, the decimal form of the number does not terminate.

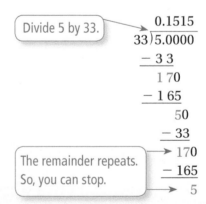

Use long division to divide 5 by 33.

Divide 5 by 33.

$$\begin{array}{r} 0.1515 \\ 33\overline{)5.0000} \\ -33 \\ \hline 1\,70 \\ -1\,65 \\ \hline 50 \\ -33 \\ \hline 170 \\ -165 \\ \hline 5 \end{array}$$

The remainder repeats. So, you can stop.

▷ So, $\frac{5}{33} = 0.\overline{15}$.

Try It Write the fraction or mixed number as a decimal.

1. $\dfrac{3}{15}$ 2. $-\dfrac{2}{9}$ 3. $4\dfrac{3}{8}$ 4. $2\dfrac{6}{11}$

Laurie's Notes

Scaffolding Instruction

- Students explored writing repeating decimals as fractions. Now they will continue converting between different forms of rational numbers.
- **Emerging:** Students may need to review writing fractions and mixed numbers as decimals. They also need more work with writing repeating decimals as fractions or mixed numbers. They will benefit from guided instruction for the examples.
- **Proficient:** Students have demonstrated that they can write repeating decimals as fractions. They can also write fractions and mixed numbers as decimals. These students should read the information at the tops of pages 396 and 397 before proceeding to the Try It Exercises 5–8 and the Self-Assessment exercises.

Discuss

- Review the definition of a *rational number*. Emphasize that *every* rational number can be written as a decimal that will either terminate or repeat.

EXAMPLE 1

- This example reviews skills from the previous course.
- Work through each part as shown, asking students to provide the reasoning.
- **Teaching Tip:** This is another opportunity to remind students to analyze the problem before solving it. Determining if the decimal will terminate is more efficient than jumping into long division only to find that the fraction can be written as a terminating decimal.

Try It

- **Neighbor Check:** Have students work independently and then have their neighbors check their work. Have students discuss any discrepancies.

ELL Support

After demonstrating Example 1, have students work in groups to discuss and complete Try It Exercises 1–4. Provide guiding questions such as, "Is the number a fraction or mixed number? Can the denominator be written as a power of 10? Will the decimal terminate? What is the decimal?" Expect students to perform according to their language levels.

Beginner: Write out the steps of writing the decimal and answer "yes" or "no."

Intermediate: Use simple sentences to answer the guiding questions and contribute to discussion.

Advanced: Use detailed sentences and help guide discussion.

Scaffold instruction to support all students in their learning. Learning is individualized and you may want to group students differently as they move in and out of these levels with each skill and concept. Student self-assessment and feedback help guide your instructional decisions about how and when to layer support for all students to become proficient learners.

Extra Example 1

a. Write $-3\frac{3}{20}$ as a decimal. -3.15

b. Write $\frac{4}{11}$ as a decimal. $0.\overline{36}$

Try It

1. 0.2	**2.** $-0.\overline{2}$
3. 4.375	**4.** $2.\overline{54}$

Try It

5. $\frac{8}{9}$

6. $2\frac{1}{15}$

7. $\frac{64}{99}$

8. $-4\frac{50}{99}$

ELL Support

Allow students to work in pairs for the Self-Assessment for Concepts & Skills exercises. Have two pairs form a group to share their answers to Exercise 9. Have each pair display their answers for Exercises 10–17 on a whiteboard for your review.

Self-Assessment
for Concepts & Skills

9. A rational number is any number that can be written as a terminating decimal, a repeating decimal, or as $\frac{a}{b}$, where a and b are integers and $b \neq 0$.

10. 0.18

11. $-0.3\overline{8}$

12. $3.\overline{4}$

13. $-12.1\overline{6}$

14. $-1\frac{7}{9}$

15. $\frac{2}{9}$

16. $8\frac{31}{33}$

17. $-6\frac{233}{990}$

Discuss

- Have students read the information at the top of the page. Then have students *Turn and Talk* with a neighbor to explain the process of writing a repeating decimal as a fraction.
- Use *Popsicle Sticks* to select students to explain the process to the class.

EXAMPLE 2

- "What is 1.25 written as a mixed number in simplest form?" $1\frac{1}{4}$
- "What does this mixed number tell you about $1.\overline{25}$?" $1.\overline{25}$ is approximately $1\frac{1}{4}$.
- Let $x = 1.\overline{25}$. Because there are two repeating digits, multiply by 100.
- "If $x = 1.\overline{25}$, then what is $100x$?" $125.\overline{25}$
- Subtract the equations and solve for x. Note that you are solving a system of two equations in one variable. Equation 1 is $x = 1.\overline{25}$ and Equation 2 is $100x = 125.\overline{25}$.
- Use a calculator to check the answer.
- "Could you multiply by a power of 10 other than 100? Explain." Yes, you can multiply by any power of 10 that aligns the repeating decimal portions (any even power of 10).
- Ask students why multiplying by 10^n works in the second step. Tell students to focus on the portion that repeats and how the decimal point moves. Encourage them to try some examples with more repeating digits. They need to make sure that the repeating portion is "aligned" when subtracting in the fourth step. So, the repeating decimal is eliminated.
- **Extension:** If time permits, you can explore with students what happens when you use the given steps for a repeating decimal that is not written in its "most abbreviated" form. For example, a repeating decimal written as $0.\overline{44}$ instead of $0.\overline{4}$. These steps still work, but you must simplify a more difficult fraction.

Try It

- Give students sufficient time to work through the exercises.
- For Exercise 8, students can ignore the negative sign. The negative sign can be "put back in" after converting the decimal.
- Ask volunteers to explain their work at the board.

✓ Self-Assessment for Concepts & Skills

- Students should work on these exercises independently.
- ◉ After students solve the exercises, they should use *Turn and Talk* to explain their solutions to each other.

The Success Criteria Self-Assessment chart can be found in the *Student Journal* or online at *BigIdeasMath.com*.

All terminating decimals and all repeating decimals are rational numbers, so you can write them as fractions.

You have previously written terminating decimals as fractions. To write a repeating decimal d as a fraction, subtract the equation $x = d$ from the equation $10^n x = 10^n d$, where n is the number of repeating digits. Then solve for x.

EXAMPLE 2 **Writing a Repeating Decimal as a Fraction**

Write $1.\overline{25}$ as a mixed number.

Let $x = 1.\overline{25}$.

$$x = 1.\overline{25}$$ Write the equation.

$$100 \cdot x = 100 \cdot 1.\overline{25}$$ There are 2 repeating digits, so multiply each side by $10^2 = 100$.

$$100x = 125.\overline{25}$$ Simplify.

$$- (x = 1.\overline{25})$$ Subtract the original equation.

$$99x = 124$$ Simplify.

$$x = \frac{124}{99}$$ Solve for x.

Calculator
$$124 \div 99$$
$$= 1.2525252525$$

▶ So, $1.\overline{25} = \dfrac{124}{99} = 1\dfrac{25}{99}$.

Try It **Write the decimal as a fraction or a mixed number.**

5. $0.888\ldots$ 6. $2.0\overline{6}$ 7. $0.\overline{64}$ 8. $-4.\overline{50}$

Self-Assessment for Concepts & Skills

Solve each exercise. Then rate your understanding of the success criteria in your journal.

9. **VOCABULARY** How can you identify a *rational number*?

WRITING FRACTIONS OR MIXED NUMBERS AS DECIMALS **Write the fraction or mixed number as a decimal.**

10. $\dfrac{9}{50}$ 11. $-\dfrac{7}{18}$ 12. $3\dfrac{4}{9}$ 13. $-12\dfrac{1}{6}$

WRITING A REPEATING DECIMAL AS A FRACTION **Write the repeating decimal as a fraction or a mixed number.**

14. $-1.\overline{7}$ 15. $0.\overline{2}$ 16. $8.\overline{93}$ 17. $-6.2\overline{35}$

EXAMPLE 3 Modeling Real Life

The weight of an object on the moon is about $0.1\overline{6}$ times its weight on Earth. An astronaut weighs 192 pounds on Earth. How much does the astronaut weigh on the moon?

Write $0.1\overline{6}$ as a fraction. Then use the fraction to find the astronaut's weight on the moon.

Let $x = 0.1\overline{6}$.

$x = 0.1\overline{6}$	Write the equation.
$10 \cdot x = 10 \cdot (0.1\overline{6})$	There is 1 repeating digit, so multiply each side by $10^1 = 10$.
$10x = 1.\overline{6}$	Simplify.
$\underline{- (x = 0.1\overline{6})}$	Subtract the original equation.
$9x = 1.5$	Simplify.
$x = \dfrac{1.5}{9}$	Solve for x.

The weight of an object on the moon is about $\dfrac{1.5}{9} = \dfrac{15}{90} = \dfrac{1}{6}$ times its weight on Earth.

▷ So, an astronaut who weighs 192 pounds on Earth weighs about $\dfrac{1}{6} \cdot 192 = 32$ pounds on the moon.

Self-Assessment for Problem Solving

Solve each exercise. Then rate your understanding of the success criteria in your journal.

18. A fun house mirror distorts the image it reflects. Objects reflected in the mirror appear $1.\overline{3}$ times taller. When a five-foot-tall person looks in the mirror, how tall does he appear?

19. An *exchange rate* represents the value of one currency relative to another. Your friend visits a country that uses a local currency with an exchange rate of $1.2\overline{65}$ units of the local currency to \$1. If a bank charges \$2 to change currency, how many units of the local currency does your friend receive when she gives the bank \$200?

20. **DIG DEEPER!** A low fuel warning appears when a particular car has $0.014\overline{6}$ of a tank of gas remaining. The car holds 18.5 gallons of gas and can travel 36 miles for each gallon used. How many miles can the car travel after the low fuel warning appears?

Laurie's Notes

EXAMPLE 3

- Ask a volunteer to read the problem. Ask another volunteer to explain what the problem is asking.
- Have students complete the first two squares of a Four Square for the problem-solving plan.
- ❓ "How can you find the astronaut's weight on the moon?" Multiply the astronaut's weight on Earth by $0.1\overline{6}$.
- ❓ "Why would you want to convert the repeating decimal to a fraction first?" *Sample answer:* To find the exact weight on the moon.
- Work through the process of writing $0.1\overline{6}$ as a fraction. Students should complete the third square of their Four Squares.
- You may want to write a few more digits of the repeating decimals.

$$x = 0.1666\ldots$$
$$10 \cdot x = 10 \cdot (0.1666\ldots)$$
$$10x = 1.666\ldots$$
$$\underline{-(x = 0.166\ldots)}$$
$$9x = 1.5$$
$$x = \frac{1.5}{9}$$

- After writing the repeating decimal as a fraction, multiply $\frac{1}{6}$ by 192 pounds to find the astronaut's weight on the moon.
- **Check:** Students should complete the last square of their Four Squares. They could divide 32 pounds by 192 pounds to verify that the quotient is $0.1\overline{6}$.

✔ *Self-Assessment* for Problem Solving

- Encourage students to use a Four Square to complete these exercises. By now, most students should be able to get past the first square.
- Give students sufficient time to work through the exercises. Ask volunteers to explain their work at the board.

The Success Criteria Self-Assessment chart can be found in the *Student Journal* or online at *BigIdeasMath.com*.

Closure

- **Quick Write:** Explain the steps of writing $2.\overline{35}$ as a mixed number.

Extra Example 3

The weight of a kitten is $0.2\overline{7}$ times the weight of the mother. The mother weighs 9 pounds. How much does the kitten weigh? $2\frac{1}{2}$ lb

Self-Assessment
for Problem Solving

18. $6\frac{2}{3}$ ft

19. 250.6 units

20. 9.768 mi

Learning Target

Convert between different forms of rational numbers.

Success Criteria

- Explain the meaning of rational numbers.
- Write fractions and mixed numbers as decimals.
- Write repeating decimals as fractions or mixed numbers.

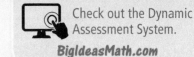

▶ Review & Refresh

1. 5

2. −1

3. 23

4. 15°, 75°, 90°

5. 40°, 60°, 80°

6. 10°, 30°, 140°

▶▶ Concepts, Skills, & Problem Solving

7. $\dfrac{7}{9}$

8. $\dfrac{85}{99}$

9. $\dfrac{23}{99}$

10. −0.15

11. $9.08\overline{3}$

12. $0.13\overline{8}$

13. 6.025

14. $0.14\overline{6}$

15. $-2.3\overline{8}$

16. 0.3125 in.

17. $-\dfrac{5}{9}$

18. $4\dfrac{1}{9}$

19. $-\dfrac{353}{990}$

20. $6\dfrac{89}{990}$

21. $\dfrac{103}{550}$

22. $11\dfrac{170}{333}$

23. $\dfrac{8}{9}$

Assignment Guide and Concept Check

Scaffold assignments to support all students in their learning progression. The suggested assignments are a starting point. Continue to assign additional exercises and revisit with spaced practice to move every student toward proficiency.

Level	Assignment 1	Assignment 2
Emerging	3, 6, 7, 10, 11, 12, 13, 17, 19, 20	14, 15, 16, 21, 22, 23, 25, 26, 28, 31, 35, 38
Proficient	3, 6, 8, 10, 12, 15, 18, 20, 22, 24	21, 23, 25, 26, 27, 28, 29, 31, 32, 34, 35, 38
Advanced	3, 6, 9, 10, 12, 15, 20, 21, 22, 24	25, 26, 27, 28, 29, 30, 32, 33, 36, 37, 38

- Assignment 1 is for use after students complete the Self-Assessment for Concepts & Skills.
- Assignment 2 is for use after students complete the Self-Assessment for Problem Solving.
- The red exercises can be used as a concept check.

Review & Refresh Prior Skills

Exercises 1–3 Evaluating Expressions
Exercises 4–6 Using Interior Angle Measures

▯ Common Errors

- **Exercises 10–15** When using long division, students may divide the denominator by the numerator. Remind them to always divide the numerator by the denominator, regardless of the size of the numbers.
- **Exercises 17–22** Students may ignore the repeating bar and write the decimal as a fraction or mixed number with a denominator that is a power of 10. For example, in Exercise 17, they may write $-0.\overline{5} = -\dfrac{5}{10} = -\dfrac{1}{2}$ instead of $-0.\overline{5} = -\dfrac{5}{9}$. Remind students that a repeating decimal cannot be written as a fraction with a denominator that is a power of 10.

9.4 Practice

? Go to *BigIdeasMath.com* to get
HELP with solving the exercises.

▶ Review & Refresh

Evaluate the expression.

1. $2 + \sqrt[3]{27}$

2. $1 - \sqrt[3]{8}$

3. $7\sqrt[3]{125} - 12$

Find the measures of the interior angles of the triangle.

4.

5.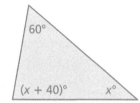

6.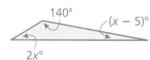

▶▶ Concepts, Skills, & Problem Solving

WRITING REPEATING DECIMALS AS FRACTIONS **Write the repeating decimal as a fraction.** (See Exploration 1, p. 395.)

7. $0.777\ldots$

8. $0.858585\ldots$

9. $0.232323\ldots$

WRITING FRACTIONS OR MIXED NUMBERS AS DECIMALS **Write the fraction or mixed number as a decimal.**

10. $-\dfrac{3}{20}$

11. $9\dfrac{1}{12}$

12. $\dfrac{5}{36}$

13. $6\dfrac{1}{40}$

14. $\dfrac{11}{75}$

15. $-2\dfrac{7}{18}$

16. **MP** **PRECISION** Your hair is $\dfrac{5}{16}$ inch long. Write this length as a decimal.

WRITING A REPEATING DECIMAL AS A FRACTION **Write the repeating decimal as a fraction or a mixed number.**

17. $-0.\overline{5}$

18. $4.\overline{1}$

19. $-0.3\overline{56}$

20. $6.0\overline{89}$

21. $0.18\overline{72}$

22. $11.\overline{510}$

23. **MP** **STRUCTURE** A *forecast cone* defines the probable path of a tropical cyclone. The probability that the center of a particular tropical cyclone remains within the forecast cone is $0.\overline{8}$. Write this probability as a fraction.

24. **MP** **STRUCTURE** Describe how to write a decimal with 12 repeating digits as a fraction.

25. **MP** **STRUCTURE** An approximation for the value of π is $\frac{22}{7}$. Write this number as a repeating decimal.

26. **MP** **MODELING REAL LIFE** The density of iodine is about $6.28\overline{1}$ times the density of acetone. The density of acetone is about 785 kilograms per cubic meter. What is the density of iodine? Write your answer as a repeating decimal.

27. **MP** **MODELING REAL LIFE** A disinfectant manufacturer suggests that its product kills $99.9\overline{8}\%$ of germs. Write this percent as a repeating decimal and then as a fraction. How many germs would survive when the disinfectant is applied to an object with 18,000 germs?

28. **MP** **MODELING REAL LIFE** You and your friend are making pear tarts for a bake sale. Your recipe uses $\frac{7}{6}$ times the weight of the diced pears used in your friend's recipe. Your friend's recipe calls for 0.3 pound of diced pears. How many pounds of pears should you buy to have enough for both recipes?

29. **MP** **PROBLEM SOLVING** The table shows the principal and interest earned per year for each of three savings accounts with simple annual interest. Which account has the greatest interest rate? Justify your answer.

	Principal	Interest Earned
Account A	$90.00	$4.00
Account B	$120.00	$5.50
Account C	$100.00	$4.80

30. **DIG DEEPER!** The probability that an athlete makes a half-court basketball shot is 22 times the probability that the athlete makes a three-quarter-court shot. The probability that the athlete makes a three-quarter-court shot is $0.00\overline{9}$. What is the probability that the athlete makes a half-court shot? Write your answer as a percent.

MP **NUMBER SENSE** Determine whether the numbers are equal. Justify your answer.

31. $\frac{9}{22}$ and $0.4\overline{09}$

32. $\frac{1}{999}$ and 0

33. $\frac{135}{90}$ and 1.5

ADDING AND SUBTRACTING RATIONAL NUMBERS Add or subtract.

34. $0.4\overline{09} + 0.6\overline{81}$

35. $-0.6\overline{3} + \frac{5}{99}$

36. $\frac{11}{6} - 0.2\overline{7}$

37. $0.\overline{03} - 0.0\overline{4}$

38. **MP** **STRUCTURE** Write a repeating decimal that is between $\frac{9}{7}$ and $\frac{10}{7}$. Justify your answer.

Mini-Assessment

Write the fraction or mixed number as a decimal.

1. $\dfrac{7}{20}$ 0.35

2. $-3\dfrac{11}{18}$ $-3.6\overline{1}$

Write the repeating decimal as a fraction or a mixed number.

3. $0.\overline{1}$ $\dfrac{1}{9}$

4. $0.\overline{75}$ $\dfrac{34}{45}$

5. $-3.\overline{81}$ $-3\dfrac{9}{11}$

Section Resources

Surface Level	Deep Level

Resources by Chapter
  • Extra Practice
  • Reteach
  • Puzzle Time
Student Journal
  • Self-Assessment
  • Practice
Differentiating the Lesson
Tutorial Videos
Skills Review Handbook
Skills Trainer
	Resources by Chapter
	  • Enrichment and Extension
	Graphic Organizers
	Dynamic Assessment System
	  • Section Practice

Concepts, Skills, & Problem Solving

24. Let x equal the repeating decimal d. Subtract the equation $x = d$ from the equation $10^{12}x = 10^{12}d$. Then solve for x.

25. $3.\overline{142857}$

26. $4930.67\overline{2}$ kg

27. $0.999\overline{8}$; $\dfrac{8999}{9000}$; 2 germs

28. 0.65 lb

29. Account C;
Account A interest rate:
$$\dfrac{\$4.00}{\$90.00} = 0.0\overline{4} = 4.\overline{4}\%$$

Account B interest rate:
$$\dfrac{\$5.50}{\$120.00} = 0.0458\overline{3} = 4.58\overline{3}\%$$

Account C interest rate:
$$\dfrac{\$4.80}{\$100.00} = 0.048 = 4.8\%$$

30. 22%

31. equal; $9 \div 22 = 0.40909\ldots$

32. not equal; $1 \div 999 = 0.001001\ldots$

33. equal; $135 \div 90 = 1.5$

34. $1\dfrac{1}{11}$ or $1.\overline{09}$

35. $-\dfrac{58}{99}$ or $-0.\overline{58}$

36. $1\dfrac{37}{66}$ or $1.5\overline{60}$

37. $-\dfrac{1}{99}$ or $-0.\overline{01}$

38. *Sample answer:* $1.\overline{3}$;
$\dfrac{9}{7} = 1.\overline{285714}$ and $\dfrac{10}{7} = 1.\overline{428571}$

Learning Target

Understand the concept of irrational numbers.

Success Criteria

- Classify real numbers as rational or irrational.
- Approximate irrational numbers.
- Solve real-life problems involving irrational numbers.

Warm Up

Cumulative, vocabulary, and prerequisite skills practice opportunities are available in the *Resources by Chapter* or at *BigIdeasMath.com.*

ELL Support

Review the meaning of the word *rational*. Write the word *ir/rational* on the board with a slash as shown. Ask students what they think the prefix *ir-* means. If necessary, explain that it means "no" or "not" and the newly formed word has the opposite meaning of the original word. So, an irrational number *cannot* be written as $\frac{a}{b}$, where a and b are integers and b does not equal 0.

Exploration 1

a. $\sqrt{2}$; irrational number; $\sqrt{2}$ cannot be written as $\frac{a}{b}$, where a and b are integers and $b \neq 0$.

b. 1 and 2; $\sqrt{1} = 1$ and $\sqrt{4} = 2$. $\sqrt{1} < \sqrt{2} < \sqrt{4}$, so $1 < \sqrt{2} < 2$.

c. 1.4; *Sample answer:* Use tracing paper to trace the length of the diagonal and compare it to a distance on the number line.

d. See Additional Answers.

Laurie's Notes

Preparing to Teach

- Students have found square roots of perfect squares. Now they will approximate square roots.
- **MP1 Make Sense of Problems and Persevere in Solving Them:** To help students make sense of square roots, they will approximate square roots geometrically.

Motivate

- Make a large Venn diagram based on student characteristics.
- The diagram can be made on the floor with yarn. Have students write their names on index cards.
- Use the diagram shown for students to place themselves. Sample labels for the groups: A = girls in our class, B = boys in our class, C = wears glasses/contacts, D = brown hair, E = taller than 5 feet 4 inches, F = wearing a short-sleeved T-shirt

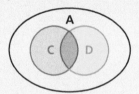
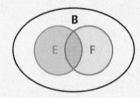

- Discuss what it means to be in certain sets and not in other sets.
- Later in the lesson, students will use a Venn Diagram to describe the set of **real numbers**.

Exploration 1

- In part (a), students should use the Pythagorean Theorem to find $x = \sqrt{2}$.
- Review the definition of a *rational number:* a number that can be written as $\frac{a}{b}$, where a and b are integers and $b \neq 0$.
- **?** Ask, "Is $\sqrt{2}$ a rational number?" no
- Explain that an **irrational number** is a number that cannot be written as $\frac{a}{b}$, where a and b are integers and $b \neq 0$.
- Discuss students' answers and reasoning for part (b).
- **?** Ask, "Why is $\sqrt{2}$ between 1 and 2?" Because $\sqrt{1} = 1$ and $\sqrt{4} = 2$. "Is $\sqrt{2}$ closer to 1 or 2? Explain." 1; 2 is closer to 1 than 4, so $\sqrt{2}$ is closer to 1 than 2.
- **Teaching Tip:** Technology is available online at *BigIdeasMath.com* to help students with part (c). Students could also use compasses, transparencies, or tracing paper to trace the length of the diagonal and compare it to a distance on the number line.
- The goal is for students to recognize that irrational numbers can have a length associated with them. They are numbers that you can approximate. When students approximate the length of the diagonal, it should be close to 1.4.
- For part (d), have students make a conjecture and then use calculators to test their conjectures.

9.5 Irrational Numbers

Learning Target: Understand the concept of irrational numbers.

Success Criteria:
- I can classify real numbers as rational or irrational.
- I can approximate irrational numbers.
- I can solve real-life problems involving irrational numbers.

EXPLORATION 1

Approximating Square Roots

Work with a partner. Use the square shown.

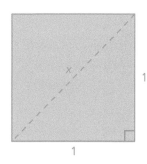

Math Practice

Communicate Precisely

How does the prefix "*ir-*" help you understand the term *irrational number*?

a. Find the exact length x of the diagonal. Is this number a *rational number* or an *irrational number*? Explain.

b. The value of x is between which two whole numbers? Explain your reasoning.

c. Use the diagram below to approximate the length of the diagonal to the nearest tenth. Explain your method.

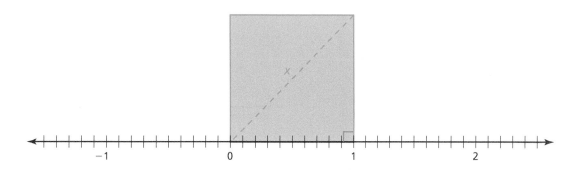

d. Which of the following is the closest approximation of the length of the diagonal? Justify your answer using inverse operations.

| 1.412 | 1.413 | 1.414 | 1.415 |

Key Vocabulary 🔊
irrational number,
 p. 402
real numbers, p. 402

An **irrational number** is a number that is not rational. So, an irrational number *cannot* be written as $\frac{a}{b}$, where a and b are integers and $b \neq 0$.

- The square root of any whole number that is not a perfect square is irrational. The cube root of any integer that is not a perfect cube is irrational. Another example of an irrational number is π.
- Every number can be written as a decimal. The decimal form of an irrational number neither terminates nor repeats.

🔑 Key Idea

Real Numbers

Rational numbers and irrational numbers together form the set of **real numbers**.

Remember

The decimal form of a rational number either terminates or repeats.

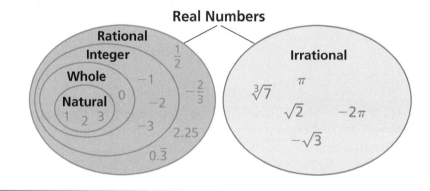

EXAMPLE 1   Classifying Real Numbers

Classify each real number.

When classifying a real number, list all the subsets in which the number belongs.

	Number	Subset(s)	Reasoning
a.	$\sqrt{12}$	Irrational	12 is not a perfect square.
b.	$-0.\overline{25}$	Rational	$-0.\overline{25}$ is a repeating decimal.
c.	$-\sqrt{9}$	Integer, Rational	$-\sqrt{9}$ is equal to -3.
d.	$\sqrt[3]{15}$	Irrational	15 is not a perfect cube.
e.	π	Irrational	The decimal form of π neither terminates nor repeats.

Try It **Classify the real number.**

1. $0.121221222\ldots$ **2.** $-\sqrt{196}$ **3.** $\sqrt[3]{2}$

Laurie's Notes

Scaffolding Instruction

- Students investigated $\sqrt{2}$ geometrically. Students will continue to approximate square roots of irrational numbers. They will also classify real numbers as rational or irrational.
- **Emerging:** Students may struggle with the concept of irrational numbers and approximating square roots. They will benefit from guided instruction for the definitions, Key Idea, and examples.
- **Proficient:** Although students may have grasped the concept of irrational numbers, they still need to understand how irrational numbers fit into the real number system. They should review the definitions, Key Idea, and Example 1 before working on the Self-Assessment exercises.

Discuss

- Explain the definition of irrational numbers. Ask students to give some examples.

Key Idea

- Write the Key Idea. It is important for students to understand that any real number is either rational or irrational. The two sets do not intersect.
- Explain that a *subset* is a set in which every element is contained within a larger set. The sets of rational numbers and irrational numbers are subsets of the set of real numbers. The sets of natural numbers, whole numbers, and integers are subsets of the set of rational numbers.
- Natural numbers are also called *counting numbers* because they are used to count objects. Whole numbers include the natural numbers and 0. Integers include the natural numbers, 0, and the opposites of the natural numbers.
- Mention that all square roots of perfect squares are rational.
- ❓ "Can you think of a repeating decimal and its fractional equivalent?"

  Sample answer: $0.333\ldots = \dfrac{1}{3}$

- ❓ "Can you think of a terminating decimal and its fractional equivalent?"

  Sample answer: $0.5 = \dfrac{1}{2}$

EXAMPLE 1

- ◉ Students will gain a better understanding of how to classify real numbers in this example.
- Discuss the push-pin note with students. In part (c), point out that because $-\sqrt{9} = -3 = \dfrac{-3}{1}$, $-\sqrt{9}$ is an integer *and* a rational number.

Try It

- **Think-Pair-Share:** Students should read each exercise independently and then work in pairs to complete the exercises. Then have each pair compare their answers with another pair and discuss any discrepancies.

Scaffold instruction to support all students in their learning. Learning is individualized and you may want to group students differently as they move in and out of these levels with each skill and concept. Student self-assessment and feedback help guide your instructional decisions about how and when to layer support for all students to become proficient learners.

Extra Example 1
Classify each real number.

a. $\sqrt{15}$ irrational

b. 0.34 rational

c. $\sqrt[3]{27}$ natural, whole, integer, rational

d. $-\sqrt{25}$ integer, rational

e. $\dfrac{0}{4}$ whole, integer, rational

Try It

1. irrational
2. integer, rational
3. irrational

Extra Example 2

Approximate $\sqrt{23}$ to the nearest (a) integer and (b) tenth.

a. 5

b. 4.8

Try It

4. **a.** 3

   b. 2.8

5. **a.** −4

   b. −3.6

6. **a.** −5

   b. −4.9

7. **a.** 4

   b. 4.5

Extra Example 3

Which is greater, $\sqrt{0.49}$ or 0.71? 0.71

Try It

8. π; π is to the right of $\sqrt{8}$ on a number line.

9. $\sqrt{26}$; $\sqrt{26}$ is to the right of $\sqrt[3]{65}$ on a number line.

10. $-\sqrt{2}$; $-\sqrt{2}$ is to the right of $-\sqrt[3]{10}$ on a number line.

T-403

EXAMPLE 2

- It is important for students to make an estimate before using a calculator. Use reasoning first!
- ? "What are the first 10 perfect squares?" 1, 4, 9, 16, 25, 36, 49, 64, 81, 100
- ? "What type of number do you get when you take the square root of any of these perfect squares?" integer
- ? **MP3 Construct Viable Arguments and Critique the Reasoning of Others:** "Between what two perfect squares is $\sqrt{71}$? How do you know?" 8 and 9 because $\sqrt{64} = 8$ and $\sqrt{81} = 9$, so $\sqrt{71}$ has to be a number between 8 and 9.
- ? "Is $\sqrt{71}$ closer to 8 or 9? Why?" It is closer to 8 because 71 is closer to 64 than to 81.
- You may wish to allow students to calculate squares of decimals using a calculator.
- You could explore more about square roots using a calculator approximation. For example, $\sqrt{71} \approx 8.4261498$. So, you can rationalize that $\sqrt{71}$ is between 8 and 9, between 8.4 and 8.5, between 8.42 and 8.43, etc., by truncating the decimal.

Try It

- Ask volunteers to share their thinking about each problem.

EXAMPLE 3

- **MP5 Use Appropriate Tools Strategically:** A number line is used as a visual model. Students will ask where to place $\sqrt{35}$. Knowing that $\sqrt{35}$ is between $\sqrt{25}$ and $\sqrt{36}$ does not tell you where to graph it on the number line.
- ? "Is $\sqrt{35}$ closer to 5 or 6? Why?" It is closer to 6 because 35 is closer to 36 than to 25.
- Similarly, $\sqrt[3]{80}$ is between $\sqrt[3]{64} = 4$ and $\sqrt[3]{125} = 5$, but closer to 4 than to 5.
- Students should use calculators to check their approximations. Make sure they are comfortable using a calculator to find square roots and cube roots.
- Plot the approximations on a number line. Because $6 > 4$, $\sqrt{35} > \sqrt[3]{80}$.

Try It

- Ask volunteers to share their thinking about each problem.

ELL Support

After demonstrating Examples 2 and 3, have students work in pairs to discuss and complete Try It Exercises 4–10. Provide guiding questions such as, "What is the closest perfect square (or perfect cube)? What is its square root (or cube root)? What is the approximation to the nearest tenth?" Expect students to perform according to their language levels.

Beginner: Write tables of squares (or cubes) and identify the approximations.

Intermediate: Use phrases and simple sentences to answer the guiding questions and contribute to discussion.

Advanced: Use detailed sentences to answer and contribute to discussion.

EXAMPLE 2 **Approximating an Irrational Number**

Approximate $\sqrt{71}$ to the nearest (a) integer and (b) tenth.

Number	Square of Number
7	49
8	64
9	81
10	100

a. Make a table of numbers whose squares are close to 71.

The table shows that 71 is between the perfect squares 64 and 81. Because 71 is closer to 64 than to 81, $\sqrt{71}$ is closer to 8 than to 9.

So, $\sqrt{71} \approx 8$.

Number	Square of Number
8.3	68.89
8.4	70.56
8.5	72.25
8.6	73.96

b. Make a table of numbers between 8 and 9 whose squares are close to 71. Because 71 is closer to 70.56 than to 72.25, $\sqrt{71}$ is closer to 8.4 than to 8.5.

So, $\sqrt{71} \approx 8.4$.

Try It **Approximate the number to the nearest (a) integer and (b) tenth.**

4. $\sqrt{8}$ **5.** $-\sqrt{13}$ **6.** $-\sqrt{24}$ **7.** $\sqrt{20}$

EXAMPLE 3 **Comparing Irrational Numbers**

You can use the same procedure to approximate cube roots as you used for square roots.

Which is greater, $\sqrt{35}$ or $\sqrt[3]{80}$?

Approximate $\sqrt{35}$.

Notice that 35 is between $5^2 = 25$ and $6^2 = 36$. Because 35 is closer to 36 than to 25, $\sqrt{35}$ is a little less than 6.

Approximate $\sqrt[3]{80}$.

Notice that 80 is between $4^3 = 64$ and $5^3 = 125$. Because 80 is closer to 64 than to 125, $\sqrt[3]{80}$ is a little greater than 4.

So, $\sqrt{35} > \sqrt[3]{80}$.

Try It **Which number is greater? Explain.**

8. $\sqrt{8}, \pi$ **9.** $\sqrt[3]{65}, \sqrt{26}$ **10.** $-\sqrt{2}, -\sqrt[3]{10}$

EXAMPLE 4 **Using the Pythagorean Theorem**

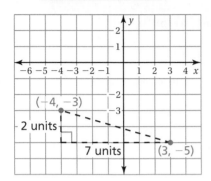

Approximate the distance between $(-4, -3)$ and $(3, -5)$ to the nearest tenth.

Plot the points in a coordinate plane. Then draw a right triangle with a hypotenuse that represents the distance between the points.

Use the Pythagorean Theorem to find the length of the hypotenuse.

$a^2 + b^2 = c^2$	Write the Pythagorean Theorem.
$2^2 + 7^2 = c^2$	Substitute 2 for a and 7 for b.
$4 + 49 = c^2$	Evaluate the powers.
$53 = c^2$	Add.
$\sqrt{53} = c$	Take the positive square root of each side.

▶ The distance between $(-4, -3)$ and $(3, -5)$ is $\sqrt{53} \approx 7.3$ units.

Try It **Approximate the distance between the points to the nearest tenth.**

11. $(-3, -1)$ and $(-2, -2)$ **12.** $(1, -1)$ and $(5, 4)$

13. $(5, 4)$ and $(9, 8)$ **14.** $(-7, 10)$ and $(3, -5)$

Self-Assessment for Concepts & Skills

Solve each exercise. Then rate your understanding of the success criteria in your journal.

15. VOCABULARY How are rational numbers and irrational numbers different?

CLASSIFYING REAL NUMBERS Classify the real number.

16. $\dfrac{48}{16}$ **17.** $-\sqrt{76}$ **18.** $\sqrt[3]{-216}$

APPROXIMATING AN IRRATIONAL NUMBER Approximate the number to the nearest (a) integer and (b) tenth.

19. $\sqrt{51}$ **20.** $-\sqrt{87}$ **21.** $\sqrt[3]{60}$

22. WHICH ONE DOESN'T BELONG? Which number does *not* belong with the other three? Explain your reasoning.

$-\dfrac{11}{12}$	25.075	$\sqrt{8}$	$-3.\overline{3}$

Laurie's Notes

EXAMPLE 4

- This example may look familiar to students, as it is similar to Example 4 in Section 9.2. The procedure is the same, but the answer will be an irrational number.

- **?** "How can you solve this problem?" Allow time for students to make a plan before discussing them as a class. Guide students to the plan of plotting the points, drawing a right triangle, using the Pythagorean Theorem, and then approximating the square root using the method from Example 2.

- As you work through the solution, ask students to supply the justification for each step.

Try It

- Have students work with a partner on Exercises 11 and 12. Then have students work independently on Exercises 13 and 14.

Formative Assessment Tip

3-2-1

This technique provides a structured way for students to reflect on their learning, typically at the conclusion of a lesson or chapter. Students are asked to respond to three writing prompts: giving 3 responses to the first prompt, 2 responses to the second prompt, and 1 response to the third prompt. All 6 responses relate to what students have learned during the lesson or chapter. Collect and review student responses to help you plan instruction for the next day.

✔ Self-Assessment *for Concepts & Skills*

- **Neighbor Check:** Have students work independently and then have their neighbors check their work. Have students discuss any discrepancies.

- **3-2-1:** Ask students to write 3 new things (concepts, skills, or procedures) that they learned so far in this section, 2 things they are struggling with, and 1 thing that will help them tomorrow.
  - The next day, begin class by sharing positive responses and clarifying any questions or misunderstandings.

- ◉ Have students use *Thumbs Up* to indicate their understanding of the first two success criteria.

ELL Support

Allow students to work in pairs for additional support and to practice language. Have two pairs present their explanations for Exercises 15 and 22 to one another and discuss any misunderstandings. Have each pair display their answers for Exercises 16–21 on a whiteboard for your review.

The Success Criteria Self-Assessment chart can be found in the *Student Journal* or online at *BigIdeasMath.com*.

Extra Example 4

Approximate the distance between $(-3, 1)$ and $(4, 5)$ to the nearest tenth.
8.1 units

Try It

11. 1.4 units

12. 6.4 units

13. 5.7 units

14. 18.0 units

Self-Assessment
for Concepts & Skills

15. A rational number can be written as $\frac{a}{b}$, where a and b are integers and $b \neq 0$. An irrational number cannot be written as $\frac{a}{b}$.

16. natural, whole, integer, rational

17. irrational

18. integer, rational

19. **a.** 7
    b. 7.1

20. **a.** -9
    b. -9.3

21. **a.** 4
    b. 3.9

22. $\sqrt{8}$; $\sqrt{8}$ is irrational and the other three numbers are rational.

Laurie's Notes

Extra Example 5

Using the equation in Example 5, about how far can you see when the periscope is 6 feet above the water? about 3 nautical miles

EXAMPLE 5

- Ask a volunteer to read the problem. Ask another volunteer to explain what the problem is asking.
- ❓ "What do you know?" the equation relating the distance you can see with a periscope to the height of the periscope above the water, and the height of the periscope above the water
- ❓ "How can you find how far you can see?" Substitute 3 for h in $d^2 = 1.37h$ and solve for d.
- Work through the solution as shown.
- ❓ "Why do you only take the positive square root?" d represents a distance and distance cannot be negative.

Self-Assessment
for Problem Solving

23. 1.7 m^2

24. Plane B;
Plane A: $5^2 + 6^2 = c^2$,
so $c = \sqrt{61} \approx 7.8$ km
Plane B: $7^2 + 3^2 = c^2$,
so $c = \sqrt{58} \approx 7.6$ km

✓ Self-Assessment for Problem Solving

- Students may benefit from trying the exercises independently and then working with peers to refine their work. It is important to provide time in class for problem solving, so that students become comfortable with the problem-solving plan.
- ⊙ Have students use *Thumbs Up* to indicate their understanding of the last success criterion.

The Success Criteria Self-Assessment chart can be found in the *Student Journal* or online at *BigIdeasMath.com*.

Closure

- **Exit Ticket:** Order the numbers from least to greatest.

$$\sqrt{38}, \sqrt{\frac{100}{3}}, 6.\overline{5} \qquad \sqrt{\frac{100}{3}}, \sqrt{38}, 6.\overline{5}$$

Learning Target

Understand the concept of irrational numbers.

Success Criteria

- Classify real numbers as rational or irrational.
- Approximate irrational numbers.
- Solve real-life problems involving irrational numbers.

EXAMPLE 5 Modeling Real Life

The equation $d^2 = 1.37h$ represents the relationship between the distance d (in nautical miles) you can see with a periscope and the height h (in feet) of the periscope above the water. About how far can you see when the periscope is 3 feet above the water?

Use the equation to find d when $h = 3$.

$d^2 = 1.37h$	Write the equation.
$d^2 = 1.37(3)$	Substitute 3 for h.
$d^2 = 4.11$	Multiply.
$d = \sqrt{4.11}$	Take the positive square root of each side.

To approximate d, notice that 4.11 is between the perfect squares 4 and 9. Because 4.11 is close to 4, $\sqrt{4.11}$ is close to 2.

▶ So, you can see about 2 nautical miles when the periscope is 3 feet above the water.

Check
Use a calculator to approximate $\sqrt{4.11}$.

```
√(4.11)
        2.027313493
```
✓

 Self-Assessment for Problem Solving

Solve each exercise. Then rate your understanding of the success criteria in your journal.

23. The equation $3600b^2 = hw$ represents the relationship among the body surface area b (in square meters), height h (in centimeters), and weight w (in kilograms) of a person. To the nearest tenth, approximate the body surface area of a person who is 168 centimeters tall and weighs 60 kilograms.

24. Which plane is closer to the base of the airport tower? Justify your answer.

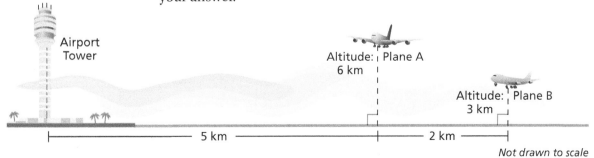

Airport Tower

Altitude: Plane A
6 km

Altitude: Plane B
3 km

5 km

2 km

Not drawn to scale

Go to *BigIdeasMath.com* to get HELP with solving the exercises.

▶ Review & Refresh

Write the repeating decimal as a fraction or a mixed number.

1. $0.\overline{4}$
2. $1.0\overline{3}$
3. $0.\overline{75}$
4. $2.\overline{36}$

Simplify the expression. Write your answer as a power.

5. $(5^4)^2$
6. $(-9)^4 \cdot (-9)^7$
7. $a^8 \cdot a$
8. $(y^3)^6$

▶▶ Concepts, Skills, & Problem Solving

APPROXIMATING SQUARE ROOTS Find the exact length x of the diagonal of the square or rectangle. The value of x is between which two whole numbers? (See Exploration 1, p. 401.)

9.

10.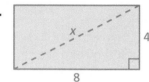

CLASSIFYING REAL NUMBERS Classify the real number.

11. 0
12. $\sqrt[3]{343}$
13. $\dfrac{\pi}{6}$
14. $-\sqrt{81}$

15. -1.125
16. $\dfrac{52}{13}$
17. $\sqrt[3]{-49}$
18. $\sqrt{15}$

19. **MP YOU BE THE TEACHER** Your friend classifies $\sqrt{144}$. Is your friend correct? Explain your reasoning.

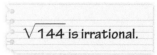
$\sqrt{144}$ is irrational.

20. **MP MODELING REAL LIFE** You cut a photograph into a right triangle for a scrapbook. The lengths of the legs of the triangle are 4 inches and 6 inches. Is the length of the hypotenuse a rational number? Explain.

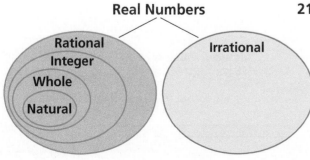
Real Numbers
Rational
Integer
Whole
Natural
Irrational

21. **MP REASONING** Place each number in the correct area of the Venn diagram.

   a. the last digit of your phone number

   b. the square root of any prime number

   c. the quotient of the circumference of a circle and its diameter

Assignment Guide and Concept Check

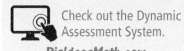
Scaffold assignments to support all students in their learning progression. The suggested assignments are a starting point. Continue to assign additional exercises and revisit with spaced practice to move every student toward proficiency.

Level	Assignment 1	Assignment 2
Emerging	2, 5, 7, 9, 11, 13, 14, 15, 16, 17, 19, 22, 23, 28, 29, 37	20, 21, 24, 26, 30, 31, 34, 39, 49, 53, 55
Proficient	2, 5, 7, 10, 11, 12, 13, 14, 15, 17, 19, 21, 24, 25, 29, 31, 39	27, 33, 34, 35, 36, 42, 43, 44, 45, 46, 47, 48, 50, 53, 54, 55
Advanced	2, 5, 7, 10, 11, 12, 13, 14, 15, 17, 19, 21, 24, 27, 31, 32, 42	34, 35, 36, 43, 44, 46, 47, 48, 51, 52, 53, 54, 55, 56, 57

- Assignment 1 is for use after students complete the Self-Assessment for Concepts & Skills.
- Assignment 2 is for use after students complete the Self-Assessment for Problem Solving.
- The red exercises can be used as a concept check.

Review & Refresh Prior Skills

Exercises 1–4 Writing a Repeating Decimal as a Fraction
Exercises 5–8 Finding Powers

 Common Errors

- **Exercises 11–18** Students may not classify the real number in as many ways as possible. For instance, they may classify $\frac{52}{13}$ as rational only, because it is written as a fraction. Remind students that real numbers can have more than one classification. Point out that they should simplify the number, if possible, before classifying it.
- **Exercises 12, 14, 17, and 18** Students may think that all square roots and cube roots are irrational. Remind them that square roots of perfect squares are rational and that cube roots of perfect cubes are also rational.
- **Exercises 14, 15, and 17** Students may think that all negative numbers are irrational. Remind them of the set of integers and that negative numbers can be rational or irrational.

Review & Refresh

1. $\frac{4}{9}$

2. $1\frac{1}{30}$

3. $\frac{25}{33}$

4. $2\frac{4}{11}$

5. 5^8

6. $(-9)^{11}$

7. a^9

8. y^{18}

Concepts, Skills, & Problem Solving

9. $\sqrt{18}$; 4 and 5

10. $\sqrt{80}$; 8 and 9

11. whole, integer, rational

12. natural, whole, integer, rational

13. irrational

14. integer, rational

15. rational

16. natural, whole, integer, rational

17. irrational

18. irrational

19. no; 144 is a perfect square. So, $\sqrt{144}$ is rational.

20. no; 52 is not a perfect square.

21. **a.** If the last digit is 0, place it in the set of whole numbers. Otherwise, place it in the set of natural numbers.

    b. irrational number

    c. irrational number

Concepts, Skills, & Problem Solving

22. **a.** 7
    b. 6.8
23. **a.** −10
    b. −10.2
24. **a.** −2
    b. −2.3
25. **a.** 7
    b. 6.8
26. **a.** 3
    b. 2.6
27. **a.** −13
    b. −12.9
28. $\sqrt{135}$; $\sqrt{135}$ is to the right of $\sqrt{125}$ on a number line.
29. $\sqrt{22}$; $\sqrt{22}$ is to the right of $\sqrt[3]{34}$ on a number line.
30. $-\sqrt[3]{100}$; $-\sqrt[3]{100}$ is to the right of $-\sqrt{42}$ on a number line.
31. π; π is to the right of $\sqrt{5}$ on a number line.
32. $\sqrt{28}$; $\sqrt{28}$ is to the right of $\sqrt[3]{130}$ on a number line.
33. $-\sqrt{38}$; $-\sqrt{38}$ is to the right of $\sqrt[3]{-250}$ on a number line.
34. false   35. true
36. false   37. 7.2 units
38. 5.4 units 39. 6.3 units
40. 9.2 units 41. 8.5 units
42. 11.2 units
43. **a.** 5.8 km
    b. 8.6 km
    c. 7.1 km
    d. 11.7 km
44. Create a table of numbers between 8.4 and 8.5 whose squares are close to 71, and then determine which square is closest to 71.
45. 8 ft   46. 118.4 cm

Common Errors

- **Exercises 22–27** Students may struggle with knowing what integer is closest to the given number. To help make comparisons, encourage them to write the first 10 perfect squares. If the radicand is greater than 100, then students should *Guess, Check, and Revise* to find two integers on either side of the number. When determining which integer is closer to the rational number, encourage students to use a number line.
- **Exercises 28–33** Students may guess which is greater just by looking at the numbers. Encourage them to use a number line to compare the numbers. Also remind students to simplify and/or estimate the numbers so that they are easier to compare.

APPROXIMATING AN IRRATIONAL NUMBER Approximate the number to the nearest **(a)** integer and **(b)** tenth.

22. $\sqrt{46}$

23. $-\sqrt{105}$

24. $\sqrt[3]{-12}$

25. $\sqrt[3]{310}$

26. $\sqrt{\dfrac{27}{4}}$

27. $-\sqrt{\dfrac{335}{2}}$

COMPARING IRRATIONAL NUMBERS Which number is greater? Explain.

28. $\sqrt{125}, \sqrt{135}$

29. $\sqrt{22}, \sqrt[3]{34}$

30. $-\sqrt[3]{100}, -\sqrt{42}$

31. $\sqrt{5}, \pi$

32. $\sqrt[3]{130}, \sqrt{28}$

33. $-\sqrt{38}, \sqrt[3]{-250}$

```
√(10)
         3.16227766
√(14)
         3.741657387
```

USING TOOLS Use the graphing calculator screen to determine whether the statement is *true* or *false*.

34. To the nearest tenth, $\sqrt{10} = 3.1$.

35. The value of $\sqrt{14}$ is between 3.74 and 3.75.

36. $\sqrt{10}$ lies between 3.1 and 3.16 on a number line.

USING THE PYTHAGOREAN THEOREM Approximate the distance between the points to the nearest tenth.

37. $(1, 2), (7, 6)$

38. $(2, 4), (7, 2)$

39. $(-1, -3), (1, 3)$

40. $(-6, -7), (0, 0)$

41. $(-1, 1), (7, 4)$

42. $(-6, 5), (-4, -6)$

43. **MODELING REAL LIFE** The locations of several sites in a forest are shown in the coordinate plane. Approximate each distance to the nearest tenth.

   a. How far is the cabin from the peak?

   b. How far is the fire tower from the lake?

   c. How far is the lake from the peak?

   d. You are standing at $(-5, -6)$. How far are you from the lake?

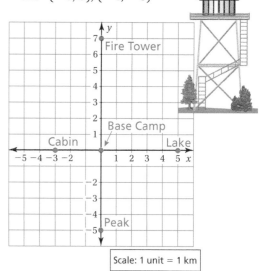

Scale: 1 unit = 1 km

44. **WRITING** Explain how to continue the method in Example 2 to approximate $\sqrt{71}$ to the nearest hundredth.

45. **MODELING REAL LIFE** The area of a four square court is 66 square feet. Approximate the side length s of the four square court to the nearest whole number.

46. **MODELING REAL LIFE** A checkerboard is 8 squares long and 8 squares wide. The area of each square is 14 square centimeters. Approximate the perimeter (in centimeters) of the checkerboard to the nearest tenth.

47. **GEOMETRY** The cube has a volume of 340 cubic inches. Approximate the length d of the diagonal to the nearest whole number. Justify your answer.

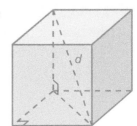

48. **CRITICAL THINKING** On a number line, π is between 3 and 4.

    a. Use this information to draw a number line and shade a region that represents the location of π^2. Explain your reasoning.

    b. Repeat part (a) using the fact that π is between 3.1 and 3.2.

    c. Repeat part (a) using the fact that π is between 3.14 and 3.15.

MP **NUMBER SENSE** **Approximate the square root to the nearest tenth.**

49. $\sqrt{0.39}$　　　　　50. $\sqrt{1.19}$　　　　　51. $\sqrt{1.52}$

52. **MP** **STRUCTURE** Is $\sqrt{\dfrac{1}{4}}$ a rational number? Is $\sqrt{\dfrac{3}{16}}$ a rational number? Explain.

53. **MP** **MODELING REAL LIFE** The equation $s^2 = 54r$ represents the relationship between the speed s (in meters per second) of a roller-coaster car and the radius r (in meters) of the loop. Approximate the speed of a roller-coaster car going around the loop shown to the nearest tenth.

$r = 16.764$ m

54. **OPEN-ENDED** Find two numbers a and b that satisfy the diagram.

55. **DIG DEEPER!** The equation $d^3 = t^2$ represents the relationship between the mean distance d (in astronomical units) of a planet from the Sun and the time t (in years) it takes the planet to orbit the Sun.

    a. Jupiter takes about 11.9 years to orbit the Sun. Approximate the mean distance of Jupiter from the Sun to the nearest tenth.

    b. The mean distance of Saturn from the Sun is about 9.5 astronomical units. Approximate the time it takes Saturn to orbit the Sun to the nearest tenth.

56. **MP** **MODELING REAL LIFE** The equation $h = -16t^2 + 26$ represents the height h (in feet) of a water balloon t seconds after it is dropped. Approximate the time it takes the water balloon to reach the ground to the nearest tenth. Justify your answer.

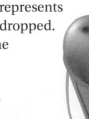

57. **MP** **NUMBER SENSE** Determine whether the statement is *sometimes*, *always*, or *never* true. Explain your reasoning.

    a. A rational number multiplied by a rational number is rational.

    b. A rational number multiplied by an irrational number is rational.

    c. An irrational number multiplied by an irrational number is rational.

Common Errors

- **Exercises 49–51** Students may struggle estimating the square roots because of the decimals. Remind them of the method they used in Exercises 22–27. Tell students to use the list they wrote, but with the decimal points moved two places to the left. These new squares will help students estimate the square roots.

Mini-Assessment

1. Classify $\sqrt{65}$. irrational

Approximate the number to the nearest (a) integer and (b) tenth.

2. $\sqrt{99}$ 10; 9.9

3. $\sqrt{\dfrac{15}{2}}$ 3; 2.7

Which number is greater? Explain.

4. $2\dfrac{11}{12}$, $\sqrt{8}$ $2\dfrac{11}{12}$; $2\dfrac{11}{12}$ is to the right of $\sqrt{8}$ on a number line.

5. $\dfrac{4}{5}$, $\sqrt{\dfrac{49}{64}}$ $\sqrt{\dfrac{49}{64}}$; $\sqrt{\dfrac{49}{64}}$ is to the right of $\dfrac{4}{5}$ on a number line.

6. Approximate the distance between $(2, -3)$ and $(-3, 4)$ to the nearest tenth. 8.6 units

Section Resources

Surface Level	Deep Level
Resources by Chapter • Extra Practice • Reteach • Puzzle Time Student Journal • Self-Assessment • Practice Differentiating the Lesson Tutorial Videos Skills Review Handbook Skills Trainer	Resources by Chapter • Enrichment and Extension Graphic Organizers Dynamic Assessment System • Section Practice

Concepts, Skills, & Problem Solving

47. 12 in.;
edge length of cube $= \sqrt[3]{340}$
≈ 7 in.
length of diagonal of base
$\approx \sqrt{7^2 + 7^2} = \sqrt{98} \approx 10$ in.
$d \approx \sqrt{7^2 + 10^2} = \sqrt{149} \approx 12$ in.

48. a.

Because π is between 3 and 4, π^2 is between 3^2 and 4^2, or 9 and 16.

b.

Because π is between 3.1 and 3.2, π^2 is between 3.1^2 and 3.2^2, or 9.61 and 10.24.

c.

Because π is between 3.14 and 3.15, π^2 is between 3.14^2 and 3.15^2, or 9.8596 and 9.9225.

49. 0.6   **50.** 1.1

51. 1.2

52. yes; $\left(\dfrac{1}{2}\right)^2 = \dfrac{1}{4}$, so $\sqrt{\dfrac{1}{4}} = \dfrac{1}{2}$; no;
$\left(\dfrac{\sqrt{3}}{4}\right)^2 = \dfrac{3}{16}$, and $\sqrt{3}$ is irrational.

53. 30.1 m/sec

54. *Sample answer:* $a = 82, b = 97$

55. a. 5.2 astronomical units
b. 29.3 yr

56. 1.3 sec; $0 = -16t^2 + 26$, so $t = \sqrt{1.625} \approx 1.3$ sec.

57. a. always; If $\dfrac{a}{b}$ and $\dfrac{c}{d}$ are rational numbers, then ac and bd are integers and $bd \neq 0$. So, $\dfrac{ac}{bd}$ is rational.

b. sometimes; *Sample answer:* $\pi \cdot 0 = 0$ is rational, but $2 \cdot \sqrt{3}$ is irrational.

c. sometimes; *Sample answer:* $\sqrt{2} \cdot \pi$ is irrational, but $\pi \cdot \dfrac{1}{\pi}$ is rational.

Learning Target

Understand the converse of the Pythagorean Theorem.

Success Criteria

- Explain the converse of the Pythagorean Theorem.
- Identify right triangles given three side lengths.
- Identify right triangles in a coordinate plane.

Warm Up

Cumulative, vocabulary, and prerequisite skills practice opportunities are available in the *Resources by Chapter* or at *BigIdeasMath.com*.

ELL Support

Explain that *converse* comes from the Latin meaning "turn around." Lead students to understand that if you are walking in one direction and then turn around, you will be walking in the opposite direction. Explain that *converse* means "opposite." If the converse of a statement or theorem is true, then its opposite is true.

Exploration 1

a. See Additional Answers.

b. Check students' work.

Exploration 2

a. If the equation $a^2 + b^2 = c^2$ is true for the side lengths of a triangle, then the triangle is a right triangle; *Sample answer:* true

b. See Additional Answers.

Laurie's Notes

Preparing to Teach

- **MP3 Construct Viable Arguments and Critique the Reasoning of Others:** Students will develop a "proof" of the converse of the Pythagorean Theorem. It is important that students are able to explain the steps in their work and compare them to the reasoning of their classmates.

Motivate

- Explain what the converse of a statement is.
- **Example:** If I live in Orlando, then I live in Florida.
  The converse is: If I live in Florida, then I live in Orlando.
  The original statement is true, but the converse is false.
- Ask students to write four true if-then statements. Have students share some examples. Ask the class to decide if the converse of each statement is true.

Exploration 1

- For each true statement, students should construct a valid explanation versus simply saying the statement is true. Classmates are expected to listen and critique the explanation offered.
- Point out the Math Practice note and review the meaning of the word *counterexample*.
- It is important for students to understand that a statement might be false even if they cannot think of a counterexample.
- **Big Idea:** Even when a conditional statement is true, its converse does not have to be true. Students should keep this in mind for the next exploration.

Exploration 2

- Students often say that the Pythagorean Theorem is simply $a^2 + b^2 = c^2$. Tell them that it is actually a conditional statement. If a and b are the lengths of the legs and c is the length of the hypotenuse of a right triangle, then $a^2 + b^2 = c^2$.
- ❓ "What is the converse of the Pythagorean Theorem?" If $a^2 + b^2 = c^2$, then a triangle with side lengths a, b, and c is a right triangle.
- ❓ "Do you think the converse of the Pythagorean Theorem is true?" Students may simply guess at this point.
- In part (b), students should use deductive reasoning to show that the converse is true. They may need guidance in linking their reasoning.
- ❓ "What does the Pythagorean Theorem tell you about $\triangle JKL$?" $a^2 + b^2 = x^2$ "What does this tell you about c and x?" Students can substitute c^2 for $a^2 + b^2$ in $a^2 + b^2 = x^2$. So, $c^2 = x^2$ and $c = x$. Remind students that this is not always true. It is true in this case because c and x represent side lengths, so they must be positive.
- In the previous course, students learned that two triangles with the same side lengths are the same size and shape. There is a sequence of rigid motions that takes one triangle to the other, which means $\triangle DEF \cong \triangle JKL$. So, $\angle E$ is a right angle and $\triangle DEF$ is a right triangle.

9.6 The Converse of the Pythagorean Theorem

Learning Target: Understand the converse of the Pythagorean Theorem.

Success Criteria:
- I can explain the converse of the Pythagorean Theorem.
- I can identify right triangles given three side lengths.
- I can identify right triangles in a coordinate plane.

The *converse* of a statement switches the hypothesis and the conclusion.

Statement:	Converse of the statement:
If p, then q.	If q, then p.

EXPLORATION 1

Analyzing the Converse of a Statement

Work with a partner.

a. Write the converse of each statement. Then determine whether each statement and its converse are *true* or *false*. Explain.

- If I live in California, then I live in the United States.

- If my heart is beating, then I am alive.

- If one figure is a translation of another figure, then the figures are congruent.

b. Write your own statement whose converse is true. Then write your own statement whose converse is false.

Math Practice

Use Counterexamples

Is the converse of a false statement always false?

EXPLORATION 2

The Converse of the Pythagorean Theorem

Work with a partner.

a. Write the converse of the Pythagorean Theorem. Do you think the converse is *true* or *false*?

b. Consider $\triangle DEF$ with side lengths a, b, and c such that $a^2 + b^2 = c^2$. Also consider $\triangle JKL$ with leg lengths a and b, where the measure of $\angle K$ is 90°. Use the two triangles and the Pythagorean Theorem to show that the converse of the Pythagorean Theorem is true.

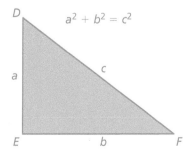
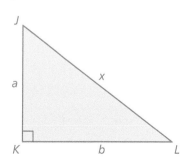

Key Idea

Converse of the Pythagorean Theorem

If the equation $a^2 + b^2 = c^2$ is true for the side lengths of a triangle, then the triangle is a right triangle.

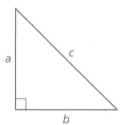

EXAMPLE 1 **Identifying Right Triangles**

Tell whether each triangle is a right triangle.

A *Pythagorean triple* is a set of three positive integers a, b, and c, where $a^2 + b^2 = c^2$.

a.

41 cm
9 cm
40 cm

$$a^2 + b^2 = c^2$$ Write the Pythagorean Theorem.

$$9^2 + 40^2 \overset{?}{=} 41^2$$ Substitute 9 for a, 40 for b, and 41 for c.

$$81 + 1600 \overset{?}{=} 1681$$ Evaluate the powers.

$$1681 = 1681 \ \checkmark$$ Add.

▶ The triangle *is* a right triangle.

b.

18 ft   12 ft
24 ft

Common Error

When using the converse of the Pythagorean Theorem, always substitute the length of the longest side for c.

$$a^2 + b^2 = c^2$$ Write the Pythagorean Theorem.

$$12^2 + 18^2 \overset{?}{=} 24^2$$ Substitute 12 for a, 18 for b, and 24 for c.

$$144 + 324 \overset{?}{=} 576$$ Evaluate the powers.

$$468 \neq 576 \ \times$$ Add.

▶ The triangle is *not* a right triangle.

Try It Tell whether the triangle with the given side lengths is a right triangle.

1. 28 in., 21 in., 20 in.

2. 1.25 mm, 1 mm, 0.75 mm

Laurie's Notes

Scaffolding Instruction

- Students "proved" the converse of the Pythagorean Theorem. Now they will use the converse of the Pythagorean Theorem to identify right triangles.
- **Emerging:** Students need practice using the converse of the Pythagorean Theorem. They will benefit from guided instruction for the Key Idea and examples.
- **Proficient:** Students can use the Pythagorean Theorem and its converse. They should complete Try It Exercises 3 and 4 before proceeding to the Self-Assessment exercises.

Key Idea

- Write the Key Idea stating the converse of the Pythagorean Theorem. It is one way of determining whether given side lengths form a right triangle.

EXAMPLE 1

- If the three numbers satisfy the theorem, then it is a right triangle. Explain that you are not using eyesight to decide if it is a right triangle.
- Substitute the side lengths for each triangle. Remind students that the longest side is substituted for c.
- Point out the push-pin note. Because 9, 40, and 41 satisfy the theorem, they form a Pythagorean triple and the triangle is a right triangle.
- Because 12, 18, and 24 do not satisfy the theorem, it is not a right triangle.
- **❓ Extension:** Tell students that a 12-18-24 triangle is similar to a triangle with side lengths 2, 3, and 4 (scale factor is 6). Then ask, "Is a 2-3-4 triangle a right triangle?" no

Try It

- **Common Error:** Students may not substitute the longest side for c. This is particularly true because the measures are listed longest to shortest.

ELL Support

After demonstrating Example 1, have students work in pairs to discuss and complete Try It Exercises 1 and 2. Remind students of the steps they need to take: (1) Write the Pythagorean Theorem, (2) Substitute the values for the variables, (3) Evaluate the powers, and (4) Add. Expect students to perform according to their language levels.

Beginner: Write out the steps.

Intermediate: Use phrases and simple sentences to discuss the process.

Advanced: Use detailed sentences to discuss the process.

Scaffold instruction to support all students in their learning. Learning is individualized and you may want to group students differently as they move in and out of these levels with each skill and concept. Student self-assessment and feedback help guide your instructional decisions about how and when to layer support for all students to become proficient learners.

Extra Example 1
Tell whether each triangle is a right triangle.

a.

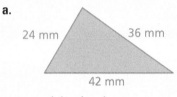

not a right triangle

b.

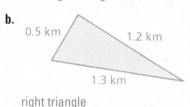

right triangle

Try It
1. no
2. yes

Extra Example 2

Tell whether the points $D(2, 3)$, $E(6, 0)$, and $F(4, -2)$ form a right triangle. no

Try It

3. no

4. yes

Self-Assessment

for Concepts & Skills

5. If the square of the longest side length of a triangle is equal to the sum of the squares of the other two side lengths, then the triangle is a right triangle.

6. no

7. no

8. 3, 6, 8; It is the only set that is not a Pythagorean triple.

EXAMPLE 2

- Write the problem on the board.
- ❓ Ask, "How can you determine if the points form a right triangle?" Plot the points in a coordinate plane and find the distance between each pair of points. Then use the converse of the Pythagorean Theorem.
- Plot the points and find the distances.
- ❓ "How do you decide which length to substitute for each variable in the Pythagorean Theorem?" Substitute the greatest value for c because the hypotenuse is the longest side. Substitute the other two values, in any order, for a and b.
- Work through the remainder of the solution as shown.

Try It

- There are multiple steps required to solve each exercise. You may want to divide the class into two groups and assign a different exercise to each group.
- Select a student from each group to present his or her solution to the class.

✔ Self-Assessment *for Concepts & Skills*

- **Neighbor Check:** Have students work independently and then have their neighbors check their work. Have students discuss any discrepancies.
- ◉ Put students into groups of three. Assign each group member one of the three success criteria. Each student should explain his or her success criterion to the other two group members. Students should not interrupt while another student is speaking. At the end of the explanation, the other group members can ask questions for clarification. Select three students to present their explanations to the class.

ELL Support

Allow students to work in pairs for additional support and to practice language. Have two pairs form a group and come to an agreement on their explanations for Exercises 5 and 8. Then have groups present their explanations to the class. Check answers for Exercises 6 and 7 by asking the questions and having students indicate *yes* or *no* using a thumbs up or down signal.

The Success Criteria Self-Assessment chart can be found in the *Student Journal* or online at *BigIdeasMath.com*.

EXAMPLE 2 **Identifying a Right Triangle**

Tell whether the points $A(1, 1)$, $B(3, 5)$, and $C(3, 0)$ form a right triangle.

Plot the points in a coordinate plane. The distance between points B and C is 5 units. Use the Pythagorean Theorem to find the distance d_1 between points A and B and the distance d_2 between points A and C.

Distance between Points A and B	Distance between Points A and C
$d_1^2 = 4^2 + 2^2$	$d_2^2 = 1^2 + 2^2$
$d_1^2 = 20$	$d_2^2 = 5$
$d_1 = \sqrt{20}$	$d_2 = \sqrt{5}$

Use the converse of the Pythagorean Theorem to determine whether sides with lengths 5, $\sqrt{20}$, and $\sqrt{5}$ form a right triangle.

$$\left(\sqrt{20}\right)^2 + \left(\sqrt{5}\right)^2 \overset{?}{=} 5^2$$

$$20 + 5 \overset{?}{=} 25$$

$$25 = 25 \checkmark$$

▶ So, the points form a right triangle.

Try It **Tell whether the points form a right triangle.**

3. $D(-4, 0)$, $E(-2, 3)$, $F(1, 0)$ **4.** $J(4, 1)$, $K(1, -3)$, $L(-3, 0)$

Self-Assessment for Concepts & Skills

Solve each exercise. Then rate your understanding of the success criteria in your journal.

5. **WRITING** Explain the converse of the Pythagorean Theorem.

6. **IDENTIFYING A RIGHT TRIANGLE** Is a triangle with side lengths of 2 millimeters, 2.5 millimeters, and 3 millimeters a right triangle?

7. **IDENTIFYING A RIGHT TRIANGLE** Do the points $(-1, 1)$, $(-3, 5)$, and $(0, 8)$ form a right triangle?

8. **WHICH ONE DOESN'T BELONG?** Which set of numbers does *not* belong with the other three? Explain your reasoning.

| 3, 6, 8 | 6, 8, 10 | 5, 12, 13 | 7, 24, 25 |

EXAMPLE 3 **Modeling Real Life**

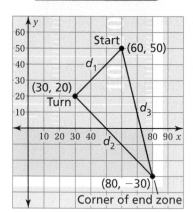

You design a football play in which a player runs down the field, makes a 90° turn, and runs to the corner of the end zone. Your friend ran the play as shown, where each grid line represents 10 feet. Did your friend run the play correctly?

Your friend ended in the corner of the end zone as planned. Determine whether your friend made a 90° turn.

The start, turn, and end locations form a triangle. Use the Pythagorean Theorem to find the side lengths of the triangle.

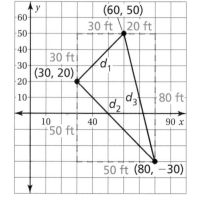

$$d_1 = \sqrt{30^2 + 30^2} = \sqrt{1800} \text{ feet}$$

$$d_2 = \sqrt{50^2 + 50^2} = \sqrt{5000} \text{ feet}$$

$$d_3 = \sqrt{20^2 + 80^2} = \sqrt{6800} \text{ feet}$$

Use the converse of the Pythagorean Theorem to determine whether the sides form a right triangle.

$$\left(\sqrt{1800}\right)^2 + \left(\sqrt{5000}\right)^2 \overset{?}{=} \left(\sqrt{6800}\right)^2$$

$$1800 + 5000 \overset{?}{=} 6800$$

$$6800 = 6800 \checkmark$$

The sides form a right triangle. So, your friend made a 90° turn.

▷ Your friend ran the play correctly.

 Self-Assessment for *Problem Solving*

Solve each exercise. Then rate your understanding of the success criteria in your journal.

16 in.

14 in.

7 in.

9. You practice archery as shown. Determine whether the arrow is perpendicular to the vertical support. Justify your answer.

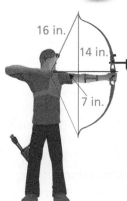

10. **DIG DEEPER!** Three fire hydrants in a neighborhood are represented on a map. The coordinates of the fire hydrants are $(0, 0)$, $(2, 5)$, and $(7, y)$. The fire hydrants are arranged in a right triangle, where y is a natural number less than 10. Find y.

Laurie's Notes

EXAMPLE 3

- Ask a student to read the problem. Then ask another student to explain what the problem is asking.
- **MP4 Model with Mathematics:** Sketch the coordinate plane shown with the ordered pairs identified.
- ❓ "How do you determine if the receiver ran the play as designed?" Check whether the triangle is a right triangle.
- ❓ "How do you determine if the triangle is a right triangle?" Use the converse of the Pythagorean Theorem.
- ❓ "How can you find the side lengths of the triangle?" Use the Pythagorean Theorem.
- ❓ "Is it helpful to approximate the square roots before using the converse of the Pythagorean Theorem? Explain." No, when you substitute the square roots into the Pythagorean Theorem, they will be squared.
- Use the converse of the Pythagorean Theorem to show that it is a right triangle.

> ### Teaching Strategy
>
> Review the problem-solving plan with students. Divide the class into four groups. Assign each group a part of the problem-solving Four Square. Ask them to make a list of items that should be completed in that square. Have groups write their lists on large pieces of paper and display them in the classroom. Some possible items for each square are provided below.
>
> **Understand the problem.** Read the problem, re-read the problem, explain the problem in your own words, and draw a picture or diagram.
>
> **Make a plan.** Use the given information to plan how you are going to solve the problem, decide what method(s) will be useful, and how you are going to implement those methods.
>
> **Solve.** Use your plan to solve the problem, write a verbal model, define a variable, translate the model into an equation or inequality, use properties to isolate the variable, and write a sentence to answer the question.
>
> **Check.** Use another method, check for reasonableness, test values of the variable to check the solution, and make sure that the answer includes any appropriate units of measure.
>
> Discuss each group's list and ideas as a class. As you discuss, add any new ideas to the lists.

✅ Self-Assessment for Problem Solving

- **Teaching Strategy:** Review the problem-solving Four Square.
- Encourage students to use a Four Square to complete the exercises. By now, most students should be able to get past the first square.
- In Exercise 9, make sure students understand that if the triangle is a right triangle, then the legs are perpendicular.

The Success Criteria Self-Assessment chart can be found in the *Student Journal* or online at *BigIdeasMath.com*.

Closure

- **Exit Ticket:** Do the points (2, 3), (−5, 4), and (−6, −3) for a right triangle? yes

---

Extra Example 3
In Example 3, your friend starts at (40, 40). Did your friend make a 90° turn? no

Self-Assessment
for Problem Solving

9. no; $7^2 + 14^2 = 245 \neq 16^2$

10. 3

Learning Target

Understand the converse of the Pythagorean Theorem.

Success Criteria

- Explain the converse of the Pythagorean Theorem.
- Identify right triangles given three side lengths.
- Identify right triangles in a coordinate plane.

Review & Refresh

1. a. 6

   b. 5.6

2. a. −3

   b. −2.6

3. a. 3

   b. 2.9

4. 4

5. 4.5

 ## Concepts, Skills, & Problem Solving

6. If a^2 is odd, then a is an odd number; statement: true; The product of two odd numbers is an odd number; converse: true; The square of a number is odd only when the number is odd.

7. If $ABCD$ is a parallelogram, then $ABCD$ is a square; statement: true; A square is a parallelogram; converse: false; Not all parallelograms have 4 right angles and 4 congruent sides.

8. yes

9. yes

10. no

11. no

12. yes

13. yes

14. yes; $15^2 + 20^2 = 25^2$

15. no; $(12.6)^2 + (12.6)^2 \neq (12.6)^2$

Assignment Guide and Concept Check

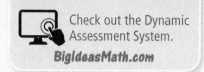
Scaffold assignments to support all students in their learning progression. The suggested assignments are a starting point. Continue to assign additional exercises and revisit with spaced practice to move every student toward proficiency.

Level	Assignment 1	Assignment 2
Emerging	2, 3, 5, 6, 7, 8, 10, 11, 13, 19, 20, 21	12, 14, 15, 17, 24, 26, 27, 28
Proficient	2, 3, 5, 6, 7, 9, 10, 12, 13, 19, 22, 24	15, 18, 25, 26, 27, 28
Advanced	2, 3, 5, 6, 7, 9, 10, 12, 13, 19, 24, 25	18, 26, 27, 28, 29

- Assignment 1 is for use after students complete the Self-Assessment for Concepts & Skills.
- Assignment 2 is for use after students complete the Self-Assessment for Problem Solving.
- The red exercises can be used as a concept check.

Review & Refresh Prior Skills

Exercises 1–3   Approximating an Irrational Number

Exercises 4 and 5   Using Similar Figures

Common Errors

- **Exercises 8–13** Students may substitute the wrong value for c in the Pythagorean Theorem. Remind them that c will be the longest side, so they should substitute the greatest value for c.

9.6 Practice

Go to *BigIdeasMath.com* to get HELP with solving the exercises.

▶ Review & Refresh

Approximate the number to the nearest (a) integer and (b) tenth.

1. $\sqrt{31}$ **2.** $-\sqrt{7}$ **3.** $\sqrt[3]{25}$

The figures are similar. Find *x*.

4. The ratio of the perimeters is 2 : 5.

5. The ratio of the perimeters is 4 : 3.

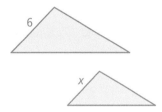

▶▶ Concepts, Skills, & Problem Solving

ANALYZING THE CONVERSE OF A STATEMENT **Write the converse of the statement. Then determine whether the statement and its converse are *true* or *false*. Explain.** (See Exploration 1, p. 409.)

6. If a is an odd number, then a^2 is odd.

7. If $ABCD$ is a square, then $ABCD$ is a parallelogram.

IDENTIFYING A RIGHT TRIANGLE **Tell whether the triangle with the given side lengths is a right triangle.**

8.
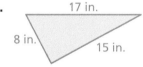
17 in.
8 in.
15 in.

9.

45 m
36 m
27 m

10.
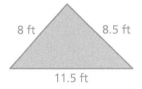
8 ft
8.5 ft
11.5 ft

11. 14 mm, 19 mm, 23 mm   **12.** $\frac{9}{10}$ mi, $1\frac{1}{5}$ mi, $1\frac{1}{2}$ mi   **13.** 1.4 m, 4.8 m, 5 m

14. **MP MODELING REAL LIFE** A post-and-beam frame for a shed is shown in the diagram. Does the brace form a right triangle with the post and beam? Explain.

15. **MP MODELING REAL LIFE** A traffic sign has side lengths of 12.6 inches, 12.6 inches, and 12.6 inches. Is the sign a right triangle? Explain.

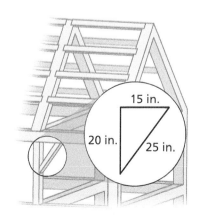
15 in.
20 in.
25 in.

IDENTIFYING A RIGHT TRIANGLE Tell whether a triangle with the given side lengths is a right triangle.

16. $\sqrt{63}, 9, 12$

17. $4, \sqrt{15}, 6$

18. $\sqrt{18}, \sqrt{24}, \sqrt{42}$

19. **MP YOU BE THE TEACHER** Your friend determines whether a triangle with side lengths of $3, \sqrt{58}$, and 7 is a right triangle. Is your friend correct? Explain your reasoning.

$$a^2 + b^2 = c^2$$
$$3^2 + (\sqrt{58})^2 \stackrel{?}{=} 7^2$$
$$9 + 58 \neq 49$$

The triangle is not a right triangle.

IDENTIFYING A RIGHT TRIANGLE Tell whether the points form a right triangle.

20. $(0, 0), (0, 5), (2, 0)$

21. $(0, 8), (2, 2), (11, 6)$

22. $(-1, 0), (5, 0), (2, -3)$

23. $(-1, -2), (2, 6), (4, -1)$

24. $(-8, 6), (7, 9), (0, -13)$

25. $(0.5, 1.5), (7.5, 5.5), (9.5, 0.5)$

26. **MP LOGIC** The equation $a^2 + b^2 = c^2$ is *not* true for a particular triangle with side lengths of a, b, and c. What can you conclude about the type of triangle?

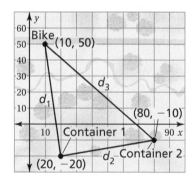

27. **MP MODELING REAL LIFE** You spend the day looking for hidden containers in a wooded area using a Global Positioning System (GPS). You park your bike on the side of the road, and then locate Container 1 and Container 2 before going back to your bike. Does your path form a right triangle? Explain. Each grid line represents 10 yards.

28. **DIG DEEPER!** The locations of a fishing boat, buoy, and kayak are represented by the points $(0, 0), (16, 12)$, and $(10, -5)$. Each unit represents 1 nautical mile.

a. Do the boat, kayak, and buoy form a right triangle?

b. The boat travels at 8 nautical miles per hour. How long does the boat take to reach the buoy if the boat travels directly toward it?

29. **MP STRUCTURE** The vertices of a quadrilateral are $(1, 2), (5, 4), (6, 2)$, and $(2, 0)$. Use the converse of the Pythagorean Theorem to determine whether the quadrilateral is a rectangle.

Common Errors

- **Exercises 16–18** Students may substitute the wrong value for c in the Pythagorean Theorem. Remind them that c will be the longest side, so they should substitute the greatest value for c.

Mini-Assessment

Tell whether the triangle with the given side lengths is a right triangle.

1. 32 m, 56 m, 64 m no

2. 1.8 mi, 8 mi, 8.2 mi yes

Tell whether the points form a right triangle.

3. $(-1, 3), (4, 3), (3, 1)$ yes

4. $(-2, 4), (0, -1), (2, 0)$ no

Concepts, Skills, & Problem Solving

16. yes

17. no

18. yes

19. no; The length of the longest side, $\sqrt{58}$, should be substituted for c, and the lengths of the two shorter sides, 3 and 7, should be substituted for a and b.

20. yes

21. no

22. yes

23. no

24. no

25. no

26. The triangle is not a right triangle.

27. no; The side lengths are $\sqrt{5000}$, $\sqrt{3700}$, and $\sqrt{8500}$, and $(\sqrt{5000})^2 + (\sqrt{3700})^2 \neq (\sqrt{8500})^2$.

28. **a.** no

   b. 2.5 h

29. yes

Section Resources

Surface Level	Deep Level

Resources by Chapter
  • Extra Practice
  • Reteach
  • Puzzle Time
Student Journal
  • Self-Assessment
  • Practice
Differentiating the Lesson
Tutorial Videos
Skills Review Handbook
Skills Trainer
	Resources by Chapter
	  • Enrichment and Extension
	Graphic Organizers
	Dynamic Assessment System
	  • Section Practice

Transfer Level	

Dynamic Assessment System
  • End-of-Chapter Quiz
	Assessment Book
	  • End-of-Chapter Quiz

Exercise 1

- Finding an Actual Distance
- Finding a Missing Length in a Right Triangle

Exercise 2

- Describing a Cross Section of a Prism
- Finding a Missing Length in a Right Triangle
- Finding the Surface Area of a Prism

Exercise 3

- Finding a Missing Length in a Right Triangle
- Identifying a Function
- Interpreting Diagrams

ELL Support

Students from Japan, Taiwan, or the Caribbean may be familiar with baseball, but many others may not. You may want to explain the basics of how baseball is played, so students understand what measurement they are finding.

Using the Problem-Solving Plan

1. 1539 in.

2. See Additional Answers.

3. 1; 4; 7; 10; yes; The rate of change is constant.

Performance Task

The *STEAM Video Performance Task* provides the opportunity for additional enrichment and greater depth of knowledge as students explore the mathematics of the chapter within a context tied to the chapter STEAM Video. The performance task and a detailed scoring rubric are provided at *BigIdeasMath.com*.

Laurie's Notes

Scaffolding Instruction

- The goal of this lesson is to help students become more comfortable with problem solving. These exercises combine students' work with real numbers and the Pythagorean Theorem with prior skills from other chapters and courses. The solution for Exercise 1 is worked out below, to help you guide students through the problem-solving plan. Use the remaining class time to have students work on the other exercises.
- **Emerging:** The goal for these students is to feel comfortable with the problem-solving plan. Allow students to work in pairs to write the beginning steps of the problem-solving plan for Exercise 2. Keep in mind that some students may only be ready to do the first step.
- **Proficient:** Students may be able to work independently or in pairs to complete Exercises 2 and 3.
- Visit each pair to review their plan for each problem. Ask students to describe their plans.

▶ *Using the Problem-Solving Plan*

Exercise 1

⇨ **Understand the problem.** You know several measurements and the scale factor in a scale drawing of a baseball field. You are asked to approximate the distance from home plate to second base on the actual baseball field.

⇨ **Make a plan.** The distance from home plate to second base is the hypotenuse of a right triangle. Find the distance in the scale drawing. Then use the scale factor to approximate the distance on the actual field.

⇨ **Solve and check.** Use the plan to solve the problem. Then check your solution.

- Find the distance of the hypotenuse in the scale drawing.

$$a^2 + b^2 = c^2 \qquad \text{Write the Pythagorean Theorem.}$$
$$4^2 + 4^2 = c^2 \qquad \text{Substitute 4 for } a \text{ and 4 for } b.$$
$$16 + 16 = c^2 \qquad \text{Evaluate the powers.}$$
$$32 = c^2 \qquad \text{Add.}$$
$$\sqrt{32} = c \qquad \text{Take the positive square root of each side.}$$

To approximate c, notice that 32 is between the perfect squares 25 and 36. Because 32 is close to 36, $\sqrt{32}$ is close to 6. Because 32 is closer to $5.7^2 = 32.49$ than to $5.6^2 = 31.36$, $\sqrt{32}$ is closer to 5.7 than to 5.6.

So, the distance of the hypotenuse in the scale drawing is about 5.7 inches.

- Use the scale factor to find the distance on the actual field.

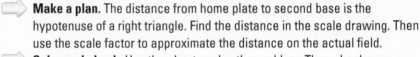

$$\frac{1}{270} = \frac{\text{Scale drawing distance}}{\text{Actual distance}}$$

$$\frac{1}{270} = \frac{5.7}{x}$$

$$x = 1539$$

So, the distance from home plate to second base on the actual baseball field is about 1539 inches.

- **Check:** Verify that the value of the ratio of the distances (in inches) is equal to the scale factor.

$$\frac{\text{Scale drawing distance}}{\text{Actual distance}} = \frac{5.7}{1539} = \frac{1}{270} \checkmark$$

Connecting Concepts

▶ *Using the Problem-Solving Plan*

1. The scale drawing of a baseball field has a scale factor of $\dfrac{1}{270}$. Approximate the distance from home plate to second base on the actual baseball field to the nearest tenth.

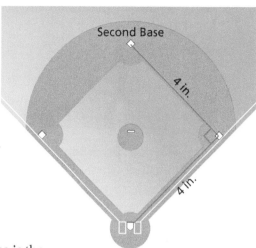

Second Base

4 in.

4 in.

Home Plate

Understand the problem.
You know several measurements and the scale factor in a scale drawing of a baseball field. You are asked to approximate the distance from home plate to second base on the actual baseball field.

Make a plan.
The distance from home plate to second base is the hypotenuse of a right triangle. Approximate the distance in the scale drawing to the nearest tenth. Then use the scale factor to approximate the distance on the actual field.

Solve and check.
Use the plan to solve the problem. Then check your solution.

8 cm

2. You cut the wood cube shown into two identical triangular prisms. Approximate the surface area of each triangular prism to the nearest tenth. Justify your answer.

3. Complete the mapping diagram representing the relationship between the lengths of the hypotenuse and the legs of an isosceles right triangle. Is the relationship linear? Explain.

Hypotenuse   Legs

$\sqrt{2}$

$\sqrt{32}$

$\sqrt{98}$

$\sqrt{200}$

Performance Task

Identify and Correct the Error!

At the beginning of this chapter, you watched a STEAM Video called "Metronome Design." You are now ready to complete the performance task related to this video, available at *BigIdeasMath.com*. Be sure to use the problem-solving plan as you work through the performance task.

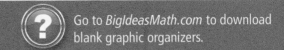
▶ Review Vocabulary

Write the definition and give an example of each vocabulary term.

square root, *p. 374*   theorem, *p. 381*   cube root, *p. 390*

perfect square, *p. 374*   legs, *p. 382*   perfect cube, *p. 390*

radical sign, *p. 374*   hypotenuse, *p. 382*   irrational number, *p. 402*

radicand, *p. 374*   Pythagorean Theorem, *p. 382*   real numbers, *p. 402*

▶ Graphic Organizers

You can use a **Four Square** to organize information about a concept. Each of the four squares can be a category, such as definition, vocabulary, example, non-example, words, algebra, table, numbers, visual, graph, or equation. Here is an example of a Four Square for *Pythagorean Theorem*.

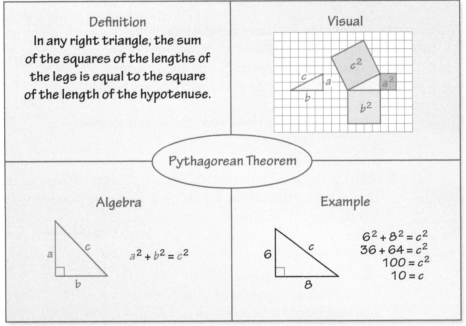

Choose and complete a graphic organizer to help you study the concept.

1. square roots

2. cube roots

3. rational numbers

4. irrational numbers

5. real numbers

6. converse of the Pythagorean Theorem

"I'm taking a survey for my Four Square. How many fleas do you have?"

Review Vocabulary

- As a review of the chapter vocabulary, have students revisit the vocabulary section in their *Student Journals* to fill in any missing definitions and record examples of each term.

Graphic Organizers

Sample answers:

1.

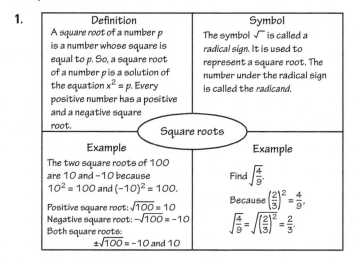

2.

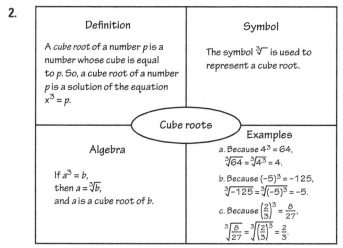

3–6. Answer at *BigIdeasMath.com*.

List of Organizers

Available at *BigIdeasMath.com*
Definition and Example Chart
Example and Non-Example Chart
Four Square
Information Frame
Summary Triangle

About this Organizer

A **Four Square** can be used to organize information about a concept. Students write the concept in the oval. Then students use each of the four squares surrounding the oval to represent a related category. Related categories may include: definition, vocabulary, example, non-example, words, algebra, table, numbers, visual, graph, or equation. Encourage students to use categories that will help them study the concept. Students can place their Four Squares on note cards to use as a quick study reference.

1. 1

2. $-\dfrac{3}{5}$

3. -1.3 and 1.3

4. -9

5. $3\dfrac{2}{3}$

6. -3

7. 2 in.

8. 37 in.

9. 0.4 cm

10. yes; You can reach 16 feet above the ground.

11. 20 units

✅ Chapter Self-Assessment

The Success Criteria Self-Assessment chart can be found in the *Student Journal* or online at *BigIdeasMath.com*.

ELL Support

Allow students to work in pairs to complete the first section of the Chapter Self-Assessment. Have pairs display their answers on whiteboards for your review. Use similar techniques to check the remaining sections of the Chapter Self-Assessment. For discussion questions, have two pairs compare ideas and reach an agreement. Monitor discussions and provide support. Review explanations as a class. For answers to *yes* or *no* questions, have students use a thumbs up for *yes* or a thumbs down for *no*.

Common Errors

- **Exercises 1–3** Students may divide the number by two instead of finding a number that, when multiplied by itself, gives the radicand. Remind them that taking the square root of a number is the inverse of squaring a number.

- **Exercises 4–6** Students may not follow the order of operations when evaluating the expression. Remind them of the order of operations. Because taking a square root is the inverse of squaring, it is evaluated before multiplication and division.

- **Exercises 8 and 9** Students may substitute the given lengths in the wrong part of the formula. For example, in Exercise 8, they may write $12^2 + c^2 = 35^2$ instead of $12^2 + 35^2 = c^2$. Remind students that the side opposite the right angle is the hypotenuse c.

- **Exercises 8 and 9** Students may multiply each side length by two instead of squaring the side length. Remind them of the definition of exponents.

▷ *Chapter Self-Assessment*

As you complete the exercises, use the scale below to rate your understanding of the success criteria in your journal.

1	**2**	**3**	**4**
I do not understand.	I can do it with help.	I can do it on my own.	I can teach someone else.

9.1 Finding Square Roots *(pp. 373–380)*

Learning Target: Understand the concept of a square root of a number.

Find the square root(s).

1. $\sqrt{1}$

2. $-\sqrt{\dfrac{9}{25}}$

3. $\pm\sqrt{1.69}$

Evaluate the expression.

4. $15 - 4\sqrt{36}$

5. $\sqrt{\dfrac{54}{6}} + \dfrac{2}{3}$

6. $\left(\sqrt{9}\right)^2 - 12$

7. The total area of a checkerboard is 256 square inches. What is the side length (in inches) of one of the small squares?

9.2 The Pythagorean Theorem *(pp. 381–388)*

Learning Target: Understand the Pythagorean Theorem.

Find the missing length of the triangle.

8.

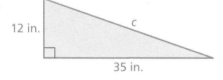

9.

10. You lean a 13-foot ladder on a house so the bottom of the ladder is 5 feet from the house. From the top of the ladder, you can safely reach another 4 feet higher. Can you reach a window that is located 13 feet above the ground? Explain.

11. Find the distance between $(-6, 8)$ and $(10, -4)$.

9.3 Finding Cube Roots (pp. 389–394)

Learning Target: Understand the concept of a cube root of a number.

Find the cube root.

12. $\sqrt[3]{-2197}$

13. $\sqrt[3]{\dfrac{64}{343}}$

14. $\sqrt[3]{-\dfrac{8}{27}}$

15. Evaluate the expression $25 + 2\sqrt[3]{-64}$.

16. Solve the equation $-55 = \dfrac{1}{4}x^3 + 73$.

17. You are shipping a puzzle cube to your friend using the cube-shaped box shown. What is the difference between the height of the puzzle cube and the top of the box when you place the cube in the box?

$V = 216 \text{ cm}^3$

5.7 cm

9.4 Rational Numbers (pp. 395–400)

Learning Target: Convert between different forms of rational numbers.

Write the fraction or mixed number as a decimal.

18. $-2\dfrac{5}{6}$

19. $\dfrac{27}{80}$

20. $3\dfrac{8}{9}$

21. Write $1.\overline{36}$ as a mixed number.

22. The gas mileage of a hybrid car is $3.0\overline{3}$ times the gas mileage of a regular car. The regular car averages 24 miles per gallon. Find the gas mileage of the hybrid car.

23. Your friend's cat weighs $0.8\overline{3}$ times the weight of your cat. Your friend's cat weighs 10 pounds. How much more does your cat weigh than your friend's cat?

24. An apple dessert recipe makes $2.\overline{3}$ pounds of dessert and serves 6 people. What is the serving size (in pounds)?

Common Errors

- **Exercises 12 and 14** Students may disregard the negative in the radicand. Remind them to pay attention to the sign of the radicand and to check the sign of their answers.
- **Exercise 15** Students may not follow the order of operations when evaluating the expression. Remind them of the order of operations. Because taking a cube root is the inverse of cubing, it is evaluated before multiplication and division.
- **Exercises 18–20** When using long division, students may divide the denominator by the numerator. Remind them to always divide the numerator by the denominator, regardless of the size of the numbers.
- **Exercise 21** Students may ignore the repeating bar and write the decimal as a fraction or mixed number with a denominator that is a power of 10. For example, they may write $1.\overline{36} = 1\frac{36}{100} = 1\frac{9}{25}$ instead of $1.\overline{36} = 1\frac{4}{11}$. Remind students that a repeating decimal cannot be written as a fraction with a denominator that is a power of 10.

12. -13

13. $\dfrac{4}{7}$

14. $-\dfrac{2}{3}$

15. 17

16. $x = -8$

17. 0.3 cm

18. $-2.8\overline{3}$

19. 0.3375

20. $3.\overline{8}$

21. $1\dfrac{4}{11}$

22. 72.8 mi/gal

23. 2 lb

24. $\dfrac{7}{18}$ lb

25. rational

26. irrational

27. natural, whole, integer, rational

28. **a.** 4

   b. 3.7

29. **a.** 9

   b. 9.5

30. **a.** 13

   b. 13.2

31. $\sqrt{48}$; $\sqrt{48}$ is to the right of $\sqrt[3]{127}$ on a number line.

32. 11.2 units

33. 25 m/sec

34. yes

35. no

36. yes

37. no; Cut 0.2 meter off.

Common Errors

- **Exercises 25–27** Students may not classify the real number in as many ways as possible. Remind students that real numbers can have more than one classification.

- **Exercise 27** Students may think that all square roots and cube roots are irrational. Remind them that square roots of perfect squares are rational and that cube roots of perfect cubes are also rational.

- **Exercises 28–30** Students may struggle with knowing what integer is closest to the given number. To help make comparisons, encourage them to write the first 10 perfect squares. If the radicand is greater than 100, then students should *Guess, Check, and Revise* to find two integers on either side of the number. When determining which integer is closer to the rational number, encourage students to use a number line.

- **Exercise 31** Students may guess which is greater just by looking at the numbers. Encourage them to use a number line to compare the numbers. Also remind students to simplify and/or estimate the numbers so that they are easier to compare.

- **Exercises 34 and 35** Students may substitute the wrong value for c in the Pythagorean Theorem. Remind them that c will be the longest side, so they should substitute the greatest value for c.

Chapter Resources

Surface Level	Deep Level
Resources by Chapter • Extra Practice • Reteach • Puzzle Time Student Journal • Practice • Chapter Self-Assessment Differentiating the Lesson Tutorial Videos Skills Review Handbook Skills Trainer Game Library	Resources by Chapter • Enrichment and Extension Graphic Organizers Game Library
Transfer Level	
STEAM Video Dynamic Assessment System • Chapter Test	Assessment Book • Chapter Tests A and B • Alternative Assessment • STEAM Performance Task

9.5 Irrational Numbers *(pp. 401–408)*

Learning Target: Understand the concept of irrational numbers.

Classify the real number.

25. $0.81\overline{5}$

26. $\sqrt{101}$

27. $\sqrt{4}$

Approximate the number to the nearest (a) integer and (b) tenth.

28. $\sqrt{14}$

29. $\sqrt{90}$

30. $\sqrt{175}$

31. Which is greater, $\sqrt{48}$ or $\sqrt[3]{127}$? Explain.

32. Approximate the distance between $(-2, -5)$ and $(3, 5)$ to the nearest tenth.

33. The equation $d = \dfrac{v^2}{15.68}$ represents the relationship between the distance d (in meters) needed to stop a vehicle and the velocity v (in meters per second) of the vehicle. Approximate the velocity of the vehicle when it takes 40 meters to stop.

9.6 The Converse of the Pythagorean Theorem *(pp. 409–414)*

Learning Target: Understand the converse of the Pythagorean Theorem.

Tell whether the triangle with the given side lengths is a right triangle.

34.

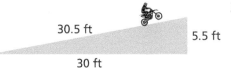

30.5 ft   5.5 ft

30 ft

35.

Kerrtown

98 mi

Snellville

104 mi

40 mi

Nicholton

36. Tell whether the points $A(1, -1)$, $B(3, -4)$, and $C(4, 1)$ form a right triangle.

37. You want to make a wooden border around a flower bed in the shape of a right triangle. You have three pieces of wood that measure 3.5 meters, 1.2 meters, and 3.9 meters. Do these pieces of wood form a right triangle? If not, explain how you can cut the longest piece of wood to make a right triangle.

1. Find $-\sqrt{1600}$.

2. Find $\sqrt[3]{-\dfrac{729}{64}}$.

Evaluate the expression.

3. $12 + 8\sqrt{16}$

4. $\left(\sqrt[3]{-125}\right)^3 + 75$

5. Find the missing length of the triangle.

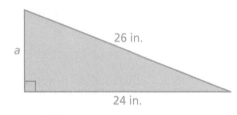

Classify the real number.

6. 16π

7. $-\sqrt{49}$

8. Approximate $\sqrt{83}$ to the nearest (a) integer and (b) tenth.

9. Write $1.\overline{24}$ as a mixed number.

10. Tell whether the triangle is a right triangle.

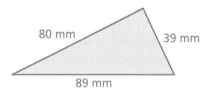

Approximate the distance between the points to the nearest tenth, if necessary.

11. $(-2, 3), (6, 9)$

12. $(0, -5), (4, 1)$

13. How high is the hand of the superhero balloon above the ground?

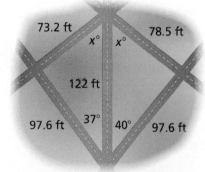

14. The area of a circular pool cover is 314 square feet. Write and solve an equation to find the diameter of the pool cover. Use 3.14 for π.

15. Five roads form two triangles. What is the value of x? Justify your answer.

Practice Test Item References

Practice Test Questions	Section to Review
1, 3, 14	9.1
5, 11, 13	9.2
2, 4	9.3
9	9.4
6, 7, 8, 12	9.5
10, 15	9.6

Test-Taking Strategies

Remind students to quickly look over the entire test before they start so that they can budget their time. Students should estimate and check their answers for reasonableness as they work through the test. Have them use the **Stop** and **Think** strategy before they write their answers.

Common Errors

- **Exercise 5** Students may substitute the given lengths in the wrong part of the formula. For example, they may write $24^2 + 26^2 = a^2$ instead of $a^2 + 24^2 = 26^2$. Remind students that the side opposite the right angle is the hypotenuse c.
- **Exercises 6 and 7** Students may not classify the real number in as many ways as possible. Remind students that real numbers can have more than one classification.
- **Exercise 8** Students may struggle with knowing what integer is closest to the given number. To help make comparisons, encourage them to write the first 10 perfect squares. If the radicand is greater than 100, then students should *Guess, Check, and Revise* to find two integers on either side of the number. When determining which integer is closer to the rational number, encourage students to use a number line.
- **Exercise 10** Students may substitute the wrong value for c in the Pythagorean Theorem. Remind them that c will be the longest side, so they should substitute the greatest value for c.

1. -40
2. $-2\frac{1}{4}$
3. 44
4. -50
5. 10 in.
6. irrational
7. integer, rational
8. **a.** 9
   b. 9.1
9. $1\frac{8}{33}$
10. yes
11. 10 units
12. 7.2 units
13. 66 ft
14. $3.14r^2 = 314$; about 20 ft
15. 53; $73.2^2 + 97.6^2 = 122^2$, so the triangle on the left is a right triangle. $x + 90 + 37 = 180$, so $x = 53$.

Test-Taking Strategies

Available at *BigIdeasMath.com*

After Answering Easy Questions, Relax

Answer Easy Questions First

Estimate the Answer

Read All Choices before Answering

Read Question before Answering

Solve Directly or Eliminate Choices

Solve Problem before Looking at Choices

Use Intelligent Guessing

Work Backwards

About this Strategy

When taking a timed test, it is often best to skim the test and answer the easy questions first. Read each question carefully and thoroughly. Be careful that you record your answer in the correct position on the answer sheet.

Cumulative Practice

1. A

2. I

3. A

4. G

Item Analysis

1. **A.** Correct answer

   B. The student adds 1.1 and 2.

   C. The student multiplies 1.1 and 4.

   D. The student adds 1.1 and 4.

2. **F.** The student evaluates the function for $x = 3$ instead of $x = -3$.

   G. The student evaluates the function for $y = 3$ instead of $x = -3$.

   H. The student evaluates the function for $y = -3$ instead of $x = -3$.

   I. Correct answer

3. **A.** Correct answer

   B. The student incorrectly thinks that the coefficients of x and y are the x- and y-intercepts.

   C. The student switches the x- and y-intercepts.

   D. When finding the x-intercept, the student gets the equation $3x = 12$ and then subtracts 3 from 12 instead of dividing 12 by 3. When finding the y-intercept, the student gets the equation $2y = 12$ and then subtracts 2 from 12 instead of dividing 12 by 2.

4. **F.** The student divides the exponents instead of subtracting the exponents.

   G. Correct answer

   H. The student subtracts the bases instead of keeping the same base.

   I. The student divides the bases and the exponents instead of keeping the same base and subtracting the exponents.

Cumulative Practice

1. The period T of a pendulum is the time (in seconds) it takes the pendulum to swing back and forth once. The period can be found using the formula $T = 1.1\sqrt{L}$, where L is the length (in feet) of the pendulum. A pendulum has a length of 4 feet. What is the period of the pendulum?

   A. 2.2 sec   **B.** 3.1 sec

   C. 4.4 sec   **D.** 5.1 sec

2. What is the value of $y = 5 - 2x$ when $x = -3$?

   F. -1 **G.** 1

   H. 4   **I.** 11

3. Which graph represents the linear equation $3x + 2y = 12$?

   A. 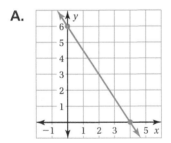   **B.**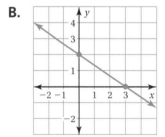

   C. 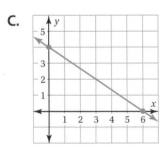   **D.**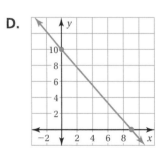

4. Which expression is equivalent to $\dfrac{(-3)^{12}}{(-3)^{3}}$?

   F. $(-3)^4$ **G.** $(-3)^9$

   H. 0^9 **I.** 1^9

5. A football field is 40 yards wide and 120 yards long. Approximate the distance between opposite corners of the football field to the nearest tenth. Show your work and explain your reasoning.

6. A computer consultant charges $50 plus $40 for each hour she works. The consultant charged $650 for one job. This can be represented by the equation below, where h represents the number of hours worked.

$$40h + 50 = 650$$

How many hours did the consultant work?

7. Which triangle is *not* a right triangle?

A.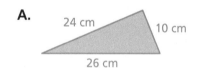
24 cm   10 cm
26 cm

B.
53 m
28 m   45 m

C.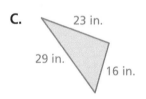
23 in.
29 in.
16 in.

D.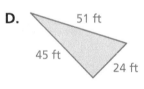
51 ft
45 ft
24 ft

8. What is the distance between $(-3, -1)$ and $(-1, -5)$?

F. $\sqrt{12}$ **G.** $\sqrt{20}$

H. $\sqrt{40}$ **I.** $\sqrt{52}$

9. An airplane flies from City 1 at $(0, 0)$ to City 2 at $(33, 56)$ and then to City 3 at $(23, 32)$. What is the total number of miles it flies? Each unit represents 1 mile.

10. The national debt of Country A is $398,038,013,519. The national debt of Country B is $2,137,348,918. Approximately how many times greater is the debt of Country A than the debt of Country B?

A. 2 times greater   **B.** 20 times greater

C. 133 times greater   **D.** 200 times greater

Item Analysis (continued)

5. **2 points** The student's work and explanations demonstrate a thorough understanding of how to apply the Pythagorean Theorem to the problem. The student calculates the distance accurately. The distance between opposite corners is $\sqrt{16{,}000} \approx 126.5$ yards.

   1 point The student's work and explanations demonstrate a partial but limited understanding of how to apply the Pythagorean Theorem to the problem. The student provides some correct work and/or explanation. The Pythagorean Theorem is misstated or, if stated correctly, is applied incorrectly to the problem.

   0 points The student provides no response, a completely incorrect or incomprehensible response, or a response that demonstrates insufficient understanding of how to apply the Pythagorean Theorem to the problem.

6. **Gridded Response:** Correct answer: 15

   Common error: The student adds 50 to the right side of the equation instead of subtracting and gets an answer of 17.5.

7. **A.** The student makes a computation error.

   B. The student makes a computation error.

   C. Correct answer

   D. The student makes a computation error.

8. **F.** The student sets up the equation incorrectly, writing $4^2 - 2^2 = c^2$ instead of $4^2 + 2^2 = c^2$.

   G. Correct answer

   H. The student incorrectly thinks that the distance between the y-coordinates is 6 instead of 4.

   I. The student finds the distance between $(-3, -1)$ and $(1, 5)$ instead of the distance between $(-3, -1)$ and $(-1, -5)$.

9. **Gridded Response:** Correct answer: 91

   Common error: The student only finds the distance between City 1 and City 2, getting an answer of 65.

10. **A.** The student incorrectly approximates the debt of Country B as 2×10^{11} dollars.

   B. The student incorrectly approximates the debt of Country B as 2×10^{10} dollars.

   C. The student incorrectly approximates the debt of Country B as 3×10^9 dollars.

   D. Correct answer

5. 126.5 yd

6. 15

7. C

8. G

9. 91

10. D

11. H

12. D

13. F

Item Analysis (continued)

11. **F.** The student switches the *x*- and *y*-coordinates of the solution.

   G. The student selects the point where one of the lines crosses the *x*-axis.

   H. Correct answer

   I. The student selects the point where one of the lines crosses the *x*-axis.

12. **A.** The student incorrectly thinks supplementary angles are congruent.

   B. The student incorrectly thinks the angles are alternate interior (or alternate exterior) angles.

   C. The student incorrectly thinks the angles are corresponding angles.

   D. Correct answer

13. **F.** Correct answer

   G. The student chooses the graph of a line with a slope of 2 instead of −2.

   H. The student chooses the graph of a line with a *y*-intercept of 2 instead of −2.

   I. The student chooses the graph of a line with a *y*-intercept of 2 instead of −2 and a slope of 2 instead of −2.

11. What is the solution of the system?

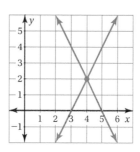

  F. $(2, 4)$

  G. $(3, 0)$

  H. $(4, 2)$

  I. $(5, 0)$

12. In the diagram, lines ℓ and m are parallel. Which angle has the same measure as $\angle 1$?

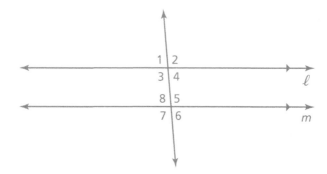

  A. $\angle 2$ **B.** $\angle 5$

  C. $\angle 7$ **D.** $\angle 8$

13. Which graph represents the linear equation $y = -2x - 2$?

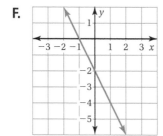

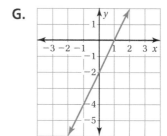

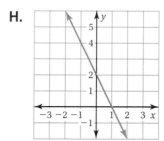

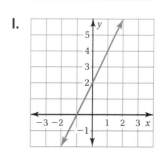

10 Volume and Similar Solids

10.1 Volumes of Cylinders

10.2 Volumes of Cones

10.3 Volumes of Spheres

10.4 Surface Areas and Volumes of Similar Solids

Chapter Learning Target:
Understand volume.

Chapter Success Criteria:
- ◻ I can explain how to find the volumes of cylinders, cones, and spheres.
- ◻ I can use formulas to find volumes of solids.
- ◼ I can find missing dimensions of solids.
- ◼ I can find surface areas and volumes of similar solids.

STEAM Video: "Canning Salsa"

Laurie's Notes

Chapter 10 Overview

This is the last chapter of the book and certainly one of my favorites! The geometric solids explored are shapes that students see in the world around them. I have a collection of solids that I have saved over the years, from package containers and party hats to mailing tubes and rubber balls. Nothing takes the place of students being able to hold and examine the solid. Looking at a two-dimensional picture of a three-dimensional object is just not the same.

Students have prior experiences with finding volume and should be familiar with this type of measurement for prisms and pyramids. Volume measurement is now extended to include cylinders, cones, and spheres.

To develop each new volume formula, students explore a connection to a formula they already know. They reason about the volume of a cylinder by relating it to the volume of a prism. Then they build the volume formulas for a cone and a sphere from the volume formula for a cylinder. Connecting the similarity of structure of the solids helps students understand how the formulas are related. These formulas are used to find volumes of common objects and solve for missing dimensions. Students will need to recall volume formulas for prisms and pyramids when finding volumes of composite figures.

The chapter concludes with a lesson on similar solids. Students will use relationships between similar solids to find surface areas and volumes of similar solids. Their previous work with scale models and areas of similar figures helps prepare them for this lesson. The big idea is that when the dimensions of a solid are all multiplied by a scale factor of k, the surface area is multiplied by a scale factor of k^2, and the volume is multiplied by a scale factor of k^3. For example:

Can A

4 cm

7 cm

Can A
Radius = 4 cm   Height = 7 cm
Surface area = $2\pi(4)^2 + 2\pi(4)(7) = 88\pi$ cm^2
Volume = $\pi(4)^2(7) = 112\pi$ cm^3

Can B

8 cm

14 cm

Can B
Radius = 8 cm   Height = 14 cm
Surface area = $2\pi(8)^2 + 2\pi(8)(14) = 352\pi$ cm^2
Volume = $\pi(8)^2(14) = 896\pi$ cm^3

$$k = \frac{\text{Radius of B}}{\text{Radius of A}} = \frac{8}{4} = 2 \text{ or } k = \frac{\text{Height of B}}{\text{Height of A}} = \frac{14}{7} = 2$$

$$k^2 = \frac{\text{Surface area of B}}{\text{Surface area of A}} = \frac{352\pi}{88\pi} = 4 = 2^2$$

$$k^3 = \frac{\text{Volume of B}}{\text{Volume of A}} = \frac{896\pi}{112\pi} = 8 = 2^3$$

If you have not started collecting three-dimensional models, begin now. Next year you will be glad you did!

Suggested Pacing

Chapter Opener	1 Day
Section 1	2 Days
Section 2	2 Days
Section 3	2 Days
Section 4	2 Days
Connecting Concepts	1 Day
Chapter Review	1 Day
Chapter Test	1 Day
Total Chapter 10	12 Days
Year-to-Date	146 Days

Chapter Learning Target
Understand volume.

Chapter Success Criteria
- Explain how to find the volumes of cylinders, cones, and spheres.
- Use formulas to find volumes of solids.
- Find missing dimensions of solids.
- Find surface areas and volumes of similar solids.

Chapter 10 Learning Targets and Success Criteria

Section	Learning Target	Success Criteria
10.1 Volumes of Cylinders	Find the volume of a cylinder.	• Use a formula to find the volume of a cylinder. • Use the formula for the volume of a cylinder to find a missing dimension.
10.2 Volumes of Cones	Find the volume of a cone.	• Use a formula to find the volume of a cone. • Use the formula for the volume of a cone to find a missing dimension.
10.3 Volumes of Spheres	Find the volume of a sphere.	• Use a formula to find the volume of a sphere. • Use the formula for the volume of a sphere to find the radius. • Find volumes of composite solids.
10.4 Surface Areas and Volumes of Similar Solids	Find the surface areas and volumes of similar solids.	• Use corresponding dimensions to determine whether solids are similar. • Use corresponding dimensions to find missing measures in similar solids. • Use linear measures to find surface areas and volumes of similar solids.

Progressions

Through the Grades		
Grade 7	**Grade 8**	**High School**
• Decide whether two quantities are proportional. • Represent proportional relationships with equations. • Use scale drawings to compute actual lengths and areas. • Solve problems involving the area and circumference of a circle. • Solve real-world and mathematical problems involving surface areas and volumes of objects composed of prisms, pyramids, and cylinders.	• Know and apply the formulas for the volumes of cones, cylinders, and spheres.	• Find and use volumes of prisms, cylinders, pyramids, cones, and spheres.

Through the Chapter				
Standard	**10.1**	**10.2**	**10.3**	**10.4**
8.G.C.9 Know the formulas for the volumes of cones, cylinders, and spheres and use them to solve real-world and mathematical problems.	●	●	★	■

Key

▲ = preparing ★ = complete
● = learning ■ = extending

Laurie's Notes

STEAM Video

1. 27 cm^3

2. **a.** yes; The values of the ratios y to x are all 3.

    b. 5 in.^{3}

Performance Task

Sample answer: It allows a company to determine the number of boxes it will need to package a certain quantity of jars.

Mathematical Practices

Students have opportunities to develop aspects of the mathematical practices throughout the chapter. Here are some examples.

1. **Make Sense of Problems and Persevere in Solving Them**
   10.3 Exercise 25, *p. 444*
2. **Reason Abstractly and Quantitatively**
   10.1 Exercise 17, *p. 431*
3. **Construct Viable Arguments and Critique the Reasoning of Others**
   10.3 Exercise 28, *p. 444*
4. **Model with Mathematics**
   10.2 Exercise 23, *p. 438*
5. **Use Appropriate Tools Strategically**
   10.4 Math Precision note, *p. 445*
6. **Attend to Precision**
   10.4 Exercise 25, *p. 452*
7. **Look for and Make Use of Structure**
   10.2 Exercise 18, *p. 438*
8. **Look for and Express Regularity in Repeated Reasoning**
   10.4 Math Practice note, *p. 445*

STEAM Video

Before the Video

- To introduce the STEAM Video, read aloud the first paragraph of Canning Salsa and discuss the question with your students.
- ❓ "In what other real-life situations is it helpful to know the volumes of objects?"

During the Video

- The video shows Robert and Tory canning salsa using proportions and volumes.
- ❓ Pause the video at 3:17 and ask, "What three-dimensional shape do they use to represent a tomato? a bell pepper? a jalapeño pepper? an onion?" sphere; square prism; cone; sphere
- ❓ "What shape is the jar?" cylinder
- Watch the remainder of the video.

After the Video

- Have students work with a partner to answer Questions 1 and 2.
- As students discuss and answer the questions, listen for understanding of finding the volume of a cube and using proportions.

Performance Task

- Use this information to spark students' interest and promote thinking about real-life problems.
- ❓ Ask, "Why is it helpful to know how many jars of salsa fit in one box?"
- After completing the chapter, students will have gained the knowledge needed to complete "Packaging Salsa."

Canning Salsa

You can estimate the volumes of ingredients to predict the total volume of a finished recipe. In what other real-life situations is it helpful to know the volumes of objects?

Watch the STEAM Video "Canning Salsa." Then answer the following questions.

1. You can approximate the volumes of foods by comparing them to common solids. A cube of cheese has side lengths of 3 centimeters. What is the volume of the cheese?

2. The table shows the amounts x (in cubic inches) of tomato used to make y cubic inches of salsa.

Tomato, x	1	2	3	4
Salsa, y	3	6	9	12

   a. Is there a proportional relationship between x and y? Justify your answer.

   b. How much tomato do you need to make 15 cubic inches of salsa?

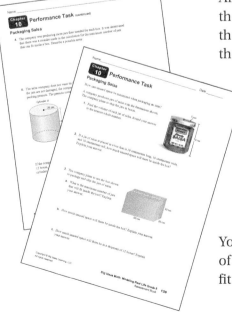

Packaging Salsa

After completing this chapter, you will be able to use the concepts you learned to answer the questions in the *STEAM Video Performance Task*. You will be given the dimensions of a jar and a shipping box.

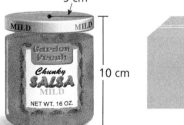

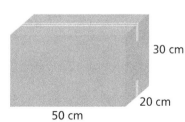

You will be asked questions about how to package jars of salsa. Why is it helpful to know how many jars of salsa fit in one box?

Getting Ready for Chapter

1. **Work with a partner.**

a. How does the volume of the stack of dimes compare to the volume of a single dime?

b. How does the volume of the stack of nickels compare to the volume of the stack of dimes? Explain your reasoning. (The height of each stack is identical.)

c. How does the volume of each stack change when you double the number of coins?

d. **MP LOGIC** Your friend adds coins to both stacks so that the volume of the stack of dimes is greater than the volume of the stack of nickels. What can you conclude about the number of coins added to each stack? Explain your reasoning.

Vocabulary

The following vocabulary terms are defined in this chapter. Think about what each term might mean and record your thoughts.

cone   hemisphere
sphere   similar solids

Laurie's Notes

 Check out the digital flash cards. *BigIdeasMath.com*

Chapter Exploration

- In the previous course, students explored volume as a layering process. Now they will use a similar method to explore volumes of cylinders.
- In part (a), students should not have difficulty reasoning that the volume of the stack is 13 times the volume of a single dime.
- Part (b) requires more thought. Although the stacks are the same height, the diameter of a nickel is greater than the diameter of a dime, so the volume of the stack of nickels must be greater than the volume of the stack of dimes. Because the diameters are not given, students can only make a general comparison.
- In part (c), listen for understanding that the volume is doubled because the height is doubled and the radius remains the same.
- In part (d), have each pair compare their answer and explanation with another pair. Discuss any discrepancies as a class.

Vocabulary

- These terms represent some of the vocabulary that students will encounter in Chapter 10. Discuss the terms as a class.
- Where have students heard the term *cone* outside of a math classroom? In what contexts? Students may not be able to write the actual definition, but they may write phrases associated with a *cone*.
- Allowing students to discuss these terms now will prepare them for understanding the terms as they are presented in the chapter.
- When students encounter a new definition, encourage them to write in their *Student Journals*. They will revisit these definitions during the Chapter Review.

ELL Support

Hold up a ball and say that it is a type of sphere, a round object. To check understanding, ask students to provide examples of other spheres, such as a globe, a planet, or an orange. They may know the word *hemisphere* from science. Explain that the prefix *hemi-* means "half," and a hemisphere is half of a sphere. Explain that in math, *sphere* has a very specific definition that they will learn later in this chapter.

Topics for Review

- Cross Sections of Three-Dimensional Figures
- Finding Areas of Composite Figures
- Finding the Areas of Circles
- Perimeters and Areas of Similar Figures
- Square Roots and Cube Roots
- Surface Areas of Prisms, Pyramids, and Cylinders
- Volumes of Prisms and Pyramids
- Writing and Solving Proportions

Chapter Exploration

a. The volume of the stack of dimes is 13 times greater.

b. The volume of the stack of nickels is greater; A nickel has a greater diameter than a dime.

c. The volume doubles.

d. More dimes were added than nickels; The volume of a dime is less than the volume of a nickel.

STATE STANDARDS
8.G.C.9

Learning Target
Find the volume of a cylinder.

Success Criteria
- Use a formula to find the volume of a cylinder.
- Use the formula for the volume of a cylinder to find a missing dimension.

Warm Up
Cumulative, vocabulary, and prerequisite skills practice opportunities are available in the *Resources by Chapter* or at *BigIdeasMath.com*.

ELL Support
Students may be familiar with the word *volume* from a radio or sound system. You may want to discuss its multiple meanings. Remind students that in Chapter 1, they learned that the word *formula* may refer to milk for babies or a category of racecar (Formula 1), but in math it refers to a rule that is expressed using symbols. Explain that a formula can be used to find the volume or the surface area of a figure.

Exploration 1
a. $V = Bh$ for each prism.

b. Multiply the area of the base by the height of the prism.

c. Multiply the area of the base by the height of the cylinder; As the number of sides of the bases of a prism increases, the prism begins to look like a cylinder. So, the volume of a cylinder is found in the same way as the volume of a prism.

Exploration 2
a–b. Check students' work.

Laurie's Notes

Preparing to Teach
- Students should know that cylinders are composed of two circular bases and a rectangle. Now they will use their understanding of volumes of prisms to reason about volumes of cylinders.
- **MP2 Reason Abstractly and Quantitatively:** In these explorations, students will model and reason about the volume of a cylinder. You want students to make a connection to the formula they learned for the volume of a prism, where they found the area of the base and multiplied by the height.

Motivate
- ❓ "Why might you want to know the volume of a cylinder?" To know how much of something will fit inside the cylinder.
- Hold two different-sized cans for the class to see. I often use cans of whole tomatoes—not only are the dimensions what I want, but the contents are the same, so you can do a little cost analysis at the end of class.
- ❓ "How do the volumes of these two cans compare?" The purpose here is to get students thinking about dimensions, not to do computations.

Exploration 1
- Part (a) reviews finding volumes of several different prisms.
- **MP1 Make Sense of Problems and Persevere in Solving Them:** In part (b), the goal is for students to see that as the number of sides of the bases increases, the prism starts to look like a cylinder. This helps students make the conjecture that the volume of a cylinder is found in the same way as the volume of a prism, by multiplying the area of the base and the height.
- After students complete the exploration, use *Popsicle Sticks* to select students to share with the class.
- Explain that today students will use their conjectures to find volumes of cylinders.

Exploration 2
- **Note:** A simulation of this exploration is available online at *BigIdeasMath.com*.
- This exploration works much better when the cube has a greater volume than the cylinder, so students only have to fill the cube one time. If the cylinder has a greater volume, then students will have to fill the prism completely, empty the rice from the prism, and then pour the remaining rice into the cylinder. Templates for the nets are available online at *BigIdeasMath.com*.
- Have students complete part (a) with their partners.
- In part (b), if you prefer that students do not pour the rice, you could demonstrate the experiment instead. Students should observe your actions and then perform their own calculations.
- Discuss students' answers in part (b).
- Ask volunteers to compare their results from the experiment to their conjectures in Exploration 1(c). Discuss students' reasoning as a class.

10.1 Volumes of Cylinders

Learning Target: Find the volume of a cylinder.

Success Criteria:
- I can use a formula to find the volume of a cylinder.
- I can use the formula for the volume of a cylinder to find a missing dimension.

EXPLORATION 1

Exploring Volume

Work with a partner.

a. Each prism shown has a height of h units and bases with areas of B square units. Write a formula that you can use to find the volume of each prism.

Triangular Prism   Rectangular Prism   Pentagonal Prism

Hexagonal Prism   Octagonal Prism

Math Practice

Find Entry Points
What does a regular polygon with an area of B square units start to look like as you increase the number of sides?

b. How can you find the volume of a prism with bases that each have 100 sides?

c. Make a conjecture about how to find the volume of a cylinder. Explain your reasoning.

EXPLORATION 2

Finding Volume Experimentally

Work with a partner. Draw a net for a cylinder. Then cut out the net and use tape to form an open cylinder. Repeat this process to form an open cube. The edge length of the cube should be greater than the diameter and the height of the cylinder.

a. Use your conjecture in Exploration 1 to find the volume of the cylinder.

b. Fill the cylinder with rice. Then pour the rice into the open cube. Find the volume of rice in the cube. Does this support your answer in part (a)? Explain your reasoning.

🔑 Key Idea

Volume of a Cylinder

Words The volume V of a cylinder is the product of the area of the base and the height of the cylinder.

Algebra $V = Bh$

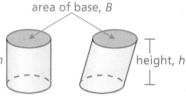

area of base, B

height, h height, h

EXAMPLE 1 **Finding the Volume of a Cylinder**

Find the volume of the cylinder. Round your answer to the nearest tenth.

Because $B = \pi r^2$, you can use $V = \pi r^2 h$ to find the volume of a cylinder.

$V = Bh$	Write the formula for volume.
$= \pi(3)^2(6)$	Substitute.
$= 54\pi \approx 169.6$	Use a calculator.

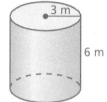

3 m

6 m

▷ The volume is about 169.6 cubic meters.

Try It

1. Find the volume of a cylinder with a radius of 4 feet and a height of 15 feet. Round your answer to the nearest tenth.

EXAMPLE 2 **Finding the Height of a Cylinder**

Find the height of the cylinder. Round your answer to the nearest whole number.

The diameter is 10 inches. So, the radius is 5 inches.

$V = Bh$	Write the formula for volume.
$314 = \pi(5)^2(h)$	Substitute.
$314 = 25\pi h$	Simplify.
$4 \approx h$	Divide each side by 25π.

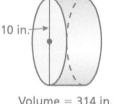

h

10 in.

Volume $= 314$ in.^{3}

▷ The height is about 4 inches.

Try It

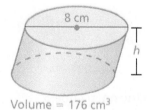

8 cm

h

Volume $= 176$ cm^3

2. Find the height of the cylinder at the left. Round your answer to the nearest tenth.

Laurie's Notes

Scaffolding Instruction

- Students discovered how to find the volume of a cylinder by comparing it to volumes of prisms. Now they will work with a formula for the volume of a cylinder.
- **Emerging:** Students need help finding the area of the base and using the volume formula. Provide guided instruction for the Key Idea and examples.
- **Proficient:** Students recognize the similarity in finding the volume of a prism and finding the volume of a cylinder. After reviewing the Key Idea and the Remember note, they should proceed to the Self-Assessment exercises.

Key Idea

- "How are cylinders and rectangular prisms alike?" Each has two congruent bases and a lateral portion.
- "How are cylinders and rectangular prisms different?" Cylinders have circular bases, but rectangular prisms have rectangular bases.
- Write the formula in words.
- Before writing the formula in symbols, ask how to find the area of the base.
- Note the use of color to identify the base in the formula and the diagram.
- "Can the formula be written as $V = \pi r^2 h$? Explain." Yes, $B = \pi r^2$.
- Read the Remember note aloud. Students may be surprised to discover that the volume of an oblique solid is calculated in the same way as the volume of a right solid. The Key Idea shows both a right and oblique cylinder.
- **Teaching Strategy:** Have students summarize the information they know about a cylinder.

EXAMPLE 1

- Model good problem solving by writing the formula first.
- Notice that the values of the variables are substituted, simplified, and left in terms of π. The last step is to use the π key on a calculator. If the calculator does not have a π key, use 3.14. Note that if 3.14 is used, the answers may not agree exactly with the answers shown in this text. Remind students of how they approximated irrational numbers in Chapter 9.
- Write " $\approx$ " on the board. "What does this symbol mean?" approximately equal to "Why do you use this symbol here?" Because π is an irrational number.
- **Extension:** Discuss the size of this cylinder. Its diameter and height (6 meters) are wider than my classroom and more than twice its height.

EXAMPLE 2

- **MP7 Look for and Make Use of Structure:** Students may be unsure of how to divide 314 by 25π. One way is to find the product 25π and then divide 314 by the product. Another way is to divide 314 by π and then divide the quotient by 25.

Try It

- **Neighbor Check:** Have students work independently and then have their neighbors check their work. Have students discuss any discrepancies.

Extra Example 1
Find the volume of a cylinder with a radius of 6 feet and a height of 3 feet. Round your answer to the nearest tenth. $108\pi \approx 339.3 \text{ ft}^3$

Try It

1. $240\pi \approx 754.0 \text{ ft}^3$

Extra Example 2
Find the height of a cylinder with a diameter of 4 yards and a volume of 88 cubic yards. Round your answer to the nearest whole number. 7 yd

ELL Support

Have students work in pairs to discuss and complete Try It Exercises 1 and 2. Provide guiding questions: What do you substitute for *B*? *h*? *V*? How do you round? Expect students to perform according to their language levels.

Beginner: Write the steps.

Intermediate: Use simple sentences to discuss and provide answers.

Advanced: Use detailed sentences to discuss and provide answers.

Try It

2. 3.5 cm

Extra Example 3

Find the radius of the cylinder. Round your answer to the nearest whole number.

Volume = 236 cm³

5 cm

Try It

3. 1.5 m

4. 6.5 mm

Self-Assessment
for Concepts & Skills

5. $14\pi \approx 44.0$ yd³

6. 12.0 ft

7. How much does it take to cover the cylinder?;
$170\pi \approx 534.1$ cm²;
$300\pi \approx 942.5$ cm³

EXAMPLE 3

- Remind students that the volume of an oblique cylinder is found in the same way as the volume of a right cylinder.
- Write the formula for volume. Substitute 226 for V and 8 for h. Solve for r^2.
- **?** "How can you solve for r?" Find the square root of both sides of the equation. Remind students that because r represents a distance, they should only take the positive square root.
- Be sure to write the units in the answer, 3 feet. Students may be tempted to write 3 cubic feet because they used the volume formula. Remind them that they used the volume formula to find the *radius*.

Try It

- Give students sufficient time to complete the exercises before asking volunteers to share their work on the board.

✓ Self-Assessment for Concepts & Skills

- ◉ **Fist of Five:** Ask students to indicate their understanding of each success criterion. Discuss any questions students may have.
- **Think-Pair-Share:** Students should read each exercise independently and then work in pairs to complete the exercises. Then have each pair compare their answers with another pair and discuss any discrepancies.

ELL Support

Allow students to work in pairs. Have each pair display their answers to Exercises 5 and 6 on a whiteboard for your review. You may also want students to display their equations to make sure they are using the correct formula. Have two pairs discuss their ideas for Exercise 7 and come to an agreement. Review as a class.

The Success Criteria Self-Assessment chart can be found in the *Student Journal* or online at *BigIdeasMath.com*.

EXAMPLE 3 **Finding the Radius of a Cylinder**

Find the radius of the cylinder. Round your answer to the nearest whole number.

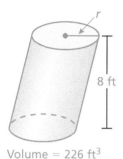

Volume = 226 ft³

$V = Bh$	Write the formula for volume.
$226 = \pi r^2(8)$	Substitute.
$\dfrac{226}{8\pi} = r^2$	Divide each side by 8π.
$\sqrt{\dfrac{226}{8\pi}} = r$	Take the positive square root of each side.
$3 \approx r$	Use a calculator.

▶ The radius is about 3 feet.

Try It **Find the radius of the cylinder. Round your answer to the nearest tenth.**

3.

4 m

Volume = 28 m³

4.

4.25 mm

Volume = 564 mm³

Self-Assessment for Concepts & Skills

Solve each exercise. Then rate your understanding of the success criteria in your journal.

4 yd

3.5 yd

5. FINDING THE VOLUME OF A CYLINDER Find the volume of the cylinder at the left. Round your answer to the nearest tenth.

6. FINDING THE HEIGHT OF A CYLINDER Find the height of the cylinder at the right. Round your answer to the nearest tenth.

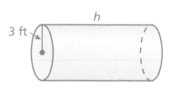

3 ft   h

Volume = 340 ft³

7. DIFFERENT WORDS, SAME QUESTION
Which is different? Find "both" answers.

> How much does it take to fill the cylinder?

> What is the capacity of the cylinder?

> How much does it take to cover the cylinder?

> How much does the cylinder contain?

5 cm

12 cm

EXAMPLE 4 **Modeling Real Life**

2.3 ft

1.8 ft

You use the cylindrical barrel shown to collect and study rainwater. About how many gallons of water can the barrel hold? (1 ft³ ≈ 7.5 gal)

Find the volume of the cylinder. The diameter is 1.8 feet. So, the radius is 0.9 foot.

$V = Bh$ Write the formula for volume.

$\quad = \pi(0.9)^2(2.3)$ Substitute.

$\quad = 1.863\pi$ Simplify.

So, the barrel can hold 1.863π cubic feet of water. To find the number of gallons it can hold, multiply the volume by the conversion factor $\dfrac{7.5 \text{ gal}}{1 \text{ ft}^3}$.

$$1.863\pi \text{ ft}^3 \times \frac{7.5 \text{ gal}}{1 \text{ ft}^3} \approx 44 \text{ gal}$$

▷ So, the barrel can hold about 44 gallons of water.

Self-Assessment for Problem Solving

Solve each exercise. Then rate your understanding of the success criteria in your journal.

8. How much salsa is missing from the jar? Explain your reasoning.

5 cm

10 cm

4 cm

9. A cylindrical swimming pool has a circumference of 18π feet and a height of 4 feet. About how many liters of water are needed to fill the swimming pool to 85% of its total volume? Justify your answer. (1 ft³ ≈ 28.3 L)

10. **DIG DEEPER!** A company creates two designs for a cylindrical soup can. Can A has a diameter of 3.5 inches and a height of 3.6 inches. Can B has a height of 4.9 inches. Each can holds the same amount of soup. Which can requires less material to make? Explain your reasoning.

Laurie's Notes

EXAMPLE 4

- It is helpful to have 3 rulers to model what a cubic foot looks like. Hold the 3 rulers so they form 3 edges of a cube that meet at a vertex.
- ❓ "About how many gallons do you think would fill a cubic foot?" There will be a range of answers.
- Ask a volunteer to read the problem aloud.
- ❓ "What are you asked to find?" how many gallons of water the barrel can hold
- It is helpful to have 8 one-gallon jugs to model what 7.5 gallons looks like, which students now know will fill about a cubic foot.
- ❓ "What do you need to find first?" the volume of the barrel
- Work through the problem, finding the volume of the barrel in cubic feet. Explain that the final answer will be more precise if they leave the volume in terms of π.
- The second part of the problem involves dimensional analysis, which students should be familiar with.
- **MP6 Attend to Precision:** Students should be comfortable with the term *conversion factor*.

✅ Self-Assessment *for Problem Solving*

- The goal for all students is to feel comfortable with the problem-solving plan. It is important for students to problem-solve in class, where they may receive support from you and their peers.
- Students should make a plan for each of the problems independently. Then have each student discuss his or her plans with a partner before solving the problems independently.
- **MP4 Model with Mathematics:** In Exercise 9, have students reason why a swimming pool would need to be filled only to 85% of its total volume.

The Success Criteria Self-Assessment chart can be found in the *Student Journal* or online at *BigIdeasMath.com*.

Closure

- Use the two cans used in the Motivate and ask students to find the volume of each. If the contents are not the same, pretend they are and ask students to compare the prices. Answers will vary, depending on the sizes and costs of the cans.

Extra Example 4

A cylindrical watercooler bottle has a diameter of 1 foot and a height of 1.25 feet. About how many gallons of water can be held in the watercooler bottle? (1 ft³ ≈ 7.5 gal) $2.34375\pi \approx 7.4$ gal

Self-Assessment
for Problem Solving

8. $150\pi \approx 471$ cm³; The empty space in the jar is a cylinder with $h = 10 - 4 = 6$ cm and $r = 5$ cm. So, $V = \pi(5)^2(6) = 150\pi \approx 471$ cm³.

9. $7793.82\pi \approx 24{,}485$ L; $C = 18\pi$ ft, so $r = 9$ ft. Then $V = \pi(9)^2(4) = 324\pi$ ft³. So, $0.85(324\pi) = 275.4\pi$ ft³, and $275.4\pi \text{ ft}^3 \times \dfrac{28.3 \text{ L}}{1 \text{ ft}^3} = 7793.82\pi \approx 24{,}485$ L.

10. Can A; The surface area of Can A is $18.725\pi \approx 58.8$ square inches, and the surface area of Can B is $19.2\pi \approx 60.3$ square inches.

Learning Target

Find the volume of a cylinder.

Success Criteria

- Use a formula to find the volume of a cylinder.
- Use the formula for the volume of a cylinder to find a missing dimension.

Review & Refresh

1. yes

2. yes

3. no

4. 3,900,000

5. 0.000067

6. 62,400,000,000

7. C

Concepts, Skills, & Problem Solving

8. 20π cubic units

9. 50π cubic units

10. 72π cubic units

11. $486\pi \approx 1526.8$ ft^3

12. $252\pi \approx 791.7$ in.^{3}

13. $245\pi \approx 769.7$ ft^3

14. $250\pi \approx 785.4$ ft^3

15. $256\pi \approx 804.2$ cm^3

16. $\frac{1125}{4}\pi \approx 883.6$ m^3

17. the cube; The cylinder could fit inside the cube with room to spare.

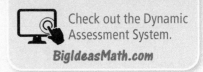

Assignment Guide and Concept Check

Scaffold assignments to support all students in their learning progression. The suggested assignments are a starting point. Continue to assign additional exercises and revisit with spaced practice to move every student toward proficiency.

Level	Assignment 1	Assignment 2
Emerging	3, 5, 6, 7, 8, 11, 13, 15, 19	12, 14, 16, 17, 18, 20, 21, 23, 26
Proficient	3, 5, 6, 7, 9, 12, 14, 16, 17, 19, 20	18, 21, 22, 23, 24, 25
Advanced	3, 5, 6, 7, 10, 12, 14, 16, 17, 18, 20	22, 23, 24, 25, 26, 27

- Assignment 1 is for use after students complete the Self-Assessment for Concepts & Skills.
- Assignment 2 is for use after students complete the Self-Assessment for Problem Solving.
- The red exercises can be used as a concept check.

Review & Refresh Prior Skills

Exercises 1–3 Identifying a Right Triangle

Exercises 4–6 Writing Numbers in Standard Form

Exercise 7 Choosing a Solution Method for a System of Linear Equations

Common Errors

- **Exercises 11–16** Students may forget to square the radius when finding the area of the base. Remind them of the formula for the area of a circle.
- **Exercises 15 and 16** When finding the area of the base, students may use the diameter instead of the radius. Encourage them to write the dimensions that they are given before attempting to find the volume. For example, in Exercise 15, students should write: radius = 4 cm, height = 16 cm.

10.1 Practice

Go to *BigIdeasMath.com* to get HELP with solving the exercises.

▶ Review & Refresh

Tell whether the triangle with the given side lengths is a right triangle.

1. 20 m, 21 m, 29 m
2. 1 in., 2.4 in., 2.6 in.
3. 5.6 ft, 8 ft, 10.6 ft

Write the number in standard form.

4. 3.9×10^6
5. 6.7×10^{-5}
6. 6.24×10^{10}

7. Which ordered pair is the solution of the linear system $3x + 4y = -10$ and $2x - 4y = 0$?

   A. $(-6, 2)$ **B.** $(2, -6)$ **C.** $(-2, -1)$ **D.** $(-1, -2)$

▶▶ Concepts, Skills, & Problem Solving

FINDING VOLUME The height *h* and the base area *B* of a cylinder are given. Find the volume of the cylinder. Write your answer in terms of π. (See Explorations 1 and 2, p. 427.)

8. $h = 5$ units
   $B = 4\pi$ square units

9. $h = 2$ units
   $B = 25\pi$ square units

10. $h = 4.5$ units
    $B = 16\pi$ square units

FINDING THE VOLUME OF A CYLINDER Find the volume of the cylinder. Round your answer to the nearest tenth.

11.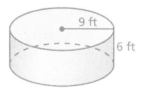
12.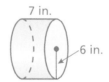
13.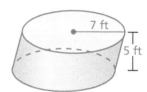

14.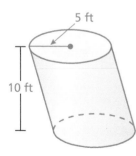
15.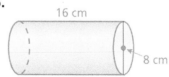
16.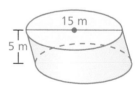

17. **MP REASONING** Without calculating, which of the solids has the greater volume? Explain.

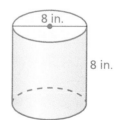
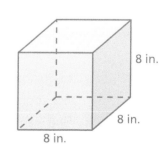

FINDING A MISSING DIMENSION Find the missing dimension of the cylinder. Round your answer to the nearest whole number.

18. Volume = $10,000\pi$ in.³

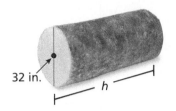

32 in. *h*

19. Volume = 3785 cm³

r

19 cm

20. Volume = 600,000 cm³

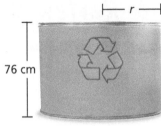

r

76 cm

21. **MP MODELING REAL LIFE** A cylindrical hazardous waste container has a diameter of 1.5 feet and a height of 1.6 feet. About how many gallons of hazardous waste can the container hold? (1 ft³ ≈ 7.5 gal)

22. **CRITICAL THINKING** How does the volume of a cylinder change when its diameter is halved? Explain.

5 ft

4 ft

Round Hay Bale

23. **MP PROBLEM SOLVING** A traditional "square" bale of hay is actually in the shape of a rectangular prism. Its dimensions are 2 feet by 2 feet by 4 feet. How many square bales contain the same amount of hay as one large "round" bale?

24. **MP MODELING REAL LIFE** A tank on a road roller is filled with water to make the roller heavy. The tank is a cylinder that has a height of 6 feet and a radius of 2 feet. About how many pounds of water can the tank hold? (One cubic foot of water weighs about 62.5 pounds.)

25. **MP REASONING** A cylinder has a surface area of 1850 square meters and a radius of 9 meters. Estimate the volume of the cylinder to the nearest whole number.

26. **DIG DEEPER!** Water flows at 2 feet per second through a cylindrical pipe with a diameter of 8 inches. A cylindrical tank with a diameter of 15 feet and a height of 6 feet collects the water.

    a. What is the volume (in cubic inches) of water flowing out of the pipe every second?

    b. What is the height (in inches) of the water in the tank after 5 minutes?

    c. How many minutes will it take to fill 75% of the tank?

27. **PROJECT** You want to make and sell three different sizes of cylindrical candles. You buy 1 cubic foot of candle wax for $20 to make 8 candles of each size.

    a. Design the candles. What are the dimensions of each size of candle?

    b. You want to make a profit of $100. Decide on a price for each size of candle. Explain how you set your prices.

Common Errors

- **Exercise 21** Students may find the volume of the container (in cubic feet), but forget to find how many gallons of hazardous waste that the container can hold. Encourage students to write the information that they know about the problem and also what they are trying to find. This should help them answer the question.

Mini-Assessment

Find the volume of the cylinder. Round your answer to the nearest tenth.

1.

4 cm

2 cm

$8\pi \approx 25.1 \text{ cm}^3$

2.

5 ft

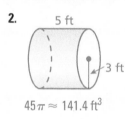

3 ft

$45\pi \approx 141.4 \text{ ft}^3$

3. Find the volume of the can of beans. Round your answer to the nearest whole number.

3 in.

4.5 in.

OLD COUNTRY STYLE
BAKED BEANS
in tomato sauce

$10.125\pi \approx 32 \text{ in.}^3$

18. 39 in.

19. 8 cm

20. 50 cm

21. $6.75\pi \approx 21$ gal

22. The volume is $\frac{1}{4}$ of the original volume; Because the diameter is halved, the radius is also halved.

So, $V = \pi\left(\frac{r}{2}\right)^2 h = \frac{1}{4}\pi r^2 h$.

23. about 4 square bales

24. $1500\pi \approx 4712$ lb

25. $8325 - 729\pi \approx 6035 \text{ m}^3$

26. a. $384\pi \approx 1206.4 \text{ in.}^3$

  b. about 14.2 in.

  c. about 19 min

27. a–b. Check students' work.

Section Resources

Surface Level	Deep Level
Resources by Chapter • Extra Practice • Reteach • Puzzle Time Student Journal • Self-Assessment • Practice Differentiating the Lesson Tutorial Videos Skills Review Handbook Skills Trainer	Resources by Chapter • Enrichment and Extension Graphic Organizers Dynamic Assessment System • Section Practice

Learning Target

Find the volume of a cone.

Success Criteria

- Use a formula to find the volume of a cone.
- Use the formula for the volume of a cone to find a missing dimension.

Warm Up

Cumulative, vocabulary, and prerequisite skills practice opportunities are available in the *Resources by Chapter* or at *BigIdeasMath.com*.

ELL Support

Point to the diagram below the definition for a cone and say, "This is a cone." Explain that an ice cream cone with a pointed bottom is an example of a cone. To check understanding, ask students for other examples of cones that they have seen in everyday life. Possible examples include traffic cones, party hats, and megaphones. Explain that students will learn the specific mathematical definition for a cone in this lesson.

Exploration 1

a. Check students' work.

b. 3

c. $V = \frac{1}{3}Bh = \frac{1}{3}\pi r^2 h$

d. Check students' work; The volume of the cone is $\frac{1}{3}$ of the volume of the cylinder.

e. *Sample answer:* yes; Volumes of oblique solids are calculated in the same way as volumes of right solids.

Laurie's Notes

STATE STANDARDS
8.G.C.9

Preparing to Teach

- In the previous course, students described cross sections of cones. Now they will find the volume of a cone.
- **MP2 Reason Abstractly and Quantitatively:** In the exploration, students will explore the relationship between the volume of a cone and the volume of a cylinder. Modeling such relationships is a powerful teaching tool.
- **Big Idea:** It is not a big stretch for students to accept that the volume relationship between the cone and cylinder is the same as the volume relationship between the pyramid and prism.
  Volume of a Cylinder = (Area of Base)(Height)
  Volume of a Cone = $\frac{1}{3}$(Area of Base)(Height)

Motivate

- Bring an ice cream cone and ice cream scoop to class.
- **FYI:** An ice cream scoop with a radius of 1-inch will make a round (spherical) scoop of ice cream that is a little more than 4 cubic inches. Share this information with students. You may also want to mention that students will study volumes of spheres in the next section.
- "If I place a scoop of ice cream (with a 1 inch radius) on this cone, and the ice cream melts, will the ice cream overflow the cone?" This question is posed only to get students thinking about the volume of a cone. Students will find the volume of this cone in the Closure.

Exploration 1

- Discuss the definition of a **cone**. Make sure students understand the difference between the height of a cone and the slant height.
- **Note:** A simulation of this exploration is available online at *BigIdeasMath.com*.
- Have students complete part (a) with their partners.
- Have students guess the relationship between the volume of a cone and the volume of a cylinder with the same base and height before they see it. If they recall the relationship between the volume of a pyramid and the volume of a prism with the same base and height, then they may guess correctly.
- In part (b), if you prefer that students do not pour the rice, you could demonstrate the experiment instead. Students should observe your actions and then perform their own calculations.
- "How many times does it take to fill the cylinder with the contents of the cone?" 3
- "How does the volume of the cone compare with the volume of the cylinder?" The volume of the cone is $\frac{1}{3}$ the volume of the cylinder.
- **Common Error:** In part (d), students may measure the slant height of the cone. Point out that the height of a cone is shown in the diagram below the definition for a cone.
- Discuss students' answers and reasoning in parts (d) and (e).

10.2 Volumes of Cones

Learning Target: Find the volume of a cone.

Success Criteria:
- I can use a formula to find the volume of a cone.
- I can use the formula for the volume of a cone to find a missing dimension.

You already learned how the volume of a pyramid relates to the volume of a prism. In this exploration, you will discover how the volume of a *cone* relates to the volume of a cylinder.

A **cone** is a solid that has one circular base and one vertex.

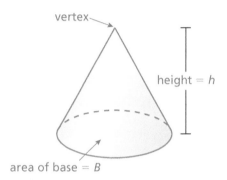

vertex

height = h

area of base = B

EXPLORATION 1

Finding a Formula Experimentally

Work with a partner. Use a paper cup that is shaped like a cone. Measure the height of the cup and the diameter of the circular base. Use these measurements to draw a net for a cylinder with the same base and height as the paper cup. Then cut out the net and use tape to form an open cylinder.

a. Find the volume of the cylinder.

Math Practice

Analyze Relationships

How does the volume of a cone relate to the volume of a cylinder?

b. Fill the paper cup with rice. Then pour the rice into the cylinder. Repeat this until the cylinder is full. How many cones does it take to fill the cylinder?

c. Use your result to write a formula for the volume of a cone.

d. Use your formula in part (c) to find the volume of the cone. How can you tell whether your answer is correct?

e. Do you think your formula for the volume of a cone is also true for *oblique* cones? Explain your reasoning.

Key Vocabulary 🔊
cone, *p. 433*

🔑 Key Idea

Volume of a Cone

Words The volume *V* of a cone is one-third the product of the area of the base and the height of the cone.

Algebra $V = \dfrac{1}{3}Bh$

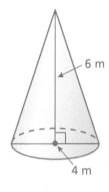

Right Cone   Oblique Cone
height, *h*
area of base, *B*

EXAMPLE 1 **Finding the Volume of a Cone**

Find the volume of the cone. Round your answer to the nearest tenth.

The diameter is 4 meters. So, the radius is 2 meters.

Because $B = \pi r^2$, you can use $V = \dfrac{1}{3}\pi r^2 h$ to find the volume of a cone.

$V = \dfrac{1}{3}Bh$	Write the formula for volume.
$= \dfrac{1}{3}\pi(2)^2(6)$	Substitute.
$= 8\pi \approx 25.1$	Use a calculator.

▶ The volume is about 25.1 cubic meters.

6 m

4 m

Try It

1. Find the volume of a cone with a radius of 6 centimeters and a height of 15 centimeters. Round your answer to the nearest tenth.

EXAMPLE 2 **Finding the Height of a Cone**

Find the height of the cone. Round your answer to the nearest tenth.

$V = \dfrac{1}{3}Bh$	Write the formula for volume.
$956 = \dfrac{1}{3}\pi(9)^2(h)$	Substitute.
$956 = 27\pi h$	Simplify.
$11.3 \approx h$	Divide each side by 27π.

▶ The height is about 11.3 feet.

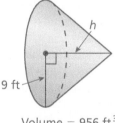

h

9 ft

Volume = 956 ft³

Volume = 7200 yd³

h

15 yd

Try It

2. Find the height of the cone at the left. Round your answer to the nearest tenth.

🔊 Multi-Language Glossary at *BigIdeasMath.com*

Laurie's Notes

Scaffolding Instruction

- Students discovered how to find the volume of a cone by comparing it to the volume of a cylinder with the same base and height. Now they will work with the formula for the volume of a cone.
- **Emerging:** Students may struggle with the formula. Provide guided instruction for the Key Idea and examples.
- **Proficient:** Students see the connection between volumes of cones and cylinders. They should proceed to the Self-Assessment exercises.

Key Idea

- Write the Key Idea.
- Write the formula in words.
- Draw the cones with the dimensions labeled. Note that the volume of an oblique cone is calculated in the same way as the volume of a right cone.
- Write the symbolic formula.
- ❓ "What shape is the base?" circle "How do you find its area A?" $A = \pi r^2$
- Remind students to make an index card for a cone.

EXAMPLE 1

- Model good problem solving by writing the formula first.
- Notice that the work is done in terms of π. It is not until the last step that you use the π key on a calculator.
- **Representation:** Encourage students to use the parentheses to represent multiplication. Using the $\times$ symbol would make the expression confusing.
- **Common Misconception:** Remind students that π is a number and because multiplication is commutative and associative, this expression could be rewritten as $\frac{1}{3}(6)(2)^2\pi$, making the computation less confusing.
- ❓ "What is being squared in this expression?" only the 2

Try It

- Have students show their work on whiteboards. Discuss any discrepancies.

EXAMPLE 2

- This example requires students to solve an equation for a variable.
- Remind students that the height of a cone is the perpendicular distance from the base to the vertex.
- Work through the problem, annotating the steps as shown.
- ❓ "How does $\frac{1}{3}\pi(9)^2 h$ equal $27\pi h$?" Only the 9 is being squared, which is 81. One-third of 81 is 27. The order of the factors does not matter.

Try It

- **Neighbor Check:** Have students work independently and then have their neighbors check their work. Have students discuss any discrepancies.

Scaffold instruction to support all students in their learning. Learning is individualized and you may want to group students differently as they move in and out of these levels with each skill and concept. Student self-assessment and feedback help guide your instructional decisions about how and when to layer support for all students to become proficient learners.

Extra Example 1

Find the volume of a cone with a diameter of 6 feet and a height of 9 feet. Round your answer to the nearest tenth. $27\pi \approx 84.8 \text{ ft}^3$

Try It

1. $180\pi \approx 565.5 \text{ cm}^3$

Extra Example 2

Find the height of a cone with a radius of 6 yards and a volume of 75 cubic yards. Round your answer to the nearest whole number. 2 yd

ELL Support

After demonstrating Examples 1 and 2, have students work in pairs to discuss and complete Try It Exercises 1 and 2. Have one student ask another, "What do you substitute for B? h? V? What is your answer? How do you round it?" Have students alternate roles.

Beginner: Write the steps used to solve the problem and state the answer.

Intermediate: Use simple sentences to provide answers.

Advanced: Use detailed sentences to provide answers.

Try It

2. 30.6 yd

Extra Example 3

Find the radius of the cone. Round your answer to the nearest tenth.

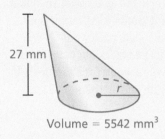

Volume = 5542 mm³

14.0 mm

Try It

3. 5 ft

4. 4 m

Self-Assessment
for Concepts & Skills

5. $100\pi \approx 314.2\ \text{yd}^3$

6. 1.5 in.

7. 1.8 cm

EXAMPLE 3

- Remind students that the volume of an oblique cone is found in the same way as the volume of a right cone.
- Write the formula for volume. Substitute 80 for V and 9 for h. Solve for r^2.
- **?** "How can you solve for r?" Find the square root of both sides of the equation. Remind students that because r represents a distance, they should only take the positive square root.
- Notice that the values of the variables are substituted, simplified, and left in terms of π. The last step is to use the π key on a calculator. If the calculator does not have a π key, use 3.14. Note that if 3.14 is used, the answers may not agree exactly with the answers shown in this text.
- Be sure to write the units in the answer, 2.9 inches. Students may be tempted to write 2.9 cubic inches because they used the volume formula. Remind students that they used the volume formula to find the *radius*.
- **?** "How can you check the answer?" Substitute 2.9 for r and 9 for h in $V = \frac{1}{3}\pi r^2 h$ to verify that $V \approx 80$.

Try It

- Ask volunteers to share their work at the board.

✅ *Self-Assessment* for *Concepts & Skills*

- **Neighbor Check:** Have students work independently and then have their neighbors check their work. Have students discuss any discrepancies.
- ⊙ **Writing Prompt:** Explain how to find the radius of a cone if you are given the height and the volume.

ELL Support

Allow students to work in pairs. Have each pair display their answers on a whiteboard for your review. You may also want students to display their equations to make sure they are using the correct formula.

The Success Criteria Self-Assessment chart can be found in the *Student Journal* or online at *BigIdeasMath.com*.

EXAMPLE 3 **Finding the Radius of a Cone**

9 in.

r

Volume = 80 in.³

Find the radius of the cone. Round your answer to the nearest tenth.

$$V = \frac{1}{3}Bh$$ Write the formula for volume.

$$80 = \frac{1}{3}\pi r^2(9)$$ Substitute.

$$80 = 3\pi r^2$$ Simplify.

$$\frac{80}{3\pi} = r^2$$ Divide each side by 3π.

$$\sqrt{\frac{80}{3\pi}} = r$$ Take the positive square root of each side.

$$2.9 \approx r$$ Use a calculator.

▷ The radius is about 2.9 inches.

Try It **Find the radius of the cone. Round your answer to the nearest whole number.**

3.

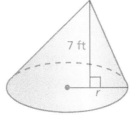

7 ft

r

Volume = 183 ft³

4.

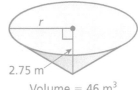

r

2.75 m

Volume = 46 m³

Self-Assessment for *Concepts & Skills*

Solve each exercise. Then rate your understanding of the success criteria in your journal.

5. FINDING THE VOLUME OF A CONE Find the volume of a cone with a diameter of 10 yards and a height of 12 yards. Round your answer to the nearest tenth.

FINDING A MISSING DIMENSION OF A CONE Find the missing dimension of the cone. Round your answer to the nearest tenth.

6.

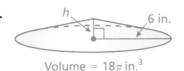

h   6 in.

Volume = 18π in.³

7.

5 cm

r cm

Volume = 16.5 cm³

EXAMPLE 4 **Modeling Real Life**

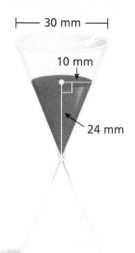

├─── 30 mm ───┤

10 mm ↓

24 mm

You must answer a trivia question before the sand in the timer falls to the bottom. Each second, 50 cubic millimeters of sand fall. How much time do you have to answer the question?

Use the formula for the volume of a cone to find the volume of the sand in the timer.

$$V = \frac{1}{3}Bh \qquad \text{Write the formula for volume.}$$

$$= \frac{1}{3}\pi(10)^2(24) \qquad \text{Substitute.}$$

$$= 800\pi \qquad \text{Simplify.}$$

The volume of the sand is 800π cubic millimeters. Use the rate at which the sand falls to determine how much time you have to answer the question.

$$800\pi \, \text{mm}^3 \times \frac{1 \text{ sec}}{50 \text{ mm}^3} \approx 50.27 \text{ sec}$$

▷ So, you have about 50 seconds to answer the question.

Self-Assessment for Problem Solving

Solve each exercise. Then rate your understanding of the success criteria in your journal.

8. A *stalactite* is a mineral formation that hangs from the ceiling of a cave. A cone-shaped stalactite has a height of 48 centimeters and a base circumference of 3.5π centimeters. What is the volume of the stalactite?

9. A store sells two cone-shaped funnels. What is the height of each funnel? (1 pt = 28.875 in.³)

4.5 in.

Volume: 0.5 pint

6 in.

Volume: 1 pint

10. You fill cone-shaped pastry bags with icing to a height of 1 foot and a diameter of 3.5 inches. You use about 1.35 cubic inches of icing per cupcake. About how many cupcakes can you decorate with 2 bags of icing?

Laurie's Notes

Formative Assessment Tip

Muddiest Point

This technique is the opposite of *Point of Most Significance*. Students are asked to reflect on the most difficult or confusing point in the lesson. Their reflections are often collected at the end of the lesson so that the following day's instruction can address any confusion, however, this technique may be used at any time. It is important for teachers to know whether there was a point in the lesson that was confusing so that the lesson can be modified. Share with students what you learned from their reflections. Students will take reflections more seriously when they see that you value and use them.

EXAMPLE 4

- If you have a timer of this type, use it as a model.
- Ask a volunteer to read the problem. Ask students for ideas about how to solve this problem.
- ❓ "How long is 30 millimeters?" 30 millimeters is equal to 3 centimeters, which is a little more than 1 inch. This helps students form a visual image of the actual size of the sand timer.
- **Teaching Tip:** Again, explain that $\frac{1}{3}(24)$ is a whole number. Then multiply $8(10)^2 = 800$.
- Be sure to use units in labeling answers. Dimensional analysis shows that the answer will have units of seconds.
- **Extension:** Use a sand timer in your classroom. Have students calculate the volume of the sand, measure the amount of time it takes to fall to the bottom, and use this information to calculate the rate at which the sand is falling.
- ❓ Stop and ask students, "What was the *Muddiest Point* in the lesson and what helped you clarify your thinking?"

✅ Self-Assessment for Problem Solving

- Allow time in class for students to practice using the problem-solving plan. By now, most students should be able to get past the first step.
- Ask students to make a plan for each problem. Before they solve the problems independently, ask students to share their plans with the class.

The Success Criteria Self-Assessment chart can be found in the *Student Journal* or online at *BigIdeasMath.com*.

Closure

- Have students find the volume of the ice cream cone used in the Motivate.
  Answers will vary, depending on the dimensions of the cone.

Extra Example 4

In Example 4, you use a different timer with the same dimensions. The sand in this timer has a height of 36 millimeters and a radius of 15 millimeters. The sand falls at a rate of 150 cubic millimeters per second. How much time do you have to answer the question?
about 57 sec

Self-Assessment
for Problem Solving

8. $49\pi \approx 154 \text{ cm}^3$

9. smaller funnel: about 2.7 in.; larger funnel: about 3.1 in.

10. 57 cupcakes

Learning Target

Find the volume of a cone.

Success Criteria

- Use a formula to find the volume of a cone.
- Use the formula for the volume of a cone to find a missing dimension.

▶ Review & Refresh

1. $63\pi \approx 197.9$ cm^3

2. $16\pi \approx 50.3$ ft^3

3. $500\pi \approx 1570.8$ yd^3

4. $x = 3$

5. $y = -2$

6. $h = 4$

▶ Concepts, Skills, & Problem Solving

7. 8π cubic units

8. 15π cubic units

9. $\dfrac{16}{3}\pi \approx 16.8$ in.^{3}

10. $9\pi \approx 28.3$ m^3

11. $\dfrac{250}{3}\pi \approx 261.8$ mm^3

12. $\dfrac{2}{3}\pi \approx 2.1$ ft^3

13. $\dfrac{200}{3}\pi \approx 209.4$ cm^3

14. $\dfrac{147}{4}\pi \approx 115.5$ yd^3

15. $\dfrac{112}{3}\pi \approx 117.3$ ft^3

16. $\dfrac{125}{6}\pi \approx 65.4$ in.^{3}

17. $\dfrac{32}{3}\pi \approx 33.5$ cm^3

Assignment Guide and Concept Check

Scaffold assignments to support all students in their learning progression. The suggested assignments are a starting point. Continue to assign additional exercises and revisit with spaced practice to move every student toward proficiency.

Level	Assignment 1	Assignment 2
Emerging	4, 6, 7, 9, 11, 13, 15, 17, 20	10, 12, 14, 16, 18, 19, 21, 22, 23, 24
Proficient	4, 6, 8, 10, 12, 14, 16, 19, 20	21, 22, 23, 24, 25, 26
Advanced	4, 6, 8, 10, 12, 14, 16, 19, 21	22, 23, 24, 25, 26, 27

- Assignment 1 is for use after students complete the Self-Assessment for Concepts & Skills.
- Assignment 2 is for use after students complete the Self-Assessment for Problem Solving.
- The red exercises can be used as a concept check.

Review & Refresh Prior Skills

Exercises 1–3 Finding the Volume of a Cylinder
Exercises 4–6 Solving Equations Using Cube Roots

▯ Common Errors

- **Exercises 9–17** Students may write linear or square units for volume rather than cubic units. Remind them that part of writing a correct answer is including the correct units.
- **Exercises 9–17** When finding the area of the base, students may not square the radius, or they may use the diameter when the formula calls for the radius. Remind them of the formula that they learned for the area of a circle.

10.2 Practice

Go to *BigIdeasMath.com* to get
HELP with solving the exercises.

▶ Review & Refresh

Find the volume of the cylinder. Round your answer to the nearest tenth.

1.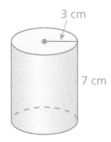
3 cm

7 cm

2.
2 ft

4 ft

3.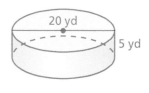
20 yd

5 yd

Solve the equation.

4. $x^3 = 27$

5. $-6 = y^3 + 2$

6. $2h^3 - 33 = 95$

▶▶ Concepts, Skills, & Problem Solving

FINDING A VOLUME The height h and the base area B of a cone are given. Find the volume of the cone. Write your answer in terms of π. (See Exploration 1, p. 433.)

7. $h = 6$ units
$B = 4\pi$ square units

8. $h = 9$ units
$B = 5\pi$ square units

FINDING THE VOLUME OF A CONE Find the volume of the cone. Round your answer to the nearest tenth.

9.
4 in.

2 in.

10.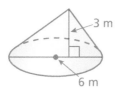
3 m

6 m

11.
10 mm

5 mm

12.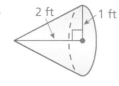
2 ft   1 ft

13.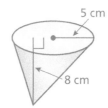
5 cm

8 cm

14.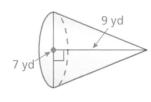
9 yd

7 yd

15.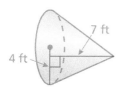
7 ft

4 ft

16.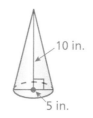
10 in.

5 in.

17.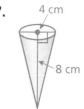
4 cm

8 cm

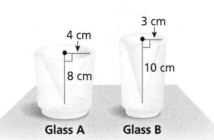

3 cm

4 cm

8 cm

10 cm

Glass A   Glass B

18. **MP STRUCTURE** The inside of each glass is shaped like a cone. Which glass can hold more liquid? How much more?

FINDING A MISSING DIMENSION OF A CONE Find the missing dimension of the cone. Round your answer to the nearest tenth.

19. Volume $= \frac{1}{18}\pi$ ft^3

h

$\frac{1}{3}$ ft

20. Volume $= 225$ cm^3

h

├─ 10 cm ─┤

21. Volume $= 3.6$ in.^{3}

r

4.2 in.

22. **FINDING A MISSING DIMENSION OF A CONE** The volume of a cone with a height of 10 meters is 20π cubic meters. What is the diameter of the cone?

23. **MP MODELING REAL LIFE** Water leaks from a crack in a cone-shaped vase at a rate of 0.5 cubic inch per minute. The vase has a height of 10 inches and a diameter of 4.8 inches. How long does it take for 20% of the water to leak from the vase when it is full of water?

24. **DIG DEEPER!** You have 10 gallons of lemonade to sell. (1 gal ≈ 3785 cm^3)

   a. Each customer uses 1 paper cup. The cups are sold in packages of 50. How many packages should you buy?

   b. How many cups will be left over if you sell 80% of the lemonade?

├─ 8 cm ─┤

11 cm

x

y

?

$2x$

25. **MP STRUCTURE** The cylinder and the cone have the same volume. What is the height of the cone?

26. **CRITICAL THINKING** In Example 4, you use a different timer with the same dimensions. The sand in this timer has a height of 30 millimeters. How much time do you have to answer the question?

27. **MP REASONING** A *vapor cone* is a cloud of condensed water that forms when an aircraft breaks the sound barrier. How does doubling both the diameter and the height affect the volume of the vapor cone?

Common Errors

- **Exercises 19–21** Students may try to use the Distributive Property before solving for h. For example, in Exercise 20, a student may incorrectly write $225 = \frac{1}{3}\pi(5^2) \cdot \frac{1}{3}h$. Remind them that factors are multiplied.

Mini-Assessment

Find the volume of the cone. Round your answer to the nearest tenth.

1.  6 yd 3 yd $18\pi \approx 56.5$ yd^3

2. 3 cm 4 cm $4\pi \approx 12.6$ cm^3

3. The volume of the ice cream cone is 4.71 cubic inches. Find the height of the cone.

⊢2 in.⊣

4.5 in.

Section Resources

Surface Level	Deep Level
Resources by Chapter • Extra Practice • Reteach • Puzzle Time Student Journal • Self-Assessment • Practice Differentiating the Lesson Tutorial Videos Skills Review Handbook Skills Trainer	Resources by Chapter • Enrichment and Extension Graphic Organizers Dynamic Assessment System • Section Practice
Transfer Level	
Dynamic Assessment System • Mid-Chapter Quiz	Assessment Book • Mid-Chapter Quiz

Concepts, Skills, & Problem Solving

18. Glass A; $\frac{38}{3}\pi \approx 39.8$ cm^3

19. 1.5 ft

20. 8.6 cm

21. 0.9 in.

22. about 4.9 m

23. about 24 min

24. a. 5 packages

b. 85 cups

25. $3y$

26. about 98 sec

27. The volume is 8 times the original volume.

STATE STANDARDS
8.G.C.9

Learning Target

Find the volume of a sphere.

Success Criteria

- Use a formula to find the volume of a sphere.
- Use the formula for the volume of a sphere to find the radius.
- Find volumes of composite solids.

Warm Up

Cumulative, vocabulary, and prerequisite skills practice opportunities are available in the *Resources by Chapter* or at *BigIdeasMath.com*.

ELL Support

Remind students of the introduction to spheres from the vocabulary discussion at the beginning of the chapter. To check their understanding of a sphere, ask students to state examples. Then explain the mathematical definition of a sphere.

Laurie's Notes

Preparing to Teach

- In the previous two lessons, students found volumes of cylinders and cones. Now they will find volumes of spheres.
- **MP2 Reason Abstractly and Quantitatively:** In the exploration, students will explore the relationship between the volume of a sphere and the volume of a cylinder. Modeling such relationships is a powerful teaching tool.

Motivate

- Bring a collection of spherical objects, such as rubber balls, to class. The objects should be of different sizes.
- ? "What is the geometric name for these solids?" *sphere*
- ? "What linear dimension or dimensions does a sphere have?" *radius*
- Discuss with students the fact that spheres have only one linear dimension. Other solids they studied have two or three linear dimensions.
- Hold several of the objects and ask students which has the greatest volume and which has the least volume. Ask them to explain their reasoning. Because a sphere has only one linear dimension, the object with the greatest radius has the greatest volume and the object with the least radius has the least volume.

Exploration 1

- Discuss the definition of a **sphere**.
- **Note:** A simulation of this exploration is available online at *BigIdeasMath.com*.
- Have students complete part (a) with their partners.
- Have students guess the relationship between the volume of a sphere and the volume of a cylinder with the same diameter and a height equal to the diameter before they see it. Because the sphere fits inside of the cylinder, students at least know that the cylinder has a greater volume.
- In part (b), if you prefer that students do not pour the rice, you could demonstrate the experiment instead. Students should observe your actions and then perform their own calculations.
- ? "How much of the cylinder is filled by the contents of the sphere?" $\frac{2}{3}$
- Make sure students answer part (b) correctly before moving on to part (c).
- Have students share their formulas in part (c). Ask volunteers to explain their reasoning.
- **Extension:** Students could verify their answers in part (b) by working with another pair to completely fill 2 cylinders with 3 spheres of rice.

Exploration 1

a. The height of the cylinder is twice the radius.

b. $\frac{2}{3}$

c. See Additional Answers.

10.3 Volumes of Spheres

Learning Target: Find the volume of a sphere.

Success Criteria:
- I can use a formula to find the volume of a sphere.
- I can use the formula for the volume of a sphere to find the radius.
- I can find volumes of composite solids.

A **sphere** is the set of all points in space that are the same distance from a point called the *center*. The *radius r* is the distance from the center to any point on the sphere. A sphere is different from the other solids you have studied so far because it does not have a base.

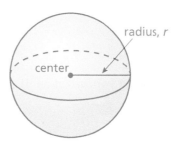

radius, *r*

center

EXPLORATION 1

Finding a Formula Experimentally

Work with a partner. Use a plastic ball similar to the one shown. Draw a net for a cylinder with a diameter and a height equal to the diameter of the ball. Then cut out the net and use tape to form an open cylinder.

a. How is the height *h* of the cylinder related to the radius *r* of the ball?

b. Cover the ball with aluminum foil or tape. Leave one hole open. Fill the ball with rice. Then pour the rice into the cylinder. What fraction of the cylinder is filled with rice?

Math Practice

Look for Structure

Why is it convenient for the height of the cylinder to be equal to the diameter of the sphere?

c. Use your result in part (b) and the formula for the volume of a cylinder to write a formula for the volume of a sphere. Explain your reasoning.

Key Vocabulary
sphere, *p. 439*
hemisphere, *p. 442*

Key Idea

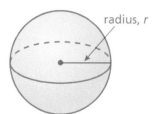

Volume of a Sphere

Words The volume V of a sphere is the product of $\frac{4}{3}\pi$ and the cube of the radius of the sphere.

Algebra $V = \frac{4}{3}\pi r^3$

EXAMPLE 1 **Finding Volumes of Spheres**

Find the volume of each sphere. Round your answer to the nearest tenth.

a.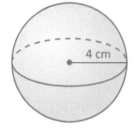

b.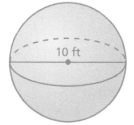

$V = \frac{4}{3}\pi r^3$ Write the formula for volume. $V = \frac{4}{3}\pi r^3$

$= \frac{4}{3}\pi(4)^3$ Substitute for r. $= \frac{4}{3}\pi(5)^3$

$= \frac{256}{3}\pi$ Simplify. $= \frac{500}{3}\pi$

≈ 268.1 Use a calculator. ≈ 523.6

▷ The volume is about 268.1 cubic centimeters.

▷ The volume is about 523.6 cubic feet.

Try It **Find the volume of the sphere. Round your answer to the nearest tenth.**

1.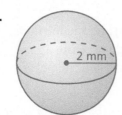

2.

◀) Multi-Language Glossary at *BigIdeasMath.com*

Laurie's Notes

Scaffolding Instruction

- Students derived the formula for the volume of a sphere by comparing the volume of a sphere and the volume of a cylinder. They will now use the formula to find volumes of spheres.
- **Emerging:** Students may not understand the formula for the volume of a sphere or how to use it. They will benefit from guided instruction for the Key Idea and examples.
- **Proficient:** Students understand the reasoning behind the formula for the volume of a sphere and can use it to find volumes and radii. They should complete Try It Exercises 3 and 4 before moving on to the Self-Assessment exercises.

Key Idea

- Have physical objects, such as a ball or a globe, available to reference.
- Draw the sphere and write the formula in words.
- Students may derive this formula again in a high school geometry course.
- Remind students to make an index card for a sphere.

EXAMPLE 1

- Notice that in both parts (a) and (b), the work is done in terms of π. It is not until the last step that you use the π key on a calculator.
- **?** "What information do you know in part (a)?" The radius of the sphere is 4 centimeters.
- **Representation:** Encourage students to use the parentheses to represent multiplication. Using the $\times$ symbol would make the expression confusing.
- **Common Misconception:** Remind students that π is a number and because multiplication is commutative and associative, this expression could be rewritten as $\frac{4}{3}(4)^3\pi$, making the computation less confusing.
- **?** "What is being cubed in this expression?" only the 4
- Remind students that the answer is an approximation because π is an irrational number.
- **Extension:** Ask students how big they think a cubic centimeter is. To help students visualize, tell them that a cubic centimeter is about the size of a sugar cube.
- **?** "How is part (b) different than part (a)?" You know the diameter instead of the radius.
- Work through part (b) as shown.

Try It

- **Neighbor Check:** Have students work independently and then have their neighbors check their work. Have students discuss any discrepancies.
- ⊙ **Thumbs Up:** Have students indicate their understanding of the first success criterion.

Extra Example 1

Find the volume of each sphere. Round your answer to the nearest tenth.

a.

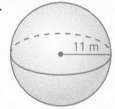

$\frac{5324}{3}\pi \approx 5575.3 \text{ m}^3$

b.

$\frac{16,384}{3}\pi \approx 17,157.3 \text{ in.}^3$

ELL Support

After demonstrating Example 1, have students work in pairs to discuss and complete Try It Exercises 1 and 2. Have one student ask another, "What number do you substitute for r? What is your answer? How do you round it?" Have students alternate roles.

Beginner: Write the steps used to solve the problem and state the answer.

Intermediate: Use simple sentences to provide answers.

Advanced: Use detailed sentences to provide answers.

Try It

1. $\frac{32}{3}\pi \approx 33.5 \text{ mm}^3$

2. $\frac{2048}{3}\pi \approx 2144.7 \text{ ft}^3$

Extra Example 2
Find the radius of a sphere with a
volume of 2304π cubic centimeters.
12 cm

EXAMPLE 2

- This example requires students to solve an equation for a variable.
- Work through the problem, annotating the steps as shown.
- Tell students not to substitute a value for π into the equation because the volume is written in terms of π, so it will divide out.
- **MP7 Look for and Make Use of Structure:** Discuss why students can write $\frac{4}{3}\pi$ as $\frac{4\pi}{3}$. You want them to see the connection to fraction multiplication: $\frac{4}{3} \cdot 7 = \frac{4 \cdot 7}{3}$, so likewise $\frac{4}{3} \cdot \pi = \frac{4 \cdot \pi}{3}$.
- Students may have difficulty solving for r in this example. As shown, you can accomplish this by multiplying each side of the equation by the reciprocal of the variable term's coefficient and then taking the cube root of each side. Provide a quick review of cube roots if necessary.

Try It

- Ask volunteers to share their work at the board.
- ◉ **Thumbs Up:** Have students indicate their understanding of the second success criterion.

✓ Self-Assessment for Concepts & Skills

- **Neighbor Check:** Have students work independently and then have their neighbors check their work. Have students discuss any discrepancies.
- Discuss Exercise 7 as a class.
- **Writing Prompt:** Explain how a sphere is different from other solids you have studied.

ELL Support

Allow students to work in pairs. Have each pair display their answers on a whiteboard for your review. You may also want to check their equations as well. Have two pairs discuss their ideas for Exercise 7 and come to an agreement. Then have each group of four present their ideas to the class.

The Success Criteria Self-Assessment chart can be found in the *Student Journal* or online at *BigIdeasMath.com*.

Try It

3. 3 m

4. 1.5 in.

Self-Assessment
for Concepts & Skills

5. $\frac{16,384}{3}\pi \approx 17{,}157.3 \text{ cm}^3$

6. 15 yd

7. sphere; It does not have a base.

EXAMPLE 2 **Finding the Radius of a Sphere**

Find the radius of the sphere.

Volume = 288 π in.³

$$V = \frac{4}{3}\pi r^3$$ Write the formula for volume.

$$288\pi = \frac{4}{3}\pi r^3$$ Substitute 288 π for V.

$$288\pi = \frac{4\pi}{3}r^3$$ Multiply.

$$\frac{3}{4\pi} \cdot 288\pi = \frac{3}{4\pi} \cdot \frac{4\pi}{3}r^3$$ Multiplication Property of Equality

$$216 = r^3$$ Simplify.

$$\sqrt[3]{216} = \sqrt[3]{r^3}$$ Take the cube root of each side.

$$6 = r$$ Simplify.

Math Practice

Use Expressions
Show that $\frac{3}{4\pi} \cdot 288\pi$ is equal to 216.

▶ The radius is 6 inches.

Try It **Find the radius of the sphere. Round your answer to the nearest tenth if necessary.**

3.

Volume = 36 π m³

4.

Volume = 14 in.³

Self-Assessment for Concepts & Skills

Solve each exercise. Then rate your understanding of the success criteria in your journal.

32 cm

5. **FINDING THE VOLUME OF A SPHERE** Find the volume of the sphere. Round your answer to the nearest tenth.

6. **FINDING THE RADIUS OF A SPHERE** Find the radius of a sphere with a volume of 4500 π cubic yards.

7. **WHICH ONE DOESN'T BELONG?** Which figure does not belong with the other three? Explain your reasoning.

 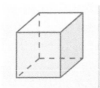

EXAMPLE 3 **Modeling Real Life**

A hemisphere is one-half of a sphere. The top of the silo is a hemisphere with a radius of 12 feet. What is the volume of the silo? Round your answer to the nearest thousand.

52 ft

> Understand the problem.

You are given the dimensions of a silo that is made up of a cylinder and a hemisphere. You are asked to find the volume of the silo.

> Make a plan.

Break the problem into parts. Find the volume of the cylinder and the volume of the hemisphere. Then add the volumes to find the total volume of the silo.

> Solve and check.

The radius of the hemisphere is 12 feet. So, the cylinder has a height of $52 - 12 = 40$ feet.

A *composite solid* is a solid made up of two or more three-dimensional figures.

Cylinder

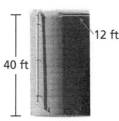

12 ft

40 ft

$$V = Bh$$
$$= \pi(12)^2(40)$$
$$= 5760\pi$$

Hemisphere

12 ft

$$V = \frac{1}{2} \cdot \frac{4}{3}\pi r^3$$
$$= \frac{1}{2} \cdot \frac{4}{3}\pi(12)^3$$
$$= 1152\pi$$

Check Reasonableness
The volume of the silo is less than the volume of a cylinder with a height of 52 feet and a radius of 12 feet.

$$V = \pi(12)^2(52)$$
$$\approx 24{,}000 \text{ ft}^3 \checkmark$$

> So, the volume is $5760\pi + 1152\pi = 6912\pi$, or about 22,000 cubic feet.

Self-Assessment for Problem Solving

Solve each exercise. Then rate your understanding of the success criteria in your journal.

8. In sphering, a person is secured inside a small, hollow sphere that is surrounded by a larger sphere. The space between the spheres is inflated with air. What is the volume of the inflated space? Explain.

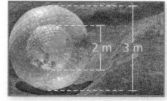

2 m   3 m

├─6 cm─┤

$1.50 each!

12 cm

9. **DIG DEEPER!** A vendor sells cones filled with frozen yogurt, as shown. The vendor has 4 cylindrical containers of frozen yogurt, each with a diameter of 18 centimeters and a height of 15 centimeters. About how much money will the vendor make when all of the frozen yogurt is sold? Justify your answer.

Laurie's Notes

EXAMPLE 3

- **3-Read Modeling:** Read the problem stem and display the diagram.
  - Ask, "What is this situation about?" a silo with a hemisphere top
  - Have students read the problem stem to a partner. Ask, "What quantities and units are involved?" radius of 12 feet and overall height of 52 feet
  - Ask students to think about what is missing while they choral or partner read. Then ask, "What mathematical questions could you ask about this situation?" *Sample answer.* What is the volume of the silo?
- "How does *3-Read Modeling* compare to the problem-solving plan?" Make sure students realize that *3-Read Modeling* helps them with the first step of the problem-solving plan.
- Discuss the push-pin note.
- "How can you find the volume of the silo?" Find the volume of the cylinder and the volume of the hemisphere, and then add.
- Use the problem-solving technique of writing the formulas first and then substituting the values for the variables.
- Work through the solution as shown. Notice that the solution is kept in terms of π until the last step.

✓ Self-Assessment for Problem Solving

- Students may benefit from trying the exercises independently and then working with peers to refine their work. It is important to provide time in class for problem solving.
- ⦿ **Thumbs Up:** Have students indicate their understanding of the third success criterion.

The Success Criteria Self-Assessment chart can be found in the *Student Journal* or online at *BigIdeasMath.com*.

Closure

- **Exit Ticket:** The radius of a sphere is 2 centimeters. Find the volume of a cube that the sphere fits snugly within and find the volume of the sphere.
  64 cm³; $\frac{32}{3}\pi \approx 33.5$ cm³

Extra Example 3
In Example 3, the radius of the silo is 9 feet and the overall height is 48 feet. What is the volume of the silo? Round your answer to the nearest thousand. $3645\pi \approx 11{,}000$ ft³

Self-Assessment
for Problem Solving

8. $\frac{19}{6}\pi \approx 10$ m³; For outer sphere, $V = \frac{9}{2}\pi$ m³, and for the inner sphere, $V = \frac{4}{3}\pi$ m³.
    So, $\frac{9}{2}\pi - \frac{4}{3}\pi = \frac{19}{6}\pi$ m³.

9. \$135; For the filled cone, $d = 6$ cm, so $r = 3$ cm.
    Volume of filled cone:
    $$V = \frac{1}{3}\pi(3)^2(12) + \frac{1}{2} \cdot \frac{4}{3}\pi(3)^3$$
    $$= 54\pi \text{ cm}^3$$
    For each container, $d = 18$ cm, so $r = 9$ cm.
    Volume of 4 containers:
    $$V = 4 \cdot \pi(9)^2(15)$$
    $$= 4860\pi \text{ cm}^3$$
    So, $\frac{4860\pi}{54\pi} = 90$ cones, and $90 \cdot \$1.50 = \$135$.

Learning Target

Find the volume of a sphere.

Success Criteria

- Use a formula to find the volume of a sphere.
- Use the formula for the volume of a sphere to find the radius.
- Find volumes of composite solids.

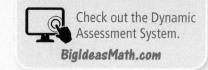

Check out the Dynamic Assessment System.

BigIdeasMath.com

Review & Refresh

1. $8\pi \approx 25.1 \text{ ft}^3$
2. $15\pi \approx 47.1 \text{ cm}^3$
3. $27\pi \approx 84.8 \text{ m}^3$
4. 8.5×10^9
5. 5×10^{-11}
6. A

Concepts, Skills, & Problem Solving

7. 288π cubic units
8. 2304π cubic units
9. $\dfrac{4000}{3}\pi$ cubic units
10. $\dfrac{500}{3}\pi \approx 523.6 \text{ in.}^3$
11. $\dfrac{1372}{3}\pi \approx 1436.8 \text{ ft}^3$
12. $972\pi \approx 3053.6 \text{ mm}^3$
13. $288\pi \approx 904.8 \text{ yd}^3$
14. $36\pi \approx 113.1 \text{ cm}^3$
15. $\dfrac{10{,}976}{3}\pi \approx 11{,}494.0 \text{ m}^3$
16. 9 mm
17. 1.5 cm
18. 3.5 ft

Assignment Guide and Concept Check

Scaffold assignments to support all students in their learning progression. The suggested assignments are a starting point. Continue to assign additional exercises and revisit with spaced practice to move every student toward proficiency.

Level	Assignment 1	Assignment 2
Emerging	3, 4, 5, 6, 7, 10, 12, 14, 16	11, 13, 15, 17, 18, 19, 20, 22, 23, 25
Proficient	3, 4, 5, 6, 8, 11, 13, 15, 16, 18	17, 20, 21, 22, 23, 25, 27
Advanced	3, 4, 5, 6, 9, 11, 13, 15, 17, 18	20, 23, 24, 25, 26, 27, 28

- Assignment 1 is for use after students complete the Self-Assessment for Concepts & Skills.
- Assignment 2 is for use after students complete the Self-Assessment for Problem Solving.
- The red exercises can be used as a concept check.

Review & Refresh Prior Skills

Exercises 1–3 Finding the Volume of a Cone
Exercise 4 Adding in Scientific Notation
Exercise 5 Dividing in Scientific Notation
Exercise 6 Using Indirect Measurement

Common Errors

- **Exercises 10–15** Students may forget to multiply by $\dfrac{4}{3}$ or cube the radius, they may use the diameter when the formula calls for radius, or they may write the incorrect units. Remind students of the formula for the volume of a sphere and that part of writing a correct answer is including the correct units.
- **Exercises 16–18** Students may not complete the solution; they may solve for the *cube* of the radius instead of the radius. Point out that they need to find a cube root, which they learned in Section 9.3, and provide a quick review if necessary.

10.3 Practice

Go to *BigIdeasMath.com* to get
HELP with solving the exercises.

▶ Review & Refresh

Find the volume of the cone. Round your answer to the nearest tenth.

1.
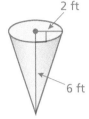
2 ft

6 ft

2.

5 cm

3 cm

3.
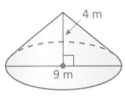
4 m

9 m

Evaluate the expression. Write your answer in scientific notation.

4. $(4.6 \times 10^9) + (3.9 \times 10^9)$

5. $(1.4 \times 10^{-4}) \div (2.8 \times 10^6)$

6. A person who is 5 feet tall casts a 6-foot-long shadow. A nearby flagpole casts a 30-foot-long shadow. What is the height of the flagpole?

A. 25 ft **B.** 29 ft **C.** 36 ft **D.** 40 ft

▶▶ Concepts, Skills, & Problem Solving

FINDING VOLUME The radius r of a sphere is given. Find the volume of the sphere. Write your answer in terms of π. (See Exploration 1, p. 439.)

7. $r = 6$ units

8. $r = 12$ units

9. $r = 10$ units

FINDING THE VOLUME OF A SPHERE Find the volume of the sphere. Round your answer to the nearest tenth.

10.

5 in.

11.

7 ft

12.

18 mm

13.

12 yd

14.

3 cm

15.

28 m

FINDING THE RADIUS OF A SPHERE Find the radius of a sphere with the given volume. Round your answer to the nearest tenth if necessary.

16. Volume $= 972\pi \, \text{mm}^3$ **17.** Volume $= 4.5\pi \, \text{cm}^3$ **18.** Volume $= 180 \, \text{ft}^3$

19. **MP** **MODELING REAL LIFE** The globe of the moon has a radius of 13 centimeters. Find the volume of the globe. Round your answer to the nearest whole number.

20. **MP** **MODELING REAL LIFE** A softball has a volume of about 29 cubic inches. Find the radius of the softball. Round your answer to the nearest tenth.

21. **MP** **REASONING** A sphere and a right cylinder have the same radius and volume. Find the radius r in terms of the height h of the cylinder.

FINDING VOLUME Find the volume of the composite solid. Round your answer to the nearest tenth.

22.
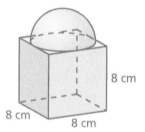
8 cm
8 cm
8 cm

23.
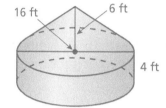
16 ft
6 ft
4 ft

24.

6 in.
11 in.

25. **MP** **PROBLEM SOLVING** A cylindrical container of three rubber balls has a height of 18 centimeters and a diameter of 6 centimeters. Each ball in the container has a radius of 3 centimeters. Find the amount of space in the container that is not occupied by rubber balls. Round your answer to the nearest whole number.

Volume = 121.5π in.³

26. **DIG DEEPER!** The basketball shown is packaged in a box that is in the shape of a cube. The edge length of the box is equal to the diameter of the basketball. What are the surface area and the volume of the box?

27. **MP** **PROBLEM SOLVING** The inner core of Earth begins about 3200 miles below the surface of Earth and has a volume of about 581,000,000π cubic miles. Approximate the radius of Earth. Justify your answer.

Inner Core

28. **MP** **LOGIC** Your friend says that the volume of a sphere with radius r is four times the volume of a cone with radius r. When is this true? Justify your answer.

Common Errors

- **Exercise 19** Students may forget to multiply by $\frac{4}{3}$ or cube the radius or they may write the incorrect units. Remind students of the formula for the volume of a sphere and that part of writing a correct answer is including the correct units.
- **Exercise 20** Students may not complete the solution; they may solve for the *cube* of the radius instead of the radius. Point out that they need to find a cube root, which they learned in Section 9.3, and provide a quick review if necessary.
- **Exercises 22–24** Students may think that there is not enough information to solve the problem. It may help to have them "break up" the composite solid into two parts, whose volumes they know how to find, and mark the dimensions on each part.
- **Exercise 24** Students may add instead of subtract the volume of the hemisphere. Point out that in contrast to the solid in Example 3, this solid is made up of a cylinder with a hemisphere *removed*, not added.

Mini-Assessment

Find the volume of the sphere. Round your answer to the nearest tenth.

1.

13 in.

$\frac{8788}{3}\pi \approx 9202.8$ in.^{3}

2.

20 m

$\frac{4000}{3}\pi \approx 4188.8$ m^3

3. Find the radius of a sphere with a volume of 7776π cubic millimeters. 18 mm

4. In Example 3, the diameter of the silo is 18 meters and the overall height is 62 meters. What is the volume of the silo? Round your answer to the nearest thousand? $4779\pi \approx 15{,}000$ m^3

Concepts, Skills, & Problem Solving

19. $\frac{8788}{3}\pi \approx 9203$ cm^3

20. 1.9 in.

21. $r = \frac{3}{4}h$

22. $512 + \frac{128}{3}\pi \approx 646.0$ cm^3

23. $384\pi \approx 1206.4$ ft^3

24. $81\pi \approx 254.5$ in.^{3}

25. $54\pi \approx 170$ cm^3

26. 486 in.^{2}; 729 in.^{3}

27. 3958 mi; $581{,}000{,}000\pi = \frac{4}{3}\pi r^3$, so $r = \sqrt[3]{435{,}750{,}000}$ mi, and $3200 + \sqrt[3]{435{,}750{,}000} \approx 3958$ mi.

28. when the height of the cone is equal to the radius; $\frac{4}{3}\pi r^3 = 4 \cdot \frac{1}{3}\pi r^2 h$, so $r = h$.

Section Resources

Surface Level	Deep Level
Resources by Chapter • Extra Practice • Reteach • Puzzle Time Student Journal • Self-Assessment • Practice Differentiating the Lesson Tutorial Videos Skills Review Handbook Skills Trainer	Resources by Chapter • Enrichment and Extension Graphic Organizers Dynamic Assessment System • Section Practice

Learning Target

Find the surface areas and volumes of similar solids.

Success Criteria

- Use corresponding dimensions to determine whether solids are similar.
- Use corresponding dimensions to find missing measures in similar solids.
- Use linear measures to find surface areas and volumes of similar solids.

Warm Up

Cumulative, vocabulary, and prerequisite skills practice opportunities are available in the *Resources by Chapter* or at *BigIdeasMath.com*.

ELL Support

Point out that the word *surface* includes the word *face*. Students may know the word face as a body part or a position a person takes, as in *I face the building*. Remind them that in math, a face is a flat side of a solid. The meaning of surface comes from the French language, with *sur* meaning "above" or "outermost" and *face* meaning "appearance." In math, surface area is the sum of the areas of all the faces of a solid.

Exploration 1

a–b. See Additional Answers.

Laurie's Notes

STATE STANDARDS
Applying 8.G.C.9

Preparing to Teach

- Students have worked with similar two-dimensional figures, surface area formulas, and volume formulas. Now they will use these skills to find surface areas and volumes of similar solids.
- **Note:** If your standards do not require finding surface areas and volumes of similar solids, you may skip this lesson.
- **MP8 Look for and Express Regularity in Repeated Reasoning:** Students may recognize and apply patterns in repeated computations they are performing, which will make this exploration go quickly.

Motivate

- Retell a portion of the story of *Goldilocks and the Three Bears*.
- Focus on the three sizes of porridge bowls, chairs, and beds.
- Share with students that Papa Bear's mattress was twice as long, twice as wide, and twice as high as Baby Bear's mattress. So, are there twice as many feathers in Papa Bear's feather bed mattress?
- This question will be answered later in the lesson.
- You may want to provide a quick review of how to find surface areas of cylinders, and surface areas and volumes of pyramids.

Exploration 1

- **Note:** Technology for this exploration is available online at *BigIdeasMath.com*.
- Tell students to leave their answers in terms of π.
- To help students see the pattern in the first table, ask students to describe the changes in the dimensions. radius and height each increase by 1
- **?** Compare each figure's height to the original figure's height. Do the same for radii, surface areas, and volumes. What do you notice?" The heights and radii are multiplied by the same number. The surface areas are multiplied by the square of this number, and the volumes are multiplied by the cube of this number.
- **?** "Are the dimensions proportional in part (a)? Explain." Yes, both the radius and height increase by the same factor.
- **MP5 Use Appropriate Tools Strategically:** It may help students to see a pattern in part (b) if they use calculators.
- **MP8 Look for and Express Regularity in Repeated Reasoning:** Ask students to describe patterns they see in the second table. Remind them to think about factors (multiplication) versus addition. The first pyramid should be referred to as the original pyramid. Describe any patterns in terms of the original pyramid.
- **?** "Are the dimensions proportional? Explain." Yes, the three dimensions are all changing by factors of 2, 3, 4, and 5 times the originals.
- To help students see the factor by which the surface areas and volumes are multiplied, they should divide the new surface area (or volume) by the original surface area (or volume). For the blue pyramid:

  Surface Area $1536 \div 96 = 16$ Multiplied by a scale factor of 4^2
  Volume $3072 \div 48 = 64$ Multiplied by a scale factor of 4^3

- **Big Idea:** When the dimensions of a solid are all multiplied by a scale factor of k, the surface area is multiplied by a scale factor of k^2, and the volume is multiplied by a scale factor of k^3.

10.4 Surface Areas and Volumes of Similar Solids

Learning Target: Find the surface areas and volumes of similar solids.

Success Criteria:
- I can use corresponding dimensions to determine whether solids are similar.
- I can use corresponding dimensions to find missing measures in similar solids.
- I can use linear measures to find surface areas and volumes of similar solids.

EXPLORATION 1

Comparing Similar Solids

Work with a partner.

a. You multiply the dimensions of the smallest cylinder by different factors to create the other four cylinders. Complete the table. Compare the surface area and volume of each cylinder with the surface area and volume of the smallest cylinder.

Math Practice

Use Technology to Explore

How can you use technology to efficiently calculate the missing values in the table?

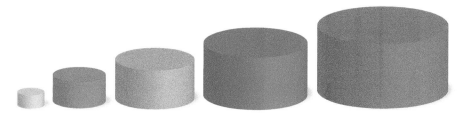

Radius	1	2	3	4	5
Height	1	2	3	4	5
Surface Area					
Volume					

b. Repeat part (a) using the square pyramids and table below.

Math Practice

Maintain Oversight

When the dimensions of a solid are multiplied by a factor of k, how many times greater is the surface area? the volume?

Base Side	6	12	18	24	30
Height	4	8	12	16	20
Slant Height	5	10	15	20	25
Surface Area					
Volume					

10.4 Lesson

Key Vocabulary
similar solids, p. 446

Similar solids are solids that have the same shape and proportional corresponding dimensions.

EXAMPLE 1   Identifying Similar Solids

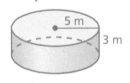

Cylinder B

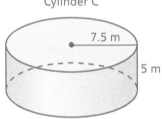

Cylinder C

Which cylinder is similar to Cylinder A?

Check to see if corresponding dimensions are proportional.

Cylinder A

Cylinder A and Cylinder B

$$\frac{\text{Height of A}}{\text{Height of B}} = \frac{4}{3} \qquad \frac{\text{Radius of A}}{\text{Radius of B}} = \frac{6}{5} \qquad \text{Not proportional}$$

Cylinder A and Cylinder C

$$\frac{\text{Height of A}}{\text{Height of C}} = \frac{4}{5} \qquad \frac{\text{Radius of A}}{\text{Radius of C}} = \frac{6}{7.5} = \frac{4}{5} \qquad \text{Proportional}$$

So, Cylinder C is similar to Cylinder A.

Try It

1. Cylinder D has a radius of 7.5 meters and a height of 4.5 meters. Which cylinder in Example 1 is similar to Cylinder D?

EXAMPLE 2   Finding Missing Measures in Similar Solids

Cone X

Cone Y

The cones are similar. Find the missing slant height ℓ.

$$\frac{\text{Radius of X}}{\text{Radius of Y}} = \frac{\text{Slant height of X}}{\text{Slant height of Y}}$$

$$\frac{5}{7} = \frac{13}{\ell} \qquad \text{Substitute.}$$

$$5\ell = 91 \qquad \text{Cross Products Property}$$

$$\ell = 18.2 \qquad \text{Divide each side by 5.}$$

The slant height is 18.2 yards.

Try It

2. The prisms at the right are similar. Find the missing width and length.

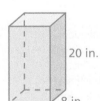

◀)) Multi-Language Glossary at *BigIdeasMath.com*

Laurie's Notes

Scaffolding Instruction

- Students explored what happens to the surface areas and volumes of solids when the dimensions are multiplied by a factor of k. Now they will use properties of similar solids to solve problems.
- **Emerging:** Students struggled with comparing similar solids. They will benefit from guided instruction for the Key Ideas and examples.
- **Proficient:** Students understand the relationships between similar solids. They should review the Key Ideas and complete the Try It exercises before proceeding to the Self-Assessment exercises.

Discuss

- Remind students that in the previous course they worked with scale models and in Section 2.7 they worked with perimeters and areas of similar figures.
- Discuss the definition for **similar solids**.
- Note that the definition simply states that the corresponding linear measures must be proportional. This means that similar solids are proportional in size.
- ❓ "What is a proportion?" an equation of two equal ratios
- ❓ **MP3 Construct Viable Arguments and Critique the Reasoning of Others:** "How do you know if two ratios are equal?" Students might say by eyesight; by simple arithmetic, like $\frac{1}{2} = \frac{2}{4}$; that the ratios simplify to the same ratio. Students should recall the Cross Products Property.

EXAMPLE 1

- Work through the example as shown.
- Be sure to write the words and the numbers. Use language such as "the ratio of the height of Cylinder A to the height of Cylinder B is 4 to 3."
- ❓ "How do you know $\frac{6}{7.5} = \frac{4}{5}$?" Answers may vary depending upon students' number sense. By the Cross Products Property $6 \times 5 = 7.5 \times 4$.

Try It

- Give students time to work independently and write their answers on their whiteboards. Discuss students' reasoning as a class.

EXAMPLE 2

- Remind students that the *slant height* of a cone is the distance along the surface of the cone from the vertex to a point on the base.
- ❓ "By the definition of similar solids, what can you determine about two similar cones?" Corresponding linear measures are proportional, so the values of the ratios are equal.
- Set up the proportion and solve for the missing slant height.

Try It

- **Think-Pair-Share:** Students should read the exercise independently and then work in pairs to complete the exercise. Then have each pair compare their answers with another pair and discuss any discrepancies.

Extra Example 1
Which prism is similar to Prism A?

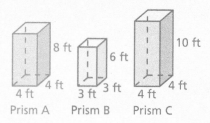

Prism A   Prism B   Prism C

Prism B

Try It
1. Cylinder B

Extra Example 2
The square pyramids are similar. Find the length of the base of Pyramid E.

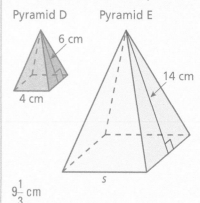

Pyramid D   Pyramid E

Try It
2. $w = 3.2$ in.; $\ell = 4.4$ in.

Laurie's Notes

Key Ideas

- Write the Key Ideas.
- **Example:** When the linear dimensions of Solid B are double the linear dimensions of Solid A, the value of the ratio of the dimensions is equal to $\frac{1}{2}$ and the value of the ratio of the surface areas is $\left(\frac{1}{2}\right)^2$, or $\frac{1}{4}$.
- Refer to the exploration to confirm that this relationship was found.
- Students may not know how to find surface areas of cones or spheres. However, they do not need this skill to determine whether two cones or two spheres are similar. The relationship given in the Key Idea applies to all similar solids.

EXAMPLE 3

? "Do you have enough information to solve this problem? Explain." Yes, the value of the ratio of the heights is $\frac{6}{10}$, so the value of the ratio of the surface areas is $\left(\frac{6}{10}\right)^2$.

- Set up the proportion and solve.
- **FYI:** The problem can be solved using the Multiplication Property of Equality or the Cross Products Property.
- **Connection:** The value of the ratio $\frac{\text{Linear measure of A}}{\text{Linear measure of B}}$ is the scale factor. The square of the scale factor is used to find the unknown surface area.

Try It

- Students should first identify the value of the ratio of the corresponding linear measurements. Exercise 3: $\frac{8}{5}$ or $\frac{5}{8}$; Exercise 4: $\frac{5}{4}$ or $\frac{4}{5}$
- Ask volunteers to share their work at the board.

ELL Support

After demonstrating Example 3, have students work in pairs to discuss and complete Try It Exercises 3 and 4. Provide guiding questions: What is the surface area of the blue solid? What proportion do you use to find the surface area of the red solid? What numbers do you substitute? What is the surface area of the red solid? Expect students to perform according to their language levels.

Beginner: Write the steps used to solve the problem.

Intermediate: Use simple sentences to discuss and provide answers.

Advanced: Use detailed sentences to discuss and provide answers.

Extra Example 3
The cones are similar. What is the surface area of Cone G?

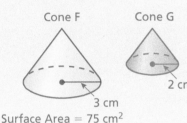

Cone F   Cone G

2 cm

3 cm

Surface Area = 75 cm^2

$33\frac{1}{3}$ cm^2

Try It

3. 237.5 m^2
4. 171.9 cm^2

 **Key Ideas**

Linear Measures

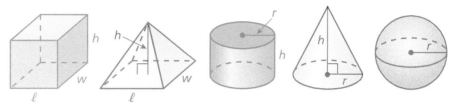

Surface Areas of Similar Solids

When two solids are similar, the value of the ratio of their surface areas is equal to the square of the value of the ratio of their corresponding linear measures.

$$\frac{\text{Surface area of A}}{\text{Surface area of B}} = \left(\frac{a}{b}\right)^2$$

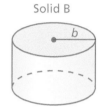

Solid A

Solid B

EXAMPLE 3 **Finding Surface Area**

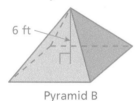

Pyramid A

6 ft

Pyramid B

10 ft

Surface Area = 600 ft²

The pyramids are similar. What is the surface area of Pyramid A?

$$\frac{\text{Surface area of A}}{\text{Surface area of B}} = \left(\frac{\text{Height of A}}{\text{Height of B}}\right)^2$$

$$\frac{S}{600} = \left(\frac{6}{10}\right)^2 \qquad \text{Substitute.}$$

$$\frac{S}{600} = \frac{36}{100} \qquad \text{Evaluate.}$$

$$S = 216 \qquad \text{Multiply each side by 600.}$$

▶ The surface area of Pyramid A is 216 square feet.

Try It **The solids are similar. Find the surface area of the red solid. Round your answer to the nearest tenth.**

3.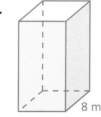

8 m

5 m

Surface Area = 608 m²

4.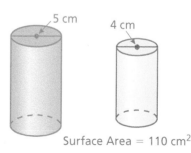

5 cm

4 cm

Surface Area = 110 cm²

 **Key Idea**

Volumes of Similar Solids

When two solids are similar, the value of the ratio of their volumes is equal to the cube of the value of the ratio of their corresponding linear measures.

$$\frac{\text{Volume of A}}{\text{Volume of B}} = \left(\frac{a}{b}\right)^3$$

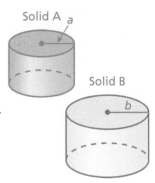

EXAMPLE 4 **Finding Volume**

The cones are similar. What is the volume of Cone A? Round your answer to the nearest tenth.

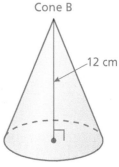

$$\frac{\text{Volume of A}}{\text{Volume of B}} = \left(\frac{\text{Height of A}}{\text{Height of B}}\right)^3$$

$$\frac{V}{288} = \left(\frac{5}{12}\right)^3 \qquad \text{Substitute.}$$

$$\frac{V}{288} = \frac{125}{1728} \qquad \text{Evaluate.}$$

$$V \approx 20.8 \qquad \text{Multiply each side by 288.}$$

Cone A 5 cm

Cone B 12 cm

Volume = 288 cm³

▷ The volume of Cone A is about 20.8 cubic centimeters.

Try It

Volume = 9 in.³   3 in.   4 in.

5. The pyramids at the left are similar. Find the volume of the red pyramid. Round your answer to the nearest tenth.

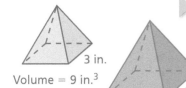 **Self-Assessment** *for Concepts & Skills*

Solve each exercise. Then rate your understanding of the success criteria in your journal.

12 ft
5 ft   Cone A

6. **IDENTIFYING SIMILAR SOLIDS** Cone A and Cone B are right cones. Cone B has a radius of 1.25 feet and a height of 3 feet. Are the cones similar?

7. **FINDING A MISSING MEASURE** A cylinder with a radius of 4 inches and a height of 6 inches is similar to a cylinder with a radius of r inches and a height of 9 inches. What is the value of r?

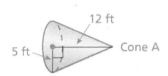
4 yd
2 yd
Surface Area = 13 yd²
Volume = 3 yd³

8. **FINDING SURFACE AREA AND VOLUME** The rectangular prisms shown are similar. Find the surface area and volume of the red rectangular prism.

Laurie's Notes

Key Ideas

- Write the Key Idea.
- **Example:** When the linear dimensions of Solid B are double the linear dimensions of Solid A, the value of the ratio of the dimensions is equal to $\frac{1}{2}$, and the value of the ratio of the volumes is equal to $\left(\frac{1}{2}\right)^3$, or $\frac{1}{8}$.
- Refer to the exploration to confirm that this relationship was found.

EXAMPLE 4

? "Do you have enough information to solve this problem? Explain." Yes, the value of the ratio of the heights is $\frac{5}{12}$, so the value of the ratio of the volumes is $\left(\frac{5}{12}\right)^3$.

- Set up the proportion and solve.
- **Connection:** The value of the ratio $\dfrac{\text{Linear measure of A}}{\text{Linear measure of B}}$ is the scale factor. The cube of the scale factor is used to find the unknown volume.

Try It

- Students should solve the exercise independently.
- **Popsicle Sticks:** Select students to share their work at the board.

✓ Self-Assessment for Concepts & Skills

- **Neighbor Check:** Have students work independently and then have their neighbors check their work. Have students discuss any discrepancies.
- Refer to Papa Bear's feather bed mattress from the Motivate. Ask, "If the dimensions are all double Baby Bear's mattress, how many times more feathers are there?" 8 times more feathers
- ◉ **Thumbs Up:** Have students indicate their understanding of each success criterion.

ELL Support

Allow students to work in pairs. For Exercise 6, have students indicate *yes* or *no* using a thumbs up or down signal. Have each pair display their answers to Exercises 7 and 8 on a whiteboard for your review. You may also want to check their work.

The Success Criteria Self-Assessment chart can be found in the *Student Journal* or online at *BigIdeasMath.com*.

Extra Example 4
The cylinders are similar. What is the volume of Cylinder J? Round your answer to the nearest tenth.

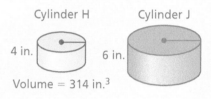

Cylinder H   Cylinder J

4 in.   6 in.

Volume = 314 in.^{3}

1059.8 in.^{3}

Try It

5. 21.3 in.^{3}

Self-Assessment
for Concepts & Skills

6. yes

7. 6

8. 52 yd^2; 24 yd^3

Extra Example 5

The dimensions of the touch tank in Example 5 are tripled. How many pounds of water are contained in the new tank? about 3,375,000 lb

EXAMPLE 5

- Ask a volunteer to read the problem and another to explain what the problem is asking.
- Students could complete a Four Square as you work through the problem-solving plan.
- ❓ "What information is given?" The original tank has a volume of 2000 cubic feet, the dimensions of the new tank are double the dimensions of the original tank, and one cubic foot of water weighs about 62.5 pounds.
- ❓ "How can you find the pounds of water contained in the new tank?" Find the volume of the new tank (in cubic feet) and then use dimensional analysis to convert to pounds.
- ❓ "How can you find the new volume (in cubic feet)?" The dimensions of the new tank are double the dimensions of the original tank, so the value of the ratio of the dimensions is $\frac{1}{2}$ and the value of the ratio of the volumes is $\left(\frac{1}{2}\right)^3$. Use this relationship to set up a proportion and solve for the new volume.
- **Common Misconception:** Many students think that when you double the dimensions, the surface area and volume also double. This big idea takes time for students to understand.
- After finding the new volume, use dimensional analysis to convert the volume in cubic feet to pounds of water.

Self-Assessment
for Problem Solving

9. 5.8 cm

10. 1670.6 lb

11. $43.80

✓ Self-Assessment for Problem Solving

- Encourage students to use a Four Square to complete these exercises. By now, most students should be able to get past the first square.
- Students should identify the value of the ratio of the corresponding linear measurements for each exercise and then compare with their neighbors before solving the exercises.
- Ask volunteers to share their work with the class.

The Success Criteria Self-Assessment chart can be found in the *Student Journal* or online at *BigIdeasMath.com*.

Learning Target

Find the surface areas and volumes of similar solids.

Success Criteria

- Use corresponding dimensions to determine whether solids are similar.
- Use corresponding dimensions to find missing measures in similar solids.
- Use linear measures to find surface areas and volumes of similar solids.

Formative Assessment Tip

Write the Test

Give each student 2 index cards. Divide students into groups equal to the number of sections in the chapter. Assign each group a different section. Tell students that they are going to write the test! Have each member of the group write 2 test questions for the assigned section. Each question should be written on an index card with the solution worked out on the back. Have each student give his or her cards to two students in the group to evaluate the questions and solutions. When students are confident in their solutions, collect the cards. Select problems from the cards to create a chapter test.

Closure

- **Write the Test:** Divide students into four groups. Assign each group a section and have them write 2 test questions for that section.

EXAMPLE 5 **Modeling Real Life**

Original Tank

Volume = 2000 ft³

The dimensions of the touch tank at an aquarium are doubled. How many pounds of water are contained in the new tank? (One cubic foot of water weighs about 62.5 pounds.)

The dimensions are doubled, so the ratio of the dimensions of the original tank to the dimensions of the new tank is 1 : 2.

$$\frac{\text{Original volume}}{\text{New volume}} = \left(\frac{\text{Original dimension}}{\text{New dimension}}\right)^3$$

$$\frac{2000}{V} = \left(\frac{1}{2}\right)^3 \qquad \text{Substitute.}$$

$$\frac{2000}{V} = \frac{1}{8} \qquad \text{Evaluate.}$$

$$16{,}000 = V \qquad \text{Cross Products Property}$$

> When the dimensions of a solid are multiplied by k, the surface area is multiplied by k^2 and the volume is multiplied by k^3.

The new tank holds 16,000 cubic feet of water. To find the weight of the water in the tank, multiply by $\frac{62.5 \text{ lb}}{1 \text{ ft}^3}$.

$$16{,}000 \text{ ft}^3 \times \frac{62.5 \text{ lb}}{1 \text{ ft}^3} = 1{,}000{,}000 \text{ lb}$$

▷ So, the new tank contains about 1,000,000 pounds of water.

 Self-Assessment for Problem Solving

Solve each exercise. Then rate your understanding of the success criteria in your journal.

9. Two snails have shells that are similar in shape. The younger snail has a shell with a height of 3.9 centimeters and a volume of 3 cubic centimeters. The older snail has a shell with a volume of 10 cubic centimeters. Estimate the height of the older snail's shell.

10. Two barrels filled with sand are similar in shape. The smaller barrel has a height of 4 feet and a volume of 4.5 cubic feet. The larger barrel has a height of 6 feet. What is the weight of the sand in the larger barrel? Round your answer to the nearest tenth. (One cubic foot of sand weighs about 110 pounds.)

11. Two trunks are similar in shape. The larger trunk has a length of 6 feet and a surface area of 164.25 square feet. The smaller trunk has a length of 4 feet. The materials needed to manufacture each trunk cost $0.60 per square foot. What is the total cost of the materials needed to manufacture the smaller trunk?

Go to *BigIdeasMath.com* to get
HELP with solving the exercises.

▶ Review & Refresh

Find the volume of the sphere. Round your answer to the nearest tenth.

1.

11 cm

2.

4.5 ft

3.

12 mm

4. Which system of linear equations has no solution?

   A. $y = 4x + 1$ **B.** $y = 2x - 7$ **C.** $3x + y = 1$ **D.** $5x + y = 3$

        $y = -4x + 1$ $y = 2x + 7$ $6x + 2y = 2$ $x + 5y = 15$

▶▶ Concepts, Skills, & Problem Solving

COMPARING SIMILAR SOLIDS **All of the dimensions of the solid are multiplied
by a factor of *k*. How many times greater is the surface area of the new solid?
How many times greater is the volume of the new solid?** (See Exploration 1, p. 445.)

5. $k = 5$

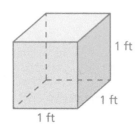

1 ft
1 ft
1 ft

6. $k = 10$

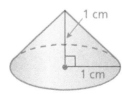

1 cm
1 cm

IDENTIFYING SIMILAR SOLIDS **Determine whether the solids are similar.**

7.

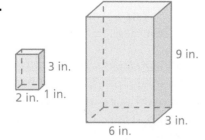

3 in.
2 in. 1 in.
9 in.
3 in.
6 in.

8.

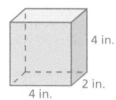

4 in.
4 in.
2 in.

4 in.
2 in. 1 in.

9.

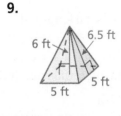

6 ft 6.5 ft
5 ft
5 ft
12 ft 13 ft
10 ft
10 ft

10.

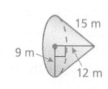

15 m
9 m
12 m

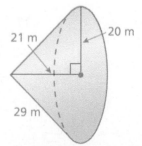

21 m 20 m
29 m

Assignment Guide and Concept Check

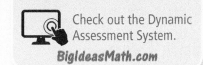

Check out the Dynamic Assessment System.
BigIdeasMath.com

Scaffold assignments to support all students in their learning progression. The suggested assignments are a starting point. Continue to assign additional exercises and revisit with spaced practice to move every student toward proficiency.

Level	Assignment 1	Assignment 2
Emerging	3, 4, 5, 7, 9, 11, 13, 15, 19, 20	8, 10, 12, 14, 16, 17, 18, 21, 22, 23
Proficient	3, 4, 6, 8, 10, 12, 14, 16, 17, 18, 20	21, 22, 23, 24
Advanced	3, 4, 6, 8, 10, 12, 14, 16, 17, 18, 20	22, 23, 24, 25

- Assignment 1 is for use after students complete the Self-Assessment for Concepts & Skills.
- Assignment 2 is for use after students complete the Self-Assessment for Problem Solving.
- The red exercises can be used as a concept check.

Review & Refresh Prior Skills

Exercises 1–3 Finding the Volume of a Sphere
Exercise 4 Solving a System of Linear Equations

Common Errors

- **Exercises 7–10** Students may compare only two pairs of corresponding dimensions instead of all three. The bases may be similar, but the heights may not be proportional. Remind students to check all of the corresponding dimensions when determining whether two solids are similar. Ask them how many ratios they need to write for each type of solid.

Review & Refresh

1. $\dfrac{5324}{3}\pi \approx 5575.3 \text{ cm}^3$

2. $121.5\pi \approx 381.7 \text{ ft}^3$

3. $288\pi \approx 904.8 \text{ mm}^3$

4. B

Concepts, Skills, & Problem Solving

5. 25 times greater; 125 times greater

6. 100 times greater; 1000 times greater

7. yes

8. no

9. yes

10. no

Concepts, Skills, & Problem Solving

11. $d = 2.5$ ft

12. $b = 18$ m; $c = 19.5$ m; $h = 9$ m

13. $\ell = 11.5$ mm; $w = 11.5$ mm

14. $\ell = 5.1$ in.; $r = 2.4$ in.

15. 90 m^2

16. 2827.7 in.^{2}

17. 673.75 cm^2

18. 196 mm^3

19. $13{,}564.8$ ft^3

20. no; $\dfrac{3}{5}$ should be cubed, not squared.

Common Errors

- **Exercises 11–14** Students may write the proportion incorrectly. For example, in Exercise 11, they may write $\dfrac{10}{4} = \dfrac{1}{d}$. Remind students to write the proportion and then check to make sure it makes sense.
- **Exercises 15–17** Students may forget to square the ratio of the corresponding linear measures when finding the surface area of the red solid or the larger can. Remind them of the Key Ideas in this section.
- **Exercises 18 and 19** Students may forget to cube the ratio of the corresponding linear measures when finding the volume of the red solid. Remind them of the Key Ideas in this section.

FINDING MISSING MEASURES IN SIMILAR SOLIDS The solids are similar. Find the missing measure(s).

11.

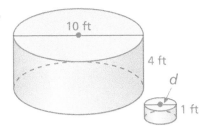

12.

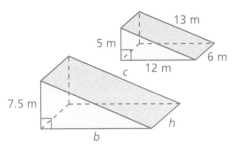

13.

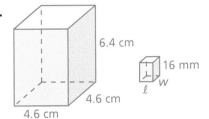

14.

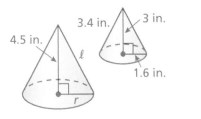

FINDING SURFACE AREA The solids are similar. Find the surface area of the red solid. Round your answer to the nearest tenth if necessary.

15.

4 m
Surface Area = 40 m²

6 m

16.

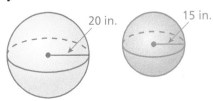

Surface Area ≈ 5027 in.²

17. FINDING SURFACE AREA The ratio of the corresponding linear measures of two similar cans is 4 to 7. The smaller can has a surface area of 220 square centimeters. Find the surface area of the larger can.

FINDING VOLUME The solids are similar. Find the volume of the red solid.

18.

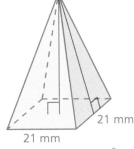

21 mm
21 mm
7 mm
7 mm
Volume = 5292 mm³

19.

10 ft
12 ft
Volume = 7850 ft³

20. **MP YOU BE THE TEACHER** The ratio of the corresponding linear measures of two similar solids is 3 : 5. The volume of the smaller solid is 108 cubic inches. Your friend finds the volume of the larger solid. Is your friend correct? Explain your reasoning.

$$\frac{108}{V} = \left(\frac{3}{5}\right)^2$$

$$\frac{108}{V} = \frac{9}{25}$$

$$300 = V$$

The volume of the larger solid is 300 cubic inches.

21. **(MP) MODELING REAL LIFE** A hemisphere-shaped mole has a diameter of 5.7 millimeters and a surface area of about 51 square millimeters. The radius of the mole doubles. Estimate the new surface area of the mole.

22. **(MP) REASONING** The volume of a 1968 Ford Mustang GT engine is 390 cubic inches. Which scale model of the Mustang has the greater engine volume, a 1 : 18 scale model or a 1 : 24 scale model? How much greater is it?

23. **DIG DEEPER!** You have a small marble statue of Wolfgang Mozart. It is 10 inches tall and weighs 16 pounds. The original marble statue is 7 feet tall.

    a. Estimate the weight of the original statue. Explain your reasoning.

    b. If the original statue were 20 feet tall, how much would it weigh?

24. **(MP) REPEATED REASONING** The nesting dolls are similar. The largest doll is 7 inches tall. Each of the other dolls is 1 inch shorter than the next larger doll. Make a table that compares the surface areas and the volumes of the seven dolls.

Wolfgang Mozart

25. **(MP) PRECISION** You and a friend make paper cones to collect beach glass. You cut out the largest possible three-fourths circle from each piece of paper.

    a. Are the cones similar? Explain your reasoning.

    b. Your friend says that because your sheet of paper is twice as large, your cone will hold exactly twice the volume of beach glass. Is this true? Explain your reasoning.

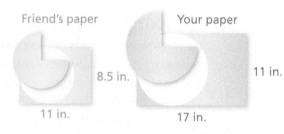

Friend's paper   Your paper

8.5 in.   11 in.

11 in.   17 in.

Mini-Assessment

The solids are similar. Find the surface area of the red solid.

1.

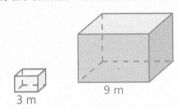

3 m

9 m

Surface Area = 32 m²

288 m²

2.

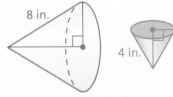

8 in.

4 in.

Surface Area = 151 in.²

37.75 in.²

3. The cylinders are similar. Find the volume of the red cylinder.

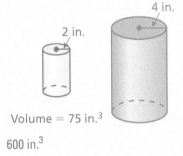

4 in.

2 in.

Volume = 75 in.³

600 in.³

Section Resources

Surface Level	Deep Level

Resources by Chapter
  • Extra Practice
  • Reteach
  • Puzzle Time
Student Journal
  • Self-Assessment
  • Practice
Differentiating the Lesson
Tutorial Videos
Skills Review Handbook
Skills Trainer
	Resources by Chapter
	  • Enrichment and Extension
	Graphic Organizers
	Dynamic Assessment System
	  • Section Practice

Transfer Level	

Dynamic Assessment System
  • End-of-Chapter Quiz
	Assessment Book
	  • End-of-Chapter Quiz

Concepts, Skills, & Problem Solving

21. 204 mm²

22. 1 : 18 scale model; about 0.04 in.³

23. **a.** 9483 lb; The ratio of the height of the original statue to the height of the small statue is 84 : 10. So, solve the proportion $\frac{x}{16} = \left(\frac{84}{10}\right)^3$.

   b. 221,184 lb

24.

Height (in.)	1	2	3	4
Surface area (in.²)	S	$4S$	$9S$	$16S$
Volume (in.³)	V	$8V$	$27V$	$64V$

Height (in.)	5	6	7
Surface area (in.²)	$25S$	$36S$	$49S$
Volume (in.³)	$125V$	$216V$	$343V$

25. **a.** yes; Because all circles are similar, the slant height and the circumference of the base of the cones are proportional.

   b. no; Your cone holds about 2.2 times as much.

Exercise 1

- Finding Lengths of Three-Dimensional Figures
- Finding the Volume of a Composite Solid
- Finding the Volume of a Cone
- Finding the Volume of a Cylinder

Exercise 2

- Finding the Volume of a Sphere
- Multiplying and Dividing in Scientific Notation

Exercise 3

- Finding Cube Roots
- Finding Missing Measures in Similar Solids
- Finding the Volume of a Cylinder

ELL Support

Explain that in Mongolia, many people live a nomadic life. One of the advantages of living in a yurt is that it is easy to take down and move to a new location. This type of living space is becoming popular for vacation homes in the United States. If any students have experiences with yurts in the United States or abroad, ask them to share their experiences.

Using the Problem-Solving Plan

1. $1950\pi \approx 6126 \text{ ft}^3$

2. about 3.1×10^{27} cubic light-years

3. Cylinder A: $96\pi \approx 301.6 \text{ cm}^3$; Cylinder B: $324\pi \approx 1017.9 \text{ cm}^3$

Performance Task

The *STEAM Video Performance Task* provides the opportunity for additional enrichment and greater depth of knowledge as students explore the mathematics of the chapter within a context tied to the chapter STEAM Video. The performance task and a detailed scoring rubric are provided at *BigIdeasMath.com*.

Laurie's Notes

Scaffolding Instruction

- The goal of this lesson is to help students become more comfortable with problem solving. These exercises combine the concepts of volume and similar solids with prior skills from other chapters. The solution for Exercise 1 is worked out below, to help you guide students through the problem-solving plan. Use the remaining class time to have students work on the other exercises.
- **Emerging:** The goal for these students is to feel comfortable with the problem-solving plan. Allow students to work in pairs to write the beginning steps of the problem-solving plan for Exercise 2. Keep in mind that some students may only be ready to do the first step.
- **Proficient:** Students may be able to work independently or in pairs to complete Exercises 2 and 3.
- Visit each pair to review their plan for each problem. Ask students to describe their plans.

▶ Using the Problem-Solving Plan

Exercise 1

⟹ **Understand the problem.** You know that the yurt is made of a cylinder and a cone. You also know several dimensions. You are asked to find the volume of the yurt.

⟹ **Make a plan.** Use the Pythagorean Theorem to find the height of the cone. Then use the formulas for the volume of a cylinder and the volume of a cone to find the volume of the yurt.

⟹ **Solve and check.** Use the plan to solve the problem. Then check your solution.

- Use the Pythagorean Theorem to find the height of the cone.

$a^2 + b^2 = c^2$	Write the Pythagorean Theorem.
$15^2 + b^2 = 17^2$	Substitute 15 for a and 17 for c.
$225 + b^2 = 289$	Evaluate the powers.
$b^2 = 64$	Subtract 225 from each side.
$b = 8$	Take the positive square root of each side.

So, the height of the cone is 8 feet.

- Use the cylinder and cone volume formulas to find the volume of the yurt.

Cylinder

$$V = Bh$$
$$= \pi(15)^2(6)$$
$$= 1350\pi$$

Cone

$$V = \frac{1}{3}Bh$$
$$= \frac{1}{3}\pi(15)^2(8)$$
$$= 600\pi$$

So, the volume of the yurt is $1350\pi + 600\pi = 1950\pi$, or about 6126 cubic feet.

- **Check:** Verify that the volume of the yurt is less than the volume of a cylinder with a height of 14 feet and a radius of 15 feet.
  $$V = \pi(15)^2(14) \approx 9896 \text{ ft}^3, \text{ and } 9896 > 6126. \checkmark$$

Connecting Concepts

▶ *Using the Problem-Solving Plan*

1. A *yurt* is a dwelling traditionally used in Mongolia and surrounding regions. The yurt shown is made of a cylinder and a cone. What is the volume of the yurt?

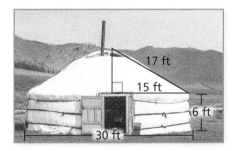

Understand the problem.

You know that the yurt is made of a cylinder and a cone. You also know several dimensions. You are asked to find the volume of the yurt.

Make a plan.

Use the Pythagorean Theorem to find the height of the cone. Then use the formulas for the volume of a cylinder and the volume of a cone to find the volume of the yurt.

Solve and check.

Use the plan to solve the problem. Then check your solution.

2. A spherical *supervoid*, a region in space that is unusually empty, has a diameter of 1.8×10^9 light-years. What is the volume of the supervoid? Use 3.14 for π. Write your answer in scientific notation.

3. The cylinders are similar. The volume of Cylinder A is $\dfrac{8}{27}$ times the volume of Cylinder B. Find the volume of each cylinder. Round your answers to the nearest tenth.

Cylinder A
4 cm

Cylinder B
9 cm

Performance Task

Packaging Salsa

At the beginning of this chapter, you watched a STEAM Video called "Canning Salsa." You are now ready to complete the performance task related to this video, available at *BigIdeasMath.com*. Be sure to use the problem-solving plan as you work through the performance task.

▶ Review Vocabulary

Write the definition and give an example of each vocabulary term.

cone, *p. 433*

sphere, *p. 439*

hemisphere, *p. 442*

similar solids, *p. 446*

▶ Graphic Organizers

You can use a **Summary Triangle** to explain a concept. Here is an example of a Summary Triangle for *volume of a cylinder*.

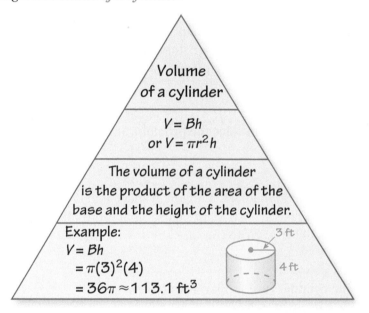

Volume of a cylinder

$V = Bh$
or $V = \pi r^2 h$

The volume of a cylinder is the product of the area of the base and the height of the cylinder.

Example:
$V = Bh$
$= \pi(3)^2(4)$
$= 36\pi \approx 113.1 \text{ ft}^3$

3 ft
4 ft

Choose and complete a graphic organizer to help you study the concept.

1. volume of a cone

2. volume of a sphere

3. volume of a composite solid

4. surface areas of similar solids

5. volumes of similar solids

Strike

Knocking all 10 pins down

Points: 10, plus points from the next 2 balls

Rolling 3 strikes in a row is called a turkey.

I thought 3 strikes and you are out.

"I finished my Summary Triangle about rolling a strike in bowling."

Review Vocabulary

- As a review of the chapter vocabulary, have students revisit the vocabulary section in their *Student Journals* to fill in any missing definitions and record examples of each term.

Graphic Organizers

Sample answers:

1.

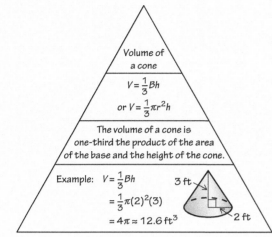

2.

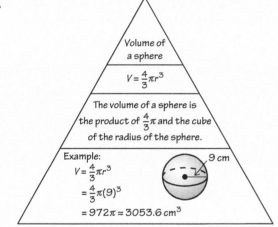

3–5. Answer at *BigIdeasMath.com*.

List of Organizers

Available at *BigIdeasMath.com*
Definition and Example Chart
Example and Non-Example Chart
Four Square
Information Frame
Summary Triangle

About this Organizer

A **Summary Triangle** can be used to explain a concept. Typically, the Summary Triangle is divided into 3 or 4 parts. Students write related categories in the middle part(s). Related categories may include: procedure, explanation, description, definition, theorem, or formula. In the bottom part, students write an example to illustrate the concept. A Summary Triangle can be used as an assessment tool, in which students complete the missing parts. Students may also place their Summary Triangles on note cards to use as a quick study reference.

1. $\dfrac{1575}{4}\pi \approx 1237.0 \text{ ft}^3$

2. $20\pi \approx 62.8 \text{ cm}^3$

3. 4 in.

4. 11 m

5. **a.** 13.5 in.

   b. $3.78\pi \approx 12 \text{ c}$

6. 9 times greater;
   $V = \pi(3r)^2 h = 9\pi r^2 h$

✅ Chapter Self-Assessment

The Success Criteria Self-Assessment chart can be found in the *Student Journal* or online at *BigIdeasMath.com*.

ELL Support

Allow students to work in pairs to complete the first section of the Chapter Self-Assessment. Have each pair display their answers on a whiteboard for your review. For the explanation in Exercise 6, have two pairs compare ideas and come to an agreement. Monitor discussions and provide support. Review explanations as a class. Use similar techniques to check the remaining sections of the Chapter Self-Assessment. For answers to *yes* or *no* questions, have students use a thumbs up for *yes* or a thumbs down for *no*.

🖍 Common Errors

- **Exercises 1 and 2** Students may write linear or square units for volume rather than cubic units. Remind them that part of writing a correct answer is including the correct units.
- **Exercises 1–4** Students may forget to square the radius when finding the area of the base, or they may use the diameter when the formula calls for the radius. Remind students of the formula for the area of a circle.
- **Exercises 3 and 4** Students may be confused about how to find the indicated dimension. Remind them to write the formula, substitute, simplify, and isolate the variable. Some students may need help with isolating the variable in these exercises, particularly in Exercise 4.
- **Exercise 4** Students may not complete the solution; they may solve for the *square* of the radius instead of the radius. If necessary, explain that they need to approximate a square root to find the radius and if they have difficulty doing so, then remind them of the approximation method they learned in Section 9.5.

▶ Chapter Self-Assessment

As you complete the exercises, use the scale below to rate your understanding of the success criteria in your journal.

1 I do not understand.

2 I can do it with help.

3 I can do it on my own.

4 I can teach someone else.

10.1 Volumes of Cylinders (pp. 427–432)

Learning Target: Find the volume of a cylinder.

Find the volume of the cylinder. Round your answer to the nearest tenth.

1.
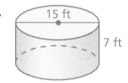
15 ft
7 ft

2.
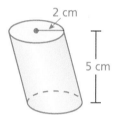
2 cm
5 cm

Find the missing dimension of the cylinder. Round your answer to the nearest whole number.

3. Volume = 28 in.^{3}

3 in.

h

4. Volume = 7599 m^3

r

20 m

5. You are buying two cylindrical cans of juice. Each can holds the same amount of juice.

   a. What is the height of Can B?

   b. About how many cups of juice does each can hold? (1 in.^{3} ≈ 0.07 cup)

6. You triple the radius of a cylinder. How many times greater is the volume of the new cylinder? Explain.

4 in.

6 in.

h

6 in.

Can A   Can B

10.2 Volumes of Cones (pp. 433–438)

Learning Target: Find the volume of a cone.

Find the volume of the cone. Round your answer to the nearest tenth.

7.

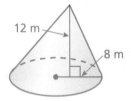

12 m

8 m

8.

4 cm

10 cm

Find the missing dimension of the cone. Round your answer to the nearest tenth.

9.

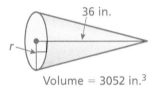

36 in.

r

Volume = 3052 in.^{3}

10.

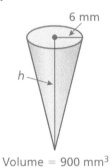

6 mm

h

Volume = 900 mm^3

6 cm

h

11. The paper cup can hold 84.78 cubic centimeters of water. What is the height of the cup?

10.3 Volumes of Spheres (pp. 439–444)

Learning Target: Find the volume of a sphere.

Find the volume of the sphere. Round your answer to the nearest tenth.

12.

12 ft

13.

22 cm

14. The volume of a *water walking ball* is $\frac{4}{3}\pi$ cubic meters. Find the diameter of the water walking ball.

Common Errors

- **Exercises 7 and 8** Students may forget to multiply by $\frac{1}{3}$. Remind them of the formula for the volume of a cone.
- **Exercises 7–11** When finding the area of the bases, students may not square the radius, or they may use the diameter when the formula calls for the radius. Remind them of the formula that they learned for the area of a circle.
- **Exercises 7, 8, 12, and 13** Students may write linear or square units for volume rather than cubic units. Remind them that part of writing a correct answer is including the correct units.
- **Exercises 9, 10, and 14** Students may be confused about how to find the indicated dimension. Remind them to write the formula, substitute, simplify, and isolate the variable. Some students may need help with isolating the variable in these exercises, particularly in Exercises 9 and 14.
- **Exercises 12 and 13** Students may forget to multiply by $\frac{4}{3}$ or cube the radius, they may use the diameter when the formula calls for radius, or they may write the incorrect units. Remind students of the formula for the volume of a sphere and that part of writing a correct answer is including the correct units.

7. $256\pi \approx 804.2 \text{ m}^3$

8. $\frac{40}{3}\pi \approx 41.9 \text{ cm}^3$

9. 9.0 in.

10. 23.9 mm

11. about 9 cm

12. $2304\pi \approx 7238.2 \text{ ft}^3$

13. $\frac{5324}{3}\pi \approx 5575.3 \text{ cm}^3$

14. 2 m

15. $360\pi \approx 1131.0 \text{ m}^3$

16. 132 ft^3

17. $\frac{64}{3}\pi \approx 67.0 \text{ cm}^3$

18. 1.1 cm

19. yes

20. $w = 2.5 \text{ in.}; h = 5 \text{ in.}$

21. 86.6 yd^2

22. 576 m^3

23. 48 in.^3

Common Errors

- **Exercises 15–17** Students may write linear or square units for volume rather than cubic units. Remind them that part of writing a correct answer is including the correct units.
- **Exercises 15–17** Students may think that there is not enough information to solve the problem. It may help to have them "break up" the composite solid into two parts, whose volumes they know how to find, and mark the dimensions on each part.
- **Exercise 17** Students may not realize that the top part of the solid is a hemisphere. Point this out to students.
- **Exercises 21–23** Students may raise the value of the ratio of the linear measures to the wrong exponent, or forget to square or cube the value of the ratio altogether. Discuss why squaring or cubing the value of the ratio makes sense.

Chapter Resources

Surface Level	Deep Level

Resources by Chapter
   • Extra Practice
   • Reteach
   • Puzzle Time
 Student Journal
   • Practice
   • Chapter Self-Assessment
 Differentiating the Lesson
 Tutorial Videos
 Skills Review Handbook
 Skills Trainer
 Game Library
	Resources by Chapter
	   • Enrichment and Extension
	 Graphic Organizers
	 Game Library

Transfer Level	

STEAM Video
 Dynamic Assessment System
   • Chapter Test
	Assessment Book
	   • Chapter Tests A and B
	   • Alternative Assessment
	   • STEAM Performance Task

Find the volume of the composite solid. Round your answer to the nearest tenth if necessary.

15.
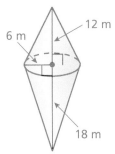
6 m
12 m
18 m

16.
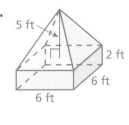
5 ft
2 ft
6 ft
6 ft

17.

2 cm
4 cm

18. The volume of water that a submerged object displaces is equal to the volume of the object. Find the radius of the sphere. Round your answer to the nearest tenth. ($1 \text{ mL} = 1 \text{ cm}^3$)

Before   After

10.4 Surface Areas and Volumes of Similar Solids   *(pp. 445–452)*

Learning Target: Find the surface areas and volumes of similar solids.

19. Determine whether the solids are similar.

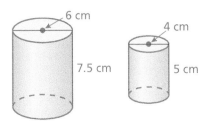
6 cm
7.5 cm
4 cm
5 cm

20. The prisms are similar. Find the missing measures.

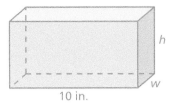
h
10 in.
w

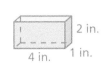
2 in.
4 in.   1 in.

21. The prisms are similar. Find the surface area of the red prism. Round your answer to the nearest tenth.

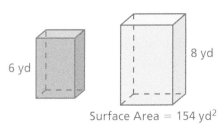
6 yd
8 yd
Surface Area = 154 yd²

22. The pyramids are similar. Find the volume of the red pyramid.

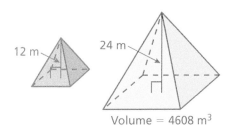
12 m
24 m
Volume = 4608 m³

23. The ratio of the corresponding linear measures of two similar jewelry boxes is 2 to 3. The larger jewelry box has a volume of 162 cubic inches. Find the volume of the smaller jewelry box.

Find the volume of the solid. Round your answer to the nearest tenth.

1.
20 mm
30 mm

2.
6 cm
3 cm

3.
26 ft

4.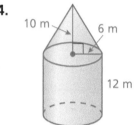
10 m   6 m
12 m

5. The pyramids are similar.

    a. Find the missing measures.

    b. Find the surface area of the red pyramid.

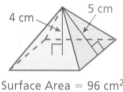
4 cm   5 cm
Surface Area = 96 cm²

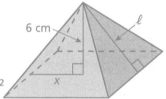
6 cm   ℓ
x

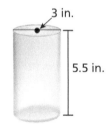
5 in.   3 in.
5 in.   5.5 in.

6. You are making smoothies. You will use either the cone-shaped glass or the cylindrical glass. Which glass holds more? About how much more?

7. The ratio of the corresponding linear measures of two similar waffle cones is 3 to 4. The smaller cone has a volume of about 18 cubic inches. Find the volume of the larger cone. Round your answer to the nearest tenth.

8. Draw two different composite solids that have the same volume but different surface areas. Explain your reasoning.

9. There are 13.5π cubic inches of blue sand and 9π cubic inches of red sand in the cylindrical container. How many cubic inches of white sand are in the container? Round your answer to the nearest tenth.

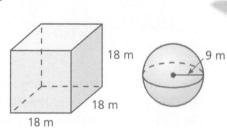
1.5 in.
16 in.

10. Without calculating, determine which solid has the greater volume. Explain your reasoning.

18 m
18 m
18 m
9 m

Practice Test Item References

Practice Test Questions	Section to Review
1, 6, 9	10.1
2, 6	10.2
3, 4, 8, 10	10.3
5, 7	10.4

Test-Taking Strategies

Remind students to quickly look over the entire test before they start so that they can budget their time. This test is very visual and requires that students remember many terms. It might be helpful for them to jot down some of the terms on the back of the test before the start. Students should make sketches and diagrams to help them. Have them use the **Stop** and **Think** strategy before they write their answers.

Common Errors

- **Exercises 1–4, 7, and 9** Students may write linear or square units for volume rather than cubic units. Remind them that part of writing a correct answer is including the correct units.
- **Exercises 1, 2, 4, 6, and 9** When finding the area of the base of a cylinder or a cone, students may not square the radius, or they may use the diameter when the formula calls for the radius. Remind them of the formula that they learned for the area of a circle.
- **Exercises 2, 4, and 6** Students may forget to multiply by $\frac{1}{3}$. Remind them of the formula for the volume of a cone.
- **Exercise 3** Students may forget to multiply by $\frac{4}{3}$ or cube the radius, they may use the diameter when the formula calls for radius, or they may write the incorrect units. Remind students of the formula for the volume of a sphere and that part of writing a correct answer is including the correct units.
- **Exercises 5 and 7** Students may raise the value of the ratio of the linear measures to the wrong exponent, or forget to square or cube the value of the ratio altogether. Discuss why squaring or cubing the value of the ratio makes sense.

1. $12,000\pi \approx 37,699.1 \text{ mm}^3$

2. $4.5\pi \approx 14.1 \text{ cm}^3$

3. $\frac{8788}{3}\pi \approx 9202.8 \text{ ft}^3$

4. $552\pi \approx 1734.2 \text{ m}^3$

5. **a.** $\ell = 7.5 \text{ cm}; x = 4.5 \text{ cm}$

   b. 216 cm^2

6. the cylindrical glass;
   $12.375\pi - \frac{31.25}{3}\pi \approx 6.2 \text{ in.}^3$

7. 42.7 in.^3

8. *Sample answer:*

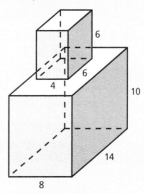

$V = 1264$ cubic units
$S = 784$ square units

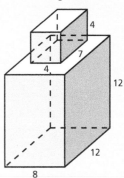

$V = 1264$ cubic units
$S = 760$ square units

9. $13.5\pi \approx 42.4 \text{ in.}^3$

10. the cube; The sphere could fit inside the cube with room to spare.

Test-Taking Strategies

Available at *BigIdeasMath.com*

After Answering Easy Questions, Relax
Answer Easy Questions First
Estimate the Answer
Read All Choices before Answering
Read Question before Answering
Solve Directly or Eliminate Choices
Solve Problem before Looking at Choices
Use Intelligent Guessing
Work Backwards

About this Strategy

When taking a multiple-choice test, be sure to read each question carefully and thoroughly. After skimming the test and answering the easy questions, stop for a few seconds, take a deep breath, and relax. Work through the remaining questions carefully, using your knowledge and test-taking strategies. Remember, you already completed many of the questions on the test!

Cumulative Practice

1. C

2. H

3. B

Item Analysis

1. **A.** The student evaluates $14 - 2^3 \left(\sqrt{64} \right)$ instead of $14 - 2\sqrt[3]{64}$.

    B. The student finds the square root of 64 instead of the cube root of 64.

    C. Correct answer

    D. The student does not follow the order of operations; subtracting before multiplying.

2. **F.** The student incorrectly uses half the radius.

    G. The student incorrectly uses half the radius and also uses the formula for a cylinder, neglecting to multiply by $\frac{1}{3}$.

    H. Correct answer

    I. The student uses the formula for a cylinder, neglecting to multiply by $\frac{1}{3}$.

3. **A.** The student finds the height of the blue cylinder instead of the volume of the red cylinder.

    B. Correct answer

    C. When writing a proportion to find the volume of the red cylinder, the student squares the value of the ratio of the radii instead of cubing it.

    D. When writing a proportion to find the volume of the red cylinder, the student does not cube of the value of the ratio of the radii.

Cumulative Practice

1. What is the value of $14 - 2\sqrt[3]{64}$?

   A. -50

   B. -2

   C. 6

   D. 48

Test-Taking Strategy

After Answering Easy Questions, Relax

How much catnip fits in a cylinder whose radius is 1 inch and height is 2 inches?
 Ⓐ 2π in.³ Ⓑ 4π in.³ Ⓒ 8π in.³ Ⓓ 2 in.³

Catnip pie, yummy for me!

"After answering the easy questions, relax and try the harder ones. For this, $\pi r^2 h = 2\pi$. So, it's A."

2. What is the volume of the cone?

   $\left(\text{Use } \dfrac{22}{7} \text{ for } \pi.\right)$

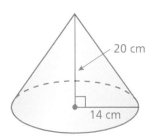

   F. $1026\dfrac{2}{3}$ cm³

   G. 3080 cm³

   H. $4106\dfrac{2}{3}$ cm³

   I. $12{,}320$ cm³

3. The cylinders are similar. What is the volume of the red cylinder?

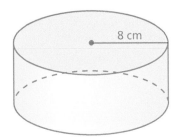

Volume = 1206 cm³

   A. 6 cm

   B. 150.75 cm³

   C. 301.5 cm³

   D. 603 cm³

4. A rectangle is graphed in the coordinate plane.

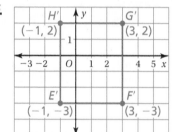

Which of the following shows Rectangle *E′F′G′H′*, the image of Rectangle *EFGH*, after it is reflected in the *x*-axis?

F.

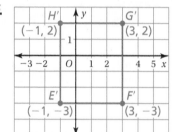

G.

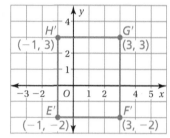

H.

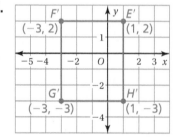

I.

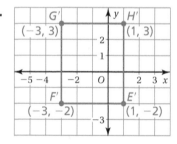

5. What are the ordered pairs shown in the mapping diagram?

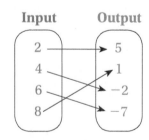

A. (2, 5), (4, −2), (6, −7), (8, 1)

B. (2, −7), (4, −2), (6, 1), (8, 5)

C. (2, 5), (4, 1), (6, −2), (8, −7)

D. (5, 2), (−2, 4), (−7, 6), (1, 8)

6. What is $0.\overline{75}$ written as a fraction?

Item Analysis (continued)

4. **F.** The student chooses the same rectangle with the vertices labeled differently.

    G. Correct answer

    H. The student reflects the rectangle in the *y*-axis instead of the *x*-axis.

    I. The student rotates the rectangle 180° about the origin instead of reflecting it in the *x*-axis.

5. **A.** Correct answer

    B. The student pairs the inputs and outputs by order from least to greatest.

    C. The student pairs each input with the output in the corresponding position.

    D. The student reverses the order of inputs and outputs.

6. **Gridded Response:** Correct answer: $\dfrac{25}{33}$

Common error: The student finds the fraction for 0.75 instead of $0.\overline{75}$ and gets $\dfrac{3}{4}$.

4. G

5. A

6. $\dfrac{25}{33}$

7. I

8. 9

9. A

10. 866.64 cm^3

Item Analysis (continued)

7. **F.** The student performs the first step correctly, but then subtracts P from $A - P$ rather than dividing.

    G. The student performs the first step correctly, but then divides A by P instead of dividing the entire expression by P.

    H. The student performs the first step correctly, but then divides P by P instead of dividing the entire expression by P.

    I. Correct answer

8. **Gridded Response:** Correct answer: 9

Common error: The student divides the volume by r instead of r^2, getting an answer of 108.

9. **A.** Correct answer

    B. The student graphs $y = \frac{1}{2}x$ instead of $y = 2x$.

    C. The student graphs $y = 2$ instead of $y = 2x$.

    D. The student graphs $y = x + 2$ instead of $y = 2x$.

10. **2 points** The student's work and explanations demonstrate a thorough understanding of finding the volume of a composite solid made up of a cylinder and a cone. The student correctly finds a volume of $276\pi \approx 866.64$ cubic centimeters. The student provides clear and complete work and explanations.

1 point The student's work and explanations demonstrate a partial but limited understanding of finding the volume of a composite solid made up of a cylinder and a cone. The student provides some correct work and explanation toward finding the volume.

0 points The student provides no response, a completely incorrect or incomprehensible response, or a response that demonstrates insufficient understanding of finding the volume of a composite solid made up of a cylinder and a cone.

7. Solve the formula $A = P + PI$ for I.

F. $I = A - 2P$

G. $I = \dfrac{A}{P} - P$

H. $I = A - 1$

I. $I = \dfrac{A - P}{P}$

8. A cylinder has a volume of 1296 cubic inches. If you divide the radius of the cylinder by 12, what is the volume (in cubic inches) of the smaller cylinder?

9. The cost y (in dollars) for x pounds of grapes is represented by $y = 2x$. Which graph represents the equation?

A.
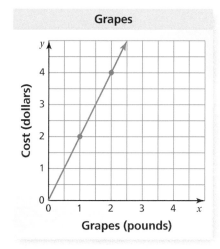

B.
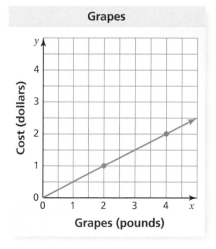

C.
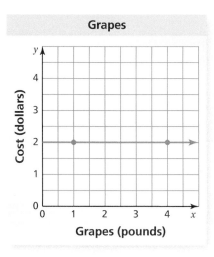

D.
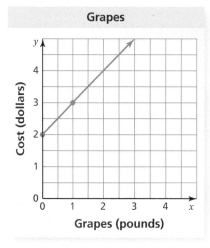

10. You are making a giant crayon.

Think Solve Explain

What is the volume (in cubic centimeters) of the entire crayon? Show your work and explain your reasoning. (Use 3.14 for π.)

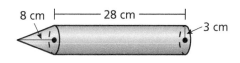

Additional Answers

Chapter 1

Section 1.1
Exploration 1
a. **Addition Property of Equality:** Adding the same number to each side of an equation produces an equivalent equation.

Subtraction Property of Equality: Subtracting the same number from each side of an equation produces an equivalent equation.

Multiplication Property of Equality: Multiplying each side of an equation by the same number produces an equivalent equation.

Division Property of Equality: Dividing each side of an equation by the same number produces an equivalent equation.

Section 1.2
Exploration 1
e. indigo: $45°, 45°, 90°$;
$$t = 90$$
$$x + x + t = 180$$
$$x = 45$$

violet: $60°, 60°, 60°$;
$$n + n + n = 180$$
$$n = 60$$

blue: $75°, 75°, 30°$;
$$x + n + p = 180$$
$$p = 75$$
$$p + p + m = 180$$
$$m = 30$$

green: $15°, 135°, 30°$;
$$p + s = 90$$
$$s = 15$$
$$s + k + m = 180$$
$$k = 135$$

yellow: $25°, 60°, 95°$;
$$w + n + (t + 5) = 180$$
$$w = 25$$

orange: $75°, 65°, 40°$;
$$w + f = 90$$
$$f = 65$$
$$p + f + y = 180$$
$$y = 40$$

Section 1.3
Exploration 1
a. blue figure: $x = 6$; $2x + 6 = 3x$, $x = 6$
yellow figure: not possible; $2x + 4 = 2x$, $4 \neq 0$
orange figure: $x = 6$; $2x + 8 = 3x + 2$, $x = 6$

b. green prism: $y = 8$; $24y + 64 = 32y$, $y = 8$
blue prism: not possible; $16y + 32 = 16y$, $32 \neq 0$

Concepts, Skills, & Problem Solving
49. $a - b = 1, c = 0$ and $a \neq b, c = 0$;

$a - b = 1, c = 0$	$a = b, c \neq 0$
$c = ax - bx$	$c = ax - bx$
$c = x(a - b)$	$c = ax - ax$
$0 = x(1)$	$c = 0$, where $c \neq 0$
$0 = x$	no solution
one solution	

$a = b, c = 0$
$$c = ax - bx$$
$$0 = ax - ax$$
$$0 = 0$$
infinitely many solutions

$a \neq b, c = 0$
$$c = ax - bx$$
$$0 = x(a - b), \text{ where } a - b \neq 0$$
$$\frac{0}{a - b} = \frac{x(a - b)}{a - b}$$
$$0 = x$$
one solution

Section 1.4
Exploration 1
a. parallelogram: $h = \dfrac{A}{b}$; Divide each side of the equation $A = bh$ by b.

rectangular prism: $h = \dfrac{V}{\ell w}$; Divide each side of the equation $V = \ell wh$ by ℓw.

triangle: $h = \dfrac{2A}{b}$; Multiply each side of the equation $A = \dfrac{1}{2}bh$ by $\dfrac{2}{b}$.

Chapter 2

Section 2.1
Exploration 1
b. The sides have the same length in the copy as in the original figure, the angle measures are the same in the figures, and parallel lines are still parallel.

Section 2.2

Try It

3. a. 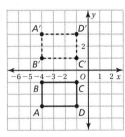 **b.**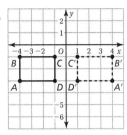

Self-Assessment for Concepts & Skills

4. a. 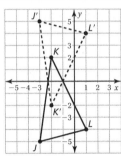 **b.**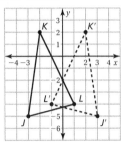

Review & Refresh

1.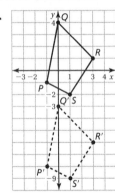

2.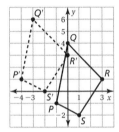

3.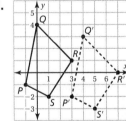

4.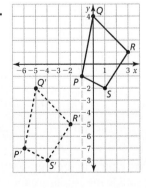

Concepts, Skills, & Problem Solving

21.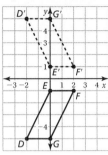

$D'(-2, 5)$, $E'(0, 1)$, $F'(2, 1)$, $G'(0, 5)$

24.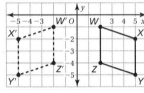

$W'(-2, -1)$, $X'(-5, -2)$, $Y'(-5, -5)$, $Z'(-2, -4)$

25.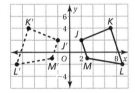

$J'(-2, 2)$, $K'(-7, 4)$, $L'(-9, -2)$, $M'(-3, -1)$

Section 2.3

Exploration 1

c. Point B: rotation of 180° counterclockwise about the origin;
Point C: rotation of 270° counterclockwise about the origin;
Point D: rotation of 90° counterclockwise about the origin

Section 2.5

Self-Assessment for Concepts & Skills

8.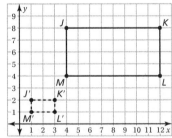

reduction

9. A dilation changes the size of a figure. The image is not congruent to the original figure.

Concepts, Skills, & Problem Solving

15.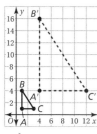

enlargement

17.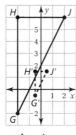

reduction

32. The transformations are a reflection in the y-axis and then a translation of 1 unit left and 2 units down; yes; The reflection produces a congruent figure and the translation produces a congruent figure, so the final image is congruent.

35. $(x, y) \rightarrow \left(\frac{1}{4}x, \frac{1}{2}y\right)$; Each x-coordinate is multiplied by $\frac{1}{4}$ and each y-coordinate is multiplied by $\frac{1}{2}$.

Section 2.6

Concepts, Skills, & Problem Solving

9.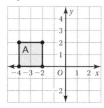

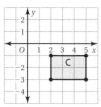

14. yes;

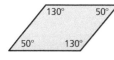 

18. yes; *Sample answer:* Because $\triangle ABC \sim \triangle DEF$ and $\triangle DEF \sim \triangle JKL$, there is a similarity transformation between $\triangle ABC$ and $\triangle DEF$ and a similarity transformation between $\triangle DEF$ and $\triangle JKL$. You can combine these similarity transformations to get a similarity transformation between $\triangle ABC$ and $\triangle JKL$. So, $\triangle ABC \sim \triangle JKL$.

Section 2.7

Exploration 1

a. *Sample answer:*

Original Side Lengths	$k = 2$	$k = 3$
$P = 6$	$P = 12$	$P = 18$

$k = 4$	$k = 5$	$k = 6$
$P = 24$	$P = 30$	$P = 36$

The perimeter of each dilated rectangle is k times the perimeter of the original rectangle.

c. *Sample answer:*

Original Side Lengths	$k = 2$	$k = 3$
$A = 2$	$A = 8$	$A = 18$

$k = 4$	$k = 5$	$k = 6$
$A = 32$	$A = 50$	$A = 72$

The area of each dilated rectangle is k^2 times the area of the original rectangle.

d. The value of the ratio of the areas is equal to the square of the value of the ratio of the corresponding side lengths.

e. To find the perimeter of the blue rectangle, write and solve the proportion

$$\frac{\text{perimeter of red rectangle}}{\text{perimeter of blue rectangle}} = \frac{\text{side length of red rectangle}}{\text{side length of blue rectangle}}.$$

To find the area of the blue rectangle, write and solve the proportion

$$\frac{\text{Area of red rectangle}}{\text{Area of blue rectangle}} = \left(\frac{\text{side length of red rectangle}}{\text{side length of blue rectangle}}\right)^2.$$

Chapter 2 Self-Assessment

12. b.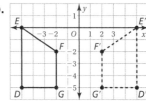

$D'(5, -5), E'(5, 0), F'(2, -2), G'(2, -5)$

Chapter 2 Practice Test

11.

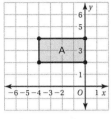

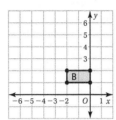

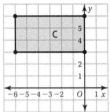

Chapter 3

Section 3.2

Exploration 2

The figure shows a triangle formed by two parallel lines and two transversals; *Sample answer:*
$\angle D + \angle B + \angle E = 180°$ because they make up a straight angle, and $\angle F = \angle B + \angle E$. Using alternate interior angles, $\angle D \cong \angle A$, $\angle E \cong \angle C$, and $\angle F \cong \angle G$. By substitution, $\angle A + \angle B + \angle C = 180°$, and $\angle G = \angle B + \angle C$.

Section 3.3

Exploration 1

g.

Number of Sides, n	3	4	5	6
Number of Triangles	1	2	3	4
Interior Angle Sum, S	180°	360°	540°	720°

Number of Sides, n	7	8	9
Number of Triangles	5	6	7
Interior Angle Sum, S	900°	1080°	1260°

$S = (n - 2) \cdot 180°$

Section 3.4

Exploration 2

Because the Sun's rays are parallel and $\angle B$ and $\angle E$ are corresponding angles, $\angle B \cong \angle E$. Because $\angle A$ and $\angle D$ are right angles, $\angle A \cong \angle D$. Because two angles of $\triangle ABC$ are congruent to two angles of $\triangle DEF$, $\angle C \cong \angle F$ and the triangles are similar. So, corresponding side lengths are proportional, and you can write and solve the proportion $\dfrac{x}{5} = \dfrac{36}{3}$ to find x.

Chapter 3 Using the Problem-Solving Plan

2. c. *Sample answer:* $\angle 1 \cong \angle 4'$ because $\angle 1 \cong \angle 1'$ and $\angle 1'$ and $\angle 4'$ are vertical angles.
$\angle 2 \cong \angle 3'$ because $\angle 2 \cong \angle 2'$ and $\angle 2'$ and $\angle 3'$ are vertical angles.
$\angle 3 \cong \angle 2'$ because $\angle 3 \cong \angle 3'$ and $\angle 3'$ and $\angle 2'$ are vertical angles.
$\angle 4 \cong \angle 1'$ because $\angle 4 \cong \angle 4'$ and $\angle 4'$ and $\angle 1'$ are vertical angles.

Chapter 4

Chapter Exploration

1. f. *Sample answer:*

Solution Points					
x	-6	-4	1	4	6
$y = \dfrac{1}{2}x + 1$	-2	-1	$1\dfrac{1}{2}$	3	4

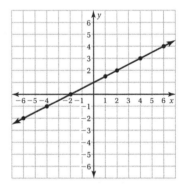

Each point lies on the line.

Section 4.1

Exploration 1

b.

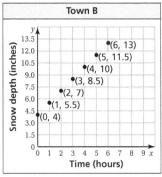

c.

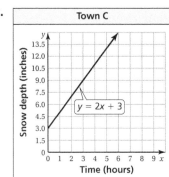

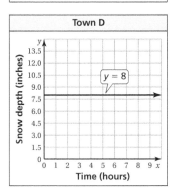

Try It

5.

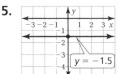

6.

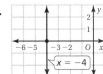

7.

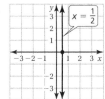

Self-Assessment for Concepts & Skills

9.

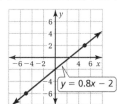

10.

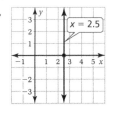

11.

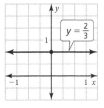

Concepts, Skills, & Problem Solving

6.

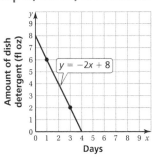

7.

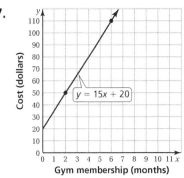

8. *Sample answer:*

x	0	1
y = 3x − 1	−1	2

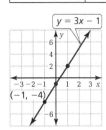

9. *Sample answer:*

x	0	3
$y = \frac{1}{3}x + 2$	2	3

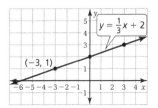

11.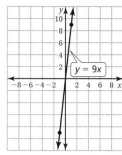

16.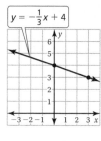

17.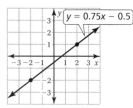

18.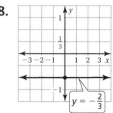

19.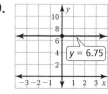

20.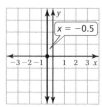

21.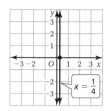

22. no; The equation $x = 4$ is graphed, not $y = 4$.

23.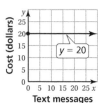

Sample answer: No matter how many text messages are sent, the cost is $20.

30. a.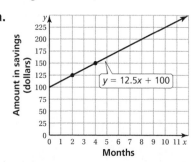

b. 11 months

31. a.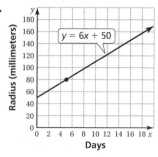

b. about 56,381.84 mm²; *Sample answer:* After 14 days, the radius is $6(14) + 50 = 134$ mm.

$$A = \pi r^2$$
$$= \pi(134)^2$$
$$= 17{,}956\pi \text{ mm}^2$$
$$\approx 56{,}381.84 \text{ mm}^2$$

32. a.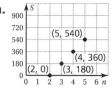

Sample answer: yes; The graph of the equation is a line.

b. no; $n = 3.5$ does not make sense because a polygon cannot have half a side.

33. a.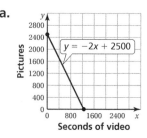

b. 2320 pictures

Section 4.2
Exploration 2

a. *Sample answer:*

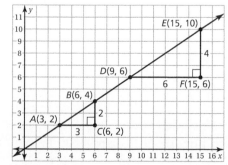

b. They are similar; *Sample answer:* $\overline{BC}$ and $\overline{EF}$ are both vertical and are parallel. The line that contains the points A, B, D, and E is a transversal. So, $\angle ABC$ is congruent to $\angle DEF$ because corresponding angles are congruent.

$\overline{AC}$ and $\overline{DF}$ are both horizontal and are parallel. The line that contains the points A, B, D, and E is a transversal. So, $\angle BAC$ is congruent to $\angle EDF$ because corresponding angles are congruent.

Both are right triangles. So, you can conclude that $\triangle ABC$ and $\triangle DEF$ are similar because their angles are congruent.

c. They are both equal to $\frac{2}{3}$. *Sample answer:* Because the triangles are similar, $\frac{BC}{EF} = \frac{AC}{DF}$ and this can be rewritten as $\frac{BC}{AC} = \frac{EF}{DF}$; The line rises 2 units for each 3 unit increase horizontally.

Self-Assessment for Problem Solving

12. *Sample answer:* Your friend's rate of change in elevation is 90 feet in one hour, which is greater than your rate of change in elevation of 30 feet in 30 minutes, or 60 feet in one hour.

Concepts, Skills, & Problem Solving

31. **b.** *Sample answer:*

2.5 ft
30 ft

Section 4.3
Exploration 1

a.

Vinegar (fl oz), *x*	3	6	9
Water (fl oz), *y*	2	4	6

For every increase of 2 fluid ounces of water in the cleaning product, there is a 3 fluid ounce increase of vinegar. The slope is $\frac{2}{3}$.

b. *Sample answer:*

Vinegar (fl oz), *x*	2	4	6
Water (fl oz), *y*	5	10	15

For every increase of 5 fluid ounces of water in the cleaning product, there is a 2 fluid ounce increase of vinegar. The slope is $\frac{5}{2}$.

Self-Assessment for Concepts & Skills

6. a. $y = \frac{5}{4}x$

b.

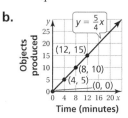

The unit rate is 1.25 objects produced per minute.

c. 75 objects

Self-Assessment for Problem Solving

7. artificial waterfall; The slope of the artificial waterfall ($m = 3000$) is greater than the slope of the natural waterfall ($m = 500$).

8. a. yes; *Sample answer:* The relationship can be represented by the equation $y = 343x$.

b. 4116 m

Section 4.4
Exploration 1

b. corresponding side lengths are proportional; *Sample answer:* The corresponding angles of the triangles are congruent, so the triangles are similar.

c. $\frac{y-3}{x-0} = \frac{m}{1}$; yes; *Sample answer:* By translating the graph of a proportional relationship up 3 units, the $y-0$ side of the triangle became $y-3$. Solving the equation for y produces $y = mx + 3$.

d. $y = mx + b$;

$$\frac{y-b}{x-0} = \frac{m}{1}$$
$$y - b = mx$$
$$y = mx + b$$

Self-Assessment for Concepts & Skills

8.

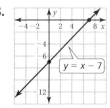

$y = x - 7$

x-intercept: 7

Self-Assessment for Problem Solving

11.

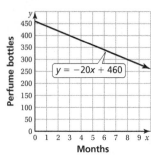

The y-intercept is 460. So, the initial number of perfume bottles in storage is 460. The slope is -20. So, the number of perfume bottles decreases by 20 bottles every month; 23 months;

$$0 = -20x + 460$$
$$-460 = -20x$$
$$23 = x$$

Concepts, Skills, & Problem Solving

24. a.

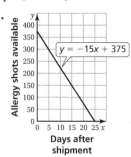

b. The slope is -15. So, the number of seasonal allergy shots decreases by 15 every day. The y-intercept is 375. There are initially 375 seasonal allergy shots available.

31. a. $y = 0.75x + 5$; The cost of going to the festival is the sum of the cost of picking x pounds of apples, $0.75x$, and the cost of admission, 5.

b.

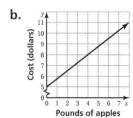

32. $y = 2x + 4$, $y = 2x + 1$, and $y = 2x - 3$ are parallel because the slope of each line is 2; $y = \frac{1}{2}x + 1$ and $y = \frac{1}{2}x + 2$ are parallel because the slope of each line is $\frac{1}{2}$.

33. a.

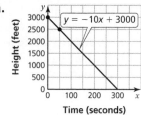

b. The slope of -10 means that the skydiver falls to the ground at a rate of 10 feet per second. The y-intercept of 3000 means the initial height of the skydiver is 3000 feet above the ground. The x-intercept of 300 means the skydiver lands on the ground after 300 seconds.

34. a. $y = 0.005x - 120$

b.

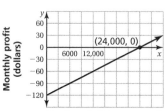

When the ads start to get 24,000 clicks a month, the profit will be $0 per month. Any additional clicks per month will start earning a profit.

Section 4.5

Exploration 1

c.

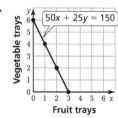

0 fruit trays and 6 vegetable trays, 1 fruit tray and 4 vegetable trays, 2 fruit trays and 2 vegetable trays, 3 fruit trays and 0 vegetable trays

$(0, 6): 50(0) + 25(6) = 150$
$(1, 4): 50(1) + 25(4) = 150$
$(2, 2): 50(2) + 25(2) = 150$
$(3, 0): 50(3) + 25(0) = 150$

Try It

3.

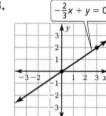

4.

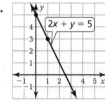

5.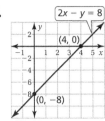

6.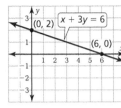

Self-Assessment for Concepts & Skills

10. *Sample answer:* 1) Write the equation in slope-intercept form ($y = -2x + 3$) and use the slope and y-intercept to graph the equation. 2) Find the x-intercept $\left(\frac{3}{2}\right)$ and the y-intercept (3), plot the points representing the intercepts, and draw a line through the points.

11.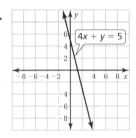

12.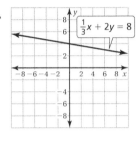

13.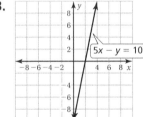

14.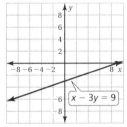

Self-Assessment for Problem Solving

15.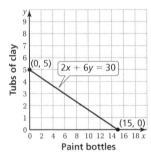

The x-intercept shows that you can buy 15 paint bottles when you do not buy any tubs of clay. The y-intercept shows that you can buy 5 tubs of clay when you do not buy any paint bottles;
6 paint bottles;
$$2x + 6(3) = 30$$
$$2x = 12$$
$$x = 6$$

16. a.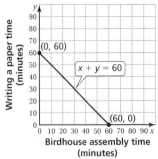

The x-intercept shows that it takes 60 minutes to assemble a birdhouse if you spend no time writing a paper. The y-intercept shows that it takes 60 minutes to write a paper if you spend no time assembling a birdhouse.

b. 20 min;
$$x + y = 60, \text{ where } x = 2y$$
$$2y + y = 60$$
$$3y = 60$$
$$y = 20$$

Concepts, Skills, & Problem Solving

7. $x =$ pounds of peaches
$y =$ pounds of apples
$$y = -\frac{4}{3}x + 10$$

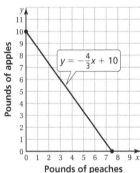

8. $x =$ hours biked
$y =$ hours walked
$$y = -8x + 16$$

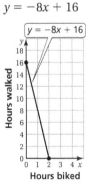

23.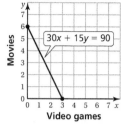

The *x*-intercept shows that your cousin can purchase 3 video games if no movies are purchased. The *y*-intercept shows that your cousin can purchase 6 movies if no video games are purchased.

24. a.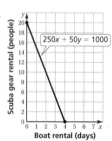

The *x*-intercept shows that the group can rent a boat for 4 days if no one rents scuba gear. The *y*-intercept shows that group can rent scuba gear for 20 people if they do not rent a boat.

b. 15 people; 10 people

c. $1000

25. a. $9.45x + 3.78y = 113.4$

b.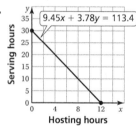

Section 4.6

Exploration 1

a. blue line: slope: $\frac{1}{2}$, *y*-intercept: 4, $y = \frac{1}{2}x + 4$

red line: slope: $\frac{1}{2}$, *y*-intercept: 1, $y = \frac{1}{2}x + 1$

green line: slope: $\frac{1}{2}$, *y*-intercept: -2, $y = \frac{1}{2}x - 2$

The lines are parallel.

b. blue line: slope: $-\frac{1}{3}$, *y*-intercept: 3, $y = -\frac{1}{3}x + 3$

red line: slope: $\frac{4}{3}$, *y*-intercept: 3, $y = \frac{4}{3}x + 3$

green line: slope: $\frac{1}{6}$, *y*-intercept: 3, $y = \frac{1}{6}x + 3$

The lines have the same *y*-intercept.

Self-Assessment for Problem Solving

9. The slope of $-\frac{1}{2}$ represents the decrease of waste, in tons, every month after relocation. The *y*-intercept of 15 represents the amount of waste, in tons, initially in the landfill; 30 months;

$$y = -\frac{1}{2}x + 15$$

$$0 = -\frac{1}{2}x + 15$$

$$\frac{1}{2}x = 15$$

$$x = 30$$

Section 4.7

Exploration 2

a.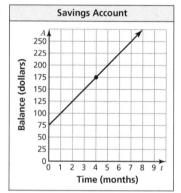

Self-Assessment for Problem Solving

12. a. $y = 30x + 15$

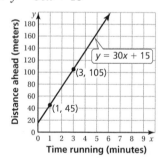

$$m = \frac{105 - 45}{3 - 1} = \frac{60}{2} = 30$$

$$y - 45 = 30(x - 1)$$
$$y - 45 = 30x - 30$$
$$y = 30x + 15$$

Chapter 4 Using the Problem-Solving Plan

2. $y = -x + 180$

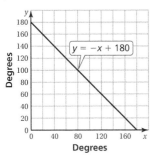

Chapter 4 Self-Assessment

8. a.

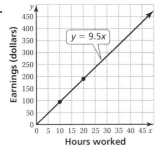

b. $380

10. a.

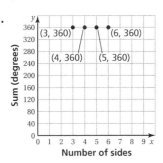

yes; The graph of the equation is a line.

b. no; *Sample answer:* It is impossible to have a polygon with 2 sides.

23. a. yes; *Sample answer:* Your friend's hair grows 1.5 cm per month. So in one year it grows $1.5 \times 12 = 18$ cm.

b.

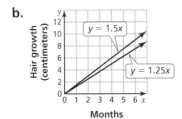

The graph for your friend's hair growth ($y = 1.5x$) is steeper than the graph for the average hair growth ($y = 1.25x$). So, your friend's hair grows at a faster rate.

28.

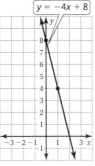

x-intercept: 2

30. a.

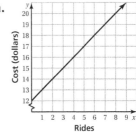

b. The *y*-intercept represents the admission price of $12 and the slope represents the unit cost of $1 per ride.

Chapter 4 Practice Test

12. a.

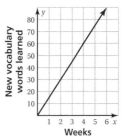

You learn 15 new vocabulary words per week.

b. 75 new vocabulary words

c. 30 more words

Chapter 5

Section 5.1

Exploration 1

a.

x (minutes)	10	20	30	40
p (headphones)	$16\frac{2}{3}$	$33\frac{1}{3}$	50	$66\frac{2}{3}$
p (phone)	35	45	55	65

x (minutes)	50	60
p (headphones)	$83\frac{1}{3}$	100
p (phone)	75	85

Sample answer: Initially, the battery power of the headphones is less than the battery power of the phone, but it increases faster and reaches 100% sooner than the battery power of the phone.

d.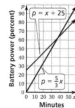

Sample answer: The intersection point of the graphs is where the devices have the same battery power at the same time.

e. Sample answer: Enter the equations into a graphing calculator. Then graph the equations and use the *intersect* feature to find the point of intersection.

Concepts, Skills, & Problem Solving

7.

x (weeks)	1	2	3	4	5
y (Country)	160	170	180	190	200
y (Pop)	135	155	175	195	215

x (weeks)	6	7	8	9	10
y (Country)	210	220	230	240	250
y (Pop)	235	255	275	295	315

Sample answer: Initially, the ticket sales for the Country Music Festival are greater than the ticket sales for the Pop Music Festival, but they increase slower and are less than the ticket sales for the Pop Music Festival for weeks 4 through 10.

Section 5.2

Try It

5. $(-4, -1)$; Explanations will vary.

6. $\left(\dfrac{4}{3}, -\dfrac{5}{6}\right)$; Explanations will vary.

Self-Assessment for Concepts & Skills

13. $(10, 2)$; Explanations will vary.

Section 5.4

Exploration 1

b. 5 backpacks

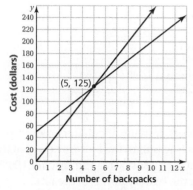

c. yes

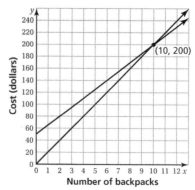

no

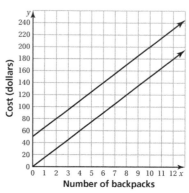

d. no solution: yes, the lines can be parallel; exactly one solution: yes, the lines can have different slopes; exactly two solutions: no, two lines cannot intersect at exactly two points; infinitely many solutions: yes, the lines can be the same

Chapter 5 Self-Assessment

32. Sample answer: $y = 2x + 7$
$y = -x + 1$

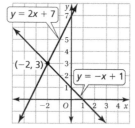

Chapter 6

Section 6.1

Exploration 1

a.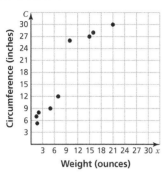

Write the weight and the circumference of each ball as an ordered pair, where the weight is x and the circumference is y. Then plot the ordered pairs in the coordinate plane.

Try It

1.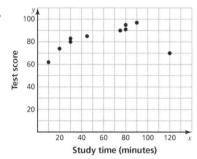

outlier: (120, 70); gaps: from 45 minutes to 75 minutes and from 90 minutes to 120 minutes; no clusters

Self-Assessment for Concepts & Skills

3.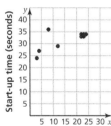

outlier: (8, 36); gap: from 12 months old to 22 months old; cluster: from 22 months old to 24 months old; positive linear relationship

Section 6.2

Try It

1. a. *Sample answer:*

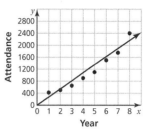

b. *Sample answer:* $y = 270x$

c. *Sample answer:* The attendance increases by 270 people each year, and the attendance in the year prior to this 8-year period was 0.

Section 6.3

Try It

3.

		Grade			
		6	**7**	**8**	**Total**
Lunch	Pack	11	23	16	50
	Buy	9	27	14	50
	Total	20	50	30	100

Self-Assessment for Concepts & Skills

5.

		Field Trip		
		Zoo	**Museum**	**Total**
Gender	Male	18	12	30
	Female	21	14	35
	Total	39	26	65

Self-Assessment for Problem Solving

7.

		Instrument		
		Play	**Do Not Play**	**Total**
Gender	Male	8	10	18
	Female	9	13	22
	Total	17	23	40

Concepts, Skills, & Problem Solving

13.

		Treatment		
		Yes	No	Total
Condition	**Improved**	34	12	46
	Did Not Improve	10	29	39
	Total	44	41	85

14. a–b.

		Eye Color			
		Green	Blue	Brown	Total
Gender	**Male**	5	16	27	48
	Female	3	19	18	40
	Total	8	35	45	88

48 males were surveyed;
40 females were surveyed;
8 students have green eyes;
35 students have blue eyes;
45 students have brown eyes;
88 students were surveyed.

Section 6.4

Exploration 1

b. *Sample answer:*

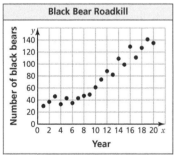

The scatter plot shows the relationship over time.

c. *Sample answer:*

Raccoon Roadkill Weights

Stem	Leaf
9	4 5
10	
11	0
12	4 9
13	4 6 9
14	0 5 8 8
15	2 7
16	8
17	0 2 3 5
18	5 5 6 7
19	0 1 4
20	4
21	3 5 5 5
22	
23	
24	
25	4

Key: 9 | 4 = 9.4 pounds

The stem-and-leaf plot shows how the raccoon weights are distributed.

Self-Assessment for Problem Solving

11. b. *Sample answer:* to attract applicants for an open position

Chapter 6 Using the Problem-Solving Plan

3.

		School Field Trip		
		Attend	Do Not Attend	Total
People	**Students**	80	44	124
	Chaperones	5	3	8
	Total	85	47	132

Chapter 6 Self-Assessment

14.

		Food Court		
		Likes	Dislikes	Total
Age Group	**Teenagers**	96	4	100
	Adults	21	79	100
	Senior Citizens	18	82	100
	Total	135	165	300

Chapter 7

Section 7.1

Exploration 2

a. Play A: one output; Play B: There are different numbers of outputs.

b. Play A: each ticket costs $8; Play B: Each ticket costs $4 or $8.

c. no; *Sample answer:* The price of a ticket for Play B varies.

Self-Assessment for Concepts & Skills

8. *Sample answer:*

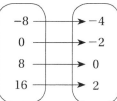

Map the input −8 to the outputs −4 and −2.

Review & Refresh

5.

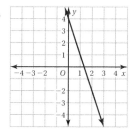

Concepts, Skills, & Problem Solving

17.

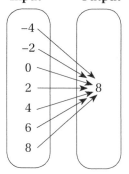

function; Each input has exactly one output.

18.

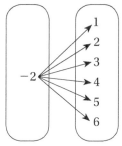

not a function; The input −2 has six outputs.

Section 7.2

Exploration 1

a.

Input, x	1	2	3	4
Output, A	1	3	5	7

Figure 41

b.

Input, x	1	2	3	4
Output, A	1	4	9	16

Figure 9

Try It

7.

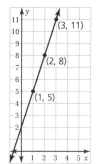

Concepts, Skills, & Problem Solving

21.

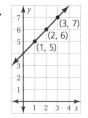

22.

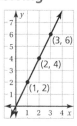

23.

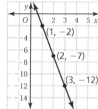

24.

40. *Sample answer:*

Side Length	1	2	3	4	5
Perimeter	4	8	12	16	20

Side Length	1	2	3	4	5
Area	1	4	9	16	25

Sample answer: The perimeter function appears to form a line, and the area function appears to form a curve. When the side length is less than 4, the perimeter function is greater. When the side length is greater than 4, the area function is greater. When the side length is 4, the two functions are equal.

Section 7.3

Try It

3. a. $y = -x + 65$

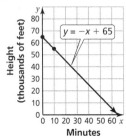

Self-Assessment for Concepts & Skills

5. a. $R = 2A + 2$

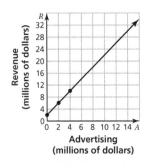

b. The slope indicates that the revenue increases by $2 million for every $1 million spent on advertising. The *y*-intercept indicates that the revenue of the company when it spends no money on advertising is $2 million.

Section 7.4

Exploration 1

b.

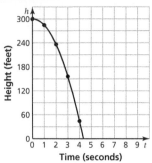

Sample answer: Plot points and connect them with a curve; nonlinear
Sample answer: Both objects fall from an initial height of 300 feet. The skydiver has a constant speed, and the bowling ball has an increasing speed. The bowling ball reaches the ground first.

Try It

5. nonlinear; You cannot rewrite the equation in slope-intercept form.

Concepts, Skills, & Problem Solving

5.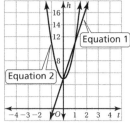

Equation 1: linear; Equation 2: nonlinear

6.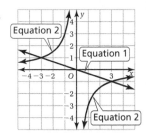

Equation 1: linear; Equation 2: nonlinear

Section 7.5

Exploration 1

d. B; *Sample answer:* The graph is horizontal when your speed is constant and decreases when you go up a hill. When you are at the top of the hill and your speed increases, the graph increases.

Exploration 2

The height increases and decreases in a cyclical pattern over time. *Sample answer:* your height above the ground over time as you ride a Ferris wheel

Self-Assessment for Concepts & Skills

4.

Snowboarding

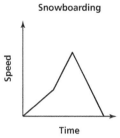

Self-Assessment for Problem Solving

6. Airplane A flies at the same height before descending at a constant rate until it reaches the ground. It remains on the ground for a while, and then ascends at a constant rate until it reaches a certain height. It then continues to fly at this height.

Airplane B travels at the same speed before slowing down at a constant rate until it comes to a stop. It remains stopped for a while, and then gains speed at a constant rate until it reaches a certain speed. It then continues to travel at this speed.

Review & Refresh

4.

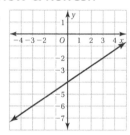

5.

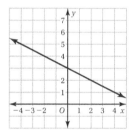

Concepts, Skills, & Problem Solving

21.

Typing

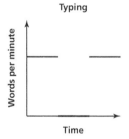

22. a.

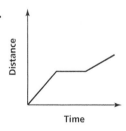

b. *Sample answer:* A person walks at a constant speed, stops to rest, and then starts to walk again at a constant speed that is about half of the original speed.

24. a. The supply curve increases at an increasing rate, so suppliers produce more and more as price increases. The demand curve decreases at a decreasing rate, so consumers buy less and less as price increases.

b.

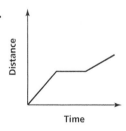

A surplus means that there is more than is needed. So, a surplus occurs when the quantity supplied is greater than the quantity demanded for a given price. A shortage means that there is less than is needed. So, a shortage occurs when the quantity supplied is less than the quantity demanded for a given price.

c. The equilibrium point moves up and to the right.

Chapter 7 Practice Test

8. a. The price of Stock A increases at a constant rate, then stays the same, then decreases at a constant rate, and then stays the same again. The price of Stock B decreases at a constant rate, then stays the same, then increases at a constant rate, and then stays the same again.

b. Stock B

c. *Sample answer:* Stock B is in direct competition with Stock A.

Chapter 8

Section 8.1

Exploration 1

a.

Power	Repeated Multiplication Form	Value
$(-3)^1$	(-3)	-3
$(-3)^2$	$(-3) \cdot (-3)$	9
$(-3)^3$	$(-3) \cdot (-3) \cdot (-3)$	-27
$(-3)^4$	$(-3) \cdot (-3) \cdot (-3) \cdot (-3)$	81
$(-3)^5$	$(-3) \cdot (-3) \cdot (-3) \cdot (-3) \cdot (-3)$	-243
$(-3)^6$	$(-3) \cdot (-3) \cdot (-3) \cdot (-3) \cdot (-3) \cdot (-3)$	729
$(-3)^7$	$(-3) \cdot (-3) \cdot (-3) \cdot (-3) \cdot (-3) \cdot (-3) \cdot (-3)$	-2187

Section 8.2

Exploration 1

a.

Product	Repeated Multiplication Form	Power
$2^2 \cdot 2^4$	$2 \cdot 2 \cdot 2 \cdot 2 \cdot 2 \cdot 2$	2^6
$(-3)^2 \cdot (-3)^4$	$(-3) \cdot (-3) \cdot (-3)$ $\cdot (-3) \cdot (-3) \cdot (-3)$	$(-3)^6$
$7^3 \cdot 7^2$	$7 \cdot 7 \cdot 7 \cdot 7 \cdot 7$	7^5
$5.1^1 \cdot 5.1^6$	$(5.1) \cdot (5.1) \cdot (5.1)$ $\cdot (5.1) \cdot (5.1) \cdot (5.1)$ $\cdot (5.1)$	5.1^7
$(-4)^2 \cdot (-4)^2$	$(-4) \cdot (-4)$ $\cdot (-4) \cdot (-4)$	$(-4)^4$
$10^3 \cdot 10^5$	$10 \cdot 10 \cdot 10 \cdot 10$ $\cdot 10 \cdot 10 \cdot 10 \cdot 10$	10^8
$\left(\frac{1}{2}\right)^5 \cdot \left(\frac{1}{2}\right)^5$	$\frac{1}{2} \cdot \frac{1}{2} \cdot \frac{1}{2} \cdot \frac{1}{2} \cdot \frac{1}{2}$ $\cdot \frac{1}{2} \cdot \frac{1}{2} \cdot \frac{1}{2} \cdot \frac{1}{2} \cdot \frac{1}{2}$	$\left(\frac{1}{2}\right)^{10}$

$$a^m \cdot a^n = a^{m+n}$$

Exploration 2

Power	Repeated Multiplication Form	Product of Powers
$(2 \cdot 3)^3$	$(2 \cdot 3) \cdot (2 \cdot 3) \cdot (2 \cdot 3)$	$2^3 \cdot 3^3$
$(2 \cdot 5)^2$	$(2 \cdot 5) \cdot (2 \cdot 5)$	$2^2 \cdot 5^2$
$(5 \cdot 4)^3$	$(5 \cdot 4) \cdot (5 \cdot 4) \cdot (5 \cdot 4)$	$5^3 \cdot 4^3$
$(-2 \cdot 4)^2$	$(-2 \cdot 4) \cdot (-2 \cdot 4)$	$(-2)^2 \cdot 4^2$
$(-3 \cdot 2)^4$	$(-3 \cdot 2) \cdot (-3 \cdot 2)$ $\cdot (-3 \cdot 2) \cdot (-3 \cdot 2)$	$(-3)^4 \cdot 2^4$

$$(ab)^m = a^m b^m$$

Section 8.3

Exploration 1

a.

Quotient	Repeated Multiplication Form	Power
$\dfrac{2^4}{2^2}$	$\dfrac{2 \cdot 2 \cdot 2 \cdot 2}{2 \cdot 2}$	2^2
$\dfrac{(-4)^5}{(-4)^2}$	$\dfrac{(-4) \cdot (-4) \cdot (-4) \cdot (-4) \cdot (-4)}{(-4) \cdot (-4)}$	$(-4)^3$
$\dfrac{7^7}{7^3}$	$\dfrac{7 \cdot 7 \cdot 7 \cdot 7 \cdot 7 \cdot 7 \cdot 7}{7 \cdot 7 \cdot 7}$	7^4
$\dfrac{8.5^9}{8.5^6}$	$\dfrac{\begin{array}{c}(8.5) \cdot (8.5) \cdot (8.5) \\ \cdot (8.5) \cdot (8.5) \cdot (8.5) \\ \cdot (8.5) \cdot (8.5) \cdot (8.5)\end{array}}{\begin{array}{c}(8.5) \cdot (8.5) \cdot (8.5) \\ \cdot (8.5) \cdot (8.5) \cdot (8.5)\end{array}}$	8.5^3
$\dfrac{10^8}{10^5}$	$\dfrac{\begin{array}{c}10 \cdot 10 \cdot 10 \cdot 10 \\ \cdot 10 \cdot 10 \cdot 10 \cdot 10\end{array}}{10 \cdot 10 \cdot 10 \cdot 10 \cdot 10}$	10^3
$\dfrac{3^{12}}{3^4}$	$\dfrac{\begin{array}{c}3 \cdot 3 \cdot 3 \cdot 3 \\ 3 \cdot 3 \cdot 3 \cdot 3 \cdot 3 \cdot 3 \cdot 3 \cdot 3\end{array}}{3 \cdot 3 \cdot 3 \cdot 3}$	3^8
$\dfrac{(-5)^7}{(-5)^5}$	$\dfrac{\begin{array}{c}(-5) \cdot (-5) \cdot (-5) \cdot (-5) \\ \cdot (-5) \cdot (-5) \cdot (-5)\end{array}}{(-5) \cdot (-5) \cdot (-5) \cdot (-5) \cdot (-5)}$	$(-5)^2$
$\dfrac{11^4}{11^1}$	$\dfrac{11 \cdot 11 \cdot 11 \cdot 11}{11}$	11^3
$\dfrac{x^6}{x^2}$	$\dfrac{x \cdot x \cdot x \cdot x \cdot x \cdot x}{x \cdot x}$	x^4

$$\frac{a^m}{a^n} = a^{m-n}$$

b. $\dfrac{2^4}{2^2} = 2^{4-2} = 2^2$;

$\dfrac{(-4)^5}{(-4)^2} = (-4)^{5-2} = (-4)^3$;

$\dfrac{7^7}{7^3} = 7^{7-3} = 7^4$;

$\dfrac{8.5^9}{8.5^6} = 8.5^{9-6} = 8.5^3$;

$\dfrac{10^8}{10^5} = 10^{8-5} = 10^3$;

$\dfrac{3^{12}}{3^4} = 3^{12-4} = 3^8$;

$\dfrac{(-5)^7}{(-5)^5} = (-5)^{7-5} = (-5)^2$;

$\dfrac{11^4}{11^1} = 11^{4-1} = 11^3$;

$\dfrac{x^6}{x^2} = x^{6-2} = x^4$;

yes

Concepts, Skills, & Problem Solving

7. $\dfrac{(-4.5) \cdot (-4.5) \cdot (-4.5) \cdot (-4.5) \cdot (-4.5) \cdot (-4.5)}{(-4.5) \cdot (-4.5)}$;

$(-4.5)^4$

8. $\dfrac{m \cdot m \cdot m \cdot m \cdot m \cdot m \cdot m \cdot m \cdot m \cdot m}{m \cdot m \cdot m \cdot m \cdot m}$; m^5

Section 8.4

Exploration 1

a.

Quotient	Quotient of Powers Property	Power
$\dfrac{5^3}{5^3}$	5^{3-3}	5^0
$\dfrac{6^2}{6^2}$	6^{2-2}	6^0
$\dfrac{(-3)^4}{(-3)^4}$	$(-3)^{4-4}$	$(-3)^0$
$\dfrac{(-4)^5}{(-4)^5}$	$(-4)^{5-5}$	$(-4)^0$

Exploration 2

a.

Product	Product of Powers Property	Power	Value
$5^{-3} \cdot 5^3$	5^{-3+3}	5^0	1
$6^2 \cdot 6^{-2}$	$6^{2+(-2)}$	6^0	1
$(-3)^4 \cdot (-3)^{-4}$	$(-3)^{4+(-4)}$	$(-3)^0$	1
$(-4)^{-5} \cdot (-4)^5$	$(-4)^{-5+5}$	$(-4)^0$	1

b. From the Multiplicative Inverse Property, you know that the product of a nonzero number and its reciprocal is 1. So, because each product in the table is 1, you can rewrite each power containing a negative exponent as the reciprocal of the power containing a positive exponent.

Section 8.5

Exploration 2

a. C   **b.** F   **c.** A

d. E   **e.** B   **f.** H

g. D   **h.** G

Sample answer: Write each number in List 2 in standard form. Then match it with the closest number in List 1.

Section 8.6

Exploration 1

a. *Answer should include, but is not limited to:* The student realizes that the number to the right of E is the exponent of a power of 10, and that the number to the left of E is multiplied by the power of 10.

Section 8.7

Exploration 1

a.

Expression 1	Expression 2	Sum	Difference
3×10^4	1×10^4	4×10^4	2×10^4
4×10^{-3}	2×10^{-3}	6×10^{-3}	2×10^{-3}
4.1×10^{-7}	1.5×10^{-7}	5.6×10^{-7}	2.6×10^{-7}
8.3×10^6	1.5×10^6	9.8×10^6	6.8×10^6

Sample answer: Write each expression in standard form. Then add or subtract the numbers and write the result in scientific notation.

Exploration 2

a.

Expression 1	Expression 2	Product	Quotient
3×10^4	1×10^4	3×10^8	3×10^0
4×10^3	2×10^2	8×10^5	2×10^1
7.7×10^{-2}	1.1×10^{-3}	8.47×10^{-5}	7×10^1
4.5×10^5	3×10^{-1}	1.35×10^5	1.5×10^6

Sample answer: Write each expression in standard form. Then multiply or divide the numbers and write the result in scientific notation.

b. To multiply, use the Commutative and Associative Properties of Multiplication to group the factors a and b and the powers of 10. Then multiply a and b, and multiply the powers of 10 using the Product of Powers Property. To divide, rewrite the expression as $\dfrac{a}{b} \times \dfrac{10^n}{10^m}$. Then divide a by b, and divide 10^n by 10^m using the Quotient of Powers Property.

Chapter 8 Using the Problem-Solving Plan

3.

		NFL Football		
		Watch	Do Not Watch	Total
Adults	Male	8.37×10^7	3.13×10^7	1.15×10^8
	Female	6.59×10^7	5.41×10^7	1.2×10^8
	Total	1.496×10^8	8.54×10^7	2.35×10^8

Chapter 9

Section 9.1

Exploration 2

$x^2 = 0$: $x = 0$; one solution
$x^2 = 1$: $x = -1$ and $x = 1$; two solutions
$x^2 = 4$: $x = -2$ and $x = 2$; two solutions
$x^2 = 9$: $x = -3$ and $x = 3$; two solutions
$x^2 = 16$: $x = -4$ and $x = 4$; two solutions
$x^2 = 25$: $x = -5$ and $x = 5$; two solutions
$x^2 = 0$ only has one solution because there is only one number, 0, whose square is 0. The other five equations have two solutions because there are two numbers whose square is the number on the right side of the equation.

Section 9.2

Exploration 1

 a.

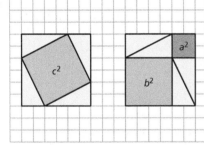

$$c^2 = a^2 + b^2$$

Section 9.4

Exploration 1

b. $9x = 3$, $x = \dfrac{1}{3}$, $0.333\ldots$ written as a fraction;

$9x = 6$, $x = \dfrac{2}{3}$, $0.666\ldots$ written as a fraction;

$9x = 1$, $x = \dfrac{1}{9}$, $0.111\ldots$ written as a fraction;

$9x = 2.2$, $x = \dfrac{2.2}{9} = \dfrac{11}{45}$, $0.2444\ldots$ written as a fraction

Section 9.5

Exploration 1

d. 1.414;
$(1.412)^2 = 1.993744$
$(1.413)^2 = 1.996569$
$(1.414)^2 = 1.999396$
$(1.415)^2 = 2.002225$
So, $(1.414)^2$ is closest to 2, which means that 1.414 is closest to $\sqrt{2}$.

Section 9.6

Exploration 1

a. If I live in the United States, then I live in California; statement: true; California is in the United States; converse: false; A person can live in one of the other 49 states and still live in the United States.

If I am alive, then my heart is beating; statement: true; A beating heart means you are alive; converse: true; Being alive means your heart is beating.

If two figures are congruent, then one figure is a translation of the other figure; statement: true; Translations produce congruent images; converse: false; *Sample answer:* One figure can be a rotation of the other figure.

Exploration 2

b. Because $\triangle JKL$ is a right triangle, $a^2 + b^2 = x^2$. Because $a^2 + b^2 = c^2$, you can substitute c^2 for $a^2 + b^2$ in $a^2 + b^2 = x^2$. So, $c^2 = x^2$ and $c = x$. Two triangles with the same side lengths are the same size and shape. There is a sequence of rigid motions that takes one triangle to the other, which means that $\triangle DEF \cong \triangle JKL$. So, $\angle E$ is a right angle and $\triangle DEF$ is a right triangle.

Chapter 9 Using the Problem-Solving Plan

2. 282.4 cm²; The height of each triangular prism is 8 centimeters, and the side lengths of the base are 8 centimeters, 8 centimeters, and $\sqrt{8^2 + 8^2} = \sqrt{128} \approx 11.3$ centimeters.

$$S \approx 2\left[\frac{1}{2}(8)(8)\right] + (8)(8) + (8)(8) + (8)(11.3)$$
$$= 282.4 \text{ cm}^2$$

Chapter 10

Section 10.3

Exploration 1

c. $V = \frac{4}{3}\pi r^3$;

$V = \pi r^2 h$ Write the formula for volume of a cylinder.

$\quad = \frac{2}{3}\pi r^2 h$ Multiply by $\frac{2}{3}$ because the volume of a sphere is $\frac{2}{3}$ of the volume of the cylinder.

$\quad = \frac{2}{3}\pi r^2(2r)$ Substitute $2r$ for h.

$\quad = \frac{4}{3}\pi r^3$ Simplify.

Section 10.4

Exploration 1

a.

Radius	1	2	3	4	5
Height	1	2	3	4	5
Surface Area	4π	16π	36π	64π	100π
Volume	π	8π	27π	64π	125π

When the radius and height are x times the smallest cylinder, the surface area is x^2 times the surface area of the smallest cylinder and the volume is x^3 times the volume of the smallest cylinder.

b.

Base Side	6	12	18	24	30
Height	4	8	12	16	20
Slant Height	5	10	15	20	25
Surface Area	96	384	864	1536	2400
Volume	48	384	1296	3072	6000

When the base side, height, and slant height are x times the smallest square pyramid, the surface area is x^2 times the surface area of the smallest square pyramid and the volume is x^3 times the volume of the smallest square pyramid.

English-Spanish Glossary

English   Spanish

A
---

angle of rotation *(p. 56)* The number of degrees a figure rotates about a point

ángulo de rotación *(p. 56)* El número de grados que gira una figura sobre un punto

---
B
---

base (of a power) *(p. 320)* The base of a power is the repeated factor.

base (de una potencia) *(p. 320)* La base de una potencia es el factor repetido.

C
---

center of dilation *(p. 70)* A point with respect to which a figure is dilated.

centro de dilatación *(p. 70)* Un punto con respecto al cual se dilata una figura

center of rotation *(p. 56)* The point about which a figure is rotated

centro de rotación *(p. 56)* El punto sobre del cual se rota una figura

cone *(p. 433)* A solid that has one circular base and one vertex

cono *(p. 433)* Un sólido que tiene una base circular y una vértice

congruent angles *(p. 64)* Angles that have the same measure

ángulos congruentes *(p. 64)* Ángulos que miden lo mismo

congruent figures *(p. 64)* Figures that have the same size and the same shape

figuras congruentes *(p. 64)* Figuras que tienen el mismo tamaño y la misma forma

congruent sides *(p. 64)* Sides that have the same length

lados congruentes *(p. 64)* Lados con la misma longitud

cube root *(p. 390)* A number that, when multiplied by itself, and then multiplied by itself again, equals a given number.

raíz cúbica *(p. 390)* Un número que, al multiplicarse por sí mismo, y luego al multiplicarse de nuevo por sí mismo, es igual a un número dado

---
D
---

dilation *(p. 70)* A transformation in which a figure is made larger or smaller with respect to a fixed point called the center of dilation

dilatación *(p. 70)* Una transformación en la que una figura se hace más grande o más pequeña con respecto a un punto fijo llamado el centro de dilatación

exponent *(p. 320)* The exponent of a power indicates the number of times a base is used as a factor.

exponente *(p. 320)* El exponente de una potencia indica cuantas veces una base es usada como un factor.

exterior angles *(p. 105)* When two parallel lines are cut by a transversal, four exterior angles are formed on the outside of the parallel lines.

ángulos externos *(p. 105)* Cuando una transversal corta dos rectas paralelas, se forman cuatro ángulos externos por fuera de las rectas paralelas.

exterior angles of a polygon *(p. 112)* The angles adjacent to the interior angles when the sides of a polygon are extended

angulos exteriores de un polígono *(p. 112)* Los ángulos adyacentes a los ángulos interiores cuando los lados de una polígono están extendidos

function *(p. 277)* A relation that pairs each input with exactly one output

función *(p. 277)* Una relación que asocia cada entrada con una sola salida

function rule *(p. 282)* An equation that describes the relationship between inputs (independent variable) and outputs (dependent variable)

regla de la función *(p. 282)* Una ecuación que describe la relación entre entradas (variable independiente) y salidas (variable dependiente)

hemisphere *(p. 442)* One-half of a sphere

hemisferio *(p. 442)* La mitad de una esfera

hypotenuse *(p. 382)* The side of a right triangle that is opposite the right angle

hipotenusa *(p. 382)* El lado de un triángulo rectángulo opuesto al ángulo recto

image *(p. 44)* The new figure produced when a figure is transformed

imagen *(p. 44)* La nueva figura producida cuando una figura esta transformada

indirect measurement *(p. 126)* Indirect measurement uses similar figures to find a missing measure when the measurement is difficult to find directly.

medida indirecta *(p. 126)* Medida indirecta usa figuras similares para hallar una medida que falta cuando la medida es dificil de hallar directamente.

input *(p. 276)* In a relation, inputs are values associated with outputs.

entrada *(p. 276)* En una relación, entradas son valores asociadas con salidas.

interior angles *(p. 105)* When two parallel lines are cut by a transversal, four interior angles are formed on the inside of the parallel lines.

ángulos internos *(p. 105)* Cuando una transversal corta dos rectas paralelas, se forman cuatro ángulos internos dentro de las rectas paralelas.

interior angles of a polygon *(p. 112)* The angles inside a polygon

ángulos interiores de un polígono *(p. 112)* Los ángulos que están dentro de un polígono

irrational number *(p. 402)* A number that cannot be written as the ratio of two integers

número irracional *(p. 402)* Un número que no puede escribirse como la razón de dos números enteros

J

joint frequency *(p. 250)* Each entry in a two-way table

frecuencia conjunta *(p. 250)* Cada valor en una tabla de doble entrada

L

legs *(p. 382)* The two sides of a right triangle that form the right angle

catetos *(p. 382)* Los dos lados de un triángulo rectángulo que forman el ángulo recto

line of best fit *(p. 245)* Out of all possible lines of fit, the line that best models a set of data

línea de mejor ajuste *(p. 245)* De todas las líneas de ajuste posibles, la línea que mejor modela un conjunto de datos

line of fit *(p. 244)* A line drawn on a scatter plot close to most of the data points; The line can be used to estimate data on a graph.

línea de ajuste *(p. 244)* Una línea dibujada en un diagrama de dispersión, cerca de la mayoría de los puntos de datos; La línea se puede usar para estimar datos en una gráfica.

line of reflection *(p. 50)* A line in which a transformed figure is reflected

línea de reflexión *(p. 50)* Una línea en donde una figura transformada está reflejada

linear equation *(p. 142)* An equation whose graph is a line

ecuación lineal *(p. 142)* Una ecuación cuya gráfica es una línea

linear function *(p. 290)* A function whose graph is a non-vertical line; A linear function has a constant rate of change.

función lineal *(p. 290)* Una función cuya gráfica es una línea no vertical; Una función lineal tiene una tasa de cambio constante.

literal equation *(p. 26)* An equation that has two or more variables

ecuación literal *(p. 26)* Una ecuación que tiene dos o más variables

M

mapping diagram *(p. 276)* A way to represent a relation

diagrama de función *(p. 276)* Una manera para representar una relación

marginal frequency *(p. 250)* The sums of the rows and columns in a two-way table

frecuencia marginal *(p. 250)* Las sumas de las hileras y columnas en una tabla de doble entrada

N

nonlinear function *(p. 296)* A function that does not have a constant rate of change; a function whose graph is not a line

función no lineal *(p. 296)* Una función que no tiene una tasa constante de cambio; una función cuya gráfica no es una línea

output *(p. 276)* In a relation, outputs are the values associated with inputs.

salida *(p. 276)* En una relación, salidas son los valores asociadas con entradas.

perfect cube *(p. 390)* A number that can be written as the cube of an integer

cubo perfecto *(p. 390)* Un número que puede escribirse como el cubo de un entero

perfect square *(p. 374)* A number with integers as its square roots

cuadrado perfecto *(p. 374)* Un número cuyas raíces cuadradas son números enteros

point-slope form *(p. 180)* A linear equation written in the form $y - y_1 = m(x - x_1)$; The graph of the equation is a line that passes through the point (x_1, y_1) and has the slope m.

forma punto-pendiente *(p. 180)* Una ecuación lineal escrita en la forma $y - y_1 = m(x - x_1)$; El grafico de la ecuación es una linea que pasa por el punto (x_1, y_1) y tiene la pendiente m.

power *(p. 320)* A product of repeated factors

potencia *(p. 320)* Un producto de factores repetidos

Pythagorean Theorem *(p. 382)* In any right triangle, the sum of the squares of the lengths of the legs is equal to the square of the length of the hypotenuse: $a^2 + b^2 = c^2$.

Teorema de Pitágoras *(p. 382)* En cualquier triángulo rectángulo, la suma de los largos de los catetos es igual al cuadrado del largo de la hipotenusa: $a^2 + b^2 = c^2$.

radical sign *(p. 374)* The symbol $\sqrt{}$ which is used to represent a square root

símbolo radical *(p. 374)* El símbolo $\sqrt{}$ que es usado para representar una raíz cuadrada

radicand *(p. 374)* The number under a radical sign

radicando *(p. 374)* El número bajo un símbolo radical

real numbers *(p. 402)* The set of all rational and irrational numbers

números reales *(p. 402)* El conjunto de todos los números racionales e irracionales

reflection *(p. 50)* A flip; a transformation in which a figure is reflected in a line called the line of reflection; A reflection creates a mirror image of the original figure.

reflexión *(p. 50)* Un reflejo; una tranformación en la que una figura se refleja en una línea llamada la línea de reflexión; Una reflexión crea un reflejo exacto de la figura original.

regular polygon *(p. 120)* A polygon in which all the side are congruent, and all the interior angles are congruent

polígono regular *(p. 120)* Un polígono en el que todos los lados son congruentes, y todos los ángulos interiores son congruentes

relation *(p. 276)* A pairing of inputs with outputs; can be represented by ordered pairs or a mapping diagram

relación *(p. 276)* Una pareja de entradas con salidas; se puede representar por pares ordenados o un diagrama de funciones

rigid motion *(p. 64)* A transformation that preserves length and angle measure

movimiento rígido *(p. 64)* Una transformación que preserva la longitud y medida del ángulo

rise *(p. 148)* The change in y between any two points on a line

desplazamiento vertical *(p. 148)* El cambio en y entre dos puntos cualesquiera de una línea

rotation *(p. 56)* A turn; a transformation in which a figure is rotated about a point

run *(p. 148)* The change in *x* between any two points on a line

rotación *(p. 56)* Una vuelta; una transformación en donde una figura se rota sobre de un punto

desplazamiento horizontal *(p. 148)* El cambio en *x* entre dos puntos cualesquiera de una línea

---

S

---

scale factor (of a dilation) *(p. 70)* The value of the ratio of the side lengths of the image to the corresponding side lengths of the original figure

factor de escala (de una dilatación) *(p. 70)* El valor de la razón de las longitudes de los lados de la imagen a las longitudes de los lados correspondientes de la figura inicial

scatter plot *(p. 238)* A data display that shows the relationship between two data sets using ordered pairs in a coordinate plane

diagrama de dispersión *(p. 238)* Una presentación de datos que muestra la relación entre dos conjuntos de datos, usando pares ordenados en un plano de coordenadas

scientific notation *(p. 350)* A number is written in scientific notation when it is represented as the product of a factor and a power of 10. The factor must be greater than or equal to 1 and less than 10.

notación científica *(p. 350)* Un número está escrito en notación científica cuando se representa como el producto de un factor y una potencia de 10. El factor debe ser mayor o igual que 1 e inferior a 10.

similar figures *(p. 78)* Figures that have the same shape but not necessarily the same size; Two figures are similar when corresponding side lengths are proportional and corresponding angles are congruent.

figuras semejantes *(p. 78)* Figuras que tienen la misma forma pero no necesariamente el mismo tamaño; Dos figuras son semejantes cuando las longitudes de sus lados correspondientes son proporcionales y los ángulos correspondientes son congruentes.

similar solids *(p. 446)* Two solids of the same type with equal ratios of corresponding linear measures

sólidos similares *(p. 446)* Dos sólidos del mismo tipo con razones iguales de medidas lineales correspondientes

similarity transformation *(p. 78)* A dilation or a sequence of rigid motions and dilations

transformación de similitud *(p. 78)* Una dilatación o secuencia de movimientos rígidos y dilataciones

slope *(p. 148)* The value of a ratio of the change in *y* (the rise) to the change in *x* (the run) between any two points on a line; Slope is a measure of the steepness of a line.

pendiente *(p. 148)* El valor de una razón entre el cambio en *y* (desplazamiento vertical) y el cambio en *x* (desplazamiento horizontal), entre dos puntos de una línea; Pediente es una medida de la inclinación de una línea.

slope-intercept form *(p. 162)* A linear equation written in the form $y = mx + b$; The graph of the equation is a line that has a slope of *m* and a *y*-intercept of *b*.

forma intersección-pendiente *(p. 162)* Una ecuación lineal escrita en la forma $y = mx + b$; El grafico de la ecuación es una linea que tiene una pendiente de *m* y una intersección *y* de *b*.

solution of a linear equation *(p. 142)* An ordered pair (*x, y*) that makes an equation true

solución de una ecuación lineal *(p. 142)* Un par ordenado (*x, y*) que hace que una ecuación sea verdadera

solution of a system of linear equations (in two variables) *(p. 200)* An ordered pair that is a solution of each equation in the system

sphere *(p. 439)* The set of all points in space that are the same distance from a point called the center

square root *(p. 374)* A number that, when multiplied by itself, equals a given number

standard form *(p. 168)* The standard form of a linear equation is $Ax + By = C$, where A and B are not both zero.

system of linear equations *(p. 200)* A set of two or more linear equations in the same variables

solución de un sistema de ecuaciones lineales (en dos variables) *(p. 200)* Un par ordenado que es una solución de cada ecuación en el sistema

esfera *(p. 439)* El conjunto de todos los pontos en el espacio que están a la misma distancia de un punto llamado centro

raíz cuadrada *(p. 374)* Un número que, multiplicado por sí mismo, es igual a un número dado

forma estándar *(p. 168)* La forma estándar de una ecuación lineal es $Ax + By = C$, donde A y B no son ambos cero.

sistema de ecuaciones lineales *(p. 200)* Un conjunto de dos o más ecuaciones lineales en las mismas variables

---

T

theorem *(p. 381)* A rule in mathematics

transformation *(p. 44)* A change in the size, shape, position, or orientation of a figure

translation *(p. 44)* A slide; a transformation that shifts a figure horizontally and/or vertically, but does not change its size, shape, or orientation

transversal *(p. 104)* A line that intersects two or more lines

two-way table *(p. 250)* A frequency table that displays two categories of data collected from the same source

teorema *(p. 381)* Un enunciado que afirma una verdad demostrable

transformación *(p. 44)* Un cambio en el tamaño, forma, posición u orientación de una figura

traslación *(p. 44)* Un deslice; una transformación que desplaza una figura horizontal y/o verticalmente, pero no cambia su tamaño, forma u orientación

transversal *(p. 104)* Una recta que interseca dos o más rectas

tabla de doble entrada *(p. 250)* Una tabla de frecuencia que muestra dos categorias de datos recogidos de la misma fuente

X

x-intercept *(p. 162)* The x-coordinate of the point where a line crosses the x-axis

intersección x *(p. 162)* La coordenada x del punto donde una línea cruza el eje x

Y

y-intercept *(p. 162)* The y-coordinate of the point where a line crosses the y-axis

intersección y *(p. 162)* La coordenada y del punto donde una línea cruza el eje y

Index

Credits

Chapter 8

316 *top* zentilia/Shutterstock.com; *bottom* OnstOn/iStock/Getty Images Plus; **317** tawan/Shutterstock.com; **318** *a.* ©iStockphoto.com/Manfred Konrad; *b.* alex-mit/iStock/Getty Images Plus; *c.* macrovector/iStock/Getty Images Plus; *d.* Kilav/iStock/Getty Images Plus; *e.* Digital Vision./Photodisc/ Getty Images; *f.* ZU_09/DigitalVision Vectors/Getty Images; *bottom* Stevyn Colgan; **319** ©iStockphoto.com/Franck Boston; **322** *top* Cecilie_Arcurs/E+/ Getty Images; *bottom* photographer3431/iStock/Getty Images Plus; **324** *top* muratkoc/E+/Getty Images; *bottom* ©iStockphoto.com/Boris Yankov; **328** *left* MR1805/iStock/Getty Images Plus; *right* Nikitin Victor/ Shutterstock.com; **330** *top* ©iStockphoto.com/VIKTORIIA KULISH; *bottom* DNY59/E+/Getty Images; **334** AndrewRafalsky/iStock/Getty Images Plus; **336** *top* ©iStockphoto.com/Petrovich9; *center* Okea/iStock/Getty Images Plus; *bottom* NASA/JPL-Caltech/L.Cieza (UT Austin); **340** *top* ILYA AKINSHIN/Shutterstock.com; *bottom* filipfoto/iStock/Getty Images Plus; **342** ©iStockphoto.com/Nancy Louie; **343** *Exploration 1a. and c.* Tom C Amon/Shutterstock.com; *Exploration 1b.* Olga Gabay/Shutterstock.com; *Exploration 1d.* HuHu/Shutterstock.com; **344** adventtr/E+/Getty Images; **347** Aslan Alphan/iStock/Getty Images Plus; **348** *right* AZ68/iStock/Getty Images Plus; *left* Crevis/Shutterstock.com; **352** *top* ©iStockphoto.com/ Oliver Sun Kim; *bottom* BORTEL Pavel/Shutterstock.com; **353** John Baker; **354** *top* ©iStockphoto.com/Christian Jasiuk; *bottom* ©iStockphoto.com/ cdascher; **358** *top* Sebastian Kaulitzki/Shutterstock.com; *bottom* asiseeit/ iStock/Getty Images Plus; **361** *top* filo/DigitalVision Vectors/Getty Images; *bottom* OnstOn/iStock/Getty Images Plus; **363** FatCamera/E+/Getty Images; **364** T_A_P/E+/Getty Images; **366** TranceDrumer/Shutterstock.com

Chapter 9

370 *top* zentilia/Shutterstock.com; *bottom* OnstOn/iStock/Getty Images Plus; **371** uatp2/iStock/Getty Images Plus; **377** *top* Perfectblue97; *bottom* Ig0rZh/iStock/Getty Images Plus; **379** *top* seregam/iStock/Getty Images Plus; *bottom* MarisaPerez/iStock/Getty Images Plus; **380** *top* ©iStockphoto.com/iShootPhotos, LLC; *Exercise 52 left* popovaphoto/iStock/Getty Images Plus; *Exercise 52 right* Dkart/E+/Getty Images; **381** claudio zaccherini/Shutterstock.com; **385** gui00878/iStock/ Getty Images Plus; **388** romeovip_md/Shutterstock.com; **394** *right* Gary Whitton/Shutterstock.com; *left* DonNichols/iStock/Getty Images Plus; **398** *top* RomoloTavani/iStock/Getty Images Plus; *bottom* tc397/E+/Getty Images; **399** NOAA; **400** *top* dial-a-view/E+/Getty Images; *center* atoss/ iStock/Getty Images Plus; *bottom* Oktay Ortakcioglu/E+/Getty Images; **405** ©iStockphoto.com/iLexx; **408** ©iStockphoto.com/Marcio Silva; **412** *left* youngID/DigitalVision Vectors/Getty Images; *right* JulieVMac/E+/Getty Images; **414** twildlife/iStock/Getty Images Plus; **415** OnstOn/iStock/Getty Images Plus; **417** Vaniatos/iStock/Getty Images Plus; **418** *Exercise 17 right* DS70/iStock Unreleased/Getty Images Plus; *Exercise 17 left* kostsov/iStock/ Getty Images Plus; *bottom* Rawpixel/iStock/Getty Images Plus; **419** supergenijalac/iStock/Getty Images Plus; **420** CD Lanzen/ Shutterstock.com

Chapter 10

424 *top* zentilia/Shutterstock.com; *bottom* OnstOn/iStock/Getty Images Plus; **425** carlosgaw/E+/Getty Images; **430** *top* Alison Hancock/ Shutterstock.com; *bottom* rasslava/iStock/Getty Images Plus; **432** *Exercise 18* ©iStockphoto.com/Prill Mediendesigns & Fotografie; *Exercise 19* MileA/iStock/Getty Images Plus; *Exercise 20* ©iStockphoto.com/ subjug; *Exercise 23* ©iStockphoto.com/Matthew Dixon; *Exercise 24* mladn61/ E+/Getty Images; *bottom* ©iStockphoto.com/Jill Chen; **436** pixeldigits/ iStock/Getty Images Plus; **438** *center* abu/E+/Getty Images; *bottom* rypson/ iStock Editorial/Getty Images Plus; **422** *top* Donald Joski/ Shutterstock.com; *bottom right* ©iStockphoto.com/Philippa Banks; *bottom left* Elenathewise/iStock/Getty Images Plus; **444** *top* ©iStockphoto.com/Yury Kosourov; *center* Carlos Caetano/Shutterstock.com; *bottom* johan63/iStock/ Getty Images Plus; **449** Tammy616/E+/Getty Images; **452** *top* Neustockimages/E+/Getty Images; *Exercise 22* Ford; *Exercise 23* ©iStockphoto.com/wrangel; *Exercise 24* Vold77/iStock/Getty Images Plus; *bottom* alfocome/Shutterstock.com; **453** *top* loca4motion/iStock/Getty Images Plus; *bottom* OnstOn/iStock/Getty Images Plus; **456** Laures/iStock/ Getty Images Plus

Cartoon illustrations: Tyler Stout
Design Elements: ©iStockphoto.com/Gizmo; Valdis Torms; Juksy/iStock/ Getty Images Plus

Mathematics Reference Sheet

Conversions

U.S. Customary
1 foot = 12 inches
1 yard = 3 feet
1 mile = 5280 feet
1 acre = 43,560 square feet
1 cup = 8 fluid ounces
1 pint = 2 cups
1 quart = 2 pints
1 gallon = 4 quarts
1 gallon = 231 cubic inches
1 pound = 16 ounces
1 ton = 2000 pounds
1 cubic foot ≈ 7.5 gallons

U.S. Customary to Metric
1 inch = 2.54 centimeters
1 foot ≈ 0.3 meter
1 mile ≈ 1.61 kilometers
1 quart ≈ 0.95 liter
1 gallon ≈ 3.79 liters
1 cup ≈ 237 milliliters
1 pound ≈ 0.45 kilogram
1 ounce ≈ 28.3 grams
1 gallon ≈ 3785 cubic centimeters

Time
1 minute = 60 seconds
1 hour = 60 minutes
1 hour = 3600 seconds
1 year = 52 weeks

Temperature
$$C = \frac{5}{9}(F - 32)$$

$$F = \frac{9}{5}C + 32$$

Metric
1 centimeter = 10 millimeters
1 meter = 100 centimeters
1 kilometer = 1000 meters
1 liter = 1000 milliliters
1 kiloliter = 1000 liters
1 milliliter = 1 cubic centimeter
1 liter = 1000 cubic centimeters
1 cubic millimeter = 0.001 milliliter
1 gram = 1000 milligrams
1 kilogram = 1000 grams

Metric to U.S. Customary
1 centimeter ≈ 0.39 inch
1 meter ≈ 3.28 feet
1 kilometer ≈ 0.62 mile
1 liter ≈ 1.06 quarts
1 liter ≈ 0.26 gallon
1 kilogram ≈ 2.2 pounds
1 gram ≈ 0.035 ounce
1 cubic meter ≈ 264 gallons

Number Properties

Commutative Properties of Addition and Multiplication
$$a + b = b + a$$
$$a \cdot b = b \cdot a$$

Associative Properties of Addition and Multiplication
$$(a + b) + c = a + (b + c)$$
$$(a \cdot b) \cdot c = a \cdot (b \cdot c)$$

Addition Property of Zero
$$a + 0 = a$$

Multiplication Properties of Zero and One
$$a \cdot 0 = 0$$
$$a \cdot 1 = a$$

Multiplicative Inverse Property
$$n \cdot \frac{1}{n} = \frac{1}{n} \cdot n = 1, n \neq 0$$

Distributive Property:
$$a(b + c) = ab + ac$$
$$a(b - c) = ab - ac$$

Properties of Equality

Addition Property of Equality
If $a = b$, then $a + c = b + c$.

Subtraction Property of Equality
If $a = b$, then $a - c = b - c$.

Multiplication Property of Equality
If $a = b$, then $a \cdot c = b \cdot c$.

Division Property of Equality
If $a = b$, then $a \div c = b \div c, c \neq 0$.

Squaring both sides of an equation
If $a = b$, then $a^2 = b^2$.

Cubing both sides of an equation
If $a = b$, then $a^3 = b^3$.

Properties of Exponents

Product of Powers Property: $a^m \cdot a^n = a^{m+n}$

Quotient of Powers Property: $\dfrac{a^m}{a^n} = a^{m-n}, a \neq 0$

Power of a Power Property: $\left(a^m\right)^n = a^{mn}$

Power of a Product Property: $(ab)^m = a^m b^m$

Zero Exponents: $a^0 = 1, a \neq 0$

Negative Exponents: $a^{-n} = \dfrac{1}{a^n}, a \neq 0$

Slope

$$m = \frac{\text{rise}}{\text{run}}$$

$$= \frac{\text{change in } y}{\text{change in } x}$$

$$= \frac{y_2 - y_1}{x_2 - x_1}$$

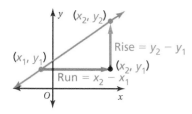

Pythagorean Theorem

$$a^2 + b^2 = c^2$$

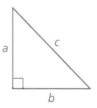

Converse of the Pythagorean Theorem

If the equation $a^2 + b^2 = c^2$ is true for the side lengths of a triangle, then the triangle is a right triangle.

Equations of Lines

Slope-intercept form
$$y = mx + b$$

Standard form
$$Ax + By = C, A \neq 0, B \neq 0$$

Point-slope form
$$y - y_1 = m(x - x_1)$$

Angles of Polygons

Interior Angle Measures of a Triangle

$$x + y + z = 180$$

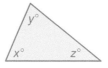

Interior Angle Measures of a Polygon

The sum S of the interior angle measures of a polygon with n sides is $S = (n - 2) \cdot 180°$.

Volume

Cylinder

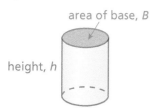

$$V = Bh = \pi r^2 h$$

Cone

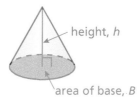

$$V = \frac{1}{3}Bh = \frac{1}{3}\pi r^2 h$$

Sphere

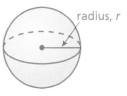

$$V = \frac{4}{3}\pi r^3$$